HISTORY OF MANKIND
CULTURAL AND SCIENTIFIC DEVELOPMENT

VOLUME IV
THE FOUNDATIONS OF THE MODERN WORLD
1300–1775

PUBLISHED FOR THE
INTERNATIONAL COMMISSION FOR A HISTORY OF THE
SCIENTIFIC AND CULTURAL DEVELOPMENT
OF MANKIND

BY

HARPER & ROW, PUBLISHERS
NEW YORK AND EVANSTON

HISTORY OF MANKIND

CULTURAL AND SCIENTIFIC DEVELOPMENT

VOLUME IV

By LOUIS GOTTSCHALK

LOREN C. MacKINNEY and EARL H. PRITCHARD

THE FOUNDATIONS OF THE MODERN WORLD

HARPER & ROW, PUBLISHERS,

NEW YORK AND EVANSTON

FOUNDATIONS OF THE MODERN WORLD (VOLUME IV OF HISTORY OF MANKIND: CULTURAL AND SCIENTIFIC DEVELOPMENT).

FIRST EDITION

LIBRARY OF CONGRESS CATALOG CARD NUMBER: 62-15718

*Prepared under the auspices and
with Financial Assistance of the
United Nations Educational Scientific and
Cultural Organization*

Editorial Consultants

Professor Roland Mousnier (Sorbonne), with the collaboration of Professors Georges Canguilhem (Sorbonne), André Chastel (Sorbonne), Alphonse Dupront (Sorbonne), Olivier Lacombe (Sorbonne), Pierre Le Gentil (Sorbonne), Raymond Picard (Sorbonne), Raymond Polin (Sorbonne) and Bertrand Gille (University of Clermont-Ferrand).

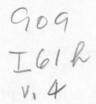

INTERNATIONAL COMMISSION
FOR A HISTORY OF THE SCIENTIFIC AND
CULTURAL DEVELOPMENT OF MANKIND

MEMBERS

Bureau

H.E. Professor Paulo E. de Berrêdo Carneiro	*Brazil*	PRESIDENT
Professor Louis Gottschalk	*United States of America*	Vice-President
Sir Julian Huxley, FRS	*United Kingdom*	Vice-President
Professor R. C. Majumdar	*India*	Vice-President
Professor Gaston Wiet	*France*	Vice-President
Professor Silvio Zavala	*Mexico*	Vice-President
Professor A. A. Zvorikine	*Union of Soviet Socialist Republics*	Vice-President
Dr Jorge Basadre	*Peru*	
Professor Jacques Freymond	*Switzerland*	
Professor Karel Krejči	*The Socialist Republic of Czechoslovakia*	
Professor Mahmud Husain	*Pakistan*	
Professor Witold Kula	*The Polish People's Republic*	
Professor Erik Lönnroth	*Sweden*	
Professor Charles Morazé	*France*	
Professor Mario Praz	*Italy*	
Mrs J. B. Priestley (Jacquetta Hawkes)	*United Kingdom*	
Professor Percy E. Schramm	*Federal Republic of Germany*	
Professor Ali A. Siassi	*Iran*	
Professor J. Pérez Villanueva	*Spain*	
Professor Caroline F. Ware	*United States of America*	
Professor C. K. Zurayk	*Syria*	
Dr Guy S. Métraux	*Switzerland*	Secretary-General

CORRESPONDING MEMBERS

HISTORY OF MANKIND
CULTURAL AND SCIENTIFIC DEVELOPMENT

AUTHORS' PREFACE

THE 'plan' of the *History of Mankind* adopted by the International Commission for a History of the Scientific and Cultural Development of Mankind, provided a blueprint for each volume[1] which was based upon the premise that, no matter how distinct the several cultures of the world might have been and may remain, they show a perceptible tendency to interchange one with another, so that in the course of time they will appear—to borrow a physiographical analogy—like a river system, each tributary rising from its own sources and running more or less independently for shorter or longer stretches but eventually (perhaps, if the world survives, only after centuries) merging to form a main stream, though without necessarily losing its own identity.

It was hoped that such a history of the scientific and cultural development of mankind would serve as a supplement to, perhaps even a substitute for, the so-called 'universal' histories which have appeared in considerable number, particularly since the eighteenth century—'so-called' because they were in fact, when not nationally oriented, histories of the world from a European or an American point of view.[2]

Volume IV was planned to trace the theme that the world's cultures developed from a stage around 1300 where mankind was largely dominated by a variety of religions in relatively isolated regions to a stage around 1775 where it was dominated largely by secular interests in increasingly interrelated regions. No significant contribution to culture, even if limited to a given time or area, was, so far as space and competence permitted, to go unmentioned and those contributions which had entered or might enter into the global diffusion of cultural achievements were to be given special consideration. Authors with such a purpose would be expected to avoid giving nearly all their space to European cultural developments and to give special attention to the lesser known achievements of non-European peoples that met the test.

The actual writing of Volume IV was entrusted to a team consisting of an author-editor, two associate author-editors, and six collaborators. The author-editor hoped at first to gather this team from all over the world, but practical considerations obliged him to limit the choice to specialists available in the author-editor's country. In the course of the work, and thanks to the procedures adopted by the International Commission, several hundred specialists scattered all over the globe have had a chance to read and criticize the several typescripts of this volume, and over sixty separate critics in fact did so.

Wherever the authors thought a criticism justified, they tried to meet it either by correcting or modifying their text, and wherever they thought they could not accept it, they informed the Secretariat of the International Commission why they could not, with a view toward having such disagreements mentioned at the disputed points in footnotes especially prepared to indicate the gist of such disputes.

In addition to the criticisms from all over the world the authors were able to exploit a series of articles published in the *Journal of World History*,[3] sometimes planned especially for their needs upon their solicitation and written by specialists from the culture under consideration.

In consequence of this international cooperation the typescript which was submitted to the French scholars who acted as the final editorial consultants for Volume IV was the product of at least four revisions and, for some parts, as many as seven. The helpfulness of this cooperation of scores of historians from all parts of the world was greater than the reader perhaps will detect, for a number of the errors and debatable statements they caught were corrected, leaving no need to mention the critic's comments in the footnotes. Those footnotes which survived were allowed to stand because they were regarded as sufficiently important supplementation, correction, or variant interpretation of the relevant text to justify the space required. In a few instances the authors felt constrained to reply to the consultant's observations and so affixed a rejoinder. They did so mostly where the critic had over-emphasized—in their opinion—the importance of his own specialty, coloured (as specialties tend to be) by focussing upon limited considerations, chrono-logical, departmental, ideological, national, regional, or denominational or combinations thereof. The critic who is a specialist in the history of music, for example, asks for more space for music and less for art; the specialist in Turkish art wants Turkish art to get more, and more favourable, attention; the economic determinist thinks too much emphasis is given to religious motivation; the Catholic critic believes the authors to be too positivistic or too Protestant, and vice-versa; the Asian historian contends that Europe has received far too much and Asia far too little wordage, and vice-versa; the historian of early science demands more pages for his centuries even at the expense of later centuries; the English critic complains that while we give too much detail about Henry the Navigator, we fail to mention that his mother was English; and so on. In cases like these, if we have responded at all, we have indicated that, no matter how justifiable the criticism, the purpose of the authors, in keeping with the philosophy which prompted the Inter-national Commission and which they subscribe to, was, so far as their competence permitted, to write a history of *mankind's* scientific and cultural development within a prescribed period (which, incidentally, everyone concerned recognized must in some regards be quite arbitrary) with special attention to the relative significance of developments and with special effort to lean over backward against their own regional, ideological, departmental, and other preferences. If we have knowingly sinned in any regard (if that be a sin), it is in our studied effort to render to the reader some account of the achievements of all known cultures in their contribution to the cultural and scientific development of mankind between the fourteenth century and 1775.

*   *   *

The authors' indebtedness to those who have provided texts, documents, ideas, corrigenda, and addenda is indicated elsewhere. Here we wish to express our gratitude also to the late Professor Ralph E. Turner and to Dr Guy S. Métraux. We owe to Professor Turner the original blue print of this volume. If we have departed from it to a considerable extent, it nevertheless served as our point of departure and as a criterion of the degree to which we were fulfilling the Commission's purpose. We are in debt to Dr Métraux and his staff not merely for the usual services of a secretariat but in addition for his assistance as an editor and critic of our text, as gatherer and editor of the illustrations in the volume, as editor (at least in part) of the articles in the *Journal of World History* which we have mined, and as editor of the footnotes which, having survived the process described above, are now at the end of each chapter of this volume.

Several foundations and libraries have also placed the author-editor in their debt. The Fulbright Commission, the Center for the Advanced Study of the Behavioral Sciences, the American Council of Learned Societies, and the Social Science Research Committee of the University of Chicago were among those that have at various times helped to provide the time, money, and assistance needed for his share in the writing and editing of Volume IV of the *History of Mankind*. The libraries of the University of Chicago, the University of Wisconsin, Cornell University, Kent State University, and Stanford University were among those whose resources he has exploited. To the staffs of these foundations and these libraries and to those that have aided the work of his associate author-editors and collaborators he wishes to present his apologies and thanks.

LOUIS GOTTSCHALK

NOTES

1. 'Plan of a History of the Scientific and Cultural Development of Mankind', *Journal of World History*, I, i (1953), pp. 223–38.

2. See *inter alia* Jean-Pierre Aguet, 'De quelques "Grands ensembles" historiques récents: Essai d'analyse historiographique', *Journal of World History*, VIII, iii (1964), pp. 395–425, and Louis Gottschalk, 'Projects and Concepts of World History in the Twentieth Century', International Committee of the Historical Sciences *Rapports*, IV (Vienna, 1965), pp. 5–19.

3. The *Journal of World History*, I- (1953–), published by Les Editions de la Baconnière, Boudry-Neuchâtel, Switzerland, for the International Commission for a History of the Scientific and Cultural Development of Mankind, under the auspices of Unesco.

NOTE ON THE PREPARATION AND EDITORIAL TREATMENT OF VOLUME IV OF THE *HISTORY OF MANKIND*

THE original typescript of Volume IV of the *History of Mankind: Cultural and Scientific Development*, prepared by Professor Louis Gottschalk and his collaborators, was submitted in 1958 to the members of the International Commission for a History of the Scientific and Cultural Development of Mankind, to a group of specialists appointed by the President of the International Commission, and to the National Commissions for Unesco in the Member States of the Organization.

The International Commission received from these sources a considerable number of comments and suggestions about this text. The author-editor and his collaborators undertook to analyze these materials and, in so far as possible, to integrate them into the original typescript. The revised text was again submitted to a group of selected scholars whose comments enabled the preparation of the final version of Volume IV of the *History of Mankind: The Foundations of the Modern World, 1300–1775*.

*   *   *

The author-editor, Professor Louis Gottschalk, and his two associates, the late Professor Loren C. MacKinney, Kennan Professor of Medieval History, The University of North Carolina, and Professor Earl H. Pritchard, Professor of History and Chairman of Oriental Studies, The University of Arizona, benefited from the cooperation of various specialists in preparing the original manuscript of this Volume. The author-editor and the International Commission would like to acknowledge gratefully the collaboration of the following scholars:

George A. Foote, Associate Professor of History, Goucher College, Towson, Md., who wrote the first draft of many passages dealing with the history of Western science and technology.

The late Marshall G. S. Hodgson, Professor of History and Chairman of the Committee on Social Thought, University of Chicago, who prepared the materials on Islamic culture.

Samson B. Knoll, Dean of the Graduate Division and Head of the Department of History, Monterey Institute of Foreign Studies, Monterey, Calif., who was responsible for the preliminary drafts of the section on the development of religion and religious history in the West after 1500.

Earl E. Rosenthal, Associate Professor of Art, University of Chicago, who wrote most of the chapters on the development of art in Europe.

Karl J. Weintraub, Associate Professor of History and Chairman of the Committee on the History of Culture, University of Chicago, who prepared the pages concerning Western literary history, and collaborated in the elaboration of Chapter I and the Conclusion (Chapter XVII).

J. A. B. van Buitenen, Professor of South Asian Languages and Civilizations, University of Chicago, who aided the authors in the preparation of the passages on India and the Indian cultures.

Margit Varro, sometime Lecturer at Roosevelt University and the Illinois Institute of Technology, Chicago, who wrote on the history of music in Europe.

In addition, the Spanish National Commission for Unesco and the Institute of History of the Academy of Sciences of the Union of Soviet Socialist Republics provided for this volume original memoranda on certain questions. Professor

Gottschalk and his associates availed themselves freely of this valuable contribution, for which the International Commission would like to express its gratitude.

* * *

In revising the manuscript, the author-editor and his associates utilized the comments and suggestions of the following scholars:

Members of the International Commission for a History of the Scientific and Cultural Development of Mankind

> The late Professor E. J. Dijksterhuis (The Netherlands).
> Sir Julian Huxley, FRS (United Kingdom).
> Professor Erik Lönnroth (Sweden).
> Professor R. C. Majumdar (India).
> Professor Mario Praz (Italy).
> Professor C. K. Zurayk (Syria).

Corresponding Members of the International Commission

> Professor Oscar Halecki, Fordham University, New York.
> Professor R. Hooykaas, The Free University, Amsterdam.
> Dr Maria Rooseboom, National Museum of the History of Science, Leiden.
> Professor Nilakanta Sastri, Institute of Traditional Cultures, Madras.

Scholars Consulted by the International Commission

> Dr T. Althin, Technical Museum, Stockholm.
> Professor J. Bonfante, University of Turin.
> Professor Fernand Brunner, Université de Neuchatel.
> Professor Hermann Heimpel, Director, Max-Planck Institut für Geschichte, Goettingen (also Corresponding Member of the International Commission).
> Mr Eric E. Hirschler, Brooklyn College, New York.
> Professor Angulo Iñiguez, Director, Instituto 'Diego Velasquez', Madrid.
> Professor Hubert Jedin, University of Bonn.
> Professor F. H. Lawson, formerly of Oxford University.
> The late Professor J. M. Romein, Co-author, *History of Mankind*, Volume VI University of Amsterdam.
> Professor Raymond de Roover, Brooklyn College, New York.
> Mr Claude Secrétan, Université de Lausanne.
> Mr A. Stowers, Science Museum, London.
> Professor René Wellek, Yale University, New Haven, Connecticut.

Scholars Consulted by the National Commissions for UNESCO

> Austria: Professor Erna Patzelt, Institute of Cultural and Economic History, Vienna.
>
> Czechoslovakia: Professor J. Polišenský, Charles University, Prague.
>   Dr František Kavka, Charles University, Prague.
>
> France: Professor Roland Mousnier, Faculté des Lettres (Sorbonne), Paris.
>
> German Federal
> Republic: Professor J. Derbolav, Institute of Education of the University of Bonn.
>   Professor Friedrich Blume, Bonn.
>   Dr Hans Schimank, University of Hamburg.
>
> Hungary: Professor László Makkai, Institute of History, Academy of Sciences of Hungary, Budapest.

Professor György Márkus, Institute of Philosophy, Budapest.
Professor Imre Révész, Academy of Sciences of Hungary, Budapest.
Dr Anna Zádor, Institute of the History of Art, Budapest.
Dr Jolán Zemplén, Technical University, Budapest.

Israel: Professor I. Katz, Kaplan School of Economics and Social Sciences, Hebrew University, Jerusalem.

Japan: Professor Suketoshi Yajima, Tokyo College of Sciences (also Corresponding Member of the International Commission).
Professor Naofusa Hirai, Kokugakuin University, Tokyo.

Lebanon: Professor David C. Gordon, American University, Beirut.

Norway: Dr Andreas Holmsen, University of Oslo.

Spain: Professor Emilio Lorenzo, University of Madrid.
Professor Luís Diéz del Corral, University of Madrid.
Professor Fernando Chueca Goitia, Madrid.

Turkey: Professor S. Kemal Yetkin, University of Ankara.
Professor Aydin Sayili, University of Ankara.
Professor Abidin Itil, University of Ankara.

Union of Soviet Socialist Republics: Dr E. A. Belaiev, Institute of Oriental Studies, Moscow.
Professor I. U. Budovnits,
Professor A. N. Chistozvonov,
Dr N. M. Goldberg.
Professor A. N. Kuznetsov,
Dr E. V. Paevskaya,
Professor V. P. Zoubov (also Corresponding Member of the International Commission).

Viet-Nam: Dr Nguyen Dình Hoà, Faculty of Letters, University of Saigon.
Professor Truöng Búu Lâm, Saigon.

In addition, critical materials were made available by the Ministry of Education, Ceylon, the Indian National Commission for UNESCO, the United Kingdom National Commission for UNESCO, as well as by the Academy of Sciences of Bulgaria and the Polish National Commission for UNESCO.

The final text of Volume IV of the *History of Mankind* was submitted in 1966 to a group of scholars at the University of Paris (Sorbonne) for the preparation of editorial notes on various aspects of the text of the author-editors. Professor Roland Mousnier, Chairman of the Centre de Recherches sur la Civilisation de l'Europe moderne, presided over a panel which included Professor Georges Canguilhem, Professor André Chastel, Professor Alphonse Dupront, Professor Olivier Lacombe, Professor Pierre Le Gentil, Professor Raymond Picard, Professor Raymond Polin, and Professor Bertrand Gille (University of Clermont-Ferrand).

The editorial notes constitute an important addition to the volume; in some cases they complement sections of the text, in others they expand the point of view of the authors or provide a variant interpretation. In each instance, it will be seen, the authorship of the notes has been clearly indicated; these notes were prepared quite independently of the work of the authors and reflect the opinions of the critics. On certain questions, however, the author-editor and his colleagues have written rejoinders in which they explain their position. The editorial matter prepared by the author-editor has been printed in italics to distinguish it from the critics' comments. This material was edited by the Secretary-General of the International Commission.

*   *   *

Several of the French scholars who examined the text of Volume IV before publication have expressed some doubt whether the authors have employed the best possible arrangement for achieving a synthesis of the main cultural and scientific developments of the period under consideration, a period which marks the inception of modern cultural and scientific developments, achievements, institutions, and conventions. In order to illustrate their point of view (and before we present the authors'), we quote at length the comments of Professor Roland Mousnier on this subject:

'Concerning the composition of the book, we find an analytic plan in which each subject is studied in and of itself (e.g. mines, wood, hunting, fishing, trade) so that the subdivisions of each chapter look like a juxtaposition of descriptive passages, a series of dictionary articles. This is good as a means of ensuring that nothing is forgotten. But the links between the facts studied in each case and those considered in other categories are rarely shown clearly enough or even not shown at all. There is lacking a general view of all these human activities, their reciprocal actions and reactions, their relationships as variables and functions. Yet it is precisely the links between these activities which are the essential material of history and the aim of monographs.

'This failure to consider things as a whole has made it impossible, on the one hand, to distinguish types—types of societies, types of civilizations, types of states—and, on the other hand, to distinguish periods characterized by the predominance of certain types. The period from 1300 to 1775 is too often regarded as a whole with little difference from beginning to end. The movement and flow of time is too often lacking in this study of history. Would it not be possible, at any rate for Europe and possibly for the world as a whole, to single out a period from 1300 to 1450 (in which Europe was moving towards a scientific and technological capitalist civilization which created the axle rudder with hinged stern-post, borrowed the magnetic needle from the Chinese, disseminated the bill of exchange and capitalism, invented the system of crank-shaft, launched the caravel—a ship suited for long ocean voyages—improved rural tools and the tools of craftsmen and, with the great nominalists, inspired by William of Ockham, Jean Buridan, Albert of Saxony, Nicolas Oresme, began the great intellectual mutation of mankind, the creation of mathematical physics), a renaissance period from 1450 to 1650, and an Age of Enlightenment from 1650 to 1775? At the very least, an effort should have been made to determine a period, or periods, allowing for all the factors and all the aspects of civilizations.

'Finally the absence of any synthesis has made it impossible to establish hierarchies between civilizations, between peoples, and between states. These hierarchies could be established according to several very different criteria: the rôle played during a given period in the general movement of history, scientific creations and inventions, the intensity and quality of religious spirituality, etc. But it would seem to be the duty of the historian to establish such hierarchies, to constitute within orders of human activity various series of growing intensity and to distribute human groups at different levels. The authors of the book undoubtedly rejected any hierarchic structure because they confused the establishment of such series with value judgments and were reluctant to call into question the dignity of a given people or state. But nobody could take offence at such observations and, in any case, all civilizations, all regions of the globe, all peoples, all states have contributed in turn to the general advancement of mankind. Could anyone have felt injured if the authors had emphasized the preponderant rôle played by Europe in the constitution of modern science, in the religious, philosophic and political movement? Such observations are also part of the historians' profession.'

Professor Louis Gottschalk and his associates, having considered Professor Roland Mousnier's strictures, wrote the following comment:

'Without denying the validity of Professor Mousnier's comments as one historian's approach to world history, the authors of Volume IV claim that, in part at least, they have conformed to his specifications and that in so far as they have departed from them, they did so in keeping with another equally justifiable concept of global history.

'Professor Mousnier, they take it, does not mean to imply that the names, developments, and periods he gives by way of illustration of his approach are not contained in their text; rather he means that individual regions, periods, etc., do not receive sufficient evaluation and characterization, and that the main interrelations among developments are not clearly enough delineated.

'On the matter of evaluation and characterization, the authors think they have assigned as much space and prominence as the chronological and geographical dimensions of their subject and physical manufacturing limitations of their book would permit to the cultural and scientific achievements which they judged worthy of selection. Of course, another team of authors would probably have made a different selection in some regards and with different relative emphasis, but that another selection might have been as good or perhaps better is debatable and, in any event, does not render theirs untenable.

'If their presentation sometimes leaves the interrelations between cultural developments obscure, as Professor Mousnier claims, it is probably because such is a more or less inevitable result of the topical arrangement which they, fully conscious of the risk, have nevertheless chosen for their presentation. They, and the International Commission as a whole, believed that the topical arrangement for a history of the cultural and scientific development of mankind, if it was not to centre upon a preferred continent, region, or culture, was preferable to a strictly chronological or geographical arrangement, since it would permit laying emphasis upon developments within the separate departments of culture and science, subordinating biographical, chronological, and geographical details to their place inside the larger subjects of the chapters. It is true that, thus the work of the same personality (Pascal, for example) may be discussed in several different contexts—as a physicist, a mathematician, a philosopher, a theologian, a man of letters, etc.—but they have tried to counterbalance this sort of vivesection by frequent cross-references and by numerous reminders that developments in a given field of endeavour depend upon developments in others, whether antecedent or concurrent.'

GUY S. MÉTRAUX
Secretary-General

CONTENTS

ILLUSTRATIONS

All illustrations are grouped together following page 542

Chinese Painting, 1300–1775

Architecture and Painting in Japan

The Evolution of Science

ILLUSTRATIONS IN LINE

All line drawings were executed especially for this work by Stella Robinson in collaboration with R. G. Hadlow.

LIST OF MAPS

ACKNOWLEDGEMENTS

Alinari, Florence
Archaeological Survey of India ASI
Archives de l'Assistance publique, Paris
Bayerisches Nationalmuseum Munich BNM
Berlin Staatlichen Museen BSM
Bibliothèque Nationale, Paris BN
Bildarchiv Foto-Marburg BFM
Central Office of Information in London BI
Cincinnati Art Museum, Cincinnati (Ohio)
Commission of the French Republic for Education, Science and
    Culture CESC
Editions Robert Laffont, Paris
Freer Gallery of Art, Smithsonian Institution, Washington D.C.
Vladimir Fyman
Giraudon, Paris
Honolulu Academy of Arts, Honolulu, Hawaii
Indian National Commission for Cooperation with Unesco
Institute of History, Moscow
Instituto Nacional de Antropolgia e Historia, Mexico INAH
Japanese National Commission for Unesco JCU
Paolo Koch
Guy S. Métraux GSM
Mexican Embassy, Paris MEP
Musée d'Art et d'Histoire, Geneva MAG
Musée du Louvre, Paris LOUVRE
Museum of the History of Science, Oxford
Museum für Kunsthandwerk, Frankfurt a.M. MKF
Museum für Völkerkunde und Vorgeschichte, Hamburg
National Gallery, London NG
National Palace Museum, Taipei, Taiwan
Oeffentliche Kunstsammlung Basel ÖKB
Josephine Powell
Roger-Viollet
Royal Museum of the History of Science, Leiden
    (Courtesy of Dr Maria Rooseboom)
Science Museum, London SML
Seattle Museum, Seattle (Wash.)
Service de Documentation Photographique des Musées Nationaux
    SMN
Spanish National Commission for Unesco SCU
Swedish National Commission for Unesco
University of Minnesota Library, James Ford Bell Collection
    (Minn.)
Yale University Library, Map Collection, New Haven (Conn.)
    YALE

CHAPTER I

THE POLITICAL, ECONOMIC, AND SOCIAL BACKGROUND

NATIONAL DEVELOPMENTS (1300–1775)

THE political geography of the world of 1775 would have appeared relatively familiar to modern viewers of the generations before World War I. It revealed a few more or less extensive states in Eurasia roughly like those known in 1914—the Japanese, Chinese, Russian, Ottoman, and Habsburg empires. It showed vast colonial realms dominated by the Dutch, the Spanish, the Portuguese, and the British in southern and southeastern Asia, parts of Africa, and the Americas. It suggested in western Europe the national consolidation of Spain, Portugal, France, Great Britain, Holland, Denmark, and Sweden. The fragmentation of Germany and Italy might still have reminded the modern viewer of the confusing political systems of the Middle Ages, but even there feudal relationships had virtually broken down, and on their ruins more powerful and centralized states or consolidated dynastic realms had arisen. Although in 1775 borders frequently were vaguely defined, unsurveyed, or in dispute, the political affiliations of many areas were fairly discernible. Several different kinds of political entities existed. Among them were to be found sprawling but contiguous empires and Western colonial empires, ethnically unified states and kingdoms that bound ethnically divergent groups together by dynastic ties, crowded city states and tiny principalities, and tight or loose tribal organizations, while some peoples formed parts of greater states without having lost their sense of being separate nations, though temporarily suppressed or frustrated.

Compare that relative clarity of 1775 with the geographical situation in 1300. For one thing, in regions remote from the more advanced civilizations the tribal structure was probably a more prevalent type of political organization at the earlier date. In general, the tribe was a loosely organized unit in which the obligations of kinship were usually more important than governmental authority. The numerical strength of the tribes was comparatively small, and the areas in which they lived were sparsely populated—e.g. the semi-deserts of north central and south central Africa or central Asia, the prairies of central North America, the steppes of Siberia, the jungles of central Africa and southern America, and the island world of the Pacific Ocean. Often the demarcations of their holdings were provided by some protective topographical feature such as a wide river, a high mountain range, or a thick forest. In general, very little is known about the political history of these tribal peoples in 1300 except where they came into contact with more urban, literate, or civilized peoples such as the Aztecs and Incas, the Chinese and Hindus, or the Muslims and Christians, or where more recently anthropologists have provided some knowledge about their culture.

*   *   *

Tribal Peoples

At times some of these nomadic peoples played an important part in the political history of the higher civilizations. Such was the role of a semi-nomadic people, the Mongols of inner Asia, who, under the leadership of great chieftains like Kublai Khan (d. 1294), founded a new dynasty in China (the Yūan dynasty, 1260–1368). In its day the Mongolian Empire was the largest relatively consolidated realm of the world. It stretched from the Yellow to the Black Sea and from Mongolia to Vietnam (Annam). At its height it included not only Mongolia, Turkistan, and other central Asian areas, where the Mongols had originated, but also Tibet and China, which they now considered their major seat; and it nominally had the allegiance of Korea, the Tatar Empire of the Golden Horde, which included the areas around Moscow and Kiev, and the enormous Persian Empire of the Ilkhans, which reached between India and the Byzantine Empire. The Mongol Empire was not destined, however, to last many decades beyond 1300.

No political achievement comparable to the formation of the enormous Mongol realm was performed by tribal peoples during our period. Timur (the fabled Tamerlane) revived the Chagatai Mongol power at Samarqand in the last decades of the fourteenth century and created an ephemeral empire from Anatolia and the Sea of Azov to northern India in imitation of the original Mongols, but, except for his beautifying of Samarqand, his role was chiefly destructive. Between the end of the fourteenth and the beginning of the sixteenth century the Turkoman tribes of the Black Sheep and the White Sheep played a significant part in Persia's history, mostly by supplanting one another in control and by becoming enmeshed in military entanglements with the successors of Timur (the Timurids). And Tai and Shan tribes were involved in Siam and Burma during the early phases of our period. But Asia's history was not to centre on tribal peoples.

Of sub-Saharan Africa knowledge even for the greater realms of our period is derived chiefly from the incomplete accounts of Muslim and other travellers. Between 1300 and 1775 some of these lands had an arresting political history. In the Sudan region, exposed to Islamic penetration from the north, lived Negro tribal peoples that had developed a high culture, now generally called Sudanic. One of the Sudanic peoples that inhabited the upper valley of the Niger was sometimes called Mandingo, from the name of its area, Mandé. This people built up a Mandingo empire[1] (1238–1488) which by any criteria was huge and which reached its peak during the fourteenth century. This empire was known to Arab geographers as that of the Mali and its people as Malinké. Their most illustrious ruler, Mansa ('king') Musa (1307-32), won the submission of the neighbouring land of Songhai and its inhabitants, the Soninké, a Negro people to their north who had already made Timbuktu a great commercial centre and Gao an impressive capital. Amid these cities of grass huts Mansa Musa's architect Es-Saheli built enduring buildings of sundried brick. Musa made a pilgrimage to Mecca in 1324 with a vast retinue and established a probably deserved reputation for piety and charity.

In the fifteenth century the Mali empire was partly conquered and superseded by a Songhai empire (1488-1591), and with the rise of the Mande-speaking Bambara kingdoms on the Niger in the seventeenth century, the Mandingo empire of the Mali lost nearly all of its remaining power. The Songhai rulers meanwhile made Jenne their commercial capital and Timbuktu a renowned Islamic cultural centre with its own university and library. Mohammed Ture (d. 1528), the most famous of the Songhai kings, is sometimes called 'the Great'. He took the dynastic name of *Askia*, which seems to apply to his unacceptability ('he is not' or 'he shall not be') to his predecessors, and founded a line of Askias. He caught the attention of the entire Islamic world by his imposing retinue and generous alms upon a pilgrimage to Mecca. The prosperity of cities like Gao, Jenne, and Timbuktu attracted raiders—twice, for example, the Mossi of the Volta valley (1333 and 1477)—and they were conquered by the Muslims of Morocco in 1591-92. Although Timbuktu achieved independence again in the 1660's, their prosperity vanished.

Farther inland, among the Hausa people in the Lake Chad region, Kano, another Islamic city, then became the metropolis of the trans-Sahara trade. Even during the lifetime of Askia Mohammed, a confederation of city kingdoms of the Hausa tribe had begun to displace the Songhai dominion in its eastern reaches. At the end of the sixteenth century King Idris Alooma (1571-1603) of Bornu conquered Kano and most of the nearby areas and, provided with firearms by the Turks, founded the Kanem-Bornu empire. Invaded in its turn by its neighbours, this empire began to crumble by the end of the eighteenth century. The Bagirmi and Wadai kingdoms were foremost among its threatening neighbours.

Other African kingdoms burgeoned at different times during our period and continued beyond it. The absolute monarchs of Dahomey won notoriety for their human sacrifices and their Amazon warriors. A powerful Ashanti federation flourished in the early eighteenth century under King Osai Tutu. In the region now called Nigeria, the Yoruba empire and the Benin kingdom developed a non-Islamic culture that won the admiration of European explorers and flourished until the nineteenth century (see Chapter XII).

These sub-Saharan kingdoms and empires were generally Negroid in race and often Muslim in religion (see Chapter II). Their chief articles of commerce were salt, gold, ivory, and slaves. Some of them suffered greatly from Berber raids and conquests as well as from wars with one another. During our period, movement among the African peoples was particularly marked. Southward migrations and invasions of Hamitic-speaking Muslim peoples (including Tuaregs and Kabyles) took place in central Africa and west Sudan, while the Arabs pushed down the East African coast. In the southern half of the African continent peoples of Bantu origin (including Zulus and Kafirs), spreading for centuries from their original homeland in the Cameroons, reached from the mouth of the Congo east to Lake Tanganyika and from the vicinity of the Cape north to the Ogoue River and today occupy approximately a third or more of Africa. They built huge empires: the realm of the *Mwenemutapa* (or Monomotapa, as the ruler at the 'royal village', the Great Zimbabwe, was called by the Portuguese) flourished from the thirteenth to the eighteenth century in the Zambesi valley; their neighbours, the dynasty of the Changamiras, created a rival stone-building culture within a state whose zenith came in the late sixteenth and early seventeenth century; the power of the Xosa-Kafirs rose to a high point under King Palo (d. 1775); and kings with the dynastic title of Mwata Yamwo founded a Luba-Linda kingdom that in the middle of the seventeenth century dominated the Angola–Congo region and remained strong until the close of the nineteenth century.

In the east central part of the African continent lay the ancient Ethiopian monarchy. Still retaining its Coptic Christian traditions, it was sometimes identified with the fabled land of Prester John. It constituted the most durable and cohesive state of sub-Saharan Africa. For a short while during the sixteenth century it established contact with the Portuguese, only to expel them as soon as differences developed over religious policies.

Contact with Europeans was generally more disastrous for tribal peoples than the continuing contact with other civilized peoples such as the Arabs. Conflict with Europeans usually ended in the subjugation, at times the eradication, of the tribes or in their gradual dispersion to the less habitable regions. Beginning in the sixteenth century, the Spanish subjugated the Philippines and the Marianas, the Portuguese and the Dutch some of the Malaysian archipelago. After 1450 much of sub-Saharan Africa's coastal regions passed step by step under the political and especially the commercial control of the Portuguese, Spanish, Dutch, British, and French. With the introduction of the plantation system in the Americas, Negro tribes of west Africa were with increasing frequency sought by slave-traders, and large numbers of Negroes, some already slaves and purchased, others brazenly kidnapped, were packed off to bondage in the New World. In our period, however, Europeans in Africa and Asia rarely went beyond their widely scattered coastal settlements. Russian expansion into central Asia and Siberia after the fifteenth century, since it went overland, was an exception to the general rule, and it was perhaps even more effective therefore in putting an end to the political, though not always the cultural, independence of many of the tribes encountered.

In America sensational, and often tragic, conflicts occurred between Europeans and Americans. The Spanish and the Portuguese established dominion not only over the highly civilized Incas, Chibchas, and Aztecs but also over many primitive Indian peoples. The Iberian rulers regarded the Indians as subjects. In the centuries that followed the initial conquests a number of tribes, especially those in *reducciones* (separated settlements) or in areas protected by missions, preserved their racial purity, but through intermarriage with and economic dependence upon Whites, others were largely absorbed in a Latin-American melting-pot of peoples, and a few, especially in the Caribbean islands, were exterminated by war or disease.

The North American Indians of the Atlantic and Great Lakes region had a somewhat different fate. In the beginning these Indian tribes were regarded as sovereign states. In the areas of French domination they enjoyed a relatively peaceful co-existence with their new neighbours, chiefly because of the sparseness of French colonization and the French settler's readiness to make alliances with them. The British, Dutch, and Swedish settlers, however, with a driving hunger for land and a marked reluctance to mingle directly with the Indians, became embroiled in frequent and embittered wilderness warfare, in the course of which whole tribes were either extirpated or pushed farther and farther inland. Attempts at peaceful cooperation (such as those of Roger Williams in Connecticut and William Penn in Pennsylvania), though conspicuous, were rare. The eastern coast of North America became largely a white man's country, while the displacement of the Indian and the Negro created problems that have remained thorny ones down to our own times.

★   ★   ★

Asian Empires

Before our period began, some regions had been organized at least nominally into states of vast dimensions. In the Far East the dominant political unit was the huge realm of China. Around this core were loosely grouped the more or less unified states of the Japanese Empire, the kingdoms of Korea and Vietnam, and to the north and northwest the tribal organizations of Manchu, Mongols, and Uighurs. The kingdoms of Burma, Cambodia, and Siam and the great island world of southeast Asia, all of which looked to India for cultural leadership, were united under the Javanese state of Singhasari. Several Muslim and Hindu kingdoms, some of them of enormous area, shared the Indian subcontinent. The Islamic states of the Middle East and the northern coast of Africa, though for a long time ruled by independent dynasties, had until 1258 owed a shadowy homage to the 'universal' caliphate of the Baghdad 'Abbāsids. In eastern Europe the Byzantine Empire was a direct descendant of imperial Rome, and in the West the myth of a Christendom united in a Holy Roman Empire was still a potent though troublesome factor, especially in the German lands. In the Americas the Aztecs, Chibchas, and Incas had also built great empires.

During the century roughly centring in the year 1300 some of these huge realms underwent tremendous turmoil and change. In Asia the great Mongol khans upset the established dynasties by imposing their vast dominion upon China and its empire. In the Malay island world the Javanese empire fell to pieces. The Muslims extended their sway almost throughout the Indian subcontinent but then broke up into several, though still strong, Islamic kingdoms. In the Middle East the existing political order was overthrown by other Mongol conquerors, and the ʿAbbāsid caliphate disappeared. In western Europe intermittent fights for the allegiance of Christendom between emperor and pope reduced the theory of the universal theocratic empire to impotence.

These turbulent events in Eurasia brought a period of readjustment during which much of the state system familiar to moderns evolved. Some of the great empires revived while others were superseded by governments of a different structure. On the ruins of some arose ethnically cohesive states, while in others strong dynasties managed to hold together divergent peoples. Sometimes previously insignificant states developed into powerful ones. Some of these states, in the main on Europe's Atlantic seacoast, created great colonial empires. Some European peoples, however, not strong enough to cope with more powerful neighbours, failed to achieve independent status.

The most interesting, and in some respects the most significant, political development in Europe between 1300 and 1775 was the growth of the national state—that is to say, a country centred on a more or less unified linguistic group, a culturally homogeneous population, or a largely accepted government. Sometimes a people was or thought it was relatively 'pure' ethnically (e.g. the Great Russians of the early Muscovite realm, the Swedes, or the Portuguese) so that it could easily be formed into a cohesive state. Sometimes a common historical background or a common cultural tradition in religion, education, literature, customs, and institutions exercised such a persuasive power that peoples within its reach could readily feel as one on current issues and anticipate a common destiny. At other times geographic compactness and common interests of commerce and defence held together culturally divergent peoples, as for instance in Spain, Switzerland, or Great Britain. Yet compactness was not always decisive: Italy, though relatively compact geographically and kindred culturally, failed to form a unified state. Dynastic policies and leadership helped to achieve political cohesion in certain instances where divergent traditions might otherwise have proved obstacles to union—e.g. France (united by Valois and Bourbon), Burgundy (itself destined to disappear but part of which was to be the precursor of the Low Countries), and Russia (in the course of its expansion after c. 1400). During our period, when popular government, and hence the feeling of personal identification with national affairs, was at best nascent and in most places unknown, the decisive factor in creating patriotism and a sense of national cohesion usually was a transcendent loyalty to the ruling dynasty.

The Chinese people had the oldest continuous sense of political solidarity. Over the centuries it had developed a cohesive civilization that was able either to absorb or to expel invading conquerors, so that it never ceased to exist as a relatively homogeneous state. The Mongols, though failing to make China the core of a lasting Mongol empire, did succeed in establishing a branch of Chingiz Khan's family as a new dynasty on the Chinese throne (the Yüan dynasty, 1260–1368). In the course of time this dynasty became partly sinified and in any case put its dynastic interests ahead of those of the Mongols. The realm grew more unified than before, with some increase in territory to the north and southeast. The native Ming dynasty replaced the Mongol Yüan dynasty in 1368 but succumbed in turn (1644) to internal revolts and the invading Manchus from the north. Under the Manchus the realm remained a unified state and for a century and a half enjoyed prosperity. The Manchu dynasty continued to rule until the Chinese Revolution of 1911–12. It increased the empire by the inclusion of Manchuria (the Manchu homeland), the Amur area, Sinkiang, and Formosa (taken from the grandson of the pirate king Koxinga in 1683) and placed Tibet and Mongolia under China's supervision.

For many centuries before 1300 the Japanese had formed in their islands a nation with its own institutions, traditions, and culture, though it borrowed heavily from those of China. Notwithstanding internal divisions and devastating civil wars, the Japanese Empire had preserved its independence from Mongol attack (1274 and 1281). In the last quarter of the sixteenth century the great military leader Hideyoshi, with the help of Tokugawa Ieyasu, brought the internal wars to a conclusion. The Japanese then embarked on a programme of expansion. In 1592 and 1597 large-scale expeditions succeeded in seizing much of Korea, but the death of Hideyoshi and the drainage of resources induced the Japanese to give way before Korean naval power and the large Chinese armies that came in from the north. Ieyasu in 1603 founded the Tokugawa shogunate, a highly centralized regime which was to rule Japan in effect while the emperors remained nominal heads. Under Ieyasu Japanese traders ranged throughout eastern Asia and Japanese shipping rivalled Muslim and Christian in Chinese waters and the Indian Ocean. In the 1630's the shoguns, fearing Christianity and desiring to insure the stability of their regime, secluded Japan from other peoples, particularly Westerners, who in the sixteenth century had established footholds for trade and missions in the islands. After 1641 a small Dutch trading settlement on the closely guarded artificial island of Deshima near Nagasaki constituted the only contact with the Western world. Chinese traders also were permitted a limited access.

In addition to Japan, several states on the fringe of the Chinese colossus achieved a considerable degree of political unity. Korea, Vietnam, and the Tai kingdom of Siam (which arose in the fourteenth century) enjoyed local cohesion and virtual independence although sometimes recognizing a tributary relationship to the Chinese Empire. From the middle of the fourteenth to the middle of the sixteenth century, the Vijayanagar Empire of India remained a powerful Hindu state despite the conquest of north India by Muslim invaders. The Delhi sultanate, for all its ups and downs, was one of the most lasting states in Islamic annals. After 1500 the Muslim rulers at Delhi fashioned a strong, centrally administered state.

Another perdurable state of Asia was the Persian Empire. The cohesiveness of the ancient Persian culture had made that country a distinguishable area even during the centuries in which it had been part of the 'Abbāsid Caliphate. Since it was situated across the routes taken by the central Asiatic invaders on their way to the Near East, Persia suffered greatly for several centuries from a constant change of rulers. Various Turkish and Turkoman tribes, the Mongol Ilkhans, Kurds, Afghans, and the Timurids ruled Persia or parts of Persia at various times. When a greater measure of political stability returned to the Islamic world towards the end of the fifteenth century, a new dynasty, the Ṣafavids, succeeded, with the aid of a fresh combination of Turkish tribes, in establishing a new Persian Empire. The great Persian shahs of our period were 'Abbās the Great (1571–1629) and Nādir (1688–1747). The Persian Empire also became embroiled in religious conflicts resulting from the ancient division of Islam into Shi'ites and Sunnites; the Persians for the most part remained loyal Shi'ites (see Chapter II). The Persians' pride in their language (though some of them did not speak Persian), the glory of their cities (especially Isfahan, 'half the world'), their preferred version of the Islamic religion, their age-old cultural traditions, and their successful maintenance of political independence enabled them to attain a cohesive loyalty and political unity during our period, despite the rivalries of clans and tribes, the succession of dynasties, and the frequency of war with their neighbours.

To the northwest of Persia arose a state that was destined to become one of the greatest powers of modern history. Until the fifteenth century most of the area now known as Russia lay under the domination of a mixed Asian people led by Mongols and generally called Tatars. Beginning in the thirteenth century the Tatars invaded Russia in two waves—first the Golden Horde and then the White Horde. Their government was the Kipchak Khanate. In the fourteenth century the princes of Moscow began the lengthy process of shaking off Tatar suzerainty. In 1380 on the Kulikovo Plain the Russian princes, united behind Dimitri Donskoi (1350–89), grand prince of Moscow, defeated the Golden Horde in a battle sometimes said to have had no fewer than 300,000 participants. Thereafter, though Moscow was again threatened, the Tatar yoke grew weaker. Towards the end of the fifteenth century the suzerainty of the Golden Horde was ended, leaving small and disunited Tatar lands on the periphery of Russia.

East Europe

Meanwhile the princes of Moscow had initiated a systematic expansion to the north and west towards the Novgorod Republic, the Lithuanians, and the Poles and to the east towards Tatar Kazan. After the end of the Byzantine Caesars (see below), Ivan III (the Great) claimed, and Ivan IV (the Terrible) actually assumed, the title of *czar*, or *tsar*. The conquests of these two rulers extended Russia by 1580 approximately to the Dnieper Valley and the Gulf of Finland in the west, the White Sea in the north, the Ural Mountains and the Ural River in the east, and the Caspian Sea and the lands bordering on the Black Sea in the south. In the early decades of the seventeenth century Russia endured a period of serious internal strife occasioned by boyar rivalries and aggravated by peasant wars and foreign interventions ('the Time of Troubles'). The country recovered quickly, however, and throughout the century energetically settled the steppes of southern Russia and explored Siberia (see Chapter XIV). Peter the Great (1672–1725) continued the work of expansion, particularly to the northwest, and in a prolonged struggle known as the Great Northern War (1700–21) with the adventurous Swedish king Charles XII (1682–1718), Peter obtained an outlet to the Baltic Sea, founded St Petersburg, and made it his capital. He also sent armies to the south against the Ottoman Empire to gain an outlet to the Black Sea, but that aim was definitely accomplished only under Catherine the Great (1729–96). Before the close of her reign, Catherine reached much farther still in both directions, at the expense of the Polish kingdom and the Turks.

While the early expansion of the Moscovite state had meant a unification of the Great Russian peoples, the conquests of the tsars brought other ethnic groups into the empire. In some instances, these were (like the White Russians and Ukrainians) closely related to the Great Russians or other Slavic peoples (like the Poles), but they also included some Europeans (like Esthonians, Livonians, and Lithuanians) who were not Slavs, as well as Asians (like Tatars, Kazaks, Kalmuks, Bashkirs, and Siberian nomads). Russians moved into the newly won lands as explorers, farmers, land owners, administrators, and soldiers. Certain 'russifying' policies were pursued by the tsars, and institutions closely associated with the rulers, such as the Russian Orthodox Church, formed a cohesive force making the vast polyglot empire a more or less united country.

To the west of the growing Russian colossus lay the largest nominally united European country of the day—the union of Poles and Lithuanians. Both peoples had been separately subjected to the *Drang nach Osten*, the eastward push of Germans during the Middle Ages, but each finally succeeded in putting a halt to inroads by the Teutonic Knights, who had been particularly active in the German expansion along the Baltic Sea. At the same time, the Poles helped to stem the Mongol advances into Europe from the east. Until the fourteenth century Lithuania and Poland formed separate and loosely organized countries, in which the power of the duke of Lithuania and the king of Poland was seldom stronger than that of the great magnates, towns, or tribal chieftains. Yet the ruling classes were ardent patriots, particularly in Poland, and their patriotic spirit grew stronger as their neighbours became more threatening.

Early in our period the two peoples were politically federated. The Lithuanian state was much larger and at first tended to be the stronger partner, but later Polish power completely overshadowed a rapidly disintegrating Lithuania. Lithuania and Poland formed a personal union when Duke Jagiello of Lithuania married Queen Jadwiga of Poland (1386). The territories of this united realm extended deep into White Russia and the Ukraine and at its southern end reached close to the shores of the Black Sea. Military successes against the Teutonic Knights, particularly the crushing Battle of Tannenberg (1410), ended the *Drang nach Osten* and helped to establish the union's closer control over the shores of the Baltic. The conversion to Catholicism of the Lithuanians, the last European people to adopt Christianity, also promoted the unity of the state.

For all its bigness, the Polish–Lithuanian kingdom was weak. The monarch was elective, and so no strong dynasty was established. The nobles who elected him frequently manoeuvred with foreign powers and candidates. Moreover, each Polish noble acquired the power to veto legislation in the Polish diet (Sejm) by the right known as *liberum veto*, and so the centrifugal tendencies continued in Poland at the very time that centralization had begun to enhance dynastic strength in neighbouring lands.

Thus the very size of the Polish–Lithuanian union was a source of weakness rather than of strength. When Russia seriously began its westward expansion and the newly founded Ottoman Empire (see pp. 17–18) pushed beyond the Black Sea regions, the union's territory shrank. After 1500 the Poles encountered on their borders a host of new powers that were interested in taking Polish lands. The consolidating Habsburg empire prevented further Polish expansion immediately to the south. To the west and northwest the growing state of Brandenburg-Prussia threatened expansion eastward at the cost of Poland. To the north and northwest the Swedish kingdom during the seventeenth century established a dominant position on the Baltic coasts and frequently clashed with Poland over trade, territory, and dynastic issues. Moments of greatness, exhibited in such feats as the daring Polish expedition into Russia (1607–09) and the valiant service rendered to western Christendom by King John Sobieski's rescue of Vienna (1683), did not suffice to save Poland from the encroachment of its neighbours. By the end of the seventeenth century Poland had become internally weak, and the Polish crown during the subsequent century became a pawn of various European powers. Although the map of Europe in 1772 still showed Poland as one of the largest continental states, it had not much longer to survive as such. That year it became the victim of its three most powerful neighbours, Russia, Prussia, and Austria. Despite Polish resistance, they took large parts of Poland's territories in the first of three partitions whereby, before the end of the eighteenth century, Poland became chiefly an historical memory and a patriotic cause.

Northern Europe

In northernmost Europe lived the Danes, Norwegians, and Swedes, whose similar languages, customs, and ethnical character might have served to unite them into one Scandinavian state. By 1300, however, they had been separate and independent kingdoms for nearly three hundred years. Dynastic inter-marriage gave Denmark and Norway in 1375 a joint ruler, and in 1389 Queen Margaret, already regent of Denmark and Norway, succeeded in ousting an unpopular German ruler from Sweden. In 1397 at Kalmar she proclaimed her nearest kinsman, Eric, king of all three realms. This so-called Union of Kalmar lasted nominally for well over a century, though punctuated by long periods of Swedish independence. In 1520 Sweden and Denmark–Norway separated definitively (see pp. 262–63). Finland, whose people were Swedish and Finnish, remained part of the Swedish kingdom.

Meanwhile, in 1450, Denmark had concluded 'a perpetual union' with Norway, which was to last actually only until 1814. Denmark–Norway engaged in several important political conflicts during our period. Among them were the struggle by which the joint kingdom freed itself from the economic control of the North German Hansa (a remarkable economic league of towns about which more will be said later), the intervention under Christian IV on behalf of the German Protestants during the Thirty Years' War, and a series of wars with Sweden over control of the Sound, the main gateway from the North Sea to the Baltic. These conflicts assured Denmark–Norway of its independence.

Sweden, despite its very sparse population, was destined to be one of Europe's greatest powers during the seventeenth century. After consolidating its home territory, the Swedish house of Vasa began to expand along the shores of the Baltic. By 1617 Sweden had wrested Karelia, Ingria, Esthonia, and Livonia from the Russian Empire. Shortly afterwards, Swedish armies under King Gustavus Adolphus played a heroic role in the Thirty Years' War, marching hither and thither in Germany to aid the German Protestant cause. From this war Sweden emerged as the greatest of the northern powers, having acquired both an enviable military reputation and new Baltic posses-sions in Pomerania and at the mouth of the Elbe River. It was able to maintain and even to promote its Baltic domination against powers like Denmark and Poland, but at the beginning of the eighteenth century the rising states of Brandenburg–Prussia and Russia began to chip away its possessions. By military victories and diplomatic skill Brandenburg–Prussia annexed part of Pomerania, while Russia moved into the northeastern Baltic area. The defensive–offensive exploits of Sweden's young king Charles XII during the long Northern War (1700–21) took Swedish armies on romantic invasions deep into Poland and Russia, but they exhausted the home country. At the war's end Sweden lost nearly all its possessions south of Finland and thenceforth played only a minor role in European political affairs.

*   *   *

Western Europe

The most notable examples of the rising national state during our period were provided by three large western European countries (Britain, France, and Spain) and three small ones (Portugal, the Netherlands, and Switzerland). Except for the Netherlands, unification began in all these countries before 1300. Four (Britain, France, Spain, and Portugal) were created by strong dynasties.

Since the time of the Angevin kings the English monarch had been accumulating power in the British Isles. By 1300 England had an uncertain claim to most of eastern Ireland and a temporary suzerainty over Scotland. In 1301 an English prince for the first time took the title of prince of Wales, though Wales was not incorporated with England until 1536. Scotland regained its independence in 1314 at the Battle of Bannockburn and preserved it by a series of wars, usually in alliance with France, until final union with England through the accession of the house of Stuart to the English throne in 1603. A formal Act of Union in 1707, by uniting the parliaments of England and Scotland, created the United Kingdom of Great Britain. A pretender's rebellion in the middle of the eighteenth century was the United Kingdom's last serious domestic war outside Ireland; it ended in failure. English dominion over Ireland, though challenged on several occasions, was not firmly established until the eighteenth century, but the British Isles nevertheless remained a single strong state. It was essentially the United Kingdom of Great Britain and Ireland, although that name did not become official until the Act of Union with Ireland in 1801.

During this time England had not been exclusively an island power. From the times of its Norman and Angevin rulers it had inherited claims to large areas of western France and in 1300 still controlled the southwestern lands of Guyenne and Gascony. In a prolonged series of wars with France, the so-called Hundred Years' War (1337–1453), the English kings attempted to exert and even to expand their continental claims. On the death of their warrior-king Henry V, the English were actually in control of the northern half of France and still retained portions of the southwest. Joan of Arc's feats at Orleans, however, turned the tide in favour of the French (1428–29), and the English began to retreat. By 1453 they retained only a narrow strip opposite Dover, and even that remnant was surrendered in 1559. England thus lost its continental empire, but about the time that it was reduced to an island realm in Europe, its seamen set out to conquer one of the greatest colonial empires of all time.

The rise of France was interwoven with England's continental losses. It was in part the outcome of the long struggle of the Capetian monarchs to establish control over every vassal and province of the land. Their progress was impeded by English conquests during the Hundred Years' War but was resumed under Joan of Arc's leadership. In subsequent centuries the forces threatening to disrupt national unity were broken. The Duchy of Burgundy, which we shall encounter again and again as one of the richest, strongest, and most cultured states of Europe during the fifteenth century, was brought down by the machinations of the French king Louis XI (1461–83) and the ambitions of its own last duke, Charles the Bold. Thereafter France's principal source of danger, which felt in turn endangered by French advances, was the Austrian Habsburg dynasty, which not only ruled in the Austrian duchies, Bohemia, and Hungary but also regularly held the imperial title in the Holy Roman Empire and, until 1700, could count on a family alliance with Spain. France's northeastern border was consistently pushed farther towards the Rhine at the expense of the Habsburgs and the Holy Roman Empire; in a series of wars that continued until 1713 some important Flemish towns and fortresses passed into French hands. Meanwhile the particularism of the Huguenot (French Protestant) towns and the prouder nobles was ended, though only after serious religious and civil conflict. By the final decades of the seventeenth century France had become a unified and centralized state in which, despite continuing regional differences, all acknowledged allegiance to the same Bourbon dynasty.

Almost as soon as it had rid itself of its English conquerors, France asserted itself as a great power in international affairs and began to strive for what later came to be called its 'natural boundaries'. In the seventeenth century, guided by able kings or statesmen like Henry IV, Richelieu, Mazarin, and Louis XIV, it acquired important border territories in drawn-out conflicts. Beyond the threshold of its 'natural frontiers', however, France frequently ran into stolid opposition and had less success. In its Italian ventures it encountered the effective resistance of the Habsburgs, both Spanish and Austrian. The same foes, supported by the Dutch and the English, thwarted France's encroachments on the Spanish Netherlands (now Belgium) and the Rhineland. A bold attempt under Louis XIV to gain control of Spain through something resembling a personal union failed because of the coalition of Europe's great powers in the War of the Spanish Succession (1701–13).

If France's more ambitious projects of expansion came to naught, its statesmen, by an effective system of alliances, succeeded in preventing inroads on French territories. Against the encircling Habsburgs, France could always bring a Turkish, Polish, Prussian, or Swedish ally into the field, but when Prussia became a common danger to them both, the Bourbons and the Habsburgs contrived a 'diplomatic revolution' by becoming allies. Against England, Scotland and Spain served France as ready assistants. And, until the nineteenth century, by playing the many states within Germany and Italy against one another, France prevented the rise of strong united powers on its eastern and southeastern frontiers.

Until the thirteenth century the Iberian peninsula had been dominated by the Moors. Only in the more rugged, mountainous areas of the north did the Christian states of Portugal, Leon, Castile, Navarre, and Aragon succeed in preserving their independence. By 1300, led by the kingdoms of Castile and Aragon and the duchy of Portugal, they had succeeded in breaking the Muslim power, now confined to a section in the south around Granada. Portugal had become a united state, incorporating all the territory it was ever destined to hold in Europe. In the Battle of Aljubarrota (1385) the Portuguese decisively upheld their independence against the Castillians and, with the exception of a sixty-year period (1580–1640) in which Portugal was bound to Spain by a personal union, remained independent. Until the Napoleonic era Portugal's status as a unified nation was not again threatened. Meanwhile its tremendous colonial exploits carried Europe's influence to several other continents.

In the country that is now called Spain the founding of a unified nation was more gradual. After the Muslim possessions were reduced, the rest of the country remained a congeries of rival Christian kingdoms, but, as frequently happened elsewhere, dynastic alliances finally provided the answer to their disunity. Leon had already been merged with Castile in this way in the thirteenth century. In 1469 the heiress of the Castillian throne, Isabella, married Ferdinand, the heir of Aragon, and as the 'Catholic Kings', this royal couple laid the foundations of a unified Spain. They tied the country together by a stern programme of administrative and ecclesiastical reforms, conquered Granada, the only remaining Moorish state on Spanish soil, and by supporting Columbus's venture (see Chapter XIII) began a vast overseas empire. The Spain that they left to their successors retained its unity thereafter, though troubled at times by particularist tendencies. Jews and Moors, although they had lived in Spain for centuries, were eliminated by mass expulsions.

By the beginning of the sixteenth century, the calculated policy of Spain's rulers had made it a powerful and homogeneous state. Through further marriage alliances they gained possession also of two of Europe's richest areas, the Low Countries and northern Italy. In 1519 the man among whose many glittering titles was that of King of Spain as Charles I (1516–56), became also Emperor Charles V of the Holy Roman Empire. For a century thereafter Spanish forces not only dominated large parts of Europe but also protected it, standing off the Turks on land and sea. Spain managed to preserve its preponderance in Italy until the eighteenth century, but in northern Europe, where it served as the great protagonist of Catholicism, it was less successful. Despite its stubbornness in a war that lasted, on and off, for eighty years (1568–1648), it failed to subdue the insurgents of the northern Netherlands, aided at times by England. The failure to reimpose control upon the Dutch and to establish superiority over the English on the seas hastened the decline of Spain's political prestige. After 1700 it was generally considered a second-rate power, save for a brief resurgence under Charles III (1759–88).

Through the very struggle that marked Spain's decline the Dutch were forged into an independent, federated republic. Before some of them declared their independence from Spain (1581), the collection of 'provinces' known as the Netherlands or Low Countries had formed no united state, for their political allegiance was divided in most complicated ways. Nominally at least they were a part of the Holy Roman Empire, although certain provinces had stronger political ties with France. Furthermore, the various provinces were engaged in feuds with one another—Flanders and Holland over the possession of Zeeland; Holland, Friesland, and Utrecht over control of the Zuider Zee. In 1363 an event occurred that ultimately was to have significant consequences for the Low Countries. King John the Good of France conferred the Duchy of Burgundy on his son Philip the Bold, who subsequently, like many other medieval dynasts, increased the size of his realm by war, diplomacy, and marriage. Philip got possession of most of the Netherland provinces by marrying Margaret of Flanders. In the ensuing century the Burgundian possessions (now including the Low Countries) developed into one of the richest and most powerful realms of western Europe. But for the rash ambitions of Duke Charles the Bold of Burgundy (1433–77) it might have become an enduring Rhineland kingdom. Charles's overreaching was foiled, however, by his Swiss, French, and German rivals, and all that remained to the immediate heir of his once far-flung holdings was the Low Countries. Nevertheless, Charles's successors continued to make illustrious matches, and thus in 1515 one of them not only inherited the Habsburg domains of Austria as well as the Low Countries but also became King Charles I of Spain. This was the young man who, as already indicated, four years later was elected to the throne of the Holy Roman Empire. He was thenceforth generally known as Emperor Charles V.

Upon Charles's voluntary abdication, the Low Countries passed (1555) to his son Philip. Philip II, unlike his father, considered himself primarily a Spaniard. He soon had a major revolt on his hands, for he disregarded local privileges and customs, tried to suppress the Protestant heresy, and sought to confine the Low Countries within the Spanish orbit. In the Eighty Years' War already mentioned the Spanish managed to keep only the southern provinces (essentially present-day Belgium), while the northern provinces succeeded in winning their independence. They thus, along with the earlier examples of Switzerland and Bohemia, provided a modern precedent of successful revolt—in this case, largely middle-class—against a disowned monarchy.

Out of these northern provinces grew a remarkable little state. Notwithstanding its loose federal structure and diversity of interests, it became one of the most prosperous and powerful nations of seventeenth-century Europe. The new United Provinces, or Dutch Republic, had a hereditary 'semi-royal' stadholder who, when an effective leader, did much to hold the divergent provinces together. The Dutch Republic became a rich country, especially after its navigators discovered and claimed a vast colonial empire. It was perhaps the greatest naval power of the seventeenth century until it lost out to the English, although by that time the Dutch stadholder, William III, had become the king of England. Gradually thereafter its status as a world power declined. Yet, despite internal crises, it continued to provide a conspicuous example of how areas with diversified backgrounds and interests but with a common memory of a common fight for a common cause might form a strong national union.

Another remarkable example of a nation composed of almost autonomous units with greatly divergent interests was the Swiss Confederation. The sharp decline of the power of the Holy Roman Empire during the thirteenth century gave some of the Swiss cantons (originally only Uri, Schwyz, and Unterwalden) a chance to begin a long fight for independence and self-determination. By successful battles over three centuries they shook off the authority of the Habsburgs, Burgundy, and Savoy, and resisted the attempts of German emperors and French kings to control their mountain passes, which formed the main avenues between Italy and northern Europe. In the course of these wars, in which the Swiss won an impressive reputation for military prowess, other cantons joined the original three in a loose federation. A federal diet guaranteed a certain unity among them against foreign powers but left the major participating cantons with their different ethnic and linguistic populations almost completely autonomous. Despite numerous inter-cantonal wars, which increased in bitterness during the Reformation, when the country divided into Protestant and Catholic cantons, the federation held together.

*　　*　　*

Heterogeneous Empires

Dynastic centralization, though often resisted by feudal nobles and imposed upon unwilling populations, yet served as a major stage on the road to modern popular nationalism. In an era of relatively primitive methods of communication and transportation, the great empires, though also created and dominated by ambitious dynasts, were, by their very size and heterogeneity, generally less effective than the more compact realms in this nationalizing process.

The Mogul Empire of India was one of these overgrown dynastic creations. At the beginning of our period the vast sub-continent of India, approximately as large in area as western and central Europe combined and probably larger in population, had been inhabited by peoples (as we shall see in the chapters below that discuss religions and languages) that were no less varied than Europeans and no less divided among conflicting states. In 1300, the northern states were more or less controlled by the Muslim sultan of Delhi, Muslims were engaged in conquering the Deccan, and Muslim conquest of the

Dravidian Hindu far-south bade fair to succeed also until (*c.* 1335) it was stopped by the formation of the Vijayanagar kingdom. At the end of the fourteenth century, the Delhi empire lost its more southerly provinces to independent Muslim dynasties and then was shattered by Timur's thrust. Thereupon several rival sultans arose in north India. At the beginning of the sixteenth century, a descendant of Timur, Bābur, king of Ferghana, conqueror of Kabul, and thereby ruler of Afghanistan, began the conquest of India. From about 1525 to about 1750 the Mogul Empire, thus founded, united great bodies of Hindus and Muslims under the rule of one powerful house. The early Mogul princes Bābur and Akbar established their sway over a host of previously disunited principalities, and Mogul dominion reached its greatest extension with the incorporation of the southern parts of the Deccan into the empire by Aurangzīb, the last great ruler (1658–1707). The empire, tied together for over two centuries by effective military relations and a sound administration, was characterized at times by an extraordinarily tolerant religious policy, which permitted Hindus and Muslims to live peaceably together (see pp. 340–42). Its eventual collapse was due to a combination of circumstances, prominent among which were the reversal by Aurangzīb of the policy of tolerance, the ineffectiveness of the later Mogul rulers, invasions of the northern areas by Afghans and Persians, the independence movements of the Sikhs, the Marathas, and some of the southern states, and the development of an Indian commercial class in the great ports.

European activities were peripheral to Indian history for most of our period but had accumulating significance as time went on. The rivalry of the Portuguese, Dutch, French, and British for territorial and commercial advantages in India began in the seventeenth century and turned decisively in favour of the British when Robert Clive, at the head of the British East India Company's sepoy and European forces, routed a larger but disaffected Bengali army at Plassey in 1757. By that time, however, the Mogul Empire had already become a mere shadow of its earlier greatness. Indian nationalism was to develop only slowly in the ensuing centuries.

Two other great dynastic realms, the Habsburg and Turkish empires, were also far-flung, multinational states. Though they lasted as powerful international forces until the beginning of the twentieth century, their contribution to the growth of modern nationalism was different from India's, for they served as irritants and obstacles against which their minorities reacted.

For some time before 1300 a small Turkish state in northwestern Anatolia had served as a kind of frontier garrison at the border between the Seljuk Empire and the declining Byzantine realm. When the Seljuk Empire collapsed under the Mongol onslaught, these Turks began to expand westward. Under Ertogrul and his son Osman (1281–1326) they embarked upon a series of conquests that was to last for about three hundred years, resulting in an immense Osmanli (or Ottoman) Empire. The first conquests, chiefly at the expense of the Byzantine Empire, reached the Aegean shortly after 1300, and

In 1354 the Turks made their first permanent settlement on the western side of the Dardanelles. Despite fierce resistance, they gained possession of Bulgaria and defeated the Serbians in the storied Battle of Kossovo (1389)—permitting them, however, until 1459 to preserve a semblance of sovereignty. By 1453, of all the once great Byzantine Empire, only the metropolis of Constantinople still withstood them, but that year it too succumbed.

After the besieging forces of Sultan Mehmet II (1451–81) conquered the city, it became the centre of the ever-expanding Ottoman realm. The conqueror now added to his empire not only Serbia but also Bosnia, Albania, Greece, Wallachia, and the land of the Crim Tatars, as well as the eastern parts of Anatolia. For a while the advances in Europe were halted and efforts were concentrated on the conquest of Upper Mesopotamia and the Mamlūk (Mameluke) realm in Egypt and Syria. For about two and three quarters centuries (1250–1517) the Mamlūks had ruled in Egypt, forcing the Crusaders out of Syria, withstanding the Mongols and Timur, and making Egypt one of Islam's most highly developed countries and Cairo one of its most beautiful cities. In 1517 Cairo surrendered to the Turks, and by 1520 the eastern Mediterranean was under Turkish rule.

That year the greatest of all Ottoman sultans, Sulaimān the Lawgiver, known in the West as 'the Magnificent' (1494–1566), came to the throne. Under him the empire was practically doubled. Most of the northern coast of Africa was either directly conquered or submitted to Ottoman suzerainty. Armenia and Mesopotamia to the Persian Gulf became Turkish provinces, and European Christendom had good reasons to grow apprehensive of the Turkish peril when Sulaimān's troops conquered Hungary (including Transylvania and Moldavia) and laid siege to Vienna.

Europe had not known such a vast contiguous empire since the great days of Rome, and gradually awakening to the danger, it began a counter-offensive. In 1571 a Christian league badly defeated the Turkish fleet at Lepanto in the greatest naval battle since Actium, but with relatively small results. Though control over the western Mediterranean stayed with the Spanish Habsburgs and their Italian allies, the Barbary States of the Maghrib (Tripoli, Tunis, Algeria, Morocco) made much of the sea unsafe until the eighteenth century. On the European continent also the Ottoman Empire reached the peak of its power. Its last great effort to push into the heart of the continent came to naught when in 1683 combined European armies, particularly the Poles under Sobieski, relieved the Turkish siege of Vienna. After that, the steady advances of Russian and Habsburg power systematically reduced the size of the Ottoman realm. By the end of the eighteenth century it was still an enormous empire but weakened internally by nationalist movements among its conquered peoples. The concessions made to Russia by the Treaty of Kuchuk Kainarja in 1774 foreshadowed that Turkey's decline would soon constitute the delicate international problem that came to be known as 'the Near East Question'.

The proud dynasty that held together the great Christian multinational state of our period originated in the modest Swiss castle of Habsburg. Count Rudolf of Habsburg (1218–91) started his family's aggrandizement by acquiring Austria, Styria, and Carniola and by establishing the precedent for choosing the Habsburg ruler as Holy Roman emperor. The Habsburgs first expanded westward, but, as we have seen, early lost control of the Swiss cantons. Until 1500 their realm was primarily an upper Danubian state. Through a fortunate series of marriages (already outlined) the House of Habsburg allied itself to Burgundy and Spain. Thus it happened that Charles of Burgundy became the ruler of the Netherlands when his father died, of Spain with its Italian and colonial possessions when his maternal grandfather died, and of Austria when his paternal grandfather died, and in 1519 he was elected emperor.

A few years before his death, Charles, baffled by the complications of ruling so vast a realm, abdicated and divided it between his son Philip and his brother Ferdinand. Ferdinand inherited the Austrian dominions and the family claim to the imperial title. Through this title, which remained in their hands until 1806 (with a brief interruption in 1742–45), the eastern branch of the Habsburgs exercised considerable control over central Europe. Their real power, however, rested upon their vast territories in the Danubian area. Back in 1526 when the king of Bohemia and Hungary, Louis II, perished in battle with the Turks at Mohacs, Ferdinand, his brother-in-law, had been elected king of Bohemia and had advanced a claim to the throne of Hungary that was disputed by both Turks and local rivals. After almost two centuries of warfare with the Turks over the rich plain of Hungary and Transylvania, the Habsburgs finally achieved (1718) complete domination of the middle Danube and its principal tributaries up to the borders of present-day Rumania. About the same time, in the partition that ended the War of the Spanish Succession, Austria acquired most of the formerly Spanish possessions in Italy and the Low Countries but soon lost all her Italian lands except Milan. Silesia, part of the Bohemian kingdom, was seized by Frederick II of Prussia in 1740, but by way of compensation the Habsburg realm was rounded out to the northeast by the acquisition of Galicia in the first Partition of Poland in 1772. Thus, by 1775 the Habsburg dynasty ruled over not only German-speaking Austria but also a vast realm of Czech, Slovak, Polish, Hungarian, Croat, Serbian, Rumanian, Italian, and Belgian peoples.[2]

*   *   *

Colonial Expansion

The type of political organization that consisted of a mother country and overseas settlements—i.e. the colonial empire—was not unknown before 1300, and with the global expansion of Europe's Atlantic nations after 1500, such empires became a familiar part of the international pattern. The forms of colonial possession varied a good deal. Some colonies consisted of areas in the Americas or Africa that were settled by Europeans themselves, as, for example, the Spanish in Mexico and the Rio de la Plata region, the Portuguese in Brazil, the Dutch in the Cape Colony, the French in the St Lawrence River valley, the English, the Dutch, and the Swedes along the Atlantic seaboard of North America, or the Spanish, the French, the English, the Dutch, and the Danes in the West Indies. In other instances, a small number of European conquerors imposed their rule upon a large indigenous population, gradually interbred with it, and thus eventually formed a new 'nation'. Interbreeding of this sort happened with the Spanish colonization of Mexico, Central and South America, and the Philippine Islands, and with the Portuguese coloniza-tion of Brazil and the Azores. In still other instances European traders, often employees of great, government-protected trading companies, gained within more or less civilized and sovereign states control over specified areas, to whose inhabitants they left a varying degree of autonomy so long as their own trading interests remained unaffected. Such control was established by the Portuguese in parts of India and the Indonesian archipelago, by the Dutch on Ceylon and in Malaysia (where they succeeded in largely eliminating Portu-guese and British competition), and by the British in India (where they superseded without totally replacing the Portuguese and the French). (Map I.)

The Portuguese and Spanish monarchies were the first great modern colonizing powers. Seafarers in their service early understood oceanic explora-tions (see Chapter XIII) and staked out claims for their masters in the lands they discovered. In order to forestall fruitless competition on the American continents, the two Iberian countries twice (1493 and 1494) submitted their rival claims to papal arbitration. Accordingly, by the Treaty of Tordesillas (1494), the Spanish laid claim to all of America from the Gulf of Mexico to Cape Horn with the exception of Brazil, which was claimed by the Portu-guese. Spanish conquerors, at times with amazingly small armies, overran the great realms of the Aztecs, the Chibchas, and the Incas, and won fabulously rich lands for the Spanish crown, reaching well into the areas that now form the south and southwest of the United States. In the Pacific Spanish con-quests were limited to the Philippine Islands and other scattered archi-pelagoes. The Portuguese empire extended westward to the Azores and Brazil, southward to some coastal areas of west and east Africa, and thence to scattered trading settlements on the coast of India and to the Moluccas in southeastern Asia. These empires lasted, with some modifications, throughout our period.

If the papal division of the world could have been effectively upheld, other European powers might never have acquired new colonies. France, the United Provinces, and England, however, were at times engaged in war with Spain (which for a time, as already mentioned, included Portugal). Moreover, as Protestant countries, the United Provinces and England, paid little attention to papal lines of demarcation. Even before the English and Dutch defeat of

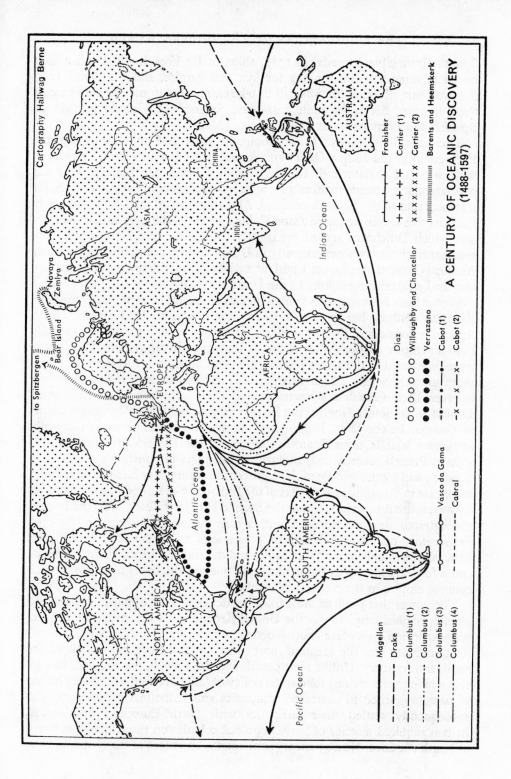

A CENTURY OF OCEANIC DISCOVERY
(1488-1597)

Cartography Hallwag Berne

Magellan	Diaz
Drake	Willoughby and Chancellor
Columbus (1)	Verrazano
Columbus (2)	Cabot (1)
Columbus (3)	Cabot (2)
Columbus (4)	
Vasco da Gama	Frobisher
Cabral	Cartier (1)
	Cartier (2)
	Barents and Heemskerk

Pacific Ocean

Atlantic Ocean

Indian Ocean

NORTH AMERICA

SOUTH AMERICA

EUROPE

AFRICA

ASIA

CHINA

INDIA

AUSTRALIA

Novaya Zemlya

Bear Island

to Spitzbergen

Spain's 'Invincible Armada' in 1588, ships under French and English flags began to roam the seas looking for loot and empire, and the Dutch soon followed suit, obliging the Spanish to take extraordinary measures to protect their treasure fleets. In some instances, Spain's rivals made inroads on Spanish and Portuguese land possessions. (Map I.)

Thus the Dutch East India Company succeeded in supplanting the Portuguese in the Indian Ocean and founding a fabulously wealthy empire, with its centre at Batavia, in the East Indies, Ceylon, and Malaya. This was predominantly a commercial empire with less explicit political power than, for instance, that of the Spanish colonies. As a stopover on the long sea route to the East the Dutch acquired Cape Colony in 1652, the only major overseas area which Dutchmen settled extensively. In the Western Hemisphere they established themselves permanently in Dutch Guinea and some of the Lesser Antilles (Curaçao, Aruba, etc.), and for a while during the seventeenth century they had a flourishing colony in the Hudson valley.

France likewise engaged in several major colonizing enterprises. During the sixteenth century her explorers staked out claims to land on the North American continent. French settlers, missionaries, and garrisons gradually built an empire on both sides of the St Lawrence River system. They penetrated westward to the Great Lakes region and finally came to the wide rivers that run to the south. The Mississippi and its tributaries served as an avenue between their Canadian possessions and their semi-tropical settlement in Louisiana. In South America the French encroached upon Portuguese claims in Guiana. In the West Indies they managed to wrest some economically important islands from Spanish control. In the Eastern Hemisphere farsighted French seamen and military commanders established a foothold in Senegal, and by the middle of the eighteenth century they had begun to build an empire in the southeastern part of the Indian sub-continent. In a long series of wars, sometimes referred to as the Second Hundred Years' War, the French concentrated upon the European rather than the overseas issues, and by 1763 France lost her North American possessions to Britain and Spain. But Senegal, the islands in the West Indies and the Indian Ocean, French Guiana, and a few settlements in India remained to form the bases of a new French colonial empire in the nineteenth century.

The power that profited most from the decline of the Spanish, Dutch, and French colonial empires was the United Kingdom. Its first attempts at overseas expansion took place shortly before 1600 on the North American continent, and this was the scene of most of its efforts before the middle of the eighteenth century. Unlike the Spanish and the French, the English, though also making wide claims, followed a policy of 'effective settlement'. By means of patents granted to chartered companies and individual proprietors, who subsequently settled their territories with north European immigrants, Britain acquired a series of fairly populous colonies on the Atlantic seaboard of North America. Nearby enemy settlements, like those of the Dutch in New

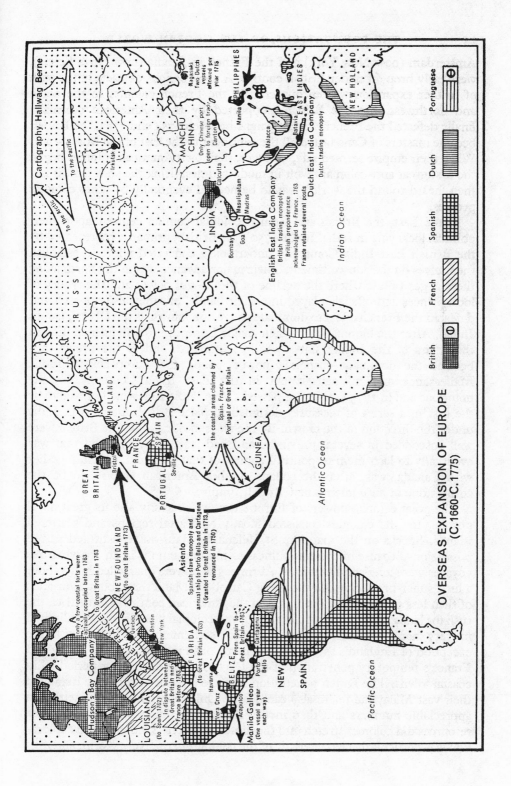

OVERSEAS EXPANSION OF EUROPE
(C.1660-C.1775)

Cartography Hallwag Berne

British   French   Spanish   Dutch   Portuguese

English East India Company
British trading monopoly.
British preponderance
acknowledged by France, 1763.
France retained several posts

Dutch East India Company
Dutch trading monopoly

to the Arctic

to the Pacific

RUSSIA

Irkutsk

MANCHU CHINA

Only Chinese port
open to foreign trade

Canton

Nagasaki
Two Dutch
vessels
allowed per
year 1715

PHILIPPINES

Manila

EAST INDIES

Malacca

Batavia

INDIA

Calcutta

Masulipatam

Madras

Goa

Bombay

Indian Ocean

NEW HOLLAND

GREAT BRITAIN

Bristol

HOLLAND

FRANCE

PORTUGAL   SPAIN

Seville

the coastal areas claimed by
Spain, France,
Portugal or Great Britain

GUINEA

Atlantic Ocean

Asiento
Spanish slave monopoly and
annual ship to Porto Bello and Cartagena.
(Granted to Great Britain in 1713,
renounced in 1750)

Hudson's Bay Company

NEW FRANCE

Quebec

Boston

New York

NEWFOUNDLAND
(to Great Britain 1713)

LOUISIANA
(to Spain 1762)
in dispute between
Great Britain and
France before 1763

FLORIDA
(to Great Britain 1763)

Only a few coastal forts were
actually occupied before 1763
to Great Britain in 1763

BELIZE
From Spain to
Great Britain 1763

Havana

Cartagena

Porto
Bello

Vera Cruz

Acapulco

NEW
SPAIN

Manila Galleon
(One vessel a year
each way)

Pacific Ocean

Amsterdam (now New York) and the French in Acadia (now Nova Scotia), were early brought under British control. A more serious obstacle in the path of further expansion was encountered in the French colonies to the north and northwest, but the British, supported by their American colonials, finally defeated the French. In campaigns between 1754 and 1763, the British became masters of Canada and all the continent to the east of the Mississippi. When their empire seemed safe, however, their own American colonies began the first great anti-colonial revolt in modern times, firing the shot that, if not then 'heard round the world', was to be heeded eventually by other colonial peoples.

In the East, the British and French colonial conflict centred upon their political jockeying in India. In the 1750's the British, primarily represented by the British East India Company, undertook a concerted effort to establish themselves on the sub-continent. Their major advance was in the north along the Ganges valley, where the decline of the Mogul power and the rivalry of local princes and officials played into their hands, but they also opposed and defeated the French effort to dominate the region known as the Deccan (south India). After the elimination of their major European foe, their meddling in the affairs of the Indian states was less impeded, and in the 1760's they became the dominant economic power among the Europeans in India. Malfeasance and mismanagement in the East India Company became notorious and in 1773 Parliament passed a Regulating Act, which proved to be the first in a series of measures designed to place British interests in India under the direction of the crown. By the close of our period the British were well ensconced in several provinces and had started on the road that was eventually to lead them to political control of that vast land, which, together with Canada, was, after the collapse of her American empire, to be the cornerstone of an immense new British Empire.

The great colonial powers of Europe were of necessity also its great naval powers, for the colonies consisted mostly of coastal regions and scattered islands. Specks on the map like St Helena or Mauritius constituted prized possessions because of their usefulness as marine stations in an era when sea voyages were long and hazardous. At times the powers quarrelled more about a little sugar-producing, slave-buying Caribbean island than about thousands of then less profitable square miles on the American continent. In Africa the rush for lands did not begin before 1870, and colonial possessions were limited to very narrow coastal strips. European settlements in India, with the exception of England's as yet quite tenuous push into the Ganges valley and France's temporary penetration of the Deccan, were during our period all in coastal towns. The Dutch penetration into the interior of the huge islands of their vast Malaysian realm also came later. Only where Europeans settled in appreciable numbers and then inched forward in the everlasting search for resources did colonies stretch into the hinterland. This kind of inland exploration was particularly characteristic of the colonies in the New World, and they proved the ones least amenable to the control of the mother-country and quickest to acquire national independence.

*   *   *

Local and Particularist Tendencies

During our period, several peoples of the world, for one reason or another, failed to achieve either dynastic cohesion or national independence. The most glaring examples of European peoples of this type were those of Italy and Germany. Both had once constituted powerful states and were destined to do so again; both made significant cultural contributions to the history of our period; yet until the nineteenth century, both remained divided into a number of little countries.

Some of the Italian states (for example, Venice, the Papal States, and Savoy) were of great antiquity, wealth, power, or spiritual importance. None of them seemed willing to relinquish any part of its sovereignty in favour of a unification of Italy, and their reluctance to unite was reinforced by foreign powers, like Spain, France, and Austria, which coveted or already had possession of some parts of the peninsula or were dynastically allied with some Italian prince. These powers proposed to prevent the rise of a united Italy that they might not be able to manipulate, and papal interests also tended to discourage the attainment of Italian unity under secular leadership.

Germany was even more thoroughly disunited. The number of German states was immense; in 1775 several hundred German principalities, ecclesiastical states, knighthoods, and towns were still more or less independent of each other. In theory at least, they constituted, all together, the Holy Roman Empire, but in fact the emperor was nearly powerless as such, and the Imperial Diet was an ineffective body. For all practical purposes, such as internal administration, taxation, and the conduct of foreign affairs, every prince of a large state was a sovereign, and the lesser princes likewise strove, usually with success, to be sovereign. With great difficulty an emperor might obtain military aid from some states for a campaign against a foreign foe like Turkey or France, but in general the brunt of these wars was borne by the emperor's own people, the Austrians, whose attention was frequently drawn away to Turkey, Italy, Poland, and other non-German areas. As a result of the Reformation, which failed to make Germany wholly Protestant, and of the Counter-Reformation, which failed to make it wholly Catholic, the division of the country was deepened. A series of civil conflicts aimed at creating greater religious unity, the Thirty Years' War (1618–48), brought foreign powers like Denmark, Spain, Sweden, and France into the country and left it exhausted, possibly retarding the development of nationalist sentiment for a century or more. In the eighteenth century, on foundations laid by the Great Elector of Brandenburg-Prussia, Frederick William (1620–88), and by King Frederick William I of Prussia (1688–1740), a strong, essentially German nation arose. The latter's son, Frederick II (1712–86), generally known as 'the Great', left Prussia a world power, whose interest would eventually point in the direction of German unity.

The peoples of India were divided, like those of Europe, by language, religion, and political loyalties, and, more than those of Europe, by a multiplicity of castes. In addition, foreign invasions were frequent, and neighbouring rulers, especially those of Afghanistan, encouraged intrigues and warfare among India's rival dynasties and states. Even after the Mogul conquest, unity, as we have seen, was precarious. Gujarat, for instance, was not conquered by Akbar until 1573. Bengal was taken from its Afghan princes only in 1576, and in 1765 it passed under the jurisdiction of the British East India Company. In 1674 the Marathas established a strong and independent state under Sivājī Raja (1627–80). Though it fell apart under his successor, who was captured by Aurangzīb, it survived to form the basis of the Mahratta States. In the eighteenth century the Marathas seemed ready to create a strong northern nation but were crushed by the Afghans and Persians under Ahmad Shah Durani in the Battle of Panipat (1761). Meanwhile, the Sikhs of the Punjab had developed from a religious community (c. 1500) into a militant people under their guru Govind Singh (1666–1708) and during the Mogul–Afghan wars of the eighteenth century succeeded in establishing a semi-independence of both Delhi and Kabul. In south India a vast Muslim realm, the Bahmani kingdom, vied through most of the fourteenth and fifteenth centuries with a vast Hindu realm, the Vijayanagar kingdom. At the end of the fifteenth century the Bahmani kingdom broke up into several independent viceroyalties, but they eventually combined, destroyed the capital city of Vijayanagar (1565), and liquidated its empire. The Bahmani successor states themselves finally were conquered in the seventeenth century by Aurangzīb. In the disruption which followed that emperor's death, the nizam of Hyderabad became the dominant ruler in the Deccan, but disputes among the nizam's successors gave the British and the French a chance to take opposing sides, with the results already suggested. Several Indian nationalities, like some European nationalities, were able to achieve a lasting political unity with a highly conscious cultural tradition. Thus, until divided by the British in the twentieth century, Bengal, even when part of larger empires, maintained its distinctive political personality. For all that, in India over-all unity among the conflicting nations appeared at times more attainable than in Europe because of the preponderant strength of a single ruler.

In Europe, several populations that once had formed or were in the course of time to form separate nations or peoples were after 1300 incorporated in the dynastic states. The Habsburgs and the Ottomans were masters, sometimes alternatively, of the countries of the Balkans and southeast Europe—Serbia (which for a time in the fourteenth century was itself a great independent empire), Bulgaria, Greece, Albania, Croatia, Rumania, Hungary (a powerful sovereign state until the Battle of Mohacs), and Bohemia (which, as Chapter

III will explain, until the 1430's successfully defied the German Catholic crusades that sought to crush her Hussite heresy). Castillians ruled over Catalonians and Andalusians; Frenchmen over Provençals and (later) Alsatians; Englishmen over Welsh and Irish. The Belgians changed masters about every hundred years. Norwegians were ruled by Danes, and Finns by Swedes. The big Russian realm swallowed up numerous ethnic groups distinctly separate from the Great Russians—among them Estonians, Letts, Tatars, and various Siberian tribes. In Spain, Moors were forcibly converted. Jews were unwanted wherever they went in their centuries-long history of suppression, segregation, and expulsion, mitigated by a limited toleration only toward the end of our era. Everywhere, and particularly in Rumania and Hungary, the Gypsies carried on their nomadic tradition apparently without desire to create a united Gypsy nation.

THE CENTRALIZATION OF POLITICAL POWER

The proper balance of central and local interests is a major political problem for all societies at all times. Of the few states that by 1300 had found a lasting answer to this problem, China, though one of the world's largest empires, was most conspicuous. It had established a fairly centralized bureaucratic government long before 1300, and the subsequent changes of dynasty hardly affected the traditional domestic structure. With the coming of the Manchus, government offices were reshuffled, but the general organization of the empire was maintained with provinces, prefectures, and districts headed by governors, prefects, and magistrates, who, in theory at least but not always in practice, acted upon directives from Peking and supervised the actions of officials subordinate to themselves. This system presupposed a well-selected and well-controlled class of administrators, which, when it functioned efficiently, was the envy and model of other rulers. In Egypt and Syria the Mamlūks had in the thirteenth century inherited a fairly well developed administrative machinery. In Europe the Byzantine Empire, heir to the Roman emperor Diocletian's regimented administration, could boast a somewhat similar civil service, which, despite civil wars and the inroads of Serbs, Bulgars, Turks, Venetians, and Genoese, remained effective until the Empire's demise in the fifteenth century. At the beginning of the fourteenth century peculiar circumstances had permitted certain relatively small areas also to achieve a fair degree of governmental centralization. Norway, for example, was a quite centralized monarchy, largely because its aristocracy was reduced by economic decline to a few families, while its mountainous terrain made the heavily armoured feudal horseman ineffective. The England of Edward I (1239–1307) was well on the way toward royal administrative control, largely because of its insularity.

The idea of centralizing Europe as a whole into a Christian empire had recurred from time to time but had never been more than a dream. Even within the separate European states the process was a complex one. In Poland, for instance, for a number of reasons an elective kingship never achieved enough power and prestige to dominate the feudal lords, and the king was hardly ever able to persuade them to participate in a united effort, particularly after the middle of the seventeenth century, when the *liberum veto* became the rule. The centrifugal tendency thus illustrated was not political alone. The Polish peasant economically as well as politically was in the main dependent on, and felt responsible to, his local lord and not his king. The same held true largely for the peasants of Hungary and of the numerous principalities of Germany. The Russian serf, the Prussian peasant, and the French, English, or Spanish tenant farmer (to give but a few examples) continued to live in subservience to local landlords.[3] Feudal services and payments were exacted from large sections of the agricultural population by local lords until the nineteenth century.

*   *   *

The Rise of the Middle Class

In those countries that were able to establish a strong government, the population was subjected to the central regime as well as, and sometimes more than, to the local lords. Even before 1300 military allegiance was shifting from local lords to sovereign governments, and certain taxes tended to drift into the king's treasury rather than the lord's. Regulation of trade was passing into the hands of the central authority, and jurisdiction over many kinds of behaviour and obligation once left to the lord's court was passing to the king's courts.

The processes by which feudal powers were gradually transferred to the central government varied. In some instances the political complications of feudalism diminished as a single feudal family rose to prominence. Japan provided an instance of this phenomenon. The imperial power had seriously declined since the twelfth century, and at times two competing courts demanded allegiance. During the first three centuries of our period the Japanese suffered prolonged civil wars among various feudal factions, but from this exhausting civil strife emerged one dominant feudal family, the Tokugawas. By means of the shogunate, a kind of *major palatii* with extensive centralized powers exercised nominally in the emperor's name, they managed to hold the empire together.

Unlike the Tokugawas, the Tudors, the Bourbons, and some of the other dynasties of Europe that likewise rose to dominance over the prostrate bodies of rivals assumed the regal title. In some western European states, royal power had been ascendant long before 1300, and the processes, whether peaceful or warlike, by which this ascent had been achieved were still being successfully applied. Some kings strengthened their hands by exploiting the ecclesiastic domains within their realms, as when Philip the Fair (d. 1314) contrived to get possession of the French properties of the military order of the Knights Templars (see Chapter III), and this procedure became particularly enticing after the decline of papal power in the fourteenth century. The Protestant Revolt gave to Protestant kings an especially good opportunity to confiscate church properties, and to Catholic kings a good reason or pretext to confiscate the properties of Protestant nobles, and to keep them or reassign them to royal supporters. Occasionally a European sovereign was sufficiently strong to dominate powerful nobles without civil war and to sequester the domains of contumacious vassals, a procedure favoured by the French rulers after the Bourbon Henry's accession (1598). In general a strong king could take advantage of whatever winds might blow. Concerted opposition of the nobles could generally be averted by fostering rivalries among them.

In Europe effective support for the monarchs in their centralizing efforts often came from the cities and their middle-class populations. Urbanization was fairly well advanced in western Europe even before 1300. Urban population until the nineteenth century constituted, to be sure, only a small portion of the total, and society everywhere remained basically agricultural, but the political and social influence of city-dwellers was greater than their numbers alone would have warranted. The walled city, with its burgher militia, its guilds, and its income from trade and industry, frequently became independent of the feudal lord or, if it remained subject to him, was generally autonomous and might even be hostile to him. It sometimes gave asylum to serfs who wanted to escape from his rule, for, as an old medieval proverb declared, 'City air makes free', and its market, which stimulated the development of cash crops, frequently enabled a peasant to substitute money payments for degrading servile dues and thus to buy higher status and a freer disposal of his time.

Urbanization, therefore, was seriously undermining the power of the feudal barons at the same time that royal centralization was also working towards the same end. To promote this common objective effectively a town would sometimes frankly ally itself with the royal power. Although some towns were merely bureaucratic or ecclesiastical capitals or sites of agricultural fairs rather than true commercial or industrial centres, urban society was predominantly commercial and industrial, and as such it was interested in the creation of a strong central power that might further trade by eliminating tolls and provincial customs-barriers, suppressing local disorders, highwaymen, and robber barons, building roads and canals, dredging rivers and ports, granting monopolies, charters, and privileges, and providing the protection of arms and tariffs against outside competition. The monarch, for his part, found in the commercial activities of this new class a source of revenue, mostly in the form of cash, wherewith he could build his own administrative and military systems, independent of the more cumbersome and less reliable feudal contributions of a stiff-necked aristocracy. In times of emergency the merchants and city banking circles could be approached for loans to be repaid in coin or commercial concessions rather than in lands and political privileges, which were the usual methods of compensation for feudal vassals.

At times, however, the considerations impelling king and town to ally against their common enemy, the nobility, did not counterbalance the burghers' fear of autocracy or their desire for political power of their own, and in such instances the centralizing power encountered solid opposition from the towns. The political ambitions of the Flemish cities, for example, were a serious obstacle for the French kings during the early centuries of our period. Emperor Charles V was at times more dependent on the support of the cities of his realm than was compatible with his political plans, and the support of Paris and of London had to be purchased dearly by their respective French and English rulers and sometimes could not be obtained at all. The revolt of an important city could be crucial for a ruler, as was exemplified by the role of London in the constitutional crisis of seventeenth-century England. When cities were controlled by forces at odds with the central government, as was the case of the Huguenot towns in France before Richelieu's day, they constituted a seriously disruptive element in the body politic. Despite the price, however, the allegiance of the towns was always a desideratum—in times of war or revolution, since they were usually strategically located and fortified, and in times of peace, since the wealth and influence of the middle class often was decisive in political manoeuvring.

So sovereigns in a number of countries came to look to the middle class for support. Louis XI of France counted heavily upon the help of a strong urban population. Henry VIII, Elizabeth I, and other Tudor rulers of England sought the aid of the country gentry as well as of urban middle-class advisers. In Russia, Ivan IV acquired the assistance not only of the gentry in his service but also of the Moscow townsfolk (posad), and Peter the Great frankly courted the middle class, promoting commerce, industry, and other bourgeois interests.

*   *   *

The Decline of the Feudal Nobility

Some of the struggles between Europe's kings and feudal lords were long and fluctuating. France, England, and Spain during the fourteenth and fifteenth centuries were at times close to a state of complete political anarchy in which rival noble families battled as they pleased for superiority without being curbed by monarchical rule. In the 'Time of Troubles' (1604–13) after Ivan IV the newly consolidated Russian realm was rent asunder by the resurgence of the great nobles. About the middle of the same century the grand French magnates, having been deprived only recently of many of their powers by the late Cardinal Richelieu, staged a major but futile attempt—the so-called 'Fronde'—to regain their previous position at the expense of the monarchy.

Hardly anywhere (England was a notable exception) was the feudal power of the nobility totally eliminated before the close of our period. Thus, centralized rule did not generally bring the tightly totalitarian form of government which modern technology and politico-economic practices have made possible. Conditions in that day rendered so high a degree of centralization difficult if not inconceivable. Centralization then meant not so much the concentration of power in the hands of a central authority as a *modus vivendi* whereby the national ruler and the various particularist forces could cooperate towards a well-ordered state and the prevention of feudal chaos. It meant absolutism rather than totalitarianism, the king being regarded as the head but not the whole of government. His power, to be sure, was checked or balanced only by tradition, local custom, corporate rights, grants, capitulations, and charters rather than by countervailing force. Such checks, however, were ordinarily respected. Since the kingly power was hereditary, the obligation to observe these traditional or historical limitations was also inherited, and it was not easily disregarded. Hereditary absolutism was thus more restrained than revolutionary totalitarianism. In the states that developed into coherent units, the disruptive aspects of feudalism were curbed, but the great nobility, though bereft of the powers that the ruler thought he needed to monopolize for the conduct of royal policy, was nonetheless still able, as a strong, privileged, and honoured order, to influence the conduct of affairs.

Naturally, in some countries the nobles were more powerful than in others. In the great dynastic states of the Turks and the Habsburgs, the magnates, and to a certain extent the smaller landowners (such as the Hungarian gentry), actually ruled their provinces in much the same way as in medieval times, though with a greater readiness to accept the guidance of the sovereign dynasty. Even in some of the more thoroughly centralized states like France, Prussia, and Russia the great landlords retained a fair amount of their feudal privileges and local power. Moreover, their social standing, their still great economic power, and their still considerable political and military prestige enabled them to continue to play a significant role in public affairs. Up to the very end of our period important levelling programmes (such as proportional taxation, free access to certain professions, or an even chance for the common-born to reach the higher ranks of church or army) could be successfully advanced almost nowhere, except perhaps in Britain, because of opposition from aristocratic interests. The so-called absolute monarchs of the late seventeenth and eighteenth centuries, therefore, had predominant but not unlimited political power within their realms. Their power was checked, to some extent at least, not only by the nobility but also by various other influential groups such as the church, the chartered cities, the guilds, and the privileged provinces, as well as by the rising middle class.

In the process of centralization the rulers strove to obtain control of the most important governmental functions. Where they succeeded, command of the military, which is likely to be the *ultima ratio* of all effective political power, passed into their hands. The system of feudal levies, by which the sovereign was dependent on the cooperation of his vassals, was replaced by a system of standing (frequently mercenary) armies, made possible by the monarch's new sources of income, whose rank and file were His Majesty's soldiers and ultimately subject only to his command. Wherever feasible, private forces of great lords were altogether eliminated or became privately raised and more or less proprietary regiments in the royal army. A statesman bent on centralization, like Henry IV or Richelieu, nullified even the defensive power of the magnates by destroying castles and fortresses and transforming them into peaceable chateaux. By the eighteenth century the primary vestige of the feudal lords' once unquestioned military eminence was that the highest ranks in the army were as a general rule reserved for nobles. In other words, feudal independence in this as in most other regards had been converted into aristocratic privilege.

*   *   *

The Rise of Royal Legal Systems

Another significant increase of power for the central government resulted from the consolidation of judicial functions in the hands of the rulers. The development of a royal judicial system was well on the way before 1300. Yet local courts with jurisdiction over only local affairs, adjudicating cases by the application of local custom and of laws differing from region to region, still created confusion. In Europe, until about 1500, the process of creating a unified system of courts and law codes and of providing a more rigid super- vision of justice was retarded by the disintegrating effects of the Black Death, a plague that spread from India to Europe in the fourteenth century, and by frequent wars, invasions, and baronial conflicts. After 1500 the process was considerably accelerated. The justice dispensed at the king's court by the king's judges came in general to be looked upon as superior, not only because the king usually could employ men of greater talent but also because it stemmed from the actually or potentially best source of law enforcement in the land. The appellate function of royal justice was thus greatly strengthened. For certain types of cases, such as those involving taxation or tariff, military affairs, constitutional questions, and more serious criminal offences, juris- diction came to rest with the royal rather than the seigniorial courts. Besides, after 1500, in Christian countries, the partition of legal authority between the secular power and the church, with its separate ecclesiastical courts and canon law, became less sharp, for the independence of the church from the crown was considerably weakened. Although, until the French Revolution and beyond, the church retained jurisdiction over marriage, divorce, inheritance, and similar civil-law issues, and in cases involving clergymen, it too became more and more an instrument of the crown.

The judicial systems that resulted in most countries from the centralizing efforts of the monarchy were mixed systems, since the royal courts did not replace the old courts but rather took places beside them. The courts of the church continued to function. The seigniorial courts retained a certain, though diminished jurisdiction over feudal obligations and other relations of lord with tenant. Since, except in the United Kingdom, serfdom still survived and in some countries had even been intensified by the end of our period (as, for instance, in Prussia, Russia, Poland, and parts of the Habsburg realm), these feudal courts remained a significant force in rural society. In urban society many issues involving artisans and workers continued to be adjudicated in the courts of the guilds. As the guild structure gradually collapsed, its judicial functions were absorbed by royal courts. Mercantile law after 1300 was generally enforced by the merchants themselves (either through guild courts or through municipal courts, which they controlled), but it tended to become a province of royal jurisdiction in the last century or so of our period, most notably in England. In almost none of these fields of law, however, was a clear-cut distinction made between the royal and the other forms of justice. Jurisdictional disputes were frequent between the royal courts and local or church courts but were resolved more and more in a fashion that enhanced the royal power.

In due course the king's courts came to be looked upon as higher courts. Some of them were ambulatory, travelling through assigned districts with the express purpose of holding appellate jurisdiction over the local courts. In England, for instance, itinerant royal judges heard indictments brought before local justices of the peace, who were themselves royally appointed, although they continued to be chosen from the local gentry. In France a similar system of legal appeal developed, for the king was likewise regarded as the source of justice, but there the highest courts of the land were the parlements. Until the fifteenth century the Parlement of Paris had been the single highest court of the land, but then various provincial parlements were created, and in the eighteenth century there were thirteen (at one time fourteen). Because of their claim on the right to 'verify' constitutional changes, frequently they came into opposition with the crown. The king, however, as the fount of law and justice was able to dominate the parlements except in instances when public feeling ran high in their favour. In addition to the regularly constituted courts, royal administrative appointees in towns or provinces on occasion exercised appellate function. The trend towards taking the administration of justice away from church, local, or private authority and placing it under the central government was general and persistent during our period.

In Europe, and its spheres of influence across the seas, the movement towards a centralized system of justice was greatly furthered by the influence of Roman law in the west and of Roman–Byzantine law in the east. By 1700 Roman law had largely replaced customary feudal law or at least had greatly modified the customary law everywhere in western Europe except in England, Scandinavia, and Switzerland. We shall return to the legal consequences of the Reception of Roman law in Chapter VIII. The political consequences were also significant. Justinian's *Corpus Juris*, in particular the *Digest*, became a common meeting-ground for all lawyers, a sort of common domain of jurisprudence. The principles of Roman law greatly influenced the royal administration of justice. It appealed especially to monarchs because it emphasized the powers of the ruler. Aided by lawyers trained in Roman law (the so-called civilians), they applied its principles increasingly in jurisdictional disputes.

Another factor in the process of judicial centralization was the tendency towards codification of the laws. In Europe codification had been common to a certain degree before 1300. The rise of the middle class gave impetus to the movement towards clear and uniform law, and the most remarkable secular codes between 1300 and approximately 1500 were of laws merchant, or commercial laws, which we shall examine in Chapters VIII and IX. Yet the codification of the laws of the respective nations proceeded rather slowly, and indeed was notably successful only after our period. No European monarchy entirely succeeded before 1775 in creating either a uniform legal system or a truly centralized administration, for the monarchs could not entirely eliminate particularism and feudal vestiges. Local custom and tradition persisted and did not readily yield to national legal concepts, whether of written or common law. Everywhere a mixture of the old and the new continued, although the trend towards the new was evident.

＊　　　＊　　　＊

The Rise of Bureaucracy

The gradual centralization of royal government brought with it a bureaucratic system and the rise of a bureaucratic 'class'. The courts of even the least practical sovereigns were becoming more and more dependent upon a trained and experienced personnel dedicated to administrative affairs—in royal councils, chancelleries, tribunals, and exchequers as well as armies. By 1300 most sovereigns had at their command at least a core personnel out of which a central bureaucracy might arise and with which the local government machinery had to cope. At the beginning of our period the most highly developed administrative systems were to be found in the states with the greatest centralization, the Chinese, the Mamlūk, and the Byzantine empires. The Chinese civil service with its selective examinations seems to have engaged the interest, at least during the later centuries of our period, of those who contemplated a similar system in central Europe.

Royal administrative policies varied with the intensity of centralization. Countries that retained a large part of the feudal system, as did Russia and the Ottoman Empire, inevitably also retained a number of local administrative agencies and left governmental functions in the hands of the feudal lords or military leaders of the provinces. An important new element, however, was introduced into this arrangement: the nobles serving as district and provincial governors were gradually deprived of freedom to act on their own discretion and were made more responsive to the basic decisions of their sovereigns. In Russia, to be sure, where the boyars, at first mostly high-born servants of the tsars, were being displaced by hereditary landlords, especially in the eighteenth century, this tendency seemed to be reversed, since the landowner steadily acquired greater control over his serfs and sometimes exercised considerable independence of the tsar. Yet in most states, Russia included, in the course of time the central governments developed media through which they could supervise and check the conduct of feudal administrators. Imperial and royal officials periodically inspected the work of the district governors. Royal fiscal agents checked their books and tax records; itinerant judges provided royal courts of appeal with power to correct the injustices of local judges; military inspectors kept watch on the district commanders and their commands. Though many of the provincial posts were still hereditary in the local noble families, rulers steadily increased their hold upon them by insisting upon formal appointment, by designating officers of their own with parallel or overlapping powers, and by occasional dismissals and replacements. The resulting administrative patterns in such instances were a composite of feudal and royal—the ruler, however, emerging, with growing frequency, as the dominant figure.

Wherever feasible, the central government sought to place its own appointees in local administrative posts or to replace agencies of long-standing particularist interests with new ones that owed allegiance to the crown alone. In that fashion, the French provinces were, after Richelieu's reforms, governed by royal *intendants* as well as by members of the great noble houses, and the once autonomous towns of Spain increasingly lost their independence to royal agents such as the *corregidores*. In military affairs lines of command came to reach more directly from the monarch down to the newest recruit, and since centralization at times depended on the army as the means of preventing rebellion and disobedience, civil administrative functions were often united with the military in a district commander (e.g. the beys and pashas in the Ottoman Empire and the military commanders in the Mogul realm). Fiscal administration was usually centralized at the top but frequently the actual collection of taxes and excises was in the hands of local tax collectors if not of semi-private 'tax farmers' who bought their posts. Administrative and judicial posts could sometimes also be bought from the king (as, for example, certain magistracies in France) and thereby become a hereditary property.

In medieval Europe, because learning had been restricted for the most part to ecclesiastical circles, the clergy had been dominant in royal administration. With the increase in lay education, the development of universities, and in particular the availability of laymen trained in civil law, many positions came to be filled by members of the legal profession. Nevertheless, the king's highest advisers, his governors, and the regional representatives of the crown still were frequently drawn from the most eminent aristocratic families, whether or not trained as clergy or lawyers. Even after the Reformation, certain positions—in the universities, for example—continued to be regarded as the special prerogative of clergy. Members of the bourgeoisie who managed to rise to high governmental positions were sometimes promoted to an aristocratic status by the granting of a title or, as in France, came to form a separate 'aristocratic' administrative class (the nobility of the robe). While the trained members of the middle class were most often employed in the central bureaucracy (i.e. the royal councils, the bureaus of the capital, etc.), others were used in municipal governments, as they came increasingly under royal control, or were put in charge of local offices dealing with the crown's economic or fiscal affairs. Many middle-class persons found employment also as scribes, clerks, and minor officials in the royal service. The interest and participation of 'the third estate' in the nation's government was thus both cause and effect of the bourgeois stake in the centralization of royal authority.

With the help of its administrative machinery the central government widened its control of the people's activities. As we shall note in more detail in Chapters II–V, administrative centralization helped to establish the supremacy of the state over the church. In the countries where Greek Orthodox Christianity prevailed, no pope had achieved independence of the emperor, and the church had been subjected to state domination for ages. The Russian tsar, especially after the Turkish capture of Constantinople and still more so with Peter's church reforms, was the chief authority for all Orthodox Christians in his realm. In Roman Catholic Europe monarchs exploited the weakness of the papacy after 1300 to arrogate powers that had previously resided in the church hierarchy. They established close supervision over ecclesiastical appointments and fiscal affairs, and curtailed the foreign activities of the clergy. Papal relations with a national church were subjected to the approval of the crown. Church institutions (the Inquisition in Spain, for instance) were used by the monarchs as instruments of state. Even in Catholic countries after the Reformation, the church tended to become a national institution, and like other subjects, ecclesiastics tended to become loyal subjects first and faithful members of the Roman Catholic hierachy afterwards. In Protestant countries rulers usually were more than nominal heads of their state churches; the clergy were appointed by them and subject to their control. Many of the administrative functions that had previously resulted from the clergy's feudal status as landowners were eliminated when the state 'nationalized' church lands. In a sense, therefore, the ecclesiastical hierarchy became the branch of the civil service in charge of the religious, and sometimes the educational and welfare functions of the state.

In political affairs the royal councils and officers in charge of judicial, fiscal, military, and economic administration became the highest governmental agencies. In the course of time these councils were divided into various 'ministries', which were sometimes under the general supervision of a high administrative official (e.g. the Turkish viziers and the eighteenth-century English 'prime' ministers). At other times they were coordinated only through the monarch (as in Spain under Philip II and in France under Louis XIV). The councils maintained contact with the regional officials of the crown and its plenipotentaries abroad, mostly through a system of correspondence and written accountings, thereby laying the foundations of the modern 'paper bureaucracy'.

*   *   *

Distance usually dictated that the administration of colonial enterprises be divided between the crown and local authorities. Colonial administration was in certain instances in the hands of chartered companies, like the various East India companies, rather than directly under royal officials. Where, however, it actually was a function of the home government, it manifested in a striking fashion the characteristics of the centralized system; for in establishing governmental agencies for newly acquired lands, colonizing monarchs rarely had to cope with obsolescent feudal or ecclesiastical institutions and interests. One of the most impressive of such colonial systems was devised by the Spanish. Under direct control of the king, a Council of the Indies, responsible for formulating laws and policies for the colonies, studiously scrutinized the conduct of colonial officials, who were its appointees. High officials like viceroys, governors, and captains-general were usually assigned to their posts for a relatively short time, in order to keep them from acquiring too much personal power. During their terms of office they were subject to inspection by visiting officials (*visitadores*), and at the conclusion of his service each was expected to render a careful accounting of his administration. Over the centuries, further checks and regulations were inserted in this highly centralized system until the machinery became so cumbersome as to raise doubts regarding its effectiveness.

As Spanish colonial experience illustrates, the high degree of centralization that absolutism entailed carried with it the seed of its own destruction. It alienated first the class that had been the king's allies—the nobles—causing him to seek allies among the commoners; and sometimes it alienated also the class that had helped him to build up his absolutism—the middle class—but not until centralization had served its major purpose, which was to counteract the centrifugal forces of feudalism. The middle class was an uncertain ally at best. Even while it fought beside the king in the common fight against decentralization, it was aware that the fight was a three-cornered one.

THE QUEST FOR LIBERTY AND SOCIAL JUSTICE

In Europe the erection of safeguards against absolute royal power was largely (but not exclusively) the work of the rising bourgeoisie. At first, members of this class had usually been eager to exchange the tyranny of the few (the feudal lords) for the rule of one (the prince who might make common cause with them against the lords). Ultimately, however, the bourgeoisie did much, occasionally in conjunction with rival classes, to foster the growth of institutions and ideas that helped to secure individual freedom and responsible government, neither of which was always welcome to princes.

Before 1300 the nobles and the churchmen of a realm were on occasion summoned by their king to advise and approve some policy or to function in some other special capacity. Around 1300 such assemblies began to be more representative, including deputies from the cities and the higher strata of the common or *roturier* (i.e. neither noble nor ecclesiastic) class. With the addition of bourgeoisie, gentry, and smaller landowners, these assemblies of the 'estates' (or orders of society) developed rapidly as parliamentary bodies and began to assume an important position in their countries' affairs. The Cortes of the various Spanish kingdoms, the Estates General in France, the Parliament of England, the Riksdag of Sweden, the Sejm of Poland, and, to a much more limited extent, the Diet of the Holy Roman Empire and the Staende in the Habsburg realm acquired certain concessions in return for financial or other aid to their princes. Among these concessions, in addition to the right to be convoked periodically for consultation and to be heard on fiscal matters affecting the whole realm, was the right to petition for redress of grievances. By coupling the granting of finances with petitions for redress, parliamentary bodies fashioned a powerful weapon against monarchs in need. They acquired a certain degree of legislative power, thus foreshadowing their main later function. On occasion, kings had to change their policies because of the unwillingness of the estates to grant the necessary finances, and a balking parliament might delay or entirely prevent an accretion of royal powers. In some countries in which the monarchs established firmly centralized rule (e.g. Spain, France, and Denmark) representative bodies declined during the period of absolutism and enlightened despotism; in others, however, they remained as at least a slight check on otherwise absolutist rule (e.g. Hungary, the Belgian Netherlands, and other realms of the Habsburgs).[4]

The English Parliament eventually became the outstanding example of a representative assembly in a monarchy. It had developed out of the great councils of the English kings, and by the beginning of our period was on its way to becoming more generally representative through the inclusion of the lower feudal order (the knights of the shires) and the burghers. Soon these elements of the population began to meet as a separate body and became the House of Commons. Parliament was an extension of the king's council, summoned to give its approval to great acts of state and appearing most frequently when the monarch had most need of public support. The real basis of Parliament's power resided in its ability to grant or withhold needed revenues. The rule of the impoverished Lancastrian kings was characterized by frequent Parliaments, but the first Tudor, Henry VII (d. 1509), as soon as his independent revenues were sufficient, summoned Parliament no more. The decisive change in the status of Parliament occurred in the reign of his successor, Henry VIII, who was compelled to invoke a representative legislature to sever connections with the Roman communion (see Chapter IV). In each of the next three reigns Parliament was called to legislate on fundamental changes in the nation's religious creed and establishment.

The effect of the Reformation in England was initially to increase the power and wealth of the monarchy and of the classes represented in Parliament. But the Reformation also divided opinion. The Parliaments contained groups that opposed the policies of the successive monarchs. As the wealth of the classes represented in the House of Commons increased and that of the crown declined by comparison, the position of the monarch weakened. Queen Elizabeth I (1533–1603) successfully withstood most attempts of the Commons to meddle with state policy, but under the Stuart kings, James I (1566–1625) and Charles I (1600–49), Parliament (and particularly the House of Commons) continued to enlarge its claims to initiate policy and control the government. Numerous conflicts now arose between the crown and the House of Commons over several issues of royal prerogative. These issues, coupled with the religious conflict of Puritans and episcopalians, finally resulted in the Civil War, in which the monarchy was overthrown, and England was for a time (1649–53) governed as a republic (the Commonwealth) by a surviving faction of the House of Commons.

On the whole, this pseudo-parliamentary government proved to be unstable and ineffectual. For one thing, it could not control the army, where the more radical of the puritan factions (the Independents and other sectaries) predominated and demanded church disestablishment and toleration. Nor could it compose the differences between this army and the Presbyterian party, which had once dominated the House of Commons and had hoped to acquire an exclusive control over both the monarchy and the established church. Parliamentary rule without a strong executive was discredited, and the vacuum was now filled by a written constitution that provided a strong executive, subject to parliamentary safeguards (the Protectorate). An able protector was found in Oliver Cromwell, leader of the army, who quarrelled with his Parliament, dissolved it, and was driven to secure a modification of the constitution after a brief period of military rule. The regime did not long survive his death, and in 1660 the Stuart dynasty was restored to the throne, on condition of ruling with Parliament. Many of the old political and religious issues, however, revived in somewhat different forms. The new king, Charles II (1630–85), improved his position by skilful manoeuvres and was able to rule without Parliament for the closing years of his reign. His successor, James II, was emboldened to advance further, and led on by initial success, he gave mortal offence to the Anglican Church by his preference for Roman Catholics, which also lost him the support of non-Anglican Protestants. These Protestants eventually joined the bulk of Anglican England and Presbyterian Scotland in welcoming William of Orange as a deliverer in the 'Glorious Revolution' of 1688.

Subsequently Parliament assumed greater and greater responsibilities. Various areas of conflict remained, but on the whole the crown and Parliament learned how to cooperate, forming a system that preserved many of the good features of centralized rule without jeopardizing the rights of the governed. Representation in Parliament, and corresponding political influence, was restricted to the nobility, the gentry, and the wealthy burgher class, but the idea of representative government and of limited monarchy had been established as a working principle. Unlike the French aristocracy, the British aristocracy was not privileged in taxation, and movement into the higher civil and military offices was easier for the poor and low-born in Britain than in France. On the whole, the people in Britain who made policy also carried it out and paid a fair share of its cost. The machinery for representative processes developed to such an extent that the nineteenth-century transition from limited to mass suffrage would take place in England without extensive civil strife.

If the Puritan Revolution failed to create a Puritan commonwealth, it nevertheless demonstrated that even strong monarchs could not always with impunity dispense with the consent of the governed. Revolution or the threat of revolution (as we shall see in Chapters VIII and IX, where we shall analyse the political thought of our period) thus became a more effective check than ever before upon the exercise of arbitrary power.

★   ★   ★

Republicanism

The contemporary instances of republicanism provided examples of another political force that might be employed to counteract the trend towards royal absolutism. Republicanism (i.e. government by some sort of representative body), which had been a vital and characteristic element of the culture of Antiquity, reasserted itself during our era, particularly in the cities. For the most part European cities were run by oligarchies working through guild organizations. The major exceptions to this general rule were to be found in those Italian Renaissance cities that were ruled by hereditary autocratic despots. Even before 1300 the Visconti dynasts (and later the Sforzas) in Milan, the house of Este in Ferrara, the Malatestas in Rimini, and other Italian ruling families had created highly developed absolutist systems. Occasionally during one period certain Italian republics also fell under the sway of a single ruling family, as Mantua under the Gonzagas and Florence under the Medici. The intense political rivalry within and among the Italian city-states, complicated by the frequent interventions of Spanish, Austrians, and French, was not conducive to the maintenance of the balanced political leadership always desirable for and frequently characteristic of republics. Continual strife usually left them with governments too weak for effective defence or conduct of foreign affairs. Nevertheless, the republican form of government prevailed in some Italian cities, such as Siena, Genoa, and Venice, which for centuries was the most successful of all republican states. Even Medici-dominated Florence retained at least the outward forms of republicanism. The cities of western and northern Europe, especially in the regions with limited centralization of government such as Germany and the Low Countries, were usually republican in form, even though they owed allegiance to the emperor or a local prince.

Originally many city governments had derived their power from their guilds as well as from the local aristocracy. But with 'the commercial revolution' of the thirteenth and fourteenth centuries the richest merchants came to dominate municipal government. For reasons to be taken up when we come to deal with economic matters, the guild system eventually weakened under the impact of early industrialization and concurrent changes in commercial and financial practices, and between 1300 and 1450 the lesser workers of some areas attempted by violence to gain a share of power. Occasionally these attempts were lower-class uprisings, like that of the Ciompi (wool-carders), who in 1378 took over temporary control of the government of Florence, but usually the only lasting success of such uprisings was to gain some representation on the town councils. They were not able to eliminate the overwhelming political, social, and economic influence of the great merchant families. For the most part, the plutocrats continued to dominate the councils and, in consequence, the entire city administration. Often in the civil strife between a town's rich and poor, help from a neighbouring feudal lord or monarch was obtained by one of the opposing factions. Many cities thus lost their autonomy to a nearby potentate.

Nevertheless, the republican spirit remained alive. The humanist movement, which was strong among the patricians of Renaissance Italy, tended to do honour to the old republican virtues of Rome as well as to its caesarism. Brutus and Cicero, prototypes of the true republican, were glorified, and tyrannicide, the assassination of political oppressors, was sometimes openly defended in principle. By deference to a different set of models, the republican ideal found favour among the religious radicals of the fourteenth century, the Lollards of England and the extreme Hussites (Taborites) of Bohemia; they harked back to the democracy of government and the community of property among the primitive Christians (see Chapter III). During the Reformation, the religious thought of some of the great reformers—Zwingli, Calvin, and especially the Anabaptists and Levellers (see Chapter IV)—was likewise compatible with republican institutions. Zürich, Strasbourg, and Geneva were outstanding both as city republics and as early centres of Reformed or Calvinistic activities. Later this Protestant movement became prominent also in the urbanized areas of southwestern Germany and the Netherlands. Calvinism in France, too, was concentrated in the cities, and some of them (as mentioned above) became independent enough to threaten to become little *imperia in imperio*. Moreover, each of the sects, whether old or new, in the communities which it did not itself control was dependent upon the exercise of religious toleration by others for its very survival. Hence they all kept up a lively interest in safeguards against religious and political oppression where they were weak (even though they might ruthlessly persecute dissidents where they themselves were strong). We shall deal with such political views in Chapters IV and IX.

By 1700 republics were few, and republican institutions seemed to be giving way completely to the monarchical form of government. Small states like the provinces of the Netherlands and the cantons of Switzerland were able to retain republican or semi-republican constitutions only, according to Montesquieu and some other eighteenth-century observers, because they had joined together into confederations for mutual protection. Venice and Genoa were still strong states but had long passed the peak of their glory. The German free cities managed to preserve their republican institutions against princely encroachments, but sometimes only with difficulty. London remained a semi-independent commune. Most of the other European towns, however, had lost whatever republican structure they might once have had. In so far as the Polish monarchy and the Holy Roman Empire might be considered republics by virtue of having elective rulers, they lent little prestige to the republican tradition. Few principles and lessons derived from the history of ancient and contemporary republics seemed relevant to the philosophy (see Chapters VIII and IX) of those concerned with the limitation of governmental authority in Europe.

★   ★   ★

Federalism

The story of federalism is closely associated with that of republicanism. Most of the federations of our period were leagues of small republics, each of which retained some degree of control over its internal affairs while otherwise submitting to a central authority. Usually federations arose out of the need for united effort against an actual or potential enemy. During the Middle Ages towns banded together for defence of their local independence and the preservation of their privileges against strong rulers or feudal magnates. The resulting leagues as a rule were loosely organized, but they had been strong in northern Italy. After 1300, stronger ones emerged in the German Empire, where the central government was steadily losing power. The German leagues had predominantly political aims, seeking to obtain more influence in the imperial Diets and the general affairs of the realm by presenting a united front. Among them were a league of the Swabian cities, a league of the important Rhenish towns, a short-lived league of the Westphalian towns, and, by far the most eminent, the Hanseatic league of northern Germany and the Baltic areas.

In the final decades of the thirteenth century, a number of north German towns had crowned their earlier cooperative enterprises by forming a league called the Hansa or the Hanseatic League, primarily for commercial purposes. With Lübeck as its centre this union, which may have included at times as many as seventy or eighty members, adopted a common legal code (the Sea Laws of Lübeck), sought to standardize its trading activities, offered military and naval protection to its members, and tried to procure and safeguard monopolies in the areas which it controlled. It never developed into a strong political federation, since member cities were not only independent in their internal affairs but also free to withdraw. From time to time delegates from participating towns met to deal with urgent political, military, and commercial matters. The League's common foreign policy was to protect and further its commercial position in the Baltic and the North Sea, where for decades it encountered opposition especially from the Danish kingdom. It negotiated with the important princes of northern Europe for trading privileges, established *kontors* ('trading settlements') abroad, improved port facilities, and policed piracy. During much of the fourteenth and fifteenth centuries the Hansa dominated north European trade and also exercised considerable political power. Then the strengthening monarchies began seriously to curtail its trading privileges; the League, unable to compete effectively with the state-protected trade of the Dutch and the English, declined and in the seventeenth century, though it never formally dissolved, ceased to have significance. Nevertheless, the mercantile achievement and the civic independence of this remarkable commercial–political federation engendered a pride that is still discernible in former league cities like Hamburg, Lübeck, and Bremen.

Only three European countries (if we exclude states united only by virtue of a personal union under the same ruler) had governmental structures that were based upon the application of federal principles to a group of contiguous areas. They were Switzerland, the United Provinces, and the Holy Roman Empire. We have already seen that Switzerland began as a federation. Each of its cantons was practically independent in the conduct of its internal affairs and jealous of its independence, since the population differed widely from canton to canton in language and economic interests, and after the Reformation also in religion. Some of them were only 'allied' to the Confederation or to some of its members; others, along with some areas now outside Switzerland, were 'protected' cantons; and some (twenty about the year 1600) were territories 'subject' to one or more cantons. All of them were bound by a series of treaties promising mutual defensive aid against attacking powers. Foreign and other common affairs were handled by a diet chosen by a complicated representational system. By the Treaty of Westphalia of 1648 the Swiss Confederation was finally recognized as independent of Austria (thereupon passing under the political influence of France). Although the practically complete autonomy of the cantons resulted in several civil wars, the Swiss showed that divergent areas could cooperate to achieve a joint strength that could be reconciled with a high degree of local autonomy.

When the seven northern provinces of the Netherlands united in 1579 to form the Dutch Republic or United Provinces a federal structure was indicated for their union. The provinces were left autonomous. They elected representatives to a States General, which, with its executive Council of State, acted as a government for the entire land. This body, however, could make no major policy decisions without instructions and directives from the provincial estates, which were dependent on the nobility in the eastern provinces, where agriculture was the major pursuit, and on the municipal councils in the provinces of Holland and Zeeland, where financial and commercial interests prevailed. In time of peace this complex arrangement made the formulation of a generally acceptable federal policy extremely hard.

Two forces, nevertheless gave great cohesion to the union. One was the predominance of the province of Holland and its chief executive official, the grand pensionary. Holland was the most populous and economically as well as culturally the most eminent area of the Netherlands, and its agents were so frequent and prominent abroad that foreigners often assumed 'Holland' to be identical with 'The Dutch Netherlands'. Under the leadership of strong men like Jan van Oldenbarneveldt (1547–1619) and Jan De Witt (1625–72) it tended to dominate federal politics. The other cohesive force was the House of Orange. As the great opponent of the bourgeois Democratic Party of Holland, it was the rallying-point of an Orangist movement. The Orangists sought greater national centralization under the leadership of the stadholders, who were at first elective in the separate provinces but were so regularly taken from the House of Orange that the office became practically hereditary before 1747 and then became officially hereditary. Despite republican opposition, the stadholder was elected by the provincial estates also as captain-general and admiral-general of the realm in times of war and so played a most important role in cases of national emergency such as the wars of liberation and the conflict with Louis XIV. The stadholder's office steadily accumulated responsibilities, but because of the strong republican tradition, especially in Holland, the Netherlands were not turned into a monarchical country until the Napoleonic era. Although before the later decades of the seventeenth century the United Provinces began to lose their powerful international position, this decline was not due primarily to the weaknesses of their federal structure and resultant domestic disputes. The provinces generally held together firmly as a federation in times of foreign invasion, and the union was envied and respected for its peacetime achievements. In many ways the Dutch Netherlands, despite religious and political dissensions, were an example of good government, in which a large degree of freedom was available to the individual within the provinces and to the provinces within the union.

The Holy Roman Empire may in a way be considered an aristocratic federation. Its numerous separate states, particularly after the Treaty of Westphalia formally gave them *Landeshoheit* ('domestic sovereignty'), governed their own domestic affairs. Yet they also acknowledged a certain allegiance to the central authority, feeble though it was, of the emperor, who was elected by those German princes who had the title of 'elector'; they all were represented somehow in one of the three houses of the Imperial Diet; and they all looked upon the Golden Bull of Charles IV (1356), which set forth the fundamental law of the Empire, as more or less constitutionally binding. Though the Treaty of Westphalia modified the provisions of the Golden Bull considerably, weakening the emperor's position still further and giving the member states freedom in foreign affairs, it still required them to make no alliances against the emperor or the Empire. If, however, the Holy Roman Empire was a federation, it was a weak one at best.

★   ★   ★

Government and Individual Rights

Conflict over the distribution of domestic power—like that of the Swiss with Austria, the Dutch with Spain, and the English with the Stuarts—and opposition to the menace of a foreign master state or ruler helped to reinforce old concepts and institutions or to evolve new ones that became fundamental in the development of Europe's liberal principles. In Britain, the seventeenth-century revolutionary movement brought or reconfirmed certain 'rights', protecting the individual from arbitrary arrest, star-chamber proceedings, and torture to elicit testimony and assuring him of *habeas corpus* and trial by jury. In Chapter IX we shall find political philosophers assuming, largely on the basis of the English experience, that a systematic division of governmental powers was necessary if tyranny was to be avoided and advancing the need of intercedent bodies between the potentially despotic ruler and the potentially suppressed people. Though for different reasons, both the bourgeoisie and the privileged classes subscribed to these principles.

Certain arguments essential to the case for the strong nation-state, by a strange irony, contributed to the growth of the philosophy (of which more will be said in Chapters VIII and IX) upon which the egalitarian democracies of later eras were based. The theory of divine-right monarchy stressed the assumptions that government was instituted for the benefit and welfare of the whole community and that God held the monarch responsible for it. Louis XIV's comment on his place in the state (which has been reduced by legend to the succinct '*L'état c'est moi*') implied responsibility proportionate to power. In the Enlightenment notion of benevolent despotism, this sense of responsibility received greater emphasis, and the ruler was considered the 'first servant' of his people, as one ruler, Prussia's Frederick II, liked to put it. The true monarch, in other words, was expected to be either God-fearing or paternalistic or both. Coupled with this expectation went the concept that there existed a 'social contract' between the governors and the governed which was binding on both parties. Even though apologists for monarchy stressed the obligations incumbent upon the governed, they held to the age-old principle that the individual possessed certain basic 'natural' rights that were superior to man-made laws and that no ruler ought to disregard. In general, monarch and people were thought to be engaged in a common quest for good government. Although this quest often led to the centralization and hence the strengthening of the monarchical state, the people at least insisted on 'just' government and the fulfilment of the 'contract' by the ruler. They were frequently disappointed to find that power corrupts.

The idea of a social contract carried the implication that men under given circumstances had the right, and perhaps even the duty, to revolt against oppression. If a ruler neglected the obligations imposed upon him by the contract, his subjects were freed of their obligation to give him loyalty and obedience; or if he so carried out his obligations as to infringe on the natural rights of groups and individuals, they were entitled to resist and, if they succeeded, to overturn his government. If the major premises were granted, the theory worked with even greater logic in the field of religion, where in fact it was applied earlier (see Chapter IV). Radical religious sects nearly always felt that they must obey God rather than man, and that in case of conflict between the things that were God's and the things that were Caesar's they must prefer God and, if necessary, resist Caesar, at least passively. This philosophy was eventually elaborated to justify the efforts of the Dutch to gain political independence by the use of force or of the Catholics in England and the Huguenots in France to resist their rulers in church matters.

On occasion the assassins of tyrants claimed to have acted in the name of a higher justice. Tyrannicide, we said above, was familiar to the humanist scholar from his study of Roman history; it was no less familiar as an actual event in the turbulent atmosphere of Renaissance Italy. In northern Europe of the sixteenth century and after, assassination was scarcely less common, but there it often was associated also with religious controversy. Thus ended the lives of eminent men like William the Silent, the Duc de Guise, Henry III and Henry IV of France, and Wallenstein; Charles I of England was condemned to death after a civil war by perhaps legal but certainly revolutionary procedures; and Louis XV of France barely escaped assassination by a religious fanatic.

*   *   *

Social and Political Revolt

Popular uprisings against the prevailing order, particularly prominent in the earlier centuries of our period, often followed a similar pattern. They tended to burst forth suddenly and for a while sweep everything before them, only to subside just as suddenly. Frequently they were based on economic and social grievances, taking the form of a bourgeois repudiation of patrician claims, a peasant revolt against noble or ecclesiastical landlords, an uprising of the urban proletariat against the dominant bourgeoisie, or a complex of these and other socio-economic conflicts. The fourteenth century, the era of the recurrent Black Death, witnessed several violent uprisings of a proletarian nature. We have already mentioned the Ciompi of Florence. In the same century, the Flemish cities, in one of the most densely populated, urbanized, and industrial regions of Europe, suffered violent insurrections. Departing from the usual pattern, they began as revolts of powerful bourgeois and urban artisans, chiefly weavers, against patrician domination but quickly took on wider significance because of the related political claims and interests of French and English kings and Flemish counts. In Italy the civic disorders time and again appeared to be mere struggles among conflicting factions of the leading families. Perhaps the most spectacular, though probably not the most important, was that led by Cola di Rienzi (1313–54), who believed himself called to restore the old Roman Republic in the city of the absent popes. Though encouraged by no less a personage than Petrarch, Rienzi's fantastic experiment lasted but a few months. A revolt led by Etienne Marcel (d. 1358), who aimed to put the government of France under the control of the Estates General rather than the king, was similarly vain (see Chapter VIII). Many of the subsequent urban uprisings in Europe were not so much social conflicts between the rich and the poor as political protest against a sovereign's curtailment of municipal liberties and privileges. Thus, for instance, Ghent revolted against Charles V, Paris refused to pay allegiance to Henry IV until he had gone over to Catholicism, and Amsterdam resisted Maurice and William II of Orange.

These revolts were for the most part urban in origin and ran their course inside the confines of cities. Unrest among Europe's peasantry likewise resulted in open rebellions that failed to achieve their objectives. As a rule failure was due to inadequate formulation of objectives and lack of effective leadership but also to the abiding strength of the conservative forces. Many insurrections were directed against practices and conditions, which we shall shortly analyse, that the peasants (and others) felt to be unjust but for which solution would be forthcoming only with a thorough overhaul of the economic and social structure for which society was not yet ripe. At times peasant outbursts were fuelled by religious fervour and supported by clerics. Pious expectations and longing for a better world in which each would have his needs fulfilled, where justice, equality, and, for some devotees, a communistic type of economy would prevail, took the place of a reasoned revolutionary programme. The revolts usually started rather suddenly, quickly assumed dangerous proportions, and were brutally suppressed. Among the most famous were the 'Jacqueries' of the fourteenth century in France (interwoven in a complex pattern with the merchants' uprising in Paris under Marcel), the great Peasants' Revolt of 1381 in England under the leadership of Wat Tyler and John Ball, the German Peasants' War of 1524–25, and the peasant rebellions in Russia led by Ivan Bolotnikov in 1606–07, Stepan Timofeevich Razin in 1667–71, and Yemelyan Pugachev in 1773–75. Their achievements were small, but their frequency and intensity gave easily credible testimony that even the lowest layers of European society were not always cowed by authority and might yet share in the search for a better world.

Philosophical justification of resistance to the point of tyrannicide and lower-class protests to the point of revolt thus contributed substantially to a revolutionary tradition (to use a term that in itself may be a contradiction). But a more effective carry-over came from political revolutions. The most significant before 1775 have already been mentioned and will be mentioned again—the Hussite wars of Bohemia, the Dutch War of Independence, and the civil strife in England that culminated in the Puritan Revolution and the Glorious Revolution of 1688. These were insurrections of peoples against their sovereigns with the aim of protecting or obtaining what they considered their rights. In their course arose many of the important issues concerning the reciprocal rights and duties of kings and subjects. The Hussite wars broke out largely over the questions of liberty of conscience that were to loom over a much greater area during the Reformation. The Dutch Revolution, we have seen, created a new federal republic that long served as a model of toleration and freedom in a Europe where such attitudes were rare. The Puritan Revolution failed for many complex reasons, but its impact on the future of political developments in England was tremendous, and the Glorious Revolution finally confirmed the principle of parliamentary participation in government, setting prescribed limits to royal prerogative and giving precise privileges to Parliament.

Roughly contemporaneously with the Puritan Revolution a wave of less important revolts swept over several continental countries. Two of them reflected the on-going contest between the forces favouring the centralizing dynasties, real or potential, and those favouring local and particularist rights, privileges, and tendencies. William II of Orange, stadholder of the Netherlands, faced with stalwart opposition from the town of Amsterdam, was foiled in an attempt to convert the Dutch Republic into a centralized monarchy. More serious was the insurrection known as the 'Fronde' in France, where dissatisfied nobles, threatened by the centralization engineered by Cardinals Richelieu and Mazarin, rebelled and, with the aid of various dissatisfied elements of the population which sought to defend their local liberties and privileges, threw the country headlong into fruitless turmoil, which lasted a number of years. Several other contemporaneous movements were based upon a more popular type of protest—a people desiring greater autonomy or independence and rising up against a sovereign whom it did not consider a good or a rightful ruler. Examples of such protests were the outbreaks in Catalonia, which had a hoary tradition of opposition to Castilian rule, and in Naples, which had not had a truly Neapolitan dynasty for centuries. Both failed. The contemporary insurrection in Portugal, however, was a successful attempt to regain national independence, which had been lost—and lost for decades (1580–1640)—when Philip II brought the country into a personal union with Spain.

Some observers have maintained that the most influential single political development of the period before the great revolutions of the eighteenth century was 'the new Leviathan'—the dynastic state. The evolution of cohesive states, characterized by a steadily increasing centralization of administration, a growing tendency of government to intervene in religious, economic, cultural, and social affairs, a perhaps greater insistence upon uniformity of law, legal codes, and legal systems, and mounting demands upon the allegiance of subject or citizen, must have left very few men and women unaffected and unconcerned. Not least among those affected were the ones who, either because they had lost (or feared to lose) power to Leviathan or because they had gained (or hoped to gain) power along with Leviathan, were concerned about institutions and opinion hostile to the strong, centralized state. Those who had lost most were the privileged orders; and those who had gained most were the urban middle class. The latter thus was faced with a dilemma, of which some who stopped to think were conscious: the middle class was highly instrumental in a long-run process of furthering both strong government on the one hand and protection of the individual from the all-encompassing state on the other; in consequence, at times middle-class sympathy lay with the kings against the privileged classes, at other times with the privileged classes against the kings. To be sure, the voices of Anabaptists, Levellers, and other radical revolutionary or millennial groups proclaimed that the fight was more than three-cornered, that the complex grouping which might be called a 'fourth estate' was also involved. But for the most part the middle class, sometimes in paradoxical alliance with the privileged orders, was as yet the chief standard-bearer of liberty, since liberty still meant to most men freedom from dynastic absolutism on the one hand and from the claims of feudal, corporate, or constituted authorities on the other. The time when it would mean to many economic and social equality, too, was not far distant.

Concepts of liberty and social justice, we shall point out in Chapters VIII and IX and elsewhere, were not peculiar to Europe. To cite only outstanding examples, in Confucian China 'the mandate of Heaven' was thought to depart from rulers who became 'bad emperors', and in Anglo-America a set of institutions and an ideology were taking shape that in 1775 was to light 'the spark that changed thought into action'.[5] In Europe, however, natural rights first became a political creed widely accepted and nurtured as a tradition and championed (as well as by others) by a full-grown Third Estate, politically conscious, able, strong, and energetic. The identification of that powerful class with that liberal creed was one of the important factors in the West's departure from the feudal, privileged, and patrician or dynastic political structure which until 1300 had been fairly common throughout the world.

ECONOMIC CHANGES AND THEIR POLITICAL IMPORT

The economic and social changes, too, of the period from 1300 to 1775 ultimately led to a markedly altered life for much of mankind. In Europe and its growing dominions overseas an economic system arose that differed considerably from the predominantly peasant societies which had previously been common to all cultures. Of the several forces that interacted to remould Europe's socio–economic structure, three call for special emphasis: the growing significance of the city, the expanding intercourse between Europe, Asia, and America, and the increasing tendency to apply scientific knowledge to industry, trade, and agriculture.

Change in social life and in the direction of economic developments generally tends to be set by the urban communities. The growth of cities helped to break up the old feudal and manorial order, to substitute a money economy for one of barter and payment in service, and to cause a marked increase in agricultural specialization, the number of free tenant farmers, and the rural standard of living. The art of trading was improved immeasurably by refinements in the methods of payment, in the transfer of goods and money, and in the safeguarding of accumulated wealth. Banks and financial corporations, characteristic of a capitalistic society, began to flourish. Religious opposition to a philosophy of life whose major end is material gain diminished, and the acquisition of wealth became an approved social practice. 'Conspicuous consumption' and the use of luxuries greatly increased.

The era of the Black Death and the Hundred Years' War, which came close upon the heels of the 'commercial revolution' mentioned above, was marked by economic setbacks. Until the end of the fifteenth century recovery was slow. After that, however, the long-run trend was almost uninterruptedly upward toward prosperity. Despite rising prices and resulting hardship for wage earners, the general material standards of the ordinary man also rose because of cheaper and more accessible goods (textiles, hardware, fuel, etc.), richer harvests, better methods of animal husbandry, and, above all, the introduction of new crops from overseas that yielded not only luxuries such as sugar, tobacco, tea, and coffee, but also cheaper staples such as potatoes and maize, not to mention new fowl, fruits, and vegetables.

Colonialization cooperated with urbanization to effect economic change. For those who were economically or otherwise bold or desperate, the overseas colonies beckoned, promising rewards from the exploitation of new lands, resources, and markets. At the same time emigration somewhat relieved the congestion in Europe. The virgin soil of the New World held the promise of a larger agricultural yield, and the vastly expanded possibilities for trade in exotic goods provided new sources of wealth for those who dared to invest labour or money in producing or marketing them. More and more of those who stayed at home found employment in slowly evolving industries, which, though a far cry from the large-scale factories of our time, nonetheless provided a greater industrial potential than could the small shops of the Middle Ages.

With the multiplying changes in political, religious, and cultural life came changes in the professions. Lawyers, soldiers, doctors, engineers, artists, ministers, and teachers were among the professional men whose special interests and skills reshaped and were reshaped by the new tendencies. Pressure to apply the growing technological and scientific knowledge (see Chapters XIII–XV) gave rise to new professional and technological procedures. They were particularly productive in industrial pursuits, and towards the end of our period a large-scale 'industrial revolution' was in the making in England, France, and Belgium. In 1776 Adam Smith was to publish his famous *Wealth of Nations*, which advanced the arguments basic to most subsequent economic theorists of the *laisser-faire* school. The readiness of some of the nascent political parties to accept the new economic philosophy was to a large degree a result, and at the same time a crystallization, of a conviction (see Chapters VIII and IX) that the hitherto prevalent theory and practice of government regulation (mercantilism) was not adaptable to an expanding world market.

Agriculture

These economic and social effects of urban, colonial, and other developments came only slowly. As before 1300, agriculture continued to be the primary mode of production; for the great majority of mankind the traditional agricultural systems underwent very little modification until recent times. In Japan, China, southeast Asia, India, and the Islamic world, as well as in most of the tribal societies, the system of landholding, the methods of planting, cultivating, and harvesting crops, the theory and practice of animal husbandry, the types of crops grown, and the preparation of meals remained more or less what they had been for centuries. In some of the advanced civilizations, where imposing cities already existed, urban influences attained no greater comparative prominence after 1300 than they had earlier. By the beginning of our period, therefore, the economy of those civilizations was already fairly well balanced between urban and rural interests, and it changed but little until the nineteenth century. This kind of stability was particularly prevalent outside of Europe, in societies that did not undergo a scientific or ideological 'revolution' and whose rate of agricultural productivity and consumption varied appreciably only with the incidence of war, drought, flood, and similar acts of God or man.

In Europe, however, urbanization had advanced so far that as early as the thirteenth century its effects upon the social structure were easily discernible. The manor or village community that under an almost autonomous landlord was able to provide its own material and spiritual needs had already been widely replaced by a village structure that permitted more frequent economic and social relations with the growing population centres. Whether commercial and industrial compounds, garrisons or fortresses, bureaucratic, ecclesiastical, or university centres, or large villages whose population still earned a living by agriculture (a type that could be found particularly in southern Europe), towns were dependent upon the surrounding countryside for their food supply, and the country folk in turn relied on the town markets for the disposal of their cash crops. Agriculture, therefore, had to adapt itself to the needs of the nearby urban population. This urban demand extended not only to food but also to the raw materials required for industrial processes.

What happened in the Flemish textile industry at the beginning of our period well illustrates the growing economic interdependence. That mushrooming industry demanded ever greater amounts of woad for dye and of wool and flax for yarn and thread. Thus the cities of Flanders stimulated both the growth of woad and flax in neighbouring Picardy and the conversion of crop fields to pasture in England, which, climatically suited for the production of a superior type of wool, soon began to compete with Flanders in textile manufacture. The consequence was a considerable degree of regional specialization in agriculture. With the intensification of agricultural specialization, the neighbouring countryside became incapable by itself of provisioning the Flemish cities, and so foodstuffs and textile materials, sometimes cheaper and frequently better, had to be imported by sea from far-off regions. A considerable amount of the grain used in Flanders came from the Baltic countries, of the raw wool used in England from Spain and Germany, and of the wool yarn used in Italy from England, while Normandy and Provence helped to provide the needs of the urban areas of Spain and Italy.

Cash crops gave peasants the means to substitute money payments for the obligations in kind or services that they owed their lords. In this way the feudal and manorial order in western Europe was gradually transformed into a tenant system. The tenant system often meant considerably higher living standards for the peasant and a rise in their self-esteem. It also brought greatly increased social mobility. Being no longer necessarily tied to the soil, more and more farmers worked for their own profit rather than in subjection to the programmes of their lords. Many peasants actually moved into cities and thus relieved the pressure upon the land that from about 1100 to about 1350 resulted from the general increase in western Europe's population.

In fact, the increase in population at times outstripped the ability of the land to provide food. Seriously unbalanced situations resulted that were responsible for some of the dreadful famines of the late thirteenth and fourteenth centuries. These famines explain in part why certain areas contemporaneously experienced a sudden reversal in the demographic trend. During the second half of the fourteenth century the appalling epidemics known as Black Death inflicted additional losses upon Italy, Spain, France, England, Germany, and Norway. Plague combined with famine and the general economic depression already mentioned to cause a general decline in Europe's population after 1350—in some countries a decline of 40 per cent or more. The ravages of war also at times decimated the peasant population, particularly in France during the Hundred Years' War (1337–1453) and in Germany during the Thirty Years' War (1618–48). Yet such catastrophies, horrifying and spectacular though they were, did not mean a permanent setback to the population growth of the smitten areas. By the sixteenth century population figures were again at their earlier levels except in Norway, where losses seem not to have been overcome for at least another century. Thereafter Europe's population rose steadily. In 1650 it was about 100,000,000, while Asia's was about 250,000,000. In 1750 the respective figures were about 140,000,000 and 406,000,000. By 1800 they had risen to about 187,000,000 and 522,000,000 respectively. The world's population had meanwhile grown from 465,000,000 to 660,000,000 and then to 836,000,000. China's alone rose from about 60,000,000 in 1368 to 583,000,000 in 1953.[6]

The demand for food and space grew correspondingly. New land was constantly exploited for agricultural purposes both through territorial expansion to the east of Europe and through cultivation of fields that had previously lain fallow. Forests diminished in number and size on the Continent, and even more in the British Isles, where profit from the raising of sheep increased the demand for pasture even at the sacrifice of tilled fields. Morasses and swamps were drained, and the Dutch developed amazing proficiency in reclaiming land from the sea and rivers. In 1600 the Low Countries were able to put a much larger area under cultivation than three hundred years earlier. On the other hand, China, Ceylon, India, Mesopotamia, Egypt, North Africa, Italy, Spain, and other regions clamouring for water had long made use of irrigation and were thus able to turn arid stretches into fertile fields. The New World and south Africa also provided virgin lands for Europe's relatively dense agricultural population to exploit.

A more intensive exploitation of the available soil was simultaneously under way. China, Japan, and southeast Asia, nearly always congested, had made a transition to the intensive farming of rice at an early stage of their development. In Europe soil conservation by field rotation had become traditional before our period, but in the seventeenth century a change from field to crop rotation and therefore from extensive to intensive cultivation began; and in the eighteenth century came the 'industrial revolution' described in more detail in Chapter XV. Improved agricultural tools and techniques saved labour, enlarged the scope of a day's work, and considerably furthered the use of fertilizer and fodder crops. New staples like maize and potatoes had meanwhile entered from America into the European agricultural system, providing a highly satisfying yield and considerably increasing the food supply of the poorer classes. At the same time, horticulture, one of the most intensive forms of agriculture, developed all over Europe, especially in the Low Countries, and some farmers prospered by concentrating on the production of fruit trees, vegetables, flowers, and ornamental shrubs in orchards, suburban gardens, and even the parks of patricians. The techniques of animal husbandry, which together with farming was the major source of rural wealth, also made great strides. In short, between 1300 and 1775 the average yield per acre, and, therefore, the average income to the farmer, was greatly enhanced, with benefit to the population as a whole.

*　　　*　　　*

Agricultural Labour

These developments worked toward the economic emancipation of the smaller farmers. To be sure, by 1775 serfdom was far from extinct in western Europe and indeed had probably grown worse east of the Elbe, and even the free peasant anywhere was often miserable. Nevertheless, a large number of peasants whose ancestors had been serfs during medieval times had become either independent or tenant farmers, with a greater degree of freedom in running both their farms and their personal affairs. On the less fertile soils many had become *métayers* ('sharecroppers'), and though their lot as such was also wretched, it tended to improve. The size of these more emancipated groups was especially impressive in western Europe. Although emancipation often meant no more than membership in a landless rural class that made a living only by hiring out as agricultural labour, a number of peasants acquired their own land and livestock. Some leased lands for a money rental, most frequently on long-term arrangements, from a lord who left them free as long as they paid the still surviving dues and respected his seigniorial rights. Even where they were still dependent on the local lord or still responsible for *corvées* to the government (often no more than a few days' labour *per* year on roads and bridges), the freeholders and tenant-farmers of 1775 were considerably better off than serfs and sharecroppers. If the lord remained a dominant figure in rural affairs, he was no longer the undisputed master of the local peasantry. Independent or partly independent farmers could now grow what they wanted, sell their harvests where they could get the most for them, marry off their daughters without seigniorial consent, appeal to royal administrators when they felt unjustly treated, and move away if they preferred. The increased productivity of agriculture and the rising prices for his produce induced the peasant to seek more land and greater freedom from his remaining servile obligations. For similar reasons, the landlords sought to retain feudal dues, cheap labour, and good lands. Thus the peasant's 'land hunger' in some places collided with the lord's 'feudal reaction'. Even though much of the peasant's servile heritage remained a burden when, in the 1780's, the revolutionary era began in western Europe, he had already taken some meaningful steps towards economic emancipation in the more advanced areas.

In eastern Europe agrarian conditions were less promising. During the *Drang nach Osten* the new settlers had in general formed the freest and most emancipated peasantry of Europe. This enviable situation lasted for a few centuries after 1300. Towards the close of our period, however, the increasing demand for agricultural products in the more rapidly urbanizing countries made the stabilizing of the labour supply more desirable for eastern landowners, and the great lords of eastern Germany, Austria, Bohemia, Poland, the Baltic areas, and Russia managed to stabilize theirs so well that serfdom of a highly restrictive kind ensued. As land ownership passed more and more into private hands, more peasants became permanently tied to the soil and passed completely under seigniorial or church jurisdiction. The Russian church was one of the worst exploiters of serf labour, the Troitse-Sergiev Monastery alone, according to one estimate, owning over 106,000 male serfs in the 1760's, when the largest noble landowner had fewer than 5,000.[7] The serfdom that ultimately developed in the eastern countries lacked some of the mitigating features of western serfdom. The lord was virtually absolute. He determined the hours of labour; he fixed the taxes; he meted out punishment; he decided who was allowed to marry whom; and he had the right to recapture any runaway serf. At times it was not easy to distinguish this type of serfdom from outright slavery. Occasionally a more enlightened monarch attempted to alleviate the peasants' lot, but the results of such attempts usually proved only temporary. Peasant revolts were frequent.

Under such conditions the general level of agricultural production in eastern Europe failed to rise. Although Russian peasants brought vast areas in northeastern Russia, the southern steppes, and Siberia under cultivation and initiated the peoples of Siberia into the knowledge of agriculture, Russian agricultural methods and tools remained relatively primitive. Animal breeding in eastern Europe never reached the point attained in the west, and of the new crops only the potato played a major role, though as fodder more than as food in our period. Some rulers like Peter the Great in Russia or the Great Elector and Frederick II in Prussia made serious attempts to introduce some of the refinements of western European agriculture but seldom were able to advance beyond the experimental stages. A splendid model farm established at Oranienburg did little to ameliorate the traditional methods and squalor of the vast multitude of Prussian peasants. For the peasant masses east of the Elbe notable improvement of personal and economic status did not come before the nineteenth century.

Rural social conditions in the New World were a strange mixture of what was good and advanced with what was bad and backward in European agriculture. Besides independent settlers, numerous indentured servants and *engagés* (bound by contract, written or understood, for a definite period) went as colonists to the English and the French colonies of North America. Whether their engagements were involuntary (for example, to escape imprisonment for debt) or voluntary, these servants and *engagés* joined the ranks of independent settlers, once their contracts were fulfilled. Such settlers, as well as many Spanish and Portuguese farmers in Central and South America, were probably among the freest farmers in the world. Each had his own land (often plenty of it), houses, tools, and livestock. He could move almost whenever it suited him and carve out a new holding in the immense stretches of unclaimed wilderness. He was more or less subject to officials who derived their power ultimately from the home country, but in the distant new lands governmental authority was generally very little felt. Most of these settlers, having possessed no land or having been only small holders in the Old World, had improved their lot tremendously.

In some areas, however (especially in the southernmost English colonies on the north Atlantic seaboard, in Mexico, and in large sections of Central and South America, as well as on the islands of the Caribbean), while Europeans enjoyed an enviable position, the non-European agricultural labourers were either serfs or slaves. The pre-Columbian Indian population in the Spanish colonies of America has been estimated at 14,579,500. By 1570 it had dropped to 9,253,850. By 1650 it had begun to climb (10,359,000), and by 1825 it was up to 15,814,000.[8] In the Spanish colonies with a large Indian population an institution known as the 'encomienda' flourished. The encomienda was a later-day version of a medieval fief. It was usually the right to exploit (along with the obligation to care for) the native population in an assigned area granted (without outright title to the land) to a European conqueror or governor by the Spanish crown. It might include several native communities, whose inhabitants were obliged to pay tribute and render services to the 'encomendero' (proprietor of an encomienda). The encomienda gave way later in the sixteenth century to a more thoroughly organized, state-controlled labour system called the 'repartimiento', which in the seventeenth century was in its turn largely displaced by the privately owned plantation, or 'hacienda'.

The hacienda was often a latifundium in which not only the land but also the labour of the Indian farmers residing on it belonged to the European colonist. The home government and the church had intended that the Indians should be free and should be converted to Christianity. Notwithstanding the efforts of some humanitarian reformers, these intentions were seldom put into practice. Instead, the natives, subject to tribute in encomienda or reparti- miento if they remained in their own communities, went off to the haciendas. There they usually acquired greater indebtedness than they could pay off and so became peons. The peon was legally free but economically a kind of serf. He was either a paid labourer or a tenant farmer on a big estate, but in either case for all practical purposes he remained perpetually indebted to the landlord and thus bound to him. Even where native village communities persisted, they were frequently subject to the neighbouring 'haciendado', or proprietor of a hacienda. The Spanish conquests thus superimposed a few rich and powerful European colonists upon vast masses of Indians, who were reduced to the status of peons.

In Brazil the Portuguese crown at first attempted to create a feudal system. It divided the country among fifteen 'donatorios' with powers limited only by the rights reserved for the crown. But from the start this system did not work well. A governor-general took over the donatorios' political powers after a few years, and in the eighteenth century the crown also took over their land grants. Meanwhile, a few thousand white settlers had been importing Negro slaves and enslaving Indians except where the Jesuits were able to settle Indians in *aldeas* ('missions'). The Marquis de Pombal, the Portuguese minister who expelled the Jesuits from Brazil (1759), also made Indians equal to white men in the eyes of the law.

Another agricultural institution, the plantation system, came into special prominence in what is now the southern part of the United States, the West Indies (whether Spanish, English, French, Dutch, or Danish), and Brazil. These were areas where the European landowner found the climate too uncomfortable for hard manual labour but very favourable for the cultivation of cash crops such as tobacco, cotton, and sugar cane. The answer to his dilemma proved to be the plantation (large farm) worked by indentured or slave labour, which enabled him to secure both comfort and profit. The plantation was much like the European manor or, though generally less extensive, like the Spanish–American hacienda.

The labour force for the plantation consisted primarily of Negro slaves, most of whom were imported from the west coast of Africa, and the trade in slaves became a most profitable enterprise for the merchants of the seafaring nations. Originally the right to import slaves into the Spanish colonies—the *asiento*—was limited, having to be purchased from the Spanish crown. By the Treaty of Utrecht in 1713, the British gained this right as a prize of war. A country's slave trade was, however, much too profitable to remain a monopoly; it attracted so many merchants of other lands that it was never easy to protect it against slave runners. The actual capture of slaves was usually the enterprise of West African chiefs. European shippers bought them cheap and transported them to America under conditions so abominable that appalling numbers died during the ocean voyage. This traffic brought to the American shores thousands upon thousands of unfortunate chattels whose descendants created a thorny political and social problem that abides to this day. Their labours, however, made the land productive, and thus they were an important factor in shaping the culture of the tropical and subtropical regions of North and South America.

One of the arguments advanced to justify Negro slavery was similar to that used (by the sixteenth-century historian Juan Genés de Sepúlveda, for example) to excuse the reduction of the Indian populations to the status of forced labourers in the encomiendas: according to Aristotle, part of mankind was set aside by nature to be slaves, and through slavery pagans could be introduced to civilization and Christianity. Some representatives of the Catholic Church—Bartolomé de Las Casas foremost among them—felt responsible for preventing the exploitation of the natives on this basis, and wherever they succeeded in exercising influence, the position of the Indians was relatively improved. At Valladolid in 1550 Sepúlveda and Las Casas presented their respective arguments before an illustrious gathering of officials, clergy, and lawyers. After several papal and royal protests and prohibitions, the sale of Indians into slavery in the Spanish colonies gradually came to an end (with exceptions in regions where nomadic warfare continued), but Negroes replaced them in the slave markets. On the whole, the lot of Negro slaves in the Spanish and Portuguese colonies was less harsh than in the English colonies of North America. By virtue of certain precedents in Roman civil law, Spanish and Portuguese slaves were manumitted more readily and were better protected in property and family affairs than slaves, for instance, in Virginia or the Carolinas, where the common law was silent on slavery and so left them subject to the mercy of their masters. Since civil law recognized marriage with slaves as binding, intermarriage further helped to improve the lot of the Negro in Spanish and especially Portuguese areas. To a large extent the more humane attitude of the Iberian governments is attributable also to the intervention of the crown and to the abolitionist efforts of such churchmen as Las Casas and Alonso de Montúfar in the sixteenth century. Toward the end of our period some Protestants—the American Quaker John Woolman (1720-72) and the English philanthropist Granville Sharp (1735-1813), for instance—campaigned against the institution of slavery with equal fervour, and eighteenth-century *philosophes* and humanitarians made abolition one of their numerous reform causes.

The use of slave labour on immense tropical and semi-tropical plantations made possible the production of lucrative crops of sugar, tobacco, indigo, and rice, which would have been less economically produced on small-scale farms. Cotton also was grown but, before the patenting of the cotton gin (1794), in quantities too small to compete with Eastern sources. The plantation provided large-scale, specialized farming, very different from the subsistence farming of most other agricultural areas, and it flourished as long as European and North American markets demanded tropical products. Between the lands in which the plantation system prevailed and the older countries a simple trading pattern emerged. The planters had to export their specialized crops and to import other agricultural necessities as well as much of the labour and equipment they required. At first, dependence on the mother country's economy was natural and convenient, a fact that made it easier for the mother country to retain a monopolistic position even after the colonies might otherwise have preferred independence.

*   *   *

Relative Stability in the East

While the conditions and methods of the agricultural classes were undergoing these marked changes in the West, only few variations took place in the agricultural methods of Asia, Africa, and the Islamic world. In China the two-crop-per-year system spread in the south, and the sweet potato and Indian corn were introduced from America via Manila, contributing to a remarkable growth of population in the eighteenth century. Where Islam established itself in India, it brought about the rise of some new Hindu sects and some new attitudes towards caste, labour, and Muslim–Hindu relations (Chapters II, III, and V), but it left the village structure essentially unchanged. Emperor Akbar (1542-1605) allowed Hindu rajahs to rule in some states and Muslim nawwābs in others, contenting himself with fairly heavy but systematic taxation, and his successors retained his system with certain modifications.9 In Japan, once the Tokugawas ended the feudal warfare of the Ashikaga period and inaugurated their own centralized regime, considerable new land was brought under cultivation, and by the 1720's the population increased to about 30,000,000. It long remained at that figure because no new agricultural techniques were introduced. Meanwhile, the gradual expansion of commerce promoted the growth of towns, undermined the feudal system, and further impoverished the peasants, many of whom lost their rights in their land to money-lenders, either of merchant or of peasant origin. Many peasants also, despite prohibitions, moved into the towns.

★   ★   ★

Industry

Modern industry was born long before James Watt meditated upon his tea-kettle. The impressive speeding-up of industrial methods in the eighteenth century was preceded by a long and important evolution in which various complex technological and interrelated factors had prepared the ground (see Chapters XIII–XV).

Despite the cumulative impact of the new forms of production, some medieval industrial practices persisted. The small artisan's shop, protected to some degree by guild organization or caste rules, continued in all countries to provide many of the manufactured articles that are now generally produced by large-scale industrial processes. Articles were seldom ready-made. If a coat was needed, one ordinarily turned to the local tailor; for a pair of shoes the local shoemaker was engaged; what furniture was not inherited and could not be made at home was provided by the local carpenter or, for finer work, by the cabinet-maker. In some localities tailors, potters, or weavers were not needed, since the farming population was quite capable of manufacturing many of its own necessities. Shopkeepers were craftsmen when they sat at their workbenches and merchants when they stepped to the sales counters. Except for man-made regulations they could in most instances ply their trade wherever they decided to set up shop, for ordinarily they were not dependent on ready access to raw materials and markets or to running water and other sources of energy. The things they required could generally be provided by the town market, the surrounding countryside, and itinerant merchants.

Even in medieval times, however, certain trades were dependent upon special conditions. Some industrial processes required a fast flow of water or steady winds, for water and wind were, next to humans and animals, the primary sources of power for mills before the development of the steam engine. At times enterprises remained localized because their raw materials were bulky or otherwise uneconomical for distant transportation. Thus, some specialization of production was necessitated by simple facts of nature—the availability, for example, of running water, forests (for charcoal), clay, or stone quarries. But since such natural features were abundant, such industries could grow up in many regions. Intensive specialization began only when differences in the quality and supply of raw materials and, above all, in the costs of their manufacture became significant considerations in fixing prices in a competitive market.

Even before 1300 physiographical features along with local craftsmanship and other factors had worked toward a regional specialization of production. The wool yarn and cloth produced in Spain, England, and the Low Countries was found to be superior to most other wool. The silk grown in the warm climates of Italy, Spain, and southern France proved superior to that produced farther north, and the best silk was produced in China. The flax of Ireland, Flanders, and Holland surpassed that used for linen in other regions. Kaolin made much finer pottery than common clays, and the finest porcelains acquired the generic name of 'chinaware' in tribute to their place of origin. The best cotton goods, as their names indicated—calico (from Calicut), chintz (from a Sanskrit word meaning *spotted*), and even muslin (though probably first made in Mosul)—came from India. Muslim craftsmen had long exhibited extraordinary skill with steel as armourers and cutlers, and extraordinary taste as well as skill in silk weaving, carpet making, and embroidery. Some Spanish towns in close contact with the Moors had learned Moorish methods of production of armour and blades, and some Italian towns, by their contact with the Levant, had learned how to manufacture most beautiful brocades. Venetians and Bohemians knew how to blow exceptionally beautiful glass. The finest rugs came from Persia. After 1300 other than regional factors combined to intensify the specialization of industry (see Chapter XV).

*   *   *

Beginnings of Capitalism

Between 1300 and 1775 the development of industry was speeded up, for one thing, by extraordinary improvements in the techniques of finance and commerce. One of the most patent drawbacks to industrial progress around 1300 was the lack of adequate capital for the creation of bigger workshops, the acquisition of new tools and machinery, the purchase of larger quantities of raw materials, the better financing of long-term sales, and larger reserves to weather the fluctuations of the market. If a town's artisans, united as they were in a guild, had massed their capital in a cooperative enterprise, the necessary expansion of money and credit might have been achieved. But the general attitude of guild members was that their guild's purpose was protective—to restrict production, prices, and labour conditions—and by such monopolistic policies to guarantee for themselves a certain standard of living and of production without free competition. With all its corporative features the guild system worked against the abandonment of the small independent craftshop for the large-scale corporative factory.

Industrial capital had to come from other sources. In Florence and other towns of Italy increasing urbanization made investments in land a good basis for further profits. Furthermore, the expansion of Italy's trade made possible the accumulation of capital by commercial activities. Gradually this accumulated capital was invested in industrial processes, and some merchants became both traders and industrial entrepreneurs. Investments in industry earned additional money, which could be reinvested in the further expansion of realty, commercial, and industrial establishments. The interplay of land, commerce, and industry made for an effective interaction of financiers with landlords, merchants, and manufacturers. Simply stated (but we shall have to consider many complications later), it produced marketable articles which, when sold by the merchant, brought profits, which, when deposited with banker or broker, were reinvested in the production of additional marketable articles. Capitalism, or the investment of accumulated wealth for purposes of further gain, became a much more familiar process in the world's economy after the fourteenth century than it had been before.

Industry first developed on a large scale in Europe in the manufacture of textiles, especially wool and linen cloth, in some of the towns of Lombardy and Tuscany and, above all, Flanders. Flemish entrepreneurs found it profitable to import the superior wools of England and Spain in great amounts and 'put it out' to Flemish farmers for spinning and weaving. In this way they avoided the regulations of the guilds, which usually dominated the manufacture of cloth in the towns. Since the farmers and their families could give them only their spare time, they found that they had to employ fairly large numbers of workers. They were thus using many hands to work numerous but individually small quantities of raw material into large quantities of finished goods—the basis of large-scale manufacture. In this way extensive capitalistic enterprises either grew up beyond the reach of the guilds or, where bold entrepreneurs chose to make a stand against guild restrictions, were eventually constrained to try to break the power of the guilds.

The 'putting-out' or 'domestic' system was cumbersome, and a natural urge developed to concentrate manufacturing processes in one location or 'factory' and under the entrepreneur's immediate direction. In the textile industry specialized labour had long been the rule and a large number of employees in separate operations washed, combed, dyed, carded, and spun raw wool into yarn for weavers to make into cloth. Innovation here took the form of combining some of these operations under the same roof and under the financial and managerial supervision of the same entrepreneur. As specialization of production set in, compensation for skill in the various steps of the manufacturing process fell while that for speed in one of the diversified operations rose. Workers might find prolonged repetition of the same process monotonous, but output was tremendously increased by such division of labour and unification of management, and the goods thus produced, though not necessarily better, were generally cheaper, especially where labour-saving devices and improved tools were employed (see Chapter XV).

Because industry characterized by technical and regional specialization proved able to supply existing demands most economically, it expanded steadily, especially in England in the eighteenth century, but not without tremendous social opposition. The ever growing centres of these specialized industries, the factories, brought smoke and slums, and some of the opposition was on aesthetic and humanitarian grounds. The loudest and most constant denunciation of the capitalistic entrepreneur, however, came from the guilds, and in some countries they were successful in delaying the rise of large-scale industries. In the long run they succumbed before the capitalist's economic strength. The small craftshop was in no position to compete with the new-comer's greater output and cheaper prices. By 1775 the guild system was moribund, and the small artisan was being driven to the wall by the large-scale producer. Nevertheless, he was to outlast his guilds and to survive until our own day as a craftsman.

The development of large-scale industries gave a new impetus to the growth of the urban proletariat, already under way because of the increasing need for labour in small-scale industry and in commercial enterprises. A mounting number of workers ceased to be skilled journeymen with relatively secure social positions and became semi-skilled or unskilled labourers owning no part of the tools of production and enjoying no guild protection. Even where the guilds managed to maintain themselves, the medieval system of graduation from apprentice to journeyman to master became limited to fewer and fewer aspirants, for the new competition induced the masters to keep down the number of journeymen. In consequence, apprenticeship was prolonged, and many a journeyman was forced to remain a journeyman for his entire life. Thus social conflict was intensified in two different ways: between journeymen and masters in the guild structure, and between entrepreneur and proletarian in the capitalist system. As we have seen, these conflicts sometimes assumed a violent character, and the towns experienced serious unrest, especially during the early centuries of our period, when the capitalist system was slowly establishing itself more effectively. Since strikes were illegal and were frequently accompanied by violence and political tension, they often merged with or developed into revolt. Once the larger industries were firmly founded and enjoyed the protection of the governments, which could effectively meet violence, this type of social disorder became less frequent. By 1775 such workers' 'insurrections' were rare, but the intrinsic tension persisted, to break out more widely and more successfully in the nineteenth century. Meanwhile they served, in a day when other channels of public opinion hardly existed, as a means, though usually latent, of pressure upon governments.

*   *   *

Mechanization and Mining

After 1700, industrialism began to be characterized by rapid mechanization. This development was based on a series of technological innovations to be described in Chapter XV. The especially striking changes in industry during the eighteenth century are sometimes called 'the Industrial Revolution', with the same justification and with the same inaccuracy as in the case of 'the Scientific Revolution'. While some of its palpable effects seemed sudden and startling, it was the result of a process that was long and slow and has been continuous ever since. When James Watt finally patented a steam engine which was really usable (1769 and 1775), a type of industrial expansion that was destined to bring a thorough change in man's productive methods got under way. England, especially in textile manufacture, laid the foundations of its later industrial superiority in the last decades of our period. France and Belgium at first unsuccessfully tried to keep pace, but the revolutions and wars of the succeeding decades impeded them, and they fell considerably behind.

As Chapter XV will show in greater detail, only when machinery became relatively familiar did mining gain substantially in safety against its numerous hazards and therefore in productivity. After 1500, technological devices like fans, rails, and, above all, pumps were installed in some European and American mines, and they became more common after 1700. The improvement in mining operations, by making 'precious metals' less precious helped to cause an inflation of prices, already discernible at the close of the fifteenth century. In the sixteenth century a number of factors—among them a strike of silver in Bohemia, Portuguese importations of gold from Africa, and the discovery of the 'patio' process of producing silver, which made Mexico and Peru the source of abundant Spanish treasure—aggravated this so-called 'price revolution'. Although Europe's and Peru's output of silver diminished as lucrative mines were depleted, Mexico's grew, and the discovery of gold in Brazil at the close of the seventeenth century brought a gold rush to the wilderness. The rise in prices, except for a downward trend from about 1660 to about 1745, continued. Conservative calculations indicate that the prices of a number of staples almost tripled in Europe between 1500 and 1800. This increase, however, was due not alone to the abundance of precious metals but also to government manipulations like debasing the coinage.

The output of iron, copper, and tin also mounted sharply, but perhaps the most remarkable mining development of the age was the steady expansion of the production of common coal, especially in England. With the invention of the coking process in 1735, coal rapidly became an indispensable component of the British metallurgical industry, and coal mining became a leading source of goods, wages, and profits.

*   *   *

Wood, Game, and Fish

The coal mine gradually replaced the forest as the chief source of fuel. Wood, however, was not only an important fuel; it was also indispensable for buildings, shorings, vehicles, furniture, and ships. In the fourteenth century the supply of wood was sufficient nearly everywhere for fuel, timber, veneers, and similar needs. With the increasing deforestation and the growth of industry and ship-building, the traffic in wood spread and the areas of Europe around the Baltic (Russia and Scandinavia, in particular) profited greatly because of the superiority of their timber. Some of the more far-sighted monarchs of Europe awakened to the dangers of deforestation and attempted to stem it. Relatively late in our period a scientific approach to forestry manifested itself in the development of silviculture.

Hunting, which in the earlier centuries of our era was still an important source of meat, was associated with forestry. Since in many regions it formed one of the most cherished privileges of royalty and nobility, the biggest and best forests were generally the possessions of kings and aristocrats, and hunting rights were jealously guarded. Popular resentment against these privileges was outspoken and persistent. With the growth of animal husbandry, hunting lost some of its economic significance, which passed to the rancher. Cattle were important not only as a source of meat and hides but also as an incentive in the settlement of the New World, where the *bandeirantes* of Brazil, the *vaqueros* of Spanish America, and the cowboys of North America were often pioneers. Edible game was practically wiped out in England before the eighteenth century, and in civilized lands, hunting became more of a sport for gentlemen with leisure than a way of procuring food. To the peasant it also represented a nuisance, since, if the game he might not freely shoot or trap did not eat his crop, the hunter might trample it.

Fish, unlike game, never lost its importance as part of the staple diet of civilized man, and for many island peoples, primitive or advanced, sea food continued to be the major article of diet. In Europe fish had gained special significance because the church considered it permissible for meals on fast days. At first the only ways of preserving fish were to dry it or to smoke it (a process which was known to some people from time immemorial and to Europeans by the fourteenth century). A Dutchman named William Beukelszoon devised an improved process of gutting and salting herring (c. 1375). From then on fishing developed into a large-scale industry, and the countries located around the North Sea grew rich on it; Amsterdam is sometimes said to have been 'built on herring bones'. In the seventeenth and eighteenth centuries the fishing banks near Newfoundland were so profitable that their possession became a factor in international diplomacy from the Treaty of Utrecht (1713) on. As a source of oil, spermaceti (important in making candles and cosmetics), and whalebone, whaling was a special branch of fishing, producing huge profits at great risk by filling needs now generally supplied by petroleum, plastics, and steel. Spitsbergen was the centre of 'the Greenland fishery', which slaughtered whales by the thousands.

★   ★   ★

Expansion of Trade

The increasing productivity of seas, soil, and mines might well have been only of localized benefit had it not been for a concomitant development in the ways of distributing goods and services. The expansion of trade was a natural result of the expansion of geographical knowledge during the centuries between 1300 and 1775.

Before 1300 Europeans had been outclassed in trade and finance by the great trading nations of other regions. Japanese shipping went out into much of the world, rivalling Muslim and Christian traders as far west as the Indian Ocean. The Chinese also had long distinguished themselves as merchants. Their powerfully developed guild system protected their common interests and regulated many aspects of their trade and competition. Chinese merchants knew of bookkeeping, paper credit instruments, trading associations, complicated methods of payment for transactions between distant points, and other refinements for facilitating the exchange of goods long before such practices became common in the West. Much of Chinese trade was domestic and independent of export and import, since the vast regions comprising China were relatively self-sufficient, and until the nineteenth century the Chinese professed only limited interest in relations with European traders. Even so, Genoese and Venetian merchantmen could be seen in Chinese waters in the fourteenth century, the Portuguese established a prosperous post at Macao in 1557, and the annual visit of the Spanish galleon from Acapulco brought Chinese junks in droves to Manila to exchange their wares for those of Europe and America.

Still more spectacular perhaps than the trading activities of the Chinese were those of the Muslims, particularly the Arabs. The central position of Islam in the Afro-Eurasian land mass had long made the Muslims the natural middlemen for the flow of goods among the several regions. Their caravans travelled to far-off places; their ships roamed the seas southward to East Africa, westward all over the Mediterranean, and eastward to Ceylon, the Malay Archipelago, and the China coast. In Asiatic waters Muslim traders had built a commercial empire centring upon Malacca, and Arab dhows competed successfully with Chinese, Japanese, Javanese, Persian, and Indian junks and sampans before the end of the fifteenth century, and after that with Portuguese and other European caravels as well. Merchants held a respected position in Muslim society and literature, and the acquisition of money by hard work and trade carried no social disapproval such as was expressed in certain quarters of contemporary Europe.

On foundations laid in the eleventh, twelfth, and thirteenth centuries, the economic system that we have already identified as capitalism grew up in western Europe. In this system an essential role is assigned to the investment of money and to the drive to accumulate more money—for a higher standard of living and for the expansion of economic enterprises as well as for the satisfaction of basic material needs. In the capitalist system economic rationalization (i.e. careful calculation of the most efficient means of exploiting the various sources of wealth) is cultivated, a clear social differentiation may and frequently does separate the owners (whether of factory, trading establishment, or bank) from those who work for them, manufacturing and selling ordinarily occur on a grand scale, production does not take place upon order but rather on the basis of anticipated demand or even of studied creation of new demand, and motivation, frankly based upon the incentive of profit in an autonomous, competitive market, at times eludes the restraints of custom or religious precept.

The growth of capitalism during our period took place in the face of many obstacles but also under the protection of the dynastic state. Although significant in agriculture and industry too, between 1300 and 1500 its effects were most notable in the development of commerce and finance. The merchant guilds were gradually replaced by independent merchants, many of whom became veritable 'merchant-princes' (such as Jacques Coeur of Bourges, the Medici family of Florence, and the Fuggers of Augsburg) or by group organizations (such as partnerships, trading companies, and commercial leagues like the Hansa). The guild, emphasizing local control and regulation, was not adaptable to the rapid expansion of trade; it could not readily reach out geographically or lend itself to quick manipulations, as could the more ambitious entrepreneurs. Independent commercial groupings were easily initiated and in general gave greater leeway to their members, thus facilitating commerce over vast areas and taking advantage of special opportunities. The new businessmen did not always advocate unrestricted competition and freedom of enterprise; on the contrary, they frequently sought monopolistic rights and privileged status from their sovereigns. Independence from government regulation and freedom of trade became the businessman's objectives only later, when the new master, the powerful state (especially if a foreign state), became an obstacle to capitalistic enterprise.

Some of the richest traders were strong enough to go their individual ways without partners. The biggest among them had their own quarters and offices, tended by stewards or minor partners, in scattered trading centres such as Venice, Florence, Bruges, Augsburg, Nuremberg, or London, and later Antwerp or Amsterdam. They had their own pack trains or, if they engaged in maritime trade, their own ships. The ambitious Jacques Coeur actually had a whole fleet for his Levantine trade and branch offices in the major towns of France and Italy. Only the really wealthy or venturesome merchants dared run the risks of trading as lone entrepreneurs, for ships and pack trains were too frequently destroyed by natural disasters, piracy, and highway robbery, and markets were often undependable. For the more cautious, the mutual sharing of profit and loss through some kind of short-term (*commenda*) or long-term (*compagnia*) partnership constituted a safer arrangement. In addition, marine and commercial insurance was inaugurated in Italy before 1300 and spread to other regions in the fifteenth century, though only toward the end of our period was it widely employed. Occasionally partnerships involved unfamiliar legal complications, but they were gradually regularized in a separate branch of civil law based on Roman practices.

The development of trans-oceanic trade after 1500 stimulated the rise of the trading company with numerous partners. Such a company frequently included individuals who merely made a contribution toward the purchase of 'stock' in return for a share in the expected profits without being actively engaged in the trading activities. Some of these 'joint-stock' companies, such as the British and the Dutch East India Company, founded respectively in 1600 and 1602, grew so powerful that they controlled vast colonial empires, each with a standing army of 10,000 or more and with a huge administrative personnel. Most of these associative forms of commerce (as noted also in connection with manufacturing) found a powerful protector in the state. Rulers were interested in safeguarding the welfare of the companies they chartered and granted them protective tariffs and subsidies in addition to privileges and monopolies, in the expectation that the royal treasury would profit as the companies' revenues increased. When the dynastic states grew strong enough, they sometimes took over the role of protector-exploiter that had been filled earlier by great commercial leagues. In the course of time merchant and monarch seemed to become ever more closely linked by a chain of gold.

★   ★   ★

Transportation and Travel

During the Middle Ages long-distance trade was particularly profitable in luxury goods. Because of the general self-sufficiency of the manorial system and because of transportation difficulties, bulk goods constituted but a small part of Europe's trade. Although trade in luxury goods remained important after 1300, the character of the principal commodities changed as specialization by region became more pronounced in industry and money economy gradually superseded manorial and feudal economy. Bulk goods like textiles, grains, wine, fish, and lumber became more common as articles of commerce. Regular fleets, first annually and then at more frequent intervals, went from Italy to carry luxury goods to the north and to bring Flemish cloth from Bruges. Other ships brought Baltic grain and wood to Flanders and England. Wine was shipped from Gascony and Portugal to England. Swedish ores went to northwestern Europe. From Novgorod the Western countries imported furs and candle wax. Where possible, bulk goods were moved by important inland water routes such as the Rhine, Loire, Seine, or Danube. Even overland traffic increased, though on a much smaller scale, profiting from new types of wagons, better methods of harnessing horses, and improved roads. The separate parts of Europe gradually learned to depend upon various other regions for varied goods. (Map III.)

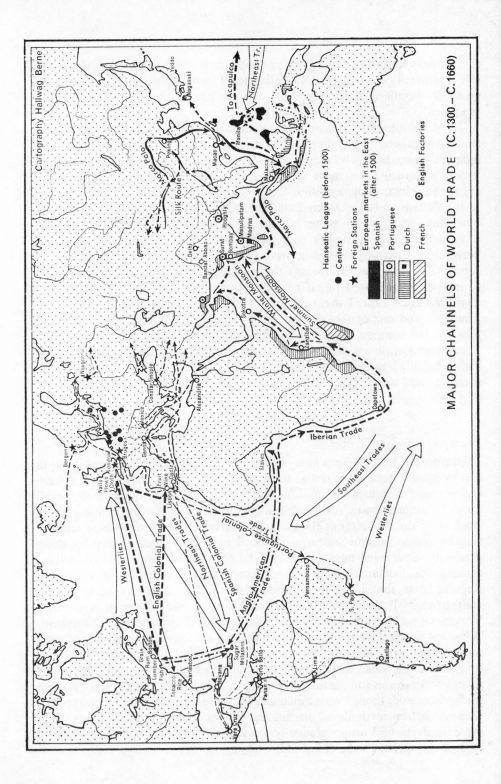

MAJOR CHANNELS OF WORLD TRADE (C.1300 – C.1660)

The greatest increase in trade came when European sailors, with improved ships, marine instruments, and navigational methods, found their way to the great productive centres of Asia and the almost untouched resources of the New World. After 1500 the products of the Orient that previously had trickled to Europe by long, broken overland stages could arrive directly oversea and *en masse*. A shipload of spices or cottons or chinaware, for example, might bring immense profits in regions that had developed a taste for things like those, which helped make life pleasanter. The Asian civilizations had little demand for European goods and generally preferred payment in precious metals, thus causing a flight of gold and silver from Europe to India and China.

Europe's colonies in the New World, in compensation, constituted an expanding market for European manufactures and a source of precious metals. As long as the overseas dominions could be prevented from creating industries to meet their own needs, they were dependent upon the homeland for manufactured goods like hardware and cloth, for which they paid with colonial products (gold, silver, sugar, rum, timber, tobacco, pelts, hides, etc.). But this trading pattern, particularly favourable to England, encountered serious disruption when the colonies began to produce their own textiles and metal goods. The Anglo-American settlers also built excellent ships, and their merchant fleets rivalled the home country's. Besides, they participated in smuggling on a wide scale, thereby further undermining the British mercantilist system. Despite French, British, and other pirates and smugglers, the Spanish and the Portuguese proved more successful in controlling the trade of their colonies, and the exchange of colonial raw materials for Iberian goods and African slaves was not seriously interrupted. Hence the Latin-American colonies, unlike the Anglo-American ones, failed to develop their own industries (except gold and silver mining).

Trading activities increased in large part because of the improvement of transportation. The advances in science and technology that helped to bring about that improvement will be considered in Chapter XV. Ships were built that made sea voyages more economical and safer. First, the less manoeuvrable but more profitable carrack replaced the galley, and about the same time came the small pioneering caravel of the Portuguese and Spanish; then the big, lumbering galleon; later, the speedier merchantmen of the Dutch and British; and, finally for our period, the fast American vessel, ancestor of the clipper. Considerable numbers of Europeans became skilful sailors provided with ever-improving nautical instruments, maps, and techniques with which to conquer the vast spans separating their homelands from the rest of the world. The seas also became better highways, to the distinct commercial and strategic advantage of the thalassocratic countries. Port facilities improved as wharves, docks, repair shops, and supply depots were built. Better and more abundant markers, lighthouses, and buoys helped the sailor find his way more safely. Piracy remained a serious problem (especially as it was

condoned by other nations as a means of harming the commerce of rivals).
The Barbary corsairs, the terror of the Mediterranean, roamed as far as
Iceland. Toward the end of our period European governments began to
cooperate to reduce piracy.

Better transportation developed simultaneously on land. Carts with
increased capacities, stronger draft animals, and better harness made possible
bigger loads. The road net of Europe slowly expanded, and the French and
other governments required a special *corvée* for work on road surfaces. Inns
and rest places grew up on all highways for the ever-growing number of
travellers, who were thus no longer dependent on monastic hospices and
mission houses. Regular postal systems (longer known and better developed
in some of the eastern civilizations) were introduced into several European
countries. Additional bridges and ferries were installed. Highway robbery
remained a scourge, and attempts to counter the danger led to better policing
and severer penalties. In general, until the end of our period, roads were bad,
and since shipping was cheaper than land transportation, the seas, rivers, and
canals carried the bulk of trade. On the whole, transportation facilities,
especially by sea, kept pace with the expanding needs of merchants and in
many cases made possible trade achievements that might well have astonished
former generations.

★   ★   ★

Banking and Finance

With the expansion of trade, the exchange of coin grew more common,
and the transportation of bullion became a serious problem. For a while
shipments, especially those to Rome, were entrusted to the knightly orders
(Templars in particular), but as the quantities became larger and more
cumbersome, other methods were sought. Italian money-lenders, particularly
Lombards and Genoese, had learned, despite church scruples, to make a
profitable business out of exchanging one coinage for another, and many of
them were engaged in collecting papal revenue from all over Europe. In
transactions with some of the Italian merchants travelling to northern
European fairs, they gradually developed customs and institutions from
which the modern banking system has evolved (see Chapter VIII).

Instead of transporting money throughout the Continent and actually
handling vast cash sums in large transactions, merchants came to deposit cash
in 'banks' in some of the important trading centres of Europe. Originally such
institutions were 'exchange banks', where it was possible to exchange one
coinage for another, a process which contributed only slightly to solving the
problem of money transportation. Realizing that business could be conducted
in a much more efficient way by a system of credit that would eliminate the
necessity of transporting large sums of hard money, Italian bankers established branches all over Europe at which merchants could complete transactions without actually having to handle coin. In this way a note, or 'bill of

exchange', issued by the agent of an Italian banker in England might be redeemable in cash in Milan, Florence, Venice, Genoa, or Siena; and instead of hauling Florentine coins to Bruges to pay for cloth bought there, the Bruges agents of the bankers, whether Bardi, Peruzzi, or Medici, would draw on their Florentine deposits there.

Some such method of branch agencies whereby ownership of money might shift by means of notes, bills of exchange, or other banking paper had been known to the ancient Sumerians and to the Arabs, Jews, Chinese, and Japanese at various times before 1300. In Europe, however, it developed into a banking system. From the private banks established by the Italian dynasties of money-changers eventually evolved state banks such as San Giorgio in Genoa and Rialto in Venice. The steps at first were simple. International loans were floated by groups of private bankers, a noteworthy example being the 'consortium' (partnership) of several Florentine families to provide Edward III of England (1312–77) with funds for an invasion of France at the outset of the Hundred Years' War. The handling of papal revenues and the proceeds of the English wool trade came to be dominated by Florentines and other Italians. The giro-bank, or deposit and transfer bank, in which one could deposit money and transfer it to others for business payments, appeared about 1300 and gradually became more ambitious and complex.

Only, however, with the development of double-entry bookkeeping during the fourteenth and fifteenth centuries could banks become more than simple institutions. Double-entry bookkeeping made possible a better understanding of assets and liabilities, profits and losses, and thus enabled banker and customer to have a complete financial statement and accounting at any stage. It was used by the great trading companies as well as the banks of the day, and it is hard to see how big business could be conducted without it. Some of the greatest exchange banks such as the Amsterdamsche Wisselbank, the Bank of Hamburg, and Venice's Banco del Giro were founded or acquired importance only after 1600.

These exchange institutions at first did not perform a function which is essential to the development of the modern bank: in general, they made no loans from bank deposits. Church scruples against certain kinds of interest restricted the ways in which such transactions could be made profitable. But with increasing accumulations of cash and growing needs of merchants for capital, loans of bank deposits became an accepted feature of economic life. The early loan offices of the Flemish cities (*tables de prêt*), often set up temporarily at fairs, made loans in forms which resemble modern promissory notes. Italian and Catalonian bankers often united in city-wide associations (such as the Genoese, Barcelonian, or Florentine deposit banks). German merchant families like the Fuggers and the Welsers began to refine the system by using cash deposits, funded debts, and even notarized contracts of business transactions for making loans, on which they collected interest according to varied and rather complicated principles. Subsequently, bankers in the Low

Countries developed a system of negotiable commercial paper (much like cheques), which were backed by deposits in their banks. About 1650, acceptance of such negotiable credit papers became general. Still later national banks such as the Bank of England were established and issued national currencies.

In the beginning many banking enterprises were closely associated with political activities. Sometimes such association brought disaster. The Italian houses of the Bardi and the Peruzzi were ruined when Edward III repudiated his Hundred Years' War loans. The financial wizard Jacques Coeur went bankrupt because of the machinations of numerous enemies at the French court. On the other hand, bankers could exert tremendous political pressure. Some became international powers, as the Medici and the Fuggers.

As commerce developed, it became more and more dependent upon an improved monetary system. While some primitive societies continued to use shells and glass beads as a means of exchange, the more advanced cultures depended on metallic coinage, usually of gold, silver, and copper. The need for reliable standards and close supervision of coinage grew as trade on an international basis prospered and coins of various types had to be interchanged. It became essential that coinage be kept constant in weight and alloy. Paper money began to be acceptable as a substitute for precious metals in the seventeenth century in some European countries. The population could be expected to accept such paper promises only if assured that they were backed by adequate deposits of bullion. The minting process therefore became more than ever the concern of monarchs and municipalities that coined their own money. The confidence in the money of Florence was so general that after the thirteenth century its monetary unit, the 'florin', was the most commonly acceptable coin in Europe, a sort of international monetary standard, comparable to the 'pound sterling' of later centuries. Although the mints at first were in the hands of privileged semi-private entrepreneurs, they came to be more thoroughly regulated by law and supervised by government fiscal agents. By gradually nationalizing mints governments reduced the profusion of coinage so that only a few remained in international circulation and national currencies moved towards uniformity.

Governments were not always above dubious practices such as debasing their coinage. They soon found, however, that they were not really at liberty to manipulate finances at will but were subject to certain laws of economics. Populations refused to accept paper that was not backed by sufficient confidence or by precious metal, as the English and the French discovered in the booms of the late-seventeenth and early-eighteenth centuries. Neither could rulers improve the wealth and living standards of their countries by merely accumulating precious metals without concurrent expansion of production through industry and commerce. This lesson became painfully manifest with 'the price revolution' already mentioned. Inflation benefited only a few elements of the population, particularly the trading classes, which could count on resulting rises in prices, while those with fixed or slowly rising incomes suffered. Prices soared especially in Spain, which neglected to build its own industries since it could afford to purchase abroad whatever it needed.

* * *

Government and Business

Between 1300 and 1775 governmental intervention in economic affairs both by direct intent and by the indirect effects of governmental processes tended to become more frequent. Princes recognized that the international relations of their countries were an important factor of domestic economic strength. War, of course, was generally assumed to be potentially either detrimental or beneficial to the total economy of a country. The circumstances that might render it detrimental were obvious. Agriculture might suffer from the impact of battles and a looting soldiery, especially since this was an era of mercenary armies. Warfare might also mean heavy taxes, levied primarily upon the commercial classes, and a serious disruption of trade. Long and intense fighting, indeed, might altogether paralyze trade and gravely retard the development of industry.

On the other hand, a war might sometimes be profitable. Armies rarely numbered more than 50,000 men before the French Revolution and were not so serious a drain on blood and treasure as in subsequent eras. On the other hand, they brought business to the suppliers of munitions (the manufacture of which tended to become nationalized), horses, food, and, when uniforms became common, cloth and clothing. War also furthered the aims of the mercantile classes in less direct ways. For example, when a ruler needed taxes, he might have to make political concessions to those whom he taxed, thereby fortifying the bourgeoisie in particular. Furthermore, victory in battle or diplomacy frequently benefited a country's commerce, winning strategic territory, eliminating customs lines, forcing trade concessions, and consolidating newly acquired markets and resources with the old. The Hansa trade in the eastern Baltic would in all likelihood have been less feasible without the pacification of that area by the Teutonic Knights; the Mongol conquests enabled a considerable amount of goods to flow from east to west directly; British trade gained explicit advantages from the War of the Spanish Succession; and the Dutch might never have acquired a colonial realm if they had not been fighting Spain during the late-sixteenth and early-seventeenth centuries. State-supported piracy, as practised by English and Dutch marauders on the Spanish Main and by the Barbary *reises*, was a lucrative business. The moral issue of war was not lost on contemporaries like Hugo Grotius (1583–1645) and the Quakers (see Chapter IX), and some questioned whether commercial advantages could not better be procured by peaceful means. Nevertheless, since military action could generally be localized, *raison d'état*, the overriding interest of the state, was regarded as well served by the triumphant sword, and so the threat of war and war itself were regular instruments of diplomacy and persuasion.

Yet political decisions, if based on considerations of power or national unity alone, might have significant economic consequences. Political motives took precedence over economic ones in the expulsion of Jews and Moors from Spain and of Huguenots from France. The granting of monopolies and other mercantilist practices, and certain taxes (for example, ship money), were sometimes justifiable by the logic of politics rather than of economics. Invasions commonly meant some degree of destruction for the fortified cities in the invader's path. Merchants tried to find protection against political arbitrariness or miscalculation through mercantile leagues, commercial codes, guilds, municipal charters, and royal grants of special privilege. When necessary, they did not hesitate to take part in open revolt against their sovereigns and, as indicated earlier, were conspicuously involved in some of the great rebellions and civil wars of the period.

At certain times and places the hazards of domestic competition were kept somewhat under control through guild supervision of production, markets, prices, weights, measures, and the training and accrediting of the labour force. In some areas the interests of the state and of the mercantile classes were more or less identical (as in Venice, Holland, and Geneva). In the rising dynastic states, however, the overall concern was less for the protection of guild interests than for the safeguard and advance of the economic and political power of the total state. Whereas guilds generally looked after their members only and often worked at cross-purposes with one another, a ruler usually identified himself with his realm as a whole and manifested concern for its economic welfare. For this reason and others already discussed, the guilds steadily lost their importance, and various of their functions were taken over by the political authorities. The tightening grasp of the state through state supervision of markets, state protection of trade, and state support of commercial and industrial enterprises hastened the decline of the guilds perhaps more rapidly than exclusively economic factors.

The deliberate, vigorous participation of the state in economic life during our period is known as 'the mercantilist system', a term made common by the system's major critic, Adam Smith (see Chapter IX). This system was dominant during the latter half of our period. It was the reflection in the economic sphere of the growing political importance of the national state. The basic unit of mercantilistic concern was not the single individual, a *homo economicus*, or any special group of producers or consumers but rather the state as such, the national wealth as seen from the rulers' point of view and as expressed in terms translatable into money. In broadest terms the mercantilist system aimed at creating a strong economic foundation for a strong political state by regulating private economic interest and making the state as far as possible autarkic, or self-sufficient. The policy was regarded as working satisfactorily if the state exported more than it imported in commodities and imported more than it exported in bullion (i.e. if it had what was called a 'favourable balance of trade'), for then it was held to be using its own resources beneficially, to be independent economically of its neighbours, and to be in some way indispensable to the countries with which it maintained a trade balance in its favour.

With these aims in view, governments did other things than regulate trade. They did their best also, for example, to build and control overseas colonies and to gain commercial advantages by diplomacy and war. At home they sought to improve agricultural self-sufficiency so that foodstuffs would not have to be purchased abroad, permitting the export of grain in case of surplus. They encouraged new products and methods that might yield richer harvests. Model farms and agricultural societies were subsidized by state funds in order to present to farmers improved ways of using the soil. New tools and crops would often be introduced on royal estates, stimulating imitation elsewhere. A decision between conflicting systems of agriculture sometimes depended on the preference of the ruler (as in the case of the victory for enclosures and sheep farming in England). Agriculture ceased to be an activity merely of landlords and farmers and became in addition an area of interference by het state for reasons and by means other than taxation.

The concern of governments for industry was perhaps still more serious. Colbert, Louis XIV's 'economic tsar', provided a pat example of a mercantilist statesman. He subsidized and otherwise promoted new industries in France in order to make her independent of imports and capable of earning additional bullion by exports. He encouraged skilled foreign workmen to settle in France (without being able, however, to prevent a flight of skilled workers when his master revoked the Edict of Nantes, which had until then granted toleration to Huguenots). He tried to stimulate shipping and shipbuilding (but had trouble finding sailors to man the ships). Like many other statesmen before and after, he attempted to regulate the flow of goods out of and into France by decree and by the manipulation of tariffs and excises. Like other mercantilists he considered colonies important in this policy and therefore exerted himself to found new ones and to exploit existing ones more efficiently, counting on them to provide raw materials for manufacture in France, markets for the manufactured goods of the home country, and outlets for France's surplus population.

Mercantilism and Cameralism

Mercantilism's basic tenet—government control of economic life for the sake of fortifying the power of the state—aimed also at the advance of the general welfare and thus corresponded closely with the political doctrines by which absolute monarchs sought to justify their position. When some of the eighteenth-century *philosophes* cast the prince in a paternalistic role and made of the 'enlightened monarch' an ideal (see Chapter IX), they gave particular emphasis to his responsibility for his subjects' material welfare. In Teutonic countries mercantilism was frequently equated with *cameralism*, a term derived from the systematic study of state management in the Prussian schools that provided training for government office (*camera*). Impressive examples of rulers who raised their countries' economic level by mercantilist methods were Frederick William I (1713-40) and Frederick II (1740-86) of Prussia. Frederick II went so far as to discourage subjects from indulging in exotic beverages like coffee when the need existed for guns, ploughs, and seed-grains. Mercantilism was a guiding principle of the reforming tsars Alexis (1645-76) and Peter the Great (1682-1725). Charles III of Spain (1759-88) and Joseph I of Portugal (1750-77) extended their paternalism also to their empires in America and the East.

Although mercantilism and cameralism remained the prevalent politico-economic philosophies of this era, they incurred a good deal of criticism, too. Traders and manufacturers naturally were satisfied with government interference if it took the form of protecting their own monopolies and privileges, but if state control interfered with their business or if they did not belong to the groups that benefited from the privileges, they were likely to be resentful. The more advanced colonies began to object to their home governments' regulation of their industries and commerce. When, for example, England changed the long-standing policy of 'salutary neglect' of her navigation acts to one of stricter enforcement, bitterness grew among the colonists who had engaged in illegal (though hitherto rarely policed) industrial and commercial operations. In addition, mercantilism suffered in practice through inevitable loopholes and exceptions. In order to enforce regulations a numerous personnel was needed, and its cost went far to wipe out the profits that theoretically ought to have accumulated. As will become more apparent in Chapter IX, criticism of mercantilism found expression also among certain economic theorists of the late-seventeenth and the eighteenth centuries, particularly in the writings of the Physiocrats, who taught that rulers might improve the economic welfare of their lands by taxing land, relaxing commercial and industrial regulations, and permitting an autonomous market. Finally, in 1776 appeared Adam Smith's *The Wealth of Nations*, which laid the theoretical foundations of the free-enterprise economy of subsequent generations. It was no mere chance that the American Declaration of Independence, the classical statement of anti-colonialism and self-determination of nations, was also promulgated that very year. Absolutism, mercantilism, and colonialism followed hard upon one another and so encountered antagonists about the same time.

SOCIAL CHANGES AND THEIR POLITICAL IMPORT[10]

Before the revolutions of the eighteenth and nineteenth centuries all peoples with the possible exception of certain primitive ones, were divided into readily recognizable strata. Between these strata frequently existed rigid legal barriers and nearly always an appreciable difference in political, economic, and cultural status. Men of different strata were rarely considered by the law equal either in rights or in opportunities, and they derived their standing in society as a rule from the stratum in which (often unalterably) they belonged. One's professional training and social function thus depended upon the social structure of one's culture rather than upon personal aptitude, preference, or achievement. Women suffered or benefited not only from these social classifications but also from special considerations appertaining to their sex.

For a large part of Asia the social structure had become stabilized on foundations laid before 1300. Hindu society had numerous castes, sharing some of the features of the clan, the social class, and the guild. Allegedly derived from the four traditional castes (described in Vol. II, pp. 190–91), they were in our period based more upon birth, geographical location, and modes of employment. While the formation of a group into a new caste was always possible, custom made it hard for an individual to change his caste.[11] In the northern parts of the Indian peninsula the Muslim way of life had flourished since about AD 1000 and became even more dominant under the Mogul Empire (1526–1857). In general, despite periods of Muslim persecution of Hindus (see Chapter V), the newer Muslim culture adjusted in some ways to the Hindu culture, while remaining distinct. Where Muslims had established themselves, either a mixed society had grown up in which Hindu and Muslim lived more or less amicably together or, more frequently, where the Muslims had come as conquerors, they formed a separate stratum that considered itself superior to the Hindu population. In China the general social order was scarcely changed by the several invasions of foreign peoples. The central Asian peoples (Mongols, Tatars, Mamlūks, etc.) remained basically nomadic, even though they had become better acquainted with more advanced civilizations (Chinese, Islamic, and Russian) and had learned new techniques from them.

In some areas of the Pacific, on the other hand, significant cultural change took place during our period. In the Malay Archipelago (particularly Sumatra and Java, its most populous and civilized islands), after 1400, a majority of the people gradually and voluntarily substituted Islamic beliefs and patterns of behaviour for their earlier Hindu–Buddhist ones. In Japan internal upheavals during the later Heian period (see Volume III) had led to the rise of a new class, and with it new social ideals. In the resulting feudal society the *daimyos*, or feudal lords, and their retainers, the *samurai*, emerged with their own specific code of behaviour and with substantial economic and legal privileges. During our period this class further entrenched itself and rose far above the Japanese farmers; and the leading daimyo, the shogun, particularly after the beginning of the seventeenth century, followed an earlier precedent of ruling in fact, though in the name of the mikado. The ideals of the samurai—their faithfulness to duty, their obedience to higher authority, their low regard for life itself (especially if it meant life without honour), and their martial spirit—

were to help shape *Bushido*, the strict though unwritten Japanese code of chivalry (see Chapter III).

In the Islamic world the stratification of society underwent a variety of changes. In India, new governors (nawwābs) were appointed to administer newly conquered areas. The Ottoman Turks, like many other Muslim regimes that controlled large populations of different stock and religion, made efforts to absorb at least those who belonged to the upper social layer. This process was supplemented by a unique system of assimilation: Christian children who showed aptitude were taken from their parents, raised in the Islamic faith, and turned into loyal and carefully trained slaves of the sultanate. The crack troops of the Porte, the Janissaries, were recruited in this fashion, to the exclusion, at least at first, of the free-born Ottoman aristocracy. So were some of the best civil administrators. This system achieved its purpose—complete devotion to the sultan—until the Janissary corps was opened to free Muslims (c. 1600), when discipline gave way to competition for advantage.

Until Ottoman rule was firmly established, the Turks ravaged Bulgaria, Serbia, and other countries that resisted, deporting or forcibly converting stubborn Christians. Once submissive, however, conquered peoples generally received, except for the tribute in children, a considerable measure of economic freedom and religious tolerance. For some important functions, especially in commercial and financial affairs, the Turks made direct and open use of the skill of their Greek-Orthodox, Armenian, and Jewish subjects. Yet—aside from the Bogomils, a heretical Christian sect that, though persecuted since its origin in the tenth century, still survived in Bulgaria, Serbia, and especially Bosnia (see Chapter II)—Turkey's Christians did not voluntarily turn Muslim in large numbers, and their desire for religious and political independence remained strong.

The Structure of European Society

During the centuries between 1300 and 1775 (except in England, where class lines tended to lose some of their distinctness) European society as a general rule was divided into three basic social classes—nobility, bourgeoisie, and peasantry. These classes, however, did not grow in quite the same way in the several regions of the Continent over the centuries. The social configuration of the eastern countries (Poland, the eastern Baltic regions, and the huge Russian realm) differed from that of the western countries in at least one significant respect: eastern European society seemed, in contrast with western society, to be divided into landowners and peasants alone, with relatively negligible middle classes. To be sure, the eastern countries had a well-to-do bourgeoisie in the cities and some more or less free farmers in the country districts, but towards the close of our period these middle classes, primarily because of their failure to keep pace in commerce and industry, did not achieve an influence comparable with that of their counterparts in western Europe. Stratification essentially into two classes—servile and ruling—had a profound effect on the culture of the eastern populations. A rich folk-culture survived among the lower classes and was particularly varied and impressive in tales, fables, song, dance, and handicrafts. It was fortified and encouraged by the churches—Orthodox in Russia, and Catholic and Uniate in Poland. The upper classes, however, largely imported their culture from western Europe (particularly France, but also Germany and Italy). They adopted western fashions, ideologies, and speech, along with western art, architecture, and literary standards, to an extent that their nineteenth-century nationalists were to consider unforgiveable.

Social cleavage was likewise intensified in the central European area (Austria, Hungary, Bohemia, and eastern Germany, for instance). Even more than in France, the nobility tended to move toward the court and away from the farms, and in so doing they moved in spirit away from the farming population. In post-Reformation Hungary, religion confirmed the gap between the great landlords (the magnates), most of whom were Catholic, and the lesser nobles, many of whom adopted, for a time at least, the Calvinist or Lutheran faiths. Two factors, however, distinguished the social pattern of central Europe from that of Russia and Poland. In the first place, although the majority of central as well as eastern European peasants were either tenants or serfs, there was also in central Europe, especially in the mountainous areas, a type of farmer that was relatively free from, or merely nominally subject to, a landlord. Perhaps more important, the urban middle class of central Europe, despite the weakening of the Hansa, did not lag so far behind western European standards as did the middle class of eastern Europe. The German middle class was prominent especially in Saxony, Bohemia, and such Hansa towns as still throve, and it was sufficiently effectual to help assure a measure of commercial and industrial advance and a significant cultural development. By the eighteenth century, if not earlier, many of the trends and purposes characteristic of the western European middle class were to be found among the bourgeois inhabitants of Vienna, Budapest, Prague, Leipzig, Dresden, Munich, Nuremberg, Augsburg, and Berlin. Though to a degree that was not so regularly attained as it was farther west, an urban middle class flourished even in Moscow, St Petersburg, or Warsaw (which owed their prominence, however, chiefly to being royal or ecclesiastical capitals and bureaucratic centres rather than commercial and industrial metropoles).

In western Europe seigniorial society was obviously declining, even if still very much alive, foreshadowing a future in which middle-class sentiments, with a strong penchant for anti-aristocratic, if not egalitarian, philosophies, would ultimately prevail. As already explained, the middle class arose among the citizens of the towns, the bourgeois. By the eighteenth century the terms *bourgeoisie* and *middle class* were generally, if somewhat inaccurately, interchangeable. Members of the middle class penetrated the ranks of the nobility to an ever-increasing degree through marriage, elevation to nobility by sovereign decree, or appointment to certain ennobling functions. Although many bourgeois gentlemen doubtless tried to adapt themselves to the outlook and conduct of the highest social class, they also gave a bourgeois cast to aristocratic social standards. By a similar process middle-class norms and preferences were accepted in turn as ideals by those lower social groups that sought to be identified with the bourgeoisie. Unlike the nobility, the middle class was 'open' at both bottom and top, and, unlike the peasantry, it enjoyed some social prestige. Since advancement into and out of it was legally permissible and relatively feasible, it became accountable for a good measure of social mobility. The scion of a peasant or urban workman might become a merchant and accumulate wealth. He might invest again in land in the hope that future generations of his family might enter the nobility with a good place-name. Some added place-names to their family names without titles of nobility. The possibility of *anoblissement* often provided an incentive for a bourgeois capitalist who aimed to rise above his status. The *philosophe* Montesquieu suggested ennoblement as a regular device for recruiting the ablest bourgeois for the nobility (provided they left their bourgeois activities behind). Largely because of the mobility of the bourgeoisie, despite its support of institutions (like guilds) and principles (like property qualifications for voting) which tended to make it a closed and privileged cast, society was not 'frozen' and the push-and-pull toward social advancement became a powerful political force. In Britain, where primogeniture deprived younger sons of titles and estates and often forced them into trade or commerce, and where the lines between yeoman and gentry and between gentry and nobles were indistinct, social mobility was more pronounced than in other monarchies.

The professions also provided a good avenue towards social advancement. As previously remarked, before our period specialization of labour was rarely found in Europe in any field of endeavour. A feudal lord might be judge, administrator, soldier, and landlord. A barber was very likely also a surgeon. An artist might well be also an engineer, an architect, or a craftsman in a variety of crafts. And a churchman might combine several functions, such as social worker, teacher, writer, councillor, and librarian, with that of spiritual leader. In the well-developed civilizations of the Far and the Near East, as in Classical Antiquity, specialization of labour had been more common than in medieval Europe. After 1300, even in Europe, the trained and specialized professional man assumed an ever greater significance in society. As education and specialization became more common (see Chapter XVI), the rapidly maturing professions gradually displaced the clergy from some of its activities. Lawyers were often named to political offices previously held normally by high clerics. With the spread of learning among laymen, it was less often necessary to call upon clergymen for work that required an ability to read, write, and cipher or some fuller measure of education. Secular artisans and artists developed techniques and arts that had previously been largely monopolized by monks.

Conspicuous changes in the importance of the cleric as professional factotum came with the Renaissance and the Reformation. Wherever teaching was influenced by humanists, many teachers were not clergy at all or were so only in name. At the higher social levels private tutors became more common, and in keeping with humanist educational ideals, they tried to equip their pupils with the secular knowledge and skills required of ladies and gentlemen as well as with Christian doctrine. The arts and sciences were with growing frequency pursued by laymen, and for purposes unconnected with the church. After the Reformation, although the political power of the clergy did not vanish in either Catholic or Protestant lands, its hold upon government offices was greatly diminished. The Jesuits until their temporary suppression in 1773 and other teaching orders rebuilt the church's educational influence in Catholic countries, but there were no Protestant charitable and teaching orders or, for that matter, monastic farms, wineries, commercial enterprises, or convent hospitals and almshouses. Although the clergy still engaged in numerous activities not directly religious in character, even Catholic church-men became concerned with religious affairs more exclusively than before, while the state took over other functions they had previously performed. Some of the more radical sects held that a true Christian life could be led altogether without the help of an organized priesthood (see Chapter IV), but they nowhere gained control long enough to abolish the church entirely. In fact, even in Protestant countries the churchman remained an influential figure in society and politics, whose presence was practically indispensable at baptisms and funerals and highly desirable at weddings, if the participating parishioners wished to be considered Christians, and he was frequently consulted on ethical problems. Yet most of the clergy, once Europe's most ubiquitous and versatile professional group, tended towards the close of our era to wander less frequently outside the field of religion and theology. The national church organization had become, so to speak, that part of the bureaucracy which handled the spiritual needs of the community, although its subordination to the government was rarely complete even in Protestant countries.

The lay professions acquired importance as the clergy lost it. The trend towards specialization in such fields as medicine and law had already set in before 1300. Ancient Greek medicine was well known among the Arabs and, when spread in Europe, brought more specialized medical training from the twelfth century on. Advances in physiology, anatomy, and drugs during the Renaissance and after made more obvious the need for specialization within the curative arts. Although the medieval physician had always been held superior to the surgeon and the pharmacist, the reason had been the method of his work (speculative as opposed to manual) rather than its subject matter. Great surgeons and pharmacists (see Chapters XIII–XV) dotted the genera-tions before the Royal College of Surgeons was founded in London (1800). As their arts became more refined and effective, and as manual labour acquired dignity, the surgeon and later the pharmacist, but rarely the dentist, became esteemed members of society, although they (and the physician, too, but less so) remained the butt of satire in art and literature. The healing professions in general attempted, with the aid of governments, to exclude quacks from their ranks, to increase their never-ending accumulation of knowledge, and to raise their standards.

The expansion of legal knowledge and the demand of the developing nation-state for minds trained in law resulted in the evolution of a profession that became one of the most powerful and respected in Western society. We have already alluded to the lawyers' significance in political and administrative service to their governments. Their training (see Chapter XVI) and interests tended to make them the spokesmen of the middle class, and they were found in large numbers in middle-class representative bodies. They became judges and chancellors, and as such they were in a very real sense the repository of the law, and hence the protectors of society against arbitrary power. Although they were in general faithful servants of their rulers, they did on occasion oppose the royal policies, as the frequent friction between French kings and parlements demonstrates. The British justices of the peace, who were generally unpaid members of the gentry commissioned by the crown to administer justice in the counties, received an excellent training in law and administration without necessarily being professional lawyers. Since the legal profession had articulate rational and secular principles, derived from Roman law and the concept of natural right, its influence on the development of a rational and secular approach to the problem of justice will call for closer examination (see Chapters VIII and IX).

Relevant chapters below (X and XVI) will deal with the developments by which the artist and the technical expert became distinct from the artisan classes to which they had previously belonged. Until the thirteenth century, although Far Eastern painters were personally recognized and esteemed as artists, a European artist rarely signed his work. After 1300 Europe's painters, musicians, and sculptors worked less often in anonymity, becoming instead proud lions of a society that prized their individual talents. We know the names of only few architects of the Gothic cathedrals, but eventually engineering and architecture became so individualized that designing was entrusted to reputed experts, trained in the sciences, draughtsmanship, and mathematics, whose names became bywords. No longer restrained by guild regulations, such experts could aspire to a prestige and remuneration inaccessible to the mere artisan.

Military duty had been one of the obligatory services of the feudal lord and his vassals during the Middle Ages. Although this feature of the feudal system continued in several countries after 1300, in general it gave way, with the advent of new methods of warfare and with the decline of feudalism, to reliance upon specialized, professional soldiers. In place of feudal levies, rulers preferred to raise standing armies, sometimes of mercenary soldiers. Mercenaries were an expensive commodity, and often they were hired only for specific campaigns, passing from one employer to another. For Italian *condottieri* or German and Swiss *Landsknechte* the hiring-out of veterans was a profitable business. Mercenary captains were in general competent officers with expert knowledge of the new firearms and the latest defence and siege tactics. Their men were long-term regulars (sometimes enlisted for life) who hoped to amass small fortunes from their pay and loot. They normally showed greater loyalty to their leaders than to their employers. They were frequently capable of highly specialized services (see Chapter XV).

Mercenary armies remained a fairly familiar military institution until the French Revolutionary era. Although eventually replaced by national standing armies, they persist, after a fashion, in such corps as the French Foreign Legion and the Papal Swiss Guard. The professional officer and the soldier of fortune did not disappear *pari passu*; and some of the great military leaders of the eighteenth century served countries in which they were foreigners (e.g. Prince Eugene of Savoy and Marshal de Saxe), giving their loyalty to appreciative sovereigns rather than to their native countries. Many noblemen of ancient lineage still considered the officer's profession their chief and most fitting field of activity, but they were no longer complete masters of their own troops (even when, as was still permissible, they commanded contingents regarded as proprietary), for they were now subordinate to the king's service. They remained, however, a privileged military class (except in England, where army commissions were easily bought), since non-nobles could advance to the higher ranks only with difficulty and in certain units not at all. The common soldier or sailor was to an ever-increasing extent drawn from the native population. Military life might be tough, but soldiers and sailors were not generally hard to get in times of peace, since soldiering presented a considerable economic and social advancement for the poorer classes. In times of war conscription and impressment sometimes were resorted to. The practice of sentencing prisoners to the galley oars of the French navy persisted until 1748.

Professional specialization helped to change Europe's social structure by enhancing the opportunities for economic reward and social advancement through recognition of individual worth rather than of family status. Modern culture would be inconceivable without the specialized services of many different kinds of experts commanding various degrees of pecuniary compensation and prestige. Though professional distinction was not unknown in the earlier Middle Ages, in large part the modern elite in so far as it is a professional elite arose during our period.

* * *

The Status of Women

Before the nineteenth century women occupied an inferior position in most cultures. Although some polite circles accorded highborn women great respect and even chivalric gallantry, in nearly all civilized societies wives were considered both by law and by social usage subject to their husbands. While a woman might own property in her own right, a European woman of property would rarely remain a spinster or a widow outside a nunnery for long. Even in Protestant countries single women of good family might enter Protestant nunneries. Women might do the larger share of physical labour or contribute significantly to cultural life and yet not enjoy the rights and privileges of men. Variations in the legal and social standing of women were numerous. Their rights in a monogamous society differed from those in a polygamous one. Their position in rural communities was not the same as in the cities. Different religious cults regarded them differently. In addition, caste and class divisions inside the same culture made for differences in the roles assigned to them. In general, except in some primitive matriarchal societies, the master of the household had ultimate control over property, wife, and children, and was the arbiter of everyday decisions.

The European attitude toward women had been subtly changing since at least the twelfth century. Woman was becoming something more than a drudge or a plaything between breeding periods. For one thing, she began to be economically more independent. The church provided one avenue of economic emancipation. Women from all walks of life had always been permitted to join the religious orders, and in a society that had a high esteem for such institutions the nun's or sister's habit brought security and public admiration. Nuns took 'solemn vows' (including poverty); lay sisters took 'simple vows', permitting them to retain property. The number of orders of sisters in hospital and school work increased during our period, giving to a large number of women a chance for useful and dignified occupation without male interference.

The rising economic importance of the bourgeoisie provided another means of raising the economic status of women. The marriage of daughters of merchants to scions of the nobility often meant economic advantage for the latter and social advantage for the former. Land, the primary source of wealth in a feudal society, lost none of its value when it passed to a daughter (in those societies where land could be inherited through the female line), but possession of land had been largely limited to the nobility before the rise of the bourgeois class. The new wealth, readily transferable, played havoc with such class distinctions. It easily became part of a rich dowry, whether the bride or groom was noble or ignoble, since feudal practices and obligations did not apply to it. A wife with a good negotiable dowry was not so easily disregarded as a wife with entailed and enfeoffed land, dependent on her husband for the performance of her feudal services.

Meanwhile the intellectual standing of women was also improving. We shall from time to time below encounter women who played a significant part in the politics and letters of India. In Europe, Renaissance artists and writers portrayed women, sacred and profane, as possessed of wit as well as beauty and grace. Renaissance women of the higher classes often were well educated, and in the eighteenth century quite a number achieved fame as writers, actresses, and artists; witness Madame de Lafayette, Madame de Sévigné, Mrs Siddons, Vigée Le Brun, and Angelica Kauffmann. The hostesses of the famous salons of the eighteenth century added to the spirit of the Enlightenment. Learned men of the Enlightenment like Fontenelle and Voltaire dedicated books to women who had helped them in their scholarly work. Writers and teachers throughout our period concerned themselves with the education of girls, and special girls' schools were founded, of which Louis XIV's St Cyr and Catherine the Great's Smolny were outstanding examples (see Chapter XVI).

Of course, women, as always, played an important part in politics. When not themselves generals or rulers, they were the mothers, wives, sisters, mistresses, or friends of generals and rulers. Lucretia Borgia as a useful pawn in the designs of her brother Caesar was one of several women active in Renaissance governments. The political destiny of France lay at times in the hands of women—Joan of Arc, Anne of Brittany, Catherine de Medici, and Madame de Pompadour. Isabella of Castile and Leon helped shape the course of the Spanish Empire. England has good reason to regard the reign of Elizabeth I as one of her periods of highest glory. Catherine the Great was among Russia's most capable rulers. The Habsburg realm was preserved from disintegration by the vigour of Maria Theresa. St Catherine of Siena and St Theresa of Avila in different ways, helped to determine church policies (see Chapters III and IV). Such an array of gifted and influential 'petticoats' (to use Frederick the Great's term) could come only in an age that had begun to regard merit as no less important than either rank or sex. Even though women were not granted equal political rights, the new attitude prepared the ground for their future political equality.

Altogether the structure of European society during our period was gaining a fluidity that made for changing social ideas. Power, wealth, leisure, education, and cultural achievement became less of a monopoly of one stratum of society or of one sex. Together with a liberal political ideology and a rationalist notion of unlimited human perfectibility, these ideals helped to prepare the ground for the belief in a future where all human beings, enjoying equal rights, would be able by sufficient effort to raise themselves to the level of free gentlemen.

THE GROWING INTERDEPENDENCE OF PEOPLES

The cultures of Eurasia, the Americas, and sub-Saharan Africa had been largely detached from each other before 1300. Communication between Europe and Asia, however, had long been feasible and profitable to both sides, although contact between Europe and the Far East was infrequent and mostly indirect. In the era centring upon 1300, the Mongol conquests broadened Europe's direct communication with the Far East and India.

Interrelations among Eurasian civilizations were altered in a fundamental way from the fifteenth century on, and not alone because of the recession of Mongol power. Land bridges from east to west began to lose their importance, with the exception of the Siberian routes, which were continually being opened wider by the Russians. The Middle East and the Syrian coast ceased to be the great entrepot for traffic between the Indian Ocean and the Mediterranean. The Levant trade of the Italian cities (especially Venice and Genoa) gave way as the main channel for eastern goods destined for consumption in Europe. And Arab ships from the ports of the Red Sea and the Persian Gulf yielded their leading place as the chief carriers in the Indian Ocean. In contrast, the Atlantic seacoast, on the outermost western edge of the enormous Eurasian continent, became the centre of a new web that meshed the world together—and it was now an expanding world.

A lengthy series of advances in physiographical knowledge and navigational techniques had made possible a number of geographical explorations, which in turn helped to bring about this fifteenth-century geographical revolution. That story will be told in detail in Chapters XIII–XV. The land explorations of greatest consequence for Europeans before 1775 were limited to America and Asia, for the interior of Africa remained relatively untouched until the nineteenth century. In America, Europeans gradually took possession, and the vast northern steppes and forests of Siberia underwent a similar gradual occupation. The more civilized regions of Asia, however (with the exception of parts of India towards the very end of our period), resisted European penetration.

Iberian Explorations and Conquests

The first centuries of exploration of the Orient by Spanish, Portuguese, Dutch, French, and English resulted in little more than the establishment of trade relations and the founding in the coastal areas of entrepots and missionary settlements. European penetration of India and Malaysia became vigorous only about the 1750's and was not carried out on an effective scale before the nineteenth century. For a while it seemed that ardent and able missionaries might drive Christian wedges into the resisting Chinese, Japanese, and Indian cultures, but a reaction against Christianity set in. Resistance was rather early and thorough in Japan, later and far from thorough in China, and casual in India. On the whole, because of a tendency on the part of Asians and Europeans to feel culturally superior to each other, the accumulating knowledge in Europe of the great Asian civilizations (and vice versa) brought less cultural than political and economic consequences during our period. But (as we shall have occasion to observe in several contexts) the cultural consequences were also considerable.

For our period (1300–1775) the occupation and penetration of the American continents by Europeans had the most immediate and decisive cultural consequences. Other areas of the world that came into contact with the West retained their indigenous culture practically intact until the fuller development of Western technology became a major determinant of their ways. But in South and North America, either immense stretches were only sparsely inhabited by nomadic peoples or, where fixed cultures had developed, they could not match the Europeans' technology. Hence the Amerindians, unable to place great obstacles for long in the path of European encroachments, were overwhelmed with relative ease, though not without partly transforming the culture of their conquerors in the process.

Until 1518 the interest of the Spanish explorers had been largely absorbed by the West Indies and the neighbouring coastal areas of the mainland. In that year, however, the first of the great *conquistadores*, Hernando Cortes, set out with a company of 600 men, 17 horses, and 10 cannon to conquer new lands for the Spanish crown in the interior of Central America. After landing north of Yucatan and founding a settlement near the modern city of Vera Cruz, he advanced inland and was the first European to come into contact with the Aztecs.

These people, who were part of the large language group of the Nahua, had conquered the Toltec Indians and had absorbed a good part of the ancient Toltec-Mayan civilization. As the Toltec-Mayan empire declined, the Aztecs began to dominate the area around what is now Mexico City (*c.* 1325), rapidly expanding their rule over an estimated 5,000,000 subjects. They reached a high level of culture, with a fairly accurate calendar, a complex system of writing, and a well-developed sense of history, mathematics, and astronomy. They could boast some admirable achievements in various arts and engineering; they used metals for implements and ornament; their religion was far from primitive (see Chapter II). Without knowledge of the wheel or beasts of burden, they built impressive monuments, temples, and pyramids (see Chapter XII). The Aztec realm was the first advanced civilization with which the Spanish conquerors came into contact in the New World. As is clear from the reports of Cortes and his followers, the splendour of the capital Tenochtitlan, the country's apparent wealth, and the size of the population filled the invading Spaniards with amazement.

Yet at the time of Cortes' invasion the Aztec civilization, along with the others of Central America, seems actually to have begun to decline. The Aztecs had established a sort of league or confederation of subject or allied towns and a fairly centralized government based largely on a powerful army. Its aristocracy was engaged in the process of replacing the clan community of property by a system of private and hereditary property. The position of 'emperor', though nominally elective, had come to be hereditary by the regular choice of the war leader and principal spokesman from the same family. Apparently strong resentment had arisen against tribute, serfdom, slavery, conscription, human sacrifice, and the stern rule of the 'emperor', for the invading Spaniards easily found tribes that were willing to side with them against their Aztec overlords. Cortes' force, despite its paucity, conquered the land in an incredibly short time, for it had the advantages of small-arms, cannon, horses (none of which the natives had ever before encountered), and the Aztecs' expectation of a white deliverer. When they subsequently revolted, Cortes cruelly repressed them, and Spain came into full possession of her first major colony on the American continent. From there Spanish explorers, missionaries, and settlers advanced northward into California and the area of the Pueblo Indians, and southward into other regions of Central America.

South of the Isthmus of Panama, in the area of present-day Colombia and Venezuela, existed another Indian realm, the Chibcha Empire, with a sound political structure and a lively trade with the civilizations to the north and south. The Chibchas used a pictographical script, which was not, however, quite so far developed as the writing of the Toltecs and Aztecs, and they had a good calendar and system of counting. Their engineering skill was not equal to that of the Aztecs to the north or the Incas to the south, but they perhaps excelled all other American Indians in the art of working gold. The conquest of their land began on behalf of the Welsers of Augsburg, to whom Emperor Charles V, to discharge a heavy indebtedness, had given huge concessions within his Spanish overseas realm. The Welsers' exploitation of the Indians soon evoked considerable complaint and, for that and other reasons, the crown deprived them of their concession. Spanish subjects subsequently conquered the remainder of the vast Chibcha territory, and eventually it became the Viceroyalty of New Granada.

Soon after the conquest of Mexico the Spaniards learned about the great empire of the Incas located, south of the Chibchas, on the Pacific coast in the high Andes. The Inca civilization had reached the peak of its territorial expansion during the fourteenth century. It stretched along the Pacific coast roughly from south of what is now Valparaiso in Chile to what is now Quito in Ecuador, centring in Peru and Bolivia. The ruler—the Sapa (only) Inca— governed an estimated population of 8,000,000 Indians by means of a highly centralized and in many ways oppressive administrative machinery and a strictly stratified society. He was an all-powerful despot but was expected paternalistically to look after the needs of his subjects. His army was of con- siderable size and had an excellent road and messenger system at its disposal. While the Incas were inferior to the Chibchas, Mayas, and Aztecs in science, their textiles, gold-work, and ceramics were at times superior. They had not learned to write, but trained initiates could send and interpret messages by *quipus*, or knotted threads of different colours. They carried on a limited trade, especially in coastal vessels. Their music and poetry, though unrecorded, were fairly well developed; and their stone-work, architecture, and engineer- ing (particularly in irrigation and water works) still excite admiration.

Between 1524 and 1528 Francisco Pizarro, one of a family whose ruthless- ness gave a bad reputation to all *conquistadores*, undertook an expedition that took him as far south as modern Ecuador. There he learned directly of the

Inca realm farther south. In 1531 he returned with 180 men, 16 horses, and only two cannon, and began the conquest of the most powerful American Indian empire. In a fashion similar to Cortes's conquest of Mexico, the large Inca realm was overrun, and subsequent revolts failed to expel the intruders. Spain thus acquired another rich colony, one that contained the most productive silver mine (Potosi) of all America. From Peru her soldiers and missionaries advanced during the next decade into the region which now forms the state of Chile, and by 1600 the whole length of South America along the Pacific coast was hers.

On the Atlantic side of South America, with the exception of the Rio de la Plata region, the interior remained for the most part unoccupied by white men until the nineteenth century. The Portuguese settled only on the coastal fringe of Brazil and did not penetrate inland until later. The Spanish, however, founded several settlements along the Parana and Salado tributaries of the Rio de la Plata as early as the sixteenth century. The Jesuits established a colony in Paraguay in 1607 and converted the Indians to Christianity and communal life in a theocratic state which prospered as a most interesting political and economic phenomenon until the expulsion of the Jesuits. By 1775, with the exception of Patagonia and the immense valley of the Amazon and its tributaries, Europeans had claims, superficially at least, upon all the South American continent.

The American realms of Portugal and Spain underwent population changes that differed considerably from those of other European colonies. In Asia the colonizing powers encountered peoples with long-established civilizations, some of whom bowed to the Westerners' military might but were not yet deeply affected by their mode of life. Even where Europeans succeeded in establishing trading posts, garrisons, or supply depots, they left the local populations, which vastly outnumbered them, more or less to themselves. The Dutch and the English did very little to convert the Asians who fell under their military and economic control. The only place in the East where a colonizing power succeeded in making conversions on a large scale was the Philippine Islands, where the rival missionary efforts of Spanish Dominicans, Franciscans, and Jesuits produced appreciable results. In the African coastal settlements, handfuls of Europeans domineered and segregated the surrounding Negroes—except in the Portuguese colonies, where Europeans and natives mixed on a limited scale. In North America, where the native tribes were, with few exceptions, nomadic and spread rather thinly over vast areas, the European immigrants usually expelled the Indians from their lands and pushed them into the interior, massacring and being massacred in the process. In the West Indies, French and English settlers exterminated or deported the warlike Caribs, from whose name the word *cannibal* is derived. In French Canada the trappers commonly lived among the Indians, but before 1775 only a small fraction of the population was half-breed (*métis*).

In contrast, Iberian America became a great 'melting pot'. Social prejudices, to be sure, tended to keep the races apart, especially in aristocratic circles, which prided themselves on their Castilian lineage. Since, however, the civil law of the Portuguese and Spanish and the attitude of the Roman Catholic Church countenanced intermarriage, children of mixed parentage were born in increasing numbers. The mixed population included *Mestizoes* (White and Indian), *Mulattoes* (White and Negro), and *Zambos*, or *Sambos* (Indian and Negro). Eventually the basic population of the West Indies islands as well as some of the continental areas was mixed.

Nevertheless, social discrimination persisted. Colonial officials, mostly Spaniards born in Spain, though fewest in numbers, formed the highest social stratum. Next was a larger stratum of Whites born in America (Creoles). Then came the part of the population that was partly white (Mestizoes and Mulattoes). Last came the Indians, Negroes, and Zambos. Most of the wealth of the colonies was in the hands of the white strata, and they also held the most important church posts, as well as a dominant position in government, letters, education, and the arts. The increase of the mixed populations, however, tended to break down the barriers between strata, and by the time of the Wars of Liberation in the early nineteenth century the Mestizo had become a significant political and social force. Although the unmixed Indian was generally regarded as inferior and the mixed Latin American populations took centuries to win a dignified status in society, they might well have been worse off if the races had been rigidly separated from the beginning.

The Spanish and the Portuguese succeeded in creating a relatively strong cultural unity out of their colonial realms by providing all strata of society with common bonds such as church and language. From the start the religious orders (Franciscans, Dominicans, Mercedarians, Jesuits, Augustinians, and Capuchins) undertook a vigorous missionary programme by which most of the natives were converted to Catholicism. By these conversions the Catholic Church perhaps gained more adherents than it lost to the Protestants in Europe, although the Indian's devotion was often a confusion of Catholic and pagan beliefs and practices. The church in Latin America played the role of protector and educator of the native population. Largely through ecclesiastical efforts the Indians were introduced to European languages, agricultural and industrial methods, learning, pastimes, and social customs. Universities (modelled after Salamanca), Baroque architecture, and Spanish law were introduced into America rather early and exercised a deep influence. The European settlers in turn adapted themselves to certain customs and uses of the Indians, such as rubber, quinine, and various foods and dyes (see Chapter XV). Out of the symbiosis of the several races grew a mixed culture which, though basically European, yet was different. The peoples of this new culture gradually came to look upon themselves as distinct and identified their interests with the lands they inhabited rather than with the countries of their ancestry. The more enterprising among them began to feel and act as

Mexicans, Peruvians, or Brazilians rather than as Spanish or Portuguese, Inca or Aztec, Negro or White, and the time was not distant when they would become independent peoples responsible for their own destiny.

★   ★   ★

North America

After the sixteenth century the foundations were laid also for the present-day nations of the North American continent. At first the discoveries and explorations of French, Dutch, Swedish, and English led to no substantial colonization, largely because of preoccupation with religious controversy at home and with civil and international wars. After 1600 the north European powers began to found settlements, build forts, and create companies to further overseas enterprises. With the re-exploration of the St Lawrence River and several of its tributaries by Samuel de Champlain (1567–1635), French colonies along their banks began to prosper. In 1608 Quebec, and in 1642 Montreal, were founded and in subsequent decades French missionaries and soldiers (e.g. Father Marquette, Joliet, and La Salle) explored the Great Lakes region and the rivers south of it that led to the Mississippi. Shortly thereafter the French advanced along that river and founded the Louisiana colony. A great chain of rivers (with some difficult portages) linked their sparsely settled Canadian and Mississippi empires (see Map II).

During the same century English adventurers and dissenters, both Protestant and Catholic, undertook to colonize the Atlantic seacoast between the areas that are now Maine and South Carolina. Subsequently the Dutch and the Swedes entered into rivalry with them. By 1700 Europeans from other lands than Spain and Portugal occupied the New England region, the Hudson and Delaware valleys, the Chesapeake Bay area, and the coast of the Carolinas. The English predominated among them in numbers and political strength. Seventy-five years later the lowland east of the Appalachians had a population of about 2,500,000, of whom the more restless, daring, or desperate had begun to push westward across the mountains. The Indian tribes had been driven out of the coastal territory, decimated in intermittent wars, or, in rare instances, absorbed into the white population. This extermination contrasted with the fate of the Indians in Canada, where a much smaller French population had learned to co-exist with the natives.

The civilization that grew up in the English colonies was, therefore, almost entirely European. Yet these colonists had learned much that was new from the Indians, such as the use of potatoes, maize, snowshoes, canoes, tobacco, and certain methods of fighting and trapping, and they had adapted the patterns of the 'old countries' to conditions imposed by wilderness, extremes of climate, and strange surroundings. The demands of frontier life thus left an indelible imprint on the Anglo-Americans,[12] which, however, was different from that left on the 'mixed' cultures of Latin America with their majorities of non-Europeans. The Anglo-Americans also developed into a new people, one that began to feel American rather than British, particularly after the danger of the French in Canada and Louisiana was removed by British success in the Second Hundred Years' War. All thirteen English colonies had interests that differed from, and sometimes conflicted with, those of the British Isles. They had originated from a country where the individual was already fairly mobile physically and socially. The self-reliance taught by conquering a wilderness, the distance from and disputes with the mother country, and sometimes from and with each other, had led some of them to entertain relatively new ideas and try relatively new institutions—a citizen army, separation of church and state, legislative defiance of royal governors, written compacts, charters, and patents that set forth the fundamental principles of their government. They also grew rapidly in power and self-sufficiency. As the young Turgot, as early as 1750, and other observers foresaw, it was but a question of time until they would demand self-determination and independence. Their fight for those rights, the first successful anti-colonial movement of modern times, not only altered Europe's colonial practices and shifted its major colonial endeavours to other scenes but also inaugurated a series of almost continuous political revolutions that took their inspiration from 'the laws of Nature and of Nature's God'.

*   *   *

Migrations

Between 1300 and 1775 a considerable movement of peoples took place inside Europe and its vicinity. The Mongols, pushing far and wide over the immense Eurasian continent, settled in parts of eastern Europe. The Ottoman Turks found a permanent home in Asia Minor and the Balkan Peninsula, and some systematic transfer of other peoples occurred under their rule. The Russians moved farther and farther eastward. The Jews were expelled from England in 1290, from France in 1394, and from various parts of the Holy Roman Empire in the fourteenth and fifteenth centuries, and took refuge in Poland for the most part. In 1492, Spain's rulers expelled the Jews, and in 1609 the Moriscos (nominally Christianized Moors), from the Iberian peninsula. Most of the Moors crossed the Straits of Gibraltar into North Africa. The Spanish Jews and Marranos (nominally Christianized Jews) sought refuge in southern France, the Netherlands, and the Ottoman Empire. Less fortunate Jews found temporary or more permanent but still uneasy abode in various ghettoes without being welcome anywhere. During and after the Reformation religious preferences or intolerance caused population shifts of Christian minorities as well. Radical groups (Anabaptists, Moravian Brethren, Mennonites, and Socinians) were regarded with dislike by the more conservative Protestants, and some of them had a social philosophy that was unbending toward outsiders. Since they found it difficult to live with their fellow countrymen, they migrated, some to the Netherlands, some to the Bohemian mountains, Poland, and Transylvania, and some to Pennsylvania. Catholics left Protestant-dominated regions in considerable numbers, as in the Irish exodus to France in the seventeenth century. A diaspora of French Huguenots took place after 1685, when His Most Christian Majesty revoked the edict which had granted them toleration. More than 50,000 families, including many of France's learned men, industrialists, merchants, and skilled workers, left the country and found asylum in England, Scotland, Holland, and Brandenburg, as well as overseas, particularly in Dutch South Africa and the English Carolinas. France's loss thereby thus was the gain of several states that were her actual or potential enemies. During the Age of Enlightenment, as rulers began to realize the possible disadvantages to a state from religious intolerance, religiously motivated mass migrations came to an end (except for the Jews).

The migration that eventually involved the highest numbers and the widest spread was Europe's overseas expansion. It went east, west, north, and south over a period of centuries. The movement to the Orient was numerically less impressive than that to America. Missionaries, traders, adventurers, sailors, and soldiers went east in goodly numbers, but comparatively few settled there permanently. The death-rate among them was exceptionally high, but those who returned home after completion of their journeys were often enriched not only in material ways but also in experience unavailable in their homelands. They helped spread the knowledge of other civilizations and stimulated two-way cultural diffusion.

To the western half of the world flowed an ever-increasing stream of European emigrants. Spanish and Portuguese went to South America, Central America, the West Indies, and the areas that are now the Southwest and the Gulf region of the United States. Frenchmen went to Canada, Louisiana, Guiana, the West Indies, and the Carolinas. The Dutch settled in the Caribbean, Guiana, and the Hudson valley. The British constituted the major part of the white population of the wilderness bounded by Florida, Louisiana, and Canada as well as some of the West Indies and parts of Central and South America. Scotch–Irish and Germans settled in western Pennsylvania and the Appalachian valleys. Swedes and Danes also went to various parts of the western hemisphere. Other migrations were of French and Dutch to Cape Colony, of Spanish to the Philippines, and of Africans to all parts of the Americas. Wherever Europeans settled they usually exterminated, displaced, segregated, or subordinated the natives, but sometimes, especially where Roman and canon law set the precedent, they interbred to an appreciable extent.

Entire populations were not involved in these moves. Only individuals or segments of peoples left home. Some of them sought only adventure, but others were induced to undertake perilous voyages by the desire to find greater freedom, well-being, or wealth, and still others were impelled by force or missionary zeal. Peasants and artisans in debt looked upon indentured service in the lands across the oceans as a means of paying for passage away from landlords and creditors. Devout people who were not willing to bow to the religious preferences of rulers or whose religious convictions made it impossible for them to continue to live in the communities where they had been born crossed the Atlantic to build new communities more to their liking. Spanish, Portuguese, and English authorities sentenced to transportation tens of thousands of felons, paupers, and political prisoners. Black men were forced to move to America by slavetraders, white men to Africa and America by intolerant rulers, black and red men to remoter areas of Africa and America respectively by white intruders who did not want to live among independent men of colour. Thousands of monks and other missionaries took upon themselves the hardships of emigration in order to spread the Gospel and at times to protect the natives from the exploitation of fellow Europeans. Wherever settlers, traders, and missionaries went, garrisons were also likely to go.

Whatever their motives, these emigrants to the new continents ran grave risks. The means of transportation were, by our standards, primitive; the seas were dangerous; the climate of the new countries frequently was harsher than Europe's; the wilderness was often trackless and unexplored; and the natives generally were hostile. Those who ventured forth left behind the culture in which they had grown up, and probably also friends and kin. Thousands died for the lack of medical care, police protection, and defending armies. Not all of them were rewarded by economic gain or greater liberty in the new lands. Collectively, however, they contributed to mankind the concept of a new life in a new world. They brought whole continents, hitherto essentially isolated from one another, into the orbit of a potentially global civilization. They made useful to all mankind parts of the earth which before had lain fallow or had been known only to a few. As subsequent chapters will show, they spread ideas and beliefs, techniques and arts, as well as material goods from which a greater number of men could profit. They committed injustices and crimes, to be sure, and in some places they exhausted the resources of forests, mines, and soil, with consequences that were sometimes serious for future generations and disastrous for some peoples. At the same time, they performed a prodigious amount of hard work in building new cities and exploiting new resources and showed great ingenuity in solving unfamiliar problems and in achieving workable governments. Despite their own intolerance on some occasions, they passed on to future generations an abiding love of that freedom for which they had made great sacrifices. These migrants, transplanting their cultures to new lands, modifying them as pioneer conditions required, borrowing from and lending to the cultures they encountered, basically widened the outlook of man. They developed two kinds of 'new worlds'. Before their time most men knew of only a small part of mankind, but by 1775 the concept of 'humanity' comprised distant regions and strange peoples all over the planet Earth. Furthermore, the concept of 'new world' was no longer a religious concept alone; a 'new world' seemed possible also on the terrestrial globe, a promised land easier of access than the one in the heavenly spheres. And all this went on at the same time (see Chapter XV) that astronomers also were discovering new worlds in the skies.

★   ★   ★

Wars and Cultural Diffusion

Conflict and war as well as trade and exploration have meant new contacts among peoples. We shall have several occasions to note how initial contacts, as of Europeans with China and Japan, sometimes led to suspicion and aloofness. Nevertheless, as we have already found, even hostile contacts such as war or the fear of war may promote the interchange of culture. Military campaigns took soldiers to other countries and acquainted them with different civilizations (as was particularly true of the Crusades). Sometimes military conquest necessitated a reorientation either for the conqueror (as in the case of the Mongols in China) or for the conquered (as in the case of the Spanish in the Philippines), and at other times it brought something of a mutual acculturation to both conqueror and conquered (as in the Muslim subjection of India). Occasionally wars built bridges between peoples (e.g. between Europeans and Asians because of the Mongol invasions) or penetrated the seclusion behind which remarkable cultures were hidden from the rest of the world (e.g. the conquest of Mexico, Peru, and some of the African kingdoms).

For better or worse, warfare was a factor of significance in the exchange of cultural influences during the centuries covered in this volume. Some wars were negligible as instruments of intercultural exchange—mere skirmishes for the possession of fortresses or strips of land, or civil wars that frequently resulted in bitter fighting and fearful atrocities but no interchange of peoples and their ways. Some were waged between small states or neighbouring towns, adding little to their previous knowledge of each other. Sometimes, however, coalitions of great states involved whole continents in their clashes, carrying their conflicts far overseas and working important changes among distant peoples. Fought in the name of religion and with all the viciousness man is capable of, warfare on occasion altered the religious concepts of those involved. A few wars were conducted like games according to unwritten but traditionally respected gentlemen's rules, but when nations battled for their very existence or for ideals they cherished, they usually fought bitterly and ruthlessly. Some wars were practically over before they started; others, though perhaps intermittent, lasted so long that they became known by the length of time they had endured—the Hundred Years' War, the Eighty Years' War, the Thirty Years' War, the Seven Years' War.

Between 1300 and 1775 marked changes in technique, tactics, and strategy widened the area, incidence, and consequences of warfare. Warships, equipped with new firearms, became veritable floating fortresses and highly effective instruments of battle (see Chapter XV), and a country with a redoubtable fleet was a formidable power even if it had no great land forces. For the European nations engaged in overseas ventures naval power assumed an unprecedented importance, and the minister of the navy often was minister for the colonies as well. Eventually the great naval and colonial powers of the Atlantic superseded Venice and Genoa in the Mediterranean also. Small feudal cavalry armies (where generally man fought man) disappeared in Europe, though they survived in Japan and China and though in the Middle East huge armies on horseback, equipped with firearms, bows, and swords, were among the best soldiers of the period.

The introduction of firearms hastened the rise of standing armies under the control of a central government (see Chapter XV). Soldiering became a trained and regular profession from which the vast multitude was excluded, providing instead the taxes for the upkeep of the military establishment. Only for special occasions, such as defence against an invader or during a siege, did the whole population of a region or town take to arms. In general, the civil populations were innocent bystanders or unfortunate victims while the professional fighters clashed, looted, and ravaged, until, with the French Revolutionary wars, came the principle of 'the nation in arms' and popular mass armies.

Unquestionably, war wrought senseless destruction, blind havoc, and immeasurable misery. Certain states—Russia under the Tatars and Germany after the Thirty Years' War provide good examples—suffered for generations after contending armies had ravaged their cities and countryside. Ambitious conquerors wasted manpower and economic resources in fantastic and ephemeral projects of expansion, as did Tamerlane (c. 1336–1405) and Charles XII of Sweden (1682–1718). As in all ages, some of the most ruinous belligerent acts were performed by men, like Philip II of Spain (1527–98) and Aurangzīb, who professed high religious ideals and great respect for civilization.

Wars nevertheless produced results now and then that seemed worth the sacrifice entailed. Political freedom, national independence, or the right to worship with a free conscience was gained on occasion (e.g. by the Vijayanagar and the Dutch wars of independence) by means of arms. Sometimes unbearable or anarchical political situations were remedied by the use of force (e.g. the Russians' expulsion of the Tatars and the French Wars of Religion). Once in a while military conflict encouraged cultural contact between peoples that otherwise might have remained mutually aloof (e.g. Christians and Turks). From time to time invading soldiers carried home, along with disease and loot, fruitful ideas, laudable customs, or new crafts, as did those of the French king Charles VIII from Renaissance Italy. Religious faiths and aesthetic impulses spread similarly. Frequently the pressure of war stimulated or hastened economic, scientific, and technological developments at home (see

Chapter XV). Thus, warfare, man's most destructive activity, has at times proved to be a channel of cultural change.

One of the natural consequences of war is the reaction to its horror, with consequent efforts to restore peace and to regulate future relations among nations by pacific means. Philosophers, theologians, and humanists whom we shall encounter in several chapters (see especially VI–IX) were deeply concerned about the warlike proclivities of man, which they considered out of keeping with God's laws, the nobler side of human nature, and the principles of civilized international conduct. Outright pacifism and non-resistance to force were preached by certain religious sects and given serious consideration by influential thinkers. Several political treatises were written expressly to promote an international structure assuring all men undisturbed peace in their pursuit of higher values or to lay down an international law that would promote peaceful relations and diminish the horrors of war. These efforts, though they remained largely without effect during our period, contributed to a growing consensus that man must somehow achieve enduring international peace. Despite the contemporaneous maturing of nationalism and the continued reliance of statesman on force as the *ultima ratio*—and, in a way, because of nationalism and the reliance on force—the yearning spread for some kind of collective organization to preserve peace.

More concrete contributions to the civilized coexistence of nations were made by developments in the conduct of diplomacy. In order to win concessions or to negotiate differences and avoid armed conflict, rulers had always been accustomed to send *ad hoc* representatives to one another's capitals. At the beginning of our period the Italian city-states, Venice in particular, adopted the policy of requiring a diplomatic agent to stay in a given capital continuously. Other nations soon followed suit, and so began the international practice of exchanging permanent embassies. Notwithstanding the intrigue and secrecy that standing diplomatic missions tended to create, they formed a sounder basis for international relations than occasional ones. A regular international exchange of information and opinion on day-by-day affairs made possible better mutual understanding and readier negotiation of differences.

Another diplomatic amelioration of the day was the appearance of great international congresses. Perhaps the most illustrious was that of Westphalia (Münster-Osnabrück), which lasted about four years and finally in 1648 brought the Thirty Years' War to a close. Meetings of the representatives of belligerent countries for the purpose of arranging a peace were common enough before the Congress of Westphalia, but never before had deputations from so many governments negotiated a peace settlement touching so many areas of the world. Despite their exorbitant attention to trivia such as diplomatic precedence, these early congresses made at least a beginning toward the establishment of a 'Concert of Europe'. Congresses were called even in times of peace (notably that of Cambrai-Soissons in 1724–28) to forestall potential causes of a new war. But those and other schemes, we shall have to record again and again, failed to bring international peace. If anything, during our period increasing contacts among nations and peoples seemed to bring more rather than less armed conflict at the same time that they brought more cultural interchange.

NOTES TO CHAPTER I

1. For African names we have usually followed Basil Davidson, *The Lost Cities of Africa* (Boston, 1959), which is the same book as *Old Africa Discovered* (London, 1959). See also Diedrich Westermann, *Geschichte Afrikas, Staatenbildungen südlich der Sahara* (Köln, 1952); Denise Paulme, 'L'Afrique noire jusqu'au XIVe siècle (deuxième partie)', *Journal of World History*, III (1957), pp. 561–88; and Roland Oliver and J. D. Fage, *A Short History of Africa* (Harmondsworth, 1962).

2. Professor Roland Mousnier feels that certain terms should have been handled with more precision. In particular: Can the Mongol 'Empire' a victorious army occupying a conquered country, be compared to the Germanic Holy Roman Empire of Charles V or, better still, the 'Empire' formed by all the possessions of Charles V, a sort of federation of peoples united by the person of the sovereign on the basis of the principles of legitimacy and respect for the laws and customs of each political unit ?

   The same applies as regards the absolute monarchy. The monarch of Dahomey was certainly not absolute in the sense that Louis XIV was, even allowing for the dictatorial nature of the latter's war-time government. The concept of representation is not sufficiently clarified and the fundamental distinction between the *major pars*, the plurality, and the *sanior pars*, the best and healthiest part of the population, which should out-weigh the *major pars*, is not clarified. In most cases, it was, in law or in fact, a group of privileged individuals, mostly a small minority, who sent representatives to an assembly. For us, therefore, this assembly had no representative value but, on the other hand, it had a considerable value for contemporaries who would doubtless have despised our system of universal suffrage and regarded those elected under that system as being representative to only a very limited degree. In most cases, the assembly was made up of individuals whose interests were so closely tied to general prosperity that they fully expressed the inmost wishes of all and did so even better than those directly concerned could have done; alternatively, the assembly was made up of those who, by reason of their position as royal officers, were the deputies and interpreters of all, the very mirror of justice, ideal proxies for both governors and governed. In France in the eighteenth century, and in England in the seventeenth century, men made the transition from the Society of Orders to the Society of Classes on the basis of the domination of a sort of middle class, a class derived from wealth and ability, embodying sovereignty, with another type of representativity, the plurality or majority, to use a term deriving from Anglo-Saxon usage, the law of number replacing the *sanior pars* but the majority deriving from a sort of *sanior pars* designated roughly by its resources. This new *sanior pars* took a materialistic form. On this question see: L. Moulin, 'Sanior et major pars', *Revue historique de droit français et étranger* (1958, 4° série, 36, pp. 368–491); *Revue historique de droit comparé*, (1955); *Revue française de science politique* (1952); *Revue internationale d'histoire politique* (1953); *Revue internationale des sciences administratives* (1951 et 1955); *Cahiers de Bruges*, 6, (1956).

   Frequent reference is made to a republic but without sufficiently demonstrating that republic here is not equivalent to democracy unless we consider as democratic any government which is not an absolute monarchy or a dictatorship. But the republics of the Low Countries, Switzerland, and Venice were oligarchies or aristocracies with no genuinely democratic element involved. The power was not in the hands of the greatest number nor were the greatest number represented. Small groups comprising the wealthy, the well to do or those of noble birth were the only ones to participate in the exercise of political power at its various levels.

The authors were aware of these strictures. The word empire *was used in a sense which it frequently bears in English 'an extensive territory ruled over by an emperor or a sovereign state'. Absolute monarchy was used with the following connotation: 'unlimited (as opposed to limited) monarchy'. In this Introduction an attempt was made to provide a generalized summary of world-wide socio–politico–economic developments over nearly five centuries, so far as possible without undue violence to the known historical particulars: a process which demands a deliberate effort to employ judiciously flexible terminologies and classifications. In later Chapters the terminology will be found sufficiently distinctive. (See also Note 10.)*

3. Professor R. Mousnier believes that the tremendous differences between the English landholder and the French 'censitaire' and between the latter and the Russian serf would seem to exclude any possibility of grouping them in the same category.

In England as early as the fifteenth century, the precarious tenure of the peasants was widely accepted. The peasant could be dispossessed virtually at the whim of the feudal lord. In this way, enclosures were facilitated and the peasants became, so to speak, proletarians or tenant farmers. In France, on the other hand, the distinction between the 'direct' seigneury of the feudal lord and the 'useful' seigneury of the peasant became more marked as from the fifteenth century. The peasant, a free man in the majority of cases, became a genuine owner with the right to make use of his produce and to dispose of the land through sale or bequest. Where the 'Coutume de Paris' prevailed, the peasant owner was almost exactly the same as he became in the nineteenth century after the Revolution. See also F. Olivier-Martin, *Histoire de la coutume de la Prévosté et Vicomté de Paris*, (1928–31), 3 vols. In Germany, east of the Elbe, beginning in the sixteenth century, the feudal lord tended to exploit vast areas of land himself, to subjugate the peasants, and to transform them into forced labourers at his pleasure. When serfdom was paramount in Russia in the second half of the seventeenth century, the serf was virtually no more than a thing in the eyes of the lord and Russian serfdom was in fact little different from slavery.

The authors, however, feel that the generalization they made is valid in the broad context of world development.

4. Professor R. Mousnier, by way of addition writes: 'To speak of representative bodies for Spain, France, Denmark, etc. would at the very least call for some explanation as to the concept of representation. Contemporaries considered that an aristocratic or oligarchic minority very adequately represented the whole populace. They were the *sanior pars*, if not the *major pars*. In the French estates of Languedoc, membership of a body of representatives was a privilege deriving from ownership. Twenty-two barons occupied positions in the estates by virtue of a right attached to the baronies they held but four quarterings were required on both the paternal and maternal side. As far as the clergy were concerned, the archbishops and the bishops had a place in the estates by right of their position. The Third Estate was represented by the consuls of certain towns by virtue of their position: for each diocese the episcopal town, the main town which sent deputies every year; sometimes a few towns of lesser importance, which sent deputies in turn. The representivity of such an assembly seemed incontestable. The three types of deputies were regarded as an 'epitome of the provinces and the peoples' proxies'. They were the 'Fathers of the Homeland', doubtless because as great landowners or representatives of great landowners their interests were closely linked to the prosperity of all. (See also R. Mousnier, 'La participation des gouvernés à l'activité des gouvernants dans la France du XVII et XVIIIe siècles'. *Recueils de la Société Jean Bodin pour l'histoire comparative des institutions*, Vol. XXIV, pp. 246 et 256.

5. J. E. E. Dalberg-Acton, *Lectures on the French Revolution* (London 1910), p. 20.

6. R. R. Kuczynski, 'Population', *Encyclopedia of the Social Sciences*, XII (New York, 1937), p. 241; Ping-ti Ho, *Studies on the Population of China, 1368–1953* (Cambridge 1959).

7. Figures taken from 'Additional Material in Connection with the Remarks of Soviet Scientists on the Plan of Volume IV . . .' (MS, 1957), p. 105.

8. R. Barón Castro, 'El desarollo de la población hispano–americana (1492–1950)', *Journal of World History*, V (1959), pp. 325–43. For a closely similar estimate see Silvio Zavala, *The Colonial Period in the History of the New World* (Mexico City, 1962), pp. 162–63. See,

however, Woodrow Borah and S. F. Cook, *The Aboriginal Population of Central Mexico on the Eve of the Spanish Conquest* (Berkeley, 1963), which implies a much higher figure for 1519 and a much lower one for 1570. See also C. Gibson, 'The Transformation of the Indian Community in New Spain, 1500–1810', *Journal of World History*, II (1955), pp. 581–607, and Richard M. Morse, 'Some Characteristics of Latin American Urban History', *American Historical Review*, LXVII (1962), pp. 317–18.

9. Professor R. Mousnier points out that, ultimately, Akbar's successors, Jahāngīr (1605–27), Shāh-Jehān (1628–57), and Aurangzib (1659–1707), did not understand his policy and disorganized the Hindu administration. They abandoned payment of their officials by salary and reverted to payment by *jaghir* a sort of 'living', a group of villages which the official administered as his own property and from which he derived an arbitrary salary. In respect of the tax on land, the emperors abandoned Akbar's system, which involved an estimate of the areas and yields and adopted something approaching a quota tax while they also allowed the officials to divide the tax between the villages without regard to the position of individual farmers. The rulers sold the charges of governor, which often became hereditary, and exploited the peasants mercilessly. The peasantry was crushed. Agriculture and industry declined. India grew impoverished.

10. Professor R. Mousnier believes that the authors should have given more stress to the analysis of social structure, which, in his opinion, constitutes perhaps the essential phenomenon in history, more important than the economic element, which it frequently determines. As far back as Hesiod and Plato men observed the behaviour of their contemporaries and devised a mental picture of the society in which they lived as if it were composed of groups forming social levels or strata superimposed in hierarchical order. They generally called these strata *classes*. The authors follow this example and use the word *classes* at every turn. But, at the very least, a distinction must be drawn between stratification into *castes* as typified by Hindu stratification; stratification into *orders* (Stände, Estates), which is so frequent and in which social groups are placed in hierarchical levels not, in principle, according to the wealth of the members and their consumption capacity, not according to their role in the production of material goods, but according to the respect, honour, and dignity attached by society to social functions which may have no relationship with the production of material goods—the profession of arms in France from the thirteenth to the seventeenth century, the scholar with an inclination for public office in China of the Ming and Ch'ing periods, etc.; finally, stratification into *classes* when, in a market economy, it is the role played in the production of material goods and the money earned by fulfilment of this role which places the individual in the various levels of the social hierarchy. A class, then, is formed by those who have the same source of income, fortunes or income of comparable extent, a similar type of life, common interests. A class is perfect if it also recognizes everything which is held in common together with a common action. The authors have not distinguished these three types (nor several others). Similarly, they have not studied the types of family, corps, and colleges existing within each social stratum or cutting across social strata. They have not sufficiently described the territorial units, villages and communities, towns or provinces. They have not studied the relations and the balance of all these social groups between each other, i.e. the social structures. They have obviously only indirectly touched on the vast movement which in France, for example, led from a society of orders based on the pre-eminence of the warrior in the fifteenth and sixteenth centuries to a society of orders based on the magistrate in the seventeenth and eighteenth centuries and to a society of classes based on the pre-eminence of the bourgeoisie, financiers, dealers in products or producers of material goods at the end of the eighteenth century. For Professor Mousnier this is a serious shortcoming since social history while it is no more the driving force of history than economic history (man as a whole is the driving force of history) is nevertheless the most fundamental part of history for the understanding of civilizations. What is the history of technology, sciences, literature, the arts, religion, if it is impossible to relate the inventors, the engineers, the artists, the writers, the connoisseurs, the publics, the clergy, the saints, the unbelievers to specific social groups? (See R. Mousnier, J. P. Labatut, and Y. Durand, *Problèmes de stratification sociale, deux cahiers de la noblesse, 1649–51* (Paris, 1965).

In the opinion of the authors this classification is helpful and, in the chapters that follow, have they used these various terms within the proper context; however, they cannot wholly accept Professor Mousnier's refined distinctions among caste, order *and* class *since for various purposes an hereditary aristocracy, for example (or a trained clergy or landowning merchants) might even by his definitions belong in more than one of the three categories at the same time.*

11. In the opinion of Professor R. Mousnier the essential feature of the social stratification by castes is the fact that it is based on the degree of hereditary religious purity, a feature which in regard to castes outweighs all the others.

12. For a discussion of the literature on this subject, see Robert E. Riegel, 'American Frontier Theory', *Journal of World History*, III (1956), pp. 356–80.

CHAPTER II

THE MAJOR RELIGIONS (*c.* 1300)

GENERAL REMARKS

CHAPTERS II–V will deal with questions of ecclesiastical establishments and with the creeds and events that, at least in part, centred upon them rather than with questions of theology as a branch of abstract thought. Theology and related disciplines will be dealt with in Chapters VI and VII. From time to time Chapters II–V will also refer again to the political, social, and economic events that have been sketched in the preceding chapter, for church developments and conflicts cannot be well comprehended except as influenced by, as well as influencing, contemporary affairs of a secular nature. Nevertheless, a deliberate effort will be made in Chapters II–V to concentrate attention upon religious organization in order to depict the largely ecclesiastical orientation of the intellectual atmosphere of 1300 and its persistence until 1775. Subsequent chapters will describe other aspects of culture and the modifications of the prevalent intellectual atmosphere.

In a fashion and to a degree that no longer is common, reverence or fear of God, gods, or other supernatural beings was prominent in daily life at the opening of our period. The supernatural was immanent for Christians in Europe and beyond, for Moslems in Africa, the Middle East, and India, for Hindus, Buddhists, Taoists, Confucianists, or Shintoists in India, China, Japan, and other parts of southeastern Asia and the Far East, for Jews scattered through Europe, the Near East, and elsewhere, and for the various animist and polytheistic creeds that were to be found in those areas of Africa, Eurasia, Australia, and the Americas that had not yet been reached by or, if reached, not yet converted to Moslem, Christian, Buddhist, or other proselytizing religions. God (or the gods) and the Devil (or devils), demons and witches, the souls and ghosts of the departed, saints and revered ancestors were present everywhere and took an active part in life and thought. To speak to them, to demand guidance of them, to propitiate or worship them, whether by set rituals or by spontaneous acts of devotion, was no less a part of the day's activities than intercourse with one's other neighbours and generally was considered more important for lasting welfare.[1] (Map IV.)

In general, the several religions tended to centre upon a given local structure. The priest might be only a witch doctor revered by a thinly populated tribe and under the jurisdiction of no prelate, or he might be a parish curé responsible to a hierarchy headed by a pope regarded by some as responsible only to God. He might feel that his gods and demons were responsive to his prayers and his rites effective only so far as the recognized

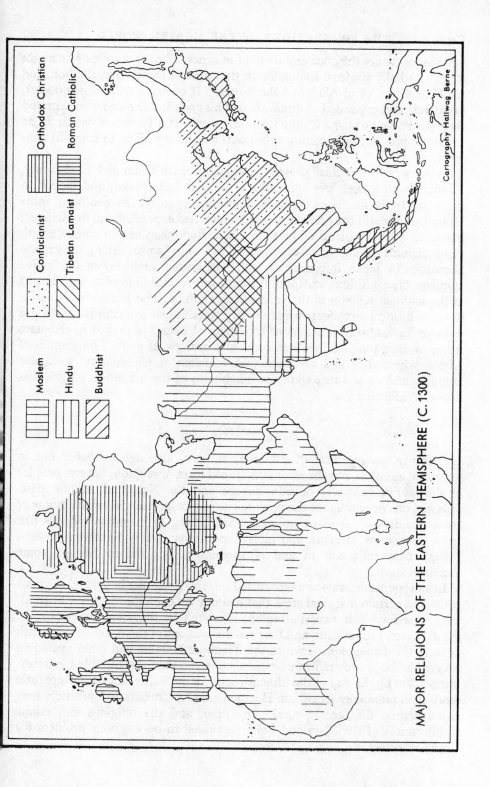

MAJOR RELIGIONS OF THE EASTERN HEMISPHERE (C.1300)

Moslem

Hindu

Buddhist

Confucianist

Tibetan Lamaist

Orthodox Christian

Roman Catholic

Cartography Hallwag Berne

boundaries where the gods and demons of other tribes took over or he might claim a catholic spiritual leadership in the name of the Father, the Son, and the Holy Ghost or of Allah and the Prophet. If he was a tribal witch doctor, his jurisdiction expanded or diminished as his gods and demons demonstrated their weakness or power by the fortunes of war. If a Christian patriarch, he counted upon not only conquest but also missionary effort to bring in converts.

In our period the chief proselytizing creeds were Islam and Christianity. Buddhism no longer was spreading as once it had spread, and indeed in northern India its followers had almost disappeared. In southern India Hinduism was still the prevailing creed, and it had expanded also to Malaysia, particularly to the island of Java. In China Buddhism had to compete with Confucianism among the more educated and with Taoism among the general populace. In Japan it competed with and even overshadowed the native animistic creed, Shinto, except in the rural areas, until Shintoism re-emerged as the national religion in the seventeenth century. The Indians of America were animistic polytheists, whether they worshipped in primitive fashion a more or less indiscriminate set of supernatural beings or prayed in elaborate Aztec or Inca temples to a well ordered hierarchy of gods. The peoples of Africa, where they had not been won to Islam or Christianity, were also animists, and so as a rule were the inhabitants of the numerous islands that dotted the Pacific.

ANIMISM

In 1300 in geographical distribution, at least, although probably not in numbers, animism was the most widespread form of religion. Several peoples of the world, generally outside Europe and the Near and Middle East, followed one or another of the polytheistic and polydemonial creeds. Some of these creeds were likewise animistic, attributing to inanimate objects like trees, mountains, streams, and idols, superhuman and supernatural powers, though frequently not in and of themselves but rather through some vicarious spirit.

In Europe, animism was a recognized system of popular belief and religious control in certain marginal areas that had not yet been thoroughly Christianized. The East-Baltic coastal region, inhabited by Slavs and Balts (Lapps, Finns, Letts, Lithuanians, and Borrussians) was one of them. In the thirteenth century the *Drang nach Osten* of the Teutonic Knights and other crusading orders had begun to eradicate heathenism in the Baltic by forcible Christianization. Yet by the end of the fifteenth century the Baltic lands still were little more than nominally Christian. Heathen animistic beliefs and practices persisted among the largely rural population, and the religious and ethnic stubbornness of the Slavs and Balts continued to be a serious problem for Christian rulers.

In the broadest sense of the term, including demonology and various sorts of kindred occultisms, animism also survived to a certain extent in many rural sections of Christendom. For example, Celtic animism hung on tenaciously among the more primitive of Irish clans, both in folklore and in upper-class literature. Animistic ideas persevered to a surprising degree even in highly civilized centres. Though a keen-minded cynic in other regards, Machiavelli believed that the air was peopled with spirits; Ficino actually defended demonology as well as astrology. The Catholic Church formally condemned witchcraft, demon worship, and pagan incantations of all kinds, and overt acts involving such heathen practices were punished. Shortly before 1300 the Inquisition began to burn witches at the stake. Despite the public stand of the church, individuals among the clergy defended, with quotations from Holy Scripture, occult practices such as palmistry, haruspices, and especially astrology. Some astrologers claimed that even the events of Jesus' life had been horoscopically predictable, since in his mortal form he had been 'under the stars'.

In a similar fashion, in the other major civilizations earlier animistic traditions survived amid more advanced religions. In areas where the great religions associated with urban cultures had not yet penetrated, animistic beliefs prevailed and in great variety—from the totemism of the Australian aborigines to the pre-animistic belief of Polynesia and Melanesia in a ubiquitous impersonal supernatural power (*mana*). These faiths revolved around special persons—medicine men, sorcerers, shamans—and practices by which the spirits could be exorcized, propitiated, controlled, or enlisted. Animistic practices ranged from offerings of flowers, liquids, foods, animals, and human sacrifice through various forms of magic, formulas, chants, and spells to very elaborate rituals. They had become engrafted on or fused with some of the higher religions to such an extent that in many cases it was impossible to indicate precisely where animism ended and a higher form of religion began. About 1300 the animistic elements in the religious practices of many areas were, it appears, of more immediate importance to the masses of the people than were higher religious concepts, which were only a veneer over the underlying culture of the masses.

Perhaps the most common and fundamental features of the religious practices of southern and eastern Asia were some form or other of nature worship and ancestor worship. In India the worship or propitiation of a host of demons and spirits, both evil and benign, was practised as an integral part of Hinduism along with the worship of higher gods. Some of the demons were the creation of higher gods; others were the spirits of departed humans. Cremation and other elaborate death ceremonies were regarded as necessary to assure that the departed would become benign rather than evil; ancestral spirits were fed and worshipped to help them in the spirit world and to preserve their friendly disposition toward the living. Male progeny was considered important as a guarantee of the continuation of ancestral worship.[2]

Persons who died sudden or violent deaths under conditions that prevented proper cremation and funeral ceremonies became spirits that roamed about with malevolent proclivities. Crimes and sins lived after their perpetrators in the form of malign demons (*bhūta* and *preta*) searching for victims who could be instigated to commit similar crimes; disease and death resulted from the acts of such spirits. These *bhūta* and *preta* were propitiated or exorcized by offerings of food, by incantations or formulas, and by the services of sorcerers. Village and household spirits were given honour to win their friendly disposition and prevent them from taking vengeance. Heroes, saints, various natural forces, trees, rivers, and animals—especially cows, snakes, and monkeys—or their spirits were invoked to confer benefit or prevent disaster.

Spiritism and ancestor cults were prominent also throughout southeastern Asia. In Burma spirits (*nats*) were thought to inhabit houses, villages, bodies of water, trees, persons, and other abodes. Most of them were considered malevolent but propitiable by offerings and ceremonials. *Nat* shrines were found outside most villages and often near homes. Siam had especially malevolent ghosts (*phi*), and the spirits of women who had died in childbirth or with unborn children were particularly dreadful. Violent spirits were sometimes provided for the defence of forts or city walls, while they were being constructed, by driving posts through a living victim, who had been well fed beforehand. In Vietnam the ancestral cult was especially strong, and the spirits of the earth, trees, animals, the heavens, the air, and the patrons of particular trades were especially important. The tiger cult was prominent on the edge of forests. The spirits of girls who had died before marriage were believed to seize upon young men to satisfy their desire for children. Most villages had temples or altars dedicated to the Fire Dame, who might prevent or diminish the destructiveness of fire in the bamboo villages. In the Philippines, certain high gods shared veneration with lesser gods and goddesses and a host of good and evil spirits (*anitos* or *diwatas*); the spirits of one's own ancestors were generally good, while those of one's enemies were bad. For the Malay-speaking peoples of Indonesia both good and evil spirits (*yang*) came from the dead and from swamps, creeks, and great trees. The Negritos of the Andaman Islands believed that various spirits of the dead might cause or cure sickness and bring death and might impart some of their supernatural powers to mortals during dreams or serious illnesses. Some Negritos believed in a superior spirit, Biliku (apparently the northeast monsoon), who insisted upon a number of ritualistic taboos. He ate, drank, slept, and reproduced like a human, and the natives would threaten him with the bite of a mythical snake if he allowed too much rain. Throughout southeastern Asia sorcerers or medicine men were commonly employed to deal with spirits, but for most purposes specialists were not indispensable, and so no dominating priesthood arose.

In Australia there existed religious totemic groups that possessed a secret mythology and ritual associated with the ancestral hero represented by the totem. This ancestor was believed to have created most of the spirits in a mythological age and to have placed unborn spirits in centres from which, when needed, they could be incarnated into human, animal, or material forms and to which they returned after death. The groups' ceremonies were regarded as essential to these incarnations; unborn spirits could be found in dreams or placed in the womb by the totemic hero. The ceremonial included the re-enactment of the appropriate part of the mythology at sacred places and the anointment of a sacred stone with blood from the arm or genitals. Serious illnesses were attributed to sorcery or the spirits and could be cured by the ministrations, partly magical, partly practical, of medicine men.

Among the Polynesians the spirits of natural forces and of reptile-like ancestors were worshipped. The Polynesians believed also in *mana* and *tapu* (from which the word *taboo* is derived). *Mana* was an inward power that might be transferred to things (weapons in particular) or persons under appropriate circumstances; *tapu* connoted the quality of being set aside for private use. The gods and spirits, certain individuals and things, and strange, mysterious phenomena possessed *mana*. A woman was *tapu* for (reserved to) her husband after marriage; the remains of a meal of a chief were *tapu* to an inferior on pain of a sore throat or other ill. A long list of taboos affected the whole range of life. Dreams were a means by which ancestors or spirits foretold coming events or guided the destinies of the living. Bloody sacrifices were common. Fingers were amputated to secure the recovery of a superior; frequently pigs and domestic animals, and occasionally humans, were immolated; in New Zealand a Maori chief might offer up a favourite child at the ceremony marking the foundation of a building.

The Ainus of Hokkaido, Japan, worshipped natural forces and objects— sometimes directly, sometimes as spirits—especially the sea, the bear, fire, and millet. Ceremonials were generally not elaborate. Millet was worshipped by cooking it and reciting a simple phrase: 'O Millet, thou hast grown well for us; we thank thee; we eat thee', and the bear by slaying a specially raised cub during a ceremonial dance and tasting its blood. Ainu practices had no doubt been influenced by long contact with the Japanese, and certain elements of Japanese nature worship, in turn, were probably derived from the partial amalgamation of the two peoples.

Although the native religion of the Japanese had been largely replaced at the top by Buddhism, indigenous animistic beliefs and practices continued among the masses. At heart this folk religion centred around the worship of natural forces or their spirits, although human beings were also deified and worshipped. *Kami*, a term usually translated as *god* or *spirit*, means *something superior, sacred, or miraculous*. The greatest of the *kami*—among a host of others, some national, most of them regional or local—was the Sun Goddess, ancestress of the imperial family. There were *kami* of the earth, soil, rivers, rain, wind, rice, mountains, waterfalls, war, learning, good luck, and clans. A simple stone resembling a phallus might be the *kami* of a field, insuring its fertility. Although the Japanese had their share of demons, their attitude towards the spirits was generally one of appreciation, love, and gratitude rather than fear. Worship was usually simple, consisting of offerings of food and liquor, bowings, clapping of the hands, and the stating of simple requests; ritualistic purity, obtained through washing, fasting, and the like, was stressed. Ancestor worship, possibly introduced from China, was almost universal by 1300. Vague elements of earlier religious practice such as shamanism, fetishism, phallicism, and perhaps totemism survived in popular religious practices. State Shintoism was distinguishable from the folk religion and will be considered separately below.

Among the Tibetans and the Mongols, Tunguses, and Koreans of northeast Asia, shamanism was widespread. Basically it was a cult of ancestral ghosts or spirits. Spirits on and above the earth were generally benign; those below were evil. Some might be approached only directly, others through mediating ancestral spirits with the aid of a shaman. A shaman was one who was capable of ecstatic spells during which he was thought to be possessed by ancestral spirits and through them to be able to communicate with, influence, and even control other spirits. This power was considered inherent in certain families. The shaman also arranged sacrifices, purified homes, drove out evil spirits, and acted as physician, prophet, and soothsayer. Popular Korean religious beliefs were a mixture of ancient shamanistic practices, ancestor worship, and the worship of various deities either borrowed from or profoundly influenced by Chinese archetypes. *Pansus* (*diviners*), who were generally blind, and *mutangs* (*sorceresses*) performed the functions of the shaman.

In China popular religious beliefs and practices contained animistic elements. The cult of ancestors formed the heart of China's religious and social structure. Although by 1300 many of the educated members of the cult may no longer have believed in its purely animistic elements, for the masses ancestral spirits seem still to have been very real. Most Chinese were practical and a bit sceptical, but they were also tradition-bound and superstitious and dared not disregard the possibility that spirits, ancestral, natural, or abstract, might really harm or help. If upon proper appeal the spirits failed to end a drought or other disaster, they might be punished but they could not be ignored. The power of heaven might be impersonal, but the spirits of the earth and soil seemed far less remote. Every village had its tutelary deity; every craft had its patron spirit; and rivers, mountains, marshes, lakes, trees, and deified heroes were worshipped. Good spirits were known as *shen*, and evil spirits as *kuei*. *Kuei* could cause death, disease, and other evils, and by committing suicide a man could cause his *kuei* to hound his enemy. At the lower levels of society *Wu* priests were employed to communicate with spirits, exorcise them, and cure disease; on a higher level Taoist and Buddhist priests (as we shall soon see) performed similar functions. In addition, local natural forces might act upon buildings, graves, and other structures to advantage or disadvantage, and *feng-shui* (*wind and water*) specialists were consulted to discover advantageous sites. Man, nature, and the spirits were thus associated in an inseparable unity.

The North American Indians, as was to be expected of peoples so widely and thinly scattered and so diverse in culture, differed in their religious practices and beliefs. The more primitive tribes believed in many kinds of spirits—of mountains, rivers, and forests, of sun, moon, and stars, of animals and departed people. Ghosts and ancestral spirits were propitiated with sometimes intricate rites, which included songs and dances and the ministrations of magicians and medicine men. Nearly all tribes worshipped a hierarchy of holy beings, ranging from mythical heroes through ogres and dwarfs to a Great Spirit, whose good will had to be courted if disease was to be cured, crops were to multiply, and battles were to be won. The North American Indians sometimes buried their dead in carefully selected mounds, although funeral rites were generally simple. Spirits were frequently represented in totems; and the totem pole as a common object of worship was a symbol of clan or tribal unity.

The more civilized Amerindians in Central and South America developed a concept of the Great Spirit that came close to monotheism. The Zapotecs of south Mexico worshipped a Creator who was himself 'uncreated, without beginning or end'.3 He was not, however, alone in his divinity but shared it with less powerful gods and spirits, who inhabited caves, rocks, trees, and other abodes. These gods were worshipped in cave temples by a hierarchy of priests, of whom the high priest was the guardian of the sacred city Mitla ('city of the dead'), whose ruins still reveal the remnants of temples, pyramids, huge stones inscribed with hieroglyphs, and other vestiges that mark it as a burial place for the mighty. Mitla apparently began to fall in ruins only late in the fifteenth century, after the Aztecs conquered the Zapotecs. The Mayans worshipped a chief god whom they called Hunab-Ku, 'the one divine existence'.4 Although he was invisible and remote from the daily life of the people, he contributed to the later Aztec concepts of divinity. The Aztecs had a well-respected priestly order, hieroglyphic records (kept on a paper that they had learned to manufacture before the Europeans knew paper), a calendar (with a surprisingly exact calculation of the year's length) probably based upon priestly knowledge, and temples that roused the admiration of the Europeans who saw them. At the head of a host of gods was Teotl, invisible and remote like Hunab-Ku of the Mayans. Teotl himself, however, owed his origin to 'a single dual principle, male and female, which had engendered gods, the world and men'5—a single Cause. The Incas also had a remote supreme god who was 'Creator of the Universe'.

The Indians generally believed in a life after death. Surviving ruins of mounds and pyramids testify to their respect for the dead; the Incas mummified their dead; the Mayans sometimes cremated their nobles. Heroic warriors went to a just reward, but dreadful hells awaited those whom the gods did not favour. Spiders were sacred to the Chibchas because they were the companions of the dead in the hereafter. Appeasement of the numerous gods was indispensable if hell was to be avoided after death, and some gods were not content with offerings of food alone; they had to be propitiated with animal and sometimes with human sacrifice; the Chibcha and the Aztec gods were particularly severe. Great numbers of captives, criminals, and even children were sacrificed to the demanding deities on terraced and truncated pyramids.

The best beloved of the Aztec gods was Quetzalcoatl. This legendary Feathered Serpent, or White God, had been the Aztecs' great teacher. His story reflects the high cultures that flourished in the area now known as Mexico and Guatemala. Originally a Toltec hero, he became identified with the hero-god Kukulcan of the Mayas when the Toltec civilization collapsed (c. 1200), and survived as an Aztec god after civil war, disease, and migration brought, in turn, the collapse of the glorious Mayan Second Empire (c. 1437). He was believed to have taught the Aztecs how to plant maize, make metals, read, and weave, and to have given them their laws, institutions, and calendar; and some day as a white, bearded leader he would return from the east to lead them again. The white men who came from the east, however, carried by large birds with great wings of canvas, were not Aztec gods but Spanish conquerors.

Priesthood and government were closely bound together in the higher Amerindian cultures. The Aztec rulers were also high priests, for the gods had given the art of government to them. Class distinctions existed in the Aztec heaven (and so were presumably still more justifiable upon earth). Human sacrifice made a religious sacrament out of the destruction of war prisoners. The Incas especially emphasized the religious sanction of their government, each tribe having its own sacred ancestor, symbolized by some bird or animal, probably with totem significance; and the Sapa Inca was considered to be a direct descendant of the Sun-God. The peoples whom the Incas conquered were forcibly converted to the Inca religion, which became in its later stages a species of sun worship, outshining but not necessarily displacing the local religions. Some elements of these Amerindian cults were to lend themselves easily to adaptation to the Christian faith and organization.

HINDUISM AND JAINISM

In 1300 Hinduism was confined mainly to the Indian peninsula and Ceylon. A form of Hinduism mixed with Buddhism was also practised in official quarters in east Java, and the rising Javanese empire of Majapahit was to expand the influence of this cult in the East Indies. It was perhaps still the formal official cult in the Khmer empire of Kāmbuja (now Cambodia) at Angkor and in Champa (southern Indo-China), but Hīnayāna Buddhism (see below) was fast becoming the dominant religion in Cambodia, and the Hindu priestly caste (Brahmans), though still employed by the rulers of the Indo-Chinese peninsula, were losing its religious influence.

In India itself Hinduism was undergoing an ordeal. As we shall soon see, Buddhism and Jainism flourished also in some parts of India; communities of Nestorian (Syrian) Christians and of Jews continued in Cochin on the Malabar coast, and a group of Persian Zoroastrians, known as Parsi (Parsee), survived in Gujarat. (In the seventeenth century the Parsis moved into the Bombay area.) Besides these old competitors Hinduism faced a newer and more militant faith—Islam. Although Islam had been known in Sind and in several mercantile cities for some time, not until Muslim conquerors established themselves in north India and the Deccan in the thirteenth and fourteenth centuries respectively did the full force of this new faith make itself felt in India. The invaders destroyed Hindu temples and seats of learning and instituted various forms of persecution but were unable to destroy the popular faith or the influence of the Brahman caste, and in the end Hinduism emerged, if not unscathed, at least unconquered. The modern Islamic state of Pakistan in the Punjab and Bengal, along with a numerous Muslim minority in the Indian Union, bears testimony to the extent of the lasting inroads of Islam into Hinduism.

Hinduism was the traditional religion of India, but in a larger sense it was the way of life, the *dharma* (law, custom, and duty—social, religious, and cosmic), of the Hindus. It was not primarily a proselytizing faith; one either was born into the faith or entered it as a member of a group that through time had accommodated itself to Hindu ways, had become a caste, and had found a Brahman to be its spiritual leader. Since freedom of religious speculation was unlimited, Hinduism developed elaborate but very diverse theological or philosophic systems. A tolerant polytheistic creed, it permitted many varieties of religious experience. Beliefs ranged from animistic magic to the absolute principle of *brahman* (or *atman*), 'eternal, unbound by time, space, and causality, consisting of pure existence, consciousness, and bliss'.[6] Practices varied from sex rites to puritanical morality; rituals from the worship of demons, spirits, and godlings to abstract monotheistic ceremonies;[7] and theology from essentially atheistic to devout theistic concepts. Among the basic requirements of the creed were (1) acceptance of the Vedas as revelation and (2) deference to the Brahmans as spiritual leaders, together with (3) the caste system associated with Brahman leadership. Exceptions, however, could be found even to these requirements.

In 1300 Hinduism was already divided into sects, generally devoted to one of the three principal divinities—Shiva the destroyer, Vishnu the preserver, and the Great Goddess Shākti. All sects, however, shared at least some of the following tenets: (1) faith in a world soul (*brahman*) or supreme being from which everything comes and to which everything returns, and in the union of the soul or self (*atman*) with this universal soul or supreme being; (2) the doctrine of metempsychosis—i.e. the rebirth, reincarnation, or transmigration (*samsāra*) of the soul from one existence to another; (3) the concept of *karma*, or the belief that the sum-total of good and bad deeds in this and all past

existences determines the condition of the next rebirth; (4) the hope of salvation, or escape (*moksha*) from the chain of rebirths, attainable through
knowledge, good works, asceticism, devotion (*bhakti*), or some combination
of them; (5) conviction of the efficacy of ritualism and hence of sacrifices,
pilgrimages, ceremonials, invocations of the deity, and the use of chants, spells,
and charms (*mantras*); (6) adherence to a rather elaborate ethical system,
which was so intimately tied up with the rules of caste and other externals
and with the aim of self-mastery as a step towards individual liberation that it
sometimes lost much of its moral tone (so that the gods were not constrained
by common standards, and temple prostitution was not considered evil if
sanctioned by caste rules or connected with the worship of some deity);
(7) respect for the contemplative ascetic (*sannyāsī*, or 'renouncer'), who was
held up as the ideal to pursue after one's duties as husbandman and householder had been discharged; (8) acceptance of the unity and sacredness of all
life with the consequent ideal of non-injury (*ahimsā*) to all living things,
especially the cow; and (9) worship of the reproductive forces, expressed in
ways such as phallic symbols, adoration of female deities, and erotic religious
literature.

The literature still sacred to Hinduism in 1300 was voluminous. It was
divided into works of three general categories: *shruti* (revelation), *smriti*
(sacred tradition), and the so-called 'later works'. The *shruti* consisted of the
four Vedas, which, despite their divine origin, were of much less importance
in our period than the other two categories.

The *smriti* for the most part consisted of certain compendia of highly
compressed aphorisms (*sūtras*), two great epics, certain legal books (*dharma-
shāstras*), and the versified works known as *purānas*. The oldest of these were
the prose *sūtras*, of which two call for specific attention: the *Brahma-sūtra* (or
Vedānta-sūtra), which epitomized the doctrine of monistic idealism, and the
Bhakti-sūtra, which set forth the idea of loving devotion to a personal god.
The two epics presented much of Hindu mythology: the *Mahābhārata* was
significant to most Hindu sects, and the *Rāmāyana* was of special interest for
the worship of Vishnu (Vishnuism or Vaishnavism). The *Bhāgavad-gītā* ('Song
of the Adorable'), one of the late sections of the *Mahābhārata*, was also
principally a Vishnuite work. The *dharmashāstras* dealt with civil and religious
obligations, the *Mānava Dharmashāstra*, or '*Laws of Manu*', being particularly
respected. The more than sixty *purānas* were the real scriptures of sectarian
Hinduism; the eighteen principal ones had been written before 1300, but
some were written later.

The 'later works' (some of which, however, were older than some of the
purānas) fell into three groups. The first, comprised of many and diverse
semi-secret sectarian manuals usually in Sanskrit, were generally known as
tantras or *agamas*. Some were composed after 1300, but their general concepts
were as old as Hinduism itself. They dealt with mythology, philosophy, the
dharma ('duty') of householders, and primarily the ceremonials and ways of

communicating with or controlling the supernatural. They expounded a system of initiation rites, drink, foods, spells, chants, charms, formulas, mystic diagrams, physical and psychic training, meditation, yoga practices, and sexual passion designed to bring the individual stage by stage to unity with *brahman*. A teacher was regarded as necessary for learning this system properly. Some of these practices were functionally analogous to Christian sacraments, but others were not.

A second group of the 'later works' comprised the poetic devotional and philosophical literature of south India written in Tamil. The *Nālāyira Prabandham*, a collection of lyrical hymns, was Vishnuite. A similar group of devotional poetry relating to Shivaism (the worship of Shiva) was collected in the *Tirumurai*, or *Drāvida-shruti* (Tamil Veda), to which, in the thirteenth and fourteenth centuries, was added a group of theological and instructional treatises known as the *Siddhānta-shāstras* or *Shaiva Siddhānta*.

A third group of 'later works' was the writings of the *āchāryas* ('systematic teachers'). These works were usually in the form of commentaries on older scriptures by leading theologians and sectarian leaders (see Chapters VI and VII). Among the most important commentaries clearly composed before 1300 (see Volume III and below) were those by Shankara, which were non-sectarian; those by Rāmānuja and Madhva, which were Vishnuite; those by Shrīkantha (Nīlakantha), which were Shivaite; and the *Gīta Govinda* ('*Song of Krishna*') by Jayadeva (c. 1170), which narrated the courtship by Krishna (an incarnation of Vishnu) of Rādhā, his beloved.

No ecclesiastical organization of the Western fashion united Hinduism's holy places and holy men. Nor did any of its three great cults—Vishnuism, Shivaism, and Shāktism—have an over-all hierarchical system. Only the sects and mendicant orders into which the great cults were subdivided were organized, and they, like some of the later Protestant sects of Christianity, were as a rule more or less loosely organized. Sub-sects had arisen that were generally independent of the parent body or autonomous. Many temples, shrines, and monasteries were completely independent, counting upon their own endowments and earning capacity. Others belonged to one or another sect, monastic order, or school and were under the general supervision of its head. Despite this loose organization Hinduism had a remarkably cohesive power, probably attributable to the Hindu social system, which tied religion, family, and caste intimately together and accepted the social, religious, and philosophical leadership of the Brahmans. Throughout the centuries the Brahmans maintained their claim to intellectual and religious leadership over the warrior and lower castes, but in the process they admitted into Hinduism almost every sort of religious or philosophical belief and practice that would accept Brahman supremacy.

If religious organization was weak, religious leadership was not. The Brahmans were the religious leaders; yet all Brahmans were not priests in the technical sense, nor were all priests Brahmans. Priests (*pūjārīs*) officiated in the temples, but these priests were not always held in the highest esteem, and their posts were often filled by low-grade Brahmans or by non-Brahmans. Some important public religious ceremonials outside the temples and many others connected with family observances could be performed only with the aid of Brahmans. In north India, generally speaking, any Brahman could perform such functions, but in most of south India only certain Brahmans would suffice. Most villages and well-to-do families and all Hindu princes had a domestic chaplain (*purohita*) to administer the necessary domestic ritual, and these *purohitas* were Brahmans. Hindu custom also required that neophites have a guru, or religious teacher or sponsor, and gurus were also to be found in most villages and attached to well-to-do families. Gurus were not all Brahmans. Gurus, like the *purohitas*, were greatly reverenced, although the amount of guidance one received from them might vary from the most perfunctory instruction to long years of intimate teaching.

Ascetics also were nearly universally admired as holy men (*sādhus*) and were held up as models. Long before 1300 Hinduism had borrowed from Buddhism the idea of the organized monastic group. Many monastic orders were open to all, regardless of caste. While nearly every sect had its special monastic orders, numerous orders had no connection with any sect. The sectarian orders were more systematically supervised and generally had monastic centres (*maths*) from which the monks set out on their pilgrimages. Most of the non-sectarian orders revered Shiva as the great ascetic, although some sought only the philosophical idea of *brahman*. Begging, contemplation, renunciation, wandering, and various other austerities (*tapas*) were common to nearly all groups, but celibacy was not universal. Some ascetics practised yoga, while others wrote theological or philosophical treatises. Some were ignorant, while others were learned. Some went naked, while others wore simple clothing. Some practised moderate austerities, while others went to such lengths as holding their hands above their heads until they could no longer be moved. The ultimate objective of all true ascetics was *moksha* (escape or salvation) through enlightenment or union with the divine.

*   *   *

Smārta and Bhakti Cults

All of the important Hindu cults and many major sects of later times were already in existence by 1300. They may be classified into three divisions: (*a*) the Smārtas, or traditionalists, (*b*) the theistic cults, which believed in salvation through *bhakti* (devotion), and (*c*) miscellaneous folk and local cults (not counting the non-Hindu tribal cults and the cults that had dissociated themselves from Hinduism). Perhaps the majority of Hindus were not specifically associated with any of the several major cults but practised an ancestral and household worship and adored one or several folk or local deities, while also paying respect to Shiva, Vishnu, or Shākti as they chose.

The Smārtas accepted and attempted to follow the Vedas and the great

body of sacred tradition (*smriti*). Intellectual descendants of ancient Brahmanism, they were essentially polytheists who accepted the monistic pantheism
of Vedānta philosophy (see Chapter VI). They were probably more numerous
then than now, and their core then as now probably consisted of the Smārta
Brahmans, centred in the Sringeri Monastery of Mysore, founded by Shankara. In domestic life and public ceremonials they aimed to follow *smriti*
ritual and practice. Animal or pseudo-animal sacrifices were performed in
open places without the use of images. Although a majority of the Smārtas
perhaps considered Shiva their favourite deity, they regarded Brahmā, Vishnu,
and Shiva alike as mere manifestations, not themselves eternal, of the impersonal, omnipotent, absolute, eternal *brahman*. For the Smārtas, *moksha* was
attainable through proper ceremonial asceticism and knowledge, and not
through emotional surrender to the divine. Their monastic adherents were
celibate, as were their great teachers.

The theistic cults, the Bhakti, were the most numerous. Their acceptance
by ancient Brahmanism betokened concessions to popular needs and to the
competition of Buddhism and Jainism. They offered a simpler, a less philosophical and ritualistic approach to religion and an easier route to salvation
than did the Smārtas. Emotional faith in the saving grace of a particular
deity was the chief article of their credo. Their separate deities possessed all
the qualities of the absolute *brahman* but were more personal. A Bhakti cult
did not deny the existence of competing deities but explained or accepted the
competitors as mere manifestations of its own omnipotent deity. The principal
Bhakti cults were those of Shiva, Vishnu, and Shākti.

*   *   *

Shivaite Sects

Shivaism was the worship of Shiva as the supreme lord of the universe, the
power that destroys and recreates, and of his wife, Pārvatī or Umā. Both took
other forms and names as well. Shiva was known also as Mahādeva (the great
lord), Bhairava (the terrible one), and Pashupati (lord of cattle—i.e. souls),
and was depicted in different forms—as a seated thinker, an ascetic smeared
with ashes, or an ecstatic dancer, often with three eyes or five faces and four
arms. He was generally represented and worshipped in the form of a *linga*
(a stone pillar, originally having phallic connotations), often combined with a
yoni (symbol of the female). He lived in the Himalayas and presided over a
heaven where his faithful worshippers, safe from transmigration, dwelt with
him in bliss. Shivaites were generally vegetarian. The theology of the major
sects of Shivaism was found in the writings of various northern teachers and
the *Siddhānta-shāstras* of south India (see Chapter V).

By 1300 practically all of the sects of Shivaism were already in existence.
The cult may be divided into northern and southern branches. Northern
Shivaism, the older, was essentially unorganized, consisting of local Shivaite
temple groups that adhered to common doctrines and practices. Its scriptures

were in Sanskrit. By 1300 it was already subjected to persecution and competition from Islamic invaders. Southern Shivaism, or the Siddhānta school, on the other hand, was by 1300 in the process of developing an effective organization and formulating a specific theology. Its canon, the *Shaiva Siddhānta*, was in Tamil; otherwise its doctrines and practices were not essentially different from those of Northern Shivaism. In 1300 it was engaged in a vigorous if essentially peaceful effort to win over the Jains and Buddhists of the south.

The Vīrashaivas were one of the offshoots of Shivaism. Heretical Shivaites, they were in revolt against the caste and ritual system, and hence the authority, of the orthodox Brahmans. Brahmans as well as lower castes took part in this revolt. The moderate among the heretics were known as the Ārādhyas, and the radicals as the Lingāyats ('*Linga* Wearers'). The Lingāyats are sometimes supposed to have completely broken with the orthodox Brahmans in the twelfth century, but more likely the schism was a gradual process extending into the fourteenth century. Although in theory the Lingāyats accepted the Vedas while rejecting later Brahmanic literature, two *purānas* in Karanese, bearing the names of their reputed founders (Bāsava and his nephew Channabāsava), became their chief scriptures. They rejected caste, repudiated sacrifice and other orthodox rites, allowed widows to remarry, did not insist on child marriage, and denied that birth, death, and menstruation defiled or that prayers for the dead were necessary. They were, after a fashion, puritans, since they forbade the eating of meat or the drinking of spirits and insisted on a rigid moral code. They rejected the use of images but worshipped Shiva in the form of a *linga*, which they always carried, generally around the neck. Theologically they took a position of qualified monism (see Chapter VI). They were divided into *jangams* or *āchāryas* (priests), laity, and followers. The married *jangams* served as ordinary priests, while the celibate lived as monks in *maths*, from which they went out as itinerant ascetics. The sect, centring in Kalyan in the Deccan, had a close-knit organization.

The Pāshupatas, another of the lesser sects of Shivaism, were the remnant of an ancient north Indian sect that had spread to the south. Their theology was more distinctly dualistic than was general among the Shivaites. As their name indicates, they emphasized both *pati* ('lord'), the lord Shiva as direct, universal, and absolute cause, and *pashu* ('cattle'), the souls or things caused by and entirely dependent upon the lord. They held that the individual soul was effective only in so far as it acted in conformity with the predetermination of Shiva and that, once saved, it remained essentially distinct from Shiva. The sect's practices included singing, dancing, gesticulation, and ecstatic acts.

Two other lesser sects of Shivaism, known as the Kashmir sect, seem to have been confined almost entirely to monastic pundits.[8] They were the Spanda and the Pratyabhijna, each founded by a different leader but not much different otherwise. Essentially philosophic in tone, they consisted of monistic idealists, for whom Shiva was the only reality, all else being unreal apart from him. The individual soul as part of Shiva was real, but its reality was obscured by *māyā* ('illusion'). Meditation helped the soul to realize its true identity with Shiva.

Numerous other orders engaged in begging and ascetic practices of varying severity. Most of them operated from some monastic headquarters. They wore either a distinctive garb or no clothes at all, carried distinguishing marks or symbols, practised special initiation rites, and buried rather than cremated their dead. The most moderate, best regulated, and most intellectual of the orders were the Sannyāsīs ('Renouncers') and the Ḍaṇḍīs ('Staff Bearers'), who traced their origin to Shankara and considered themselves followers of his monistic philosophy. Although they were generally attached to Shiva, some were Vishnuites. Some of the Sannyāsī groups accepted members from all castes, but the Ḍaṇḍīs were restricted to Brahmans. The professional Sannyāsī should be distinguished from the ordinary Brahman householder *sannyāsī* (mentioned above), who renounced the world late in life. Likewise, some Yogis were organized in Shivaite orders (although the term *yoga*, properly speaking, applied to a widespread system of self-control and meditation and not alone to a specific ascetic order). The Kāpālikas and the Kālāmukhas were ancient sects, whose extreme practices had been denounced by Shankara. They worshipped Bhairava the terrible one. The Kāpālikas used human skulls as eating dishes and ate the flesh or ashes of corpses.

*   *   *

Vishnuite Sects

If Shiva was a terrible god of power and force, Vishnu in contrast was a benevolent preserver. Vishnuism was the worship not only of Vishnu and two of his *avatāras* ('incarnations'),[9] Krishna and Rāma, but also of his beautiful and benevolent wives Lakshmī (or Shrī) and Rukminī. Vishnu was the adorable lord (Bhagavān), creator, destroyer, and preserver of the universe. He had been a minor solar deity in the *Rig Veda*, while Krishna and Rāma were deified heroes. Krishna, although in an older form a heroic warrior, appeared besides as a youthful cowherd beloved by the neighbouring milkmaids, especially Rādhā, who in time rose to divine equality with her lover, their ardour symbolizing the soul's passion for God. Rāma was the personification of chivalry, and his wife Sītā of chastity. In 1300, specific Rāma and Rādhā cults had not yet become widely popular. In some quarters Buddha too was regarded as an incarnation of Vishnu—a clear attempt to attract Buddhists to Vishnu. Vishnu, Krishna, and Rāma each presided over his own heaven. Vishnuites were strict vegetarians.

The Vishnuite sects had all developed out of an earlier Vishnuism, which had originated in north India and then spread to the south. Of the earlier Vishnuites, the Bhāgavatas, who worshipped Vishnu as their adorable lord (Bhagavān) under the names of Vāsudeva (son of Surya the sun) and Nārāyana (mover in the water), were perhaps the most important. In 1300 many little-organized Bhāgavata groups and some earlier sects still survived, and the four main sects (*sampradāyas*) of present-day Vishnuism were perhaps already in existence. These four were (1) the Shrī-Vishnuite sect or Rāmānujas, (2) the Brāhma sect or Mādhvas, (3) the Shanākadi sect or Nimāvats, and (4) the Rudra sect.

The Vishnuism of these sects was a theistic reaction to the Vedānta ('completion of the Veda') philosophy systematized and popularized by the ninth-century philosopher Shankara. The Vedānta philosophy was based on the *Upanishads*, the philosophical treatises that come at the end of the Vedas. Shankara taught an absolute monistic doctrine known as *advaita* (see Chapters VI and VII): nothing exists except *brahman*, which is identical with the individual self or soul, and our phenomenal world is only *māyā* (illusion, a world of appearances), created in sport and without purpose by *brahman*. This philosophy left little place for a warmer theism, for homage to a personal God who saved individual souls.

The first effective champion of the theistic groups was Rāmānuja (*c.* 1100), who developed a qualified monism (*Vishistādvaita*), which made room for the eternal individual soul and a personal god while remaining within the framework of the Vedānta philosophy. For most Vishnuites, *brahman* was in some way identified with God (Vishnu), from whom the universe, souls, and matter came into being. Thus the Vishnuite sects were imperfectly mono-theistic, reaching from pantheism at one extreme to polytheism at the other. All worshipped the Supreme Being (Vishnu) under various names. All rejected the sacrificialism of traditional Brahmanism as the basis of salvation and substituted in its stead knowledge and meditation accompanied by *bhakti* (or emotional homage) to a personal God, who repaid devotion with help and loving grace.

The Shrī-Vishnuite sect (Rāmānujas), established by Rāmānuja, was the first of the four great systematically organized popular sects of modern Vishnuism. It was based on his qualified monist philosophy, but its ritual and ceremony were less emotional than those of some later Vishnuite sects. Rāmānuja is said to have founded seven hundred maths (colleges or religious centres) and eighty-nine hereditary abbotships (since members of his order were allowed to marry). The sect accepted Hindu institutions, including the caste system, as part of the tradition supposedly revealed to it by Shrī, consort of Vishnu. It revered Vishnu most often under the old names of Nārāyana and Vāsudeva. A fuller account of its theology will be given in Chapter VI. By 1300 the sect was in the process of dividing into two branches.

The Brāhma sect (Mādhvas), founded by Madhva during the thirteenth century, spread especially in south India. Its doctrines were supposed to have been revealed by Brahmā. Madhva developed a dualistic philosophy (*dvaita*) based upon the *Upanishads* and so remained within the Vedānta system, but he was continuously in conflict with the monistic followers of Shankara. The

Mādhvas generally called God Vishnu or Nārāyana; Brahmā, the creator, and Vāyu, wind or spirit, were his sons. Salvation was believed impossible except through Vāyu, one of whose incarnations was Madhva. Members of the sect honoured Vishnu by taking his names, by being branded with his discus and conch shell, and by worshipping him with their voices, their bodies (giving alms), and their hearts (showing love, faith, and mercy).

The Shanākadi sect (Nimāvats) was devoted to the worship of Vishnu in the form of Krishna. It was founded by the *āchārya* Nimbārka, who is generally placed in the twelfth century but more probably lived in the fourteenth, for the later dating of the rise of the Nimāvats fits better into the general history of the Krishna-Rādhā worship.[10] According to Nimāvat doctrines those who felt their helplessness and completely surrendered in faith and devotion to Krishna received his saving grace.

The Rudra sect worshipped Vishnu in the form of Krishna, although its revelation was believed to have come originally not from Vishnu but from Rudra (i.e. Shiva). The *āchārya* Vishnusvāmī is generally said to have been the founder of the sect. According to one tradition, he lived in the thirteenth century, but another would seem to fit Indian religious development better. It places the founding of the Rudra sect in the fifteenth century, when Vishnusvāmī allegedly moved from south India to the Gujarat area and began to preach; the father of a later religious leader, Vallabha (see Chapter V) is supposed to have migrated north with Vishnusvāmī, and Vishnusvāmī's philosophic position is conceded to have been similar to Vallabha's pure monism (*shuddhādvaita*). Vallabha would thus appear to have been at least the moulder, if not the actual founder, of the sect.

* * *

Shāktism

Another of the great Bhakti cults was Shāktism, or goddess worship. *Shakti* connotes, among other things, the power of the universe as represented in the consort (*shakti*) of a god. It was identified also with *prakriti* (nature), *māyā* (the illusory world of the senses), and the energy, coexistent with *brahman*, that creates and destroys. Goddesses (Shaktis) were sometimes beneficent, but most often were awe-inspiring, demanding bloody sacrifices, especially of human males, and sexual rites. The most popular Shaktis were the consorts of Shiva—in such terrible forms as Kālī the black destroyer, Durgā the inaccessible slayer of demons, and Bhairavī the terrible. For this reason, Shāktism has sometimes been considered a part of Shivaism, but it is actually a separate cult. By 1300, goddess worship was found in all parts of India, but its centres were Bengal, Bihar, and Assam.

The rise of Shāktism was associated with the increase of Tantrism (see below) and the decline of Buddhism. Shāktism represented the amalgamation of numerous local goddess cults, brought about by time and the ingenious speculations of Brahmans presented in the *Tantras*, the sacred literature of

Shāktism. The amalgamation, however, was imperfect; Shāktism lacked formal organization, and its adherents (Shāktas) worshipped at local shrines dedicated to particular goddesses or groups of goddesses. The village mother goddesses of south India, the mothers of Gujarat, and the *Shaktis* of Vishnuism were but imperfectly integrated into the system. No single deity dominated the cult as in Vishnuism and Shivaism.

The *Tantras* represented for Shāktism the only road to salvation. They prescribed rituals, ceremonials, formulas, and practices aimed at propitiating, beseeching, and compelling the goddess. Goats and other animals were sacrificed publicly; one's own blood might be offered; but most pleasing to the goddess was a willing human male. Ritualistic uses included domestic worship of the nude image of a goddess or of a nude woman, and under certain conditions the sex act formed part of the ritual. Other uses were of mystic diagrams (*yantras*), combinations of words and sounds believed to have magical power (*mantras*), certain gestures, actions, and patterns of touch (*mudrās*), amulets, meditation, and yoga. Some of the yoga, intended to bring about union with Shakti, was perhaps based on influencing the vagus nerve and hence affecting the nervous system and bodily controls. Sometimes the ritual called for such practices as the manipulation of a corpse in a graveyard at night.

The *Tantras* held up Shāktism as a higher stage of religious development than Vedaism, Vishnuism, or Shivaism. Only after the aspirant had passed these lower stages did he enter the first real Shākta stage of development, called *dakshina* ('right-hand'). In that stage, through meditation and certain rituals and practices, including animal sacrifices, he might begin to understand the nature of the goddess. The next stage, called *vāma* ('left-hand'), was secret and required special initiation and the guidance of a guru. Here passion was directed 'upwards and inwards' and transformed into power. The fetters of ignorance, fear, caste, and ordinary conventions were cut away by the five-elements ritual (*pañcatattva*) and by certain yoga and other esoteric practices. The *pañcatattva* involved the ritualistic partaking of wine, meat, fish, and parched grain and of sexual intercourse at midnight. Several other stages followed, until the adept reached the *kaula* stage, where he became a *divya*, a divine being united with the goddess—an all-seeing, all-knowing *brahman*, who retained merely the outward form of a man.

The ultimate objective of these practices was liberation through the attainment of union with the goddess, but lesser objectives were also sought. Most of the sacrifices, and perhaps some of the sexual rituals, seem to have been primarily propitiatory, aimed at inducing the goddess to be kind and helpful rather than cruel and dangerous. This emphasis on the Shakti's terrible nature no doubt reflected a realistic appraisal of the tragic conditions of life, and Shāktism apparently flourished best in times of greatest trouble. Another objective seems to have been to gain the Shakti's aid in the destruction of one's enemies. The sexual practices, while undoubtedly reflecting older fertility rites, appear to have had an escapist component. The cult's minimization of caste, its generally favourable attitude towards women, and its emotion-packed public festivals appealed to the oppressed. The Shāktas usually were well-to-do householders, only a few adept being ascetics. Most Shāktas seem to have been guided by their local gurus and affiliated with particular temples honouring particular goddesses.

*　　*　　*

Folk and Local Cults

Alongside the major cults flourished a number of folk and local cults. They centred around mother goddesses, rivers, mountains, other geographical phenomena, disease, heroes, animals, and the patron gods of villages and particular professions. Some of these local deities had been more or less identified with Shiva, Vishnu, or a Shakti, but perhaps the majority had not. Several local cults of Bengal were particularly noteworthy. They were folk cults associated with sex, magic, and agriculture, and with goddess, snake, and animal worship, mingled with elements of Tantric Buddhism. Their amalgamation with Vishnuism, Shivaism, and Shāktism continued throughout the period of our study. Local deities were held in great respect by most Hindus, even adherents of the great cults. Although the majority of Hindus paid deference to the principal deities, the local cults provided a religious outlet second in importance only to the domestic rituals.

Hinduism was elastic and thus able to absorb a considerable variety of creeds. Nevertheless, several creeds of India remained independent, and today millions of Indians are still classified as tribals—that is, belonging to tribal groups not yet integrated either in the Hindu caste system or in the international religions. Each of these tribals had its own gods and religious practices. In 1300 they must have had as adherents a greater proportion of the population than today.

*　　*　　*

Jainism

Except for Buddhism, among the native religions that had dissociated themselves from Hinduism Jainism was the only one of importance. In 1300 although suffering from Mohammedan persecution and vigorous Hindu competition, numerous Jain communities continued in northeastern India, Gujarat, the Maratha country, and the Deccan, and in the fourteenth century they were well treated in the Vijayanagar Empire. Jainism was atheistic in that it denied the existence of a supreme being and regarded gods as other living beings subject to transmigration and *karma*. The Jain world, self-existent and eternal, was composed of souls, matter, and other separate and eternal substances. Souls occurred in all animate and inanimate matter and were basically free, but through a tendency to action and passion they followed false ways and acquired bad *karma*. The way to salvation (*nirvāna*) was to end the accumulation of bad *karma* and annihilate what had accumulated. This goal was reached by right faith, right knowledge, and right conduct. Right conduct involved the five vows (not to kill, not to speak untruths, not to take anything that was not given, not to be unchaste, and not to take pleasure in external objects) and asceticism (repentance, humility, meditation, the suppression of desire, self-denial, and self-mortification). Asceticism might culminate in death by voluntary starvation, which, if properly achieved, destroyed *karma* and led to *nirvāna*, a realm above the heavens of the greatest gods, where freed souls resided in happiness beyond compare.

The Jains were divided into laity and ascetics (both male and female). Modifications of the rigid rules were allowed for the laity, who supported the ascetics. The ascetics spent most of their time on pilgrimages and took extreme precautions to avoid injury to life other than their own. Since agriculture and other professions that might involve injury to living things were considered unbecoming though necessary, laymen were chiefly merchants.

The Jains were divided into two major sects: the Digambara, who believed in nudity for its ascetics, and the Shvetāmbara, who wore white clothes and believed women might attain *nirvāna*. Each sect had a separate canon (*Siddhānta*). The Jains had well-ordered animal hospitals, schools, rest-houses for their ascetics, and temples adorned with figures of their saints. Worship was simple, consisting of offerings to the saints of flowers, incense, lights, and praise. A long line of patriarchs had succeeded Mahāvīra, the probable founder of the religion, a contemporary of Buddha, but sacerdotalism was not strong, and the real strength of the group resided in the tight organization of the laity.

*   *   *

Hindu Ritual

Hindu worship differed materially from that of the Western creeds, but in 1300 the difference was probably not so great as now, since Protestant congregationalism has emphasized the worshippers' participation.[11] Hindu congregational participation was definitely subordinate to the service performed by the priest. There was no temple preaching, but preaching by wandering ascetics and revivalists was common. Public worship comprised regular temple ceremonies, festivals, pilgrimages, and the adoration of certain animals and rivers. The gods and their attendants were worshipped in the form of consecrated images or symbols housed in an inner sanctuary of the temple. Worship (*pūjā*) normally took place daily in the temples. The simplest form of priestly ritual was practised in Shivaite temples; leaves or flowers were placed on the *linga*, and holy water was poured over it to the accompaniment of chants or readings from sacred books. A common ritual treated the god in his image as an honoured human. He was awakened, bathed, dressed, fed, allowed to nap at the usual hours, otherwise waited upon, and finally put to bed at night; all this activity was accompanied by appropriate gestures, lights, chants, *mantras*, and scripture readings. In many south Indian temples the ritual included dances and songs by temple dancing girls. In Shākta temples animal sacrifice was normal and in Shivaite temples occasional but in Vishnuite temples unknown. Cows, monkeys, and snakes were especially holy and were not to be molested or injured. Cowdung was used for many ceremonial purposes.

The god held court at certain times, which were the most appropriate for individual worshippers to pay homage. The devout usually entered the shrine individually, rang a bell, washed his hands, bowed or prostrated himself, presented his offering, recited a prayer or incantation, made a personal petition, and backed away. In some temples daily, in others at less regular intervals, and particularly in Vishnuite and Shākta temples, a type of worship took place in which priest and congregation took part. Such congregational participation involved offerings, music of gongs and drums, hymns, prayers and incantations, flaming lights, dancing and singing by the temple dancers, acts of homage, the distribution or eating of consecrated food, and ablutions in the sacred tank or pond. In Vishnuite and Shivaite temples offerings usually consisted of flowers, leaves, rice, oil, perfume, water, and money. Wine and sandalwood as well as animals and the devotee's own blood were favourite offerings to the Shaktis.

Numerous festivals and holy days provided occasions for special ceremonies and rejoicing. The gods were taken in processions through the streets or into the countryside and received offerings and adoration as they went. Special religious ceremonials open to all were performed by the priests on the premises of some wealthy worshipper. Sectarian lines were largely disregarded on festival occasions, and spectators thronged the temples. During the ten-day Durgā (Shakti) festival in September great crowds witnessed the decapitation of large numbers of goats in the goddess's temples. Pilgrimages were an integral part of Hindu religious life. Holy places like Benares and Puri were continually crowded by pilgrims with offerings. To bathe in or drink the waters of holy rivers like the Ganges was deemed particularly efficacious for washing away sin or effecting cures.

Public religious observances were of much less importance than those performed in the home. Domestic rites consisted of (1) traditional ceremonies associated with caste and obligatory for all caste Hindus, (2) special household obligations for those who belonged to certain sects, and (3) ancestor worship. In a sense, all caste rules were religious obligations, but some of them had a more explicit religious bearing than others.

Every family that could afford it had a private chapel or domestic shrine, where the gods—Brahmā, Vishnu, Shiva, and others special to the household —were worshipped. Prayers, food, and flowers were offered to the gods before meals. Specific rituals were prescribed for rising, cleaning the teeth, bathing, greeting the sun, preparing the hair, putting on sacred marks, meditating, reading sacred books, eating, and other daily acts, each accompanied by appropriate gestures and prayers or incantation. Fasts were required twice a month as well as on special occasions. Twelve household sacraments were provided in the ancient Manu code, but undoubtedly by 1300 many observed some of these only loosely. The more important ones related to birth, name-giving, food-giving, tonsure, betrothal, initiation (when a boy began his education), marriage, and death. All required the service of a private domestic chaplain (*purohita*) or the village Brahman. These household requirements varied in some details from caste to caste. Since their full performance needed four or five hours daily and was very costly, their abbreviation was necessary for many Brahmans, to say nothing of the poorer castes.

For the separate sectarians special rites replaced some of the above ceremonies. Shivaites adored a small stone *linga*, Vishnuites a stone *sālagrāma* (a black ammonite with spirals) or a *tulsī* plant, and Shāktas a diagrammatic *yoni*. Some rites in the private worship of the goddess were very elaborate, including breath control and burnt offerings.

Ancestor worship was a fundamental part of the Hindu religion. Elaborate funerals included cremation and the offering of enough food for the ten days considered necessary to transform the departed soul from a dangerous ghost into a proper ancestral spirit. After these obsequies, which were regarded as inauspicious, came the auspicious *shrāddha*, or act-of-faith ceremonies. The male relatives of a head of a household for three generations before and three generations after him were called his *sapindas*, and all surviving *sapindas* of the head of the deceased's household normally took part in the *shrāddha*, together with Brahmans, friends, and local notables. The central feature of the *shrāddha* was the offering of food to all the deceased within the *sapinda* circle. The ceremony was repeated monthly for a year and thereafter annually, and a feast regularly followed. Rites like these were deemed essential to the well-being of one's ancestors and hence of the living, because ancestors, if properly treated, would give aid and protection. The ceremonial of ancestor worship solidified and strengthened the family but usually was costly and helped to impoverish many.

BUDDHISM

The movement traditionally ascribed to Gautama (the Buddha) in the sixth century BC was a reaction against contemporary religious practices in India. It rejected the pretensions of the Brahmans, sacrificial rites, and extreme forms of asceticism in favour of a 'middle way'. It preached a high standard of moral conduct and laid special emphasis on gentleness, impersonal love and kindness, and the sanctity of life. Its approach to salvation was essentially personal; salvation could be attained here and now through individual initiative and effort by anyone who had the stamina, courage, and capacity to follow and understand the programme of conduct and training outlined by the

'Awakened', the Enlightened One, the Buddha. It accepted the ideas of trans-migration and *karma*, *karma* being portrayed as a universal principle of causality by which any action inevitably caused an appropriate effect. It also denied the existence of the immutable soul or self (*atman*), i.e. of the soul as a permanent, unitary entity that would be reborn, and advanced instead the idea of *anatta* (non-soul or non-self), in which existence or consciousness was conceived as a constantly changing combination of material and mental qualities (*skandhas*),[12] which were reconstituted in another form after death as determined by its *karma*, much as one wave of the ocean grows out of another in a varying but endless process.

The Buddha had proclaimed the Four Noble Truths. They were (1) that existence was suffering, (2) that suffering originated in desire and the thirst for life, its wants and ambitions, all of which, by *karma*, led to rebirth, (3) that suffering ceased with the cessation of desire, and (4) that the Eight-Fold Path—the middle path between indulgence and austerity—led to the cessation of desire. The Eight-Fold Path consisted of right belief, right resolve, right speech, right behaviour, right occupation, right effort, right contemplation or mindfulness, and right concentration or rapture. The last involved mental application and yoga practices. The continuation of desire and of rebirth could be ended, and enlightenment (*nirvāna*)[13] attained, only by properly following the Four Noble Truths. *Nirvāna* thus meant the extinction of desire and the attainment of an infinite state of calm joy and inner peace. The understanding *arhat* (disciple of Buddha) might personally attain *nirvāna* by a rigorous following of the Eight-Fold Path, and the way to pursue the Eight-Fold Path was to become a member of the *sangha* (Buddhist monastic order).

As time went on, Gautama's doctrines were elaborated by accretions from Hindu and Far Eastern practices and by the speculations of fertile Indian minds, and were organized into elaborate religious systems. The three main systems, Hīnayāna, Mahāyāna, and Tantric, despite their wide divergencies, shared some basic tenets and practices. The most important were (1) belief in Buddha and enlightened beings (Buddhas) who are superior to all deities and from time to time appear on earth to teach *dharma*, the eternal law or way; (2) the idea of transmigration; (3) the concept of *karma*; (4) the doctrine of *anatta* (non-soul), although the distinction made between soul (self) and conscious-ness (existence) was such as to render *anatta* of no practical significance in ordinary life; (5) the conviction that the aim of life was to escape re-birth and attain *nirvāna*; (6) a highly ethical code, which often, however, became corrupted in peculiar ways; (7) gentleness, kindness, helpfulness, and respect for the sanctity of all life, although the sacredness of human life in certain local practices was almost forgotten; (8) emphasis on monastic life to an extent that made monastic groups the centre of Buddhism; (9) lay participation in the Buddhist ideal, which varied greatly from country to country but everywhere failed to integrate the laity effectively; (10) a democratic and equalitarian attitude, which helped to promote Buddhism's popularity; and (11) tolerance towards and readiness to adopt local practices and ideas, which facilitated Buddhism's spread to many lands.

*   *   *

Main Systems of Buddhism

Around 1300 Buddhism was still divided into three main systems. Hīnayāna (Little Vehicle) Buddhism, also called Pali or Southern Buddhism, was the oldest and simplest of them. It emphasized self-centred discipline and knowledge, epitomized in the ideal of the *arhat*, who aimed at personal salvation and enlightenment (*nirvāna*) by means of monastic life. Mahāyāna (Great Vehicle) Buddhism, also called Northern Buddhism, was a later form; it was more theistic and devotional. It held up as the ideal the *bodhisattva*,[14] who aspires to salvation through many incarnations devoted to the salvation of others. Tantric Buddhism was a late form of the Mahāyāna, best represented by the Lamaism of Tibet. Emphasizing the esoteric and demoniac elements of Tantrism, it aimed at identification with or control of the deities through magic and self-hypnosis.

Hīnayāna Buddhism was found in south and southeast Asia, for the most part outside of India. It was predominant in southern Ceylon (the Sinhalese-speaking areas), Burma, Siam, Cambodia, and Laos, and some remnants still survived in south India, Java, and Sumatra. In these areas it had adopted certain native ideas and practices or was in the process of doing so; in some parts of Cambodia at least, it was also in competition with a still surviving Mahāyānaism assimilated with Shivaism. It was known but no longer actively practised in China, Korea, and Japan. Although it showed no great originality, it exhibited considerable ability to assimilate and expand, and remained vigorous if not creative.

China, Korea, and Japan were the major centres of the Mahāyāna. Although it had originated in north India and perhaps central Asia, China became its foster home, from which it spread to Korea, Japan, and Vietnam. In China Mahāyāna ideas had been supplemented and modified, and still further adaptations took place in Korea and Japan, but the essential characteristics of Indian Mahāyāna were preserved wherever it went. Although it never displaced native religious practices and had to compete with Confucianism and Taoism, it became a strong force in China; and in Japan for a time it bade fair (as we shall see) to absorb Shintoism. By 1300, however, the Mahāyāna, except in Japan, had lost its appeal and creative power, and in China it had definitely begun to decline before the assaults of a revived Confucianism (Neo-Confucianism). In central Asia, except at Turfan and perhaps other points, Buddhism had given way before the Muslim conquest.

Certain Tantric elements were to be found in the Mahāyāna, but as Buddhism lost ground in the land of its birth to Hinduism, the Tantric practices which affected both religions came to dominate Indian Buddhism's remaining centres. These were Bihar, Bengal, and Orissa. From these centres

Tantric Buddhism was transmitted to the East Indies, Nepal, and Tibet, where it assimilated various native practices. Tibetan Buddhism, or Lamaism, developing a missionary zeal, established centres in Mongol China, was accepted by Kublai Khan in 1261, and was thus enabled to expand among the Mongols. In southeast Asia a Tantric form of the Mahāyāna, apparently largely assimilated to Hinduism (principally Shivaism) and to native practices, was dominant in Malaya, Champa (Cochin-China), Sumatra, and Java and had centres of influence in other East Indian islands. Indian Buddhism barely survived the destruction of its centres by the Muslims, and after 1300 the more or less leaderless Tantrics of eastern India gradually degenerated, to be absorbed ultimately by Hinduism or converted to Islam.

Each of the major divisions of Buddhism had a canon of sacred literature, called *Tripitaka* (*Three Baskets*). The Hīnayāna *Tripitaka* was written in Pali, probably the literary language of Magadha, the scene of much of Gautama's activity, and it unquestionably constituted the oldest surviving Buddhists teachings. Its three sections or *pitakas* (baskets) were the *Vinaya* (rul es of the monastic order), the *Suttas* (largely sayings or dialogues attributed to the Buddha or his disciples), and the *Abhidhamma* (metaphysical and philosophical treatises), which were certainly later than the other parts. The Pali canon was accepted in Ceylon, Burma, Siam, and Cambodia.

Mahāyānaist literature, arising in north India and central Asia, was originally written in Sanskrit. No specifically Mahāyānaist canon probably ever was defined. Both Mahāyānaist and Hīnayānaist works in Sanskrit tended to disappear as Buddhism died out in India, and they have survived only partly in Nepal and central Asia, and in Chinese and Tibetan translations. The Chinese *Tripitaka* (*San Tsang*), which also served Japan, Vietnam, and Korea, was a collection of 1662 works of Hīnayānaist, Mahāyānaist, and Chinese genesis, in which the Mahāyāna texts predominated. Although the original scriptures were of Sanskrit derivation, in 1300 the Chinese collection was the basic canon of Mahāyāna Buddhism.

The scriptures of Tantric Buddhism were preserved in Tibetan in the *Kanjur*, or Tibetan canon, supplemented by the *Tanjur*, a thesaurus of exegetical literature. The two collections together were considerably larger than the Chinese canon. They contained most of the originally Sanskrit texts found in the Chinese canon and had many more *Tantras* besides. Translated between the seventh and thirteenth centuries, they formed the sacred literature of the late Tantric Buddhism of Bihar and Bengal also.

* * *

Buddhist Organization and Practices

Although a world religion, Buddhism never has had a world organization. By 1300 India, once the well-spring of the faith, was no longer its source of inspiration. Ceylon had come to be the seat of authority for Hīnayāna (Pali) Buddhism, and China for the Mahāyāna, while Tibet had replaced Bihar and Bengal as the centre of Tantric Buddhism. None of the three creeds as yet had a unified structure, but Tantric Buddhism was to develop one as the grand lama of Tibet became a sort of pope.

From the very beginning the core of Buddhism was its monastic system, and consequently the various monastic orders became the bases of Buddhist organization. A Buddhist sect consisted of a group of monasteries and their lay adherents, who accepted a common body of beliefs centring upon particular scriptures and a certain degree of supervision from a head or patriarch. Since the *sangha* (monastic order) cultivated a distinct sense of carrying on a sacred institution founded by the Buddha, considerable attention was paid to ordination. Hence sects founded in new lands or whose purity of descent had come into question tried to get started or restarted through properly ordained monks from older centres. China originally depended on India and central Asia, and Korea, Japan, and Vietnam in turn on China; Burma and Siam at times sent to Ceylon for authentic monks, and Ceylon later had to call on Siam and Burma; Tibet originally counted upon India. Once proper succession was established, a monastery might carry on under its own abbots with a minimum of supervision from a sectarian head.

Buddhist organization tended to develop along national lines, as in Japan, Burma, Siam, and Tibet, although it might vary from country to country and from time to time in the same country. No country except Tibet, however, developed a theocracy or close identification of church and state of the Christian or Islamic type.[15] Rulers often patronized, regulated, or in various ways interfered with the Buddhists, and at intervals Buddhism occupied the position of a state religion, but the state seldom, except in Tibet, became an agency for enforcing religious orthodoxy.

Buddhism's inadequate provision for lay participation probably accounted for its failure to develop a strong organization outside the monastic sects. Despite its emphasis upon kindliness and compassion, for a long time the only road that led to *nirvāna* was a life of monastic asceticism; and although the Mahāyāna developed easy and popular routes to salvation, monastic life remained the ideal, thereby discouraging the establishment of churches for the laity. Men who were prepared to practise a prescribed though less rigorous discipline than the monks were nevertheless admitted to the monastic groups as a sort of lay brotherhood. And the laity in general was encouraged to follow as much of the Buddhist doctrine and moral discipline as their knowledge and condition would permit; they were in particular encouraged to adhere to the Five Precepts (not to take life, drink intoxicants, lie, steal, or be unchaste), to honour the Three Jewels (Buddha, *dharma*, and *sangha*), and to support the monasteries. Merit was also to be won by avoiding garlands and perfume, sleeping on mats, not eating after midday, practising such social virtues as pleasant speech, kindness, and helpfulness, going on pilgrimages, listening to the reading of the *sūtras*, having the *sūtras* copied, engaging in religious conversations, giving alms, endowing monasteries building temples, preserving respect for the law, and performing the mutual obligations of parent or child, pupil or teacher, husband or wife, friend or befriended, master or servant, and layman or cleric. The laity might win merit too by visiting temples and shrines to offer gifts, perform acts of respect or worship, make supplications, observe ceremonials performed by the monks, and listen to the preaching or the reading of scriptures on certain days of the month.

In early Buddhism and subsequently in Hīnayānaism these good deeds could do no more than improve one's *karma*. Mahāyāna, however, held out the possibility of redemption through *bodhisattvas* and through faith in Amitābha (one of the Buddhas), and thus opened an easier way to salvation for layman and ascetic alike. Still, except to a limited extent in Japan and to a lesser extent in China, no effective lay-oriented sects developed. The monastic life was arduous, permissible lay participation was basically passive, and, above all, no secular clergy were provided to organize and promote the *dharma* among the laity. As a result, only where Buddhism became a sort of national religion did the monks take on the functions of a secular clergy sufficiently to develop large and close-knit followings.

Monastic practices in 1300 differed considerably from country to country and from sect to sect. The early ideal of the wandering mendicant had declined outside India, and most monks now resided permanently in a monastic establishment, although they engaged in pilgrimages and itinerant activities. Major differences distinguished Hīnayāna from Mahāyāna monasticism. The life of a Hīnayāna monk, whose ideal was the *arhat* and whose purpose was personal salvation, tended to be somewhat more strictly ascetic than that of the Mahāyāna monk, whose ideal was that of the *bodhisattva* who accumulated merits for the benefit of mankind. Monastic vows were generally revocable. Poverty was the established rule for Hīnayāna monks but seems not to have been universally demanded of Mahāyāna monks, and in neither group did it apply to the monastic foundation. One of the important functions of the abbot and the administrative staff of a monastery was to husband its properties, and some monasteries became extremely wealthy. Celibacy was the general rule in both Hīnayāna and Mahāyāna monasticism, except in Japan, where some sects abandoned it and many monks became essentially secular, marrying and living among the laymen they served. Among Tantric Buddhists of this period celibacy seems to have been largely abandoned. Vegetarianism was also the general rule except among the Tantrics. An alms bowl, certain vestments, a staff, a razor, a toothpick, and a water-strainer (to avoid taking insect life) were standard equipment for monks.

Most monastic recruits seem to have been young boys, pledged to monk-hood by their parents. They were trained either at monastic schools or within the monastery prior to taking their first vows (see Chapter XVI). Monastic orders for nuns existed, but they seldom had wide appeal and were generally under the control of the male orders.

The daily routine in most Buddhist monasteries was similar. It included morning and evening devotional services, reading and memorization of sacred texts, worship of the Buddhist images, meditation, and domestic work. In Hīnayāna lands the monks usually ate only at noon, and begging was a daily occupation, but in Mahāyāna countries three meals were normal, begging was rare, and the monks appear to have lived in greater ease and comfort. Certain days of the month were fast days, and on the bi-monthly Uposatha fast-and-confessional days the monks in congregation recited the Prātimoksha, a catalogue of 250 vows or prescriptions concerning conduct.

Monks performed a large variety of public services. They instructed the young (especially those destined for monkhood), read the scriptures aloud on certain days each month, occasionally preached and lectured, distributed food (often obtained by begging), and chanted *sūtras* and other formulas in connection with public festivals, holidays, sickness, death, and the exorcism of evil spirits. In Tibet Tantric charms and formulas were considered especially efficacious in the general war on demons. The average level of learning and piety seems not to have been very high in most of the monastic orders, and standards in Tantric Buddhism often seem low. In Japan some of the orders maintained troops and engaged in conflict with the feudal lords. Most of the orders in Japan, Korea, and Tibet engaged in politics.

*   *   *

Southern Buddhism

Hīnayāna Buddhism corresponded more nearly to early Buddhism than did the Mahāyāna. In a way the Hīnayāna was more a rationalist ethical system than a religion; it held out no promise of salvation through faith, and it called for individual self-reliance and discipline. It paid devotion to only one Buddha, the terrestrial Shākyamuni, although it also recognized previous Buddhas and the *bodhisattva* Maitreya, who would come to preach the law sometime in the future. Strictly speaking and for the learned few, the Buddha was not a god but a superman superior to all gods. Out of compassion for mankind he had come and shown the way to salvation; he had then passed on to *nirvāna* and was beyond the reach of prayers or supplications;[16] only his *dharma*, his teaching of the way to salvation, remained. In the popular mind, however, he was in practice a supreme deity who could answer prayers and petitions. In the minds of learned and untutored alike, the important purpose of human existence was the improvement of one's *karma* by appropriate acts and a meritorious life. The idea of a series of universes, heavens, and hells had also grown up, along with a group of supernatural beings ranging from ghosts and tempters through saints to *devas*, or gods. In popular thought rebirth in one of the hells was greatly dreaded. Native animistic beliefs had been grafted to Buddhism in all Hīnayāna countries, and charms, spells, images, relics, and pilgrimages to holy places remained Hīnayāna practices.

In Ceylon the Hīnayānaism of the large Mahāvihāra Monastery, which had preserved the Pali canon, had won out over Mahāyānaist ideas. Sinhalese

Buddhism, having accommodated ancient animistic beliefs, was in the process of accepting also a group of *devatas* as attendants of the Buddha. These attendant deities, often appealed to for personal help, included Brahmā and especially Vishnu. A type of Hīnayānaism similar to that of Ceylon survived in various localities of south India too.

In Burma the Talaing school of Buddhism long was dominant. The collapse (*c.* 1298) of Pagan as the political centre of Upper Burma appears to have left Thaton, in the Talaing country of Pegu, the leading Buddhist centre. Nevertheless, before 1300 each of several groups of Burmese monks, having been ordained at the Mahāvihāra Monastery in Ceylon and having established monasteries in Burma and Pegu, claimed to represent the only proper descent by ordination. The old Talaing and five new Sinhalese schools thus competed for control in the fourteenth century. The Pali canon of Burma contained some works that were not recognized in the Sinhalese canon. Otherwise Talaing Buddhism was essentially the same as that of Ceylon (except perhaps for a few Mahāyānaist elements). It, too, had to adapt itself to the popular worship of native spirits (*nats*), some of which were accepted as attendants to Buddha or as guardian spirits.

By 1300 the Thai kingdom of Sukhothai and the Khmer Empire were essentially Hīnayānaist. Pali Buddhism was a well-organized state religion in Sukhothai, probably having come from Pegu and Burma. The worship of native spirits (*phis*), ancestors, and natural forces had to be accommodated, as in Ceylon and Burma, along with certain Mahāyāna elements, such as the belief in *bodhisattvas* and merits, which had probably come from the Khmer Empire of Cambodia. In Cambodia itself, however, Hīnayānaism was in the process of displacing that combination of Hinduism and Mahāyānaism which was mentioned above as perhaps the official cult. When the Chinese traveller Chou Ta-kuan visited Angkor, the capital of the Khmer Empire, in 1296, Hīnayāna Buddhism was already becoming its dominant religion.

* * *

Northern Buddhism

Just as Hīnayāna Buddhism moved southeastward, so Mahāyāna Buddhism moved northeastward. Although transformed, as it moved, by Persian, central Asian, Greek, and local adaptations, Mahāyāna had developed logically from early Buddhism. Prominent among its distinctive features were the belief in *bodhisattvas* and the idea that their merit could be transferred. A *bodhisattva* was a sort of saviour, a potential Buddha, who, out of compassion for mankind, had renounced Buddhahood and laboured through countless ages to accumulate merits (something like Christian 'good works') which could be transferred to the use of ordinary people. Gautama was believed to have been such a being prior to attaining *nirvāna*. Seven *bodhisattvas* became especially prominent. Among them Avalokita, saviour and personification of divine mercy, transformed into a goddess of mercy (Kuan-yin in China, Kwannon in

Japan), became the most important, and Maitreya (Mi-lo or Miroku) remained significant as the future Buddha. Heavenly *bodhisattvas* who had never been on earth also laboured constantly for the salvation of mankind. The idea developed that anyone might become a *bodhisattva*, and the final stage of monkhood was initiation as a *bodhisattva*.

Another prominent idea of Mahāyāna Buddhism comprised a sort of composite of polytheism and trinitarianism. Buddhas were regarded as innumerable and distributed through infinite space and time, but they were conceived of also as forming a kind of trinity. This idea was set forth in the doctrine of *trikāya* and *dharma-kāya* and in the concept of Ādi-Buddha (see below) in essentially the same way though in different forms. *Trikāya* was the concept of the three bodies or personalities of the Buddha. The highest form of this trinity was the *dharma-kāya* (literally, 'the body of the law'). It was the essence of all Buddhas—in fact, the essence of all things; it was true knowledge, the ultimate reality underlying phenomena; it was the norm of being or the principle of the universe; and it was personified, capable of willing and reflecting. In other words, the first form of the trinity was a personalized, omnipresent, absolute, and supreme being. The second was the blissful heavenly Buddhas in their paradises. The third was that of the Buddhas who had appeared on earth as humans.

The figure of Ādi-Buddha arose in late Indian Buddhism (and, as we shall soon point out, remained especially important in Tantric Buddhism). Ādi-Buddha was the original essence, the basic stuff from which all Buddhas came. Ādi-Buddha by contemplation created five *dhyāni* (contemplational or heavenly Buddhas), who in turn created human Buddhas, *bodhisattvas*, and other sacred beings. Out of the multiplicity of Buddhas that were thus conceived, six stood out. Foremost among them were Shākyamuni (known as Shih-chia-mu-ni in Chinese or Shaka in Japanese), who was Gautama, and Amitābha (O-mi-to in Chinese, Amida in Japanese), who was the Buddha of measureless light and infinite compassion. Shākyamuni was the human Buddha, and Amitābha was one of the *dhyāni*. Amitābha had a great treasury of merits that he could dispense to those who in true faith called upon him. The invocation of Amitābha's name might thus assure the supplicant rebirth in the Blessed Land, or Western Paradise.

The Mahāyāna developed a distinctive system of metaphysics that anticipated but was basically very similar to the monistic Vedānta (see Chapter VI). The concept of the *dharma-kāya* was essentially the same as that of the Hindu *brahman*. Different philosophical absolutes arose among several Mahāyāna schools, but they were all identified with the *dharma-kāya*, which in turn was identified with *nirvāna*. Philosophical *nirvāna*, or enlightenment, thus came to mean the realization that the Buddha essence was everywhere, that hence it was within oneself, and that we are all one with the *dharma-kāya*.

The Mahāyāna also developed an elaborate system of universes, heavens, hells, and spiritual beings (many of them evil). Among the host of attendants of the Buddhas were the Four Kings of Hīnayānaism, the Sixteen *Arhats* (Eighteen *Lohans* in China), the Five Hundred *Lohans*, and the twenty-four tutelary deities (including Brahma, Confucius, and Kuan-ti, the Chinese god of war). This complicated system of heavenly and hellish hosts gave to Mahāyāna Buddhism another of its distinguishing features, a complex ritual involving the use of numerous formulas and charms with an elaborate iconography and art.

* * *

Sects of Mahāyāna Buddhism

A number of Mahāyānaist sects flourished in 1300. Some of them were either ascetic or philosophic in character (such as the Lü or Vinaya, the Fa-hsiang or Yogācārya, and the Hua-yen or Avatamsaka) and did not attract a great following. Other sects or schools were more influential. The Pure Land or Lotus sect (Chinese, Ching-t'u; Japanese, Jōdō), infused with much Taoist language and imagery, expounded the ideas of salvation through faith in Amitābha. Its special scriptures were the three *Pure Land Sūtras*, which portrayed the Western Paradise. Its doctrine of simple salvation had affected all the sects in China, and it had spread rapidly in Japan, where the *nembutsu* (the formula *Namu Amida Butsu*, 'home to Amida Buddha') became the popular route to salvation. It divided into many sub-sects in Japan.

The Shin or Ikko sect of Japan was a logical extension of the Pure Land doctrine. It held that faith in Amida was all important, that one sincere *nembutsu* was adequate, that while penance, fasting, pilgrimages, and celebacy were useless, prayer and purity were desirable. The successors of its founder married, becoming a hereditary clergy living among the people. It was numerous and met in congregations for worship and preaching. It denounced other sects, arousing keen opposition, which kindled into physical conflict as the Buddhist sects became feudalized (see Chapter III).

Hardly less popular, and in some ways more important, was the Meditative (*Ch'an*; *Zen*) or Sudden Enlightenment sect. It seems to have been the outcome of a long evolution, in the course of which it unquestionably was profoundly influenced by Taoist ideas. It emphasized that the only reality was the Buddha quality in every man, that prayer, asceticism, good works, and learning were of no real importance to salvation or enlightenment, but that through meditation, self-study, and introspection enlightenment might come in an intuitive flash. It honoured no scriptures beyond the lives of the Ch'an (Zen) saints, gave little regard to systematic doctrine or instruction, and recommended occasionally slapping or kicking neophytes to help bring on the flash of enlightenment. Great lovers of nature and solitude, the Ch'an (Zen) monks located their monasteries in out-of-the-way scenic spots and developed important schools of poetry and landscape painting in both China and Japan. The simplicity, austerity, and self-discipline of the Zen sect appealed to the Japanese, especially the military class.

Among the popular sects the T'ien-t'ai (Tendai), which took its name from a monastery near Ningpo, was the one most given to intellectual pursuits. Rejecting the Ch'an's disregard of instruction, it became a many-sided school that advocated learning as well as meditation, discipline, and ecstasy. It endeavoured to harmonize Buddhist ideas by suggesting that the Buddha had set forth different levels of teaching during his lifetime—first the doctrine of heavenly beings of the *Avatamsaka-sūtra* (which expounded the *dharma-kāya* doctrine), then the Hīnayāna ideal of the *arhat*, then the Mahāyāna ideal of the *bodhisattva*, then the transcendental knowledge of the *Prajñāpāramitā-sūtras* (a well-known part of the Buddhist canon), and, in his old age, the quint-essence of Buddhism in the *Lotus Sūtra* (*Saddharma-pundarīka*), the favourite text of the T'ien-t'ai.

The Hokke or Nichiren sect of Japan exhibited some of the popular and militant tendencies of the Shin sect. Its founder, Nichiren (1222–82), a Tendai monk, was interested in the masses and attacked other sects as heretics who sapped the vitality of the people and corrupted the state. The sect upheld Shākyamuni as the eternal, omnipresent Buddha and believed that faith in the teachings of the *Lotus Sūtra* was the only route to salvation. They contended that the world had entered the *mappō* era (the period of the destruction of the law) and that Nichiren was the *bodhisattva* Vishishtacāritra (Jōgyō), whom Shākyamuni had designated to propagate the faith in that era. Because of their sharp, abusive criticism of government, society, and other sects, they were in constant conflict with the state and rival sects but popular with the poor (see Chapter III).

The Chen-yen (Shingon) or True Word sect was the only Tantric per-suasion in Far Eastern Buddhism. It revered Vairocana, the great sun Buddha, as the eternal Buddha, all other Buddhas, the *bodhisattvas*, and the world being regarded as mere emanations. It divided Buddhist thought into ten classes, the highest of which comprised the 'true-word' tantric practices by which the adept became a living Buddha. Its promise of a short cut to salvation through easily performed ceremonies and magic made it popular and to a considerable extent determined procedure at Chinese funerals. Its practices tended to become diffused in China, but in Japan it acquired power and influence. Its principal scripture, *The Great Sun Sūtra* (*Dainishikyō*), was supplemented in Japan by later writings which developed the theory that Shinto deities were but emanations of Vairocana (Dainichi).

Korea's Buddhism was imported from China along with the main Chinese sects. It exhibited no very original developments and was infiltrated by older native beliefs. Its monastic groups became involved in politics, maintained armed forces, and depended heavily on government patronage. By 1300 Korean Buddhism had to compete with a revived Confucian movement but still enjoyed government support.

Buddhism entered Vietnam from China long before 1300, but really distinctive sects did not develop there. Instead Vietnamese Buddhism became an amalgam of several beliefs. To be sure, Buddhist temples (*Chua*) were distinct from Taoist, Confucian, and Dinh temples (the last dedicated to native municipal gods and heroes), but they also contained Taoist, Confucian, and native deities. The *bodhisattva* Kuan-yin (Quan-am), in the form of legendary heroines, was especially popular.

*   *   *

Tantric Buddhism

Tantric Buddhism had been exported from Bihar and Bengal in its least erotic form, the Mantrayāna, to the East Indies and the Far East, and in a later and more modified form to Tibet (*c.* 747) and Nepal. It readily accepted and incorporated local cults and practices. In its most erotic form, Buddhas and *bodhisattvas* were supplied with female counterparts, union with whom constituted *nirvāna*, the highest state of bliss, which might be attained on earth by the adept. Buddhism thus absorbed Shākta as well as Tantric features, Tārā, the female companion of Avalokita, becoming an influential deity. While the Mantrayāna form used the magic formulas and similar rites of Tantrism, the erotic elements in it were not marked. It considered Vairocana the original and chief of the five celestial Buddhas.

The East Indies seem at one time or another to have been influenced by all three main forms of Buddhism. The principal religion of the Majapahit Empire, which, beginning in 1293, dominated Java and some of the neighbouring islands about a century, was a mixture of Hinduism (principally Shivaism), native practices, and late Tantric Buddhism, the last being perhaps the most important. Shiva-Buddha was a popular deity, and several other Hindu deities were identified with Buddhas. The Old Javanese work *Kuñjarakarna* (perhaps eleventh century) included an exposition of the faith attributed to Vairocana, and the *Kamahāyānikan* (thirteenth or fourteenth century) expounded various Mahāyāna and Tantric tenets, including the doctrine of the void, the utility of magic formulas, reverence for the five celestial Buddhas (with female counterparts), and the evolution of everything from Advaya (apparently Ādi-Buddha). The *Kamahāyānikan* also identified the highest principles of Hinduism with Buddhism.

Tibet about 1300 had four main Buddhist sects. All had adopted many features of the native Bon religion, including its demonophobia, necromancy, shamanism, and magic. The oldest, the Nying-ma-pa (Old Ones), dated from the introduction of Mantrayāna Buddhism in the eighth century; Vairocana was its cosmic Buddha, and it also worshipped its founder. The other three—the Kadampa, Sakyapa, and Kargyupa sects—grew out of the Vajrayāna (Thunderbolt Vehicle) or Kalacakra system, which, having spread in the eleventh century from Bihar and Bengal to the East Indies, was taken to Tibet by Atisha about 1040. The Vajrayāna developed the idea that Ādi-Buddha was the primordial Buddha, from whom everything else evolved. It supplied the Buddhas and *bodhisattvas* with wives and adopted the erotic and other elements of the *Tantras*, with their ensuing effect on monastic and religious life. Atisha himself founded the Kadampa sect. The Sakyapa sect was established in 1071 by a royal prince in a great monastery about fifty miles north of Mount Everest, and from 1270 to 1340 its abbots were the real rulers of Tibet. It mixed the *Tantras* of the Old and Kadampa sects. The Kargyupa sect, also founded in the eleventh century, emphasized the solitary, wandering life. None of the four Tibetan sects insisted on celibacy or abstinence from alcohol, all dabbled in politics, and a major occupation of the monks was summoning Buddhas or *bodhisattvas* to combat demons. Tārā was an especially popular goddess; Avalokita and Maitreya were popular *bodhisattvas*; Amitābha, Shākyamuni, and Vairocana were popular Buddhas. A brand of this late Tantric Buddhism mixed with Hinduism also flourished in Nepal.

CONFUCIANISM

Around 1300 Confucianism as a religion was confined to China, Korea, and Vietnam, but certain of its ideas and practices were also widespread in Japan. In many ways it was more an ethical than a religious system, but since it required certain rituals and beliefs that were theistic in nature, it must be regarded also as a creed. Along with Taoism and Buddhism, it was one of China's leading creeds. Confucianism, Taoism, and Buddhism, the *san-chiao* ('the three teachings') of China, were separate, but they were easily alloyed. A few scholars were exclusively Confucianists, a few adepts exclusively Taoists, and some monks and nuns exclusively Buddhists, but the vast majority of Chinese in 1300 were at the same time Confucianists, Taoists, and Buddhists (as well as animists).

This plural loyalty was a parallel to, and perhaps a reflection of, the current attitude of the Chinese towards life in general. Essentially eclectic and tolerant, they tended to adopt whatever usages seemed to meet their needs and customarily permitted any that did not seem to endanger the state or the social order. Their common pattern of behaviour was at bottom ethical, this-worldly, and social, the supernatural being called upon primarily to promote well-being here below. A practical ethical code like Confucianism was found congenial as contributing to harmony among the living.

Ceremonies and rituals were nevertheless extremely meaningful to the Chinese as a rule. Their ethical code was embodied in a system of ceremonial behaviour, and their approach to the supernatural was invariably clothed in elaborate rites. Ceremonies and rituals were generally assumed to have value in themselves but at any rate were useful as educative devices and as a means of social control. Chinese social attitudes tended to be at once superstitious, optimistic, and sceptical. Although the life of the people was difficult and their world was inhabited by harmful spirits and forces, they usually believed that human nature was fundamentally good, that evil spirits could be vanquished, and that conditions would thus be improved, but they tended to be somewhat uncertain about the power of the various gods and demons. This lack of certainty undoubtedly accounted for their eclecticism in religion; if no supernatural forces should prove totally effective, common sense suggested honour to all that might help and propitiation of all that might harm.

Confucianism was in essence a way of life and a system of social and political control. In this regard it resembled the *dharma* of Hinduism—with the difference, however, that Confucianism was interested in the problems of this life and was little preoccupied with the soul and life after death. It more nearly resembled the religious outlook of classical Greece than of India. The Confucianism of 1300 was the product of a long evolution. In the course of time it had incorporated (1) a group of ideas and ceremonials relating to ancestral and natural spirits that predated Confucius (d. 478 BC), (2) a body of moral principles and practices expounded by Confucius and developed by his early followers, and (3) various accretions and adaptations that had taken place since his time. The whole scheme of thought had been systematically organized and sharply defined by the Neo-Confucian writers of the Sung Dynasty (960–1279).

*   *   *

Ancestors, Heaven, and Other Deities

Ancestor worship, which seems to have been as old as the Chinese people, was the core of Confucianism as a religion. Confucius had strengthened the ancestral cult by building a progressive, this-worldly, ethical order around the family. Emphasis upon filial piety and other family loyalties tended to diminish the importance of the supernatural elements in ancestor worship, without eliminating them. About 1300 ancestral worship thus combined ancient Chinese beliefs and practices with Confucian ceremonial and social ideas. Buddhist and Taoist doctrines relating to the after-life had also entered the combination.

The supernatural elements of the ancestral cult centred in the conviction that the spirits of the dead had the power to befriend or injure the living and that, if they were to be friendly, they must be honoured, fed, and cared for. Funeral ceremonies were designed to help a departed spirit safely to an appropriate resting place as well as to demonstrate filial reverence. Funeral days and burial sites were carefully selected, and funeral processions were elaborate. The more important the individual or the more wealthy the family, the more costly the ceremonies, because the competition in ostentation was keen. They included fasting, mourning costumes, and the offering of wine, food, paper money, memorial scrolls, and other gifts. Friends and neighbours attended to pay their respects. Generally Buddhist monks chanted prayers for the soul or Taoist priests exorcized evil spirits.

The spirits of the dead were worshipped in the home, in ancestral tablets, and at the grave. Worship in the home began immediately after the funeral. An ancestral tablet was installed with ceremonious kowtowing and chanting of passages from the classics, usually followed by the chants and formulas of Buddhist or Taoist priests. The deceased was next provided with things needed in the future life by burning paper effigies of them in an open place. Further ceremonies were conducted at fixed intervals during twenty-seven months of mourning, after which annual memorial services were required. The spirits of departed forefathers were also worshipped daily, under the supervision of the head of the family, with kowtows, the burning of incense, and the offering of food and wine (which were later removed and used by the family). They were appealed to in times of crisis and were informed of significant events. A high point in the marriage ceremony was the kowtow of the bride and groom before the ancestral tablets, and ancestral spirits were worshipped at the grave site during the spring and autumn festivals and upon other special occasions. Families that were members of a clan which maintained an ancestral hall sent representatives there at the winter and summer solstices to join other clan members in making offerings and requesting the help and protection of their forebears' spirits. In all these ceremonies, the oldest male, as head of the family, was the key figure.

The Chinese state officially worshipped a considerable pantheon of natural forces and heroes. Some far-reaching phenomena such as heaven (*t'ien*) and earth had long enjoyed official reverence, but other deities had been elevated to the national pantheon from a distinctly local ranking. After the coming of Buddhism the tendency to deify legendary heroes and famous persons increased, and such deities were gradually included in the national pantheon, among them Confucius himself. The ancestors of the reigning emperor were also included, since they were worshipped by the emperor, and he himself was worshipped by the officials on state occasions. Worship of some of the pantheon was confined exclusively to the emperor or officials acting for him, while others like the city gods, local gods of the soil and grain, and various mountains and rivers were also worshipped directly by the people. At the head of the pantheon was the god called T'ien (Heaven) or Shang-ti (Supreme Ruler). T'ien was respected as a sort of impersonal power or force from which the emperor's right to rule was supposed to come. Sacrifices to Shang-ti were reserved exclusively to the emperor, but all people might and did call upon Heaven, although they did not sacrifice to it. More will be said below about the State Cult.

*   *   *

Confucian Ethics

The Chinese early developed a theory resembling the Western concept of natural law; man and nature, they held, were harmoniously united, and the welfare of man depended upon the maintenance of this unity. Hence man must follow a course of action (*tao*) that preserved and promoted the harmony between nature and the human spirit. Proper behaviour, including sacrifices to the appropriate spirits, was part of the *tao*, and the emperor, as high priest of the state and intermediary between man and nature, was responsible for carrying out the necessary sacrifices.

The Confucians always emphasized the ethical nature of the *tao*, and it would be extremely difficult to say whether or to what extent about 1300 the supernatural prevailed over the ethical elements of the State Cult. The natural forces and the great men that were worshipped were essentially of an impersonal character, and although supplications were often couched in highly personal terms, the whole sacrificial procedure was routine. The will of Heaven was interpreted to mean the will of the people. The very fact that the emperor promoted or demoted deities in the official pantheon indicated the system's rationalistic nature. Whether or not the majority of the lettered elite, the literati, believed that deities could directly influence the course of human affairs, certainly the more rationalistic Confucians looked upon their cult as primarily a way of showing respect for nature and as a traditional procedure useful in promoting social and political control.

The ethical standard of Confucianism was extremely high. Based upon a patriarchal conception of the family as the key social unit, it extended to the clan, the community, and the state, which was the family writ large. The emperor and his officials were expected to rule the state as a patriarch ruled his family—by virtue, benevolence, reasoned guidance, and, when necessary, appropriate chastisement; if those above set the proper example, those below were expected to respond with respect, obedience, and helpfulness. Moral responsibility began with the individual, who was called upon to perfect his heart and conduct, but the individual, of course, first learned the proper ideals and modes of conduct from his family.

The ethical code that the family inculcated may be considered under six headings—filial piety (*hsiao*), the 'five relationships', the five cardinal virtues (*te*), proper conduct (*li*), the norm of life (*tao*), and the ideal of the gentleman (*chün-tzu*). Hsiao meant devotion to the family and its ancestors, and special love, respect, and obedience to parents. A child's first duty was to parents, family, and ancestors, but a girl after marriage turned her devotion to her husband's family. The patriarchal family was organized in a hierarchy of privileges and corresponding responsibilities, ranging from the father as head through the mother, elder brothers, younger brothers, elder sisters, and younger sisters to grandchildren and collateral relatives. A mode of behaviour was prescribed for each member of the family in relation to every other. The head of the family was responsible for all, and they owed him reverence and obedience. The 'five relationships', when fully developed, laid down the principles that should govern one's social relations: probity between ruler and minister, affection between father and son, proper division of labour between husband and wife, proper order of precedence between older brother and younger, and fidelity between friend and friend; justice should govern relations even with one's foes. *Te* (somewhat inadequately defined as 'virtue') was a personal quality everyone was called upon to cultivate. It subsumed the five cardinal virtues: benevolence (*jen*), righteousness (*i*), reverence (*chung*), wisdom (*chih*), and sincerity (*hsin*). *Jen* is variously translated also as 'love', 'altruism', and 'human-heartedness'; it conveyed the idea of reciprocal forebearance and was perhaps best expressed in the Chinese equivalent of the Golden Rule: 'What one does not want done to himself, he should not do to others'. *Li*, propriety or proper conduct, is often given as one of the cardinal virtues in place of *chung*. *Li* involved more than good taste and the proprieties like etiquette, ceremonials, and rituals; it stood also for a type of outward behaviour that reflected an inward grace.

One who properly coordinated all the above requirements would approach the Confucian *tao*, or way of life. This Confucian *tao* (to be distinguished from the *tao* of the Taoists, which will be described below) was essentially ethical rather than metaphysical and consisted of the ideal norms of conduct. Individuals who possessed it would live in cooperation and harmony with their fellow men; states that possessed it would be properly governed. He who possessed it was a *chün-tzu* (ideal man), a prince or gentleman in the highest sense.

Concepts like *li* and *chung* made Confucianism ceremonious and ritualistic. Sacrifices and rites were carried out according to carefully prescribed rules. The way to act and speak in different situations and in accordance with the hierarchy of relationships involved was set forth in elaborate codes of etiquette (*li*). Even in cases where *li* did not in fact reflect an inward grace, the Chinese considered it an efficacious means of both education and social control. Sacrificial rituals were thus often practised for their own sake—for their presumed inherent social value—regardless of whether the participants believed in the spirits to which the sacrifices were offered.

*   *   *

State and Popular Confucianism

The Confucian canon was rather concise and clearly defined. It consisted of the sayings of Confucius and some of his disciples, the writings of Mencius, one of his chief successors, and some supposedly older classical works either used by Confucius or in some way associated with him. By 1300 the canon had been reduced to the Five Classics (*Wu-ching*) and the Four Books (*Ssu-shu*). The Five Classics were the *Shih ching* (*Book of Odes*), a collection of about 300 ancient poems and folksongs; the *Shu ching* (*Book of History*), a collection of early historical documents (some of them unquestionably forgeries); the *I ching* (*Book of Changes*), an enigmatic volume consisting of a rural omen calendar, a divination manual, and other materials; the *Ch'un ch'iu* (*Spring and Autumn Annuals*), a history of Lu, the native state of Confucius, which he was supposed to have edited but probably did not; and the *Li chi* (*Record of Rites*), a collection of ancient rituals and practices, much of which was later than Confucius. Two complementary works on ritual, the *I li* (*Book of Etiquette and Ceremonials*) and the *Chou li* (*Rites of the Chou*), although no among the Five Classics, were almost equally esteemed. Parts of the *I li* were among the oldest ceremonial records, and the *Chou li* was a late idealized description of the government of the Chou dynasty. The Four Books included the *Lun yü* (*Analects of Confucius*), the *Meng-tzu* (*Book of Mencius*), the *Ta hsüeh* (*Great Learning*), and the *Chung yung* (*Doctrine of the Means*). The last two were extracted from the *Li chi* and given special attention by the Neo-Confucians; the *Ta hsüeh* expounded a theory of higher learning; and the *Chung yung* set forth a theory of the golden mean. Still another respected work was the *Hsiao ching* (*Book of Filial Piety*), which although no longer considered a classic, was a basic textbook. The civil-service examinations were based on these canonical books, and the commentaries of the great twelfth-century Neo-Confucian Chu Hsi constituted the authoritative interpretation of them.

In one sense Confucianism lacked organization as a religion: no church of Confucianism existed, and no specific body propagated it. But in another sense it was highly organized. A formally organized Cult of the Scholars, whose patron saint was Confucius, was a part of the State Cult, which was headed by the emperor and formally administered by one of the government's main offices, the *Li-pu*, or Board of Rites. The Cult of Scholars involved all scholars, whether official or not, but was in general confined to the literati; purely military officials without literary degrees had their own patron saint. The official philosophy was Confucian, the civil-service examinations were based on the Confucian canonical books, and the whole governmental system of cults, education, and training was organized to promote and teach Confucianism (see Chapter XVI). Moreover, the patriarchal family, out of which so much of Confucianism grew, propagated Confucianism in almost every one of its activities. China was thus thoroughly and completely a Confucian state and society. If the emperor neglected to worship the state deities or failed to rule in an ethical manner, disaster could be expected to overtake the country, and ultimately Heaven would remove his family from the throne (see Chapter VI).

The deities in the official pantheon were grouped in three classes. At the top were Heaven, Earth, and imperial ancestors, and the gods of the soil and grain. In the second class were the sun, the moon, the year star (Jupiter), the gods of the sky, of the clouds, of rain, of wind, of thunder, and of the ten mountains, the four oceans and the four rivers, some legendary rulers, and other distinguished men and women, including Confucius and several of his disciples. The third class included the city gods and the gods of healing, of literature, of war, of fire, of architecture, and of the gate and door. Worship of Heaven, Earth, and imperial ancestors was reserved to the emperor, and he was also required either in person or by proxy to sacrifice to the sun, the moon, the gods of the soil and grain, and several other gods. He often sacrificed also to Confucius. On the longest night of the year, after appropriate fasting and purification, he tendered to Shang-ti burnt offerings of bullocks, silk, jade, wine, and other things of value in an elaborate, impressive ceremony at the Altar of Heaven. At the summer solstice somewhat similar offerings were buried at the Altar of Earth. The farming season opened in the spring with ceremonial ploughing at the Temple of Soil and Grain. Provincial and local officials sacrificed at local temples, where the city gods, the gods of the soil and grain, and Shen-nung, the patron of husbandry, were particularly revered. All the deities were represented by either symbols or images; the symbol of Heaven was circular, that of Earth square.

By 1300 the worship of Confucius was a highly developed cult, promoted by the emperors. An especially revered temple at Ch'ü-fu, Shantung, the home of Confucius, was maintained by the state under the management of a lineal descendant of Confucius. Kublai Khan had built another august temple in Peking. Every territorial subdivision of the country had a Confucian temple, or *Wen Miao* (Temple of Literature or Culture), in which were placed the names or images of Confucius, Mencius, other outstanding Confucian scholars, and illustrious supporters of the doctrine. Side rooms or separate buildings housed tablets or images of Confucius's ancestors and of famous local scholars and officials. These temples were normally open to the public, and twice a year, in spring and in autumn, sacrifices in honour of the sage were offered, with local scholars, officials, and students participating. Everything about the ceremonies suggested deification except the verbal expressions, which honoured Confucius only as a great teacher. All efforts to give him the title *ti* (god), however, were resisted by the scholars, who apparently preferred to venerate him as a sage.

Confucianism as practised by the people, however, was essentially unorganized and varied considerably from family to family. Popular Confucianism involved (1) worship at the local shrines of the Confucian pantheon; (2) training in Confucian ethics and in the various *li*; and (3) participation in the ancestral cult. The city gods and the village gods of the soil were particularly revered by the common people, who prayed, announced births and deaths, and presented offerings to them. Their temples were community centres. Pilgrimages to Confucian holy places were common. Almost everyone reverenced Confucius and T'ien, was acquainted with the *li* associated with his station in life, was able to quote sayings from the classics, and knew and endeavoured to practise the essentials of Confucian ethics. Figures of the Buddhist Kuan-yin, the female transformation of Avalokita, or of the Taoist Tsai-shen, god of wealth, and of the household gods were likely to be associated with the ancestral tablets, and at times of crisis Buddhist and Taoist priests might be called in. Unless the head of the family were an extraordinarily rigid Confucian, womenfolk in particular tended to utilize the services of Buddhist or Taoist priests at weddings and funerals, during serious illness, and at other periods of stress.

Confucianism had spread from China to Vietnam, Korea, and Japan. In both Vietnam and Korea it was a rather watered-down version of that in

China, but in 1300 it probably was somewhat stronger in Vietnam than in Korea. In both countries the ancestral cult was basic and had become thoroughly impregnated with Confucian ideas of *li* and filial piety, and Heaven was officially worshipped. In Vietnam, there was a state cult which resembled that of China, but the worship of Heaven was not exclusively reserved to the ruler as in China, and territorial officials also took part in it; not only did Confucian temples promote the cult of Confucius but also Buddhist temples displayed images of him. In Korea, where Buddhism was the state religion and was much stronger than in Vietnam, no Confucian cult was prominent at this time, but Confucian ideas and practices had fused with native elements. In Japan the Confucian family cult strengthened certain native tendencies. It contributed to the development of a cult of ancestor worship and filial piety, modelled on that of China, and of Confucian ethical and ceremonial ideas. In 1300 the Chinese impact on Japan's state cult was, however, of minor importance; Buddhist religious ideas were far more influential.

TAOISM

Taoism, strictly speaking, was confined to China. A cult bearing the Chinese name existed in Vietnam and Korea but was, in fact, a local occultism modified by a few Chinese practices and, despite the many Taoist temples in Vietnam, not sharply distinguished in the popular mind from Buddhism. Taoism may also have had a modifying influence upon Shinto occultism in Japan, especially in connection with the mountain priests of the Ashikaga period (1336–1568).

Taoism as a religion has to be clearly differentiated from Taoism as a philosophy. In fact, the religion was antithetical to nearly everything in early Taoist philosophy. Although customarily regarded as a degeneration of Taoist philosophy, more probably the Taoist religion emerged from the activities of priests, sorcerers, and magicians of the animistic folk cults, who used oracles, formulas, alchemy, herbs, charms, breath control, and similar means to divine the future, restore youth, gain superhuman powers, or attain immortality. These cults appropriated to their own use the name *tao* and ultimately deified Lao Tzu and other early Taoist philosophers, canonizing their writings. Outside influences also were absorbed, so that religious Taoism in 1300 was an unrationalized mixture of many things. Among them was perhaps something of Persian Mazdaism and Christian Nestorianism, certainly something of Confucian ethics, and a great many Buddhist ideas, such as those relating to monastic organization, sacred literature, a trinity, *karma*, transmigration of souls, ethics, heavens, and hells. Above all, however, still loomed the ideas and practices growing out of the folk cults of China and the activities of their wonder-working priests and adepts.

In contrast to the dominant this-worldly, rationalist Confucianism,

Taoism, whether as a philosophy or as a religion, reflected the mystical, supernatural, and superstitious side of the Chinese. In some respects it shared Hinduism's mysticism and metaphysics. The transcendentalism of Taoist philosophy somewhat resembled Hindu doctrine; the eternal way of nature (*tao*) did not seem far different from the absolute *brahman*; and the Taoists' search for immortality, their numerous gods, heavens, and hells, and their dependence on yoga, magic, and occultism were superficially reminiscent of Hinduism. The two creeds differed fundamentally, however. The central preoccupation of Hindu thought was with the soul, while Taoism concentrated on the body. Taoist philosophy laughed at death and taught that man could best enjoy life by living in harmony with nature; and if the native Taoist religion feared death and endeavoured to find the key to immortality, it was immortality not of the soul but of the body (the totality of the person). Thus Taoism, like Confucianism and unlike Hinduism, was this-worldly.

Taoism's search for immortality generally took the form of a hope for prolonged life, supernatural powers, and special advantages. The immortality sought was that of the mundane body or personality. The aim was to prolong life as long as possible and then to assure the continued existence of the individual as a genie or an immortal (*hsien*), able to move freely between this world, the heavens, and various earthly abodes of the immortals, such as the Isles of the Blest in the eastern seas, or the K'un-lung Mountain in the west, where the Hsi-wang-mu, the Fairy Queen, resided. Taoist literature was full of stories about humans who, having become immortal, could fly through space or pass through solid walls.

Nevertheless, devotion to a single deity through the intercession of a well-knit hierarchy in order to obtain immortality did not emerge, for separate deities were regarded as having separate jurisdiction over wealth, good fortune, and success of various other kinds. In most situations some adept was needed to serve as intermediary between the layman and the supernatural. This need produced a class of adepts, the Taoist priests (*tao-shih*), who knew the lore and tricks of the trade and the value of their services. The Taoist religion thus became a repository of numerous magical and occult practices devised by the *tao-shih* to promote the wishes of his clients.

Some of the *tao-shih* seriously sought the elixir of life or the pill of immortality; most were content to cater to popular superstitions and dispensed, for a fee, whatever combination of ethical teachings, occult practices, and Taoist lore they possessed. In the search for immortality cinnabar (which contains mercury), gold, jade, pearls, and herbs were used. Herbs, seeds, and various drugs were prescribed to treat disease and prolong life. Potions were concocted to inspire love or hate and to restore virility. On the assumption that evil spirits (*kuei*) were the cause of misfortune, exorcism was widely practised to treat disease and insanity, protect or save the dead, release the living from their troubles or shield them from harm, and stop droughts, floods, and other disasters. Chants, formulas, diagrams, extracts from scriptures, charms, amulets, pictures of deities or of virtuous people, and sudden noises as from gongs or firecrackers were used to frighten away evil spirits. Various kinds of fortune-telling flourished—among them astrology, divination, physiognomy, the interpretation of dreams and omens, and communication with the spirit world by means of trances and the ouija board. Shamanism and sorcery were cultivated, particularly by Wu priests, the sorcerers of the folk cults, in the effort to communicate with deities, spirits, and immortals and to command their services or gain information from them. Self-hypnosis, breath control, and perhaps drugs were used to bring on trances. Yoga practices (or 'cultivating the inner embryo'), comprising meditation, posturing, breath control, fasting, and sex rituals, were deemed effective in the search for prolonged life, immortality, supernatural power, and harmony with the *tao*. Geomancy, or *feng-shui*, was considered the best method of calculating the occult forces of nature and discerning a propitious location for graves, temples, houses, and other sites. Systems of dietetics were devised, mainly to prolong life and cure disease. Most *tao-shih* were vegetarians, but they often avoided the use of grains, too, preferring special herbs or seeds and resins.

Despite the prominence of occultism in the Taoist religion, it contained a moral system. According to Taoist ethics: 'One carries his own fate with him in the process of living. The recompense of good or evil follows one, as the shadow follows the object.'[17] The ethical system enjoined the Five Precepts of the Buddhists, the Ten Virtues (filial piety, loyalty, kindness to all living things, patience, remonstrance against evil, helpfulness to the poor, planting trees and setting free living creatures, digging wells and building roads, teaching the unenlightened, and studying the scriptures and making offerings to the gods), and other precepts. The popular *Kan-ying p'ien* (*Books of Rewards and Punishments*) promised that he who observed the virtues would be preserved by providence, respected by all, and assured success and office, and he might hope for immortality. The record of men's deeds was therefore kept eternally, and if one's rewards or punishments were not balanced out during this life, they were credited or debited to one's descendants or to oneself in the heavens or hells of the future life; evil deeds reduced one's life or brought other punishments, while good deeds extended it, brought other earthly rewards, or helped to make one immortal. To become an immortal on earth 300 good deeds were deemed necessary, and to become one in heaven, 1300. Three spirits that dwelt in the body, as well as the city god and the hearth spirit, or kitchen god, were supposed to report man's acts to the recorder of deeds. The kitchen god was often bribed by smearing the face of his image with something sweet. An elaborate system of heaven and hells was pictured in large drawings and detailed written descriptions, making this scheme of *tao* essentially like the law of *karma*.

Taoist mythology included a cosmology and an elaborate pantheon but remained for the most part unrationalized. No consistent explanation of the origin of things was vouchsafed, but change always involved the interaction of *yin* or *yang*, the negative (female) and the positive (male) principles respectively. The universe was sometimes depicted as having come from the *t'ai-i* (great unity), a personalized idea often equated with *tao* or with the dipper god (Hsüan-wu) and sometimes depicted as having come from the Heavenly Honoured One of Origin and Beginning (Yüan-shih T'ien chün), often identified with Yü-huang, the Jade Emperor. Perhaps the most honoured in the Taoist pantheon was the trinity (*san-ch'ing*) of the purities (essence, vital force, spirit), personalized respectively in Yüan-shih T'ien-chün, who presided over the Heaven of Jade Purity populated by holy men, Tao-chen (Lord of Tao), who presided over the Heaven of Superior Purity populated by pure men, and Lao Tzu, who presided over the Heaven of Great Purity populated by immortals. In the popular mind, however, the most important deity was the Jade Emperor, who was often not only identified with the first of the trinity but also depicted as the ruler, from his residence in the Great Bear constellation, of the universe and judge of rewards and punishments. The universe was divided into provinces, districts, and so on, in which the other deities occupied office as his minions. The pantheon also included Tsai-shen (god of wealth), Wen-ti (god of literature), Wen-shen (god of epidemics), Ho-shen (god of fire), Lung-wang (the dragon king connected with floods), the mountains T'ai-shan in Shantung and Hua-shan in Shensi, the kitchen god, other Confucian deities, Buddhas, *bodhisattvas*, local deities, deified heroes, stars, forces of nature, and the spirits of animals, insects, and human actions such as robbery, drunkenness, and fornication.

Secret lay societies were a common offshoot of Taoism. Some of them had a deep religious motivation—such as the Chin-tan Chiao (Golden Elixir of Life Society), which, organized during the T'ang period, still exists in China. Others were harmless vegetarian or self-culture groups. Still others—among them, the White Lotus Society (Pai-lien-hui) of the Mongol period—were of a criminal or immoral nature or became involved in revolutionary activities. The White Lotus Society also had Buddhist elements in it.

The Taoists had a sacred literature (*Tao Tsang*), which was in many ways an imitation of the Buddhist *Tripitaka*. It included the well-known philosophical works of early Taoism, various later ones attributed to early Taoist worthies, some Buddhist and Confucian writings, and those of the early utilitarian philosopher Mo Ti. The greater part of the canon was composed after the beginning of the Christian era though often attributed to legendary or mythological figures. Some of it was lost in the general destruction of Taoist works ordered by Kublai Khan in 1281, but it now consists of 5,200 *chüan* ('chapters'), as reconstituted in an edition of 1446 and supplemented in 1607.

Since the T'ang dynasty, the descendants of the first-century teacher Chang Tao-ling had been recognized by the emperors as titular heads of Taoism. They were in charge of a large establishment on the Dragon-Tiger Mountain in Kiangsi and had the title of *T'ien-shih*, heavenly teacher. The

T'ien-shih was supposed to possess great power over evil spirits, and charms from him were highly prized. The city gods and guardian deities of some of the territorial units of government were technically supposed to receive their appointments from him. Actually he possessed little control over Taoist organizations, and some of the sects did not recognize his authority at all.

Strictly speaking, the only Taoists were those *tao-shih* who had gone through some form of apprenticeship and had been formally admitted to one of the organizations. Most Chinese, however, were influenced to a greater or lesser extent by Taoist ideas and used the services of the *tao-shih*. These priests generally wore blue robes, let their beards and hair grow, and tied their hair up in a 'bun' on the head. They were divided roughly into three kinds: (1) a relatively small group of wandering ascetics or hermits; (2) a considerable group of celibate monks and some nuns who resided in monasteries, although the monks might spend considerable time in pilgrimages; and (3) a larger group of home *tao-shih*, who were married and had families, presided over some temple or shrine, and made a living largely by selling their services to the public. Monastic organization and discipline, while modelled to a certain extent on those of Buddhism, had to take account of the more individualistic nature of Taoism. Some of the wandering ascetics and hermits were almost certainly irregular *tao-shih*, never formally admitted to the ranks; they were those who, drawn by the mysticism of philosophic Taoism, late in life perhaps, had decided to abandon the world and seek contentment in meditation, solitude, and a life as simple and as near to nature as possible.

During the Yüan (Mongol) dynasty (1260–1368) the regular *tao-shih* comprised four main sects. One was the Chen-ta-tao sect, about which little is known. Another was the T'ai-i sect, which used charms and magic in an effort to recover the Great Unity that had existed before the separation of heaven and earth. Both of these sects gradually disappeared. The Cheng-i (True Unity) sect was orthodox, recognizing the headship of the Chang family. Most of its members were home *tao-shih*. It emphasized man's spirit or true self, using charms, magic, and ceremonials to preserve his original nature and prolong life. It was dominant in the south. The Ch'üan-chen (Preserve Purity) sect did not recognize the headship of the Chang family. It was organized along monastic lines. It emphasized the importance of man's vital force (*ch'i*), using potions, medicine, herbs, diet, meditation, breath control, and sex practices to prolong life. The White Cloud Monastery outside Peking was its headquarters, but it also had monasteries in the great monastic centres, T'ai-shan in Shantung and Hua-shan in Shensi. It had its principal strength in the north.

Most Chinese were acquainted with a considerable smattering of Taoist lore and were plenteously supplied with superstitions, which the *tao-shih* on occasion stimulated for their own benefit. Blocks of stone, allegedly from T'ai-shan, were considered a sure defence against demons. Worshippers and onlookers attended services in Taoist temples, and the *tao-shih* with his bag of tricks was always treated with awe and respect. In times of drought, flood, prestilence, or other calamity the services of the *tao-shih* were invariably utilized by public officials as well as private individuals. The numerous vegetarian and self-culture societies of laymen reflected Taoist influence. As we shall see in subsequent chapters, Taoist mythology and lore profoundly affected Chinese literature and art, and Taoist philosophy exerted great weight upon Chinese systematic thought, political theory, and political practice.

SHINTOISM

In the discussion of animism above, Shintoism was mentioned as the native religion of Japan. By 1300 Shintoism had been so nearly amalgamated with Buddhism as to make its future as an independent creed appear doubtful. It proved, however, to be so thoroughly embedded in the folkways of the people, and its deities, shrines, ceremonies, and mythology so tied up with national traditions and with the affairs of the imperial and other important families, that it never quite lost its independence. Although some of its shrines and rites were taken over by Buddhism, the worship of local Shinto deities, and the ancient rituals, legends, and animistic practices of the Japanese folk, continued.

The Shinto state cult also survived. It subscribed to a rationalized mythology according to which the islands and people of Japan were a special creation of the gods (*kami*) whereof the imperial family as direct descendants of the sun goddess (Amaterasu), chief of the gods, were the divinely appointed rulers. Under the sun goddess, with her principal shrine at Ise, came a pantheon of lesser deities. Okuninushi (Onamochi) was the great earth god of Idzumo. Ukemochi was the food goddess, worshipped at the Outer Shrine of Ise and (under the name of Inari, the rice god) at the Inari Shrine near Kyoto. Hachiman, generally revered as a god of war, was apparently a deification of the Emperor Ojin, with shrines at Usa, Kyoto, and Kamakura. Temmangu, god of learning, was a deified human. And a host of minor deities helped to supervise the welfare of the imperial family, the state, and an agricultural people.

A department of the imperial government had charge of the national Shinto shrines and was nominally responsible for the proper observance of festivals and ceremonials, but because of the decay of the imperial government the shrines were actually supported by pious shoguns, warriors, and commoners. Twenty-two of them were singled out for special imperial offerings, since their deities were often officially consulted and gave replies in the form of oracles. The priesthood attached to these shrines or assigned to the observance of Shinto ceremonies was hereditary. It boasted some of the most important families of Japan, such as the Nakatomi ritualists, the Imibe abstainers, the Urabe diviners, and the Sarume musicians and dancers. The established system of festivals and ceremonials included coronations, prayers and thanksgiving for harvests, appeasement of the deities of epidemic, fire, storm, and other disasters, and the two annual rituals in which the impurities of the people were washed away. In certain of these events the emperor played an important part. Offerings of rice, vegetables, meat, weapons, and implements were made to the *kami*, to the accompaniment of music and dances. Shinto's sacred literature included the *Kojiki* and *Nihonji*, which gave the official mythology and early history; various prayers (*norito*), ceremonials, and oracles were preserved in the *Engi shiki* (*Ceremonials of the Engi Era*) and in the records of the great shrines.

Buddhism early invaded the Shinto state cult, Buddha being identified with the sun goddess as early as 742. The Tendai sect of Buddhists gradually adopted the system of Ichi-jitsu (One-Truth) Shinto, in which Shinto deities were regarded as manifestations of the one transcendent Buddha. Shingon Buddhism penetrated Shinto even more effectively with its system of Ryōbu (Double-Aspect) Shinto. It considered all phenomena, including Buddhas, *bodhisattvas*, and other deities, mere manifestations of Vairocana (Dainichi), the one absolute reality, and fitted the Shinto *kami* into various circles of phenomena of decreasing permanence or reality moving outward from Vairocana; the sun goddess herself was identified with Dainichi, the Great Sun Buddha. More and more Shinto-Buddhist sanctuaries were set up, and an amalgamated priesthood (*shasō*) was established in many shrines. The Tendai centre at Mount Hiyei, near Kyoto, at one time alone had twenty-one large and one hundred small Shinto-Buddhist shrines, with others scattered throughout the country. In some places an outer shrine housed traditional Shinto ceremonials while Buddhist ceremonies were conducted in an inner shrine.

The close association with Buddhism, while threatening Shinto from one direction, strengthened it from another. Early Shinto had lacked a well developed philosophy or ethical system. In Buddhism, as well as in the Confucian ideas widely current in intellectual circles, the Shinto priesthood and other intellectuals whose fortunes were in one way or another associated with the national cult found building material for an effective philosophical foundation for Shintoism. The oracles of the Kamakura period (1192–1333) began to show a much greater ethical content. The priesthood of certain of the major Shinto shrines successfully resisted the encroachments of the Buddhist monks, and in the thirteenth century the Urabe family, which provided the priests for the Hirano and Yoshida shrines in Kyoto, and the Waterai family, which provided them for the Outer Shrine of Ise, began to develop a Shinto philosophy and ethics. The threat of the attempted Mongol invasions (1274 and 1281) and the efforts of the Emperor Go-Daigo after 1333 to establish himself as an actual ruler greatly stimulated Japanese nationalism. Interest in the imperial family grew and hence invigorated the native religion associated with it. A Shinto revival movement followed (see Chapter III).

ISLAM

Let us briefly recall the story, detailed in Volume III, of Islam's remarkable spread from its original domain. Under the leadership of Mohammed's successors (the caliphs), Muslim warriors quickly overran the Tigris–Euphrates valley, Iran, the lands to the east, including Sind, and to the west Syria, Egypt, the Maghrib, and Spain, at the same time threatening Constantinople with great armadas. By 750 the advance had been checked at Tours-Poitiers in Gaul, at Constantinople, in India, and in Transoxania. Another era of gradual expansion began in the eleventh century, and it went on unevenly throughout our period. The Punjab, Anatolia, and parts of western Sudan were among the areas opened to Islamic soldiers, saints, and merchants in the eleventh century, and later the expansion continued in these and other directions despite occasional setbacks. In the thirteenth century parts of Syria and Spain were conquered by Western Crusaders, and larger areas by the pagan Mongols. The Mongols were, however, Islamized and helped to spread Islam.

The god of the Muslims was Allah, the same God the Jews and Christians revered. Although Mohammed was considered his final and most perfect prophet, the holy figures of the Old and New Testaments were likewise respected as prophets and founders of true religions. Allah was worshipped through prayer (especially on Friday), alms, pilgrimages, fasting, and, above all, observance of the ritual law, which governed all aspects of life. This worship was based on the *Koran*, God's words spoken to Mohammed, and the *Ḥadith*, sacred reports of Mohammed's own words and deeds. The mosques were centres of ritual worship, education, and much of civil life. There was no Muslim priesthood, but *'ulamā'*, religious learned men, preserved the faith and usually served as *imāms*, or prayer leaders.

At the beginning of the fourteenth century Islam as a religion and as a social order had largely recovered from the worst immediate effects of the Mongol invasions of the preceding century and was vigorously expanding its hold in all directions. With the end even of the dubious claim of the Baghdad caliphate to general sovereignty, Islam was now undisguisably decentralized politically, as indeed it had long been in practice. The spiritual and intellectual issues that had arisen at the time of the caliphate had by now been in large measure replaced by others. In religious life the orders, or brotherhoods (*ṭarīqas*), of Islamic mystics (Ṣūfīs) had come to be more important, whether as actively creative groups or as disputatious rivals, than the earlier sects and schools of law or doctrine. In intellectual life the Hellenistic philosophical and scientific tradition had ceased to play a major independent role, while Persian, as we shall see, replaced Arabic for most purposes as the prevalent vehicle of culture in the large area stretching from Anatolia to Bengal, carrying with it a rich harvest of Iranian aesthetic and historical ideals.

In 1295, when the Mongol rulers of Iran adopted the Muslim faith of the population, Islam was more widespread than any other religion. It was predominant throughout northern Africa, the Middle East from Egypt and Anatolia through the Iranian plateau, and much of central Eurasia, and it was professed by the ruling minority in the Indus and Ganges basins and also by small groups along most of the coasts of the Indian Ocean and in some parts of China. Yet it was held together effectively as an international social and cultural body (despite the lack for some centuries past of any central political or other organizational ties) by a self-perpetuating system of personal and social law, the *sharī'a*.

The *sharī'a* was the sacred law of Islam. It governed personal behaviour ranging from etiquette, ritual, and profession of belief to points of marriage, inheritance, and civil contract. For generations it had been worked out in minute detail and was regarded as binding on all Muslims, but in fact it had never been the only law in Islamic life, and it had come to be applied with varying degrees of completeness among different Muslim peoples. For instance, many of the Berbers, of North Africa, followed an older customary law in such points as inheritance, and Turkish women were granted greater freedom than was the Islamic norm. Nevertheless, the *sharī'a* secured sufficient uniformity to make it possible for a Muslim from any country to be allowed full civil rights throughout the Dār al-Islām, the vast area ruled on Muslim principles. Accordingly, Islam in this period was not only a religion in the narrower sense but also the legal and cultural nucleus of an entire civilization.

The earlier divisions among Muslims as to the interpretation of their religion had to a large extent been overcome before 1300. Almost everywhere the predominant form of Islam was the Sunnī (or Sunnite) form, marked by acceptance of the principle of *ijmā'*—that agreement on points of law among the broad community of believers in the Koran established the validity of the points agreed upon. Among the Sunnīs four schools, each of which interpreted the *sharī'a* differently in secondary matters, had survived all competition and had become mutually recognized as definitive. The Mālikite school prevailed in the relatively rigoristic west, centred in North Africa. Elsewhere the Ḥanafite school—adopted among most of the Turkish peoples—and the Shāfi'ite school, slightly more active theologically, existed side by side, along with a sprinkling of rudiment-minded Ḥanbalites, who persistently criticized the compromises that Muslims in actuality accepted. The principle of *taqlīd*— that further schools were not to be developed and the already recognized schools were no longer subject to basic changes—insured them stability so long as the general social conditions of the world remained as they were. Their several traditions were by now so close together that they could be taught under a common roof.

Scattered widely among the Sunnī, and in emotional opposition to them, were the Shī'ites. The Shī'ites exalted the special claims of 'Alī, a son-in-law of Mohammed, and his descendants. They were divided into a variety of often mutually hostile persuasions, but the Twelver Shī'a (accepting twelve *imāms*, or spiritual leaders, of the house of 'Alī) was the most common during our period. Though the Shī'ites continued to be distrusted by the majority, their principle of *taqiyya* (pretence of conformity) allowed them to take part in the general Islamic life.

In the late Middle Ages, especially after 1300, arose a number of Shī'ite movements in the form of Ṣūfī *ṭarīqas* (brotherhoods). With the downfall (thirteenth century) of Ismā'īlism as a political power and with the failure of orthodox Shī'ism to gain power under the Mongols, Shī'ite tendencies of an unorthodox type gained wide acceptance among Persians, Kurds, Turks, and Arabs. These groups stressed a secret wisdom which the believer could share and which Islamic orthodoxy merely symbolized in its legalistic doctrine. The Ḥurūfīs, for instance, interpreted the Koran in terms of a letter and number symbolism, with which they expressed a gnostic doctrine. Such ideas were especially popular among the Turkish and the Kurdish tribes, which sometimes attached themselves as units to one or another line of Shī'ite teachers. By calling the teachers Ṣūfīs, they shielded themselves from Sunnī persecution. In fourteenth-century Iran amid the political uncertainties that followed upon the collapse of Mongol power there, a large part of Khurāsān was ruled by a Shī'ite group called the Sarbadārs. Their republican disorders were condemned bitterly by the courts of the surrounding amirs, but they were not finally put down until the fanatically Sunnī Timur (Tamerlane) brought devastation among them.

In its Sunnī form, Ṣūfism, Islamic mysticism, had come to be accepted by most Sunnīs as an essential part of the faith, and as a personal religion Islam was largely dominated by it as expressed through the Ṣūfī *ṭarīqas*. These brotherhoods had been developing in the preceding two centuries, and by 1300 they offered varied channels for emotional or speculative piety. Some of the most important were already widely spread, but all the *khānaqāhs* (convents or local meeting-places) remained under the authority of a common head, resident ordinarily at the revered tomb of the founder. The Qādiriyya, with its tendency to extravagant exaltation of its founder's eminence, was found far beyond its centre in Baghdad. The pattern of *ṭarīqa* organization had been established by orders such as the sensitively ethical Rifā'iyya in Iraq, the Iranian Kubrāwiyya, the wonder-working Aḥmadiyya (recently founded) in Egypt, the at first lay-oriented and then orthodox Shādhiliyya in the west, the ecstatic Mawlawiyya (the 'whirling dervishes') in Anatolia, and the Chishtiyya in India, marked by the humane and unworldly spirit of Niẓām al-Dīn Awliyā' (d. 1325). Quite outside the regular orders there wandered throughout the Muslim territories such ascetic or antinomian devotees as the Qalandars, who rejected even the limited institutionalization of Ṣūfism.

In 1300 Islam was in the midst of an active wave of expansion, the result partly of political activity and partly of individual missionary effort in both

Islamic and other areas. The disappearance of the Baghdad caliphate did not handicap this expansion, for the caliphs had rarely contributed to the spread of Islam beyond their own subjects, and for a long time the caliph's powers, except in a narrow area around Baghdad, had been reduced to purely ceremonial functions. After 1300 the title of caliph lost even ceremonial importance. Many independent and God-fearing Muslim rulers assumed the rather empty title and therewith claimed command over the military and administrative forces of Islam. Matters of worship or doctrine as such remained outside any caliph's province except as he taught by example or enforced by the sword the decisions of the *'ulamā'*. Rulers freely called each other 'caliph' out of courtesy, and the title was never the most important in any ruler's etiquette. Its exact use was significant in our period to none save a few rigorist *'ulamā'*.

As Islam expanded, a number of *ghāzī* (frontier warrior) states carried it into the Aegean and southeastern Europe. Ultimately the greatest of these was the Ottoman state, which in the fourteenth century was ready to absorb the larger part of the Balkan Peninsula. This advance into southeastern Europe was offset by the reduction of the Muslim area in southwestern Europe to a small corner of Spain, but there (and more permanently in the Maghrib) the Muslims stabilized their position for a long time.

Islam was meanwhile being more widely accepted in western Sudan. There Islam replaced not one of the great world religions but tribal faiths. The trade and political organization of western Sudan, already well developed (see Chapter I) before the advent of Islam, was furthered by the Muslims, who were able to offer a broader world outlook and contacts with the international society of civilized peoples. Islam was rapidly adopted in the Sudanese cities and among the ruling classes, and was gradually brought to more backward elements of the population.

By 1300 Muslim political domination of India was already far advanced. Islam had long controlled the Indus valley, and Islamic merchants had been known in Gujarat and other Indian coastal areas for centuries. When Delhi, occupied in 1193, became the capital of a series of Islamic dynasties in the north, all India felt the full pressure of Islam. By 1300 north India except parts of Rajputana had fallen under Islamic rule, and by 1327 the Deccan, and for a time even the far south, was under Muslim sultans. The Islamic conquerors brought with them Afghan, Turk, and Persian soldiers, officials, and fortune hunters, many of whom took Hindu wives; and many Hindus embraced Islam out of conviction or as a means of social advancement. Even so, the number of Muslims in India remained relatively small, though significant in the main cities. Their greatest strength was in the Punjab and Sind, where their influence had been exerted longest. While the Delhi sultans were Sunnites, not all of their followers were. Moreover, quite apart from the activities of the sultans, the Ismā'ili Shī'ite sect won many converts in India, sometimes whole castes.

The tide of Islam also swept into central Asia and farther east. From central Asia, Islamic traders and adventurers reached north China at an early date, and Islamic traders were known in Canton from the T'ang dynasty onward. By 1300 much of the Tarim Basin was Muslim, while important Islamic elements were to be found in Kansu, north Burma, and Yunnan. Islam was first introduced into Malaya and the East Indies by Arabic, Gujarati, and Bengali traders, who had been well-known throughout the area for a long time. It acquired its first political foothold in the Pacific islands, however, only in the late thirteenth century, when the seaport kingdoms of Perlak and Pasai in western Sumatra came under the rule of Islamic sultans. Marco Polo in 1292 noted that many of the inhabitants of Perlak were Muslim.

JUDAISM

Judaism in 1300, as during many previous centuries, was international in scope. Beginning in some instances before the rise of Christianity, Jewish communities had grown up all over the Eastern Hemisphere—in China and India, as well as in the Middle and Near East, Ethiopia, and Europe.

Small communities of Jews or sometimes isolated families and individuals had lived in most of the commercial regions of Europe since the early Middle Ages or earlier. In eastern Europe they were to be found in Byzantine centres such as Thebes (as silk manufacturers) and in the Balkan provinces of the Eastern Empire; in central Europe in Hungary, Poland, the Rhineland (especially at Mainz), Italy, and Sicily; and in western Europe in France, England, and both Christian and Mohammedan Spain. Although sometimes segregated in ghettoes, persecuted as infidels, and occasionally massacred in pogroms (especially during the Crusading period), in most regions of the West they prospered. This was particularly true of the Sephardic Jews (those of Spain and Portugal), who in Moorish territory were permitted to rise in social status and frequently acted as 'cultural middlemen' between Moors and Christians. The Ashkenazim (Jews of eastern and central Europe) were less privileged but generally were permitted, though on a precarious basis, to engage in commerce and money-lending.

To the east the Jews generally found more friendly conditions. An isolated community of *Bene Israel* lived for centuries in Cochin, India, and possibly elsewhere along the Malabar coast. In Syria a remnant of undispersed Jews, having endured the hardships of Roman imperial and Byzantine Christian rule, continued to enjoy relative tolerance under various Muslim dynasties. By 1300 Palestine itself was overwhelmingly Muslim, with only a weak minority of Jews. Under the tolerant rule of Persian Muslims, Judaism had flourished in the Euphrates Valley, developing near Baghdad an intellectual centre of international influence in the Gaonate (see Volume III), but intellectual leadership of the Jews had passed before 1300 to Europe, particularly Spain, France, and Germany. The ravages of the Mongols and the expansion of the Ottoman Turks ended the growth and importance of the Persian wing of Judaism, though until the seventeenth century Persian Jews were not actively persecuted. Smaller settlements of Jews existed in the *mellahs* (ghettos) of North Africa, among the Falashas of Ethiopia, in Arabia, and in the Far East. They were frequently isolated from, and exercised little influence on, Jews elsewhere.

The religion of the Jews was a forerunner of the religions of the Christians and the Muslims, but the Jews accepted neither Jesus as the messiah nor Mohammed as a prophet. They had no explicit creed, but a number of basic beliefs were common to them. Judaism was strictly monotheistic. It held high in the minds of its adherents as the 'chosen people' the hope of an ideal end to history—a messianic era, which some of them conceived as a resurrection at some future time of supernatural judgment and others as a possibly near natural event, the return of the Jews to control of Zion. Their sacred literature comprised particularly the unalterable revelation of God's will to Moses in the *Torah*—i.e. the Pentateuch—and parts of the *Talmud*, which comprises the collection of their oral law (*Mishnah*) and of the commentary upon it (*Gemara*).

The scattered Jewish communities had only a loose hierarchy. The descendants of the ancient priests (*Kohanim*) were honoured wherever they could be found, but the diaspora had created conditions under which any Jew, if he were sufficiently versed in the sacred literature, might take upon himself the leadership in performing religious services. Every community that had a synagogue, nevertheless, had a *hazzan* ('prayer leader') and a *rabbi* ('teacher'). The rabbis by 1300 had become the chief figures in their respective communities, some of them enjoying great prestige in other communities as well. Hebrew was the learned and holy language of the synagogue, but Jews commonly spoke also the vernacular of the countries in which they lived, though they might sometimes write it in Hebrew characters. Among the practices that distinguished them from Christians was their strict observance of their Sabbath (from sundown on Friday to sundown on Saturday) and of the Mosaic dietary code (*kashrut*).

In north Africa and in Spain, Judaism was perhaps beginning to decline at the beginning of the fourteenth century. In Europe the Black Death intensified the intolerance of the Jews, fortifying the traditional hatred of them because they were infidels, aliens, property-holders, and money-lenders with the charge that they were deliberate spreaders of the plague. In the cities of Germany, by the second half of the fourteenth century they were more often confined to ghettoes. Several public disputations regarding tolerance took place between Christians and Jews from 1200 to 1500 in France and Spain. That at Tortosa in Spain (1413–14) was perhaps the most important and the longest, lasting a year and a half,[18] but with foregone conclusions. At best the debates confirmed each side in its beliefs. The expulsion of the Jews from various parts of Europe during the early centuries of our period is noted elsewhere (see Chapters I and III).

CHRISTIANITY

The numerous administrative, political, and theological conflicts that beset Christianity also are noted elsewhere (see Chapters I, III, and IV). Here only certain features of Christian organization and geography will be indicated.

*   *   *

Orthodox Christianity

About 1300 Christianity was dominant in nearly all of Europe. In eastern Europe, Orthodox (i.e. Greek Catholic) Christianity, already divided into national units (Russian, Bulgarian, Serbian, etc.), was on the defensive. From Asia Minor the Turkish Muslims of the Ottoman dynasty were threatening invasion, and the Tatars ruled in Russia. In the Balkans the independent Christian rulers of Serbia and Bulgaria had shattered the already weakened authority of the Orthodox patriarchate of Constantinople. The spiritual influence of Greek Catholicism still prevailed, but the machinery of church administration was controlled by the local rulers, and, in addition, a number of heretical sects weakened the hold of the separate local church systems upon the minds of the people. Of these heresies, in the fourteenth century, the Bogomils (see Chapter I) were the most numerous. Originating in Bulgaria, the Bogomils had spread to Serbia and to Bosnia, where they became particularly prominent. Other heretics with similar Manichaean and gnostic beliefs also challenged the Orthodox faith. The heretical creeds were frequently recruited from malcontents whose dissidence was due less to doctrinal convictions than to protest against ritualistic formalism and patrician control of the church.

Under Tatar domination the Russian church continued, as before essentially independent of Byzantine Constantinople's control, while, thanks to the opportunistic Mongolian religious policy, its metropolitans grew wealthy and powerful. The metropolitan see, located in Kiev until 1299, moved permanently in 1325 to the much younger and thitherto less renowned city of Moscow, where its independence and prestige as a symbol of national unity mounted. The Russian metropolitans were appointed by the patriarch of Constantinople and remained nominally subordinate to him and the Constantinople synod until 1439 (see Chapter III). All in all, however, before the Turks conquered the Byzantine capital, though Orthodox Greek Catholicism remained strong in cultural and spiritual influence, it constituted only a loose federation of regional churches.

*   *   *

Roman Catholicism

In the West about 1300, the Roman Catholic Church was rounding out its most successful century. It had been stronger and more firmly unified during the thirteenth century than ever before or since. The new mendicant orders of

Franciscans and Dominicans had given the papacy an effective army of spiritual warriors. But for the clash of Boniface VIII (1294–1303) with the English and French national monarchs, the papacy might have continued its spiritual supremacy and political domination in Western Europe (see Chapter III).

Even so, the Catholic Church preserved its effective control over doctrine. The Inquisition discouraged heresy, and the preaching friars spread devotion. Canon law was respected, and the church courts were powerful. Universities continued to be strongholds of rationalized but conservative orthodoxy, thanks to the learning and keenness of Scholastics such as Thomas Aquinas (see Volume III). Secular education also was a province of the clergy, who in that realm could enjoy a life that was secure and prosperous. The arts were willing handmaidens of the church, and social life still centred largely in cathedral or parish.

In northern Europe, under the guise of 'crusades', Germans and Poles were continuing the *Drang nach Osten*, expanding eastward and northward into the Baltic regions beyond the Vistula River. In the thirteenth century the Teutonic Knights, recently removed from the Holy Land to Hungary, had transferred their crusading activities to the Prussian frontier. They had suffered serious setbacks at the hands of the Mongols (1241) and of Duke Alexander (Nevsky) of Novgorod (1242) and some bloody revolts on the part of their non-Christian subjects in Prussia and Lithuania. Nevertheless, by 1309, when the grand master of the Teutonic Order established headquarters at Marienburg in Prussia, they had extended an iron Germanic Christian control over the Baltic regions and were dominant in Poland.

The Teutonic regime meant forced conversion and enslavement of the native populations to German landlords. Besides, German immigrants, both peasants and burghers, kept thronging to the east, attracted by favourable conditions of settlement on the land and in the towns. The Teutonic Order reached its greatest power and prosperity during the fourteenth century, only to decline thereafter, and a united Poland–Lithuania was to break its military power at the Battle of Tannenberg in 1410. Nevertheless, until 1466 (the Peace of Thorn), when the order's territories became subject to Polish overlordship, it remained practically a sovereign government. The history of the Teutonic Order bears eloquent testimony to the rapid secularization of Europe's crusading ideals. Though never altogether spiritual, Christendom's earlier failure to capture the Holy Land contrasts vividly with the brutal success of the 'crusades' against the Spanish Muslims and the Baltic heathens.

Catholic expansion during the fourteenth and fifteenth centuries was not impelled by national, secular, or materialistic considerations alone. King Louis IX of France and Raimon Lull of Spain tried to persuade the church of the possibility of converting rather than slaying Muslims in northern Africa. Lull learned Arabic, established a missionary college, and died (ca. 1315) a martyr in Tunis. At the beginning of the fourteenth century Pierre

Dubois, in *De Recuperatione Terrae Sanctae*, set forth detailed suggestions for pacific missionary methods. His programme included the conversion of the heathen not only to the Christian faith but also to Christian civilization. He urged that the training of young men and women for missions should comprise the study of oriental languages and medicine as well as Christian theology. This ideal, of course, was not put into operation.

*   *   *

Christianity in Asia

A considerable number of non-Catholic Christians were scattered throughout Asia from Syria and Mesopotamia to Peking and from Samarkand to south India. The Mongol conquerors of the early thirteenth century had, to be sure, killed or dispersed many of them, but during the following century, the religious tolerance of the Mongols, their policy of employing learned or technically trained personnel regardless of race or creed, and their generally favourable attitude towards trade and travel contributed to the growth of Christian communities in their lands. Among the non-Catholic Christians there were several Monophysite groups—the Armenian Christians of Asia Minor and Iran, the Jacobite Christians of Syria, and the Coptic Christians of Egypt and Abyssinia—and the Nestorian Christians, who were the most numerous. The major Nestorian centres were in Mesopotamia, Persia, and Russian Turkestan, but they were also widely scattered throughout India, and the 'Syrian' Christians of south India, if not Nestorians, were closely related to them. Many of the Uighurs and Keraits of Chinese Turkestan and the Naimans and Onguts of southwestern Mongolia were Nestorians. The Mongol conquests scattered these people as far westward as Persia, but the largest groups probably went to China. In the early fourteenth century Nestorians were widely dispersed in China and at one time or another had flourishing churches at Khanbaliq (today's Peking), Chin-chiang, Yang-chou, and Hangchow. The Alans, who originated in the Caucasus and were introduced into China as Mongol military contingents, seem to have been Greek Orthodox at first but were later won over by the Franciscans.

During the late thirteenth and early fourteenth centuries the Dominicans and the Franciscans were active as missionaries. The former were especially occupied in Mesopotamia and Persia, and the latter in south Russia, Turkestan, and China, while both had missions in India. The Dominican Jordanus (Jordan Catalani) disappeared in the course of some daring missionary enterprise in India in the 1320's and 1330's. The Franciscan Giovanni di Monte Corvino (1246–1328), after some success in Persia and India, went by sea to China, where he established a Franciscan mission in Khanbaliq (1294). In 1307 he was made archbishop of Khanbaliq, aided eventually by suffragan bishops in China, central Asia, and south Russia. The China mission flourished, with imperial support for some time, and the Mongol government created a special bureau to regulate Christians. As reinforcements arrived from the West, other Franciscan centres were gradually established—at Hangchow, Ch'üan-chou (Zaitun, a bishopric), Yang-chou, and probably Nanking, Shantung, and other places. The last successful effort to reinforce the Peking (Khanbaliq) mission seems to have been the expedition in which Giovanni di Marignolli participated as papal legate; he was in central Asia (Almaliq in Ili, a bishopric under Peking) in 1340, Peking in 1342, and India (Quilon) in 1348, and back in the papal see at Avignon in 1353. Although Dominican and Franciscan missionaries made a serious effort to proselytize Muslims, they appear to have given more attention to winning non-Catholic Christians to Roman allegiance than to converting Muslims, for which they ran the risk of capital punishment in Islamic countries.[19] Their zeal often brought them into conflict with the Nestorians, particularly in Islamic countries.

After 1350, as the Mongol kingdoms of western and central Asia disintegrated or their rulers were converted to Islam, conditions grew less favourable to Christianity. Travel became more difficult, and missionary reinforcements failed to reach their destinations. The Ming rulers (1368–1644) proved more hostile to foreign faiths than their predecessors had been, and at the same time Muslim opposition increased in the Middle East, central Asia, and India. Under these circumstances all types of Christianity declined in Asia. Both Roman Catholics and Nestorians gradually disappeared in central Asia, and though Nestorians remained on in Mesopotamia and Persia, their number diminished. Christianity in India was eventually confined largely to the Christians of the Malabar coast. Catholic missionary activity throughout the East fell off from about 1350 until after the great discoveries of the 1490's.

* * *

Of all the adherents of the religions that in modern times have proved to have major importance, in 1300, with the exception of the Shintoists and the Jews, the Christians were probably the least numerous. Like the devout almost everywhere, they believed that life was but a brief interval between birth and the hereafter, which might bring eternal reward or punishment but in either case was not reached by human volition alone. This other-worldly view was to be more thoroughly questioned by Europeans than by others in the centuries to follow.

NOTES TO CHAPTER II

1. In Professor O. Lacombe's opinion there is a distinction to be made as follows: 'While all religions are characterized by the feeling that the sacred is quasi-immediately present to the profane, the group of great monotheistic religions—Judaism, Christianity, Islam—emphasizes the transcendence of God, not omitting His immanent presence. In the main religions of the Far East, on the contrary, the emphasis is more frequently placed on immanence.'

2. While this is so, Professor O. Lacombe also stresses that the persistence of matriarchal institutions in more than one region of the world here described should not be forgotten.

3. Juan Comas, 'Principales contribuciones indigenas precolombinas a la cultura universal', *Journal of World History*, III (1956), pp. 196–230.

4. *Ibid.*, p. 227.

5. *Ibid.*, quoting A. Caso, 'El Pueblo de Sol' (Mexico, 1953), p. 18.

6. W. Norman Brown, *The United States and India and Pakistan* (Cambridge, Mass., 1953), p. 28.

7. To Professor O. Lacombe while it is permissible to speak of the monotheistic *tendency* of certain forms of Hindu religious life, Hinduism as a whole makes no claim to be monotheist in the Christian or Islamic sense of the term.

8. Professor O. Lacombe indicates that Kashmir Shivaism, now becoming better known, is of great doctrinal importance and occupies a unique place in the history of Indian philosophies.

9. The literal meaning of the word 'avatāra' is 'descent', that is to say the descent of the divine into the earthly condition.

10. Surendranath Dasgupta, *A History of Indian Philosophy* (Cambridge, 1940), III, pp. 399–402.

11. Professor O. Lacombe emphasizes that whatever the differences in theological concept as to the nature of the Christian cult which distinguish Protestant 'congregationalists' from preceding Christianity, the essence of the Christian cult is to be at once communal and personal. Hindu temple rites cannot be viewed in this perspective. The domestic rites referred to on pp. 123–24, on the other hand, concern essentially the family group.

12. The word *skandha* describes literally a major ramified articulation such as a shoulder or a tree trunk. This leads us to the idea of a class-determining group. The five *skandhas* of Buddhism are the five main differentiated groups into which are divided the physical and psychic elements of the universe. (O. Lacombe.)

13. Nirvāna means literally 'extinction': that is the extinction of the miseries and servitudes of transmigration.

14. Bodhisattva: a being destined to Awakening, a future Buddha.

15. Professor O. Lacombe points out that despite the empiric resemblances pointed out here, it is important not to lose sight of certain essential differences between Christian, Islamic, Hindu, and Buddhist concepts concerning the relationship between spiritual and temporal powers.

16. Professor O. Lacombe emphasizes, however, that after attaining Awakening, Buddha deliberated within himself whether it was opportune to show others the difficult way of deliverance he had discovered. Despite the danger of misunderstanding, he opted for the way of compassionate preaching.

17. From the *Kan-ying p'ien*, as quoted in K. L. Reichlet, *Religion in Chinese Garments* (London, 1951), p. 91.

18. Salo W. Baron, 'Some Recent Literature on the History of the Jews in the Pre-Emancipation Era (1300–1800)', *Journal of World History*, VII (1962), pp. 145–6.

19. R. P. Beaver, 'Recent Literature on Overseas Missionary Movements from 1300 to 1800', *ibid.*, I (1953), pp. 142–3.

CHAPTER III

MAJOR RELIGIOUS EVENTS (1300–1500)

BEFORE 1300, religion and politics were, generally speaking, so closely bound together that, despite the frequent clash of temporal with spiritual authority, they constituted a natural and unquestioned association, separable only by a more or less conscious intellectual effort. Europeans, however, had begun to depart to a conspicuous degree from this common pattern even before 1300. In the succeeding ages the Christian church was to be relegated in some areas to a position subordinate to the state, and in others to a sphere altogether separate, at least in theory, from government. Still, in Christian as in other countries religion retained a close identification with society and politics. (Map V.)

HINDUISM

By 1300 all of north India except parts of Rajputana was under Muslim control, and in 1310–11 a great raid overran the extreme south. By 1327, of the southern kingdoms only the Pāndyas in the extreme south and Warangal and Orissa on the east coast were fully independent. In 1336 around the city of Vijayanagar a Hindu empire began to rise, and from 1373 until the city's destruction in 1565 it was the centre of Hindu power and influence in the south. From the middle of the fourteenth century onward, most of the rest of India except for Orissa and the knightly Rajput clans, which were never fully subjected, was under Muslim rule.

The Koran was less friendly to the eastern religions than it was to Judaism and Christianity, and, at least partly for that reason, most of the early Muslim rulers in India were more fanatical than their counterparts to the west. No systematic effort was made to wipe out Hinduism or convert all Hindus to Islam, but sporadic attacks, varying in intensity from place to place and ruler to ruler, were frequent. Muslim rulers destroyed the temples, images, schools, monasteries, and religious books of Hindus, Buddhists, and Jains alike. They persecuted Hindus in general and slaughtered monks and priests in particular. They forbade or discouraged Hindu religious festivals and pilgrimages and subjected non-Muslims to the *jizya* (poll tax) regularly and on occasion to a pilgrim's tax besides. Since, however, the invaders were relatively few, they had to run their government with the aid of submissive Hindu princes and administrators, who contrived to blunt the cutting edge of Muslim persecution. At times influential groups escaped the poll tax altogether or paid it at a reduced rate.

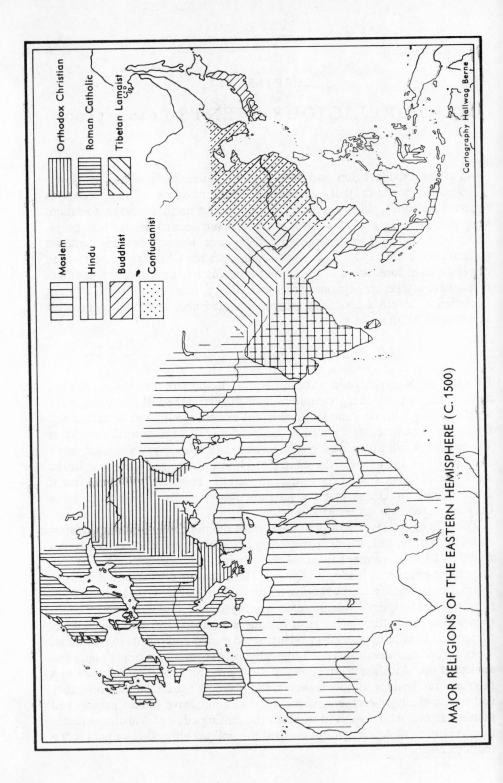

MAJOR RELIGIONS OF THE EASTERN HEMISPHERE (C. 1500)

Orthodox Christian

Roman Catholic

Tibetan Lamaist

Moslem

Hindu

Buddhist

Confucianist

Cartography Hallwag Berne

The Muslim conquest affected Hindu religious developments in a number of ways. (1) Hinduism lost ground to Islam, which gradually became established as a major religion in north India. The immigration of Afghans, Persians, Turks, and Arabs, and the offspring of mixed marriages (usually Hindu women to Muslim men) augmented the Islamic ranks. Besides, many Hindus, usually from the lower castes, became Muslims, sometimes out of religious conviction, sometimes to avoid the poll tax or persecution, often to escape the caste system itself. (2) Both Hinduism and Islam gained at the expense of Jainism and especially Buddhism. Buddhism, already declining in India when the Muslim conquest began, had become concentrated in monastic foundations and popular Tantric cults. The destruction of monasteries and monks dealt the *coup de grâce* to the older forms of Buddhism in India. The Tantrics, when they did not turn to Islam, adopted Shāktism or the most emotional forms of Vishnuism. All three religions are still strong in Bengal and Assam. (3) The popular *bhakti* cults grew in numbers and influence. The monotheism of Islam and the miseries of constant war and persecution seem to have encouraged emotional surrender to a god through whose grace salvation could be attained by loving devotion. The Brahmans, perhaps in order to maintain their position against Islamic competition, conceded more and more to the need of the masses for a simple, emotional solution of the problem of salvation. Many of them accepted the *bhakti* ideas, which became less austere and meditative, more emotional, and even sensual. The more personal and lovable *avatāras* of Vishnu—Rāma and Krishna—came to the fore, as did also the terrible but personal goddesses of Shāktism. (4) Cults arose which borrowed from both Muslim and Hindu. Hindus under Muslim rule eventually took over Islamic ideas about dress, ceremonials, the seclusion of women, and other features of Islamic culture, and some Persian Ṣūfīs who settled in India found in turn much of interest and merit in Hindu thought and religion. Leaders then arose who tried to unite Muslim and Hindu in cults that combined elements from the religions of both. (5) Finally, Hinduism gave way to Hīnayāna Buddhism or Chinese influences in the Indo-Chinese peninsula and to Islam in Malaya and the East Indies.

Developments within the several Hindu sects differed considerably. The Smārta traditionalists, for example, underwent few major changes during this period. The Muslim persecutions and the growing emphasis on *bhakti* seem to have caused a reduction in their ranks, since some of them tended to concentrate their affections on Shiva as the most intellectual of the *bhakti* deities, but they continued as a strong group. They unquestionably flourished in the Vijayanagar Empire, which apparently protected all Hindu cults including the Jains. Many of Vijayanagar's emperors were traditionalists or Shivaite, though some were Vishnuite.

Northern Shivaism appears to have suffered considerably at the hands of the invaders. Kashmir Shivaism ceased altogether except among a few scholars. The Pāshupatas vanished from the north and survived only as relatively isolated groups in the south. Despite persecution and massacres, however, northern Shivaism remained a powerful cult, imbued by hardship with greater devotion. It probably also began at this stage the process of absorbing the local Nāth cult of Bengal.

In the south the Shiva Siddhānta school continued under the protection of Vijayanagar. Great Shivaite temples prospered at Madura, Tinnevelly, Tanjore, and elsewhere despite Muslim raids. The theologian Umāpati (fl. 1313) completed the Tamil canon with eight doctrinal treatises, which took the form of poetical commentaries on earlier works, discussions of divine grace, and catechisms and critiques of other faiths (see Chapter X). The devotional element remained strong in this school.

Anti-Brahman influences added vigour to the Lingāyats. This sect flourished, while the affiliated sect of the Ārādhyas probably declined. The Lingāyats spread throughout the Kanarese-speaking areas of south India, and their creed is said to have been the state religion of Mysore (1399–1600).

With Buddhism's decline Shāktism seems to have expanded in Bihar, Bengal, and Assam despite Muslim persecutions. Pillage and carnage seem to have stimulated the worship of destructive goddesses, and local goddess cults like those of Chandī and Manasā, which had already become the last refuge of Tantric Buddhism in India, acquired new importance. Brahmans began to serve these cults and to integrate them with Shāktism. Thus Manasā, partly snake goddess and partly Buddhist figure, ultimately became the daughter of Shiva, and Chandī, partly female *bodhisattva*, became Shiva's wife, identified with Durgā.

This process of amalgamation went on until the eighteenth century or later. An extensive oral tradition relating to these goddesses appeared in Bengali writing (see Chapter X). Shakti *tantras*, such as the *Kālikā-purāna* (which gave prescriptions for human and animal sacrifices), became so numerous that digests for the use of Shāktas were compiled. Shākta saints also emerged. One of them, who may have flourished in the late-fifteenth century, was Sharvānanda, a poor illiterate of Mehar, to whom the Divine Mother was reported to have revealed Herself one night as he was repeating a *mantra* in accordance with a particularly dangerous ritual. Mehar has since become a place of pilgrimage, with an annual festival in January.

*   *   *

Developments in India

The most spectacular Hinduist developments of the period came within Vishnuism. Equalitarian tendencies arose in opposition to the caste system. Devotional intensity increased with the growth of Rāma and Krishna worship. Efforts to unite Hindu and Muslim emerged.

No striking changes took place among the Mādhvas, who remained aristocratic and puritan. Dancing girls were not allowed in their temples; cleanliness was demanded; and although members of most castes could belong to their sect, only Brahmans could be ecclesiastics. The Mādhvas gradually became separated into two groups, the Vyāsakūtas, who accepted only Sanskrit scriptures, and the more numerous Dāsakūtas, who had somewhat more popular tendencies and accepted Kanarese scriptures.

The origin of the Nimāvat or Shanakādi sect of north India is very obscure. We have already mentioned the debate regarding the date of birth of Nimbārka, its founder (see Chapter II). He lived and taught near Muttra, and the sect developed there and in Bengal. If Nimbārka is placed in the fourteenth century, the rise of the Nimāvats coincides with the upsurge of the popularity of Krishna and Rādhā. Because of their devotion to Krishna the Nimāvats were unquestionably connected with the popular Krishna–Rādhā cults of the period.

The widespread adoration of Krishna and Rādhā was expressed by the Rajput poetess Mīrā Bāī and the great vernacular poets of Bihar and Bengal in the early fifteenth century (see Chapter X). So devoted to Krishna was Mīrā Bāī that he is supposed to have engulfed her in his embrace. A Krishnaite sub-sect, generally considered a branch of the Vallabhas (i.e. of the Rudra sect; see Chapter II), bears her name. These earthy poets seem to have had a deep spiritual affinity with the Rudra sect. In fact, their affinity seems deeper than that of the restrained Maratha religious poets, who are sometimes, though with less reason, also associated with the Rudra sect.

The sect to which these Maratha poets belonged centred upon the temple of Pandharpur. Its deity was named Vitthobā, Vitthala, or Pāndurang. The first two of these names were dialectal variations of Vishnu, and the last was an epithet of Shiva, but the Maratha deity was popularly associated with Krishna and his wife Rukminī. The sect, as portrayed by its mystic poets, accepted the pantheistic monism of Shankara but believed intensely in the saving grace of Krishna. It emphasized the importance of knowledge, meditation, humility, preservation of life, moral purity, and devotion, and largely ignored Rādhā and Krishna in his cowherd character.

Of the mystic Maratha poets, Nāmdev (c. 1400) was the outstanding one. His message was that God was everywhere, accessible to all without ceremonials, austerities, philosophy, or pilgrimages through love and steadfast faith, praise, and devotion. At times Nāmdev denounced images as limitations of God. Except for its adoration of Krishna, this school resembled the Rudra sect less than it did the Rāmāt sect of Rāmānanda (see below), and Nāmdev may have been under the influence of Rāmānanda.

The Shrī-Vishnuite sect of Rāmānuja was in the process of dividing into two groups as the fourteenth century opened. The two were known as the Tengalais, or Southerners, and the Vadagalais, or Northerners, although both were confined to south India. The Southerners were inclined to innovation, tending to disregard the Vedas and Sanskrit tradition, and to consider the

Tamil *Nālāyiram* sufficient as scripture, while the Northerners insisted upon the Sanskrit as well as the Tamil tradition. The Northerners held that true surrender to God can follow only upon good works and individual effort; in order to be saved, one must exert oneself and grasp God as a young monkey grasps its mother. The Southerners, on the other hand, discounted personal effort, aside from faith and self-surrender, and insisted that the grace of a forgiving God grasped the soul as a cat does its kittens. The Southerners held that Lakshmī was created and finite, though divine, and hence merely a mediator without power to bestow grace directly, while the Northerners held her to be equal with Vishnu. Both groups laid great stress on guidance by gurus, though each had a different succession of religious teachers and quarrelled with the other for control of the temples which they used in common. Each developed different sectarian marks and ceremonials, although both branded members with the conch shell and discus. Both were scrupulous about caste observances and the ceremonial purity of their food and meals. Although each admitted lower castes (*shūdras*), a special class of priests, called *satanis*, had to minister to them. The Southerners, being, on the whole, more tolerant towards the lower castes, gradually became the more numerous. Pillai Lokācārya (d. 1327), the effective founder of the Southerners, wrote numerous treatises in Tamil, including simple guides for women and the lower castes. Perhaps the Southerners' chief saint and teacher was Manavāla Mahāmuni (*c.* 1370–1443), who wrote numerous commentaries and poems and a small treatise on daily worship in the home. Vedānta Deshika (*c.* 1269–1369), 'the lion of poets and philosophers', was the most famous of the Northerners. Though a poor householder who travelled a great deal, he was the author of over a hundred works in both Tamil and Sanskrit (see Chapter X).

The Rāmāts differed little from the Vadagalais in doctrine, and although the Rāmāts dispensed with branding, both wore the same sectarian marks. Rāmānanda, founder of the Rāmāt sect, probably flourished about 1400. Whether he was a southerner or a northerner by birth, the scene of his main activities certainly was the north. He was a follower of Rāmānuja but, for infringing its rules regarding eating, was reputedly expelled from the Rāmānuja sect—with, however, permission to found a new sect. Although a few hymns ascribed to him have survived, he was not a writer but a popular teacher who voiced a general desire for a more equalitarian and devotional creed. He formulated no new philosophical system but combined the emotional ritualism of the south with the more restrained meditative philosophy of the north. His love of God seems to have been joined with compassion for mankind. His devotionalism, his use of the vernacular (Hindi in his case), and his disregard for caste were to affect all later Indian sectarian developments. His humanity and moral quality led him to oppose the growing sensuousness associated with Krishna and to favour the worship of the knightly hero Rāma. The heroism of Rāma and the virtue of his wife, Sītā, appealed to a Hindu world threatened by Islam and served as rallying symbols for a highly moral *bhakti* cult.

Rāmānanda inspired the founding of many congregations and monasteries, and numerous disciples carried on his work. The Rāmāts emphasized the role of the guru; their ceremonies included initiations, in which the initiates were given the secret *mantra*, and sacramental meals; they believed in salvation through faith in the saving grace of God; and they tended to disregard caste and seclusion in the preparing and eating of meals. They were divided into celibate ascetics, clerical Brahman householders, and laity. The ascetics in turn were divided into several groups, of which one was reserved for Brahmans and three others were open to all castes.

Rāmānanda was supposed to have had twelve principal disciples, some of whom certainly were not his contemporaries. Among them were men of all castes and of different callings (including a raja, a weaver, a cobbler, a peasant, and a barber) and a woman. They propagated the sect throughout north and central India, and some of them established sub-sects. Rāidās, the cobbler, who established a sub-sect especially popular among the caste of leather workers, wrote hymns in praise of the 'One Infinite God, who is above and beyond all religious sects' and who 'resides within the hearts of his devotees.'[1] Senā, the barber, who also founded a sub-sect, became the guru of a raja. The raja, Pīpā, was born about 1425 (i.e. after Rāmānanda's death); he established a monastery at Pipawat near Dwarka, and his wife took up the religious life with him. The most famous of the disciples was Kabīr, the weaver.

Whether Kabīr was a personal disciple of Rāmānanda or only a later follower is uncertain. He seems to have flourished during the middle and end of the fifteenth century. At first, he probably was a follower of the Rāmāt sect, but eventually he sloughed off much of its mythology, emphasized its monotheism, and added elements from Islam in an effort to unite Hindu and Muslim. He was not a systematic writer but a religious poet and teacher. His sayings and poems have been preserved in the *Bījak* (compiled about 1570), the chief scripture of his sect, and the *Ādi Granth* of the Sikhs.

As these sources were compiled only after Kabīr's death, what he actually taught is uncertain. Clearly, however, he believed in one personal God, who was the same whether called Allah or Rāma, although his God, whom he preferred to call Rām, was more Indian than Semitic. Kabīr rejected reincarnation, maintaining that the world of transmigration and illusion existed in men's hearts and no one could free himself from it except by finding God there instead. Kabīr condemned the formalities of both Hinduism and Islam. Human beings, he held, were of one blood, and caste distinctions were prideful, corrupting fictions. He rejected idolatry, circumcision, austerities, ritualism, haughty self-confidence, and the pursuit of wealth and sensual pleasure, and he extolled respect for all forms of life, hard work, helpfulness to others, love of mankind, the moral way, and service to God. His God says:

'If you want me, give up your desire for every other thing and become mine, and then everything will be yours.'[2] For Kabīr external religious observances possessed no truth:

'The difference among faiths is due only to difference in names; everywhere there is yearning for the same God. Why do the Hindus and Mohammedans quarrel for nothing?'[3]

Kabīr attracted both Hindu and Muslim followers, who were known as Kabīrpanthīs. His teachings were particularly popular among the lower classes of north-central India. After his death his disciples organized the movement and, ironically enough, practically deified him. His sect is generally considered as belonging to Vishnuism despite its wide departure from traditional Hinduism, and he is revered by the Vishnuites. Along with Rāmānanda, Kabīr is by some historians numbered among the world's great spiritual leaders. Certainly the emphasis of these two teachers upon human brotherhood and their supreme devotion to God place them high in the ranks of those who helped to develop mankind's religious and humanitarian ideals.

*   *   *

Developments outside India

Forced to give ground to Islam in India, Hinduism underwent even greater losses in the Indo-Chinese peninsula and Malaysia. During the fourteenth century the dominant people of this area were the Khmers of Cambodia, and some of the Khmer rulers were nominally Shivaite. The famous temples of their capital, Angkor, helped to make it one of the lesser centres of Hinduism. Hīnayānaist Buddhism, however, not only was more generally accepted in Cambodia but also became the religion of the expanding Thai, even though the Thai rulers obtained Brahmans from the Khmer Empire as political advisers and accepted the Hindu concept of the god-king. The Thai sacked Angkor in 1431. Thereupon the Khmer rulers abandoned it, and Cambodia completely forsook Hinduism for Buddhism. In the rival kingdom of the Chams in Champa, Hinduism gradually gave ground before the advancing Vietnamites from the north, and by 1500 the quasi-Chinese religious ideas and practices that they brought with them dominated the Cham area.

In the East Indies Hinduism and Buddhism both fared badly. The expansion of the powerful Majapahit Empire throughout Malaysia assured the strength of its mixed Hindu-Buddhist religion during the 1300's. During the next century, however, Hindu-Buddhism began to meet the competition of Islam spreading eastward from west Sumatra. With the rise of Malacca as a commercial power the spread of Islamic influence was hastened, and with the decline of Majapahit after 1470, Hinduism and Buddhism as independent religions of the Indies rapidly declined, ultimately to disappear except in Bali. Nevertheless, they left a residue of practices and ideas, which, mixed with the pervading animistic beliefs, was amalgamated into Islam to form the dominant religion of Malaya and the East Indies.

BUDDHISM

By 1300 Buddhism's great creative and missionary period was over. Although it lived on as an important religious force in eastern Asia, no significant new doctrines or sects appeared. In India and central Asia its struggling remnants gradually vanished, although in south India survivals of Hīnayānaism seem to have persisted until the sixteenth century. In China, Korea, and Vietnam it lost ground to Neo-Confucianism or other native creeds. Sinhalese, Japanese, and Tibetan Buddhism, however, remained energetic.

In Ceylon much of the north was gradually lost to Hinduism as a result of the Tamil invasions. The great Mahāvihāra Monastery at Anuradhapura had to be abandoned, and the monks with their precious relics, including a tooth of Buddha, were shifted to new and less resplendent locations in the south. The Mahāvihāra brand of Hīnayānaism continued to dominate the south, however, and the prestige of Sinhalese Buddhism remained high in other Hīnayāna lands as well. Pilgrims and students came to Ceylon from Burma and Siam to observe and study. In 1361 Siam asked Ceylon for learned Buddhists, and in 1476 Pegu sent a large group of monks and its highest prelates to be taught and properly ordained by the Mahāvihāras. The process of accepting various Indian *devas* as guardian deities in Sinhalese Buddhism no doubt went on during this period.

In Burma the fourteenth and fifteenth centuries formed an era characterized by sectarian disputes. The collapse of Pagan (*c.* 1298) as the political centre of a united Burma and the invasion of the Shans probably caused some decline of monastic activities, but Pegu remained an important monastic centre, and for a time Pagan, too, revived as such. Besides, various Shan rulers and nobility in the north soon became patrons of the monks, and new centres developed; after 1364 Ava gradually emerged as the political and monastic capital of Upper Burma. In Pegu, King Dhammaceti or Rāmādhipati (*c.* 1472–91), a former monk, succeeded in putting an end to the rivalry between the Talaing and Sinhalese sects and tightening monastic discipline. It was he who sent some monks and prelates to Ceylon for study and ordination. After their return all the monks in Pegu and many from upper Burma, estimated to have numbered together 15,666, were re-ordained. The conflicting sects were thus united, and the Sinhalese school remained the standard for all Burma thenceforth.

In Siam Hīnayāna Buddhism continued to flourish as the national religion under the Thai rulers. In 1361 the ruler of Siam sent to Ceylon for an abbot, or *sangharāja*, who was received with great pomp and ceremony. This abbot no doubt helped to secure the dominance of Pāli (Hīnayāna) Buddhism and reduce the Mahāyāna elements in Thai Buddhism. Also about this time a bodhi-tree (holy wild-fig tree) was brought from Ceylon, and some sacred relics from Patna. Great monasteries prospered under royal patronage. When after 1350 Ayuthia eclipsed Sukhothai as the political centre of Siam, the rulers continued to be great patrons of Pāli Buddhism, which spread down the Malay Peninsula with the Thai conquests. Ayuthia's rulers remained liberal patrons of Buddhism, as the ruins of Wat Somarokat and Wat Chern with their huge bronze Buddhas testify, until its destruction by the Burmese in 1767.

By 1300, although the Mahāyāna-Brahman cults still flourished at Angkor, Pāli Hīnayānaism, generally accepted by rulers and peoples alike, spread as the national religion. In 1358 the Laotian king was converted to Hīnayāna Buddhism through the influence of his Khmer wife and the ruler at Angkor. A statue of the Buddha known as the Luang Prabang is said to have been sent to the Laotian king from Angkor, and it became the palladium of the Laotian kingdom. After the abandonment of Angkor in 1432, the Mahāyāna-Brahman cults were not revived at the new Cambodian capital of Phnom-Penh, and Cambodia became almost entirely Hīnayānaist.

*   *   *

Developments in China, Vietnam, and Korea

Under the Mongol (Yüan) dynasty (1260–1368) the fortunes of the Buddhists reached an apogee in China. Kublai Khan (1260–94) adopted Lamaism and imposed it on the Mongols. The Tibetan lama, Pagspa (Pa-ssu-pa), was given the title of *Kuo–shih* (National Teacher) and placed at the head of China's Buddhist hierarchy. The ninth collection of the *Tripitaka*, published in 1285–87 under Pagspa's supervision, was in 1312 ordered to be translated into Mongol. Lamas continued to fill Pagspa's post and were favoured in other administrative positions for the duration of the Yüan dynasty. Lamaist temples were established in Peking and elsewhere in north China, and Kublai and his successors generally acted as lavish patrons of other forms of Buddhism as well. Old restrictions on Buddhists were removed, and their buildings and lands were exempted from taxation. The lamas sometimes abused their privileges by allowing the wealthy to register lands in their name in order to escape taxation.

Most rulers of the Ming dynasty (1368–1644) also patronized the Buddhists, giving them lands, endowments, and at times, through the favouritism of eunuchs, special advantages. Still, the Ming emperors did not favour the Buddhists so much as the Mongol emperors had done. The official philosophy of the Ming was Neo-Confucianism, and the administrative hierarchy was controlled by Confucian scholars. Since all religions were officially under the supervision of the government, a Buddhist office (*Seng-lu Ssu*) regulated and supervised the Buddhist monastic establishments, and two Buddhist patriarchs (*Shan-shih*) were officially maintained with a staff of subordinates. Ming religious policy in general was to conciliate the lamas of Tibet because of their influence over the Mongols, to patronize all religions more or less impartially, to restrict the number of monasteries, monks, and nuns, and otherwise to keep a tight control over the clergy. This policy was instituted by the founder of the dynasty, the Hung-wu emperor (T'ai-tsu, 1368–98), who had spent some time in a monastery. He received Buddhist monks, appointed them among others as tutors to his sons, decreed that all monks should study the *Prajñāpāramitā* and certain other revered works, ordered the compilation of commentaries on these works, and patronized the publication of the tenth collection of the *Tripitaka*.

The third Ming ruler, the Yung-lo emperor (Ch'eng-tsu, 1403–24), was still more friendly to Buddhism. He elevated his Buddhist tutor, Yao Kuang-hsiao, to high office. He brought lamas to the capital, restored to them the title of *Kuo-shih*, and made them the highest prelates in Buddhism. He wrote prefaces to the eleventh collection of the *Tripitaka* and to several other Buddhist works and had a *sūtra*, allegedly revealed to his empress, included in the *Tripitaka*. Yet he also restricted the number of persons that might be ordained.

Under the lax administration of the lamas, clerical celibacy had not been enforced, and under the Hung-wu emperor the number of secular clerics (that is, priests who were married and did not live in monasteries) was considerable. They probably had already begun to be numerous during the Mongol period, and they continued to increase under the Ming despite decrees against them (1394 and 1412), for married priests filled a popular need and provided a means of exceeding the limitation placed on the total number of monks. In 1458 a decree restricted the number of ordination ceremonies to one a year. The Ch'eng-hua emperor (1464–87) was under the influence of eunuchs and Buddhist monks (bonzes), but his successor (1487–1505) cleared the monks and eunuchs out and otherwise restricted Buddhist influence.

Despite official patronage, Chinese Buddhism lacked creative qualities in the fourteenth and fifteenth centuries. A few new translations from Sanskrit were made during the Mongol era, but none under the Ming. Nor did native scholarship contribute anything original in theology, confining itself to the preparation of histories, lives of saints, eulogies of the three religions (Confucianism, Taoism, and Buddhism), collections of poetry, and various compendia. During the Ming period, among the intellectuals Buddhism lost ground to Neo-Confucianism. No new sects appeared, and the old ones tended to assimilate, absorb general Chinese practices, and cease to be distinctive. The Sudden Enlightenment or Ch'an (Zen) sect remained the strongest and most original; among the monks the T'ien-t'ai (Tendai) was next in importance; and for the laity the ideas of the Pure Land or Ching-t'u (Jōdō) were by all odds the most significant. Mantrayāna practices spread among all the sects.

Much the same is true of Buddhism in Vietnam and Korea. In both countries, and especially Vietnam, it tended to lose distinctiveness and fuse with Confucianism, Taoism, and the native cults. In Korea, after the fall of the Mongols, a revolt deposed the native dynasty, which had submitted to them, and set up the Yi dynasty (1392). The leaders of the revolt favoured Neo-Confucianism, and identifying Buddhism with the old regime, subjected it to persecution. They issued a set of decrees that restricted Buddhist learning, obliged marriages and burials to conform to Confucian rites, required Buddhist statues to be melted down, and (1472 and 1512) closed monasteries in the capital and other cities, limiting them to rural areas.

*   *   *

Developments in Japan

In Japan, Buddhism during this period showed some energy and originality, but, largely because of the contemporary political instability, it became militarized and intolerant. The Kamakura Shogunate suddenly collapsed in 1333 as a result of the Emperor Go-Daigo's efforts to restore imperial authority. He was unable, however, to establish control, and soon there were two royal courts, one at Kyoto under the control of the Ashikagas, who set themselves up as shoguns, and one at Yoshino under Go-Daigo and his successors. Thus ended a long period of relative peace. The bitter struggle that ensued came to a close only in 1392, with a compromise that brought seventy-five years of relative stability. The civil war that then began (1467) inaugurated a period of relentless feudal strife that lasted until Hideyoshi united the country in 1590.

During most of this age of strife, compromise, and renewed strife the Ashikaga shoguns were in power, and it is known as the Ashikaga or Muromachi period. It brought several important changes to Japanese Buddhism. (1) Many sub-sects were established and widely distributed throughout the country, serving as centres for the spread of Buddhist ideas and a modicum of learning. (2) Higher learning and culture were kept alive largely by the Zen monks, who served as advisers to the shoguns but kept largely aloof from the military conflict, maintained trade and contact with China, and became eclectics in learning and masters of landscape painting. (3) A code of military ethics, *Bushido*, emerged that was an amalgam of Zen ideas of discipline, Confucian ideas of loyalty and family responsibility, and Japanese ideas of bravery and clan loyalty. *Bushido* somewhat offset a contemporaneous moral depression characterized by extreme pessimism, intolerance, persecution, obscene cults, magic, sorcery, exorcism, and divination. (4) Many of the Buddhist sects became militarized, maintaining considerable armies, turning their establishments into fortresses, and waging war with one another and with the feudal lords.

The Zen sect emerged as probably the most important Buddhist group in Japan, with five great monasteries in Kamakura and five in Kyoto. Its discipline appealed to the military, and its monks gained prestige as advisers of the Ashikaga shoguns. Soseki (Musō Kokushi, 1275–1351), tutor and adviser of

Ashikaga Takauji and abbot of the Tenryuji Monastery, initiated the Zen-Ashikaga commercial voyages to China in 1342 and persuaded the shogun to order the establishment of a Zen monastery and pagoda in every province. Eisan (1268–1325) and Gazan (1275–1365) also laboured to extend Zen in the provinces. Zen monks were record keepers, accountants, tutors, teachers at the Ashikaga college, librarians, chroniclers, essay writers, painters, art collectors, and masters of the tea ceremony. They introduced Neo-Confucian ideas from China and wrote sophisticated works like the *Tsuré-zuré-gusa* of Yoshido Kenkō (1283–1350), which spoke sympathetically of Shinto, Confucianism, and Taoism. In addition, they produced collections of moral maxims, poetry, and devotional tracts suitable for children and common people, and they were instrumental in initiating the transcription of the *Tripitaka*, which was begun in 1354.

Of the other sects the competing Shin and Nichiren were the most militant in the provinces. The Shin sect was especially active in central and north central Japan. Its hereditary clergy dominated it, but it divided into ten sub-sects, each with a different abbot as administrative head, although they all paid general allegiance to the abbot of the Hongwanji Temple in Kyoto, established in 1272. The abbot Ryōgen (1294–1335) was known for promoting Shin influence around Kyoto and the central provinces, but the pre-eminent Shin leader was Rennyo (1415–99). Forced to leave Kyoto in 1465, when the Tendai sect destroyed the Hongwanji, he spent many years wandering and teaching throughout Japan and established a major centre at Yoshizaki in Echizen. In 1480 he rebuilt the Hongwanji at Yamashina, near Kyoto. His *Ofumi*, or Epistles, and *Ryōgemon*, a sort of creed, did much to unify the sect upon a sound moral basis, gradually putting an end to the internal faction called 'Evil Doers', who argued that deeds did not matter if one's belief was correct. The Shin had large groups of poor lay followers and engaged in constant conflict with other sects and with feudal lords. Its congregations, each with its own fortified temple, spread throughout the land. It virtually dominated the province of Kaga and in 1496 established a centre at Osaka. It was driven out of Yamashina in 1532 by the Nichiren sect, whereupon it turned its centre at Osaka into an impregnable stronghold.

The radical Nichiren sect was reported to have established as many as 80,000 centres throughout the country. In 1440 its leader Nisshin (1407–88) won broad renown for withstanding the tortures heaped upon him by the shogun as punishment for criticism. It expanded especially in central and eastern Japan under an effective organizer, Nitchō (1422–1500). The belligerent social philosophy and quarrelsome character of the Nichiren kept them in constant conflict with the feudal lords and other sects. After they drove the Shin sect out of Yamashina, the Bakufu (the government of the shogun) and the Tendai sect joined forces with the Shin (1536). The coalition destroyed twenty-one temples of the Nichiren in Kyoto and drove them from the city. This catastrophe, coupled with internal dissensions and the attacks of feudal lords, caused the Nichiren to decline as the century advanced, while the Shin became probably the most numerous sect in the land.

Only a few other sects continued to thrive. The Tendai monks of Mount Hiei, Kyoto, were not active in the provinces, but in the capital their military forces had to be restrained on numerous occasions by the shogun. The Shingon sect entrenched on Mount Koya, Kyoto, was also turbulent, and a branch developed in Kii province which controlled 2,700 temples, a great fortified centre at Negoro, and a large army of mercenaries. It remained for Ryōto Shōgei (1341–1420), of the relatively inactive Jōdo, or Pure Land, sect, to formulate the most important new religious doctrine of the period. In his *Jugi*, he asserted that the Pure Land was not in another region but represented a change of mind and condition here below. At the other extreme the Mountain Priests, or Yamabushi, a group of wandering teachers, appealed to ignorance and superstition, promoting occult practices and Chinese *yin-yang* ideas.

*   *   *

Tantric Buddhism

In north India, although the main centres of Tantric Buddhism in Bengal and Bihar were destroyed by the Muslims, some monasteries seem to have survived. Tibetan sources indicate that a king of Bengal about 1450 restored some others and that *sūtras* were still being copied in Bengal in the fifteenth century. Undisguised Buddhism probably survived longest in Orissa, which was not fully conquered by the Muslims until 1568. Although one of Orissa's rulers persecuted Buddhists in 1529, its last Hindu ruler was reputedly a Buddhist. Elsewhere, fusion with Hinduism or acceptance of Islam had already gone a long way by 1300 and continued during the succeeding centuries. Groups of wandering monks and nuns, generally in pairs, propagated a degenerate sort of Buddhism for a long time. Other unedifying forms of Buddhism, mixed with local practices and Hinduism, survived in Bengal's local cults such as those of Chandī, Manasā, and Dharma (a form of the Buddha). These cults were gradually absorbed by Shāktism, Shivaism, or the Chaitanya movement (see Chapter IV). The Dharma cults were especially strong in western and southern Bengal.

Tantric Buddhism languished in several other regions also. As already indicated, the mixed Buddhist-Hindu religion of Majapahit rapidly declined after 1470. A form of Tantric Buddhism mixed with Hinduism existed in Nepal when in 1324 the Hindu king of Tirhut, fleeing from the Muslims, seized the Nepalese throne. Later in the century his successors, under Brahman influence, organized Hinduism and Buddhism in parallel groups, which tended to become more and more alike and to absorb new Hinduistic elements from India. In the fourteenth century wandering ascetics, or Nāthas, who combined elements of both creeds and were honoured by both, came into prominence.

Tantric Buddhism developed its maximum strength in Lamaism, its Tibetan form. In Tibet the abbots of the Sakya Monastery continued to dominate until around 1340, when the decline of Mongol power enabled other sects and various temporal princes to establish their independence. The Ming dynasty after 1368, apparently content to see authority in Tibet divided, did not interfere actively but recognized the abbots of eight monasteries as well as a secular dynasty.

Coincident with the rise of the Ming dynasty was the career of Tsong-ka-pa (c. 1358–1419). He studied at a number of monasteries and may have known something of Christianity. He was convinced that Lamaism was not in harmony with its own scriptures and undertook to reform it. Originally a member of the Kadampa sect, he reorganized it, making it into the Gelukpa, or Order of the Virtuous Way. He instituted stricter monastic discipline, insisting on celibacy, frequent prayer services, the reduction of tantric and magical elements, and the carrying of the begging bowl. Since his sect wore yellow robes and hats, it was known as the Yellow Bonnets, to distinguish it from the old unreformed sects, or Red Bonnets. He established a close-knit organization and a highly ritualistic service. He founded the Gandan Monastery near Lhasa, his disciples established others, and his sect rapidly developed into the most powerful in Tibet.

About this time the belief emerged that each of the abbots of the Gelukpa was the incarnation of some Buddhist figure and that upon death he was reincarnated in a child who was to be found by oracular means and installed as the new abbot. Tsong-ka-pa came to be considered the incarnation of the *bodhisattva* Mānjushri, while his nephew, Geden-dub, who became the first grand lama of the Gelukpa at Lhasa in 1439, was considered the incarnation of Avalokita. One of Tsong-ka-pa's disciples, as first abbot of Tashilhunpo (founded 1447), was considered the incarnation of Amitabha. The Yung-lo emperor (1403–24), at whose court the *Kanjur* was printed in 1410, greatly advanced the political fortunes of the new Tibetan group in China, and the Ch'eng-hua emperor (1465–88) recognized Lhasa and Tashilhunpo, in that sequence, as superior to the other monastic sees of Tibet. The second grand lama (1479–1541) put the hierarchy in good order, distinguishing clerical posts, to be filled by incarnations, from merely administrative ones.

CONFUCIANISM, TAOISM, AND SHINTOISM

No arresting changes occurred within Confucianism during the period here under consideration, which covers much of the Mongol dynasty (1260–1368) and the first half of the Ming dynasty (1368–1644). Neo-Confucianism had come forward during the Sung dynasty (960–1279) as a genuine effort to revive the ancient thought of China, blurred by centuries of competition with Buddhism and Taoism. The Sung Neo-Confucians, however, did not themselves escape the Buddhist and Taoist influences they sought to throw off. In their efforts to develop a system of thought that would retain the moral, social, and political aspects of the ancient doctrine and yet appeal to a more sophisticated age, they borrowed freely from the very systems they were fighting. Their cosmology, metaphysics, and meditative practices drew heavily upon Taoism and Ch'an Buddhism, introducing much that was alien to early Confucianism. This new Confucianism was accepted under the Mongol rulers as the formal philosophy of the Imperial College but had less effect upon the national bureaucracy than might have been expected, since civil-service examinations were held only intermittently.

The Mongol rulers carried on the official cult much as usual. Although they themselves favoured Buddhism, most of them endeavoured also to please China's scholars by honouring Confucius and supporting the Confucian cult. Kublai built a Confucian temple in Peking, in 1308 Confucius received a new and higher title, and in 1316 the emperor sacrificed to him. In 1313 the names of Chu Hsi and a number of the other Neo-Confucians were added to those honoured in Confucian temples. Sacrifices in these temples became more elaborate, and the tendency to deify Confucius grew.

Under the Ming dynasty, despite the predilections of some emperors, Neo-Confucianism became the unquestioned philosophy of the state (see Chapter VI). The official cult, meticulously carried on, occasionally added a new deity and raised or demoted old ones. Thus, in 1409, new titles were conferred on the T'ien-fei, or Celestial Spouse, a guardian deity of sailors, because of aid supposedly rendered to imperially sponsored voyages into the Indian Ocean. The Yung-lo emperor had the Neo-Confucian writings condensed into the *Hsing-li ta-ch'üan*, or Great Philosophy, and in 1416 ordered that, together with the Five Classics and Four Books, the condensation should be the basis of instruction in the official schools and in civil-service examinations (see Chapter XVI). The rationalistic tendencies of Neo-Confucianism steadily gained ground, finding expression not only in edicts against yoga, exorcism, Buddhist, and Taoist masses for the dead, and various other allegedly superstitious practices but also in the tendency in the Cult of the Scholars gradually to replace deification of Confucius by respect for him as a mortal sage.

Elsewhere in the Far East Confucianism also flourished. In Korea after the establishment of the Yi dynasty (1392), it became the official philosophy and was liberally patronized by the state. For a time its high ethical and moral principles contributed to good government and a flowering of culture, but as time went on, the bureaucracy forgot its high ideals and became corrupt and grasping. The forms were maintained, but the spirit died. Nevertheless, ancestor worship and Confucian family ceremonials and ethics remained an important part of Korea's popular religion. In Vietnam it also received official patronage. In Japan, its ethics and philosophy contributed to the warrior's code (*Bushido*) and to Japanese ideas in general.

Taoism likewise underwent no profound change in the Mongol and early Ming periods. Kublai Khan ordered the destruction of Taoist books about 1281, and some Taoist writings were lost as a result. Otherwise the Taoists appear to have suffered little from the Mongols, who indeed were attracted by its shamanistic elements. The Ming dynasty subjected Taoists as well as Buddhists to restrictive legislation, requiring the registration of monks and nuns, limiting the number that could be ordained, prohibiting the building or enlarging of monasteries and temples without official permission, specifying the age at which men and women could enter monastic life, fixing the number of pupils that the married secular clergy could have, and placing all Taoist affairs under a national board, the Tao-lu Ssu, with branches in the local subdivisions. Restrictive legislation was not, however, rigorously enforced, and some emperors were veritable patrons of Taoism. Both Mongol and Ming rulers recognized the position of the Chang family as *T'ien-shih* (see Chapter II), but the Mings seem to have recognized also a rival patriarch. Under imperial patronage publication of the Taoist canon began in 1446, but with the Hung-chih emperor (1487–1505) further destruction of Taoist books took place. During the Ming period, though Taoism seems to have discarded some of the practices that had invited criticism—among them orgies in their monasteries on certain festival occasions, it appears to have generally declined. At least two of its sects, the Chen-ta-tao and the T'ai-i, gradually became extinct.

* * *

The Revival of Shintoism

During the Ashikaga shogunate, when the fortunes of both the imperial house and the native religion of Japan reached their lowest point, Shintoism began to develop a clearly independent system of thought and to assert its freedom from Buddhism. The roots of this revived Shintoism can be traced back to the thirteenth-century *Shinto Gobusho* (*Shinto Pentateuch*) of the Waterai family priests of the Outer Shrine at Ise. Waterai Yukitada (1236–1305) and other members of the family vigorously asserted the superiority of their deities and ceremonials at Ise over the Buddhist ones, and the new spirit was taken up by officials attached to the imperial court as well as by the priestly families.

The revival of Shinto was soon associated with the restoration of the divine emperors to their position as actual heads of the government. In the formulation of the philosophical basis of Shintoism the work of Kitabatake Chikafusa (1293–1354), a court noble and warrior, stands out. He supported the efforts of the Emperor Go-Daigo to regain control of the government upon the overthrow of the Kamakura Shogunate in 1333. In his various works, especially the *Jinnō shōtōki* (*History of the True Succession of the Divine Emperors*), Kitabatake expounded the uniqueness of Japan as a country of the gods (*kami*) properly ruled only by direct descendants of the Sun Goddess. The three sacred treasures of the imperial regalia—mirror, necklace, and sword— were symbolic of sun, moon, and stars and represented respectively sagacity (or intelligence and veracity), benevolence (or mercy), and courage (or strength and justice). These virtues were the Shinto national inheritance from the Sun Goddess; they were the living facts of national life—the foundations of the state. If the government were to be successful, Shinto ways and the descendants of the Sun Goddess had to be restored and revered. Actually, Kitabatake's ideas were eclectic, for he borrowed heavily from Confucianism and Buddhism, but he presented his borrowed ideas as an essential part of native Shinto.

As Japan's feudal disorders worsened in the fifteenth century, another court noble, Ichijo Kaneyoshi (1402–81), developed the symbolism of the imperial regalia further. In the effort to promote national unity under the divine emperors he fused Buddhist, Confucian, and Shinto ideas and presented them as the Shinto tradition. He identified the cosmic soul of Buddhism and Shinto with the individual soul and argued that ethics consisted of bringing the individual soul and everyday life into harmony with cosmic unity. Although the Shinto *kami* were many, they were in reality but individual manifestations of the universal soul (*kami*) and shared alike the three qualities symbolized in the imperial regalia, which he equated with the three aspects of Buddhahood, wisdom (*prajnā*), emancipation (*moksha*), and truth (*dharma*). The duty of mankind as individuals and of the Japanese as a people was to live in harmony with these Shinto virtues, thus realizing the unity of man with the cosmic *kami* through the divine emperor. This was true Shinto —the Way of the Gods.

Probably the first Shinto school of thought to be formed in distinct opposition to the Ryōbu Shinto of the Buddhists was the Waterai or Outer Shrine Shinto, based on the teachings of Waterai Yukitada and other priests of the Outer Shrine at Ise. It taught an ethical, pantheistic Shinto. Outer Shrine Shinto's high development was not to come until the seventeenth century, but the position of the Ise Shrine was strengthened during the period of imperial poverty before 1500 because its priests formed lay associations for its support and attracted widespread interest and devotion. It thus changed from an imperial-family shrine into a national one, to which the faithful tried to make at least one pilgrimage.

Another early school to oppose Ryōbu Shinto was the Yui-itsu (One and Only, or Unique) Shinto. Since it was developed by the Urabe diviners of the Yoshida and Hirano shrines at Kyoto and most fully by Urabe (Yoshida) Kanetomo (1435–1511), it was also called Urabe or Yoshida Shinto. It was a pantheistic creed that claimed to be a direct revelation from the Japanese gods. It stressed sorcery and divination, laying less emphasis on ethics than previous writers had done.

This Urabe system too was a compound—of Shingon and Tendai Buddhism, Taoism, Confucianism, and native ideas and practices. Contrary to Ryōbu Shinto, however, it asserted that the Japanese *kami* were the original deities, the Buddhist deities being mere manifestations of them. The original *kami* was the self-existent, eternal absolute from which the other *kami*, the universe, and all its manifestations came. *Kami* was soul (*kokoro*), and the soul was *kami*. Japan and her people, by virtue of their more intimate connection with the *kami*, were uniquely divine, and the emperor, as the direct descendant of the Sun Goddess, was a *kami* in human form, who ruled by virtue of his unique descent. Urabe Kanetomo used this doctrine not only to strengthen native Shinto but also to extend the influence of his family in Shinto affairs; ultimately the Urabes virtually monopolized the ordination of Shinto priests and the establishment of sanctuaries.

ISLAM

Between 1300 and 1500 Islam established firm roots in India and spread widely throughout Malaya and the East Indies. In India its spread was largely due to military conquest, which opened up a field favourable to proselytizing, and farther east to the missionary activity of merchants and teachers and to matrimonial alliances. Shī'ite and non-orthodox elements were influential in Muslim conquests and conversions in India, but, whether Shī'ite or Sunnite, the brands of Islam that developed were often heavily intermixed with Hinduistic practices. Many of the traders and teachers who carried Islam to the East Indies were from Gujarat and Bengal, and they generally were willing to accept converts upon a simple affirmation of faith. Hence local practices persisted, and the type of Islam that developed in the East Indies differed markedly from the orthodox Islam of the Near East. Shī'ite elements were also strong in the East Indies during this early period. In central Asia and northwestern China Islam gained some ground, but its cultural advances in China were relatively inconsequential.

During the two centuries under review, Islam grew slowly in north India and the Deccan. Teachers, mystics, merchants, refugees, and adventurers of all sorts accompanied or followed the conquerors. Most of the newcomers were Persians and Afghans, but some were Turks and even Arabs. A majority belonged to one or other of the four main orthodox Sunnite schools, the Ḥanafites predominating, but some were Shī'ites, and many of both groups had only imperfectly assimilated Islam before their entrance. Some brought wives with them, but many took Hindu wives or concubines, and a considerable portion of the Islamic growth was due to natural increase. The children of Muslim fathers were reared as Muslims, even though their beliefs might be thoroughly coloured by Hindu views. Some converts came from the Brahman and other upper castes, but most from the lower classes, who saw in conversion a chance to escape from the Hindu caste system as well as the poll tax (*jizya*) imposed by the conquerors. Converts were especially numerous in Bengal, where many of the leaderless Tantric Buddhists turned to Islam. Islam likewise became significant in the Punjab, which was more thoroughly subjected to Islamic invasion and colonization than other areas. In addition, a considerable Islamic commercial element developed in Gujarat, and Muslims moved also into the Deccan, though the number there was not large. Among those in Gujarat and the Deccan the Shī'ite elements seem to have been strong.

The most important Shī'ite group in India was the Imāmiyya, or Twelvers, whose major strength lay in the Bahmani kingdom of the Deccan. Shī'ite influence was evident from the very founding of this kingdom in 1347, and the ninth ruler, Aḥmad Shāh I (1422–36) openly embraced the Imāmiyya faith. Rulers of some of the states that replaced the Bahmani kingdom were Shī'ites and promoted the faith there.

Of the Ismā'īliyya, another branch of the Shī'a, there were two sects in India. The Tayyibīs (or Bohrahs, as they were called in India) had been established in the Cambay area of Gujarat by missionaries from Yaman before 1300. They were persecuted by the Sunnite rulers of Gujarat after 1396, and a large group became Sunnites in the fifteenth century. The Nizārīs (or Khojahs, as they were called in India) were established in the Multan area of the Punjab and in Sind, Gujarat, and Kashmir by missionaries, principally from Persia, at various times between the twelfth and fifteenth centuries. Both groups recruited heavily from Hindu converts, were active in mercantile affairs, and accepted many Hindu customs, ideas, and legal practices. Each had its separate literature and paid its tithe directly to its respective religious head. The Bohrahs retained their Hindu laws of inheritance, but their literature, mainly in Arabic and Gujarati, generally continued the tradition of Fatimid Egypt. The Khojahs tended to consider 'Ali the tenth incarnation of Vishnu, as set forth in *Das Avatar* (*The Ten Incarnations*), written in the fifteenth century by Ṣadr-ud-Dīn, a Khojah missionary. They regarded their head very much as a god. Their literature was in Persian and Gujarati or other Indian vernaculars. Both groups seem to have been active as traders and missionaries in the East Indies and east Africa.

Islamic Ṣūfism became popular in India. Most of the Ṣūfīs were Sunnites, for the Shī'ites generally held that spiritual oneness with God could be attained only through the *Imām* and not through mystic practices. Large numbers of Islamic *faqīrs* (mendicant Ṣūfīs) appeared in India, and their mystic approach led many Ṣūfīs to be receptive of pantheistic Hindu ideas. Two of the regular Islamic *faqīr* orders—the Chishtiyya and the Suhrawardiyya—were introduced into India immediately after the conquest, and the Shaṭṭāriyya order was inaugurated in the late-fourteenth century by Abd Allāh Shaṭṭāri. In 1482 the Qādiriyya order was introduced to Sind, which had already become famous as the home of Indian Ṣūfism. Many Ṣūfīs were important as missionaries. Numerous irregular Ṣūfī orders that did not emphasize learning or observe the Ṣūfīs' customary ritual of fasting, prayer, and other stringent practices also appeared in India during this period. Some of them were founded by outright charlatans, and their begging, singing, magic, fortune telling, amulets, charms, and other unsavoury practices wholly misrepresented the regular orders of *faqīrs*.

In general, Islam took firmer hold in India's towns and cities than in the rural areas. It ranged in form from the most orthodox of Sunnite practice to mere lip-service to Allah and his prophet Mohammed. The Islamic conquerors were not generally accompanied by a well-organized company of teachers and missionaries. Hence, although the essentials of Islam—the confession of faith, daily prayers, giving of alms, the month's fast of Ramadān, and pilgrimages to Mecca—gradually took hold among most of the converts, many elements of Hinduism persisted, particularly among the groups that only nominally embraced Islam. A host of new saints, some of whom were borrowed from Hinduism, appeared; Hindu festivals were incorporated into Islam, as were Hindu godlings and demons and the methods of revering or propitiating them; Hindu rather than Islamic law regarding property was applied in many areas; caste attitudes were often retained, as were Hindu customs relating to family life, eating, marriage, worship of ancestors, and the burning of widows. Pantheism and Hindu ideas regarding the absorption of the individual soul into the divine being affected Indian Ṣūfism in particular. Even Sunnite and Shī'ite differences were sometimes obscured.

* * *

Developments in Malaya and Malaysia

In the East Indies around 1300 Islam centred in the two petty sultanates of Perlak and Pasai at the western end of Sumatra. Since the Hindu-Buddhist kingdom of Majapahit dominated Java, while that of Malayu (Jambi) dominated south Sumatra, and the Hīnayānaist Thais were expanding in the Malay Peninsula, the spread of Islam at first was slow. But from 1400 onward, and especially after 1440, as the power of Malacca rose while that of Malayu and Majapahit declined, the political domination of petty Islamic rulers spread. The success of Islam was closely associated with the development of trade between the East Indian areas on the one hand and India (especially Gujarat and Bengal), Persia, and the Red Sea region on the other. Islamic merchants from western Asia, and especially from the Cambay area of Gujarat, either settled or spent long periods of time in the trading cities of the East Indies. Encouraged by the local rajas and their overlords for economic reasons, they became influential in many of the cities and, together with the Islamic teachers associated with them, began the process of conversion. In some cases the local rajas were themselves converted or married daughters of Muslim merchants, and so, sooner or later, Muslims sat on their thrones. Once this stage was reached, matrimonial alliances between the petty kingdoms, commercial pressure, or outright conquest extended the sway of Islam. By 1500 most of the commercial towns of Malaya and the East Indies that were the capitals of small kingdoms were Muslim and were ruled by Islamic sultans.

Two major centres of dispersion developed. One was Malacca, the other the trading cities of Grisek and Tuban in the Surabaya area of East Java. Islam spread from Perlak and Pasai to the Malaya peninsula and thence to

Malacca. The kingdom of Malacca was founded about 1403. It soon developed into an important commercial city, in which many Gujarati and Javanese merchants settled, and its first ruler, Parameshvara (Megat Iskandar Shah, 1403–24), embraced Islam at the time of his marriage to a Pasai princess. Despite the threat of an expanding Siam, Malacca maintained its position and from the time of Muzaffar-Shah (c. 1446–59) was a spearhead in the Islamic advance. It extended its dominance to the lower Malay Peninsula, the north-eastern coast of Sumatra as far south as Jambi, and Borneo. Its connections throughout the Indies and especially with East Java made it by 1511 the strongest commercial power in the area. The Gujarati merchants at Malacca were said at times to number a thousand, and it always had a large contingent of East Javanese.

Grisek, the commercial port of Majapahit, to which Gujarati merchants came directly from India, became a distributing centre for the spice trade. With the neighbouring commercial town of Tuban it early developed some important Islamic communities. The oldest Islamic tombstone of Grisek is of 1419. In this area about 1450 appeared Raden Raḥmat (Sunan Ampel), who, together with his sons and foster son, was to be numbered among the most famous *walīs* (Islamic saints) of Java. Raden Raḥmat came from Champa, where an important Islamic community had arisen. He was a nephew of the queen of Majapahit and the son of an Islamic merchant and a princess of Champa. On his way to Majapahit he had converted the Javanese governor of Palembang on the island of Sumatra. After he reached Majapahit, its Hindu-Buddhist ruler gave him a large estate near Grisek, and his estate became a training centre for Islamic teachers. His son rose to be the first Islamic ruler of Tuban, and his foster son, Raden Pahu (d. 1482), founded the ecclesiastical power of the priestly princes of Giri near Grisek, which exerted enormous influence throughout the Indies for centuries. A son of the governor of Palembang married a daughter of Raden Raḥmat and made Demak, to the west of Tuban, another important Islamic centre (c. 1468). About this time the rulers of Majapahit, yielding to a combination of forces, retired to the island of Bali, although Majapahit itself fell into Islamic hands only after 1516.

In the meantime, Islamic rulers had established themselves at Brunei, in northern Borneo, and other points. Moro chronicles place Islamic teachers in ihe Sulu Islands as early as 1380, and the islands were certainly under effective Islamic control shortly after 1450, when Abu Bakr of Palembang, who had married the raja's daughter, established himself as sultan of Jolo (or Sulu). Islam was brought to Mindanao about 1475 by a band of Islamic conquerors from Johore under a leader whose father, Ali Zainul-Abiden, had himself been an immigrant to Malaya from Hadramut in south Arabia. It also spread to points in south Borneo, and before 1500 sultanates had been established at Tidore and Ternate in the Moloccas.

Islam was largely confined, however, in Malaya and the Indies to the coastal commercial towns. In the interior most of the islands, little affected by the Koran, preserved their mixed animistic-Hindu-Buddhist beliefs. Furthermore, many of the coastal inhabitants, though they had crossed over to Islam, retained a large part of their traditional beliefs and practices. Of the few Islamic teachers available, some spread an Indianized Islam of a Persian background, and many of the merchant-missionaries, being Shī'ites, brought to the Indies their Shī'ite practices. Certain so-called mystical elements of Islam, often consisting of faith in charms, spells, and the yoga magic of the irregular *faqīrs*, had a particular appeal for the Indonesians, while the incentive of commercial gain had been important among rajas, officials, and aristocracy. The Islamization of Malaya and the Indies thus was far from complete or whole-souled when the Portuguese arrived.

* * *

Developments from Transoxania to Grenada

Much the same factors that brought about Islam's advance in Malaysia held good also farther west. Sometimes this advance was achieved by the conversion of rulers. Thus, the Mongols of Transoxania soon adopted, as had the rulers of Iran, the religion of their Muslim subjects, and in 1326 the dynasty of hitherto Hindu Kashmir also embraced Islam. Sometimes advance came by the expansion of strong frontier powers. Thus, when most of India south of the Ganges was conquered by the Delhi sultanate and the Balkans by the Ottomans, in each area converts were attracted by the prestige of the new faith. Sometimes expansion was more attributable to individual penetration by merchants and mystics. In one way or another, Islam continued likewise to push on in the Sudan and to extend along the east African coast at the same time that it spread in Malaysia, so that most of the Indian Ocean trade with the Middle East came to be in Muslim hands.

The advance of Islam into Europe under Ottoman banners began about 1350, when one of the warring factions in Constantinople made a marriage alliance with the Turkish ruler Orkhan I (1326–59). Within ten years the Turks were in possession of both Gallipoli and Adrianople. In spite of the Byzantine emperor's appeals to the Avignon popes for western aid, the Turks soon took over most of his European provinces and subjected the independent states of Bulgaria, Bosnia, and Serbia as well. Thus the Islamic faith was introduced into the Balkans, in parts of which it still survives. Sultan Murad (1359–89) began the imposition of the 'blood-tax', training Christian boys to become hardy warriors (Janissaries) and civil servants. At the same time Turkish immigrants spread the faith and civilization of the conquerors throughout the Balkans. The Byzantine Empire was essentially conquered long before the fall in 1453 of its already isolated capital city, Constantinople.

Both before and after this storied event Hungary remained crucial in the Christian defence. Under their general Janos Hunyadi, Hungarian armies drove back the invaders and crossed the Danube into Turkish Bulgaria. The treachery of his allies and the inadequacy of western assistance paved the way to his final defeat. Only one vigorous stand was made—at Varna in 1444, where 'crusading' forces fought along with King Vladislav of Hungary-Poland and Hunyadi. The king did not survive the defeat, and Hunyadi was forced to retreat. His last exploit before dying of the plague was to raise the siege of Belgrade, invested by the Turks in 1456. The Hungarian resistance continued until it collapsed at the Battle of Mohacs in 1526.

In contrast, the Iberian Muslims were being overwhelmed by the Christians of Portugal, Castile, and Aragon. By 1300 Islamic rule survived in Iberia only in the little southeastern kingdom of Granada, which maintained a precarious existence until 1492. In the regions taken over by the Christian conquerors, Muslims who held to their faith were called Mudejars. Like Jews they were forced to wear a distinctive garb, live in segregated sections of the towns, and pay special taxes. Even though they were an economic asset, they were expelled from Seville in 1248 and from Castile late in the fifteenth century.

After the fall of Granada in 1492, followers of Islam were subjected ഥ persecution. The terms of the surrender of Granada provided for toleration, but they were disregarded by Archbishop Ximenes de Cisneros of Toledo (1436–1517) and Queen Isabella. A Muslim revolt ended in a decree (1502) giving the Muslims of Spain a choice between becoming converts (Moriscos) and going into exile. Many ostensible Moriscos remained in Castile, holding secretly to their Muslim beliefs and customs. Mudejars were suffered to remain in Aragon, but only as serfs on the estates of exploiting landlords.

*   *   *

The Great Age of the tariqas

All over Islam during the fourteenth and fifteenth centuries the Ṣūfī movement grew. The number of ṭarīqas multiplied, especially from the branching-out of established ṭarīqas, and some, old as well as new, were particularly enterprising. The Suhrawardiyya, for example, rivalled the Chishtiyya in India after the time of the lordly Makhdūm-i Jahāniyān in the mid-fourteenth century; the Qādiriyya maintained its lead in Islam as a whole; the Naqshbandiyya, more recently founded, became prevalent especially in Iran and Turkestan; the Shī'ite Bektāshī order rose to prominence in the growing Ottoman domains and in the fifteenth century grew dominant among the Janissaries.

The ṭarīqas disputed with each other for pre-eminence. Each tended to take the position that it alone possessed the full inner truth of Islam and that its heads ruled the mystical saintly hierarchy in which Ṣūfīs had come to believe. In fact, the several ṭarīqas often stood for quite diverse approaches to the problems of the time. The Suhrawardiyya in India tended toward greater orthodoxy in relation to the sharī'a and to the acceptance of government office than the more ascetic Chishtiyya. Likewise, orders like the Qādiriyya and the Naqshbandiyya stood by a relatively cautious orthodoxy. Some *bī-sharʿ* (without law) orders, on the other hand, asserted, on the model of the Qalandars, their freedom from the whole *sharīʿa*. Some orders catered more to wonder-working and popular superstition, like the Saʿdiyya in Egypt. Some made concessions to the non-Islamic customs of peoples newly won to Islam; thus, the Bektāshīs in Anatolia and the Balkans, who seem to have played a significant role in converting part of the Christian population, retained in their ritual and cult certain pre-Islamic elements. The *ṭarīqas* differed also in their attitude toward the manner of life of their members. Celibacy was recommended by some but not by others; some required Ṣūfīs to engage chiefly in wandering, while others gathered them into fixed convents; the Khalwatiyya of Turkey demanded of each member a solitary retreat once a year. The *ṭarīqas* differed also in their hospitality to mystical speculation and in the degree of freedom with which they treated the philosophical problems then exercising the Muslims (see Chapter VI).

Significant opposition to the *ṭarīqas* arose from time to time among the *ʿulamāʾ* (repositories of the *sharīʿa*). Some *ʿulamāʾ* felt that the popular reverence for the Ṣūfī saints, around whose memories and tombs the *ṭarīqas* were organized, went ill with the basic Islamic emphasis on a simple obedience to the impersonal sacred law. Thus in Syria in the fourteenth century the Ḥanbalites Ibn-Taymiyya and Ibn-Qayyim-al-Jawziyya held forth turbulently against the prevailing alliance of Ṣūfīs with the more complacent majority of *ʿulamāʾ*. Their lead was followed much later by the reforming Wahhābīs of Arabia (see Volume V), but their protest at first was not widely heeded. Not only did the saints in their tombs receive the often superstitious reverence of the masses, but the popular following of the Ṣūfīs increased. Large numbers of people who were not themselves under the full mystical discipline of a *ṭarīqa* formed a lay affiliation with it, reciting its prayers and accepting guidance from its leaders. Though most of the actual members of the *ṭarīqas* were men, some convents were at this time founded for women also.

The Shīʿite *ʿulamāʾ* were generally more hostile to Ṣūfism than were the Sunnite *ʿulamāʾ*, but even the Shīʿite tradition was at this time largely expressed through *ṭarīqas*. The growing Bektāshī order taught allegiance to the *imāms* of the Twelver Shīʿites as well as other esoteric Shīʿite doctrines. The remains of the Ismāʿīlī movement in Syria and Iran took the outward form of a Ṣūfī *ṭarīqa*. Many Sunnī orders showed Shīʿite influences, but one, the Ṣafawiyya, turned frankly Shīʿite and was the instrument of the subsequent conversion of Iran to the Shīʿa.

During this great age of the *ṭarīqas*, the Dār al-Islām was fragmented politically into numerous and, for the most part, unstable powers, but the resulting political divisions were of less importance than ever before or after. As a social order, Islam continued to gain territory as well as more complete adherence within territory already gained. During the two centuries after 1300

Muslim rule receded seriously only in the far south of India and at the western end of the Mediterranean; otherwise, Islamic power and the Muslim religion gained as compared with rival religions till the end of the fifteenth century.

JUDAISM

The years just before and after 1300 marked a new era of Judophobism in western Europe. Exiles from England and France and refugees from the pogroms of Germany and Austria searched for comparative security elsewhere. East European rulers, seeking to repeople their countries after the Mongolian ravages of the mid-thirteenth century, encouraged immigration from the west. For example, the code of King Casimir III of Poland (1333–70) granted religious toleration and local self-government. Thus Poland became an asylum for persecuted Jews. Although again restricted in many ways and subjected to sporadic persecution in the fifteenth century, the Polish Jews enjoyed a degree of prosperity and of religious and intellectual freedom unknown to Jews farther west. The Jewish population of Poland at the close of the eighteenth century is estimated at somewhat more than ten per cent of the total—about 900,000 out of 8,790,000; they nearly all lived in the towns, where they outnumbered the Christian population by about 9 to 5.4

The Spanish Jews (the Sephardim) were well treated until the late thirteenth century. A turning came in that century with the conquests in the Muslim south by the Christian kings. As Spanish cities passed from Muslim to Christian control, the generally tolerant attitude of the Muslims of that day toward Jews gradually gave way to Spanish resentment. The new rulers preferred to chasten the Jews as infidels, sometimes as wealthy competitors, and in any case as aliens. In Aragon Jews were excluded from governmental offices (1283), and in Castile segregation decrees were so rigid as to forbid them to employ Christians as servants (1313). The Castilian law code (*Siete Partidas*), initiated in 1256 but not proclaimed until 1348, formalized the new policy, obliging Jews, among other restrictions, to reside in ghettos. These restrictions, however, were not strictly enforced, largely because the rulers found the Jews useful, whether as sources of loans and taxes or as civil servants, in their conflict with the nobles. Hence, in contrast to the rest of western Europe, Spanish Jews remained, despite sporadic outbreaks, relatively safe from mass violence through most of the fourteenth century.

The first epidemic (1347–50) of the Black Death rekindled slumbering anti-Semitism in Germany and elsewhere, but in Spain, although occasionally mercenary troops plundered the ghettos, no mass attacks took place until late in the century. Then, in 1391, at Seville, the preaching of an eloquent court clergyman named Fernando Martinez roused the populace to frenzied action. His attacks started a chain of pogroms, which swept through Castile and Aragon. Jews who accepted conversion were alone spared, and most of them preferred baptism to death. Later pogroms increased the number of converts, popularly referred to as *Marranos* (i.e. *pigs*). Many of the Marranos were converts in name only, continuing their Jewish worship in secret. Thus freed from legal restrictions, Marranos recovered their former places in government and society. Some genuine, or at least zealous, converts became Christian clergymen, fanatically dedicated to the eradication of crypto-Judaism.

With the advent of Ferdinand and Isabella as the 'Catholic sovereigns' of Spain, the pseudo-Christians were considered so serious a problem that the Inquisition was established (1478), primarily to extirpate heresy among the *conversos*. It did its work so well that most of the *conversos* quickly were eliminated, and many Marranos eventually migrated to more tolerant countries. The Inquisition, which had authority over heretics but not infidels, nevertheless advocated the expulsion of the remaining unconverted Jews, whose public practice of Judaism was a bad example to their converted brethren. Accordingly, in 1492 all unconverted Jews were expelled from the Catholic sovereigns' possessions—Castile, Aragon, Sicily, and Sardinia. Navarre followed suit, and Portugal, not permitting emigration, tried forcibly to convert its Jews. Thus, formally Judaism came to an end in the Spains. The exiles settled in North Africa, Palestine, and (in large numbers) in the northern regions of the Turkish empire, where Sultan Bayezid II (1447–1512) gave them a place of refuge comparable to that in Christian Poland, which now harboured the largest Jewish population.

Instances of tolerance sometimes brighten the contemporary record of the vendetta against the Jews. Where the rulers were friendly, as in Poland and, until the fifteenth century, Spain, Jewish scholarship and business enterprise prospered. Among the Avignon popes some advocated the study of Hebrew, although their purpose often was only that Jews might be confuted or converted. Humanist scholars such as Pico della Mirandola saw good in Judaism and tried to reconcile it with Christianity, Islam, and Platonism (see Chapter VI). In northern Europe Johann Reuchlin (1455–1522) not only studied and taught Hebrew (at Orleans and Stuttgart) but also defended Judaic scholarship against clerical extremists who would have confiscated all Jewish books. Other German humanists likewise encouraged the intensive study of the Old Testament in Hebrew and the collecting of Hebrew manuscripts. In some parts of the Islamic world Judaism held on, though its cultural achievements were not so remarkable in this period as in preceding centuries.

GREEK ORTHODOX CHRISTIANITY

During the fourteenth and fifteenth centuries, the Byzantine Empire with its Greek Orthodox populations gradually was subjected to Turkish rule. The outlying provinces succumbed first, Constantinople and its environs last.

Various groups of Balkan Christians had seceded from the harsh control of Orthodox Constantinople long before the Balkan countries were overrun by the Turks. Serbia was the first to do so. Tsar Stephan Dushan (1331–55) made that country the centre of a west Balkan empire, and he set up an independent patriarchate at Ipek (Pec) in 1346. In a striking exhibition of politico-religious ambition, he raised Serbia to equality with Byzantium. The archbishopric of Serbia became a patriarchate, and Stephan himself became tsar and emperor of Serbs and 'Romans' (i.e. east Romans). The ceremony took place at Uskub in northern Macedonia and was attended by the head of the monasteries at Mount Athos. Stephan intended that his Balkan empire and patriarchate should supersede the decadent Byzantine Empire and patriarchate of Constantinople, but all that he accomplished was a secession.

Stephan's ambitions died with him, and by the end of the century Serbia was subject to the Turks. His patriarchate, like his empire, comprising heterogeneous peoples, disintegrated into semi-autonomous communities of Orthodox Serbs, Orthodox Greeks, Roman Catholics, and Bogomil heretics. These irreconcilable ethnic and religious groups failed to co-operate with Janos Hunyadi in his heroic stand against the Turks in the Danube valley immediately after the fall of Constantinople. One by one they succumbed to the victorious Sultan Mehmet II, and the Bosnian Bogomils turned wholesale from heresy to Islam. The dwindled Serbian patriarchate at Ipek was repressed in 1459, and for nearly a century Serbs as well as Bulgars had to look to the archbishopric of Ochrida (Ohrid) in Macedonia for spiritual guidance. After the Ipek patriarchate was restored (1557), it persisted until 1690, but the Serbian Church passed under the ecumenical patriarchate at Constantinople only in 1766.

The Bulgarians, when dominated by Stephan, were compelled to transfer both their religious and their political allegiance from Constantinople to Belgrade, but upon his death and the disintegration of his Serbian empire, they regained an independent Bulgarian church and state. Within half a century, however, Bulgaria fell to the Turks, and the Bulgarian church likewise came under Turkish control (1393). It recovered a fleeting independence during the Hunyadi episode (1456), only to fall permanently under Turkish rule later. The Ochrida archiepiscopate was not abolished, however, until 1767. Thereafter, according to a popular saying, just as the Turks governed the bodies of the Bulgarians, the Greeks ministered to their souls. By the end of the eighteenth century the disintegration of the Eastern church, begun in pre-Turkish times, had in a sense been checked; at any rate the Orthodox Christians within the Turkish empire tended to accept the leadership of the sultan-controlled ecumenical patriarchate at Constantinople.

*   *   *

The Failure of Union with Rome

The patriarchate at Constantinople had meanwhile suffered serious local crises. Long before 1300 it had inherited a factional conflict over the relationship of the priestly with the monastic clergy. In Constantinople, as elsewhere in Christendom, monks were the nucleus of organized movements for rigid, puritanical reform. Under the leadership of the monks of Mt Athos, the 'Zealot' faction was particularly determined to preserve the faith of the fathers. They had successfully organized a violent opposition to union with the Roman Catholic Church despite the fact that such a union had been arranged in 1274 (see Volume III). In the succeeding century they gained control of the patriarchate so completely that invariably the patriarchs were chosen from the Mt Athos congregation.

The Zealot monastic party was further strengthened by a wave of mysticism. Under the name Hesychasts (i.e. Quietists) ascetics who stressed silent contemplation in complete seclusion from the world came to exercise a powerful influence on Orthodox religious thought and action. Their strength was shown in conflict with Barlaam, a learned pro-Roman Greek monk from southern Italy who criticized the regime at Mt Athos and the Hesychast movement. The specific issue was Barlaam's accusation that Hesychasts who attained the highest degree of contemplative ecstasy claimed to be able to see 'with corporal eyes the divine and uncreated light'⁵ which was identical with that which had transfigured Jesus. If so, God was directly visible to men—a doctrine unacceptable to the Roman Catholic Church and to the secular clergy of the Eastern Orthodox Church.

War between rival claimants of the imperial throne, the steady nibbling away of the empire's territory by Stephan Dushan, the Turks, and other neighbours, the decline in Constantinople's trade in competition with Venice, and the complaints of the empire's numerous poor mixed with the dispute over mystical dogma to create an explosive internal atmosphere. The Hesychasts, led by Archbishop Palamas of Thessalonica, won the support of a leading contender for the Byzantine throne, John Cantacuzene, and after an indecisive council in the Church of St Sophia (1341), Baarlam returned, defeated, to Italy. The populace of Constantinople in contempt and anger dragged the dead body of one of the leading anti-Hesychasts about the streets. Revolt broke out also, for mixed religious, social, and political reasons, in Adrianople; and in Thessalonica, the second city of the empire, the Zealots took control for seven years (1342–49), during which they confiscated the property of the nobles and the church and massacred or expelled a number of nobles before the rival emperors combined and restored peace.

Mystical and ascetic influences remained strong in the fifteenth century and inspired violent popular opposition to all proposals of union with the Roman Church. The fruitless efforts of the Roman Catholic pope to bring the Greek Church into the Catholic fold is part of the story of the conflict of the popes with the councils, which will be described below. Any hint of compromising ancient Orthodox dogmas so as to make them acceptable to western Christians whipped the populace of Constantinople into a religious frenzy in which there were mingled bitterness over social and economic grievances and an intense desire for continued cultural independence. So it was with regard to the addition of the words *and the son* (*filioque*) to the portion of the Nicene creed concerning the procession of the Holy Spirit 'from the Father (and the Son).6' The additional phrase raised the question of the nature of the Trinity and remains for some a fighting shibboleth to this day. It was accepted as permissible, along with other compromises, by Byzantine diplomats at the Council of Florence in 1439, and thence issued an Act of Union intended to combine the two churches and assure western aid against the Turks. When announced in the East, however, the agreement precipitated outspoken condemnation on the part of ecclesiastical leaders and violent protests from the populace. Many churchmen refused to sign the Act of Union, and those who had signed it were forced to withdraw their signatures. In Alexandria, Jerusalem, and Antioch the action of the ambassadors at Florence was disavowed. In Constantinople and Moscow the conflict of opinions was more violent still.

Emperor John VIII Paleologus (a convert to Roman Catholicism) and the patriarch had negotiated the Act of Union. Emperor John and his successor, Constantine XI, along with the patriarch, now led the Unionists, and thanks to their commanding position they were able to maintain the external formality of union and alliance with the West. Below the official level, however, allegiance to ancient orthodoxy was unbending. In the forefront of the opposition were the monastic Zealots. No matter what price must be paid in political or military defeats, the Athos-led orthodox masses insisted on keeping the faith. In 1450 (according to historical records that some scholars reject) a council in the Church of St Sophia condemned the Act of Union and restored the Orthodox creed and organization.

If (as some insist) such a condemnation did not actually take place, it was because of the imminence of the Turkish attack on Constantinople, which forced the emperor to appeal to the West once more for immediate aid. In 1452 he welcomed a Roman cardinal (the exiled Metropolitan Isidore of Moscow), who proclaimed in St Sophia the union of the Roman and Greek churches under the primacy of Rome. The reaction of the Orthodox bishops and their flocks to the decree of union showed how intense was their dislike of imperial church policy. Even though the city was already in a state of siege, Orthodox mobs cursed the 'Romanists', and one of the imperial princes expressed an unabashed preference for turbans (of the Turks) rather than red hats (of the Roman cardinals) in Constantinople. He got his wish. After the Turkish conquest of the city the new patriarch, George Gennadios, chosen by the sultan, denounced the hated union. Obviously, whatever their political and ecclesiastical leaders might do in the name of expediency, the populace and their monastic-mystic leaders preferred to go down to defeat with their orthodoxy intact.

* * *

Autonomy for the Russian Orthodox Church

Only in Russia did Orthodox Greek Christianity emerge from the era of Asiatic conquests independent and powerful. The seat of Russian Orthodox Christianity moved from Kiev to Moscow early in the fourteenth century. Here, in a frontier region, the Holy Church of Russia grew to maturity. As elsewhere in Christendom, a strong, mystically ascetic impulse led missionaries to build wilderness monasteries that developed into dynamic centres of Christian culture. A close alliance of church with state favoured the growth of a strong ecclesiastical hierarchy. Moscow, from which the metropolitan and the prince ruled their respective spheres, became an active capital of religious and political nationalism. By the third quarter of the fourteenth century, Metropolitan Alexis, a man of noble birth in close alliance with other nobles of the royal council, constituted the real power behind the throne. By the middle of the next century, having broken the power of the Golden Horde, Moscow combined a rapidly expanding political regime with an effective ecclesiastical organization.

This vigorous development resulted in final emancipation from the patriarchate of Constantinople. In 1436, the noted Greek humanist Isidore was named metropolitan of Kiev, then dominated by Lithuania, and temporarily was accepted as metropolitan of all the Russias. In 1439 Isidore accepted the Act of Union with Rome. but it proved repugnant to the Russian grand prince, Basil II, and to the Russian clergy, since it required recognition of the primacy of the Roman pope. On his return from the Council of Florence to Moscow, Isidore was put under arrest and subsequently deposed by a synod of Russian bishops. The Unionist patriarch of Constantinople thereupon excommunicated the Russian Church, which in turn refused to accept the patriarch's authority. Thus began the complete autonomy of the Russian Orthodox Church.

ROMAN CATHOLIC PAPACY

A century after Innocent III and his successors had triumphed over the kings of Europe and the Hohenstaufen imperial dynasty (see Volume III), the Catholic papacy suffered defeat and humiliation at the hands of a rising temporal power, the king of France. Boniface VIII, pope from 1294 to 1303, might have maintained a semblance of papal authority over all Christendom had he not alienated those whose help he sought. To begin with, Boniface imprisoned his predecessor, Celestine V, whose abdication smacked of undue influence on Boniface's part and led to charges of illegality. The new pope's Italian policy reflected secular ambitions. In the south he strove, though vainly, to take Sicily by force of arms from its intractable Spanish rulers and restore it to its former Angevin rulers and thus to papal vassalage. Meanwhile he manoeuvred with greater success to keep under his control the Angevin rulers of Naples, a traditional fief of the papacy. Furthermore, in order to round out the properties of his own family in the region of Gaeta, he planned to take over the nearby holdings of the Colonna family.

The Colonnas were formidable foes. They were firmly entrenched both materially, with huge holdings in south Latium, and politically, with two members of their family in the college of cardinals. Cardinal Giacopo Colonna, an energetic opponent of Boniface's Sicilian ambitions, was dangerous also because he questioned the legality of Pope Celestine's abdication. Both Boniface's position as pope and the aggrandizement of his family demanded the elimination of Colonna power. Young Sciarra Colonna by raiding papal property provided a pretext for action. Boniface retaliated by depriving the two Colonna cardinals of their ecclesiastical benefices, and they in turn proclaimed the illegality of his pontificate and appealed to a general church council. Boniface responded by preaching a crusade against them, destroying their Palestrina stronghold, and confiscating all Colonna lands, merging them into a feudal state for one of his nephews. The Colonnas sought refuge in France.

Boniface was less successful in his ambition to gain control of Tuscany. There the bitter strife between the pro-papal party, the 'Blacks' or Guelphs, and the anti-papal party, the 'Whites' or Ghibellines, provided ample opportunity for papal intervention, ostensibly in the interests of peace and amity. A May Day brawl in 1300 between young 'Blacks' and 'Whites' precipitated an uproar in Florence and provided the pope with a pretext for action. First he sent a cardinal to 'mediate' the feud between the in-power 'Whites' and the out-of-power 'Blacks'. When the 'White' rulers (including Dante, who was one of the priors) refused to withdraw their condemnation of the 'Black' conspirators or to agree to the selection of priors from both factions, the papal mediator interdicted the city and departed. Disorder infected other Tuscan towns, and Boniface could, with ostensible justice, send his partisan, Charles of Valois, with an army to pacify Tuscany (1301). Charles entered Florence, 'unarmed', as Dante expressed it (*Purgatorio* 20, 73), 'save with the lance of treachery with which Judas tilted.'

Charles' mediation clearly favoured the 'Blacks'. Exiled members of the papal faction returned in force and, in the name of public reconciliation, virtually took control. Over five hundred 'Whites' were sentenced to death, others to confiscation and fines. Dante went into exile rather than risk trial by prejudiced officials. Early in 1302, having restored the papalists to control, Charles left Florence. But complications elsewhere were to render Boniface unable to reap the fruits of his intrigue in Italy.

Shortly before the accession of Boniface, Edward I of England and Philip IV ('the Fair') of France drifted from diplomatic tension to war. Both kings, in desperate need of funds, applied financial pressure to clergymen as well as to nobles and merchants. In 1296 Boniface precipitated an open conflict with both monarchs by issuing his famous bull 'Clericis Laicos' (see Volume III), which forbade laymen to make or clerics to pay levies except by papal permission. Edward countered by outlawing the recalcitrant clergy and taking over their temporal holdings, and Philip cut off all export of coin from France. The pope admitted defeat by acknowledging the legality of clerical 'gifts' to the crown in times of national emergency.

Boniface might have hesitated to challenge monarchical nationalism a second time but for the accident that 1300 was a centenary year. The jubilee of that centenary was a spectacular success. The promise of spiritual rewards brought throngs of pious pilgrims to Rome, and Christian rulers sent embassies to pay their respects to the spiritual head of Christendom. With coffers and prestige replenished, the pope's self-confidence revived. But Philip IV was equally confident. The year after the jubilee he demanded of Boniface the degradation of a troublesome French bishop on various charges. The pope felt obliged to refuse but ordered that the trial, as one involving clerical jurisdiction, be remanded to the papal curia at Rome.

Had Boniface been content with this plausible legal stand, he would have had a strong case. Instead, he broadened the issue to the moot question of papal *versus* royal authority. He renewed the prohibition of clerical contributions, condemned royal encroachments of various kinds, and summoned the French clergy to Rome for consideration of a programme for reforming the realm of France, and in a papal bull reflected a determination to discipline the king. Philip promptly burned the bull in public and circulated through the realm a garbled version, along with his reply, which opened with the phrase, 'Philip to Boniface, who pretends to be sovereign pontiff, little or no greeting'.

The case of the offending bishop was promptly pushed into the background. The cardinals and the French clergy attending the papal conference at Rome protested against the outrageous language of the French proclamation, and the pope in the bull 'Unam Sanctam' asserted that 'it is necessary for salvation that everyone be subject to the Roman pontiff'. In response, Philip and his lawyers persuaded the three orders (clergy, nobility, and commons) attending the Estates General of 1302 to send open letters denying the pope's political authority over France and questioning the validity of Boniface's election.

For a time the pope seemed to have the better position. In an invasion of Flanders in 1302 Philip's knights suffered an ignominious defeat at the hands of the embattled burghers of Courtrai, and shortly afterward about fifty French clergymen arrived in Rome to attend the council called by the pope. The low state of Philip's cause was revealed by his tactful response to the demands presented by a papal legate. But again Boniface pressed his opponent too far. He demanded unconditional surrender, on pain of excommunication, and Philip, upon the advice of an aggressive counsellor, Guillaume de Nogaret, determined to fight on. The three orders of the Estates General and the populace were flooded with violent charges against Boniface, notably the illegality of his election, and with demands for a general council of the church to judge him for his irregularities and crimes. Scriptural passages were broadcast to make it appear a Christian duty for the French king and people to correct the pope and purge the papacy. Thus the pope's council, a weapon forged for the correction of Philip, was to be matched with the king's council, a weapon to be forged for the correction of the pope. While Boniface sought allies, Nogaret found an eager collaborator in Sciarra Colonna. Nogaret set out for Italy with about 1600 men, intent upon bringing the pope either to terms or to trial by a general church council.

The affair came to a climax in 1303 at Anagni, the pope's summer retreat near Rome. Nogaret's little army forced its way into the town and took possession of the pope. Despite Colonna and other bitter enemies, Boniface apparently was not manhandled, although he refused to consider resigning or submitting willingly to arrest and trial. While his captors hesitated for several days to carry him off by force, papal partisans among the townsfolk took up arms, and the invaders beat a hasty retreat. Boniface was escorted by a senatorial delegation to safety in Rome, where, however, he died within a month.

The short pontificate of Boniface's successor, Benedict XI (1303–4), was dominated by his desire for peace. Benedict, instead of condemning the attack on the spiritual head of Christendom, compromised. Nogaret and the Colonna were excommunicated, but King Philip was officially exonerated. Meanwhile Italy split into pro-French and pro-papal factions. When Benedict died, the choice of a successor took place only after a year of manoeuvering between the Italian majority of the cardinals and the French-Colonna faction.

★   ★   ★

The 'Babylonian Captivity'

Finally Philip's lobbying won the election for Clement V, a Gascon nobleman who had served as archbishop of Bordeaux. On Philip's invitation Clement was crowned pope at Lyons, with the king holding his stirrup in token of royal subservience to spiritual authority. Nevertheless, the pope soon found himself in a royal trap. Philip created complications that induced Clement to postpone departure for Rome. Thus began the so-called 'Babylonian Captivity' of the Avignon popes. It lasted for over seventy years (1305–78).

One of Clement's most notorious complications was the dissolution of the Knights Templars. At the opening of the fourteenth century that order was powerful, wealthy, and corrupt. Unlike the Hospitallers and Teutonic Knights, they could boast no active crusading after the loss of the Holy Land to Islam. Refusing to consider union with the Hospitallers, who were entrenched as far east as Rhodes, they came to be known as luxury-loving aristocrats. Philip decided that it was high time to reform the order, incidentally replenishing the royal treasury by appropriating Templar wealth. Accordingly, he suddenly (1307) ordered an investigation on charges of heresy and immorality. All Templars in France, about two thousand, were arrested and subjected to rigorous examination, first by royal officials, then by inquisitors. Under orders to get confessions, by torture if necessary, the examiners extracted admissions of immoralities, heretical initiation rites, and other secret misdeeds. So impressive was the list of confessed crimes against God and man that Clement sent a papal commission to take over the investigation.

The papal investigation appeared to be objective in purpose and method. In all Christian lands governmental officials were ordered to take the Templars into custody for examination or re-examination, high officers to be given special examination by the pope. The new investigations revealed that many of the original confessions had been obtained by torture or fear of torture. One victim testified that after seeing cartloads of fellow Templars on their way to be burned alive, he would have admitted having killed Christ himself. Many of the prisoners retracted their forced confessions.

Philip and his henchmen now felt obliged to defend their procedure. This they did by inflaming the Estates General and the public to demand punishment of the Templars as secret subverters of religion and morality. Their propaganda prevailed. After four years, the pope gave in and abolished the order, declaring, however, that the evidence was not conclusive. Two years later, Grand Master de Molay and another aged Templar of high rank, both unbroken by their examiners, were executed for protesting against the injustice of the investigations. All Templar property was ordered transferred to the Hospitallers or (in Spain) to other military orders. Eventually, with reluctance, Philip complied with this order, and so his victory over the Templars was less profitable financially than politically. It had warded off penalties for the 'crime of Anagni,' and it placed the papacy still further under royal influence.

Clement V died at Avignon in 1314. Although the town and the surrounding Comtat Venaissin were papal enclaves, the papacy was anything but independent of French control. In his seven-year pontificate Clement created twenty-eight new cardinals, of whom all but three were Frenchmen, and the papacy could presumably be counted on to avoid antagonizing the king of France. The hearings on Nogaret and the other 'criminals of Anagni' dragged on and ended eventually in virtual absolution. The memory of Boniface was blackened by the pope's formal approval of Philip's zeal in endeavouring to purge the church of heresy and corruption.

Although several of Clement's French successors were high-minded, pious, and upright men—for example, Benedict XII (1334–42), Innocent VI (1352–62), and Urban V (1362–70)—they had to keep constant vigil against the mounting bane of wealth and politics in ecclesiastical affairs. John XXII (1316–34) sold church offices and squeezed money from all possible sources so effectively that he left a well-filled treasury to his successor. Clement VI (1342–52), a luxury-loving nobleman from Limoges, expanded the money-raising machinery of the curia and spent freely on artists, poets, women, horses, and other worldly amusements. Urban V completed, in regal magnificence, the papal palace at Avignon. Erected amidst similarly worldly establishments of cardinals, envoys, lawyers, secretaries, lobbyists, sycophants, and prostitutes, and manned by armies of servants, the palace elicited pious condemnation from Petrarch: 'Babylon of the West'; 'hell on earth'; 'sinkhole of vice, glorying not in the Cross of Christ but in feasting, drunkenness, fornication, incest'. Catherine of Siena compared the worst aspects of Avignon to 'the odours of hell'.

The fundamental defect of the papacy even before the 'Captivity' had been the increasing secularization of church administration. It was revealed most spectacularly in two kinds of activity—papal elections and finances. The packing of the electoral College of Cardinals by Clement V was but an accentuation of an older practice rendered still more notorious by the pope's residence in France. Secular influences and interest were perhaps even more crassly revealed in the election of Clement V's successor. Little effort was made to hide that the major issue was not who was the best man but whether he was French or Italian. Twenty-three cardinals met in conclave at Carpentras, near Avignon, in 1314. Lest the minority of Italian cardinals should hold out for an Italian pope or at least for a pope who would return to Italy, the French faction organized pressure groups that mobbed the conclave, threatening death to Italians. Barely escaping with their lives, the cardinals proved stubborn and procrastinated for two years. Finally, convening at Lyons under a guard of French troops, they elected John XXII, a cobbler's son from Cahors.

The financial complications of the papacy had been rendered perhaps even more corrosive than its electoral irregularities by the removal to Avignon. The papal income was diminished by disorder and disaffection in Italy and by the hostility of anti-French nations such as England, while papal expenses increased because of not only the rise in price levels throughout the West but also the vastness of the building programme at Avignon. To meet the demands the popes created a highly successful money-raising machine. The papal chamberlain and his *camera apostolica* became the most important section of the evolving bureaucracy, which comprised departments of revenue (*camera*), correspondence (chancery, or *cancellaria*), and judiciary (*consistorium*, *audentia rota*, *penitentaria*, etc.).

The Avignon department of revenue made tax collections, never popular, particularly odious by its very success. The power of the pope as supreme pontiff to overrule any clerical appointment was turned to profit even where vested electoral rights of long standing were injured, as in the selection of new bishops and in promises of appointment to offices not yet vacant. Candidates were obliged to contribute to the papal treasury a considerable portion of their first year's income, in addition to paying fees and gratuities to all concerned with their actual taking of office. The exploitation of such provisorships, reservations, and expectatives led to violent protests everywhere. In England the reformer John Wycliffe (see below) voiced the resentment which led Parliament to pass the Statute of Provisors (1351), declaring invalid all papal appointments and provisions to English benefices, and the Statute of Praemunire (1353), forbidding the removal of suits to foreign (including papal) courts. By and large, however, the popes were successful in asserting their rights, though often they saw fit to compromise with local authorities by appointing (for a consideration) the candidates of influential patrons.

The financial machine also squeezed out existing dues, fees, taxes, and other levies more vigorously. A papal appointee to a bishopric or abbacy surrendered a *servitium* of about one third of the first year's revenue. Archbishops gave an additional fee for the *pallium*. Appointees to local benefices paid annates (the first year's income) and (for ensuing years) *decimae*, or *tithes*, amounting to about a tenth of the annual income. On the death of an appointee, his personal effects and the income of the office pending occupancy by a new incumbent went to the papal treasury. If an incumbent died leaving debts to the papal treasury, his successor was held responsible for them. Special gratuities and fees to members of the papal bureaucracy, great and small, local and central, contributed to the steady stream of revenue toward Avignon. Resentment of the increase of taxes to an absentee officialdom necessitated strict, often harsh, measures on the part of papal collectors. Severity, in turn, led to the deepening of hostility. Thus, the very success of the revenue machine was a source of misfortune. Worse than public resentment was the deterioration of church officialdom. In every locality absentee benefice-holders, foreign clerics, or pluralists cropped up. At Avignon office seekers and litigants for promised positions swarmed, and petty parasitical officials thrived upon graft, bribes, and fees.

Yet this commercialized system had its good points, too. Papal and temporal patrons often collaborated peacefully in the selection of church officials. Under honest, well-meaning popes, church revenues were put to constructive uses, such as foreign missions, literature, art, and education. For example, Petrarch, though he condemned the luxury and worldliness of the Avignon popes, lived on the benefices they bestowed. Many a university student owed his education to papal grants, and some universities sent to the pope lists of scholars deserving of benefices so that they could complete their education. Clement V and John XXII encouraged medical studies in Greek and Arabic as well as Latin at Montpellier and other universities. They urged the establishment of professorships of Hebrew, Arabic, and other oriental languages, although more for the purpose of combating infidel religions than of increasing human knowledge.

From a political point of view, the Avignon papacy recorded some noteworthy achievements. In addition to deriving political advantage from their cultural patronage, the French popes restored the morale of the papacy as a factor in international affairs. They were not browbeaten or insulted with impunity. To be sure, on occasion papal legates who threatened wayward communities might be roughly handled (at Milan in 1362 they were compelled to eat the papal bull of excommunication, parchment and all). Yet no hostile force invaded the walled town of Avignon, while papal forces reconquered several rebellious towns of Italy.

The Avignon popes carried on a vigorous drive against heretics. Remnants of ancient sects felt their displeasure, notably the Waldenses of the French Alpine regions, who, however, retreating farther into the mountains, managed to survive. In addition, stern decisions were enforced against intramural heretics. Some mystical Franciscans, having in the thirteenth century begun to preach that the era of the Holy Spirit was at hand, practised a strict poverty and the *vita contemplativa*. These 'Spiritual Franciscans' soon fell under suspicion of heresy, and after the accession of Boniface VIII at the turn of the century, those who refused to submit (viz., the Fraticelli) were harshly treated, not merely as heretical but also as rebellious. Nevertheless, numerous sects of 'poor men' sprang up. John XXII excommunicated all who advocated poverty as a fundamental tenet of Christianity, whether the older Beghards and Beguines or the newer Fraticelli. This measure raised a debate over absolute poverty in which the whole Franciscan order became involved, since some within the order favoured strict observance of St Francis' ideal of poverty. In 1323 the pope denounced as heresy the claim that the Apostles had practiced absolute poverty. Still, a number of Franciscans, the so-called 'Strict Observants', chose to follow the rule of St Francis rather than the pope's decree. Here again papal determination, backed by the efficiency of the Inquisition, won a decisive victory. By the end of the century the order had been purged of the heresy of its founder.

The papacy's policy regarding heretics was a logical outcome of its determination to organize effectively all sections of the army of Christ to defend the faith. Strict regimentation aimed at the elimination not only of well-meaning idealists but also of charlatans and vagabond monks. All the monastic orders were forced to regularize their customs in keeping with ideals considered practicable, and several of the popes (e.g. Clement V and John XXII) added valuable disciplinary rules to the existing law of the church. But international disturbances, including the calamity of the Black Death, prevented anything resembling a thorough reformation.

The Avignon popes also organized missions for the penetration of the East. John XXII's and Clement VI's naval expeditions gave allied Christian forces a temporary foothold in Smyrna and made secure the Hospitaller stronghold at Rhodes. By mid-century it was evident, however, that the combined forces of Byzantines, Hospitallers, and Venetians could not battle effectively against the rising strength of the Turks in Asia Minor. John XXII revived a foreign missionary society, first organized in the thirteenth century, and staffed it with Dominicans and Franciscans. In the Holy Land the Franciscans established permanent monastic centres at Jerusalem and Bethlehem. In Armenia monks of the early native Christian orders merged with the Dominicans under the name 'Uniats' (or United Brethren). Still greater success (as we saw in Chapter II) attended the work of missionaries farther east, in regions as distant as China. Until the 1350's the Avignon papacy could boast marked missionary progress in Asia. But in the second half of the century serious setbacks were suffered both in China, because of the fall of the friendly Mongol dynasty in 1368, and in western Asia, because of the ravages of Tamerlane.

★   ★   ★

Temporary Returns to Rome

Various considerations continually directed the absentee popes' attention to Italy. Italian sources of income assumed growing importance as English and German recalcitrance increased. The exhortations of mystic or patriotic Italians such as Catherine of Siena, Dante, and Petrarch reinforced this interest in Italy, but more cogent was the practical consideration that papal political control in the peninsula was in jeopardy. In the Papal States local despots and town authorities paid little heed to their French overlord. In Rome, deprived of its attractiveness as Christendom's centre for pilgrims and church politicians, the citizens threatened to set up their own pope. In 1328 they actually crowned the excommunicated emperor, Louis IV of Bavaria (1314–47), and for a time they supported an anti-pope of his designation. Throughout northern Italy the towns profited by this new struggle between church and state, since, to win support, both the absentee emperor and the absentee pope granted them rights which neither was anyway in a position to veto.

Innocent VI paved the way for the prodigal's return by sending (1353) Cardinal de Albornoz, formerly a Spanish warrior, to restore papal authority in Italy. With marked success Albornoz persuaded or forced the independent rulers in the Papal States to submit, eventually promulgating a code of law known as the Aegidian Constitutions (1357). In Rome itself he used the popular leader Cola di Rienzi to win the supporters of the revived Senatus Populusque Romanus to the pope's cause. Urban V actually returned to Rome for a time (1367–70) at the urging of a friendly emperor, Charles IV, amid the applause of the populace and the congratulations of Italian patriots. Three years in devastated Rome amid restive Italians, however, discouraged him, and he returned to Avignon, notwithstanding the protests of Petrarch, the saintly Bridget of Sweden, and the emperor, who had humbly submitted to coronation at his hands. He died shortly after his return.

Italian disappointment at the pope's desertion and resentment at oppression by his French agents were keen. Revolts broke out even in pro-papal Florence. Gregory XI (1370–78), Urban's successor, sent bands of mercenaries to crush the rebels, but the brutalities of the papal soldiery served only to enflame Italian hostility. Catherine of Siena, entrusted by the Florentines to negotiate with the pope, urged him, 'for the love of the crucified Saviour,' to employ weapons of peace rather than war and return to Rome. The threat of the Romans to join the revolt and set up an anti-pope was more convincing. In 1377 Gregory consented to go to Rome, and he spent several months there, but, finding it too dangerous to remain, he went back to Avignon. Resorting to diplomatic tactics, he won Italian city after city by promising self-government under papal supervisors. The Florentines were isolated by these tactics, and the victorious pope finally returned to Rome, where he soon died.

★   ★   ★

The Great Schism

The regulations governing conclaves required the election of a pope in the town in which the last incumbent had died. At the time of Gregory's death he was preparing to leave once more for Avignon, and the Romans were determined to prevent it. The dying French-born pope had authorized the cardinals to disregard regulations so as to prevent Roman domination of their conclave, but the Romans, officially and spontaneously, blocked all ways of escape from the city, even confiscating the oars of boats in the Tiber. The cardinals were threatened with death if they failed to select a Roman or, at least, an Italian. After ten troubled days they went into conclave at the Vatican. The next morning the crowds were so menacing that quick action was judged necessary, and Bartolomeo Prignano, archbishop of Bari, was elected. Without any apparent question as to the legality of the election, he was crowned pope as Urban VI (1378–89).

Soon, however, Urban's inflexible behaviour alienated most of the cardinals. As soon as they could, some of them left Rome. Within four months after the election, sixteen had escaped, and thirteen of these met at Fondi to declare Urban's pontificate illegal. A month later they elected one of their own number, Robert of Geneva, as Pope Clement VII (1378–94).

Arguments as to whether Urban or Clement was legal pope led to an open schism. It continued for over thirty years as a merely two-part schism, and then for eight years more (until 1417) as a three-part schism. The schism exacerbated the animosities created by 'the Babylonian Captivity'. Rival popes now excommunicated each other and each others' supporters. Duplicate officials were appointed to church positions. Duplicate revenues were claimed. The French generally supported Clement VII, the Italians and the English, Urban VI. The Spanish kingdoms declared for Clement, but Portugal shifted to Urban by reason of English pressure. The German emperor recognized Urban, but not all of the imperial states followed his example. Some Italian states that originally had favoured Urban were driven into Clement's camp because of Urban's fanatical and sometimes brutal treatment of any who differed with him. Neither pope and neither college of cardinals would resign, arbitrate, or even recognize the legal existence of the other. No general council could be called legally without papal consent, and that was unobtainable.

Since no orthodox solution of the muddle was possible, scholars resorted to unorthodox ones. As we shall see (Chapter VIII), the theory of popular sovereignty was widely expounded. Marsilius of Padua and John of Jandun had already set it forth in their *Defensor Pacis* (1324). This work argued that papal authority was dependent ultimately on the faithful or their representatives and, hence, that a general council called even by representatives of the laity might judge the pope, inasmuch as he was the responsible executive rather than the autocrat of Christendom. Rienzi, in defence of his republic in Rome, and William of Ockham, in defence of the Franciscans, likewise questioned whether the pope was supreme in certain temporal and spiritual matters. As the schism moved from bad to worse, theologians, such as the Germans Heinrich von Langenstein and Conrad von Gelnhausen and the Frenchmen Cardinal Pierre d'Ailly and Jean Gerson, rectors in turn of the University of Paris, applied this line of reasoning to the problem of eliminating the double papacy. Thus the idea spread that a general council called by a temporal ruler might remove a pope.

Such unorthodox views received more and more attention as the double papacy was prolongated. After the two original rivals died, the Roman cardinals elected Boniface IX (1389–1404) and the Avignon cardinals Benedict XIII (1394–1423), a Spaniard. In 1395 a council of French clergymen recommended the abdication of both popes, but neither pope would consent. In 1398, on the advice of professors from the University of Paris, among whom were Ailly and Gerson, a second French council adopted stronger measures. Charging Benedict with heresy, both clergy and king withdrew French support, financial as well as spiritual. Affairs in the separate dioceses that had been subject to papal authority were now handled by the bishops. Thus, at one stroke, the papal perquisites in the French church were taken over, ostensibly at first by the French clergy, ultimately by the king and the local nobility. Royal and aristocratic officials exploited local churches unmercifully, benefices and treasures were plundered, and the clergy profited little from their emancipation.

Benedict refused to yield to French pressure. He took refuge at Marseilles, where he received promises of renewed fidelity from outside powers including the king of Castile, and tried to initiate negotiations with his rival. Boniface refused to negotiate, condemning his rival as an obstinate rebel. On his death shortly afterward, the Roman cardinals elected an aged Venetian as Pope Innocent VII (1404–06), but he too refused to negotiate. Benedict thereupon seized the opportunity to press for a conference and, on further refusal, took the drastic step of calling on the temporal princes of Christendom to remove the obstinate Roman pope forcefully. Nothing came of the appeal, however, and on Innocent's death the schism continued, for the Roman cardinals elected Gregory XII (1406–15).

Popular pressure and especially the resentment in the Papal States induced Gregory to be less stubborn than his predecessors. He offered to abdicate if Benedict would do the same, thus permitting both sets of cardinals to unite for the election of a single pope. The two popes haggled until April 1408, when Gregory, temporarily absent from his capital, heard that Rome had been occupied by Benedict's champion, the king of Naples, and broke off negotiations.

By this time the patience of many in the rival camps was exhausted, and each college of cardinals, consenting to desert its pope, agreed to a general council. This startling decision, threatening to take the initiative from both popes, was checked by Benedict, who still hoped to determine the outcome. Retiring to Perpignan, he called his own general council. Pope Gregory shortly followed suit. Both offered to abdicate but on conditions that each was sure would not be fulfilled. Meanwhile a general council had actually met at Pisa and had deposed both popes, and the united college of cardinals elected the cardinal-archbishop of Milan as Pope Alexander V (1409–10).

The choice of a third pope proved to be no way to restore the unity of the church. The failure was partly due to the clever tactics of the other two popes, who refused to give up, but even more to the Pisa papacy's own weaknesses. Before election Alexander had been forced to promise radical reforms in the interests of the local clergy and to the detriment of the papacy. Once he was installed, he ignored his promises. He died within a year, to be succeeded by John XXIII (1410–15). (In 1958 the late pope took the same name, indicating repudiation of the fifteenth-century claimant.) John, the most ruthless of the cardinals, was a fighting man from Naples. He conquered Rome and summoned a council to meet there and sanction his manoeuvres, but it was sparsely attended and quickly adjourned.

*   *   *

The Rise of the Conciliar Movement

Sigismund, the new German ruler (chosen king in 1410 and crowned emperor in 1433), soon voiced the widespread demand of western Christians for a settlement. Ambitious to become a secular leader of the West, he promoted the now familiar idea of conciliar control of popes. He persuaded John XXIII, whose temporal enemies had driven him from Rome, to issue a formal summons to a general council. The Pisa pope consented, not only because he was hard pressed in his wars, with Sigismund presenting his only hope of survival, but also because his cardinals insisted.

Late in 1414 a general council met at Constance, in Imperial territory. Sigismund devoted his attention to the council's relations with secular powers. His efforts to win over the lay adherents of the several recalcitrant popes helped to solve the council's practical difficulties. Its theoretical problem, the justification of the doctrine of conciliar supremacy over the papacy, was the concern of the Scholastics, i.e. the university men. Some of them, notably Dietrich von Niem and Cardinal d'Ailly, thought that general councils ought to be the continuing sovereign power in church government, while Gerson and Francesco Zabarella, of the Bologna law school, thought that they ought to be merely a check on the pope's executive power. All were of one mind, however, as to the necessity not only of eliminating the schismatic popes but also of instituting drastic reform in the papal bureaucracy.[7]

The Council of Constance dragged on for four years. At one time it comprised as many as six hundred representatives, and the total number that attended is estimated at six thousand. Medieval towns were not ordinarily equipped to accommodate so many visitors, and food shortage threatened at the outset, but efficient management, to the point of enforcing schedules of maximum prices, achieved satisfactory local arrangements. International congresses were uncommon in those days, and for a time procedural issues were paramount. The proposal of John's Italian contingent to confirm the Pisa decision (thus recognizing John as pope) and merely to provide for general councils every quarter century was rejected. Two French cardinals, Ailly and Guillaume Fillastre, argued persuasively for the resignation of all three popes and a declaration of the supremacy of the council. They also opposed another Italian proposal to give votes only to bishops and abbots, of whom many were Italian. Instead, decisions ultimately were reached, as was then the custom at the universities, by a vote of the 'nations' present (Italian, German, French, and English), each 'nation' being free to decide who should vote within its own grouping. As a result voting was not restricted to the higher clergy but was extended to clerical university professors, representatives of secular powers, and a few others. The division of a Catholic Church council into 'nations' was an unmistakable sign of the times.

Early in the year 1415 the Pisa pope, John, finding the council indocile, fled from Constance and withdrew his support. This defiance unified the four 'nations'. They decreed that the council held its authority from Christ, was supreme, and must be obeyed by all Christians including a pope. John was summoned, refused to appear, was tried *in absentia*, was found guilty on seventy charges (including simony, varied immoralities, murder, and heresy), and was deposed. Soon thereafter representatives of the Roman pope, Gregory XII, submitted his resignation. But the Avignon pope, Benedict XIII, safe in his native Aragon, remained obstinate. Thereupon Emperor Sigismund left the council in order to try to solve the dispute by diplomatic negotiations. Eventually he was able to win over Benedict's Spanish and Scottish supporters, and they sent representatives to Constance to join the council.

Meanwhile the council also dealt with heresy. The heretics John Huss and Jerome of Prague (whose heresy we shall describe below) were tried, condemned, and burned at the stake. Their archetype, John Wycliffe, already safely dead, was tried *in absentia*, and his remains were ordered removed from an English churchyard. The council's uncompromising handling of the three heretics, even its disregard for Sigismund's safe-conduct for Huss, was generally approved as a necessary if harsh measure for the crushing of treason against God and the Faith. With the council's consent, the new pope, when finally elected, issued a bull condemning specific tenets of Wycliffe and Huss and required a loyalty oath of suspected heretics affirming their acceptance of the council's decrees on church doctrine.

The more subtle problem of church reform met with many differences of opinion at the Council of Constance. Like all other important matters, it was presented to each 'nation' for discussion and vote before consideration in full session. Here the conciliar procedure broke down. While the council was in session a lengthy truce between the English and the French ended, and the Hundred Years' War was renewed. To make matters worse, the French, both at home and at the council, had already split into rival factions, the Armagnacs and the Burgundians, and were at sword's point over the murder some years earlier (1407) of the Armagnac leader, Duke Louis of Orleans, by emissaries of Jean sans Peur, duke of Burgundy. Jean Petit, a French theologian, had defended the murder as justifiable tyrannicide, and Jean sans Peur had himself appealed to the Avignon pope, the still obdurate Benedict XIII, for vindication. Gerson, who had been prominent in the prosecution of Huss, led the opposition to Jean sans Peur and Petit. The issue now came before the council, where it precipitated a feud within the French 'nation' that was at least as bitter as the hostility between the French and English 'nations'.

Other regional issues aggravated the divisions in the council, drawing attention away from church reform. Even when the councillors seriously grappled with that problem, criticism of papal administration proved easier than practical remedy of bureaucratic abuses. A special commission representing the several 'nations' assembled a number of proposals for reform, which it submitted to each of them for discussion. For about two years the commission and the several 'nations' considered proposed reforms, especially of papal financial practices. In general, the German, the English, and for a time the French were more favourable, and the Italians more opposed, than the others to serious change.

The prolonged absence of Emperor Sigismund while negotiating with the schismatic factions added to the delay. On his return Sigismund found the council badly divided. The French cardinals, formerly leaders in the cause of conciliar reform and supremacy, had grown suspicious of him. He and the German 'nation' were pro-English in the Hundred Years' War and were thought to be planning to elect a pope who would be an anti-French puppet. Gradually the council degenerated into two camps, the Teutonic (English and German) 'nations' versus the Latin (French and Italian) 'nations', supported by the newly-arrived Spanish 'nation'.

After more than two years' deliberation, the council deposed the still defiant Benedict XIII and at last took up the question of choosing a new pope. The reformers preferred postponement of a choice until their programme should be adopted, but the French-Italian-Spanish coalition urged an early decision and by the old method—selection by the cardinals. A compromise was reached providing that election should be by a joint conclave of the cardinals and six representatives from each of the five 'nations' and that to be elected a candidate must receive the votes of at least two thirds of the cardinals and of each 'nation's' representatives. An additional compromise stipulated that the election and the reform programme should proceed simultaneously.

The first decision (October 1417) was a decree calling for frequent councils in the future. It was also decreed that, in event of a new schism, a council must be held within one year. Furthermore, certain unpopular papal practices were prohibited, and the new pope was required, with the assistance of the council. to make eighteen specified reforms, chiefly concerning papal revenues and appointments. A new pope was elected without undue delay. On the first vote in the joint conclave, Cardinal Otto Colonna had a two-thirds majority in the English and Italian 'nations' and some support in the others and in the college of cardinals. After three days he was chosen and became Pope Martin V (1417–31).

Martin immediately undertook to consider the specified recommendations for reform. Each 'nation' presented its views on them, and a conciliar reform commission consulted with him. Inevitable differences of opinion, combined with general weariness, played into Martin's hands. He was able to limit the programme to seven of the recommendations, and those of no great import. The council ended with a tacit recognition that universal reform was impossible. The 'nations', on the other hand, were able to make separate treaties with the pope toward the same end. By 'concordats' they tried to limit local abuses in the collection of papal revenues, the making of papal appointments, papal interference in judicial matters, and other papal prerogatives. Like much of the council's later achievements, the concordats were relatively ineffective and short-lived.

*   *   *

The Decline of the Conciliar Movement

The adjournment of the council (April 1418) was marked by certain ominous developments. The pope's announcement that the next council would meet at Pavia in Italy displeased the French 'nation'. Several minor problems, such as Petit's defence of tyrannicide, were left unsettled; the doctrine of tyrannicide was denounced as heresy, but the council, which had condemned Huss, left Petit untouched. Gerson, thus partly repudiated, temporarily exiled himself from France, dominated by the Burgundians, Petit's protectors. Many representatives departed with a sense of frustration, and immediate events justified their gloom. After the council formally adjourned, Martin proclaimed to the cardinals, in the presence of Sigismund, that the pope was the supreme judge and that none might appeal from his decisions. This view was not promulgated as a bull only because of the hostile reactions of leading churchmen such as Gerson and the suggestion that the proclamation verged on heresy. For the Italians and the Colonna pope, however, the outcome of the council was most satisfactory. Papal control was restored in Rome and most of the rest of the Papal States. Thus the Colonna family, ruthlessly ousted by Boniface VIII over a century earlier, not only returned to their patrimony but returned to it as leaders in the revival of the papacy, which Boniface had started on the road to Captivity, Schism, and degradation.

Once Pope Martin V was firmly in office, he showed no interest in carrying out the conciliar decrees. His programme was to strengthen the papacy, and that meant to undermine the doctrine of conciliar supremacy. He could not well refuse to call the promised Council of Pavia, but he could minimize its significance. Since Pavia was in the realm of the hostile duke of Milan, he did not attend in person but gave the presidency to four legates and empowered them to move the council to another place if necessary. An epidemic provided them with the pretext for removal to Siena. The poor attendance at the council, an eloquent testimonial of the apathy engendered by the last days at Constance, permitted Martin's legates to control the proceedings. Heresy, especially that of Wycliffe and Huss, was re-condemned, union with the Orthodox Greek Catholic Church was approved but found impracticable, and the reform programme of Constance was revived. When certain drastic reformers of the French 'nation' became uncontrollable, the papal legates left the council and from a safe distance in Florence dissolved it. Determined to spike the guns of the reformers, Martin appointed a commission of cardinals to investigate abuses. The result, a bull condemning some well-known abuses, accomplished nothing except to cover up the pope's aversion to reform.

All parties realized that the fate of real reform and of conciliar influence still hung in the balance. Sincere reformers, notably the scholars of the University of Paris and Sigismund, called on the pope to fulfill the expressed will of the 'nations' at Constance. The rulers of England and France also favoured a council, if for no other reason than to protect their peoples from a revival of papal exploitation. The demand grew louder as the Hussites in Bohemia successfully resisted the crusade that Martin had proclaimed against them. Two German princes went so far as to have placards posted in Rome setting forth the need for a council to combat the victorious Hussites and threatening to depose the pope and the cardinals if they refused to act. Hostile though he was to councils, Martin felt impelled to act. Accordingly in 1431 he appointed Cardinal Giuliano Cesarini, who was en route to Germany to lead the crusade against the Hussites, as his legate to open and preside at a council at Basel. Shortly thereafter Martin died, to be succeeded by Eugenius IV (1431–47), a Venetian cardinal.

Like the abortive council at Pavia, the Council of Basel was poorly attended —at least, at the outset. In fact, it seemed about to expire altogether when the collapse of Cesarini's crusade against the Hussites, impelling him to turn his major attention to Basel, saved it. He sent out a call for the pope and the clergy to attend and invited the Bohemian Hussites to send a delegation to discuss reunion with the church. Then suddenly, in December, word came from the new pope dissolving the council and forbidding negotiations with the heretics. Thereupon the members of the council, thoroughly aroused, taking matters into their own hands, renewed the Constance decrees concerning conciliar supremacy and frequent reform councils.

For two years thereafter council and pope played a desperate game.

Eugenius' plan was similar to that of his predecessor—to use evasive tactics. The council was convinced that the salvation of the church demanded reform, a constructive solution of the Hussite problem, and the establishment of conciliar supremacy. It called upon the pope to revoke his decree of dissolution and to appear in person at Basel. It ordered the cardinals likewise to appear and announced that, should the papacy fall vacant, the election of a successor would take place at the council. Cesarini, now a sincere conciliarist, accepted these decrees. The pope yielded partly, agreeing to allow the council to continue at Basel until the Hussite problem was solved, but after that he proposed to call a new council somewhere in the Papal States to end heresy, reform the church, and restore peace in western Europe. The council responded by reasserting its supremacy.

For a time, the council steadily gained in prestige and attendance. Most of the cardinals appeared. The pope did not appear, but he finally gave sanction to the council and called on all lay and ecclesiastical powers to send representatives. Eventually the attendance reached five hundred. Emboldened, the councillors called on the pope to legalize their actions from the beginning and threatened to depose him if he failed to come or to send official representatives. Eugenius temporized by naming six cardinals to preside in his absence. One of them, Cesarini, refused the appointment. By the middle of 1433 the council began seriously to consider deposing the pope, but Sigismund, whom he had recently crowned emperor at Rome, objected to such drastic action, thus encouraging the pope to take a stronger stand. In several bulls Eugenius condemned any conciliar action save on the three issues which he had named—heresy, reform, and peace. He also annulled all acts against himself and his curia and demanded recognition of his presiding officers. He was perhaps only testing his strength, for he withdrew the demands that evoked violent opposition. By the end of the year both parties seemed content with a stalemate.

Meanwhile conciliar business dragged on. This council was not organized by 'nations', though they functioned informally with considerable vigour and some serious differences of opinion. In general, the Council of Basel was less manageable than that of Constance had been. Voting was by 'head' (i.e. by individuals) rather than by 'nations', and many voting members had low rank. In the long run, the council's efficiency was hampered by this 'democratic' factor as well as by its very success in diplomatic exchanges with the pope, for democracy and success made for extreme measures that undermined public confidence.

Extremism was exemplified in the handling of the delicate problem of church reform. Not only did the council condemn generally recognized abuses and restrict blatant evils of papal finance and bureaucracy but it also made changes that were less easily justified. It set up a system of provincial and diocesan councils with a view to extending conciliar controls to the archbishops, bishops, and other regional bureaucrats of the ecclesiastical hierarchy. Any payment of fees to papal officials for appointments, ordinations, annates, and the like was prohibited. Such officials were thenceforth to depend solely on salaries, although the council not only made no specific provision for salaries but even stipulated that, for the time being, all local revenues due the pope were to be sent to Basel for conciliar supervision. Eugenius took this revolutionary blow at his financial resources with remarkable calm, merely attempting to obtain a compromise. He was encouraged by reports that many conservative members of the council were alarmed at the rising tide of radicalism. His opportunity for decisive action came with the offer of the Eastern emperor and church to negotiate concerning possible unity of the Roman and Greek churches.

The Easterners, concerned over the growing menace of the Turks, seemed willing to buy western aid at the price of reunion with the Roman Catholic Church. For some time the pope and the Council of Basel competed with each other for the right to carry on the negotiations. The Greeks, however, finally refused to go to Basel and insisted that, wherever the meeting took place, the pope must be present. This was Eugenius' first tactical victory over the council. He gained a further advantage when the council split over the place for negotiations. A majority, led by the French faction, voted to meet at Avignon or thereabouts; Cardinal Cesarini and the Italian minority held out for Florence or some other Italian city that would be agreeable to the Greeks and the pope. Differences of opinion degenerated into bitter words and physical violence, with rival spokesmen struggling for the presiding officer's chair and shouting each other down. To make matters worse, the conciliar majority renewed its charges against Eugenius, accusing him of disobeying its decrees, contributing to schism, and resisting reform. This denunciation drove Cesarini and his minority to secession. They adjourned to Ferrara, where the pope opened formal negotiations with the Greeks in January 1438. The Baselites, condemned as a rump council, continued their meetings, futilely denouncing the pope and futilely negotiating with the Hussites.

Dragging on for a decade, the Basel majority demonstrated the weaknesses of a divided parliament if pitted against a centralized authority. When already outmanoeuvred in the Greek negotiations, the council suspended Eugenius, at a time (1439) when his prestige was rising. Temporal bodies were quick to take advantage of the rent in the ecclesiastical system. Albert, who had succeeded Emperor Sigismund in 1437, and the leading German princes, the electors, took a neutral position in the struggle between council and pope, but a German diet exploited the anti-papal decisions, formally adopting the decrees on conciliar supremacy and the restrictions of papal authority in finances and local appointments. Similarly a French ecclesiastical council, convoked by Charles VII at Bourges in 1438, turned the Council of Basel's actions to France's national advantage. Without repudiating papal authority, the Pragmatic Sanction of Bourges (1438), revealing the desire of the French king and clergy for the administrative independence of the French church, declared that the king was free to nominate candidates for French benefices to the cathedral chapters, religious communities, and other ecclesiastical electtoral bodies, and limited French appeals to the papal courts and French payments to the papal treasury. Successive popes refused to honour this unilateral declaration, until a compromise was reached in the Concordat of 1516 (see Chapter IV), but it served as the basis of what later came to be called 'the Gallican Liberties'.

In the face of diminishing ecclesiastical prestige, the rump council at Basel put a finishing touch to its negative programme. It deposed the already suspended Eugenius for the heresy of opposing the council and elected a counter-pope, Felix V (1439-49). Felix at first gained some support in Germany, but Albert's successor as ruler, Frederick III, went over to the papal side in return for the generous Concordat of Vienna (1448), a highly pragmatic arrangement by which the pope purchased the support of a national prince and clergy with concessions on local ecclesiastical revenues and offices. Although the council was still three hundred strong, Frederick expelled it from Basel. It prolonged itself ineffectually at Lausanne, where Felix resided, until he abdicated.

The decade of the decline of the Conciliar Movement was a decade of ascent for Pope Eugenius. The Greeks, having accepted his Ferrara Council as the authentic one, sent to it an impressive embassy, comprising Emperor John Palaeologus, the patriarch of Constantinople, Metropolitan Isidore of All the Russias, and some seven hundred other Greek Orthodox clerics and subordinates. The papal negotiations with the Greeks were outwardly impressive but accomplished nothing permanent. The Greeks were on the defensive at home against Turkish conquest, and their real purpose at Ferrara was to obtain military aid with as little sacrifice as possible of their ecclesiastical independence. All differences except two were settled with relative ease. Both at Ferrara and at Florence (to which the pope transferred the council after a year and where he personally presided) the council heard protracted arguments concerning the supremacy of the pope and the 'procession of the Holy Spirit'. Finally (July 1439) an Act of Union was signed. The Greeks accepted the Roman doctrine that the Holy Spirit had proceeded from God the Son as well as from God the Father,[8] and also acknowledged the 'primacy' of the papacy (with a vague recognition of the autonomy of the Greek Church). In return, the pope sent two war galleys and three hundred soldiers to aid in the defence of Constantinople.

Furious resentment of rank-and-file Greeks, we have seen, kept the ecclesiastical agreements from being carried out, but, even so, Pope Eugenius gained a decisive advantage in the West. Emboldened by his freshly won prestige, he formally condemned all decrees of conciliar supremacy over the papacy, returned to Rome in 1443, and took the council from Florence to his own Lateran, to serve as a 'rubber stamp' for his decisions. Felix's resignation and the demise of the Council of Basel under Eugenius' successor, Nicholas V

(1447–55) marked a new era. The struggle for government of the Catholic Church by reforming ecumenical councils virtually ended, and in its stead came the absolutism of Italian popes. A new schism threatened briefly when a French-inspired council at Pisa in 1511–12 contemplated forcing the abdication of Pope Julius II (see below), but he counteracted it successfully by calling his own (Fifth) Lateran Council in 1512, which lasted until adjourned by his successor in 1517. This council made a few feeble recommendations for reform but did little to correct the major abuses that were to help provoke the different and deeper kind of schism known as the Reformation.

The greatest achievements of the councils must be classified as pragmatic rather than idealistic. In the end the compulsion of nationalism reduced the reform programme to a mere shifting of control of the papal spoils system from an efficient bureaucracy to scattered kings and their secular underlings. The 'nations' of the councils, the concordats, and the pragmatic sanctions were milestones on the road toward the disintegration of the medieval Catholic empire and the rise of nationally controlled churches. As once the provinces of the western Roman Empire had fallen apart among regional tribal groupings, so now the papal empire was falling apart among national dynasties. At their best, the councils had stood for international harmony, limited monarchy, and spiritual reform, but the main currents of Western civilization pushed strongly in the direction of nationalism, absolutism, and political secularism.

*   *   *

The Popes (1417–1521)

In spite of the Conciliar Movement, the autocratic power of the papacy revived. Pope Martin V was the first of a line of secular-minded popes.[9] True to his Colonna ancestry, he laid solid foundations for papal despotism in central Italy. His successor, Eugenius IV, gave ground in the struggle for control of the Papal States during nine years of absence in Cosimo de' Medici's Florence, but his deputy at Rome suppressed republican revolts and governed with such brutal efficiency that Eugenius, upon returning to Rome (1443), was able to exercise absolute power. By mid-century the pope was one of Italy's many Renaissance despots, and the papacy emerged not only as a worldly autocracy but also as a pseudo-nationalist state with the ambition of uniting Italy under its temporal sway.

The popes provided excellent exemplars of another Renaissance characteristic as well—humanistic culture. Nicholas V (1447–55) even before his election as pope had had an enviable reputation as a scholar. The first humanist pope, he aimed to make the rebuilt Vatican City a centre of learning and art and spent lavishly for Latin and Greek manuscripts, whether Christian or Classical, purchased throughout Europe. Scribes and scholars were subsidized to copy and translate. He lived to see the completion of parts of the Vatican Palace, including a library that housed some 5,000 manuscripts. Venerable churches and ancient monuments throughout the city were repaired, and plans were made for a new St Peter's. While Rome was thus rebuilt in a fashion calculated to make it once more the world's cultural capital, the medieval papal idea of spiritual leadership was eclipsed.

Though dominated by grandiose cultural ideas, Nicholas was also remarkably successful in politics. A man of peace, he was by inclination as well as good fortune to bring to an end the papal conflict with the Council of Basel and to terminate the worst of Italy's internecine wars. His jubilee of 1450 was an unprecedented success; so many pilgrims crowded the streets that hundreds were crushed in panics, and it was deemed necessary to limit each visitor's stay. The jubilee filled the papal coffers, permitting the pope to carry on his expensive programme, and brought prosperity to Rome's citizenry as well. Although he benevolently granted a certain degree of local autonomy to the city, his last years were embittered by a republican plot. The major event of his reign, however, was the fall of Constantinople.

Since about 1300 intermittent appeals had been made for Christian crusades against the rising tide of the Ottoman Turks. Christians were no longer urged to help recover the Holy Supulchre but rather to assist in defending Constantinople and Hungary, which constituted Christendom's outer bastion against the infidel. A French-Burgundian army had been annihilated on the lower Danube in 1396 by Sultan Bayezid I's forces. Constantinople's ultimate fate was thus sealed, although postponed half a century by Tamerlane's temporary destruction of Turkish power in Asia Minor. Tamerlane's onslaught might have given Christendom a golden opportunity to counter-attack and destroy the battered and divided sultanate, but no large-scale crusade was launched, and Constantinople fell in 1453.

The exploits of the Hungarian crusaders a few years later were due to a dramatic revival of the old crusading spirit, but only on a national, defensive basis. Inspired by the Franciscan Giovanni di Capistrano and led by Hunyadi, already revered as a national strategist-statesman, a Hungarian army consisting largely of badly armed but heroic peasants not only checked the Turks at Belgrade in 1456 but drove them back and invaded the Bulgarian provinces of Turkey. The lack of effective aid from the Hungarian nobility and, despite papal efforts, from other Christian nations made it impossible to follow up this victory; and it proved to be the only successful Christian crusade of the entire century. Yet in itself it was decisive. It postponed the Turkish invasion of the middle Danube area until the campaigns that led to the Hungarian defeat at Mohacs in 1526 and the siege of Vienna in 1529, and it may have saved central Europe for Christendom.

Nicholas died in 1455 in the midst of a vain attempt to organize a crusade against the Turks, and his immediate successors carried on his policy. Calixtus III, of the Borgia family, formerly a Spanish cardinal, during a short reign (1455–58) continued fruitlessly to promote a crusade. Pius II (1458–64) compared with Nicholas in scholarly interests and crusading zeal. As Bishop Aeneas Sylvius Piccolomini of Siena, Pius had been a worldly gentleman of the High Renaissance. His varied writings on history, education, and other subjects (see Chapters VIII and XVI) had a facile, piquant, classical flavour. His illegitimate children, his disapproval of celibacy for the clergy, and a risqué novel of his younger days, widely translated, embarrassed his pontificate. His shifting career in Basel and in Germany had been more fitting for an Italian humanist and diplomat than for a candidate for the throne of St Peter. Upon becoming pope, however, he not only adopted the crusading programme of Nicholas and Calixtus but in fact died of a fever while preparing personally to lead a Papal-Venetian armada against the Turks. Not until the reign of Sixtus IV (1471–84) did an expedition go off, but, except for taking a few prisoners, it came to naught, and Western Christendom thereupon took a position of passive defence.

Seven popes followed Pius II in the half century or so before the Reformation and for the most part shed little glory on their hallowed post. Even disregarding the unreliable scandal which was noised abroad about most of them, observers could detect the triumph of secularism in the See of Peter. These seven occupants of the pre-Reformation Vatican, on the one hand, showed less interest in Renaissance scholarship than Nicholas V but, on the other, glaringly promoted the triumph of worldliness. They set a spiritually questionable standard of magnificence in their lavishly decorated palaces. Witness the Sistine Chapel—i.e. the chapel of Sixtus IV.

Spiritual indifference was matched by zeal in secular enterprises as papal despotism advanced. Sixtus IV (1471–84) strengthened his control of the Papal States by nepotism and the diplomatic marriages of his kinsfolk. His efforts to extend his sway elsewhere in Italy, though equally unprincipled, were less successful. In fact, in the midst of his manoeuvres, the Turks captured the Italian seaport of Otranto, commanding the straits between the Adriatic and the Ionian Sea. Nevertheless, he showed Italy and the western world that the papacy was an aggressive political force capable of playing a leading part in Italian affairs.

The tales about the Borgian roué, nephew of Calixtus III, who became Pope Alexander VI (1492–1503) may be fantastic exaggerations, but they illustrate how low was the moral tone believed to be characteristic of the nominal leaders of Christendom. Alexander played a despot's role strikingly similar to that of Sixtus IV except that the Borgia curia was packed with Spaniards instead of Genoese. As in Sixtus' pontificate, foreign invaders hampered the pope's Italian ambitions. In Alexander's case, however, the invasion was the first in a disastrous series that came from the north; it was by Charles VIII's French 'barbarians' instead of by Turkish infidels; and it was complete, penetrating the length of the peninsula to Rome and Naples. Unprepared to resist, the pope rode out the storm with diplomatic skill. Eventually he joined with Spain, the Empire, Venice, and Milan, all of which resented Charles' conquests in Italy, in a 'Holy League', which obliged the French to retreat, and he recovered control of the Papal States. The brutal conquests of his son, Cesare, the able general who was the prototype of Machiavelli's *Prince*, were more spectacular than permanent. The pope's untimely death left the Papal States and the rest of Italy in a turmoil.

The reforging of despotism in the Papal States was left to Julius II (1503–13), an iron-willed 'Machiavellian' who had learned much about papal politics as a cardinal. In contrast to the easy-going, urbane Alexander, Julius was a man of a violent temperament who led troops in person and governed the Papal States with tyrannical efficiency. His unscrupulous diplomacy restored the papacy to its position as an international power. Allying with France and others in the League of Cambrai (1508) against Venice, he made good the papal claim to lands that had been seized by Venice. Then with Venice as one of his allies, he set about to drive the French 'barbarians' out of Italy. He fought and negotiated for three years, undismayed by illness, defeat, or threats of deposition by renegade cardinals at the Council of Pisa mentioned above, and he died victorious, absolute master of the revived Papal States, arbiter of the Italies, a leading diplomat in the melée of European power politics. More lasting than his forging of papal despotism (and at the same time a tool in the process) was his patronage of art, especially architecture (see Chapter XII).

Leo X (1513–21), one of Lorenzo de' Medici's sons, played a similar role as builder of papal despotism and patron of Renaissance culture. He strengthened the University of Rome, especially by the addition of professors of Greek and Hebrew, organized the already extensive Vatican Library more effectively, and rewarded classicists, poets, and dramatists generously. Cardinals and Roman aristocrats followed his example in building private libraries and patronizing literature and art (see Chapters X–XII). Leo's need for funds—to rebuild St Peter's Church, among other things—and the inadequacy of the reform measures undertaken by the Fifth Lateran Council (see above) aided directly to precipitate the Reformation. In March 1517 the council ended its five-year career; in October Luther posted his ninety-five theses (see Chapter IV).

MYSTICISM AND HERESY IN EUROPE

Though, and in part because, the papacy was drifting with the current of secularism, the church was fostering certain contrasting tendencies. One of these was mysticism. A dynamic outgrowth of a quieter development of earlier centuries, mysticism now tended to take at the same time the diverging paths of contemplative and of active religion. In pursuing the active aim, the path diverged again—in the directions of church reform, on the one hand, and heresy, on the other.

Mysticism had its roots in Augustine's Neoplatonism and the contemplative life of monasticism. The mystic, inspired by intuitive experience, might seek to revive some aspect of early church worship such as the veneration of the Virgin Mary, the Eucharist, or some earlier puritanical practice such as apostolic or monastic poverty. Monastic mystics were prone to emphasize the other-worldly life of the Apostles and of the early hermit-monks. Women tended to stress a more spectacular type of mysticism, that of prophetic vision or revelation. The puritanical impulse often proved to be a reaction to the worldliness of the clergy and might end in a charge of heresy, as was the case, indicated previously, of the zealots among the Spiritual Franciscans.

Even the Dominicans, although upholders of strict orthodoxy, produced some mystics. Among them were the Rhineland teachers and preachers Johannes Eckhart of Cologne (1260–1327) (generally known as Meister Eckhart), Heinrich Suso (1295–1365), and Johann Tauler (1290–1361). All three were strongly influenced by Neoplatonism (see Chapter VI). Although Eckhart was personally orthodox, certain of his doctrines were condemned as heretical, and undoubtedly they affected those German monastic mystics who followed the heretical path marked out by the Spiritual Franciscans. Suso's influence became noteworthy in Dominican nunneries of the Rhineland and (along with Tauler's) among the fourteenth-century Rhenish and Bavarian mystics known as the 'Friends of God'. Prominent in this loosely organized but effective movement were middle-class laymen and women. Perhaps because of their Dominican connections, the 'Friends of God' held firmly to orthodox doctrines and practices, intent on making themselves an inner church of dedicated souls in direct communion with God. They vigorously opposed the excesses of earlier and more radical German and Flemish groups such as the Beghards, Beguins, and 'Brethren of the Free Spirit'. Out of their midst (c. 1350) came *Eine Deutsche Theologie*, a sort of textbook of mysticism, once mistakenly attributed to Tauler. Widely circulated in manuscript, it was not printed in full until Martin Luther's approval of it led him in 1518 to supervise its publication under the title *Ein geystlich edles Buchlein*. Thus the role of mysticism as a forerunner of Protestantism was made fairly explicit.

A more radical form of mysticism was exemplified in Flanders, where Jan Ruysbroeck (1295–1381) and his disciple Geert Groote (1340–84) taught, preached, and wrote. Even though Ruysbroeck vigorously attacked the Beguins and other such heretical groups in and about Brussels, his own pantheistic tendencies were suspect in his own day and later were condemned by orthodox theologians. He and Groote were concerned to strengthen the people's faith against heresy by enlivening their spiritual lives. For that reason Ruysbroeck wrote in the vernacular, and Groote was, for a time, a popular lay preacher. Both, however, were criticized by the orthodox clergy for their condemnation of clerical faults.

Groote's principal contribution to Flemish mysticism was the establishment of the Brothers of the Common Life at Deventer. The strength of this organization lay in the teaching and practice of the 'New Devotion' (*Devotio*

Moderna), a deep inner spirituality combined with simple honest living. The movement spread widely, as branch houses and schools were established throughout the towns of Flanders. The Brothers' literature of Christian devotion extended still farther—even to Scandinavia, where Gerlac Peterson wrote the *Fiery Soliloquy of God*. With the *Imitation of Christ*, now generally attributed to Thomas à Kempis (1379–1471), the Brothers won an undying influence upon those who sought a secluded, contemplative, and devout Christianity.

England produced a few great mystics, but no English movement arose comparable to those of Flanders and the Rhineland. Richard Rolle (1300–49) came closest to the continental model. An Oxford student turned wandering preacher, he taught both orally and in writing a simple doctrine, strongly Biblical and often highly critical of the clergy. His appeal reached all classes of lay men and women, and he left behind a saintly reputation. His disciples are often unidentifiable or of little renown, but two works of contemplative devotion came from among them—*The Scale of Perfection* by Walter Hilton, which approaches the sublimity of the *Imitation of Christ*, and *Revelation of Divine Love* by Juliana of Norwich.

Juliana was far from being the outstanding woman among the mystics of the fourteenth century. The life span of Bridget of Sweden (1303–73) synchronizes almost exactly with the Avignon papacy. Born into a noble family, she lived a relatively normal life (except for mystic visions, which began at an early age) and became the mother of eight children. The death of her husband on their way home from a pilgrimage to Compostella induced her to embark upon a career that combined spiritual introspection with organized monastic service strikingly similar to that of the Franciscans. Her revelations, written down in the vernacular, included a vision of the Passion, which eventually was known in lands as far distant as Coptic Egypt and Abyssinia (perhaps as a result of her pilgrimages to Jerusalem). Her revelations also involved her in practical reforms: the temporarily successful importuning of Pope Urban V to return to Rome and the founding of the women's Order of St. Saviour (sometimes known as the 'Bridgettines'). This order exemplified the amazing increase of feminine influence in the era after St Francis. His 'Poor Clares', of which Bridget became a member, had been merely a 'tertiary' adjunct of the men's orders of Franciscans. The 'Bridgettines' were an independent order, of which Bridget's daughter Catherine became the first official head.

Bridget's younger contemporary Catherine of Siena (1347–80) is sometimes referred to as a 'politician' as well as a mystic and reformer. Catherine was the youngest of twenty-five children of a Sienese textile worker. When only seven years of age, she became a member of the Dominican tertiaries. Mystic visions led her at nineteen to become a spiritual bride of Christ and impelled her to the task of ending the 'Babylonian Captivity', reforming the church, and uniting the Italies. Like Bridget (and with more lasting effects), by personal intervention she helped to persuade a pope (Gregory XI) to go from Avignon back to Rome. Equally important was her role as peacemaker in war-torn Italy. She negotiated between the rebellious Florentines and the pope. She pleaded for a cessation of the brutalities of war, and doubtless her saintly influence was more immediately effective than the literary appeals of Dante and Petrarch in the vain cause of Italian peace and unity. She died in Rome at the beginning of the Great Schism, leaving in her *Dialogue* a passionate record both of inner spiritual love and of outspoken criticism of clerical vices.

The year of Catherine's death was that of the birth of a townsman, Bernardino of Siena (1380–1444). Bernardino helped found the Observant (i.e. relatively propertyless) Franciscans and by his eloquence persuaded calloused Romans to burn the tokens of their vanity. The Observants were ultimately (1517) recognized as a separate order by Pope Leo X. Mysticism attained great political significance with Bridget and Catherine of Sweden and Catherine and Bernardino of Siena, all of whom were eventually canonized. Yet it did not cope successfully with the church problems of the day. One of the most perceptive of the contemporary churchmen, Jean Gerson, disapproved of the political efforts of Brigdet and Catherine: by persuading the popes to return to Rome they had, in his opinion, precipitated a worse situation, the Schism.

At least in part because of this disillusionment, in the fifteenth century mysticism tended to appear in a different guise—as either the literary spiritualism of individual writers or the social radicalism of heretical or near-heretical groups. The heretical groups, we shall see below, fared badly. Literary spiritualism was exemplified in the works of Thomas à Kempis, the scholarly yet inspirational treatises of Denis the Carthusian (1402–71), and certain writings of Cardinal Nicholas of Cusa (1401–64). The only woman mystic of this century who can compare with the saints of the preceding century (Jeanne d'Arc excepted) was Catherine of Genoa (1447–1510), a cultured Renaissance lady who presided over a spiritual 'salon' and a well-organized hospital.

The belief in witchcraft of the late fifteenth and succeeding centuries may be described as a sort of mysticism in reverse—a belief that men and women could and did commune directly with the Evil Spirit. In earlier Christian times many a learned scientist (e.g. Albertus Magnus and Roger Bacon) had been popularly suspected of occult relations with the Devil. In 1405 a treatise appeared which, among other things, described and condemned seven major classes of magic, all invented by the Devil for the seduction of mankind; they were geomancy, hydromancy, aeromancy, pyromancy, chiromancy (palmistry), aromancy (by animals' shoulder-blades), and necromancy. The climax of this strange aberration came during the High Renaissance. An epidemic of witch hunting commenced during the last quarter of the fifteenth century, and death penalties for witchcraft (thitherto rare) rapidly became more common. This severity seems to have stemmed from a papal bull of 1484. Quoting the

Biblical mandate to the primitive Hebrew tribes, 'Thou shalt not suffer a witch to live' (Exodus 22: 18), the bull urged inquisitors to be more alert in prosecuting witches. Popular suspicion and imagination added oil to the fire. Never before, in Christian lands, had so many innocent women been hounded to death for imaginary crimes. In one Italian town (Como) forty-one women were burned during the next year; and in 1514, three hundred more. The religious dissensions of the Reformation were not to quench—perhaps were even to add to—the blaze.

*   *   *

Heresy and Discontent in Western Europe

Mysticism was not the era's only source of heretical persuasion. Censure was also a pitfall for the individualist irked by the regulations of a religious organization, since deviation from organizational norms is likely to be considered heresy.

Long before 1300 the Roman Catholic Church organization and creed had become relatively crystallized. Somewhere between the parish priest with his catechism, confessional, and other direct contact with his flock and the pope's curia at Rome, authoritative judgments could be pronounced on nearly everything of importance in the Christian's daily life. Canon law was a well organized and highly technical code, explained and annotated by authoritative handbooks such as Gratian's *Decretum* (c. 1140), and a long line of eminent theologians had reduced Roman beliefs to a set of fundamental dogmas. To be sure, differences of opinion arose from time to time concerning details, and commentaries of marvellous complexity had been written upon them. Nevertheless, summaries by scholars like Thomas Aquinas and Albertus Magnus had reduced the major points of Christian faith to specific statements on which one could be reasonably certain, and an episcopal inquisition in each diocese permitted bishops to distinguish dangerous divergencies from orthodoxy. As the training of ecclesiastical officials improved in theology and canon law, they became more expert in detecting perilous trends. The strict schooling of Dominican friars made them particularly competent as inquisitors. The centralization of power in the papacy permitted a strong executive in Rome to check lesser officials, enforce ecclesiastical regulations, and otherwise give direction to an effective bureaucracy. This machinery of control, taking shape for a century or more before 1300, thereafter improved its efficiency.

Like every machine, however, the church bureaucracy had its weaknesses, and papal control failed at various times and in various regions. During the fourteenth century, even though the Avignon popes perfected certain parts of the machine, national monarchs sometimes were lax in obedience to papal instructions, and laxity became still more common during the Schism, when two or three rival popes were issuing contradictory orders. At such times heresies flourished with less danger of suppression.

Expanding urban life provided a most favourable atmosphere for heresy.

Commerce, industry, town schools, universities, business, travel, and other mundane relationships that town life fostered helped to promote a desire for secular justice and for reform of the more blatant evils of an increasingly worldly church. In addition, the growing number of persons exposed to a secular education in secular institutions brought an increase in the inclination to question ecclesiastical authority. Merchants schooled in business and graduates of university schools of civil law were little inclined to accept submissively every ecclesiastical judgment based on other-worldly dogmas. Their disinclination developed into heresy at times. The zealous questioner was tempted to become a social reformer, and then a religious heretic. With poverty all around him among the masses, with luxury and immorality rife among the clergy, a reformer felt impelled to speak out boldly. On the other hand, a local ecclesiastic, faithful to his organization and perhaps also confident of its essential rightness, might feel bound to suppress troublemakers.

If the mystic-reformer-heretic was a cleric, he might easily be constrained by withholding the episcopal licence to preach. At a crucial point in a mystic's career he might have to decide whether to obey the will of God (as vouchsafed to him personally) or that of man (as presented by an unsympathetic bishop). In this manner many of the Spiritual Franciscans became heretics, and eventually the Observant Franciscans, too, parted company with the Conventuals (see above). To the more mystic among the Spirituals obedience to God meant the practice of absolute poverty; in the eyes of the official head of the church this practice was heresy. Many pious Christians, judged heretical by 'Christ's vicar', were single-heartedly following what seemed to them to be the precept and example of Christ. Still, the official judge of the law of Christ's church was the pope; therefore his decision must be obeyed or the penalty for disobedience paid. To cite one particularly horrible example, Dolcino of Novara, the messianic leader of the Apostolici, was executed by being slowly torn to bits with red-hot pincers (1307).

The mere enforcement of an orderly legalism, however, did not get at the underlying cause of many heresies, social discontent. 'Poor Men' (Waldenses), whether in Dauphiny or Piedmont or elsewhere, multiplied (until nearly exterminated by a 'crusade' in the 1480's); likewise Apostolici, Beghards, Beguins, and a host of other mendicant groups. Even in earlier times heresies had appeared in industrial regions, especially textile towns. With the expansion of commerce and industry in the thirteenth and fourteenth centuries, industrial workers tended to form a more or less self-conscious proletariat. The Black Death accentuated their discontent, evidenced by a series of revolts in industrial centres throughout the West; and an added incentive to social heresy came from the division, for over a century, of Christian loyalty and papal leadership at the time of the Babylonian Captivity and Great Schism. The grinding poverty of the masses was not so basic to social discontent as the stark contrast between the wealth of some pastors and the hard lot of their flocks. Petrarch expressed in literary indignation what many a heretic felt: the painful difference between the Christ of Galilee with his foot-sore disciples and the luxury of Avignon, 'Babylon of the West'.

At the end of the fourteenth century, Wycliffe spearheaded the widespread resentment. Using the vernacular of the English, he popularized his attacks upon the wealth of the church, his doctrine of 'civil dominion' over church property, and his doubts regarding the sacramental system and the authority of the pope, and he translated the Bible. His followers, the 'poor priests' and the Lollards, were attracted more often by his views upon wealth, whether ecclesiastical or lay, and upon clerical abuses than by his theology, and for much the same reason he lost his support in Parliament. He was condemned by the English clergy as a heretic and banished from Oxford. After his death in 1384, the Lollards remained active, but in 1401 a fearful Parliament passed the statute *De haeretico comburendo*, requiring the temporal authorities to co-operate with the church in seizing, trying, and burning heretics, and forced the movement underground.

Urban and clerical discontent was accompanied by peasant discontent. The English Peasants' Revolt (1381) under the leadership of Wat Tyler and John Ball, who was a follower of Wycliffe, sprang from a combination of both elements. Directed primarily against legal restrictions on wages, servile dues, and poll taxes, it won the sympathy of many in London and other cities. It was, however, a short-lived explosion without significant outcome save for some widespread destruction.

In certain parts of the West national sentiment was also a factor in the rise of heresy. In Bohemia the ground had been prepared during the fourteenth century by several native Czech leaders for a favourable reception of radical religious ideas, but the demand for church reform was in part also a protest against the German influence in the University of Prague and other institutions of Bohemia. The doctrines of Wycliffe were well known at the University of Prague, where Huss was rector in 1402-3, because the political ties of Bohemia and England at that time were close. Jerome of Prague had studied at Oxford. Huss and Jerome preached Wycliffe's views and won wide adherence not only because they echoed Bohemia's discontents but also because the Germans tended to oppose them. After the German ruler Sigismund delivered Huss and Jerome at the Council of Constance (see above), the national solidarity against the Germans was greatly enhanced, to the point where it was embodied in the first great representative assemblies on the European continent—those at Cheslov in 1421 and 1422. Some German Waldenses joined forces with the Hussites. The rebels achieved their major military successes when stirred by patriotic spirit to heroic effort against hated German 'crusaders'. It was also in keeping with the times that their ultimate downfall was in part due to an internal rift between the relatively conservative middle-class Utraquists, primarily concerned with ritual, and the relatively radical, peasant Taborites, primarily concerned with social justice (see Chapter VIII).

In Spain, on the contrary, nationalism worked in favour of orthodoxy. The nationalist monarchs used the legal machinery (the Inquisition) provided by the international ecclesiastical organization to crush infidel minorities (Jewish and Muslim). But, since in this case the unorthodox were social outcasts (even though many of them were wealthy), the royal-papal machinery of suppression was approved with enthusiasm by a national-minded populace. Furthermore, the leaders of the persecution, Ximenes and Thomas Torquemada (1420–98), won support because they were also diligent reformers of the evils of church and clergy.

Two mystics of the fifteenth century provided a sharp contrast to the social-minded heretic, the usual type. A curious Dutch mystic, Wessel Gansfort (1419–89), was a spiritual reformer concerned with individual salvation rather than social reform. Educated by the Brethren of the Common Life, he imbibed more of their Biblical piety than their humanism. His individualism and reliance on the Holy Scriptures as the sole guide for Christians led him to reject the necessity of priestly intercession. The individual Christian, he held, had direct access to God. In a later century he might have joined the Protestants. The same seems plausible in the case of Jeanne d'Arc. Her execution, though essentially politically motivated, had distinct theological overtones. Among the numerous offences held against her by her English captors and their theological henchmen a major one was that she held stubbornly to the conviction that she was responsible for her actions directly to God and not to the church.

*   *   *

Mysticism and Heresy in Eastern Europe

Of the mystics in the Eastern Orthodox Church perhaps the outstanding example is provided by the Hesychast movement of fourteenth-century Byzantium. The way in which it merged with social and political discontents has already been indicated. When the movement was fully systematized by the monks of Mt Athos, the aspirant Hesychast had to pass through several earlier degrees before he became 'perfect' and worthy of the highest degree of ἡσυχία (contemplation). Only the perfect were worthy enough to see the light that was identical with that which had transfigured Jesus on Mt Tabor (Matthew 17: 1–9). The hierarchy, both Roman and Eastern had good reason to suspect this doctrine of direct contact with God as potentially dangerous to the church, whether united or divided.

Of several heretical sects that survived in eastern Europe around 1300, the Bogomils (see above) were the most numerous. Their views resembled those of the Socinians and the Anabaptists of a later period (see Chapter IV). Subsequently, heretical movements occurred in the Russian church. In the second half of the fourteenth century Novgorod and Pskov, and possibly also Moscow and Tver, were the scene of a heresy that took its name from one of its champions, Carp Strigolnik (i.e. Carp the Barber). The 'Barbers' or

'Shearers' (the Strigolniki) not only accepted the heterodox theology of the Bogomils but also denied the need of a special priestly order and ritual, and decried the wealth of the clergy. Their heresy was ruthlessly put down by the church. About a century later a new heresy arose in Novgorod and Moscow. This time its adherents were known as Judaists; they drew their creed from the Old Testament and were familiar with medieval Hebrew literature, and the church contended that their strange doctrines were brought into Russia by the Jews. A church council in 1490 anathematized the Judaists, and some were executed.

The Russian clergy itself split on the question of the material wealth of the monasteries. The overwhelming majority advocated that the monastic lands should be retained and were known as *Nyestyazhateli* ('non-abstainers'); a minority of *Styazhateli* ('abstainers') opposed church ownership of land. Judaists and Styazhateli at first evoked a certain sympathy from the reigning grand prince, Ivan III (1440–1505), at least in part because of the attractive prospect of distributing church lands among the lesser feudal lords whose good will he courted. The church, however, eventually won the support of the state, which ultimately acted in the interests of centralized administration and against the further enrichment of the feudal aristocracy. A church council in 1503–4 condemned the 'abstainers', and several of them were burned at the stake, providing a distinct victory for the alliance of tsar and church against princes, boyars, and heretics. Nowhere in Europe was heresy triumphant before the sixteenth century.

NOTES TO CHAPTER III

1. *The Cultural Heritage of India* (Calcutta, 1936), II, p. 252.
2. R. G. Bhandarkar, *Vaisnavism, Śaivism and Minor Religious Systems* (Strasbourg, 1913), p. 73.
3. *The Cultural Heritage of India*, II, p. 255.
4. R. F. Leslie, *Polish Politics and the Revolution of November 1830* (London, 1956), p. 9, n. 1
5. A. A. Vasiliev, *History of the Byzantine Empire* (Madison, Wisc., 1929), II, pp. 376–77. See also Charles Diehl *et al.*, *L'Europe orientale de 1081 à 1453* (Paris, 1945), pp. 254–55.
6. The Act of Union (Council of Florence, 1439) was expressed in the following terms: 'The Holy Ghost proceeds eternally from the One and from the Other [Father and Son] as from one principle and by one aspiration. . . . The procession of the Holy Ghost from the Son is through the Father by whom He is eternally begotten.' In the absence of these details, without the formula 'as from a single principle', the Florence agreement would have been inconceivable. It was no political compromise but a theological explanation upon which the two parties were able to reach agreement. (O. Lacombe.)
7. For a discussion of recent literature on the Conciliar Movement, see Hubert Jedin, 'Nouvelles données sur l'histoire des conciles généraux', *Journal of World History*, I (1953), pp. 164–78.
8. See note 6 above.
9. Professor O. Lacombe points out that these popes, who were temporal rulers, bent upon Italian and universal politics, were none the less obliged to deal daily with a host of strictly religious problems, the religious nature of which was perfectly apparent to them. Neither individual predilections nor historical circumstances, nor yet the upsurge of lay humanism, could blind their innermost consciousness to these facts.

CHAPTER IV

CATHOLICS AND PROTESTANTS IN EUROPE (1500–1775)

DEMANDS WITHIN THE CATHOLIC CHURCH FOR REFORM

THE tribulations of the Catholic Church during the Avignon Papacy and the Great Schism stirred many clergymen and lay Christians to demand reform of the church 'in head and members'. The Council of Constance and its successors drew up lengthy reform programmes, which, however, remained empty promises thanks to the inability or unwillingness of the Renaissance popes to implement them. The Apostolici, Lollards, Waldenses, Hussites, and other heretical aggregates of the fourteenth and fifteenth centuries reflected the widespread discontent but occasioned only further vain efforts at reform.

Economic conditions combined with religious discontent to popularize the demands for reform. In an age of rising prices, the papacy had managed to establish a financial system that enabled it to live in a luxury befitting its position as one of the leading powers of Christendom. To the lower classes those who lived in luxury, whether laymen or clergymen, were suspect, the spiritual leader of Christendom more than any other. This suspicion was especially rife in the northern countries, where the pope and his Italian bureaucrats seemed to be foreigners living off the contributions of the native population, and Rome was pictured as the headquarters of an unreformable ecclesiastical hierarchy of luxury-loving exploiters.

Long before Luther the financial system of the papacy had been subjected to severe criticism. The mercenary aspects of such religious practices as relic cults, pilgrimages, and indulgences had been condemned; the Conciliar reform programmes, for example, had called for correction of the commercial aspects of indulgences.[1] The repeated demands seemed, however, to have fallen on deaf ears, and more and more Christians came to feel that the church hierarchy was callous to the physical suffering and spiritual needs of the faithful. Popular resentments helped lay princes, if indeed they needed such help, to encroach on the property and patronage of the church with impunity.

Early in the sixteenth century the French king provided a pat example of secular encroachment by gaining formal recognition of some of his extensive powers over the French church. Since the Pragmatic Sanction of Bourges (1428) a dispute had raged between France's kings and the popes over the method of selecting French prelates. To many benefices the conflict had brought great confusion, worse confounded by French invasions of Italy and the attempt of King Louis XII to depose Pope Julius II (see Chapter III). When Francis I came to the throne, he undertook to bring order into this chaos by a compromise with Pope Leo X. The result was the Concordat of Bologna (1516), which finally put an end to the French phase of the Conciliar Movement. It provided that the French crown would designate French archbishops, bishops, abbots, and priors to the pope, who would then invest them with canonical authority. Thus ecclesiastical electoral bodies were bypassed. In addition, Francis further expanded his authority over the French church by getting the power to collect an ecclesiastic tithe and to restrict appeals to the Roman curia. In return for this papal surrender the king acquiesced, at least by silence, to the right of the pope to continue to receive annates (the first year's income from new appointees) and certain other dues, and recognized—what was now a fact—the superiority of the pope over the councils. The Concordat of 1516 was bitterly opposed by the Parlement of Paris, the University of Paris, and some of the French clergy on the ground that the king had yielded too much, but in the end he had his way.[2]

In Spain a shift of control of ecclesiastical domination to the state likewise took place. The Inquisition, under monarchical control and with public approval, served as an effective instrument for purging the nation of ethnic and religious minorities. A sincere desire for reform heightened the fanaticism of the Spanish inquisitorial regime. Cardinal Ximenes de Cisneros, the pious and austere Franciscan who became primate of Spain and inquisitor-general, pressed for drastic measures not only against heretics and infidels but also against clerical abuses. After being appointed (1492), despite his reluctance, to the influential position of spiritual guide to the queen, he tried to remodel the Spanish church after his own Franciscan ideals. In an effort to improve the educational as well as the moral standards of the clergy, he made the University of Alcala the centre of the new learning in Spain. Its most remarkable achievement, a tribute to the excellence of humanist scholarship in Spain, was the *Complutensian Polyglot Bible* (so-called because the Latin name of Alcala was Complutum). Published in 1522 in six large volumes, this work was essentially a scholarly edition of the Vulgate with the texts of the component parts in the original languages. It was a formidable scholarly and religious achievement, in some ways surpassing a more famous contemporary work of Biblical scholarship, Erasmus' several editions of the Greek text of the New Testament with his own annotated Latin translation (1516–52).

Whereas the Spanish reformers remained solidly orthodox, the North produced one group composed of moderate reformers and another prepared to run the risk of rebellion. For a time, the moderate reformers, most of them humanists, dominated the northern scene. Unlike the typical Italian humanist, they combined humanistic scholarship with piety. Their very piety made them formidable critics of the bureaucrats in the church administrative system and of the Scholastic theologians in the old-line universities. The persistent religious trend of northern humanism emanated in large part from the *Devotio Moderna* of the Brethren of the Common Life. Erasmus received part of his training at perhaps their leading school, the one at Deventer; Luther at Magdeburg and Calvin at Paris were also among the fairly large number of illustrious men who as boys had gone to the Brethren's classes.

At first some of the northern humanists were allied with the radical reformers in lamenting the shortcomings of the clergy. A case in point is Johann Reuchlin (1455–1522). As an influential and tolerant professor at Heidelberg, he came into conflict with a fanatical converted Jew named Johann Pfefferkorn and his Dominican supporters, who were determined to suppress all Jewish books. In the subsequent war of ink, Reuchlin's *Eyes' Mirror (Augenspiegel)* and his *Letters of Famous Men (Clarorum Virorum Epistolae)* drew many of the German humanists into the camp of the critics of the clergy. The conflict became one of humanists *versus* Scholastics and of tolerant literary men *versus* authoritarian theologians. The humanists employed the weapon of satire with deadly effect. Ulrich von Hutten, Crotus Rubeanus, and others compiled the *Letters of Obscure Men (Epistolae Obscurorum Virorum)*, which pretended (1515 and 1517) to be the work of ignorant clerical bigots. The clergy came in for a goodly share of satire also in *Das Narrenschiff (The Ship of Fools,* 1494) of Sebastian Brant (1457–1521) and the *Encomium Moriae (Praise of Folly,* 1511) of Desiderius Erasmus (1466 ?–1536).

With his keenly satirical pen, Erasmus was not perhaps so good an example of humanistic piety as some of his contemporaries—his English friends John Colet and Thomas More, for example. Colet (*c.* 1467–1519), having studied the Classics in Italy, returned to his old school at Oxford and developed a humanistic interest in the actual texts of the Holy Scriptures. He was lecturing on the Epistles of Paul as early as 1496, about twenty years before Luther concentrated his attention on them. He preached sermons denouncing the clergy and demanding drastic clerical reforms as early as 1512. At the same time he encouraged in London a humanistic type of secondary education under lay control (see Chapter XVI).

Sir Thomas More (1467–1535), a barrister and a member of the House of Commons, exerted a somewhat similar influence, though in less vigorous fashion and on the broader front of both political and social reform. His *Utopia* (1516) indicates his more secular approach; in depicting an imaginary country that was admirable in many regards though not altogether ideal, it presented a critique of English society of the day. More, Colet, and some of their fellow humanists exemplify the attitude of those humanist reformers who, though critical, refused in the 1520's to join the revolt against the church. Erasmus got to know these 'Oxford Reformers' during several visits to England (1499, 1505, and 1509), and their mutual admiration and influence was unusually strong and lasting. The prince who was to become King

Henry VIII encouraged the activities of this friendly association of learned men.

In general Erasmus was to prove more inclined than his English friends to hold aloof from the struggle of the faiths. To him religion was a guide to right living rather than a set of established beliefs and ritualistic practices. He was intensely interested in the New Testament, especially the Sermon on the Mount, but his interest was ethical rather than devout. The contrast between Jesus' precepts and the practices of the clergy of his own day provided him with a point of origin for a double reform programme—the building of a good life for laymen and the betterment of the clergy. His *Praise of Folly* made a plea for reform of the church; his *Handbook of the Christian Soldier* (*Enchiridion Militis Christiani*, 1503) expounded the way by which a sincere Christian might attain a good life. Education, intelligent Christian effort, and careful self-training in good works, he contended, could produce right living (see Chapter XVI). Holding this philosophy of patience, Erasmus could hardly be expected, when the issues arose, to approve of doctrines like Luther's 'bondage of man's will' and 'justification by faith' or of rebellion against the church, no more than Luther could be expected to approve of Erasmus' belief in salvation by self-training and in the cure of church abuses by slow reform.3

LUTHER AND LUTHERANISM IN GERMANY (TO 1529)

When, on October 31, 1517, Martin Luther posted his ninety-five theses on the door of the castle church at Wittenberg, he did no more than follow a general practice of announcing an intention to debate with a fellow-theologian certain religious propositions. Yet this act reverberated throughout Germany, indeed throughout western Christendom, and signalled the final break-up of the traditional unity of the medieval church. Why this prompt reaction? Dissatisfaction in Germany with papal ultramontanism and the lax morality of the clergy was widespread. Resentment at the draining of German wealth into the papal treasury at Rome was fanned by a nascent sense of German unity. Social unrest was rife among German peasants and the impoverished German imperial knights; and the rising German middle class, long dissatisfied with clerical abuses and mismanagement, looked to the princes of the Reich rather than to the frequently absent emperor for protection and support.

Luther himself, when he proposed his theses, seems to have had no thought of provoking a general revolt or of breaking with the papacy. He had entered the Augustinian Order in 1505 against the wishes of his ambitious father. Though his zeal, piety, and learning had won him general respect, he remained forever troubled by the problem of divine justice. Neither the strictest observances of monastic discipline nor the most ascetic practices could deliver him from a conviction of utter sinfulness, which made him despair of salvation. In a moment of sudden inspiration, while teaching the Bible at the recently founded (1502) University of Wittenberg, he became convinced that justification must come through faith alone, not through good works. This denial of the efficacy of good works meant the abandonment of a cardinal tenet of Catholic doctrine, which looked upon good works as an indispensable part of its system of penance.

Indulgences were prominent in this system of penance. They were based upon the doctrine of the *thesaurus meritorum*, the inexhaustible treasury of merits accumulated by Jesus and the saints and dispensed by the pope for the benefit of Christians of insufficient merit. Originally indulgences were intended by the church to grant remission only of temporal punishment and only for the truly penitent sinner, but preachers of indulgence claimed for them the power of reducing punishment in purgatory as well and, following a papal bull issued in the fifteenth century, extended this power to include the souls of the departed. Purchase of indulgences thus became an act of pious concern for the dead as well as a matter of personal welfare for the living. The doctrinal errors and the practical abuses in the sale of indulgences had been sharply criticized by theologians long before Luther. In Germany it was viewed with special dissatisfaction as one of the several papal schemes to drain the national wealth into Roman coffers.

A flagrant confusion of financial and spiritual ends was involved in an indulgence issued in 1515 by Pope Leo X, ostensibly for the building of St Peter's in Rome. Albrecht of Hohenzollern, archbishop of Mainz, was made its chief commissary. Contrary to canon law, Albrecht, who was not even of the required age, had brought under his control three German bishropics. He had received papal dispensation in return for a large sum of money, which he, in turn, had borrowed from the Fuggers. In orders to enable him to repay this debt, Albrecht was authorized by a secret provision of the indulgence to pocket half of the proceeds.

To push the sale of this indulgence, grossly exaggerated claims were made about its power. Luther attacked these claims, and his sovereign, Frederick the Wise, elector of Saxony, prohibited the sale of the indulgence throughout Saxon territory. In 1517, when one of Bishop Albrecht's ablest subcommissaries, the Dominican Johann Tetzel, approached the Saxon border, Luther posted his ninety-five theses to challenge him to a public debate. The debate never took place, but the impact of the theses, soon printed and broadcast all over Germany in the vernacular as well as in Latin, was immediate. The theses indeed went far beyond attacking indulgences; they unmistakably suggested limitations of the power of the pope and upheld the Gospel as the only divinely inspired basis of Christianity. Thesis no. 36, for example, read: 'Every truly repentant Christian has a right to full remission of penalty and guilt, even without letters of pardon.'[4] Such bold propositions touched fundamental concepts of Roman Catholicism, for in Catholic doctrine the salvation of Christians depended largely upon the clergy as the ordained administrators of the sacraments.[5]

Luther enjoyed the constant protection of his sovereign, Frederick the

Wise. Neither Emperor Maximilian nor Pope Leo X could well afford to alienate this powerful prince, especially since the emperor hoped to win Frederick's vote for his grandson, Charles of Spain, as successor to the imperial crown. Private efforts in 1518 to make Luther retract his attack failed; he refused to recant unless he could be convinced by arguments from Scripture before an impartial tribunal of theologians. He later converted this demand for a tribunal into a call for a general council of the church, thereby giving Frederick justification for continuing his protection until such a council might take place. Backed by his sovereign, Luther thus became the spokesman of the conciliar party, still strong within the church even among some otherwise opposed to his views.

As public tension deepened, Luther came to deny the importance of the clergy with increasing vehemence. In a crucial debate at Leipzig (1519), a celebrated theologian, Johann Maier Eck, skilfully led him on to deny the infallibility not only of popes but, by admitting agreement with certain principles of the condemned heretic John Huss, also of ecumenical councils. In June 1520, the pope, urged by Eck and the Dominicans, issued a bull (*Exsurge Domine*) threatening Luther with excommunication unless he recanted within sixty days. By that time Maximilian had died, and Charles had been elected and crowned Holy Roman emperor. Charles's diplomatic involvements, however, tied his hands in domestic affairs. Moreover, public sentiment was overwhelmingly in Luther's favour, and drastic measures against him could be expected to provoke large-scale unrest. Luther was therefore in a relatively strong position.

In August–October 1520 Luther, without yet formally replying to the threat of papal excommunication, set down his principles explicitly in three brochures: *An Open Letter to the Christian Nobility of the German Nation*, *The Babylonian Captivity of the Church*, and *A Treatise on Christian Liberty*. In these works he proclaimed the essential priesthood of all Christians, thus repudiating the distinction between clergy and laity and directly attacking the sacrament of ordination by which the priest becomes endowed with the spiritual power of his office. The true believer, he further contended, needed only one source of truth, the Gospel, and only one means of salvation, faith. The good Christian, though 'the perfectly free lord of all, subject to none', voluntarily acted in accordance with the law to become 'the perfectly dutiful servant of all, subject to all'.[6] The performance of good works was pleasing to God if undertaken freely without the expectation of future rewards. Divine justice was not a simple saving of the righteous and damning of the unrighteous, for all men are sinners. It was rather the working of divine grace, of which man could be assured only by a faith that made him confident of the goodness and mercy of God: 'Good works do not make a good man, but a good man does good works.'[7]

For Luther, therefore, certain external practices were non-essential to true Christianity. He rejected outright four of the seven traditional sacraments as not justified by Gospel, retaining only baptism, communion, and penance, but he later abandoned penance also. Baptism was for him the most fundamental sacrament, for through it the Christian was reborn from his original sinful state, became truly a member of the Christian community, and thus might hope for ultimate forgiveness. Essentially Luther conceived of faith as a mystical bond between man and God and of the priesthood as a mere ministry of God's word.

In December 1520, long after his sixty days' grace was up, Luther burned the papal bull, along with some volumes of the canon law, in a public ceremony. It now devolved upon the young emperor, Charles V, to implement the papal excommunication with an imperial ban. According to imperial law, however, no subject of the Empire could be placed under ban unheard. Charles agreed to grant Luther a hearing before the Diet, which assembled in 1521 at Worms. Protected, at the insistence of Frederick the Wise, by an imperial safe-conduct, Luther arrived at Worms after a triumphal journey. Before the assembled princes and notables of the Empire he refused to retract his writings and asserted the authority of conscience over dogma and canon law:

'I am held fast by the Scriptures adduced by me, and my conscience is taken captive by God's Word, and I neither can nor will revoke anything, seeing that it is not safe or right to act against conscience. God help me. Amen.'[8]

The Edict of Worms, signed by Charles after the close of the Diet, pronounced the ban of the Empire upon the intransigent heretic.

*   *   *

Political and Social Complications

So far Luther's cause had been only a movement for church reform, but the forces that he had unleashed now ran an independent course, at times outrunning his leadership. On his return from Worms to Wittenberg, he was abducted on the order of his prince, and for a year he was kept safely hidden in the Wartburg, Frederick's castle near Eisenach. In a unified country ruled by a strong monarch such defiance of papal excommunication and imperial ban would speedily have been foiled, but the particularism of Germany, leaving to the emperor only a limited and begrudged authority, permitted his opponent, Frederick, to come to an understanding with rival German princes. Moreover, Charles was not free to deal with only German affairs. Though a devout Catholic sincerely eager to crush Luther and eradicate heresy, he was preparing a military campaign against the French king, Francis I, whom the pope was supporting. Frederick, skilfully manoeuvreing between pope and emperor, was able to shield Luther, all the while protesting his desire to comply with the laws of both church and empire.

Behind Frederick stood the formidable strength of incipient German nationalism, and anti-clericalism was a dominant theme in this nationalist sentiment. The establishment of strong dynastic monarchies in France, England, and Spain had left Germany one of the few western European countries still wholly subject to papal authority in church affairs, as well as a most important source of papal revenue. Papal domination had long been resented, and successive German diets had drawn up lists of grievances against the papacy. At the very Diet of Worms which in 1521 had banned Luther, feeling against the church ran so high that the papal nuncio lamented: 'The whole of Germany is in open revolt. Nine-tenths of it shouts for Luther and the other tenth, if it cares nothing for the Reformer, cries 'Death to the Roman Curia.' "9

Luther's *Letter to the Christian Nobility* had contained a calculated appeal to this national fervour. He sought to evoke the pride of his 'fellow Germans' against exploitation by unnecessary papal officials who 'lie in wait' for German benefices 'as wolves lie in wait for the sheep'.10 He called for national legislation to prevent the removal to Rome of the monies collected in Germany. He went still further in appealing to the political interests of the German princes. His concept of the essential priesthood of all believers led him to assert not only the complete separation of temporal from spiritual power but also, since all Christians are equal and temporal power is divinely ordained, the supremacy of the secular government: 'On this account the Christian temporal power should exercise its office without let or hindrance, regardless whether it be pope, bishop, or priest whom it affects.'11 With this assertion of the supremacy of the temporal power, Luther in effect commended the reform of the church to the secular rulers of Germany.

Charles V at Worms made unmistakably clear that he considered himself the champion of the traditional faith, but Luther could count not only upon Frederick of Saxony and certain other powerful princes but, more decidedly, upon the lesser nobility, as well as large sections of the middle class and peasantry. The church was one of the largest landholders in Germany; it commanded vast material wealth and was feudal lord over many nobles and multitudes of peasants and serfs. The Imperial knights, often poor and always proud, were especially prone to look upon the concentration of vast estates in the hands of a few magnates, whether ecclesiastical or lay, as a threat to their well-being. Peasants and knights readily vented their discontents in a deep-seated anti-clericalism and anti-Romanism. Among their grievances were the diminution of the knights' prestige as the cities grew and military techniques changed, and the hardening of servile status for the peasants as Roman law was substituted for traditional German law (see Chapter VIII) and as prices rose for all classes. The demand for reform of the church became also a demand for reform of the society.

Urged on by the knight-humanist Ulrich von Hutten, the knights were the first to take up arms. Hutten published in 1520 a *Complaint and Admonition against the Power of the Pope*, in which he openly espoused the cause of Luther, called upon the emperor and the German estates for a war against Rome, and called for an alliance of the nobles and the cities, if the emperor and the estates failed to take the lead in the national cause. A subsequent publication, the *Exhortation to the Free and Imperial Cities*, revealing the position of the knights more clearly, advocated an alliance of cities and knights alone against their common enemies, the great secular and ecclesiastical princes, who were usurping the rights of burgher and knight. Hutten won over Franz von Sickingen, the most renowned and powerful Imperial knight of his day.[12]

Armed revolt, however, had never been part of Luther's creed. On the contrary, he re-affirmed the ancient doctrines of unquestioned obedience to ordained authority and denied the right of revolt. In his view, where misrule and oppression occurred, they were divinely ordained punishments, to which Christians must patiently submit. His *Ernest Exhortation for All Christians, Warning Them against Insurrection and Rebellion* (1521), issued from the Wartburg when disturbances broke out in Wittenberg and elsewhere, made quite clear that for him reform of religion was the task of the ordained secular power alone and no part of a scheme for general social and political reform.

Despite Luther's exhortations the knights went to war in 1522–23. This Knights' War ended in Sickingen's death, Hutten's exile, and the destruction of the knights' power. Luther saw in their failure a terrible yet just decision of God, but he did not thunder against them so violently as he was soon to thunder against the peasants.

To a degree Luther sympathized with the demands of the peasantry. The Swabian peasants voiced their grievances in the *Twelve Articles*, deliberately phrased in a moderate tone so as to influence him in their favour. One article demanded that peasants be taught the Gospel and have the right to choose their own pastors. Another based the demand for emancipation from serfdom upon a concept that he approved: 'Christ has delivered and redeemed us all, the lowly as well as the great.'[13]

Yet Luther's sympathies with the peasants did not make him waver in his rejection of violent action. To be sure, his treatise *Secular Authority: To What Extent It Should Be Obeyed* (1523) warned the princes of the consequences of misrule; still he clearly denied to suffering subjects the right of revolt and approved of only passive resistance in matters of religion. In part his restraint was due to the growing difficulty of his situation. By this time he had returned from Wartburg to Wittenberg. Shortly after his return a first Diet of Nuremberg (1522) had deferred enforcement of the Edict of Worms against him, demanding the convocation of a general council to deal with the problem; after the knights' defeat, however, a second Diet of Nuremberg (1524) agreed to enforce the Edict 'as far as possible'. This noncommittal compromise reflected the delicate balance between conservative and reformist forces in the Empire, but the same delicacy of balance placed Luther in a dilemma. On the one hand, powerful princes charged him with responsibility for the revolt of the knights and the ferment among the peasants; on the other, a radical wing of the reformers wanted him to side openly with social revolution.

At length (1524) the peasants rose in revolt in Swabia and Franconia. In this perplexing position Luther issued (1525) his *Admonition to Peace: A Reply to the* Twelve Articles *of the Peasants in Swabia*. It denounced the tyranny of secular and especially of ecclesiastical princes, blaming them for the uprisings, yet at the same time turned against the 'false preachings' of radical reformers. It not only did not concede the right of disobedience; it went so far as to assert that the demand for freedom from serfdom was not supported by the Gospel. Despite Luther's appeal to religious principles and moderation, the Peasants' War spread throughout southern and central Germany, marked by all the savagery that characterizes warfare in any age. To Luther the peasants seemed guilty of sinning grievously against the Gospel and of endangering his reform programme. He vented his indignation in a tirade *Against the Robbing and Murdering Hordes of Peasants*, in which he called upon the princes and 'everyone who can [to] smite, slay, and stab, secretly or openly, remembering that nothing can be more poisonous, hurtful, or devilish than a rebel.'[14] The bloody repression of the peasants that followed might very well have come without Luther's appeal, for the princes scarcely needed prompting from him to protect their interests with the sword, but his appeal alienated many who identified religious with social reform.

Luther's proclamation of the religious equality of believers without conceding social and political equality thus helped to promote disunity in the reformist camp. A number of his earlier followers accused him of sacrificing principles to political expediency, and the mass support he had hitherto enjoyed vanished, taking with it all hope of making his movement truly national in scope. His stand, though revealing the essentially non-political intent of his reforms, had political implications. It forced him to rely more and more, in his efforts to organize a new church, upon friendly princes and free cities.

*   *   *

The Widening of the Rift

During Luther's months of hiding in the Wartburg, the traditional forms of worship had come under attack in reforming communities throughout Germany. In Wittenberg Luther's colleague Andreas Carlstadt (1480–1541), who had independently arrived at a position that approximated the chief reformer's theology, was a leader in a brief radical movement. Unlike Luther, Carlstadt accented the connection between religious and social reform. When Luther returned to Wittenberg, he cut short Carlstadt's ascendancy and, in the end, drove him into closer rapprochement with the more radical reformers or Anabaptists (see below). Yet Carlstadt's activities had forced the Wittenberg town council to adopt the first practical measures of reform— revision of the service, communion in both kinds (wine as well as bread), and abandonment of clerical celibacy.

Luther had at first been willing to grant a certain latitude in religious observances as long as faith and the Gospel were held superior to ritual, but the necessity for uniformity became apparent if reformist strength was not to be dissipated. Gradually the general aspects of a reformed service evolved. Mass was abolished. Regular gospel readings and sermons, both in the vernacular, became the core of religious worship. Communion in both kinds was given to those approaching it in true faith. To make the congregation active participants in the service, Luther advocated community singing of hymns in the vernacular to replace the chants and responses of traditional liturgy. He himself composed a number of hymns for this purpose (see Chapter XII).

Of necessity Luther's reforms carried beyond liturgical conventions. His attacks upon monasticism and the celibacy of the clergy led to large-scale defections from monasteries and convents and to the resumption by monks and nuns of secular life. As early as 1522, the Wittenberg chapter of the Augustinian Order voted its members the privilege of renouncing their vows; Luther himself, after some hesitation, married in 1525. The disorganization within clerical ranks in Saxony caused a disruption of schooling and other social services that the clergy had customarily performed for the poor, the sick, and the orphaned. An early step in some reformed communities was to prohibit begging, which Catholic doctrine had condoned because it offered an opportunity for charity, but as poverty did not shrink before this prohibition, Luther authorized reformed congregations to appropriate ecclesiastical funds and place them in a common chest for the support of the reform (or, as it soon came to be called, 'the evangelical') clergy, the poor, and such social enterprises as hospitals and schools. He thus transferred to the community responsibility for the social no less than the spiritual welfare of its members, as had been true of the early Christians.

By thus assigning the maintenance of the school system to the reformed community, Luther was constrained to give some thought to pedagogical problems (see Chapter XVI). His writings on education plainly reveal his intellectual debt to humanism. That indebtedness was clear also in his translation of the Bible. His searching studies of Scripture would have been impossible without the Hebrew studies of Reuchlin and others and without Erasmus' Greek edition of the New Testament, which became the basis of his translation of the Old and New Testaments into German. The translation was an inescapable consequence of his theology, for if the Gospel was to be the sole source of Christian faith, it had to be read and understood by all. The vernacular Bible became a common bond among reformed Christians. The wording of Luther's translation also had a decided impact upon German literature and the development of the German language (see Chapter XI). Its distribution throughout Germany laid the foundation for a common *Schriftsprache* that eventually became the vehicle of a truly national German literature. Despite his huge debt to humanism, however, Luther was not wholeheartedly a humanist. His repudiation of rationalism and his religious intolerance clashed with humanist secularism and cosmopolitanism. A rift shortly separated him from the leading humanists and widened as the Reformation progressed.

Many humanists in Germany and abroad—among them Crotus Rubeanus, Hutten, Johannes Oecolampadius, Martin Bucer, and, most important of all, young Philipp Melanchthon—rallied to Luther's support. Melanchthon (1497–1560) was at twenty-one professor of Greek at Wittenberg. He took part in the Leipzig Disputation, was Luther's trusted surrogate in Wittenberg during the period of hiding at the Wartburg, assisted him in translating the Bible and organizing the reformed church, and published the first systematic summary of reformed theology, *Loci Communes Rerum Theologicarum* (1521). In successive diets and at meetings with other reformers he acted as Luther's adviser. Less obstinate and more tolerant than Luther, he was inclined to make greater concessions, but he allowed himself to be overruled. Two years after Luther's death Melanchthon confessed: 'In Luther's time I was often compelled to give in and found it more than humiliating.'[15] He remained, however, a loyal lieutenant throughout Luther's life and then shouldered the leader's mantle.

A similar loyalty and community of purpose was lacking in Luther's relations with some other humanists. What at first drew most of his humanist supporters to him was a common opposition to Scholasticism and Catholic dogma, and a common desire for reform of the church. When Luther went beyond those objectives and proceeded from reform to open revolt, not all humanists could concur. His increasing popular following, some anticipated, would lead to tumult, and his deepening bitterness, intransigence, and intolerance separated them from him more and more.

The rift became unbridgeable as a result of Luther's controversy with Erasmus. Erasmus had at the outset joined Luther's appeal for freedom of individual faith. Luther never thought highly of Erasmus as a theologian but in the beginning was careful to court his support, since Erasmus was the most influential man of letters of the age. Gradually Erasmus was alienated by Luther's religious zeal, while Luther became more and more impatient with Erasmus' cautious conservatism. Erasmus' behaviour was partly motivated by a certain opportunism, for he was worried by attacks from both sides upon himself as a moderate. Yet other, perhaps more compelling, considerations influenced his attitude. His cosmopolitan spirit was offended by Luther's appeal to nationalism. His conviction that gradual education, not quick, spontaneous, popular action, was the surest way of reform constrained him to condemn the passions released by Luther's revolt. Moreover, a fundamental philosophical difference estranged the two men. Luther's pessimism made him picture mortal man as incapable of good without the saving grace of God; a captive will bent by original sin toward evil was a presupposition of the doctrine of salvation by faith alone. For the more optimistic Erasmus, such religious determinism not only cast doubt upon the possibility of educating man toward good but also implied the responsibility of God for evil. In 1524 Erasmus published *De Libero Arbitrio* (*On Free Will*), which attacked the core of Luther's theology, and Luther answered it in 1525 with *De Servo Arbitrio* (*On the Bondage of the Will*). Their alienation became final when Erasmus, although still defending Luther against Scholastic attacks, publicly refused to abandon the traditional church.

The current of the time was now against the moderation of Erasmus and his sympathizers. Luther's call for religious reform was closer to the mystical heresies of the Middle Ages than to the reforming humanism of the Renaissance. It led to a renewed preoccupation with religion all over Europe, and thus to a growing theological partisanship—to the neglect of the more secular, rational interests of the humanists. The Reformation indeed is sometimes thought to have brought a marked decline in the influence of humanism in parts of Europe as learned men turned their minds from literary pursuits to theological polemic.[16]

*   *   *

Inauguration of an Evangelical Church System

The preoccupation of Emperor Charles with diplomatic and military complications had given the reformers a relatively free hand to organize their church, and a diet at Spires in 1526 postponed action again. This (the first) Diet of Spires ended with a resolution (generally called the Recess of 1526) foreshadowing the eventual solution of the religious question—that until a general council had been convoked, each state 'should live, govern, and conduct itself as it is willing to answer before God and the Imperial Majesty'.[17] Luther interpreted the Recess to mean that each evangelical prince had the right to organize the reformed church on his own lands. Accordingly, with his chief adviser Melanchthon, he drew up plans for the administration of evangelical churches, giving the prince the functions of a bishop in administrative though not in spiritual affairs. The first 'visitation' (inspection of churches), ordered by the elector of Saxony in 1527, found church affairs in a state of confusion. Melanchthon thereupon worked out a *Kirchenordnung* (Church Ordinance), which, when revised by Luther, provided uniformity of service and supervision of the clergy through regular visitations. The *Kirchenordnung* was a major step toward the subordination of the Lutheran church to the state. The visitations provided the beginnings of a consistorial system through which ecclesiastical government was placed in the hands of a body of state officials, composed of theologians and jurists acting under the temporal authority. (The first consistory was not established, however, until that of Wittenberg was set up in 1539.)

In 1529 Charles V, having defeated his enemies and having made peace with Pope Clement VII and Francis I of France, was at last in a position to press for the strict application of the Edict of Worms throughout the Empire.

The German representatives, meeting that year at the Second Diet of Spires, revoked the latitude tentatively allowed to the local princes by the Recess of 1526 and thus placed Luther and Lutherans again under the Imperial ban. This reversal of policy met with so vigorous a protest from the evangelical princes and cities that their followers were known thenceforth as Protestants. Their protest was in favour of the right of a government (not of the governed) to choose the religion of a state.

ZWINGLI AND CALVIN

German Protestantism was able to achieve no union with a reform movement going on contemporaneously in Switzerland. The leader of the German-Swiss phase of that movement was Ulrich Zwingli (1483–1531). Although reform in Switzerland did not begin until two years after Luther published his ninety-five theses, Zwingli had developed the basic principles of his theology independently. He had become increasingly familiar with the writings of Erasmus, especially the Greek edition of the New Testament, and under the influence of that great humanist, whom he visited in Basel, his religious ideas took on a clearer shape. Although a humanistic bent made Zwingli's approach to reform more intellectual than Luther's, his decision to proceed to an open demand for reform came only after he underwent an emotional crisis during a plague that ravaged Zürich in 1519.

From the beginning Zwingli's reforms combined the political with the religious in a way that distinguished them sharply from Luther's. In fact, the Swiss reformer first became antagonistic to the papacy over a political issue— the plight of Swiss mercenaries in the service of popes and secular princes. As chaplain of Swiss troops on several expeditions into Italy, he had gained first-hand knowledge of their distress and, in verse as well as prose, tried to rouse his countrymen against the trade in human flesh, condemning their greed on theological no less than humane grounds.[18]

Like Luther, Zwingli preached the Gospel in the vernacular, attacking the validity of indulgences, pilgrimages, and similar pious works. After Luther's explicit denial of papal primacy in his disputation with Eck at Leipzig, Zwingli wholeheartedly associated himself with the efforts of his Saxon colleague. In 1519, upon recovering from the plague, he preached a series of sermons that marked the beginning of open reform in Switzerland. These sermons upheld the Gospel and ancient Christianity as the sole basis of Christian worship and church organization and denounced the veneration of saints, fasting, clerical celibacy, and other Catholic practices. Unlike Luther, Zwingli was concerned to give his measures a popular and legal footing through the assent of cantonal and municipal authorities. In a series of public and private disputations in 1523–24, he induced the Zürich town council to vote in favour of preaching the Gospel in all the canton's churches and of separating from the jurisdiction of the bishop of Constance.

By the same kind of civic assent the Zwinglian reformation spread into other cantons. After a nineteen-day disputation in 1528, Zwingli, assisted by Bucer and Oecolampadius, won an especially important ally in the canton of Berne. The backing of the civic authorities in the reformed communities gave his movement a collective sanction that the Catholic Church could not easily deal with, especially since the pope stood to lose his major source of mercenaries in case of open conflict. The fight was, therefore, left to local bishops and lower clergy. Zwingli's insistence upon majority vote proved singularly effective against them, and at the same time it greatly reduced friction within the reformed communities.

With the help of laymen as well as reformed clergymen, the Swiss reformer thoroughly simplified the content and form of the church services. Though not himself a violent iconoclast, he led groups of civic and guild representatives in a usually orderly removal of decorations from the reformed churches. Relics were burned or buried. Priests were allowed to marry, as Zwingli himself did. Permission was given to eat meat during Lent. Mass was abolished, and the service, stripped of all pomp, was built around the reading of the Bible in the ancient tongues with sermons in the vernacular. Zwingli himself collaborated in the translation of the Bible into Swiss German. In 1523 he first began to celebrate communion in both kinds, the entire congregation participating.

The Zürich leader went beyond the Lutherans in the reform of the church. He abolished all practices not sanctioned by the Gospel, including organ-playing and the singing of hymns (which were not reintroduced into the Reformed service until long after his death). He looked upon the church not only as a spiritual but also as a political democracy and placed its external direction in the hands of the constituted civic authority, which he made also the guardian of a strict moral code. He envisaged an identity of church and community that was much closer than had been achieved under the Lutheran princes of Germany. He thus prepared the ground for Calvinist governmental theory and puritanism.

With religious reform Zwingli also sought to combine political and social reform. Under his leadership Zürich for the first time refused to send mercenaries to fight in Italy. He attempted to remove the inequalities that gave the older forest cantons a certain predominance in the Swiss Federation —a proposal that would also have increased the voting strength of the Reformed cantons. He had poor laws passed in Zürich and had begging outlawed. Although he did not condone the violence of the Peasants' Revolt in 1525, in striking contrast to Luther he called for leniency and for measures to improve the peasants' lot, moving toward the abolition of serfdom.

In matters of doctrine, Zwingli's humanism made for greater optimism and rationalism than Luther revealed. Zwingli did not deny the concept of 'original sin' but softened its impact by interpreting it as man's inclination to sin; and while he also preached justification by faith alone, he did not exclude the great teachers of non-Christian societies from salvation. In his *Exposition of the Faith* he wrote: 'We may expect to see [in eternal life] the communion and fellowship of all the saints and sages and believers and the steadfast and the brave and the good who have ever lived since the world began.'[19] Unlike Luther, he did not despair of recognizing the elect, for he identified the chosen with those who had the true faith, thus making all of a reformed congregation potentially members of the true, invisible church. Like Luther, Zwingli accepted only two sacraments, baptism and communion, but, unlike Luther, he saw in them merely symbolic acts rather than true miracles. The conflict over the Eucharist proved to be the most divisive doctrinal difference between Lutheran and Zwinglian theology. For Zwingli the Lord's Supper was but a symbol of Jesus's suffering; Luther, on the other hand, while denying the Catholic doctrine of transubstantiation (i.e. that the bread and wine of the sacrament actually changed into the body and blood of Jesus), believed in consubstantiation (i.e. that Jesus was only—but really and materially—present in the bread and wine during the sacrament).

In Switzerland the balance between the contending forces of Catholics and reformers was no less precarious than in Germany. The old forest cantons in the south resisted all efforts at religious reform; only in the northern cantons (and in some neighbouring areas of southern Germany) did Zwingli and his followers make significant gains. Berne accepted the Reformation in 1528. Next to Berne, the most important canton in the north was Basel. A centre of humanism, especially since the arrival of Erasmus in 1521, it long resisted open reform. Its conversion to Zwinglianism was the work of Oecolampadius. Like Zwingli he had maintained close contact with Erasmus at first but then had actively supported Luther, and when, in 1522, he was called back from Germany to Basel as preacher, he immediately began to press for reform, allying himself closely with Zwingli. After years of preaching and stormy public disputations, his efforts met with success (1529). Erasmus and other humanists left the city for quieter precincts.

The struggle between the reformed and the Catholic cantons had by that time become so embittered that violence broke out. The Catholic cantons formed a league and made an alliance with the Habsburgs, the traditional enemies of the Swiss Federation. War was actually declared between the Reformed and Catholic forces in 1529, but peace was concluded at Kappel without bloodshed, and unity within the federation was temporarily reestablished. Yet each side continued to distrust the other. Suspecting a resumption of the alliance between the Swiss Catholics and the Habsburgs, Zwingli proposed to join forces with the Reformed cities of southern Germany and the Lutheran princes of the Empire.

This plan concurred with that of the newly converted Landgrave Philip of Hesse, who hoped to unite the two Protestant sects. He invited the leaders of both to a colloquy at his residence in Marburg in the fall of 1529—to no avail. Despite a large measure of agreement, the two parties could reach no understanding on the meaning of the Lord's Supper. On the first day of their colloquy, Luther chalked on the desk before him the words from the New Testament: 'This is my Body.' He was unwilling to allow any but the most literal interpretation of the verb *is*, although Zwingli and Oecolampadius insisted that the same verb in other passages of the Bible repeatedly had the meaning *represents*. Zwingli was ready to concede a spiritual, though not a real, presence of Jesus at the Eucharist, but compromise on this basis was blocked by the usually moderate Melanchthon. Melanchthon, possibly swayed by Charles V's recent attempt at the Second Diet of Spires to play the Zwinglian party against the Lutherans, persuaded Luther not to compromise, on the grounds that concessions in a radical direction might forever thwart reconciliation with the Catholic princes of Germany. Realizing the need for at least a show of unity, the Colloquy of Marburg issued a public declaration expressing mutual respect and listing points of agreement. The rift was nonetheless complete, for the declaration also reaffirmed their continued disagreement on the crucial issue of the Eucharist.

The failure of the Colloquy of Marburg weakened the political and military effectiveness of the entire reform movement. Check came soonest in Switzerland, where in 1531 war again broke out. It ended in defeat for the Zwinglian forces in a battle at Kappel, with Zwingli, who had gone forth as field chaplain, among the killed in action. The Second Peace of Kappel followed and put an end to the spread of religious reform in German Switzerland by accepting the emergent principle of territorialism—that the church affiliation of a people was to be determined by its civic authorities.

*   *   *

Calvinism in Geneva

Zwinglianism won adherents in a number of towns in southern Germany, the most important of which were Ulm, Augsburg, Constance, and Strasbourg. The development of Strasbourg as an important centre of Zwinglian reform was largely the work of Martin Bucer (1491–1551). On the crucial doctrine of the Eucharist, though he decidedly shared Zwingli's view, he strove for unity within the reform movement. He therefore developed a middle position between Lutheran and Zwinglian doctrines that was to influence both Anglican and Calvinist theology. For King Henry VIII of England consulted the Strasbourg theologian on his impending divorce from Catherine of Aragon, and Calvin spent three years (1538–41) in Strasbourg in close association with Bucer. In 1549, on the invitation of Archbishop Thomas Cranmer, Bucer went to Cambridge as professor of divinity and subsequently collaborated in the revision of the Book of Common Prayer.

Jean Calvin (1509–64) had originally preferred the contemplative life of the humanist scholar to that of the active reformer and had studied law, Latin, Greek, and Hebrew with notable scholars. His conversion to evangelical Christianity occurred sometime between 1532 and 1533, when he helped to prepare for his friend Nicholas Cop, recently chosen rector of the University of Paris, an address which clearly revealed the influence of both Erasmus' humanism and Luther's belief in the saving grace of faith alone.

Sorbonne orthodoxy reacted to Cop's address with wrath, and Cop fled. After vain attempts to win support, Calvin also fled, eventually reaching Basel. There he completed and published (1536) the Latin version of his *Institutes of the Christian Religion (Christianae Religionis Institutio)*, which he repeatedly revised until it reached its definitive form in 1559, his own French version appearing in 1541. Dedicated to Francis I, the *Institutes* were originally designed to promote the Reformation in France. In 1536, the very year the *Institutes* appeared, Calvin was persuaded by his compatriot Guillaume Farel, who was in the midst of the struggle for reform in Geneva, that it was his divinely ordained duty to take part in that struggle.

Geneva was particularly fertile ground for reform. Located between two aggressive neighbours, France and Savoy, it sought to maintain its independence by an alliance with the Swiss cantons of Berne and Fribourg. Berne was reformed and Fribourg Catholic. The assistance of Berne had given Farel a strategic advantage when he began his ardent campaign to evangelize Geneva. A public disputation led to no conclusive victory, but soon political dissatisfaction reinforced religious dissent. The citizens of Geneva sought greater self-government, and the Catholic bishop of Geneva, a descendant of the Savoy family, resisted, counting upon armed support from his Savoyard relatives. Continued ferment provoked Fribourg to withdraw from its alliance with Geneva, forcing Geneva into closer ties with Berne. In the midst of this tense situation a second disputation was held (May 1535) and ended in victory for Farel, but it took an iconoclastic riot of the reform party to force accession to the demand for evangelical worship. The House of Savoy now intervened, and Berne was forced to move to Geneva's defence. The Bernese defeated the Savoyards (1536), and the victory of the reformed cause was assured in Geneva. When subsequently nearby Lausanne became Protestant, Fribourg remained the only Catholic canton in French Switzerland.

Thus the circumstances were favourable when Calvin went to Geneva and decided to remain there. His task appeared to be simply to give substance and organization to the newly victorious Protestant creed. His early efforts were only partly successful, however, and in 1538, when he and Farel proposed to re-establish excommunication as a disciplinary measure and sharp disagreement broke out over the ritual of the Lord's Supper, both were banished. Calvin then spent three years in Strasbourg, where Bucer exerted the influence already noted upon his further theological development. Meanwhile Geneva was rent by opposing factions. In 1541 its desperate council recalled Calvin, giving him a free hand to put into practice his stern ideas, which had become even less flexible during exile.

Although Calvin sometimes went far beyond both Luther and Zwingli in his departure from Catholic theology, he was indebted to both. He particularly acknowledged Luther's leadership in formulating the cornerstone of Calvinist, or Reformed, belief—that justification came through faith alone and not through faith and good works. Like Luther and Zwingli, Calvin retained only two sacraments, baptism and communion, but differed from his predecessors in his interpretation of them. In its outward simplicity Calvinist worship was heir to Zwingli; yet, like Luther, Calvin believed in the efficacy of congregational singing, though of psalms in preference to hymns. Under the influence of Bucer he adopted a middle position between Luther and Zwingli in the interpretation of the sacraments. Baptism, in agreement with Zwingli, was for him a simple rite by which one became a member of the Christian church. His interpretation of communion, however, was a compromise between the Lutheran and the Zwinglian positions, similar to that which had been suggested to Luther at Marburg in 1529. Calvin retained Luther's concept of the real presence of Christ but divested that presence of all materialism and, in closer agreement with the Zwinglian concept, declared it to be a spiritual presence which the partaker could, if he had faith, appropriate, although spiritually only.

In Calvin's theology the doctrine of predestination received a more radical formulation than in either Luther's or Zwingli's. Luther had attempted to overcome any starkness implicit in the doctrine by counterbalancing his conviction of man's unworthiness with his faith in God's grace; Zwingli had admitted as potentially included among the elect all those who sincerely embraced his creed; but Calvin pursued the doctrine to its most logical conclusion. His major premise was the absolute omnipotence and omnipresence of God, Whose wisdom and will were beyond human comprehension. Convinced, no less than Luther, of the utter sinfulness of man, he considered salvation an inscrutable mystery. No man could have full assurance of his worthiness to be among the elect and therefore could find hope only in unquestioning faith in the goodness of God: 'For it is unreasonable that man should scrutinize with impunity those things which the Lord has determined to be hidden in Himself.'[20]

Calvin's doctrine of absolute predestination gave to his concept of the church a decided dualism, making it a political and a religious instrument at the same time. For Luther, the sacrament of baptism provided a bond that united all the baptized in one invisible church. Zwingli had accepted the existence of an invisible church of the elect but had regarded membership in the visible church as an outward sign of election. Calvin placed the invisible church of the elect completely outside the ken of man; yet man was saved from despair by his membership in the visible church, which not only united both elect and nonelect in this life but also was a church of equals, for the doctrine of absolute predestination made no special allowances for noble birth or privileged status. Membership in this church provided three possible tests of election; it was the outward sign of the individual's faith, permitting him to hear and preach the word of God; it enabled him to partake of the sacraments; and it bore witness to his righteousness and Christian discipline. Through this emphasis upon the righteous life (which was not the same as, but was reminiscent of, the Catholic doctrine of 'good works') the church became the moral as well as the religious guardian of the Reformed commonwealth and therefore an integral part of its government. Where Luther had subordinated the church to the state and where Zwingli had made his church the expression of the majority will, Calvin placed the civic side by side with the spiritual authority. Even if tyrannical, rulers must be obeyed, Calvin taught, except when they order impiety. The temporal government thus became also a functionary of divine power: 'Civil government is designed . . . to cherish and support the external worship of God, to preserve the pure doctrine of religion, to defend the constitution of the Church, to regulate our lives in a manner requisite for the society of men, to form our manners to civil justice, to promote our concord with each other, and to establish general peace and tranquility.' [21, 22]

The visible church thus was conceived by Calvin as a sort of theocracy, a government according to God's law, but it was a theocracy based upon a representative system. Its powers were laid down in the *Ordonnances ecclésiastiques* of 1541. Church discipline was put in the hands of a Vénérable Compagnie des Pasteurs, a board of ministers, who also were to watch over doctrinal purity. An Order of Teachers was made responsible for teaching the pure doctrine and securing a succession of well trained ministers. A Consistory, composed of six ministers and twelve elders elected by them from the city councils, was to supervise the conduct and opinions of the population. Public welfare was placed in the charge of appointed deacons. Together these orders (ministers, teachers, elders, and deacons) made up the government of the church, which held its authority directly from Christ. At first the authority of the civic bodies of Geneva (councils, assemblies, syndics, etc.) over the ecclesiastics was safeguarded, but the magistrates gradually yielded power and deference to the church orders, particularly the Consistory, and Calvin dominated the Consistory. Eventually civic and ecclesiastic authorities were inextricably intertwined. The republican tradition of Geneva was reinforced by Calvin's at least theoretical preference for an elective theocracy. Moreover, by implication the concept of predestination, no respecter of titles, power, or pelf, was democratic, for the community of the elect (the invisible church) cut across class lines.

The theocracy that Calvin eventually established in Geneva ruled public as well as private life with an iron hand. It discouraged amusements and diversions, outward adornment and manifestation of pride, and often severely punished infractions. Calvin even reintroduced, though against much opposition, excommunication and exile as forms of punishment but, like the Catholic Church, left to the civic authority the execution of the church's sentences. The expression of thought was strictly policed, and a network of informers aided the Consistory in imposing its will. As the number of cases cited before the Consistory indicated, resistance to Calvinist puritanism was widespread, but in 1555, the opposition party (which became known as 'the Libertines') was destroyed by the torture, flight, or execution of its leaders. On the surface at least, Calvin succeeded in his aim of making Geneva the goal and haven of Reformed Christians from all over Europe. John Knox, who visited the city during his exile from England, looked upon Calvinist Geneva as the perfect example of a Christian commonwealth.

In the *Institutes*, Calvin had written: 'I am not an advocate for unnecessary cruelty, nor can I conceive the possibility of an equitable sentence being pronounced without mercy.'[23] The quality of Calvin's mercy nevertheless sometimes was strained, and most conspicuously in his treatment of Michael Servetus (see below). The execution of Servetus (1553) provoked a stinging indictment by the French humanist Sebastian Castellio, whose treatise *On Heretics and Whether They Ought to Be Burned* (1554) presented an uncompromising defence of religious tolerance. Yet it was an era when humanism was being engulfed by the new dogmatism, and the replies of Calvin and Theodore Beza, his adjutant at Lausanne, who ardently sought to justify the punishment of heretics, sounded louder and more persuasive than Castellio's well-reasoned plea.[24, 25]

Despite Calvin's dogmatism, he propounded a thoroughly humanistic system of education. In Chapter XVI we shall describe the curriculum that he provided for the College and Academy of Geneva. Almost from their inception, these schools became the rallying point of students from all over Europe, many of whom were to become leaders of the reform movement in their native countries. Their presence in Geneva testified that Calvin and his commonwealth had become the focal point of the Reformation.

THE TUDORS AND ANGLICANISM

In Germany and Switzerland political action followed from the concern of theologians and humanists with religious reform. In Tudor England the reverse was true: the foundations for reform were laid by an absolute monarch who used theologians with reformist leanings to further his political and personal designs. The one theological issue at first involved, the problem of a king's divorce, entailed little more than a technicality of canon law. In seeking annulment of his marriage to Catherine of Aragon on debatable grounds, Henry VIII was moved by more than infatuation with the dark-eyed Anne Boleyn. Of greater moment were the political considerations that the Tudor succession might be endangered because Catherine was—or, at any rate, was thought to be—too old to bear him a male heir and that the absolutism to which he aspired could hardly be perfected so long as the English clergy recognized in Rome an authority outside his own.

Henry originally had no intention of provoking a rupture with Rome. He had been—and persisted in being—a professed Catholic who allowed no marked deviations from the accepted creed. His *Defence of the Seven Sacraments*, written against Luther in 1521, had, in fact, earned him the title 'Defender of the Faith', conferred by a grateful pope and still borne proudly by Henry's successors. Nevertheless, after Luther's revolt any opponents of the papacy became potential allies of the evangelical camp. Thus Henry's decision to push through his divorce with or without papal sanction gave to a family dispute a profound international significance.

As had been the case with Luther, a delicate diplomatic situation played into Henry's hands. Pope Clement VII not only had genuine religious scruples against annulling King Henry's marriage but also was victimized by the conflict between Emperor Charles V and Francis I. Clement could not well afford to offend the emperor (who was not only Catherine of Aragon's nephew but also a more willing defender of the faith than Henry), especially after imperial troops had occupied and sacked Rome (1527); and yet he also hoped to retain Henry's support in his efforts to counter Habsburg supremacy on the Continent, especially in Italy. He therefore did his best to delay a final decision concerning Henry's divorce. His temporizing tactics did not work to his benefit. Years of waiting only increased Henry's impatience and at the same time gave him the opportunity to devise measures that would give a legal semblance to his divorce if papal assent were not forthcoming.

Meanwhile Henry prepared his subjects for such an eventuality. In 1529 he summarily dismissed his lord chancellor, Cardinal Thomas Wolsey, who had failed to secure the annulment of his marriage. He then attacked some of the clerical abuses most highly resented among the English people. A series of acts forced through Parliament between 1529 and 1532 diminished the economic advantage of the clergy. They regulated charges for clerical services, limited both the number of offices and the amount of property that could be held by members of the clergy, and drastically reduced the annates paid to Rome.

Sure of popular support, Henry concurrently attacked the political position of the clergy also. He accused them in 1529 of having violated the Statute of Praemunire when they had recognized Cardinal Wolsey, archbishop of York and lord chancellor of England, as papal legate—an office that, ironically, Wolsey had accepted with Henry's consent in the hope of furthering the king's divorce. In addition to paying a substantial indemnity for this offence, the Convocation of the English clergy that year had to acknowledge the king as their 'singular protector, only and supreme lord, and, as the law of Christ allows, even Supreme Head'. In 1532, Henry renewed his attack with the 'Supplication against the Ordinaries', which denounced the legislation passed in the Convocations and the clerical administration of ecclesiastic courts. The Convocation answered with a 'Submission of the Clergy', which, in effect, made all future church legislation subject to royal approval and that of the past subject to review. Parliament was then (1533) induced to pass the

Restraint of Appeals Act, which prohibited appeals to foreign (i.e. papal) jurisdiction from decisions of English courts.[26]

Thomas Cranmer, a humanist scholar from Cambridge and a devoted advocate of royal absolutism, had recently won royal approval, for it was he who had suggested an appeal of Henry's case to the European universities, a majority of which had replied in the king's favour. Still acting with papal consent, the king made Cranmer archbishop of Canterbury (1533), and after his installation, Cranmer dissolved Henry's marriage. This action brought the final break with Rome; the pope excommunicated Henry. The authority of the English ruler over church affairs, already implicit in the 'Submission', became explicit when Parliament passed the Act of Supremacy (1534), which unconditionally recognized the king as the supreme head of the Church of England. Prominent dissenters were punished; Sir Thomas More, who in 1529 had reluctantly agreed to be Wolsey's successor as lord chancellor, was executed as a traitor (1535).

Henry was able to accomplish his religious revolution without encountering significant organized resistance. An important factor in weakening the opposition was the strength of national sentiment that had characterized English attitudes since the Hundred Years' War. The War of the Roses had eliminated the English nobility as a serious rival of royal power, and the middle class, anxious to avoid the hardships and devastation of that war, believed a strong monarch to be the best guarantor of domestic peace. Clerical reform and a national church were, besides, welcome in principle to the people of England, while Henry's confiscation and redistribution of monastic lands converted the beneficiaries of royal favour into grateful recipients who replenished the diminished ranks of the English landed nobility with powerful advocates of royal paternalism. The fate of the monasteries between 1536 and 1539, nevertheless, provoked the only serious show of resistance. The struggle was short-lived. It culminated in the so-called Pilgrimage of Grace in 1536–37, an insurrection in several northern shires by thousands of Catholic laymen and clergy, which was put down by a few dozen executions.

Another reason for the weakness of the opposition was that Henry's religious reforms were restrained. They did not impugn Catholic theology but only matters of ecclesiastical organization and administration. They, therefore, did not excite religious passions to the same extent as the Continental reform movements. Henry, in fact, assiduously avoided giving the impression that he favoured doctrinal reform. He persecuted both recalcitrant Catholic clergy and avowed reformers with apparent impartiality. In the Ten Articles, issued by the Convocation of 1536, a deliberate attempt was made to pacify doctrinal disputes and 'to stablish Christian quietness and unity'.[27] The Articles sought to appease not only the more moderate Catholics at home but also the more moderate reformers, for Henry was for the moment courting the German Lutherans. Yet no new doctrine was explicitly proclaimed, and whatever change could be read into the Ten Articles was attributable to omission rather than commission. Thus, while they mentioned only three sacraments, they did not deny validity to the other four. After the open rebellion of the Pilgrimage of Grace, however, Henry opposed even implicit accommodation to reform doctrines. The Six Articles of 1539 reasserted the basic tenets of Catholic theology except papal authority, confirming as dogmas of the Anglican Church hitherto suspect principles and practices such as transubstantiation, celibacy of priests, auricular confession, communion in one kind, vows of chastity, and private masses. Henry's divorce in 1540 from his fourth wife, Anne of Cleves, signalled the complete abandonment of his pro-Lutheran policy. Until the end of his reign, the Six Articles remained the religious law of the land and were firmly enforced.

*　　*　　*

Doctrinal and Liturgical Reform

The phase of the English Reformation which ended with Henry's death constituted little more than the secession of the Church of England from the jurisdiction of Rome and the establishment of the king as the supreme head of the church. Doctrinal and liturgical reforms were accomplished during the short reign of Edward VI, the son born to Henry from his third marriage (to Jane Seymour). The first step in these reforms is identified with the boy-king's uncle, Edward Seymour, duke of Somerset and lord protector, a convinced Protestant of Lutheran persuasion, who exerted a decided influence upon his ward.

Despite Henry's opposition to reformed ideas and his persecution of known Protestants, the writings of Luther, Zwingli, and Calvin had become widely known in England. The Oxford Reformers had helped promote the scholarly study of the Christian tradition, and the still lively persistence of Lollardy had prepared the ground for the popular acceptance of many reformed ideas. A centre of reformed opinion had developed at Cambridge, where the Lutheran leanings of William Tyndale, Cranmer, and other theologians became so well known that their meeting-place was nicknamed 'Little Germany'. Henry had kept these reform advocates in check; Somerset found a willing ally in Cranmer when he set out to add liturgical reform to the political and legal reform of Henry.

So complete now was the submission of the ecclesiastic to the secular power that the authority of the lord protector sufficed to bring about the changes that Henry himself had wanted to forestall. As a first step, the Six Articles were repudiated, and with the Order of Communion, issued in 1548, the year after Henry's death, communion in both kinds was legalized. In 1549, the first Book of Common Prayer was published, substituting English for Latin, and through an Act of Uniformity worship was standardized throughout England. Neither Somerset nor Cranmer, however, was willing to risk civil war, and they revealed their caution in the ambiguity with which they worded important parts of the Prayer Book. Many outward elements of the traditional service were retained, and new ones did not expressly controvert Catholic teaching, although they were so phrased as to enable Protestants to interpret them according to their consciences. Despite the ambivalence in high places respect for the old tradition was still profound in England, and enforcement of the Act of Uniformity led to sporadic outbursts, notably in Cornwall, where English was a foreign language. As on the Continent, the borderline between religious and economic discontent was none too clear, and the hardships caused by the enclosure movement (see Chapter 1) were undoubtedly also important factors in these uprisings.

Somerset's inability to maintain domestic peace coupled with several diplomatic failures led to his downfall and to the ascendency of the Earl of Warwick, afterward Duke of Northumberland. Northumberland cast his lot with the more radical reformers. The ambiguities of the first Prayer Book, while avoiding provocation of traditionalists, were offensive to convinced reformers, who not only pressed for a clearer statement of doctrine but also objected to the persistence of Catholic symbols in the service. They found telling support among several illustrious refugees whom the victory of Emperor Charles V over the Protestant Schmalkaldic League in 1547 (see below) and the consequent threat of persecution had forced out of the Holy Roman Empire. The Pole Jan Laski in London, the Italian Peter Martyr at Oxford, and the German Martin Bucer at Cambridge lent distinguished support to the Protestant cause. Bucer especially, although his willingness to compromise between Lutheran and Zwinglian theology was not acceptable to many, was an influential critic of the first Prayer Book.

Northumberland initiated the final phase of the Anglican revolt, making the break from Rome more definitely a break also from Catholic theology. A new Act of Uniformity, passed in 1552, imposed a second Book of Common Prayer, which went farther than the previous edition in the reform of worship and theology. The service was simplified, marriage of the clergy was permitted, and language and ceremonial more clearly approximated a Protestant interpretation. The rite of communion underwent the most important change. Cranmer, even before Bucer's arrival in England, had been converted to the Zwinglian concept of the Eucharist. Whereas the first Prayer Book had been deliberately phrased so as to allow for a varying interpretation, the second Prayer Book stated expressly that Holy Communion was merely an act of 'remembrance', for 'the natural body and blood of our Saviour Christ ... are in heaven and not here'.[28] The ceremonial itself was changed to conform with that of the Swiss Reformed Church.

With the second Prayer Book the Church of England took its place decisively on the Protestant side, but the Anglican revolt was—and remained—the least radical of the reform movements. Changes of liturgy and service were less far-reaching than in either Germany or Switzerland, notwithstanding a sudden wave of iconoclasm during Somerset's protectorate. On the Continent, Protestant church administration had been reorganized along either consistorial or presbyterian lines; in England continuity was unbroken in both ritual and organization through the maintenance of the episcopal system. In the relationship of church with state, the English Reformation consequently differed notably from its Continental counterparts; the king was acknowledged as the supreme governor of the Church of England, though without any further spiritual function or office. The crown thus symbolized the identity, almost complete, of the Anglican Church with the English realm. Tudor absolutism had established the most truly national church in western Christendom, but the studied ambiguity of Anglican doctrine contributed in no small degree to a flexibility that permitted men of different convictions to remain loyal subjects and Anglicans. Those who refused to conform altogether, however, were to create future complications.

Emphasis upon national unity at the expense of religious uniformity moulded the strength of Anglicanism. Only a year after the second Act of Uniformity, the death of Edward VI permitted the accession of Mary (1553–59), the Catholic daughter of the repudiated Catherine of Aragon. Anglicanism was to prove that it was capable of surviving Catholic reaction and retaining its predominance in English religious life. Thus to the insularity, dynastic loyalty, historical tradition, and other peculiar institutions bolstering Englishmen's national sentiment was now added the potent force of religious solidarity in an evangelical creed that distinguished them from other nationalities.[29]

THE ANABAPTISTS

The most radical reformers of the century were commonly designated as Anabaptists because advocacy of adult baptism emerged as the chief bond among them. While reform in England, Germany, and Switzerland is clearly identified with outstanding individuals, the diversity of the Anabaptist background beclouds their theological and even their geographical origins. In the Rhineland, Switzerland, Bohemia, Moravia, Poland, the Baltic provinces, and the Low Countries, elements of Anabaptist doctrine were disseminated by preachers who, though they frequently were aware of each other's views and activities, sometimes appear to have had no direct contact with one another. This diversity accounts at least in part for the fact that, while at various moments in Anabaptism's tumultuous history a number of influential preachers came to the fore, no one individual became its acknowledged theologian.[30]

The other religious groups, whatever issues divided them, were unanimous in the violence they directed against this radical wing of the Reformation. Reformers and humanists like Zwingli and Melanchthon joined hands with Catholic inquisitors and untutored feudal lords in demanding the execution of Anabaptist preachers and their followers. In 1529 the Diet of Spires, in the midst of the struggle between Catholic and Protestant factions of the Empire, took time to pass an imperial law commanding the princes on either side to remove Anabaptist 'men and women of rational age from natural life to death by fire or by the sword . . . without prior inquisition before spiritual judges'.[31] Thus Anabaptists were denied even the slender safeguard which the Inquisition, by giving offenders the chance to recant, offered to other heretics.

The passion with which Anabaptists were persecuted cannot be explained solely by the religious doctrines that distinguished them. The very name (meaning 'believers in rebaptism') by which they have become known gives undue emphasis to one of those doctrinal differences and seems to have been deliberately assigned to them by their enemies in order to bring them under the provisions of an ancient Justinian law that made repetition of baptism punishable by death. As a matter of fact, the Anabaptists, to whom this issue was not cardinal, referred to themselves simply as Baptists. The cardinal tenets of their theology were the literal interpretation of Scripture and a firm conviction of the efficacy of divine revelation. These tenets led them to assert the true believer's ability to interpret Scripture for himself and so make religion a personal matter and membership in the church voluntary. As a result, among the Anabaptist arose a host of self-appointed preachers, both men and women, and a marked diversity of teachings. None of them, however, could find in Scripture authority for infant baptism. Hence, but only as a result of their more basic tenets, they advocated adult baptism (not rebaptism).

The faith of the Anabaptists was essentially mystical. It centred upon an intimate relationship of the believer with God that was mediated not by institutions but by Christ alone and could be achieved only through the active desire of the individual. Anabaptists, therefore, revised the doctrine of predestination and insisted upon the existence of free will. Christ, they believed, had died for all men; baptism, therefore, was not a prerequisite of salvation but merely the outward expression of a free-will conversion to Christ. Infant baptism was meaningless, for only adults could knowingly symbolize by baptism their acceptance of the True Church. The True Church thus was composed of voluntary adult believers, the 'saints' who had vowed to live in imitation of Christ. No other reformed creed was ready to go so far in emancipating the immature or unwilling from institutionalized religion or to place so few formal bonds on the mature and willing. To find the true principles of Christian living, no institution or outward rites were needed—only piety and spiritual understanding, which came to the truly pious as an act of revelation. An enthusiastic fringe of the movement preached the imminence of the second coming of the Christ, and their prophesies kept the masses agitated and won adherents who did not necessarily grasp the more obstruse tenets of the creed.

Whether chiliasts or not, in general the Anabaptists demanded the most complete 'restitution' of the primitive church. This demand was revolutionary, for it implied the absolute brotherhood and equality of all believers. To maintain the purity of the True Church, a strict, self-imposed moral discipline was expected, and the state was denied all authority in the affairs of the church. The cardinal principle of complete religious freedom led also to rejection of the authority of the state in matters of individual conscience, to a doctrine of separation of church and state. Indeed, participation by the true Christian in the affairs of the state was disapproved. A true Christian would not pay certain taxes, for example, because they might be used to support un-Christian acts of the state; even church taxes were opposed, on the ground that the church should be supported entirely by voluntary contributions. The true Christian would take no oath. Nor would he hold office, since to do so would conflict with the prescribed equality of all believers and might, more-over, lead him to inflict the death penalty, thus violating Christian scruples against taking human life. The same scruples required Anabaptists to oppose war and to refuse to bear arms even in their own defence. Continued persecu-tion induced only the more radical among them to turn from meek submission to a crusade against their persecutors as enemies of the City of God.

The Anabaptists' ideal of restoring the brotherhood of the primitive church involved a radical concept of social and economic justice. Like the Catholic Church and Luther, Anabaptists not only rejected usury but in their emphasis upon a literal interpretation of the Bible went far in the direction of the primitive communism of early Christianity. In the abstract at least, Ana-baptism rejected private property, declaring that all possessions were the property of God, to be held only in stewardship by the proprietors and so ministered as to meet the needs of less fortunate brethren. In practice, Anabaptist attitudes with regard to property ranged from private philanthropy on the part of those who considered community of property impracticable to the voluntary communism practised in the Moravian communities, the compulsory community of goods demanded by Dutch and German Anabap-tists such as Jacob Wiedemann, and the violent attacks upon wealth and the hierarchic society in the writings and sermons of Thomas Münzer.

The social and political implications of the Anabaptists' religious teachings help to explain the hostility that they evoked. Their very pacifism, at a time when the Turks were threatening Latin Christendom, laid them open to the charge that they were willing to let Christianity perish. Probably most shock-ing, however, was their insistence upon the absolute separation of church and state. Luther, Zwingli, and Calvin, while with greater or less vigour asserting the primacy of religion, had submitted to or become allied with the existing civic authority and thus had helped to preserve, to one degree or another, unity of church and state. Carried to a logical conclusion, however, Anabaptist teachings might have destroyed not only the established spiritual order of western Christendom but also the established political and social order.[32]

The Anabaptists were in some regards indebted to the earlier religious revolution in Bohemia. The Hussite movement of the fifteenth century had already demonstrated by its splinterings how schism breeds schism. Nevertheless, on the eve of the Reformation in Bohemia, the more conservative, primarily religiously motivated Calixtenes had outlasted the Taborites and the other more radical, politically and socially motivated splinters, with the exception of the so-called 'Moravian Brethren' (*Unitas Fratrum*). Founded by Peter Chelčisky (d. 1460) and enjoying the protection of John Rokycana (d. 1471), the first and last archbishop of the Utraquist (Hussite) Church, the 'Moravians' during the early sixteenth century won the adherence of influential minorities in Bohemia and Moravia. Unlike future Anabaptists, they accepted infant baptism, and of late the influx of upper-class elements had brought a departure from the radical equalitarianism of the founder, but in other regards they were among the significant forerunners of the Anabaptists. Chelčisky believed in the literal interpretation of Jesus' teachings, the democratic practices of primitive Christianity, and the repudiation of war, oaths, and participation in civic matters.

Prior to the peasants' uprising in Germany in 1524-25, most Protestant reformers had viewed with only relative alarm the various extremist groups that had arisen in the wake of their more moderate revolts. One of the first of these groups was the so-called 'Prophets', Nicholas Storch, Markus Stübner, and Thomas Münzer. In the town of Zwickau, Saxony, near Bohemia, they took the lead in a movement that, going far beyond Luther in its reform efforts, revealed distinctive Moravian tendencies. After expulsion from Zwickau, in 1521, Storch and Stübner went to Wittenberg, where, in Luther's absence, they gained considerable influence over Carlstadt, already showing Taborite proclivities, and even over Melanchthon. Their ardent mysticism, chiliastic prophesies, and iconoclastic outbursts incited demonstrations that greatly disturbed Luther. As already indicated, in 1522 he hurried back from hiding on the Wartburg and regained control of the reform movement. From then on, the Prophets and eventually Carlstadt became bitter opponents of Luther, whom they denounced as a traitor to the Reformation. But Luther did not at that time propose that extreme measures be used against them. The Anabaptist movement had not yet truly begun, and Carlstadt seemed more a misguided mystic than a subversive rebel.

Münzer, Carlstadt, and a number of other mystics who were popularly, if somewhat anachronistically, later to be associated with Anabaptism made common cause with the peasants. Their influence grew as Luther's denunciations revealed him to be an ally of the ruling classes. Münzer became ever more convinced that God was on his side, would exterminate his enemies, and would soon unite the community of the faithful in an egalitarian kingdom of God on earth. A considerable popular following enabled him to create and to maintain until expelled by the local lords communal theocracies in Allstedt and Mühlhausen in turn. In 1525 he was captured after unsuccessfully leading a force of Thuringian insurgents in the Peasants' War and was executed.

Among the Zwickau Prophets adult baptism had been favourably regarded, and Münzer had openly advocated it, but it had apparently not been practised.

It is doubtful, therefore, whether strictly speaking they are to be considered Anabaptists. Anabaptist teachings are commonly believed to have first crystallized into a coherent theology in Zürich, Switzerland, where Zwingli's reform, though even in its initial phases more radical than Luther's, had not yet, in the opinion of an increasing faction, gone far enough. Among the radical leaders stand out Conrad Grebel, well educated scion of a patrician family, and Felix Manz, a humanist and Hebrew scholar. Disputations in 1523 and 1525 revealed the gulf that separated Zwingli from this group, which meanwhile had developed such tenets of Anabaptism as freedom of conscience, adult baptism, free will, and opposition to church taxes. In 1525 at Lake Zürich, Grebel performed the earliest known adult baptism, and the practice spread. With the Peasants' War resounding on the borders of Switzerland, the Zürich town council, fearful of the growing radicalism within its own domain, in 1526 made punishable by drowning not only adherence to Anabaptism but even attendance at Anabaptist meetings. In January 1527, Manz was so executed.

Confirmed now in the belief that Anabaptism was synonymous with rebellion, Luther stiffened his attitude, and Lutherans and Catholics concurred, as we have seen, at the Diet of Spires in 1529 in condemning Anabaptists. In an exegesis of the Eighty-second Psalm written in 1530, Luther distinguished two types of heretics, and with pointed reference to Anabaptist teachings said: 'There are . . . heretics who hold that one should tolerate no authority; . . . that one should own no possessions, but run away from wife and child, leave house and home, or should hold and keep all things common. Such are not only heretics but rebels, and therefore without doubt should be punished.'[33] A year later, the 'gentle' Melanchthon in a memorandum to the elector of Saxony demanded the death penalty for Anabaptists as rebels against the state church, and Luther added: '*Placet mihi Luthero.*'[34] In a letter written to the town council of Münster in 1532, he warned against leniency toward Anabaptists, 'who are always bent on rebellion, mix in political affairs, and arrogantly desire to rule'.[35]

Meanwhile Anabaptist influence had spread into the south German cities, traditionally in close association with the Swiss cantons. The prosperous commercial and industrial city of Nuremberg became a centre of Anabaptism, and several other communities soon contained more Anabaptists than Lutherans and Zwinglians combined. The Anabaptists found a particularly ripe soil in Moravia, where they established one of their earliest communities, but in 1526 Ferdinand of Austria, an ardent Catholic, became king of Bohemia and shortly ended toleration of them. The Moravian Anabaptists, ever victims of persecution, moved through Bohemia and into more tolerant Poland. By 1532, the most capable leaders of the Swiss-German Anabaptists, the men whose restraint had guided their followers and whose high standards of morality had gained for their sect a measure of respect, were dead, often at the hands of executioners.

A faction had long existed that did not accept the absolute pacifism first associated with Anabaptism. These men emphasized the mystical aspects of Anabaptist theology, its chiliastic ideas, and its correlation of religious with social reform. Hans Hut by his militant preaching of pacifism had split the Anabaptist community in Moravia even before Ferdinand's decrees dispersed it. Hut himself soon went to a horrible doom in Augsburg, but under stress of persecution the fanatical element took firmer hold, recruiting its largest following among the common people. Most of its leaders, themselves from the common class, were without formal education. Inspired chiefly by their understanding of the Bible, they derived their authority from the Anabaptist doctrine of divine revelation. Among them arose powerful preachers whose essentially nonrational appeals and prophesies kept their followers in constant agitation. Typical, and perhaps most prominent, was Melchior Hoffmann, a furrier from Swabia. Having first espoused Lutheran, then Zwinglian ideas, he was converted to Anabaptism in 1529 and became one of its most successful itinerant preachers. After wandering and preaching through northern Germany and East Friesland, he arrived in Holland in 1530, where soon a number of Anabaptist communities emerged.

Persecution now spread into Holland. The Anabaptist communities were dissolved, and their leaders were executed. Persecution, however, only raised chiliastic hopes, since according to Scripture persecution of the True Church would precede the second coming of Christ. Hoffman, self-styled prophet, predicted that the millennium would come in 1533 and that Strasbourg was to be the new Jerusalem. In 1533 he confidently entered that city, was promptly arrested, and after ten years of indignities and torture died in prison. His imprisonment having been part of his own prophesies, the expectations of his followers continued to run high. His disciple Jan Matthijszoon, a baker from Haarlem with a somewhat questionable past, became the new prophet of Anabaptism.

The role for which Hoffman had selected Strasbourg eventually went to the city of Münster in Westphalia. Largely Lutheran, Münster was in the midst of a struggle with its spiritual and feudal overlord, the Catholic bishop. That this struggle was not a purely religious one is evident from the citizens' demand during disturbances in 1525 that the clergy should refrain from trade and should surrender the tools they used in industry. Bernhard Rothmann, a teacher and preacher of wide renown, and Bernard Knipperdollinck, a wealthy cloth merchant, led the opposition to the bishop. They found strong Lutheran support, especially among the guilds. A compromise, forced upon the bishop in 1533 by the threat of open warfare, divided the city and its churches among Catholics and Lutherans, granting toleration to both. Rothmann and Knipperdollinck soon embraced Anabaptist doctrines, and Rothmann in increasingly popular sermons emphasizing the social teachings of the creed won a large number of followers. Münster was now split into three factions—the Catholics, composed mostly of the old clergy and the aristocratic element of the town; the Lutherans, strongly entrenched among the guilds; and the Anabaptists, backed mostly by the common people.

Matthijszoon, having proclaimed Münster the New Jerusalem, commanded all members of the True Church to congregate there to witness the coming of Christ. At the same time he preached abandonment of pacifism, declaring that the Anabaptists were destined to prepare the Kingdom of God by the sword. From the neighbouring towns and from Holland, Anabaptists converged upon Münster, among them one of Matthijszoon's chief disciples, Jan Beukelszoon, an adventurous but eloquent and courageous tailor, sometimes known as John of Leiden. In February 1534, after a bloodless demonstration of armed might, the Anabaptists gained control of Münster, forcing their opponents into exile, and established a theocracy under the leadership of Matthijszoon. But his reign was short-lived. The soldiers of the bishop laid siege to the city, cutting it off from the outside world. Sallying forth on Easter Day with only a few men, like another Gideon, to route the enemies of Israel, Matthijszoon was hacked to pieces. John of Leiden became prophet and ruler of the beleaguered City of God.

The new leader attempted to re-establish primitive Christianity. Community of goods was required, by force if necessary; the guilds were abolished; workers were fed and clothed by the community; meals were eaten in common. Absolute obedience to the prophet was demanded, and Knipperdollinck as 'bearer of the sword' enforced discipline by terror. For over a year the city was able to stand off the combined financial and military forces of princes and Empire, even to inflict stinging defeats upon them.

At the height of his military successes, John had himself proclaimed king of Zion and thereafter affected a regal pomp that contrasted sharply with the austerity required of his people. Soon after, he introduced the most widely execrated measure of the Münster regime, polygamy. The tremendous excess of women over men in Münster (about three to one), added to the strain of continuous war, apparently made such a step appear desirable, especially because strict laws against adultery and prostitution remained in force. Moreover, in the Anabaptist view acceptance into the True Church dissolved all previous relationships, including marriage, in order that the Church might preserve its purity by complete isolation from non-members, and so remarriage did not necessarily mean to an Anabaptist that he was taking an additional spouse. Nevertheless, the introduction of polygamy was followed by an uprising intended to overthrow John and to restore private property. The uprising was ruthlessly suppressed.

In an attempt to win relief for his beleaguered forces, John sent twenty-seven 'apostles' through enemy lines to rouse the neighbouring cities. The apostles were all captured and executed, but not before northern Germany and Holland underwent a series of rebellions and demonstrations of sympathy, attesting the widespread social dislocations and the appeal of the Anabaptist movement to the common people. The tight ring that encircled Münster prevented any support from reaching it, and when it was clear that the city was doomed, John permitted all who desired to do so to leave. The end came, hastened by treachery, in June 1535. Retaliation followed. John and Knipperdollinck were among the captured and, after brutal and prolonged torture, were executed in 1536. Their bodies, locked in iron cages, were hoisted to the top of St Lambert's Church, where they remained until 1881. The bishop's soldiers restored Catholicism as the only authorized religion.

Through the efforts of Menno Simons[36] (d. 1561) in the Netherlands and elsewhere and of Jakob Huter (executed in 1536) in Moravia moderate Anabaptism survived, dissociated from revolutionary activity. These men insistently repudiated the Münster type of Anabaptism, remained loyal to the principles of pacifism and community of property, refused to take oaths, and, in order to maintain their version of the Christian life and discipline, banned marriage with dissenters. After decades of persecution under the Spanish régime in the Low Countries, the Mennonites (i.e. the followers of Menno Simons), who were especially numerous in the northern provinces, won tolerance when the Dutch Republic became an independent state and even shared in Holland's prosperity. Holland is still a centre of their faith. From there they spread into England. In the course of time, the constantly dwindling remnants of the Anabaptist sect were hounded out of Switzerland, Moravia, Poland, and elsewhere. At the end of the seventeenth century they began to migrate to North America, where, as Mennonite, Hutterite, and Amish communities, they still flourish.

SOME OTHER PROTESTANT CREEDS

Certain other minor creeds that still survive reflected the splintering tendency of the Reformation without vitally determining the course of the Reformation. The numbers of their adherents were relatively negligible, and the very individualism they preached prevented their maturing into well organized and disciplined churches. Their importance lies rather in the fact that, despite the persistence of dogmatism and intolerance in both new and old churches, they reveal the freedom with which daring individuals began to approach traditional doctrines and the everlasting question of salvation. A marked mysticism is characteristic of some of these fringe movements, spurned alike by Catholic and Protestant because of their opposition to institutionalized religion and their refusal to submit to either new or old dogma. While some mystics, like the Spaniard Juan de Valdes (c. 1500–41) in Naples and Guillaume Postel (1510–81) in France, despite their heretical ideas remained within the Catholic fold, others showed, at least in the beginning, a preference for Protestant affiliations.

Among the most mystical ideas of the time were those of two prominent German thinkers, Sebastian Franck (1499–1543) and Kaspar von Schwenkfeld (1490–1561). Franck, an ordained priest, shortly after Luther's break with the papacy became a Lutheran preacher. His rejection of slavish dependence upon the written word and his insistence upon the greater validity of the inner light soon brought him into conflict with Lutheran authorities. Franck believed in a subjective spiritual interpretation of the Bible, and piety was for him a personal matter whose direction could not be prescribed except by the inner spirit. God was so all-embracing, he thought, that the most diverse conceptions of the Deity were compatible with His existence. This position led him to advocate complete religious tolerance, even for infidels and pagans: 'Wherefore my heart is alien to none. I have my brothers among the Turks, Papists, Jews, and all peoples.'[37] Outlawed by Lutherans as well as Catholics, he had to gain his livelihood successively as soap boiler and printer while engaged in historical and theological writing.

Individualist that he was, Franck did not found a school; Kaspar von Schwenkfeld, a Silesian nobleman, did. Schwenkfeld had at first harboured Lutheran ideas, but his mysticism brought him into opposition to the new creed. During Lutheranism's brief career between revolt and establishment as a new orthodoxy, in Schwenkfeld's eyes it had lost its spirituality and had become too dependent upon Scripture. To him the word of God had two equally valid manifestations: the external Word and the internal Spirit. The internal Spirit was everlasting and removed from the outward symbolism of ritual and sacraments such as baptism or Lord's Supper; its important element was inner experience, not formal practice.

Schwenkfeld recruited a scattered following among Anabaptists to whom his opposition to baptism appealed, and among the pietist Bohemian congregations, to whom his mysticism appealed. Forced to leave Silesia, he wandered to Strasbourg and, driven from there, to Ulm, where he died, outlawed and in hiding. His followers, now known as Schwenkfelders, broke entirely with the Lutheran Church. Persecution by all sects thinned them out and dispersed them into Silesia and elsewhere. They retained their identity, however, despite close association with the mystic Jacob Boehme in the seventeenth century and despite a special effort by the Jesuits to convert them in the eighteenth. The majority of them eventually found refuge with Count von Zinzendorf (see below), whose Moravian Brotherhood some of them joined. A very small group found their way to America, where they still preserve their identity as one of the religious sects among the Pennsylvania Dutch. Schwenkfeld's mysticism, reinforced by the ideas of Boehme, contributed to the development of the Pietist movement (see below).

Perhaps a greater danger to the established Christian churches than that derived from Franck's and Schwenkfeld's views was early reflected in the writings of Servetus. Servetus, an advocate of adult baptism, had still more daring views upon a dogma which is cardinal in Christian theology, Catholic as well as reformed, although subject to debate throughout the ages. It is the dogma that makes the Father, the Son, and the Holy Ghost a trinity and a unity at the same time. It requires faith in the pre-existence of Jesus as the

Son of God before becoming a mortal and, therefore, in his eternal divinity. As Servetus, a physician and humanist of acknowledged reputation, read Scripture, he could find no justification for belief in the Trinity. His studies led him, on the contrary, to a kind of unitarianism that identified Jesus with God. The mysticism of this position was underlined by Servetus' belief that man could conquer mortality by his union in faith with the divine. Few heretics were ever hunted with greater persistence than was Servetus by Calvin. Calvin had a hand in the denunciation of Servetus to the Inquisition at Lyons; and when Servetus, escaping from prison in France, passed through Geneva, Calvin had him arrested and tried (1553). Even after Servetus was burned at the stake (though Calvin had favoured decapitation), the discussion of his principles continued and led to their further elaboration and currency.

An unmystical Anti-Trinitarianism, emphasizing the human character of Jesus and the concomitant dignity of man, was especially strong in the countries east of the Holy Roman Empire. In Poland, Transylvania, and Hungary, the feudal nobility was still powerful, and the defence of the frontier against Turkish advance continued hazardous. Feudalism and military hazards combined to give political influence to the local lords and princes, while king and middle class remained weak and the peasantry powerless. The feudal nobility often were of a faith different from the king's. The resulting political and religious decentralization contrasted sharply with the dynastic centralization that had developed in western Europe and the larger principalities of Germany. As a consequence, radical sects—Anabaptists, for example—were sometimes able to win a local lord's favour and to find at least temporary asylum in these eastern lands.

Among the diverse peoples of the kingdom of Poland religious unity scarcely existed. While the Poles of the west were Roman Catholic, the White Russians and Ukranians of the east were Orthodox. The Reformation at first made striking gains, particularly with the conversion to Lutheranism (1525) of Albrecht of Brandenburg, grand master of the Teutonic Order. On the advice of Luther, Albrecht transformed the order's huge Prussian domain into a hereditary dukedom, which he accepted as a fief from the king of Poland. As we shall soon see, an exceptional degree of toleration of religious differences was to this stage permitted in Poland and the neighbouring principality of Transylvania. It led to an influx of Anabaptists, who added to Poland's religious disunity. And a reform movement in the form of Anti-Trinitarianism also burgeoned in both Poland and Transylvania.

The Anti-Trinitarians quickly split into two factions, one of the leaders of the more moderate splinter being Georgio Biandrata, Italian physician at the courts of Poland and Transylvania. He called upon Fausto Sozzini or (as he is more commonly called) Socinus to help him counteract the extremists. Scion of an Italian patrician family in which the practice of canon law and jurisprudence was a long tradition, Socinus had become interested in the problem of the Trinity through the controversy over Servetus. While denying Jesus' prior existence as the son of God, Socinus retained the practice of invoking—but not worshipping—him. The extreme wing of Anti-Trinitarians denied any divinity at all to Jesus and refused to worship him in any way. Their radicalism was enhanced by the support of many among Poland's and Transylvania's numerous Anabaptists.

Socinus first went to Transylvania (in 1578) and reached Poland in 1579. He was able to win a considerable following even among the extremists in both countries and succeeded in establishing at least the semblance of an ecclesiastic organization, sometimes referred to as the Socinians and sometimes as the Minor Church. Its precepts were laid down after his death in the so-called Racovian Catechism of 1605, drawn up at the communal settlement which the Anti-Trinitarians had created at Racow. Despite a distinct element of mysticism, the Socinian creed stood out for its rationalism. Although the Socinians considered Scripture, especially the New Testament, the authoritative record of divine revelation, they held that the truth of Scripture could be rightly understood only by the application of reason. While they thought God to be omnipotent and the embodiment of the supreme free will, they believed that man, too, possessed a free will, and they accepted neither original sin nor predestination. They held that religion could dispense with both rigid doctrine and sacraments, sharing the Anabapist view that baptism was simply a rite marking initiation into the Christian community. Possibly Anabaptist influences played a part in the Socinians' appeal for a revival of primitive Christianity and in some of their social tenets; they denounced war and considered it wrongful for a Christian to hold office in a secular government.

Anti-Trinitarianism was especially vigorous in Transylvania, where the Calvinistic bishop Francis David of Transylvania preached the extremist doctrine that conceded neither divinity nor adoration to Jesus. He had made the capital, Kolozvár (Klausenburg, Cluj), the seat of a numerous Anti-Trinitarian sect. Although David, denounced by Biandrata, ended his days in prison (1579), his followers struggled on and even grew in numbers. The name 'Unitarian', apparently first applied to them in debate, came to be used officially and eventually proved acceptable to them.

In Poland and Transylvania the strength and conviction of the Protestant minority, the apprehension of Catholic nobles over the Catholic clergy's power, the weakness of the kings, the tolerant humanist proclivities and the diversity of religions among the nobility, and the need for a united front against the Turks led the diets at first to concede freedom of conscience to Catholics, Lutherans, Calvinists, Hussites, and Socinians alike. In 1572–73 Poland found itself in the midst of an interregnum, and a repetition of the recent French Massacre of St Bartholomew (see below) was to be feared because of the persistent intensity of religious rivalries and the momentary lack of royal authority. Despite some opposition, the nobility drew up a

Confederation of Warsaw (1573) confirming the spirit of religious freedom, and for a long time the succeeding kings upheld it. And so until 1658 the Polish Socinian centres remained, so to speak, the capitals of Europe's Anti-Trinitarians.[38]

Then a series of domestic crises and foreign wars wrought a change in the Polish atmosphere. Perhaps the most critical of these untoward events was the uprising of the Cossacks under their hetman Bogdan Chmielnicki (d. 1657). With the Tatars as allies they fought the Poles in a war (1648–54) that began as a struggle for an independent Orthodox Ukrainia. But soon Tsar Alexis of Russia stepped in as protector of the Orthodox faith, and then King Charles X of Sweden as claimant of Poland's coastal regions. The result was a ruinous Thirteen Years' War (1654–67), which ended with a set of treaties that foreshadowed the eventual partition of Poland among its neighbours.

During this war Orthodox Cossacks massacred Jews, Catholics, and others fairly indiscriminately, and the religious policy of Poland's government changed from toleration to persecution of those who differed from it in creed. Along with other Protestant refugees, the Polish Unitarians fled. They went to western Europe, especially Holland and England, where local Unitarian movements were already under way, and Unitarianism practically vanished from Poland. It persisted, however, though not without difficulty, in Transylvania as one of the four officially tolerated creeds, and today's Unitarians of Rumania are its offspring. An offshoot of the Unitarians known as the Sabbatarians because they celebrated Saturday as the Sabbath and borrowed or were accused of borrowing other Jewish tenets were not formally tolerated at any time, but they managed to survive until the middle of the nineteenth century.

PROTESTANT EXPANSION AND CATHOLIC RESISTANCE 1521–98

The Holy Roman Empire provided an outstanding example of a state where particularism impeded the achievement of national unity and hence of a national church, and the religious reform movement in the Empire was from the beginning partly dependent upon this particularist attitude. The Protestant cause as a whole was able to hold and gain ground mainly because several important cities and powerful princes, especially in northern Germany, were won over. Under the influence of Melanchthon, Philip of Hesse was converted to Lutheranism in 1524, and other Lutheran preachers brought over Margrave Casimir of Brandenburg and Duke Ernest of Lüneburg. The exiled Duke Ulrich of Württemberg, who had much to gain from any embarrassment of the imperial authority, likewise declared his allegiance to the new faith. The spread of Protestantism was, in fact, limited to those territories where powerful converts could resist papal and imperial pressures. In southern Germany and the Rhineland, principal seat of the ecclesiastical electors, the spread of Protestantism met the determined opposition of

Catholic princes. The ardent Catholicism of Charles V, and the equally ardent, although more politic, Catholicism of his brother, Archduke Ferdinand, succeeded in keeping Lutheran ideas from conquering the Habsburg possessions, and persecutions of Lutherans began there early. *Cuius regio eius religio*, the compromise eventually adopted to halt religious strife in the Empire, was applied in practice long before it became an official formula.

The Protestant footing in Germany was further consolidated by a circumstance already mentioned: in the very year of Luther's condemnation at the Diet of Worms (1521) Charles V engaged in his first war (1521–26) with Francis I of France. The Reichsregiment was reconstituted in the hope of carrying on the affairs of Germany efficiently during the emperor's absence, but this effort to bring national unity to the Empire was hampered by the princes' determination to preserve their traditional privileges. Thus two divergent factors, the national consciousness fanned by Luther's appeals and the self-interest of the German princes, joined to build resistance to papal as well as imperial demands for enforcement of the Edict of Worms. Nearly unanimously the German estates demanded reform of the church, though not necessarily Luther's Reformation. At the Diet of Nuremberg in 1522, enforcement of the Edict of Worms was delayed. In fact, a resolution was adopted—and in the emperor's absence issued as an imperial edict—demanding convocation of a council to meet on German soil.

Earnestly concerned about some of the shortcomings of the church, Pope Adrian VI preferred to seek the support of the Catholic princes of the Empire. Some of the most important among them were persuaded to meet at Ratisbon in 1524. There they considered plans for resisting Lutheranism, discussed serious measures of reform, and concluded the first anti-Protestant alliance. Led by Archduke Ferdinand and the Duke of Bavaria, it was supported by a number of south German bishops. The alliance was instrumental in suppressing the Peasant Revolt, which broke out mostly in Catholic principalities, although the Lutherans were blamed for it. During the violent reprisals that followed, known or suspected Protestants frequently were punished along with rebellious peasants. Nevertheless, by 1525 Protestantism commanded a minority strong enough to prevent drastic legislative action by its enemies in the imperial Diet.[39]

The coalition formed at Ratisbon was counterbalanced by one formed at Torgau in 1524 among the principal Protestant princes. As we have seen, at the Diet of Spires the Protestant coalition won the Recess of 1526, but at the Second Diet of Spires in 1529, when Charles felt strong enough not to compromise with the Lutheran faction, the Catholic majority voted to rescind the Recess of 1526 and required strict enforcement of the Edict of Worms. Eight years had elapsed, however, since the Edict first was issued, and Lutheranism had meanwhile grown strong. When the reformers issued the joint protest that gave them the name of 'Protestants', the emperor simply could not disregard it. Much though his power and prestige had increased with his victory over the alliance of his French and Italian enemies in the League of Cognac, he had to move cautiously. He had no assurance of the continued submissiveness of either the pope or the French king, and the threat of the Turks was ever present. A Turkish siege of Vienna in 1529 was broken only by the concerted effort of all German estates, Lutheran as well as Catholic. Charles could ill afford the antagonize to German estates, and Archduke Ferdinand, heavily engaged in his struggle for Hungary, felt constrained to a conciliatory course.

In 1530 the emperor was able to be present at a diet for the first time since 1521. It met, with unparalleled pomp, at Augsburg. The Catholic party, emboldened by the presence of the victorious emperor and a papal legate, at first seemed ready to consider the use of armed force in suppressing the Lutheran heresy. Despite the failure of the Marburg Colloquy in 1529 to achieve the unity of Lutheranism and Zwinglianism, Protestant resistance was also determined. A formal defence of the Lutheran position was introduced at the Diet—the so-called 'Augsburg Confession', which has since become the norm of Lutheran doctrine. It was based upon seventeen points—the so-called Schwabach Articles—which, after Marburg, Luther had drawn up, firmly distinguishing the more radical Zwinglianism from his own creed. Under Melanchthon's influence, the Augsburg Confession became an effort to draw close to Catholicism, thus completely isolating Zwinglianism in the struggle between Catholicism and Lutheranism. The Lutherans at the same time declared their determination to abide by the Recess of 1526 until the religious controversy should be resolved by a general council.[40]

Despite Charles's hardly veiled intention to resort to arms in order to enforce obedience, he was not yet in a position to jeopardize the internal peace of the Empire. He could not feel sure of the support of all the Catholic princes, some of whom indeed supported the Recess of 1526. Moreover, he was concerned with securing support for the election of his brother Ferdinand as king of the Romans and thus successor to the imperial crown. He therefore had to compromise and so issued the Recess of Augsburg, which betrayed his dilemma. Under threat of severe penalties it demanded immediate enforcement of the Edict of Worms but at the same time moved from the use of force in the direction of judicial action. The highest tribunal of the Empire, the Reichskammergericht, was reconstituted and empowered to hear suits for the recovery of church property secularized in the Protestant principalities. Simultaneously Charles pressed Pope Clement VII for convocation of a general council. So strong had the emperor's ascendancy become that Clement, though reluctant, agreed, and Charles promised a council within a year.[41]

In December 1530, the Protestant princes and cities met at Schmalkalden to discuss measures of joint defence on the principle that legal action against one of them in the Reichskammergericht should be considered action against all. The more aggressive Protestant princes at Schmalkalden proposed an armed defensive league and, early in 1531, under the leadership of Philip of Hesse formed the Schmalkaldic League. Meanwhile the threat of court condemnations had led Bucer to promote a rapprochement between Zwinglians and Lutherans, which met with sympathy even from Luther. A number of Zwinglian communities in southern Germany were ready to join the proposed league, but the Swiss cities now refused to make common cause with the Lutherans. Zwingli's death in the second Battle of Kappel (1531) halted the advance of Zwinglianism in Switzerland and gave to the Lutheran forces undisputed leadership of the Reformation in Germany.

Just as the time began to seem favourable for a full settlement in Germany, Clement VII's fear of a general council and the emperor's preparations for another Turkish threat once more brought delay. At Nuremberg in 1532 a religious peace was concluded suppressing all suits against the Protestants before the Reichskammergericht and guaranteeing a truce until a new diet or a church council might make other arrangement. In 1534 came the first armed effort of the Protestant princes, and it was victorious; led by Philip of Hesse, they forcefully restored Duke Ulrich of Württemberg to his ancestral throne. At almost the same time the Lutherans ceased temporarily to be the major threat to the Empire with the outbreaks of Anabaptists revolts in Münster and other German cities, in the suppression of which Protestant and Catholics joined forces. For the next twelve years, the military and political involvements of the emperor vouchsafed a religious truce throughout the Empire.[42]

Meanwhile the Protestant cause in Germany steadily grew stronger. In 1539, Joachim II, elector of Brandenburg, openly adopted Lutheranism. Albertine Saxony likewise was converted under Duke Henry in 1540. In 1542, the reckless Duke Henry of Brunswick lost his territories, the last stronghold of Catholicism in northern Germany, by provoking a war with the Schmalkaldic League. A number of cities and minor princes, encouraged by the early successes of the league, also espoused the Protestant cause. Thus practically all of northern Germany formed a Lutheran bloc, backed by the growing strength of the solidly Lutheran Scandinavian countries (see below). Finally, twenty-six years after the Edict of Worms had called for the repression of Luther and Lutheranism, the religious controversy erupted into open war. The Schmalkaldic War of 1546–47 ended in an easy victory for the emperor, but it was now too late to root out the heresy. In parts of Germany a whole generation had grown up that knew only Lutheranism.

*　　*　　*

The Spread of Lutheranism to Scandinavia

In Scandinavian Europe, as in England, the Reformation was achieved by the political action of the ambitious monarchs. Ever since the Union of Kalmar (1397) the Scandinavian countries had been ruled in personal union by the Danish kings, who also ruled Schleswig and Holstein as principalities in the Holy Roman Empire. This union had always been disturbed by sporadic unrest in Schleswig-Holstein (united in 1386) and Sweden, and unrest grew upon the accession (1513) of Christian II, who tried to make himself an absolute ruler.

Christian's policy required that he break the power of the nobles, allying himself with the merchant class and peasants. An important step in that direction was the *Landelove*, the Danish code of 1521. Among other things the code laid the framework of a national church independent of Rome, and since clerical abuses were all too rife, this objective received popular support. The code placed ecclesiastical affairs under the jurisdiction of secular judges, prohibited the clergy from owning property, required residence of priests in their parishes, and established certain criteria for their education. It also curtailed the prerogatives of the nobility and limited serfdom. Furthermore, Christian regulated trade in such a manner as to favour domestic merchants over both domestic landlords and the Hanseatic League, which hitherto had held a near monopoly of trade in the Baltic regions.

Since he was careful to avoid antagonizing his brother-in-law Emperor Charles V, Christian kept his clerical reform within the framework of correct Catholic doctrine. Nevertheless, his ruthlessness antagonized the Catholic clergy no less than others. In Sweden he encountered open hostility, which he squelched by force in 1520, and after being crowned king of Sweden, he had the most important secular and ecclesiastic princes executed in flagrant violation of an amnesty he had granted. This 'Stockholm Blood Bath' provoked new unrest in Sweden at the very time that the king's reform measures were increasing upper-class antagonism against him in his native Denmark. In 1523, he was deposed by the rebellious clergy and nobility of his entire realm, and his uncle, Frederick of Schleswig-Holstein, was proclaimed in his place. Rapidly spreading revolt and a war with Lübeck, retaliating as leader of the Hanseatic League for his discriminatory trade regulations, forced Christian and his family to flee.

Although the new king of Denmark, Frederick I, had promised loyalty to the traditional church, he was personally inclined toward Lutheranism. Some of the Danish nobility, because they either shared his principles or coveted ecclesiastic properties, also favoured religious reform. Pope Leo X played into their hands by proposing to appoint an Italian to the important archbishropic of Lund. The general outcry against this foreign interference enabled Frederick to proceed with reform. Supported by the nobility at the Diet of Odense (1527), he forced the clergy to accept an ordinance that brought the Danish church completely under the authority of the crown. The ordinance contained a provision unusual for that age: Lutherans as well as Catholics were granted freedom of conscience, and the king was proclaimed protector of both denominations. Toward the end of his reign Frederick was able to restore peace to his uneasy realm.

Civil war broke out again upon Frederick's death (1533). The Danish

Catholic peasants and towns, supported by Lübeck, which was trying to establish a union of Baltic cities, united in an effort to restore the refugee Christian II. The nobility and the Lutherans, in alliance with the now independent king of Sweden (see below), supported Frederick's son, also named Christian. The victory of the Lutheran nobles in this so-called 'Counts' Feud' doomed Catholicism in Denmark. Frederick's son ascended the throne as Christian III (1534–58), a Danish national church was established, and shortly thereafter the Augsburg Confession was adopted as the official creed of the Danish kingdom.

In Norway and Iceland, popular sentiment was distinctly on the side of the Catholic Church, and the crown found significant support only in the towns, where Lutheranism had been introduced through foreign, mostly Hanseatic, traders. During the Counts' Feud Norway, led by Archbishop Olaf Engelbrektssön, rose in revolt against Denmark, recognizing a German Catholic claimant as the legitimate heir to the Norwegian throne. Christian III thereupon issued a proclamation (1536) depriving bishops of their power in the government and forfeiting their possessions. When no help came from Germany, the archbishop fled, and the remaining Norwegian bishops were unable effectively to resist the victorious Danish monarch with his Lutheran Church. Yet remnants of the old faith long persisted in Norway, since the scarcity of Lutheran pastors greatly delayed the spread of the new faith among the common people. In Iceland, too, years of revolt, led by the bishops of the island, followed upon the effort to establish the Reformation by royal decree. Only in 1554 did revolt end and the royal will prevail.[43]

Meanwhile, the turmoil had enabled Sweden to break completely away from the Union of Kalmar. Indignation over the 'Stockholm Blood Bath' brought on an uprising which soon turned into a war for national independence. It was led by Gustavus Vasa, a young nobleman who himself had spent some time in prison as a victim of Christian II's perfidy. Supported by Swedish peasants and Lübeck's naval forces, Gustavus emerged victorious and upon the deposition of Christian II in 1523 was crowned king of Sweden. The advent of the Reformation was closely linked to these political developments. Gustavus Trolle, archbishop of Uppsala, was widely discredited as the instigator of the Stockholm massacre. When he and the other Scandinavian Catholics abetted Christian II's attempt to regain the triple crown, the cathedral chapters voted Trolle's removal from office. Pope Clement VII not only refused to sanction this removal but, repeating Leo X's blunder in Denmark, also attempted to appoint an Italian to the see of Skara.

The consequent resentment gave Gustavus the opportunity to introduce reform in the guise of national resistance to the pressure from Rome. Secretly an adherent of Lutheranism, Gustavus took into his service Olaus Petri, a minister who had studied at Wittenberg, and Lars Andersson (Laurentius Andreas), archdeacon of Uppsala Cathedral and an ardent reformer, who became the royal secretary. Through Petri's translation of the New Testament and other theological writings, Lutheranism began to spread among the Swedish people.

Matters came to a head when it became clear that the king's financial needs could well be met by the confiscation of church properties. In the struggle for independence, most of the old nobility had perished, and the free peasantry stubbornly refused to pay the taxes needed to bring order to the exchequer. At the Diet of Västerås in 1527, by a threat to abdicate Gustavus was able to push through his demand for sequestration of church property. The resulting Recess of Vasterås gave to the crown all ecclesiastical property that in the king's judgment the church did not need, and restored to their original owners all taxable and some tax-exempt properties previously granted to the church. Subsequently the Västerås Ordinances completed the subordination of the clergy to the king by giving him, among other controls, the power to appoint and dismiss bishops. Gustavus made no attempt to decide matters of dogma by official action, but under the influence of the king and devoted preachers Lutheranism spread throughout the land. The Augsburg Confession, however, was accepted as the official creed of the Swedish Church only in 1593. Finland, as a possession of the Swedish crown, was also subject to the royal religious policies.

*   *   *

From the Augsburg Confession to the Heidelberg Catechism

The spread of Lutheranism in northern Europe was not matched by a similar expansion of the Reformed Church in the south. After Melanchthon in the Augsburg Confession had emphasized the differences between the Lutheran and Zwinglian creeds, Zwingli addressed to the emperor (July 1530) a personal profession of faith in which he, too, sharply drew the line between them. Thereupon, four German cities, Strasbourg, Constance, Memmingen, and Lindau, also dissociated themselves from the Augsburg Confession by presenting to the emperor their own joint confession, the so-called *Confessio Tetrapolitana*. Though essentially Zwinglian in character, its wording betrayed the hope of its chief author, Bucer, to bring about some measure of agreement between the two leading reform parties. Political exigencies made such a rapprochement seem desirable, and for a while it looked feasible. Luther agreed to receive Bucer at Coburg in September 1530, and Bucer's Strasbourg joined the Schmalkaldic League in December. But the Zwinglian position stiffened even as the Lutherans became less adamant. In the end the Swiss cities refused to join the Schmalkaldic League, and Berne rejected the Tetrapolitana. Reconciliation of Lutherans and Zwinglians thereafter became still more difficult.

About the same time the victory of the Forest Cantons in the Battle of Kappel brought about a considerable degree of religious tolerance in Switzerland. Despite his goal of a democratic reformed commonwealth, Zwingli had been willing to use force to secure the victory of the Reformation throughout

Switzerland. In Zürich and other Reformed cantons Catholicism was suppressed and Catholic dissenters were persecuted. Zwingli had provoked the second war with the Forest Cantons largely by his attempt to force them into submission by an economic blockade. His defeat and death marked the end of such forcible methods, and the Second Peace of Kappel secured freedom of worship for Catholics in the Reformed cantons. Eventually Catholicism was restored in the canton of Glarus, and through the efforts of Cardinal Carlo Borromeo (1538–84), who founded a Swiss College at Milan, Jesuits and (later) Capuchins gained influence in Catholic Switzerland, especially Lucerne. In 1586, Lucerne joined the six other Catholic cantons in a defensive alliance, the so-called Borromean (or Golden) League. The check of militant Protestantism was thus assured in Switzerland, but without destroying the traditional freedom of the Swiss cantons. Decisions concerning religious as well as political affairs remained subject to a majority in each canton, making Switzerland one of the first countries where a degree of religious diversity was sanctioned. The practice became the law of the land as the result of a series of *Landfrieden* (national peace treaties) from 1529 to 1712.

Under the leadership of Zwingli's successor, Heinrich Bullinger (1504–75), the Reformed Church, though not permitted to expand, was able at least to consolidate its position. Steps to mediate the difference between Zwinglianism and Lutheranism meanwhile continued. Bucer, generally recognized as a mediator, took an active part in these efforts. In 1536 some Swiss theologians formulated at Basel the First Helvetic Confession, which attempted to bridge the gulf between the two creeds. Later that year in the Wittenberg Concord a gathering of evangelical divines made an attempt to compromise on the doctrine of the Eucharist. Although the German cities of Strasbourg, Ulm, Constance, and Augsburg were ready to accept the compromise, Luther still hesitated. A second conference at Basel rejected the Wittenberg Concord, and Zürich took a similar step in 1538.

In an effort to strengthen Swiss Protestantism, Bullinger now turned to Calvinist Geneva. The Zwinglian view of the Eucharist, which saw in the sacrament merely a symbolic act, was abandoned in favour of the Calvinist doctrine, which held to the spiritual presence of Christ. In 1549, Bullinger and Calvin concluded an agreement at Zürich, the so-called *Consensus Tigurinus*, in which the Calvinist view was formally adopted. It became the basis of the Second Helvetic Confession (1566). The unity of Swiss Protestantism became complete eighty years later, when Basel finally adhered to it. The boundary between the Lutheran and the Reformed Church in the Alps region thus came to coincide with the political boundary between the Empire and the Swiss Confederation, while at the same time Protestantism and Catholicism within Switzerland were stabilized between urban and rural sections respectively.

The void left among the Protestant masses by Luther's alliance with the ruling powers was generally filled by the more democratic Calvin, who became the outstanding theologian of European Protestantism and gave to the Reformation its world-wide significance. After Luther's death, Calvin's Geneva became the undisputed centre of the Reformation to a degree never true of Luther's Wittenberg. The academy Calvin founded became the centre of Reformed learning, a magnet drawing from all over Europe reformers who desired to study with Calvin or its other famed teachers. Geneva became also the base of Protestant missionary activities, which, directed by Calvin, spread throughout Europe and beyond.

Even during Luther's lifetime a personal friendship had developed between Melanchthon and the Geneva reformer, confirming the Wittenberg humanist in his growing sympathy with Calvinist views. After Luther's death Melanchthon permitted his followers for a time to become 'adiaphorists'—i.e. uncommitted on those things which, though condemned by Luther, the Bible seemed neither to condemn nor to approve. One of Melanchthon's disciples, Zacharias Ursinus, was instrumental in making a most significant concession to Calvinist influence. Under the auspices of Frederick III, Calvinist elector of the Palatinate, he participated, after Melanchthon's death, in the formulation of the so-called 'Heidelberg Catechism' (1563). This catechism found wide acceptance as the definitive statement of the reformed creed. Though opposed by dyed-in-the-wool Lutherans, it was adopted by either the governments or a fair share of the population (or both) not only in other parts of Protestant Germany (Hesse, Anhalt, Nassau, Bremen, Brandenburg, and elsewhere) but also in the Netherlands, Poland, Hungary, and Transylvania.

*   *   *

The French Wars of Religion

In France the first phase of the reform movement was represented chiefly by a group of humanist reformers that gathered around the learned bishop of Meaux, Guillaume Briçonnet. Their intellectual leader was a famed humanist and translator of the New Testament, Lefèvre d'Étaples. For a while this group enjoyed protection in high quarters—the king's sister, the future Marguerite of Navarre, and even Francis I himself. But Francis, though a humanist, was not a reformer. The Concordat of Bologna in 1516 had more or less satisfactorily resolved the ancient dispute between kings and popes regarding the primacy of authority over the French church, giving the French kings significant control over episcopal appointments. The king, therefore, not only had no fundamental conflict with the established church but had, in fact, a vested interest in its preservation, while the upper clergy, dependent upon the crown for appointment and benefices, was a staunch ally of the monarchy. The established order was at first supported also by the nobility and the wealthy bourgeoisie. The Meaux group was forced to disperse in 1525.

Francis I's policy toward the reformers vacillated between suppression and leniency, according to the exigencies of his conflict with Charles V. Neither by conviction nor by policy was he ever interested in reform beyond the correction of certain clerical abuses. In his later years, in fact, he took increasingly violent measures against religious dissenters in reprisal for sporadic outbursts of Reformed fanaticism in Paris and other French towns. Under his son, Henry II (1547–59), persecution increased in violence, and *chambres ardentes* awaited the avowed heretic with the death penalty.

Reform persisted, however, among the small artisans and merchants in the towns and among the lower clergy, who, mostly of poor origin themselves, were familiar with the physical and religious needs of their flock. For them the French translation (1541) of Calvin's *Institutio* was a milestone. Calvin had never abandoned his attempts to carry the Reformation into his native country. His *Institutio* had been dedicated to Francis I; in subsequent pamphlets and letters he tried to guide the course of French reform. Geneva received money from France to finance Protestant missions, and several French preachers returned from Geneva devoted apostles of Calvinism, ready to accept martyrdom. The first Reformed church in Paris was founded in 1556, and in 1559 the first national synod was organized and drew up a strictly Calvinist confession of faith. Despite persecution, censorship, and book burnings, Protestant churches multiplied.

The movement remained essentially middle-class and became increasingly urban. Its strongholds were in the coastal towns of Normandy, which were in constant contact with England, in the region along the Loire River, in southwestern France, and along the Mediterranean coast, but the eastern regions, despite their closeness to Germany, proved relatively immune. Rouen, Dieppe, La Rochelle, Tours, Lyons, Montauban, and Nîmes were among the most important Calvinist centres. A significant segment of the wealthy bourgeoisie joined the smaller merchants and tradesmen, and so did a few among the military and administrative officers of the kingdom. This link with the grand nobility gave to the Huguenots (as the French Protestants came to be called) a strategic position out of all proportion to their numbers. It transformed a minority middle-class movement for religious reform into a powerful party, whose religious and political aspirations became inextricably interwoven. Bourgeois, fighting against the royal bureaucracy for administrative and economic reforms, and noblemen, fighting against royal encroachments upon their feudal privileges, united under the banner of religious reform in common enmity to the devoutly Catholic Guise family, which used its mounting power behind the ever weakening Valois throne to further its own dynastic ambitions.

On a provincial scale at first, then on a national scale, and eventually on an international scale, the Huguenots met armed resistance. A Catholic League was organized inside France, sanctioned by the pope and assisted by the king of Spain but dominated by the Guises. The League's power soon overshadowed that of the French king. The short-lived reigns of Henry II's three young and weak sons made the French throne the object of an intense struggle for mastery between France's two most powerful noble families— the Guises, who dreamed of restoring Catholicism to undisputed power in the kingdom, and the Bourbons, who had assumed leadership of the Protestant party. Since the Bourbons, as 'princes of the blood', might become the legitimate heirs to the throne if the Valois line were to die out, rivalry for succession became a salient motive in this religio-political duel. Eight religious wars, in reality forming one long and violent civil war interrupted by a series of armistices, ravaged France between 1562 and 1589.

Hoping to prevent the religious struggle from destroying France, the moderates formed a party known as the *Politiques*. Loyal Catholics, the *Politiques* yet preferred non-conformity in religion to civil anarchy. They therefore advocated religious toleration as a means of safeguarding the continued existence of the state. Their tolerant attitude was frustrated by the plotting of Catherine de Médicis, queen-mother and regent, and the Guises. Perhaps out of fear, perhaps out of cool calculation, they gave the signal for, may even have prepared, the Massacre of St Bartholomew's Day (1572), in which many Protestant leaders and thousands, by some estimates tens of thousands, of lesser Protestants were slaughtered all over France. While surviving Protestant leaders fled abroad, some Catholic rulers ordered *Te Deums*, and the pope had a medal struck to commemorate the destruction of the heretics.[44]

In the end, massacre only intensified fanaticism and increased the violence of the civil war. In its final phase, it became an open war of succession—'the War of the Three Henrys' (the Valois king, Henry III; the Catholic pretender, Henry of Guise; and the Bourbon heir-presumptive, Henry of Navarre). The Huguenots owed their military and political strength to effective organization. They formed a confederation held together by a written instrument of government that provided for the orderly and efficient conduct of governmental functions and for unity in the conduct of the war. Even before their ultimate victory, their organized power won them important religious and political concessions.

Upon the assassination of the other two Henrys, Henry of Navarre, having consented to become a Catholic, was crowned King Henry IV of France. He then made a daring bid for religious peace. His Edict of Nantes (1598) placed France among the first countries (along with Poland, Transylvania, and Switzerland) to establish some sort of religious toleration by law. It confirmed all the privileges previously granted Protestants, conferred upon them complete freedom of conscience and of private (though not public) worship, and accorded them full civil rights. The king provided money for Protestant schools and colleges, and, of gravest import for the future, the Huguenots were ceded control over numerous towns and castles, which they were permitted to fortify and garrison at royal expense. The most important among the fortified towns were Montauban and La Rochelle. The Huguenots thus became a quasi-independent power, a political and military stumbling-block on the calculated road to royal centralization.[45]

*   *   *

Calvinism in Scotland and England

In Scotland in the sixteenth century a unique combination of social, political, and religious factors led to one of the most significant triumphs that Calvinism achieved outside Geneva. Barely emerging from its clan society and still dominated by a feudal nobility, Scotland was torn by internal feuds and ravaged by repeated wars with England, whose kings coveted the Scottish crown. Fear of English aggression threw Scotland into alliance with France, involving the Scots in the intermittent duel between the French and the English rulers and making resistance to English purposes a main tenet of Scottish patriots. At the beginning of the Reformation, the Franco-Scot alliance was a leading factor in preserving Catholicism, despite some Protestant sentiment, as the essentially undisputed faith of the Scots. Still, the Scottish clergy, largely recruited from the powerful noble families, had become notoriously lax in behaviour and uneducated to the point of illiteracy. Desire for reform—at least within the Catholic Church—spread, especially among the common people and the slowly emerging merchant class.

Scotland became more closely tied to France (and therefore to the Catholic cause) when in 1538 its King James V married Mary of Guise, whose family was rapidly assuming leadership of political Catholicism in France. Upon the king's death, Mary, surrounded by French advisers, whose patronizing demeanour in Scotland was widely resented, became one of the regents for her six-day old daughter, Mary Stewart. The queen-regent's government, refusing her daughter's hand to the future King Edward VI of England, arranged instead a prospective marriage to the French dauphin. Before she was six Mary, queen of Scots, went to France (1548). She was to marry the dauphin ten years later, and in 1559, when he became King Francis II, the queen of Scotland was to become the queen of France as well but to remain such only a little over a year, for her husband died in 1560.

Meanwhile in many Scottish patriots' minds France had begun to supplant England as the major threat to Scottish independence. The queen-dowager, they thought, ruled the country, protected by unpopular French soldiers, as if it were a province of France at war with England. The Protestants grew in number, and in 1557 the Protestant nobles formed the self-styled 'Lords of the Congregation', a 'covenant' for mutual protection and advantage. In their minds Catholicism rather than Anglicanism became identified with the national enemy.

The leader of the Protestants in Scotland was John Knox (1505 ?–72). A Scottish Catholic cleric in his youth, he had become a Protestant and had been a chaplain at the court of Edward VI of England. When a Catholic reaction (1553–58) took place in England under Queen Mary Tudor ('Bloody Mary'), daughter of Henry VIII and his divorced wife, Catherine of Aragon, Knox went into exile. Eventually he reached Geneva, and there he developed into a zealous and fearless apostle of Calvinism. He became the chief adviser of the Lords of the Congregation both from exile and during a brief sojourn at home. Upon the accession (1558) of Elizabeth I, daughter of Henry VIII and Anne Boleyn, to the English throne, the Catholic reaction ceased in England, but some Catholics there and elsewhere, insisting that Elizabeth was illegitimate, recognized Henry VIII's grand-niece, Mary, queen of Scots and bride of the dauphin of France, as the true ruler of England.

Knox returned to Scotland in 1559. That year the Lords of the Congregation declared Mary of Guise deposed as queen-regent and asked Elizabeth to act as protector of their country against France. A year later, a series of laws established the Reformed Church in Scotland. The Scottish Parliament decreed that papal authority in Scotland had come to an end, that the statutes against heretics were illegal, and that celebration of the mass was punishable by death. A confession of faith drawn up by Knox was adopted as the law of the land. In 1561, the *First Book of Discipline*, prepared mostly by Knox and based upon Calvin's *Ordonnances*, prescribed the organization of the Scottish Church. Local churches—or kirks—were to be governed by presbyteries (or councils of ministers and elders), which were vested with the right to arbitrate matters of doctrine, to control education, and to ordain and induct ministers; final authority rested with the General Assembly of the Universal Kirk, in which all local presbyteries were represented. When first her mother and then her husband died (1560), Mary, still in her teens, returned to Scotland (1561). A widowed queen of France, a cultured French-woman of Catholic faith, a rallying symbol of the Catholic cause in England, she found herself the reigning monarch of a predominantly Protestant country.

Although Elizabeth greatly disliked Knox because of his *Against the Monstrous Regiment [i.e. rule] of Women*, she had little choice but to help the Scottish Protestants. Mary was widely suspected of aiming to restore Catholicism in Scotland and, eventually, in England, and though she was not herself actively engaged in such a purpose, she was supported by Catholic nobles at home and in England who were. The French, preoccupied with their own religious wars, failed to give Mary effective aid. Kidnappings, marriages, divorces, and murders now further poisoned the Scottish political atmosphere, with Mary as victim rather than perpetrator of most of the intrigues. A general uprising in 1567 forced her to abdicate and eventually to seek a forlorn refuge with her rival and cousin, Elizabeth. Twenty years more of plots and counterplots and finally Mary, accused of complicity in a plan to murder Elizabeth, was executed. With her died the hope of Catholic restoration in Scotland and England.

Calvinism also gained an important foothold in England. Calvin himself attempted to influence the English reform movement by correspondence with influential men. Upon her accession, to be sure, Elizabeth, largely for political reasons, confirmedre the Anglican compromise through the Act of Uniformity (1559). Nevertheless, many of the English reformers who returned from exile after her accession were active Calvinists, seeking a more radical break with Roman dogma and ritual, and Calvinism acquired a certain vogue. Agitation for a more thorough 'purification' of the Anglican Church gave rise to even more audacious 'Puritan' movements such as the Separatists and the Presbyterians (see below). Elizabeth decided, however, that political exigencies demanded caution in religious matters, and the Thirty-Nine Articles, adopted in 1563, confirmed the reestablishment of the Anglican compromise.

★　　★　　★

The Dutch War of Independence

In the Low Countries, the eventual triumph of Calvinism was linked with the drive of the Dutch Netherlands toward freedom from Spanish domination. Here the reform sentiment had beginnings independent of Lutheranism and Zwinglianism. Inspired by the humanist demand for a more spiritual religion, the doctrine of sacramentarianism, anticipating the Zwinglian interpretation of the Eucharist as entirely symbolic, spread among the Dutch, especially the wealthy bourgeoisie in the flourishing trade centres. For a time Anabaptism, too, gained a considerable following among the lower bourgeoisie and peasantry. The two trends reinforced the resistance to Lutheranism with its doctrines of the real presence in the Eucharist and of infant baptism.

Moreover, the Lutheran subordination of religion to the princely authority held little appeal for the Low Countries, fiercely jealous of their traditional privileges. They had small use for a church organization that might counterbalance their weight in the conduct of their own affairs through their old provincial states (or legislatures) and their more recently granted States General (representative of the provincial estates). Moreover, Emperor Charles V, who had inherited the Low Countries from his paternal side, considered them an entity separate from Spain, Austria, or the Holy Roman Empire. Having been born and brought up in the Netherlands, he had encouraged their national unity. Though he attempted to suppress religious dissent in the Low Countries through the establishment of the Inquisition there in 1522 and the publication of the so-called *Placards* against heresy, he did so in a manner consistent with the provinces' traditional privileges. His effort to suppress the Netherland Anabaptists was violent but did not provoke unrest on a large scale, since, as elsewhere, this sect was generally hated as extremist.

The relatively calm Dutch atmosphere changed after the abdication of Charles in 1555. His son, Philip II, received both the Spanish crown and the Low Countries as hereditary possessions. Philip's attempts to establish in the Low Countries the religious unity to which he was accustomed in Spain eventually alienated large sections of the Netherland nobility. His efforts to increase the number of bishropics and to turn the Inquisition into an instrument of state policy patterned after the dreaded Spanish model met with widespread opposition. The commercial classes were provoked by the new taxes and commercial restrictions imposed upon them in order to promote Spanish military and political ventures. Even among Catholics Philip's peremptory order to enforce the decrees of the Council of Trent (see below) was resented as an invasion of provincial privileges. Though Catholic, the local nobility, educated in the humanist tradition, were opposed to forcing conscience. Philip thus became identified not only with Spanish domination but also with intolerance.

Meanwhile Calvinism, introduced from England, France, Germany, and Geneva, had spread through the provinces, especially in the north. Unlike Lutheranism, Calvinism preached the absolute supremacy of 'the Word of God', even over the authority of the ruler. This doctrine appealed to the growing patriotic sentiment in the Netherlands, since it seemed to justify resistance to the ordained overlord on religious grounds. Opposition crystallized in the Compromise of Breda, concluded in 1566 and signed by over two thousand individuals, in which suspension of the Inquisition and of the *Placards* against heresy was demanded. From the epithet *Gueux* (beggars), supposedly applied to those who presented a petition to Philip's regent in the Netherlands, Margaret of Parma, the movement derived its name and emblems of solidarity (the beggar's wallet or bowl).

Among the signers of the Compromise were a number of Catholics. Violent outbursts of iconoclasm quickly alienated many of them, but the ruthless policy of repression applied by the Duke of Alba, Philip's lieutenant in the Netherlands, and the excesses of his Spanish troops rallied the Catholics once more to the support of the rebellious Protestants. In 1574, the Netherland Confession and the Heidelberg Catechism, both unmistakably Calvinist, were officially adopted in the largely urban province of Holland, though the other provinces left the religious question unsettled. Through an agreement known as the Pacification of Ghent (1576) mutual toleration, warmly advocated by William of Orange, leader of the *Gueux*, himself until recently a Catholic, was agreed upon in a common struggle against the Spanish invader. And the next year on William's instigation toleration was extended to the Dutch Anabaptists.

Toleration, however, proved hard to achieve in fact. Dissensions between the predominantly Protestant and Dutch north and the predominantly Catholic and Flemish or Walloon south were frequent and were skilfully exploited by the new regent of the Netherlands, the Duke of Parma. They led at last to the abandonment of the Pacification of Ghent. The Union of Arras, concluded in 1579, created a Catholic nucleus for the eventual reconquest of the southern Low Countries (modern Belgium) and was counterbalanced a few days later by the Union of Utrecht, creating a confederation of the seven largely Protestant provinces of the north. After a solemn abjuration of allegiance to King Philip in 1581, the Union of Utrecht became the United Provinces, whose independence, however, was formally confirmed only after decades of war by the Treaty of Westphalia in 1648 (see below). The creation of this independent, kingless confederation was a victory not only for Calvinism but also for republicanism. More prominently than in the winning of Swedish independence, the quest for religious freedom had rallied the builders of the new Dutch nation. The partial victory of Calvinism in the Dutch Republic had a special political significance besides; it prompted Johannes Althusius (1557–1638) and other Calvinists to seek to justify rebellion on more than religious grounds (see Chapter IX).

*   *   *

The Reformation in Eastern Europe

In eastern Europe, the Protestant reform movements were unable to develop the strength requisite for lasting victory. In both Poland and Hungary the ever-present tension *vis-à-vis* the Empire worked against the adoption of Lutheranism, which, suspect because of its German origin, appealed mainly to the urban population. Calvinism thus became more attractive to those who entertained a reformed opinion. In Poland, it spread among the nobility and for a while was supported in the Diets even by Catholic members of the *szlachta*, the Polish gentry, because they considered the hierarchy a threat to their political interests.

Among the important Polish reformers were the humanists Andrzej Frycz Modrzewski (see Chapter VIII) and Jan Laski. Laski during his travels in western Europe had come to know Erasmus, had embraced the ideas of Calvin, and had been a leader among the foreign refugees in England. Laski's attempts to unify Lutherans, Calvinists, and Bohemian Brethren in Poland into a national Reformed Church were frustrated by the intense rivalry among the reforming sects, especially the Anti-Trinitarians, and by the loyalty of the Polish kings and common people to the traditional faith.

In spite of occasional edicts directed against non-Catholics, Sigismund I and particularly Sigismund II generally granted them tolerance. The Catholic recovery of Poland was assured, however, when the childless Sigismund II accepted the decrees of the Council of Trent (1564) and gave up the idea of divorcing his third wife and when Cardinal Stanislaus Hosius, the leader of the Catholic reform movement, brought the first Jesuits to Poland (1565). In the brief interregnum that followed the death of Sigismund II, toleration, as narrated above, was formally guaranteed to most dissenters by the Religious Peace or Confederation of Warsaw in 1573. The Jesuits' subsequent success in restoring Poland to Catholicism was a striking example of their skill in combining political pressure with missionary zeal.

The Ruthenians (White Russians and Ukrainians) of the Polish-Lithuanian Commonwealth had been Orthodox Christians on the eve of the Reformation. But the frustrated Union of Florence (see Chapter III) was still remembered among them, and when many prominent Ruthenian families turned to Catholicism of the Latin rite or to Calvinism, the Orthodox hierarchy decided in favour of a regional reunion with Rome—one that would recognize papal primacy but would retain the Slavonic liturgy, the Eastern ritual, and the right of the clergy to marry. That union was proclaimed at the Vatican toward the end of 1595 and ratified the next year at the Synod of Brest-Litovsk by the metropolitan of Kiev and most of the Ruthenian bishops. It had the support of the Polish government but was regarded as an apostasy by Moscow and Constantinople. In Poland this 'Uniate' church was generally accepted by the formerly Orthodox at the beginning of the eighteenth century, but many peasants and a few noble families remained Orthodox, giving Russia a pretext for future intervention in Polish affairs.

After the Battle of Mohacs (1526) Hungary was divided into three parts. The Habsburgs retained a narrow strip known as Royal Hungary; the Turks took the rest, but they governed only the western part of their area directly, granting to Transylvania a large degree of autonomy. In Royal Hungary Catholicism always remained dominant, but the Reformation made speedy progress in the districts under Turkish control, for the sultans cared little what creed their Christian subjects professed. The peasants of Transylvania, being largely Rumanian, were to that extent Greek Orthodox and little affected by the schism in the Roman Church. The Turkish government and the Hungarian nobles alike, however, were opposed to the Catholic Church as the Habsburgs' ally. At the same time, the Hungarian nobles rejected Lutheranism, which vested religious supremacy in the ruling prince. Thus Lutheranism made pronounced progress only among the 'Saxon' (German) element in Hungary. The Szeklers, descendants of the ancient Magyar frontier guard in eastern Transylvania, accepted the Socinianism of the Polish reformers; and among the Magyar nobility of Transylvania, Calvinism found greatest favour, broadcast through the efforts of reformers like Peter Melius and Kasper Karolyi, translator of the Bible into Magyar. In Transylvania Calvinists at first were outlawed, but in 1546 they gained tolerance under the semi-independent prince John Sigismund. Catholics, Lutherans, Calvinists, and Socinians all gradually acquired legal status by a series of decrees of the Transylvanian diet, eventually formally included in a corpus compiled in 1669.

In the Austrian holdings of the Habsburgs, the dual problem of religious conflict and princely particularism continued to embarrass Charles V's successors. More politic than his brother Charles, Ferdinand I was a constant advocate of conciliation and compromise. Despite his own Catholic orthodoxy, he placed the unity of the Empire in the face of the Turkish aggression above religious conformity. He adopted a policy of compromise with the Protestants, and his policy at first was carried on by his son, Maximilian II. Ultimately Maximilian resumed an aggressive Catholicism in order to insure his succession to the imperial crown, and a chance of election to the throne of Poland made him still more zealous in the Catholic cause. His son and successor, Rudolf II (1576–1612), whose Spanish mother was a devout Catholic, had been reared in Spain by Jesuits. Under Rudolf Habsburg Catholicism became increasingly militant, especially in the family domain, sharpening the religious conflict.

The Jesuits had already begun their labour of education and conversion in Austria, and although Protestantism had spread widely, they were remarkably successful. In 1552 Ferdinand had summoned Father Peter Canisius from his pedagogical triumphs at the universities of Cologne and Ingolstadt, and Canisius repeated his success in Vienna. In 1556 a Jesuit college was established also in Prague. Under Rudolf II and his successors, Jesuit educational efforts were reinforced by the secular authority with a programme of persuasion, persecution, and forcible conversion of Protestants. By 1597, Catholicism was re-established in Austria and was well on the way to recovery in the other Habsburg territories.

* * *

Efforts to Restore Religious Unity by Force

The Reformation had early produced civil wars, as in Switzerland and Denmark, and foreign governments had not hesitated to intervene in them, as Lübeck intervened in Denmark. Full-scale international conflict, however, did not become a decisive factor in the course of the Reformation until Charles V undertook to suppress German Protestantism by force. He thus initiated a century of armed clashes that sooner or later involved all of western Christendom. They began with the Schmalkaldic War in 1546 and closed only with the Thirty Years' War in 1648. In these struggles political rivalries cut across religious lines and hindered concert of action by those who might have been expected to support the same religious cause. Where expediency suggested, Protestants fought on the side of Catholics against Protestants, and Catholics on the side of Protestants against Catholics, for territorial or political advantages.

The mixture of political aspirations with religious convictions was clearly apparent when (as previously noted) the Protestant duke Maurice of Saxony first allied himself with Charles V against the Schmalkaldic League and then, fearful of imperial supremacy, turned against his erstwhile ally. By the Treaty of Friedwald (1552), Maurice secured the assistance of France in the renewed struggle against the emperor, their mutual enemy. Maurice thereby established a precedent for a long series of alliances by which German princes made a willing France the guardian of their particularism against Habsburg domination. Despite the emperor's initial victory over the Schmalkaldic League, the conflict ended with a formal recognition of the compromise that had long existed *de facto* in Germany. The Religious Peace of Augsburg (1555) proclaimed liberty of conscience in the Empire for Lutheran and Catholic rulers but not for Calvinists, Anabaptists, Socinians, or others of the new creeds. Lutheran princes and free cities were granted freedom of worship and the *ius reformandi*, the right to introduce the Reformation into their territories. This legal confirmation of the principle of territorialism—*cuius regio eius religio*—was a belated recognition of a truly revolutionary break with medieval religious tradition, which had regarded the Universal Church as the supreme guardian of Christians. Luther's concept of the authority of the prince over his church thus emerged victorious in the Empire, foreshadowing the heyday of divine-right absolutism.

The effort to restore religious unity to Europe was transformed from the several domestic scenes to the international theatre by Philip II of Spain, groomed for this task by his father, Charles V. In Spain, where particularist interests and constitutional restrictions were not so strong as in the Empire, Charles had been able to impose his sovereign will, and his son inherited a centralized realm in which religious uniformity was enforced by the Inquisition. The Moriscos were to rise up ultimately against forcible Christianization (1609), but that was not to be until the reign of Philip II's successor, and then it was to result only in their expulsion.

Philip II saw in his secure national position the means of achieving an ambitious programme—Spanish predominance, his own political leadership of Catholicism, and the restoration of religious unity throughout Europe. We have already encountered some of the national antagonisms and political rivalries that frustrated him. In England his marriage (before he became the Spanish king) to Mary Tudor was highly unpopular, and his and the queen's policy of Catholic restoration was doomed to failure there. His desire to support Mary, queen of Scots, and to keep Elizabeth I from intervening effectively on the side of the rebellious Netherlands induced him openly to attack England; the ill-fated Great Armada of 1588 was the outcome. His efforts to wipe out the Protestants of the Low Countries led to rebellion and the eventual independence of the United Provinces. The fear of Protestant success in France forced him, now married to a French princess, to take an active part in the French Wars of Religion, but the inveterate competition of Spain and France for supremacy on the Continent made him reluctant to give adequate support to the Catholic side lest its clear-cut triumph make France too united and strong. Upon the victory of Henry IV in France, Philip by the Treaty of Vervins (1598) had to yield all his French conquests and more. Philip nevertheless won great prestige from the major part his navy played in temporarily checking the Turkish advance in the Mediterranean (by the victory of Lepanto in 1571), and he annexed Portugal in 1580. His policy of militant Catholicism was to be continued, but with even less success, by his son, Philip III.[46]

THE CATHOLIC REFORM MOVEMENT

Catholic humanists, clergy, popes, and princes all realized that the spread of Protestantism could not be halted by political or military measures or by persecution alone but had to be met also with a moral and spiritual regenera-tion of church and papacy. They therefore pressed for reform—as Luther himself originally had done—within the established church.[47]

The Catholic reform movement received a strong impetus from late-fifteenth-century Spain. As devout Catholics, the Spanish monarchs, Ferdi-nand and especially Isabella, had zealously supported the reform measures of Cardinal Ximenes (see above). Their Most Catholic Majesties' desire to cement the absolutism with which they ruled the national church as well as their people was an effective political spur to their interest in religious reform. Ximenes, combining religious zeal with a thorough education in the new learning, favoured church reform as much as he opposed revolt. Through his efforts, the Spanish church became perhaps the strongest and best disciplined of the national churches in the age of the Reformation. It was able to resist, spiritually as well as politically, the threat of Protestantism and to play a leading role in the Catholic reaction to it. Spanish national sentiment, which was largely identical with Spanish Catholicism, was contemporaneously intensified by the continuing struggle to eradicate the Moors and the Jews. The Spanish Inquisition (a national rather than papal institution) had been founded originally (1480) to investigate converts from Islam and Judaism, but its operation culminating (long after Ximenes' death) in the multiple executions called *autos-da-fé*, initiated in 1559, also made the dissemination of Protestant ideas exceedingly hazardous.

Nevertheless, Erasmian thought found a fairly wide acceptance among Spanish scholars and theologians. As revealed in the case of Servetus, its attacks upon the abuses of the church prepared the ground for the infiltration, even the further elaboration, of Protestant principles. Many Spanish human-ists and reformers were forced to seek refuge in neighbouring Italy or Switzerland. Most prominent among them was Juan de Valdes. Influenced by the Dutch humanist and apparently also by the German mystic Tauler, Valdes became a leader of the reform movement in Italy.

Several centres of Protestant thought prospered for a time in Italy. In Ferrara, the Duchess Renée, daughter of King Loüis XII of France, aided a group of Calvinists despite her husband's opposition. In Venice, Lutheran sympathies reached into the ranks of the clergy and the populace. In Milan, Lucca, Modena, and several other cities the number of Protestants was also significant. Often the most illustrious reformers were not heretics but were linked with heresy in official or popular thought because they favoured some of the things for which the Protestants stood. Profiting from this atmosphere of reform, Valdes gathered near Naples a group of devoted followers.

Valdes's theology is best formulated in his *Hundred and Ten Divine Considerations*. He accepted the Lutheran doctrine of justification by faith but deepened its mysticism with the precept that divine inspiration could be found through introspective contemplation. He taught a simple Christianity reflected in noble and righteous living. Some of his disciples eventually took the final step into the Reformed camp, but in general, they worked quietly and devotedly within the Catholic Church for a spiritual regeneration. They took no vows and followed no formally accepted rules but found inspiration and fulfilment as individuals in contemplation and lofty discourse. Recruited mostly from among the Italian nobility, they were held together chiefly by admiration of their mentor. After his death (1541) they dispersed throughout Italy.[48]

More formal in its organization and more direct in its approach to reform was the Oratory of Divine Love, which claimed among its members some of the most distinguished priests and laymen of Italy. It was founded in Genoa about 1500, before Lutheranism became a threat, and similar communities were shortly established in Rome (1517), Naples, and other Italian cities. Its aim was the reform of religion through both personal devotion and acts of charity. Most of the Italian leaders of church reform were in one way or another associated with the Oratory. Among its prominent members was Giovanni Pietro Caraffa (later cardinal and still later Pope Paul IV), who as bishop of Chieti had brought strict reform to his diocese even before Luther's revolt. In 1524 a new order appeared—the Order of St Cajetan. An off-shoot of the Oratory of Divine Love, it was a strict order, composed mainly of Italian nobility and devoted predominantly to the education and moral improvement of the clergy. Caraffa became its first superior, and in his honour it became known as the order of the Theatines (Thiete being the Latin name of his see, Chieti).[49]

The Theatine order scattered after the sack of Rome in 1527 but was reconstituted in Venice. Under the guidance of Senator (later Cardinal) Gasparo Contarini, Venice already contained the nucleus of a reform order. At various times the order blossomed, counting among its members such partisans of reform as the humanist Cardinal Jacopo Sadoleto, once secretary of Pope Leo X, and Cardinal Reginald Pole, who had fled England during the controversy over Henry VIII's divorce. These men, entertaining a certain respect for some Lutheran ideas, at first showed a cautious willingness to compromise, but their conciliatory attitude gradually faded. Caraffa himself became a zealous defender of papal authority, and when he became pope, was to persecute both the Oratory and the remnants of the Valdes circle. Meanwhile, however, it was largely from members of the Oratory and the Theatines that the papacy recruited the men through whom it sought to effect reconciliation with the Protestants.

The death of Leo X (1521) and the election (January 1522) of Adrian VI brought to the Holy See a pope of sincere devotion and uncompromising austerity. Born in Holland, Adrian was to be the last pope of other than Italian birth. He had been educated in the simple piety of the Brethren of the Common Life. As tutor of the future Emperor Charles V and bishop of Tortosa, he had been associated with Cardinal Ximenes, whom he succeeded in 1518 as inquisitor general of Castile and Leon. His unanimous election to the papacy seemed to augur a change in the conduct of papal and church affairs, but the reforms he attempted were resisted by papal courtiers and church officials who resented his measures of economy, his caution in bestowing gifts and offices, and his endeavour to halt the corruption that pervaded the Curia. His Dutch manners increased his unpopularity among the Romans.

Aiming to restore unity among the Christian princes, Adrian made a sincere effort to assess the clerical abuses that contributed so greatly to Luther's success. He instructed his nuncio at the Diet at Nuremberg in 1523 to accept the Curia's responsibility for ecclesiastical conditions and to announce the pope's intention to bring about reform. The need for such a step was recognized by an important segment of Catholic opinion; in 1523 Dr Eck, Luther's opponent at the Leipzig debates, paid a visit to the Vatican in order to persuade Adrian that immediate reforms alone could prevent the further spread of Lutheranism. Adrian's death later that year, however, halted the work of reform before it could get under way.

Adrian's successor, Clement VII (Giulio de' Medici), though able as an administrator and well-intentioned as a reformer, was preoccupied with preserving the temporal power of the papacy (and of his family). He therefore became heavily involved in the conflict between the Habsburg emperor Charles V and the Valois king Francis I over the control of Italy. His ill-fated alliance with the League of Cognac against Charles led to the capture and sack of Rome by imperial troops in 1527. This catastrophe shook the Renaissance papacy to its foundations and may have had some influence on Clement's refusal to grant Henry VIII's divorce. Even the most reluctant members of the Curia were now sufficiently shocked to submit to reform.

Reforms finally were initiated under Clement's successor, Paul III (Cardinal Alessandro Farnese). Although the new pope continued the sharply criticized practice of nepotism and openly strove to increase his family's power and wealth, he was genuinely concerned with reform of the Curia. He signalled his intentions by elevating to the cardinalate some of the most conspicuous advocates of mediation and reform, most of whom were or had been associated with the Oratory of Divine Love—among them Caraffa, Sadoleto, Contarini, and Pole. In 1536 a commission, composed exclusively of known reformers, was established to report on needed reforms. Again members of the Oratory were prominent.

In 1537 the commission presented a secret proposal for reforming the church (*Consilium de Emendanda Ecclesia*). The *Consilium* began with a frank admission of the ills that plagued the Curia, giving a long list of them, specifying unbridled greed and papal absolutism with consequent favouritism and nepotism as the chief causes of the corruption. The commission insisted that papal dispensations be dissociated from money payments and that the rule of law and justice be reinstated in the government of the church. Contarini minced no words in urging this unvarnished view upon Paul III:

'The law of Christ . . . is a law of freedom and forbids a servitude so abject that the Lutherans would be entirely correct to compare it with the Babylonian Captivity. . . . A pope . . . must command, forbid, or grant dispensation not according to his own pleasure but in accordance with the rule of reason, of divine commands, and of love. . . . For positive laws are not imposed by arbitrary will . . . but by bringing natural law and divine commands into harmony with existing conditions.'[50]

The *Consilium* resulted in the naming of several later commissions with the express purpose of reforming the Curia. In 1540, Paul III ordered that their proposals be initiated without delay throughout the entire church.

*　　*　　*

The Failure of Attempts at Reconciliation

While these efforts to reform the church from within were going on, liberal Catholic reformers tried to seek a reconciliation with the Protestants. The zeal of members of the Oratory for reform and their willingness to compromise on doctrine so long as the unity of the church was acknowledged made them the logical mediators between the papacy and the dissenters. In 1539, Sadoleto, at the suggestion of Pope Paul III, tried to win strife-torn Geneva back into the Catholic fold by means of a letter addressed to the city authorities and inhabitants. In a conciliatory tone, he stressed their common tradition and faith, but to no avail. His letter inspired Calvin, then in exile in Strasbourg, to answer with a cogent defence of the Reformed position.[51]

A more concerted attempt at reconciliation, on the initiative of Charles V, led finally to a colloquy at Regensburg (Ratisbon) in 1541. Preliminary conferences had induced the leaders of both parties to hope that they might find a common ground and restore unity. Political considerations also rendered a colloquy imperative. Charles V, though momentarily not engaged in open war, wanted unity within the Empire in his two-front struggle against French and Turks. The papacy, too, desired to present a united Christian front to the Turkish advance. Paul III therefore instructed his successive nuncios in Germany to take a conciliatory position and to demonstrate the new spirit of reform in the Roman Curia. Charles V likewise chose for the imperial delegation theologians known for their moderation. On the Protestant side Melanchthon and Bucer were the most active participants; Calvin attended as an observer from Strasbourg. In an early atmosphere of amity and optimism a surprising degree of agreement prevailed on four doctrinal points—the nature of man, original sin, salvation, and justification. Contarini as the papal legate made important concessions on the last point, admitting justification by faith alone, if by faith was meant a living, operative faith (which thus implied good works).[52]

In the end, however, Protestant dogma proved too widely divergent from Catholic dogma to make a reunion possible, and other than religious considerations further complicated the negotiations. The Reformation by that time had become so integral a part of the political constellation of western Christendom that, even if a theological compromise had been possible, it probably would not have resolved the controversy. For all his desire to reassert papal authority over a unified Christendom, the pope feared the power of a Germany united under Habsburg rule. A united Habsburg empire would be a grave threat also to the emperor's opponents both within Germany, such as the duke of Bavaria, and abroad, such as the king of France. Advice, protests, and warnings therefore went to Rome that could not fail to have an effect. When the discussion turned to the question of papal authority, the pope refused to consider anything but unconditional acknowledgement. Ultimately he rejected the conciliatory formulation of doctrinal points that at first had given so much hope. Nor was the Protestant camp—especially Luther—convinced of the sincerity of Catholic concessions or reform. After four months, the Regensburg Colloquy ended in failure.

*   *   *

Increased Demand for Reform within Catholicism

In Rome the failure at Regensburg brought a reaction in favour of reform in accordance with the tradition of the Catholic Church. This movement centred around heretic-hunters like Cardinal Caraffa, who now definitely opposed appeasement of those who seemed to him to be rebels. The pope repudiated Contarini's concessions and inaugurated the Roman Inquisition (1542), making it one of the most powerful weapons against Protestantism in the Italian principalities. After 1550 Protestantism survived nowhere in Italy as a serious menace.[53]

The Inquisition alone, however, did not account for that outcome. Among the other factors was the Catholic reformers' concern with revitalizing Catholic theology and its didactic method, Scholasticism, which had long been under attack by the humanists as obscuring rather than clarifying the meaning of Christianity. We shall soon encounter leading Scholasts of the sixteenth century—such as Melchior Cano and Francisco Suárez. A leading role in this revitalization was played by the Dominicans, one of whose principal domains was the teaching of theology (see Chapter XVI).

Improvement of the traditional orders and the inauguration of new ones was another part of the internal reform programme of the church, especially in Spain and Italy. The Theatines, though few in number, had already provided an imposing precedent. Gregorio Cortese reorganized the Benedictine community, and Paolo Giustiniani, a Venetian nobleman, reformed an ancient offshoot of the Benedictine order, the Camaldulians.

Matteo di Bassi, an Observant Franciscan, was not content with mere reform of an existing order. Repelled by the secularism that by the sixteenth century characterized even this stricter branch of the Franciscan friars, he led a secession from his old order. The subtleties of theological disputes were less meaningful to him than the everyday workings of the Christian spirit. If the church were to be effectively rehabilitated in the minds of the common people, he maintained, then the orders, whether old or new, must combine preaching and teaching with social service among the poor and the sick, giving a visible demonstration of the traditional concept of Christian charity. Bassi therefore aimed to restore the original Franciscan practices of poverty and austerity. Despite the opposition of his old order, he was able to win recognition of a new one, which was formally confirmed by Pope Clement VII in 1528. Members of the new order were called Capuchins because of the hood—*cappuccio*—which they wore. They not only preached to the poor but also ministered to the needy, performing especially valiant work in the trying times after the sack of Rome. Despite the withdrawal of some of their leaders to the Observant Franciscans or to Calvinism, they steadily increased in numbers and influence. Their missionary work eventually reached to Africa, Asia, and the Americas, and they played a leading role in reviving the common people's affection and respect for the Roman Catholic Church.[54]

New charitable orders followed one another in quick succession. Girolamo Miani founded the Order of the Somaschi (so-called from their centre, Somasca) to help repair the devastation wreaked by the wars of Charles V upon northern Italy; it established orphanages for the care and education of destitute children. The Barnabites (officially, the Clerics Regular of St Paul), organized (1530) in Milan by three noblemen, combined care of children with preaching and missionary work among the poor. Filippo Neri founded the Oratorians in Rome for secular priests; originally dedicated to relieving the plight of the pilgrims to that city, they sought to revive an informed piety through simple, exegetic services (they gave their name to the oratorio as a musical form), preaching, and the confessional. The Fathers of a Good Death, of Camillus de Lellis, and the Brothers of Mercy, of John of God in Spain, ministered to the sick, buried the dead, and founded hospitals, orphanages, and schools.[55]

Women, too, took an active part in these efforts at religious reform and social relief. Influential missionary and educational work was carried on by the Ursulines, founded by Angela Merici at Brescia, (1535) officially approved by Paul III (1544, and later on patronized by Cardinal Carlo Borromeo). The Ursulines were mainly devoted to the care and education of children, especially girls, as well as to the care of the sick. In Spain St Theresa was instrumental in the reform of the Carmelites, working with John of the Cross in creating an especially ascetic branch called the Discalced (barefoot) Carmelites. Notwithstanding their emphasis upon practical social work, nearly all the new orders stressed education as an important instrument of social rehabilitation and religious reform (see Chapter XVI).

A number of these Catholic reformers lived exemplary lives that were to lead eventually to sainthood—for example, Neri, John of God, Theresa, and

John of the Cross. At the Curia this saintly spirit was represented by Cardinal Borromeo (1538–84), nephew of Pius IV and archbishop of Milan. Despite the high offices he held at Rome, he scorned the opportunities for a brilliant career and, instead, devoted his life to the reform of his diocese, to the care of the sick—especially during the plague that ravaged Milan in 1576—and to the establishment of colleges and seminaries. Canonized in 1610, he belonged to a new group of saints who were sanctified by neither martyrdom nor miracles but by self-sacrificing labour among the sick and destitute and by unceasing efforts to bring to men once again the message of hope.[56]

* * *

The Organization of the Society of Jesus

Perhaps the most effective instrument in rebuilding the power of Catholicism was the order of the Jesuits, founded by Inigo Lopez de Loyola (now generally known as St Ignatius). Born in 1491 of Spanish nobility, Loyola led the life then typical of courtier and soldier until in 1521, during the siege of Pamplona by French troops, a cannon ball shattered one of his legs. In the long confinement that followed, he submitted unflinchingly to the rudimentary orthopedics of the day. To distract his mind from the agony, he turned to reading and thus came under the spell of religious books. Their spiritual message merged with the tales of chivalry that once had inspired him, and he began to dream of himself as a knight-errant consecrated to the defence of Jesus and Mary. He vowed to go to Jerusalem and fight for conversion of the Turks.

Upon his recovery and after some time spent in the most severe ascetic practices, Ignatius travelled to Italy to obtain permission for a pilgrimage from Pope Adrian VI. Finally, having survived a difficult and hazardous voyage, he arrived in Jerusalem in 1523. The Franciscans, fearful lest Loyola's proselytizing zeal incite violence from fanatical Turks, forced him by a threat of excommunication to leave. Returning to Venice in 1524, he determined to acquire the education prerequisite for priesthood and successful missionary work. After two years at Barcelona, where he studied Latin in the company of small boys, Ignatius went to the universities of Alcala and Salamanca. Already conspicuous by his ascetic life, utter poverty, and strange, ragged garb, he roused suspicion among the clergy by his public discussions of Scripture, and he and his followers were repeatedly cited before the Inquisition. Acquittal followed his courageous defence of his orthodoxy, but he decided nevertheless to move to the less inquisitorial Paris, where he enrolled in 1528 at the College of Montaigu and later at that of Sainte Barbe.

In Paris, Ignatius formed the nucleus of the future order of the Jesuits. One night in 1534, in a little church on Montmartre, he and six devoted companions took holy communion and vowed to go forth together to convert Turks or, if that mission should prove impossible, to place themselves unquestionably at the disposal of the pope. His six companions were Pierre Lefèvre (Peter Faber), once a Savoyard shepherd, who had been his tutor and room-mate at Sainte Barbe; Francis Xavier, of an aristocratic family in Navarre, who had long resisted Loyola's efforts but was to become the most ardent and effective Jesuit missionary; Diego Laynez, of Spanish-Jewish ancestry, who was to become prominent at the Council of Trent and to succeed Loyola as general of the order; Alfonso Salmeron of Toledo, who was destined to be equally prominent at Trent and to become a foremost theologian; Simon Rodriguez, a Portuguese, who was eventually to return to his native land as head of the Jesuit mission there; and Nicholas Alfonso, named Bobadillo after his home in Castile, who was to carry on important missionary activities in the Holy Roman Empire.

Shortly after their inaugural meeting the seven men dispersed. When, two years later, they reunited in Venice, their membership had increased to ten. In Venice Loyola, again suspected of heresy, drew upon himself the wrath of Cardinal Caraffa by his criticism of the Theatines, of whom Caraffa was the superior, and by his refusal to merge with them. The renewal of the Turkish wars kept Loloya and his disciples from departing for the Holy Land. In Rome, where they went in 1538, they were openly accused of heresy, but Loyola in a long audience with Pope Paul III defended his stand so skilfully that he gained the pope's approval. A trial, begun at Loyola's own request, ended in complete vindication, bringing wide recognition to the 'Inigists' (as the band was called, after its founder's Spanish name). The learning and the effectiveness of their preaching attracted the attention of Catholic princes everywhere, and they were soon in demand throughout Europe to aid in reforming Catholic institutions and strengthening the Catholic party. Laynez and Lefèvre were appointed to the University of Rome, where their success as teachers and theologians was so great that a papal decree in 1530 commanded all teachers in the holy city to adopt the new order's methods of instruction (see Chapter XVI).

If conversion of the Turks no longer seemed practical, Europe, rent by the Reformation, seemed to cry aloud for missionary devotion. When, therefore, Loyola and his followers met again (1539), they decided to reorganize their brotherhood. This meeting marked the formal founding of a new *compania* of militants for Christ, thenceforth known as the Society of Jesus. To the vows of chastity and poverty was now added that of absolute obedience to the pope and to the general of the order. The strange rules of the new order encountered stubborn disapproval in the Curia, and it took the most subtle manoeuvres on Loyola's part to overcome opposition. The new order received papal sanction only in 1540, and the next year Loyola, against his will, was unanimously elected its general. Membership was at first limited to sixty, but in 1543 a papal bull removed this restriction and unconditionally recognized the order as operating under its own rules. Loyola spent the rest of his life revising these rules, and only in 1558, two years after his death, were the society's 'Constitutions' adopted by its first General Congregation. The 'Constitutions', together with other crucial documents of the order, form 'The Institute of the Society of Jesus', which regulates it to this day.

In the Institute the church was conceived as the Church Militant, served by the order with absolute obedience and soldierly discipline. The stringent training by which the aspirant Jesuit became a full-fledged 'professed of the four vows' will be analyzed in Chapter XVI. Obedience was maintained not only through binding vows but also through the acceptance of the obligation to report infractions of rules or expressions of rebellion. Highest constitutional authority rested with the General Congregation of the Order, a body of officers recruited exclusively from the 'professed'. They elected the general, and, if paramount considerations required, might depose him. Otherwise, actual authority rested with the general—checked, however, by a body of 'assistants' representing the geographical subdivisions ('assistancies') of the order, by a special confessor, and by a monitor who brought to the general's attention the assistants' criticisms of his actions. All of these officers were appointed by the General Congregation without interference from the general. The assistancies of the order were organized into 'provinces', each headed by a 'provincial', who was appointed by the general and assisted by a body of advisers similarly appointed. The provinces had jurisdiction over the order's colleges, seminaries, novitiates, houses, and missions within their boundaries. All branches of the Society were under the centralized administration at Rome, where the general was required to reside.

While all the Jesuits took vows of obedience to the pope, they also vowed obedience to their general. In cases of conflicting interests the general might thus successfully thwart papal policies for which the efforts of the Society were required. Even so, Popes Paul III and Julius III further strengthened the general's power, but after Loyola's death Paul IV actively interfered in the affairs of the order. In addition to insisting upon greater conformity in Jesuit religious services, he issued a decree (1558) that limited the general's term of office to three years.

The Society found supporters among the most influential Catholics of Europe. The Jesuits' austerity and strict conduct, their devout obedience, their willingness to sacrifice themselves, and the obvious success of their labours made them indispensable allies in the struggle for the preservation of Catholicism. After Paul IV's death (1559), Pius IV restored the provision by which the general held office for life. Under Pius V all privileges formerly bestowed upon the Jesuits were confirmed and even extended to include all benefits enjoyed by the traditional orders. For the next two hundred years, until their temporary suppression in 1773, the Jesuits remained the most active allies of the papacy. In 1773 they numbered around 24,000, divided into 49 provinces, in which there were 669 colleges.[57]

From the outset the Jesuits purposefully concentrated upon effective control of men's minds. Jesuit aspirants were carefully trained and over a period of years were weeded out step by step until only the best adapted candidates remained (see Chapter XVI). When they were fully trained, education, both formal and informal, became one of their major activities (with dramatic results that will likewise engage our attention later). Their missionary work was perhaps still more dramatic. Even before the official recognition of the Jesuits in 1540, their assistance was requested by King John III of Portugal in converting the inhabitants of his newly acquired colonies. Francis Xavier spread the Gospel under the most difficult circumstances in India, the Indies, and Japan. In subsequent decades Jesuit missions were established in many parts of the world, including Africa and America. A key to their success was the flexibility with which they accommodated Christian teachings to the beliefs they encountered. Xavier himself did not employ this expedient of 'accommodation' though he frequently used other kinds of worldly pressure, such as promises of financial reward, commercial advantage, and threats of punishment by the civil authorities. His successors in Asia, as also those in the New World, went much farther in this direction, appearing in the religious garb familiar to the locality or permitting elements of the old religion to become part of the new as long as they seemed not to offend essential Christian doctrine. While these methods were frequently criticized both within the church—by Pascal, for instance—and by Protestant opponents, they were successful in prompting conversions *en masse* though perhaps not in depth.

A similar flexibility was in no small degree responsible for the Jesuits' success in their inner missions. As militant defenders of Catholicism, expert pamphleteers against Protestantism, and skillful organizers of the Catholic party throughout Europe, they fitted their methods to the situations confronting them. Loyola himself, though aware of the need for missionary work among the masses, had early realized the importance of gaining support among persons of authority and influence. Accordingly, Jesuits became tutors of princes and, particularly under Loyola's successors, court confessors in Catholic countries, capable by their knowledge of a ruler's mind and soul to give to their spiritual guidance a decisive political turn. Jesuits addressed themselves to all classes of society, sometimes wearing no distinctive garb and accommodating themselves even in appearance to the milieu in which they laboured. They preached sermons tailored to suit the merchant as well as the farmer, the soldier as well as the criminal. Flexibility, though a source of strength, was ultimately also a source of weakness, for it made them vulnerable to never-ending accusations of opportunism or even hypocrisy, which eventually, in the age of the Enlightenment, were among the factors that led to their temporary dissolution after 1773. The Jesuits' devotion to the cause of Catholicism, and especially of the papacy, was to be amply tested in the long and tortuous conferences known as the Council of Trent.

THE CATHOLIC COUNCILS AT TRENT (1545–63)

The Fifth Lateran Council, we have seen, lasted until 1517, the year of the Ninety-Five Theses. It accomplished little in the way of reform, for neither Julius II nor Leo X permitted any interference with papal authority or with the secular interests of the Holy See. The council, in fact, reaffirmed the doctrine of the superiority of popes over councils in the affairs of the church, thus confirming the failure of the Conciliar Movement. The idea of conciliar supremacy retained many adherents, however, especially among those who were persuaded that papal absolutism was a stumbling block in the way of religious reform.

Luther's appeal for a general council found a strong echo in Germany, where Protestant and Catholic princes alike felt the need of defending their opposing causes before a forum of all Christendom. Emperor Charles V himself at times supported the idea of a council. A devout though not fanatical Catholic, he was fully aware of the need for reform. Nevertheless, his reform efforts, like his policy toward the Protestant Reformation, were geared to the exigencies of his political problems. Habsburg rivalry with Valois France and campaigns against the Turks obliged him to be cautious in dealing with the German princes, whether Protestant or Catholic. A general council, in which conceivably Catholic strength would prevail, thus seemed to afford a possible solution of his dilemma. Furthermore, he was heir to the traditional rivalry between the emperors and the popes and therefore intent upon limiting the papel power. His sympathy with the demand for a general council thus not only betrayed his desire for moderate religious reform but also implied that in the affairs of Christendom he recognized an authority higher than the pope. This very implication, however, was the major reason why the contemporary popes for a long time refused to convoke a general council.

The papal strategy, perhaps wise for Italy, led in Germany to a louder demand for a national council to resolve the religious affairs of the Empire. Although the most powerful ruler in Europe, Charles was unable to assert full power anywhere because of the numerous involvements his very power entailed, and he was only gradually induced to take a definitive stand. When Pope Clement VII joined the alliance against him (1526), he demanded a council to arbitrate Catholic and Protestant differences; he even appealed to the cardinals to convoke it in their own name if the supreme pontiff refused. Then when the fortunes of war placed the pope for a time in his power (1527) he dropped this policy.

The accession of Paul III (1534) at first brought a change in papal attitude. Paul actually convoked two councils between 1536 and 1538, at Mantua and Vicenza respectively, but both were prorogued without material achievement because of hostilities between the emperor and the kings of France and England as well the refusal of the Protestant princes, organized since 1531 in the Schmalkaldic League, to participate. In the heat engendered by the increasingly complex political situation Paul's willingness to convene a council withered. His desire to reform the church, though real, was not so deep as to permit him to jeopardize the papacy's prestige and power as one of the great temporal states of Europe. And so, until 1545 convocation was frustrated, chiefly by the antagonistic aims of the principal Catholic rulers. Charles V, however, continued his attempts to compromise with the Protestants, with or without papal sanction, and his tactics made it imperative— as several papal legates repeatedly pointed out from Germany—that the pope should not veto a council.

Some of the most jealous manoeuvring that preceded the actual convocation of a council revolved around the issue who was to control it. The emperor and the pope were the leading contenders, with the king of France skillfully playing one against the other to further his own purposes. The pope's main concern was to confirm the position of the Fifth Lateran Council that popes were superior to councils and thus to frustrate the emperor's attempts to make the council rather than the papacy the authoritative instrument of reform. The preliminary jockeying in this race for control pivoted upon the location of the forthcoming council. The pope naturally preferred Italy, where the majority of attendants would probably be Italian bishops, who, looking to the Curia for benefices and privileges, might be counted upon to support the papal cause. German public opinion, for parallel reasons, clamoured for a location somewhere in Germany, forcing Charles to oppose the papal preference. In the end a compromise solution was agreed upon; the council was to be convoked in Trent, a city in southern Tyrol, close to the Italian border but at least nominally within the Holy Roman Empire.[58]

The rival Catholic parties also wrangled over what policy to follow regarding the Protestants. A reconciliation was for a time considered conceivable, but after the failure of the Regensburg Colloquy, as noted above, the pope considered the heretics beyond compromise and in 1542 inaugurated with the Roman Inquisition a policy of repression. Political considerations, however, forced Charles, engaged in war with Francis I, to maintain a conciliatory attitude and to acquiesce in Protestant demands for tolerance—at least until a general council might settle disputed points. Thus the emperor was concerned to delay a council until Paul might show greater signs of moderation, while the pope, wary of German reconciliation, shifted his stand, declaring his readiness to convoke a council at an early date. Charles agreed, assuring the German estates that he would convene a national council in Germany if the prospective general council should fail.

Long negotiations followed between papal legates and imperial ambassadors. The pope vainly tried to change the announced location for the council, but a summons to meet at Trent in November 1542 was finally issued. Then war between France and the emperor once more intervened; only three papal legates and the imperial chancellor appeared; and a papal bull in July 1543 suspended the council. Whether it would reconvene was left to the pope's discretion.

Charles' defeat of France and the consequent Peace of Crépy in September 1544 considerably reduced the international tension. The pope, once more in at least outward rapport with the emperor, summoned the council to assemble again at Trent in March 1545. Its formal opening was delayed until December, but even then attendance was small. The Italian and Spanish delegations outnumbered the Germans, because the German bishops were preoccupied at home by the threat of war with the Schmalkaldic League of Protestant princes. Attending the council by express order of the emperor (who, as king of Spain, was their sovereign), the Spanish delegation represented the imperial power as well as the Spanish national church. They not only pressed for reform of the Curia but also persistently defended episcopal—and by implication, conciliar—privileges against papal encroachment. Their opposition was formidable, because since the reforms of Ximenes the Spanish church had not only become the strongest and most unified in western Europe but also could boast some of the most learned theologians of the age. Their unquestioned orthodoxy and their loyal support of the papacy in matters of doctrine made their challenge of the papal legates and their emphasis upon reform doubly effective.

No Protestants participated in the council, and for a number of reasons. Although Luther and his followers had constantly appealed from the pope to a general council, their emphasis had always been upon a 'free' council not dominated by the Curia, and they declared that this one was neither general nor free and not even Christian. Political calculations likewise hindered their attendance. Various temporary agreements allowed them the exercise of their religion in the Empire until a general council should reach a definitive doctrinal settlement, but the decisions that were to be anticipated from the Council of Trent might put an end to tolerance. They, therefore, wished the emperor to guarantee in advance that the truce would continue. This, of course, the emperor would not do, and so, despite his assurances of peaceful intentions, the Protestants stayed away.

The struggle for control of the council began at the outset. Three forces openly contended with one another—the Curial party, jealous for papal prerogatives and eager to reassert papal authority over all of western Christendom; the Imperial party, still hesitant to break completely with the Protestants and intent upon reform and restriction of papal power; and the episcopal party, mostly non-Italian bishops, eager to defend their prerogatives against the pope, the most radical among them ready even to question the primacy of the bishop of Rome. The episcopal movement, identified most readily with the Spanish bishops, could have succeeded only in conjunction with a strong conciliar movement, and its advocates were indeed conspicuously conciliar in sentiment, but the conciliar theory was essentially incompatible with the concept of hierarchic priesthood, which even the most radical bishops were loath to abandon. Despite the widespread opposition to papal absolutism, the papal legates had the upper hand because the assembled bishops were unwilling to attack in any fundamental way the hierarchical structure of the church.

The first meetings of the council decided three issues in a way that portended the eventual victory of the papacy. When the full name of the council was considered, a number of delegates proposed that the words *universalem ecclesiam representans* be added. These words seemed to imply that the council, as fully representative of the church, was superior to the pope, and the papal legates induced the council to reject them. A second issue concerned the system of voting. At previous councils, votes had been counted by nations, with lesser clergy and theologians voting along with princes of the church. This method permitted a significant number of voters to avoid direct papal influence. At Trent voting by nations was rejected in favour of voice voting, only bishops and generals of orders being allowed to vote, no proxies permitted. Thus the Italian bishops, being the largest delegation, could almost alone assure the eventual success of the papal cause.

On the third issue the papal preferences met with a setback but only a partial one. Upon the express orders of the pope, who considered reform a papal prerogative, his legates insisted that dogma be made the first business of the council. This move encountered determined opposition from the Imperial camp, which was under orders to place reform first. The Spanish bishops proved their strength when against the most determined papal opposition they forced a compromise. In January 1546, it was decided that dogma and reform should be considered simultaneously by special commissions and their findings brought before the council in alternate sessions. The partial defeat of the papal party on this issue was softened when the pope's counter proposal that no reform of the Curia be discussed without his prior consent was accepted. It was further agreed that only after being prepared, discussed, and approved by preliminary bodies should a measure be brought before the general assembly, and it was to be promulgated as a definitive act only if adopted in a solemn public *sessio* (meeting) of the entire council.

The debates on dogma were the most heated. The Jesuit fathers Laynez and Salmeron played a vital part in them as the pope's theologians. Although they were not delegates, they alone among the assemblage had been granted the privilege of preaching, and their general learning and familiarity with Scripture and canon law won deep and wide respect. Although originally instructed by Loyola to mediate between pope and bishops, they were also instructed to make no concessions on dogma. Thus they became in effect the vanguard of the papal forces. Their learned discourses—especially those of Laynez—were instrumental in solidifying the front against innovation. The fact that the Jesuit theologians were Spanish offset the Spanish opposition.

The very wording employed by the papal legates in formulating doctrinal disagreements usually seemed designed to make reconciliation with the Protestants impossible. Almost every point of Protestant theology was branded from the outset as heretical and appeared to be cited only to be anathematized. The attack began with the discussion of the sources of faith and revelation. Against the Protestant conviction that Scripture was the sole source, the council decreed that tradition (i.e. the writing of the church fathers) was of equal validity and that the church alone had authority in the interpretation of both. At the same time, obviously in repudiation of Luther's translation of the Bible, the Vulgate was decreed the only authentic version, even though the more learned among the delegates, as indeed Paul III himself, realized that the work of the humanists had raised doubts concerning its adequacy.

The discussion of the sources of faith led logically to the discussion of justification. Justification by faith alone, the principal creed of Protestantism, was defended even by some of the delegates. One of the papal legates, Cardinal Pole, noted for his moderation, pleaded with the council not to reject a tenet merely because it was held by the Lutherans. Cardinal Seripando, general of the Augustinians, made an impassioned plea for a rapprochement, expounding an opinion that approximated the Protestant doctrine of justification by faith alone. In reply, Laynez made one of his longest and most effective speeches, and in the end prevailed. Justification by faith alone was anathematized.

The ancient dogma thus clinched implied many corollaries, and the public *sessio* on justification resulted in no fewer than thirty-three canons of key importance. Good works were now logically reconfirmed as a necessary part of justification. With equal logic, free will, which enabled man to choose the path of good works, was retained as part of the Catholic creed. All seven traditional sacraments were reaffirmed, and the council declared that, with the exception of baptism, they could have their true efficacy only if performed by ordained priests. Thus the dependence of the laity upon the priesthood, in opposition to Luther's assertion of the essential priesthood of all believers, was reasserted. Still later, when the sacrament of ordination was discussed, the council anathematized any who maintained that 'sacred ordination is not truly and properly a sacrament instituted by Christ' and repudiated the doctrine that priests might be elected from and by the laity; 'those who, being only called and instituted by the people, or by the civil power and magistrate, ... are not ministers of the church, but ... thieves and robbers, who have not entered by the door'.[59]

The pope was eager to publish the canonical findings of the council, since they bade fair to become a telling weapon against Protestant heresy. On the other hand, the emperor betrayed growing dissatisfaction. The Schmalkaldic War had broken out soon after the council opened, and he had won such important victories that he had reason to hope for concessions from the

Protestants. He, therefore, tried to delay publication of the conservative decisions on dogma while pressing for supplementary measures of vital reform. Thus the issue was joined whether the council was to become an instrument of reform or of counter-reform.

Though Paul III, through his legates, was determined to maintain full control over the Catholic reform movement, he had to face a significant number of non-Italian bishops. The Spanish delegation proved its strength a second time and forced another compromise. The debate on the rules for preaching and religious instruction brought a decision that members of the regular clergy would be free to preach in the churches of their respective orders but must not preach in diocesan churches without the bishop's permission. During this debate an issue arose that repeatedly dominated discussion of episcopal jurisdiction: Were episcopal privileges and obligations founded upon divine law (*iure divino*) or ecclesiastical law (*lege ecclesiastica*)? The Spanish bishops maintained that all episcopal duties existed *iure divino* —thus implying that bishops derived their obligations and authority directly from God, as did the pope himself (as bishop of Rome). This view was naturally opposed by the papal legates—to whom, besides, the corollary that bishops should reside in their sees was personally embarrassing since it called in question the papal practice of bestowing benefices in distant parts upon cardinals living in Rome. The origin of episcopal rights was so passionately argued that otherwise dignified prelates exchanged insults and came to blows. A decision was not to be reached even in the final stages of the council (1563), when the question was evaded by intentional ambiguity.

Meanwhile political considerations added to the tensions created by the disputes over theology and church administration. Shortly after the Council of Trent began, the Protestants showed some signs of becoming tractable. Luther died in February 1546, thus depriving them of their most unbending spokesman, and their military power was broken by the emperor's victories over the Schmalkaldic League. Charles still had to take into account, however, the legal rights of the Protestant princes, and he was anxious not to provoke the outbreak of new hostilities. Moreover, he saw in the Protestant opposition to the pope a means of strengthening his own bargaining position at the council.

Paul III had good reason to fear the emperor's improved position, and he urged the council to move to Italy, where he could better balance imperial influence by his personal presence. A few cases of the plague aided the papal legates to win a majority, and despite the vehement protest of the minority, composed mostly of Spanish bishops, the council adjourned, and most of the delegates reassembled at Bologna (March 1547). This move came close upon a sudden burst of public approval for the council's decisions on dogma, putting further obstacles in the way of the emperor's peace efforts. Wrathfully Charles forbade the Spanish bishops to leave Trent, and so a rump body held out there. Although it was careful, on the emperor's orders, to avoid action that might lead to schism, the council was none the less split, and no effective action could be taken at either Trent or Bologna. Charles summoned the Diet to meet in Augsburg in September and in due course (May 1548) proclaimed his own tentative compromise with the Protestants, the Augsburg Interim. But no more definitive agreement could be reached and finally in September 1549, Paul III prorogued the council at Bologna. Two months later he died.

The new pope, Julius III, while continuing to assert the power of the Holy See, proved willing to appease the emperor, even on the delicate issue of Protestant attendance at a council. The German princes demanded that the council resume at Trent, for they wanted the Protestant problem in Germany solved on German soil, and after displaying considerable reluctance, Julius consented. Two further obstacles to Protestant attendance at the council remained to be overcome—an unconditional safe conduct that would be better honoured than the one promised to Huss over a century earlier and a decision whether the new assembly was a continuation of the prorogued Council of Trent. If the new assembly was to be regarded as merely a continuation of the old, it would feel bound by its earlier decisions on dogma, rendering attendance by Protestants futile. Julius III at first left this question open, but toward the end of the new set of meetings it came to be regarded *de facto* as a continuation of the earlier council. By that time, other events had once more made apparent that debate, however free, would not alone suffice to heal the schism in Christendom.

Some lay representatives of a few German Protestant states were finally admitted to the fifteenth public *sessio* of the council (January 1552). In expounding the conditions on which Protestant theologians might agree to attend, they made stipulations that could hardly be compromised. They wanted to resume the debate on dogma, insisting at the same time that Scripture be the sole authority for further deliberations. Bishops should be freed from their oaths of papal allegiance, they argued, for otherwise the pope in effect would sit in judgement of his own case, and they insisted that the papal legates, who normally held the presidency of the council, should surrender that prerogative. The principal speech setting forth these demands, probably written by Melanchthon, made a profound impression, especially upon several Spanish delegates. 'In full session', the Bishop of Orense exclaimed, 'they have stated what we [Spaniards] dare not say'.[60] It appeared for a moment as if the entire papal opposition at the council—Spanish bishops, emperor, and Protestants—might form a united front.

Once more political forces interfered, abruptly stifling any slim chance there might have arisen of forcing papal concessions and restoring Christian unity. Certain German Protestant princes were worried by the emperor's conciliatory policies, which seemed designed to repeal territorialism, unite the Empire, and break their power. The devious Maurice of Saxony was one of them. Coveting the title and prerogatives of his kinsman the Saxon elector, he had recently changed sides and had fought under Charles V in the Schmalkaldic War. At this juncture he changed sides once more, resuming leadership in the militant Lutheran cause and taking up arms against Charles. His victorious advance forced the emperor to seek refuge in Innsbruck, only to flee again when Protestant troops converged upon that city. Fear spread that Maurice might march on Trent, about eighty-five miles away, and the council precipitately suspended its meetings again (April 1552). It had done little more since reconvening than discuss the sacraments, anathematize Protestant doctrine concerning the Eucharist, and postpone a decision on the question of communion in both kinds.

Almost ten years were to pass after the second prorogation of the council before it reconvened. In that interval several popes had succeeded to the papal throne. Julius III (d. 1555) was followed by Marcellus II, who survived his election only three weeks, and after his death, Caraffa received the tiara. During his austere reign as Paul IV he initiated no move toward reopening the council. Though as cardinal he had been a most ardent advocate of reform, he proved as pontiff to be conspicuously political-minded. His deep-seated mistrust of Spain involved him in war with that country, staunchest supporter of orthodox Catholicism in Europe, and led him to make overtures even to Protestants and Turks in a vain effort to avert military disaster. The nepotism that he practiced to the dismay of the reform party in Rome was closely related to his anti-Spanish policy, for members of his family insinuated themselves into his favour as staunch supporters of his diplomacy. Disillusioned by defeat and the realization of a favoured nephew's unworthiness, he at last concentrated on reform but did so with such fanaticism that rejoicing was general in Rome when he died (1559).

By that time, the political situation had changed materially. Charles V had abdicated, and his son had become King Philip II of Spain, and his brother Holy Roman Emperor Ferdinand I. The successes of Maurice of Saxony and the intervention of France had evened the balance between German Catholic and Lutheran princes, and (as we saw above) they had agreed to the compromise Peace of Augsburg (1555). Armed conflict ended in Germany for over half a century.

Within a year of Pius IV's accession (1559) to the papal throne, he summoned the council to reopen at Trent. But his initial willingness soon evaporated because of apprehension that a new assembly might undo some of the earlier work. Once again the threat of a separate national council—this time from France—was needed to prod the hesitant pontiff into confirming the convocation. An anticipated conflict quickly arose: Was this a continuation of the old council and therefore committed to previous decisions (as desired by the uncompromising Philip II of Spain), or was it a new one and free to revise previous decisions (as demanded by the Emperor Ferdinand and by Francis II of France, who had powerful Protestant groups among their subjects)? Pius resorted to the now familiar device of leaving the question undecided. When in January 1562 the council finally opened, the hope of reconciliation seemed dim indeed, and it soon vanished entirely. The Protestants, although safe conduct had been granted them, again stayed away, and after deliberations were well under way, Pius decreed that this assembly was a continuation of the old Council of Trent.

During this third period of the Council of Trent the constellation of powers differed from the earlier ones. France and the Holy Roman Empire were united in favouring not only a thorough reform of the Curia but also changes in ritual and religious practices, such as communion in both kinds, mass in the vulgar tongue, permission for priests to marry, and stricter observance of residence by bishops and priests. The Spanish bishops, no longer under a king identified with the Empire, while still demanding stringent reform of the church, were unwilling to make any concessions in dogmatic matters. As a result papal diplomacy was again successful in dividing the opposition, and the papal legates, having the sole right of initiative, achieved considerable control over deliberations. After a year or so of this third period, the council seemed to be headed toward a conclusion. Philip of Spain was convinced that the council was seriously contemplating reform; in fact, Cardinal Morone, who became first legate in 1563, introduced a project in July intended to satisfy some of the various national demands. Emperor Ferdinand, faced with frustration of his desire that the chalice be granted to the German laity, heeded his adviser, the Jesuit Canisius, and decided to negotiate directly with Pius IV rather than to prolong the council's discussions on the subject. Canisius's advice proved justified, for the pope eventually (1564) granted the chalice in Germany, though under specified conditions. The Cardinal of Lorraine, leader of the French delegation, also was won over to adjournment. On December 4, 1563, at the close of its twenty-fifth *sessio*, the council, having accepted Morone's project, formally terminated amid the unconcealed rejoicing of the delegates.

In the bull *Benedictus Deus* (January 1564) Pius IV confirmed the decrees of the council but asserted the pope's exclusive prerogative of interpreting them and giving them their true validity. He appointed a special commission of eight cardinals to serve as a Congregation of the Council of Trent to help him carry on its work, and later that year he published the 'Tridentine Profession of Faith' (now generally known as 'The Creed of Pius IV'), to which all holders of ecclesiastical offices still must subscribe. This creed no longer left much room for discussion. It not only restored the traditional faith but in fact reinvigorated it by the clarity and definitiveness with which it repronounced Catholic doctrine. In the centuries that followed, deviations from the Tridentine Creed were synonymous with heresy and exposed their proponents to the displeasure of the Inquisition. Thus the Council of Trent, after its many years of fierce debate and intermittent search for compromise, provided in effect an arsenal of weapons for a counter-reformation.

The papal victory probably could not have been won without internal reforms that strengthened the church as a militant organization and blunted the fittingness of its opponents' criticism. The reform decrees of the Council of Trent were intended to correct the patent abuses that had contributed to the outbreak of the Reformation. Although those decrees did not always have the desired effect, they considerably improved discipline throughout the church. They made preaching a solemn obligation of ordained priests, gave to the training of priests a firm and lasting foundation by instituting a seminary in each diocese, enjoined bishops to reside in their dioceses and priests in their parishes, denounced plurality of offices, strengthened the authority of bishops over regular and secular clergy, abolished the sale of indulgences for money and specifically restricted the conditions under which indulgences might be granted, reaffirmed the celibacy of priests, excluded the illegitimate sons of prelates from certain benefices and pensions, and prohibited clandestine marriages even for laity. The council itself did not establish a new *Index of Prohibited Books* although it appointed a commission to revise the *Index* of 1559, but it referred this matter along with other important decrees to the pope for implementation.

PAPAL POLICIES AFTER TRENT

If the Council of Trent left western Christianity irrevocably split into several sects, the Roman Catholic Church emerged stronger than it had been before. The Church, to be sure, had narrowed its geographical boundaries, but at the same time it had drawn its faithful together in a tighter, more authoritative bond. The Council of Trent not only provided added momentum in the counter-attack upon the Protestant heresy but also marked the end of the Conciliar Movement. No ecumenical council was called again until 1869, and then it was completely under papal domination (see Volume V). The authority of the pope as the spiritual overlord of the Roman Catholic fold was more fully established by the Council of Trent than ever before, and if in Europe that fold was diminishing, overseas it gained many new adherents.

Active reform was intensified under the austere Pius V (1566-72), a former Dominican monk. He issued the Roman Catechism called for by the Council of Trent. He also gave Catholic liturgy a marked degree of uniformity. Both breviary and missal had thitherto varied greatly in the different parts of Catholic Christendom, since bishops had the right to determine details of liturgy for their dioceses. A commission established by the Council of Trent had undertaken the task of revising and unifying them. Under Pius V these revisions were formally promulgated as the officially sanctioned liturgy, except for churches which could claim an unbroken local usage for two centuries. This exemption was intended in the main for the French and German Catholic churches, but so great became the influence of the papacy upon an increasingly unified Catholicism that Pius's 'reformed' missal and breviary gradually supplanted most local versions. He became a staunch ally of Philip II of Spain in his determination to wipe out the Protestant heresy and stem the advance of the infidel Turk, and, except for Rome and Ancona, he expelled the Jews from the Papal States. He made the Inquisition a powerful weapon in the struggle against Protestantism, enforced the strictest morality and discipline throughout the hierarchy, put an end to some of the more glaring types of nepotism, and thoroughly revised the system of justice in the Papal States. He prohibited future investitures in perpetuity with fiefs from the papal possessions, and to give this reform measure lasting stability, he compelled his cardinals by solemn oath to support it.

Like liturgy, canon law took final and official form as a consequence of the programme laid down at Trent. Shortly before the council ended, Pius IV had established a commission (the Correctores Romani) to compile a definitive edition of canon law, but it completed its work only in the days of Gregory XIII (1572–85). In 1582 appeared the first edition of this new compilation, which later became known as the *Corpus iuris canonici* and, together with the decrees of the Council of Trent, forms the basis of the *ius novissimum*, the latest law. Augmented by the rulings and decrees pronounced since the Council of Trent, this *ius novissimum* has remained the basic code of Roman Catholicism to this day.

Gregory's main attention was focused upon improving religious instruction, particularly for the clergy. He was an especially generous patron of the Jesuit colleges, helping to found the Roman, German, and English colleges at Rome, as well as those at Vienna and Graz and on the Greek islands. His best known contribution was the reform, in keeping with a recommendation of the Council of Trent, of the calendar (see Chapter XIV); the Gregorian calendar gave greater regularity to religious holidays by establishing a more accurate correlation between them and the four seasons of the year than had been possible under the Julian calendar. Gregory also spent vast sums of money for public works and for subsidies to Catholic princes who were fighting Protestantism, especially in the Netherlands, France, and England. To compensate for the drain on the papal treasury he resorted to such measures as the confiscation of fiefs of doubtful title. Widespread unrest resulted among the nobility in the Papal States, and the curse of private warfare with resultant large-scale banditry returned to Italy.

On Gregory's death his successor, Sixtus V (1585–90), faced with the problem of restoring peace and financial solvency, crushed brigandage and private warfare with brutal severity and replenished the papal treasury by means that could not easily be reconciled with his reforming zeal. While he cut down the expenses of the Curia, he also increased old taxes, devised new ones, and raised both the number and the price of offices put up for sale. He debased the currency and, when his tampering led to speculation in currency exchange, sold permits to the speculators. These measures provided the vast sums needed for his numerous public works in Rome and for the defence and propagation of the faith. In 1586, Sixtus gave the College of Cardinals its definitive form, and in 1588 he reorganized the Curia by establishing fifteen congregations of cardinals, each having a special advisory capacity in a specified field of ecclesiastical administration.

The Council of Trent had left to the popes the responsibility not only of interpreting but also of enforcing its decisions. To place spiritual conformity under the desired discipline, it had proposed control of the minds of the faithful. Censorship had long been known in the Catholic Church, but not until 1559, under Paul IV, was an official *Index Librorum Prohibitorum* issued with full papal authority. This *Index* was regarded as inadequate by the Council of Trent, and a commission was appointed to propose revisions. The new *Tridentine Index* was published under Pius IV in 1564, along with the famous 'Ten Rules' setting forth the criteria of censorship adopted by the Council of Trent. Under Pius V a Congregation of the Index was established, and the formal publication of lists of prohibited books ended only in 1966.

The Inquisition became an even stronger weapon in the arsenal of Roman Catholicism. The papal Inquisition had lost considerable power and prestige during the Great Schism, but the Spanish Inquisition, established by Ferdinand and Isabella, had become formidable. Yet outside Spain Catholic princes, even Charles V in his role of emperor, were reluctant to follow the example of Spain, where the Inquisition had become a power rivalling that of the crown. Moreover, popular opposition was so violent in the most important Spanish possessions in Italy that attempts to establish the Spanish Inquisition at Milan and Naples had to be abandoned. The spread of Protestantism, however, led Pope Paul III to establish the Inquisition at Rome (1542), and Paul IV and Pius V, himself once an inquisitor, used it ruthlessly and successfully not only to ferret out known or suspected Protestants but also to enforce discipline among the faithful.

The church did not rely on reform and compulsion alone to fortify Catholicism. As will be indicated in Chapter XII, church architecture and church music became part of a studied effort to make a dramatic appeal to the eye and the ear. The paganism that had characterized some of the great accomplishments of Renaissance art gave way increasingly to a new piety in which the artist again sought inspiration from Christianity. This development was at least in part consciously in opposition to the austerity of Protestant church service and church architecture. The schools, too, became an effective instrument in the battle for men's minds, especially in the hands of the Jesuits (see Chapter XVI).

Thus, a little over half a century after the first impetus of the Reformation, Catholicism rose again in a new militancy under a revitalized central authority. For all that, the attempts to make the decisions of Trent binding throughout Catholic Christendom met with considerable defiance. Catholic princes, though willing to submit in matters of dogma, were reluctant to accept the decrees on discipline, which frequently infringed cherished interests of national governments and churches. The decrees on discipline were withheld in the Empire (although Ferdinand adopted them for his hereditary dominions) and in France; Spain and Venice adopted them only with stringent reservations; in effect, only Portugal and Poland among the Catholic powers approved them outright. Yet even in those Catholic countries where, out of national or dynastic considerations the Tridentine decrees were not regarded as binding, in a very real sense the effect of the Protestant revolt had been to cement the bonds among those who had remained loyal.

RELIGIOUS CONFLICT AND NON-CONFORMITY (1598–1775)

War weariness and an emergent rational spirit led to various attempts to restore Christian unity by irenic means. We have already referred to the humanists' efforts (e.g. those of Modrzewski and Laski in Poland) to harmonize conflicting doctrines on the basis of a common Christianity. Harking back to such humanists, various conciliators of the seventeenth century sought to merge Lutheran and Calvinist, Protestant and Catholic, Roman and Greek Orthodox theologies. Hugo Grotius explored the common ground of Catholics and Protestants in his *De Veritate Religionis Christianae* (1627) and its sequel, *Via et Votum ad Pacem Ecclesiasticam* (1642). The 'pansophy' of John Amos Comenius (Komenský) (1592–1670) was designed to end the conflicts of at least the evangelical creeds through a common core of learning (see Chapter XVI). The Lutheran theologian Georg Calixtus of Helmstedt took an active part in a religious conference at Thorn (1645) that vainly tried again to reconcile the Protestant creeds. Though attacked by all parties, especially by orthodox Lutherans, he inspired the Great Elector to attempt a union between Lutherans and Calvinists in Prussia, though without avail. A disciple of Calixtus, Gerhard Molanus, participated in the most far-reaching efforts at conciliation. One of these was the negotiations between the French bishop Bossuet and the German philosopher Leibniz, whose *Systema theologicum* (1687) advocated the accommodation of all Christian creeds and whose *Théodicée* (1710) was partly intended to cut across the differences among Christian sects and present a fundamental Christian theism. Another was the overlapping efforts of Bishop Spinola, who, in the service of Emperor Leopold I, negotiated with the Archbishop of Mainz, Protestant theologians in Berlin and Hanover, and Leibniz. Watched by the papacy and supported by the emperor, who sought Protestant aid against a new Turkish advance in the 1680's, these efforts ended in an abortive religious colloquy at Hanover in 1683. In the end, all these syncretic schemes, and parallel ones in England and Sweden, failed.

In the Germanies the Religious Peace of Augsburg (1555) lasted for over sixty years. Nevertheless, the truce was a precarious one. Some Protestant princes—mostly Calvinists, from whom official recognition was withheld in the Peace of Augsburg—formed a Protestant Union, abetted by Henry IV of France; the Catholic princes, resenting the frequent secularization of their church's properties, which they considered a violation of the treaty, formed a Catholic League. Each alliance looked for support abroad among co-religionists or others who might benefit from cooperation. Germany was thus split into hostile and alert factions. Several crises nearly led to armed conflict, and a full-fledged civil war broke out in 1618.

The Thirty Years' War began that year with the rebellion of the Bohemian Protestant estates against Habsburg attempts to abrogate their religious and political liberties. It quickly broadened into an unequal struggle (1618–20) between the Protestant Union and the Catholic League and then (1620–25) merged with the age-old conflict between German particularism and imperial authority. First (1625–29) Christian IV of Denmark and then (1629–35) Gustavus Adolphus of Sweden intervened directly on the side of the German Protestants. Spain's Habsburgs supported the Catholic League and the Austrian Habsburgs, and the Habsburg compact brought in on the other side their long-standing enemy France. Meanwhile the confederation of the United Provinces continued its struggle for independence from Spain. The German war thus spread into a general conflagration in which the battle between Protestantism and Catholicism became inextricably mixed with political rivalries that at times eclipsed the religious issues. Germany remained the principal battleground, ravished by the mercenaries on both sides. Among their commanding generals the adventurer Wallenstein was one of the few moved by a far-sighted political goal—German unity based upon religious freedom and a strong, centralized monarchy.

Disunited and faced with vastly superior Catholic power, German Protestantism was almost overwhelmed but was saved by Cardinal de Richelieu. For the very reason that he sought successfully to weaken the Huguenots of France (see below), Richelieu wished to keep the German Protestants strong —i.e. as a menace in each case to the respective central authority. It was for that reason that he had induced Gustavus Adolphus of Sweden to intervene in Germany, and when the intervening Swedish forces stalled after their king's death in the Battle of Lützen (1634), he brought France into open military alliance with the Swedish forces. The final phase of the Thirty Years' War thus in a sense became a Bourbon continuation of the long duel between Habsburg and Valois.

The peace, signed in the Westphalian towns of Münster and Osnabrück in 1648 after years of negotiation, was a series of treaties adjusting a vast complex of religious and political disputes. The religious settlement extended the provisions of the Religious Peace of Augsburg to German Calvinists and removed all distinction in the affairs of the Empire between Protestant and Catholic states. Ecclesiastical properties secularized before 1624 were allowed to remain in the hands of those who had secularized them. Previously granted religious liberties were reaffirmed, but Protestants under Habsburg family rule were specifically excluded from this provision. The Treaty of Westphalia did not grant full religious toleration but accorded the right of emigration to those denied the exercise of their religion, and Lutheran as well as Calvinist princes agreed upon mutual freedom of worship in their domains. Habsburg dominance was counterbalanced by increasing French power in Alsace-Lorraine, by increasing Swedish power in the Baltic area, and by formally recognizing the independence from the Habsburg crowns of Switzerland and the United Provinces. The gravest setback to Imperial union, however, was the complete restoration of territorial sovereignty (*Landeshoheit*) to the German states, including the right to enter into alliances among themselves and with foreign powers. The holocaust of the Thirty Years' War, though perhaps sometimes exaggerated, nevertheless left the Empire materially and spiritually weakened for over a century. Moreover, with France and Sweden as its guarantors, the Treaty of Westphalia became the thin end of a wedge for constant foreign intrusion in imperial affairs.

* * *

Fragmentation and Individualism in Protestantism

Protestantism manifested a strong tendency toward fragmentation. English Protestant opinion, for example, inclined increasingly toward Calvinism, and many of the subjects of Elizabeth I's successors resented the retention of certain Catholic elements in Anglican worship. While some of these 'Puritans' never broke with the Anglican Church, others became Presbyterians or Separatists. They all strove for a greater simplicity in church service and sought to cleanse the national church of doctrinal and vestiary externals incompatible with Reformed beliefs. They tended to believe that one who was among God's elect would lead a life of practical Christianity, outwardly demonstrated by a kind of temporal asceticism, and they opposed the subordination of religion to political exigencies. The Presbyterians of England and Scotland differed from other Puritans chiefly on the issue of church administration. Presbyterians opposed government of the church by the state (Erastianism) or by bishops (episcopalianism) and advocated government by its members through a hierarchy of assemblies, representing at each step a widening circle of churches. Presbyterianism was a logical outgrowth of the Protestant belief in the essential priesthood of all Christians. It occupied a middle ground between the monarchic episcopalianism of the Anglicans and the democratic congregationalism of the Separatists, or Independents, who believed in separate organization and independent government for each congregation.

Calvinist doctrines also contributed to the development of Baptist groups. Under Mennonite guidance, the Anabaptists had abandoned their earlier radicalism, and some English Brownists (Separatists), exiled in Holland, easily fell under Mennonite influence. They soon divided into 'General Baptists', who rejected Calvinist views of predestination, and 'Particular Baptists', who accepted them. Congregationalist in matters of church government, Baptists went further than the Presbyterians in their demand for freedom of religion from civil authority. In their 'Declaration of Faith', published in 1611 in Holland, English Baptists were the first to include in a formal creed the demand both for the absolute independence of congregations and for absolute freedom of the individual conscience.

The ultimate manifestation of Protestant individualism came with the rise of the Society of Friends (or Quakers). In Quaker theology doctrinal preoccupations and formal ritual were abandoned. Worship was freed of all external and material ritual in order to make the religious experience as inward and personal as possible. Quakers built no churches and, though the first to recognize the ministry of women, ordained no ministers, believing that communication with God cannot be limited to particular places, times, ceremonies, or intermediaries. Their tolerance of doctrinal heterogeneity did not prevent their accepting a certain code of religious and social ethics expressed in such outward manifestations as pacifism, refusal to take oaths, philanthropy, and full support of civil liberty. Under the leadership of George Fox and William Penn, Quaker colonies were established in Pennsylvania, New Jersey, and Delaware, and Quakers, despite persecutions, went to live in nearly every other Anglo-American colony. They were the first religious body publicly to advocate the friendly treatment of Amerindians and the abolition of slavery. They did so before the close of the seventeenth century, and by the end of the eighteenth century, slavery virtually had ceased to exist among them. The Quaker John Woolman's *Some Considerations on the Keeping of Negroes* (1754) was the first important American abolitionist tract.

Strict personal conduct as an expression of practical Christianity became characteristic especially of the Bohemian Unity of Brethren (Unitas Fratrum). All but wiped out during the Thirty Years' War, the Bohemian Brethren survived in Saxony, where a remnant found refuge on the estates of Count von Zinzendorf at Herrnhut. Under his influence the Brethren became closely associated with Lutheran Pietism (see below) and subsequently took an active part in the religious revival of eighteenth-century German Protestantism and in the foundation of the 'Pennsylvania Dutch' communities in America. Through John Wesley's contacts with them, the 'Moravians', as they were called in America, were also to influence the development of Methodism in England and the Anglo-American colonies.

The emphasis upon active endeavour became part of an ascetic Protestant ethos that sought to realize Christian principles in all spheres of life. The good Protestant was conceived as abiding by strict standards of family discipline, morality, honesty, thrift, austerity, and philanthropy. Idleness and waste were rejected as dangerous to the Christian's state of grace, but the honest accumulation of wealth and power through toil and enterprise was regarded as a possible outward sign of an inner grace. It has long been argued pro and con whether this list of virtues made Calvinism especially attractive to the rising capitalist class,[61] for Protestant ethics seemed to give a religious incentive to 'business virtues' and 'substance', and thus sanctioned the profit motive that Catholic scruples about 'just price' and 'usury' had tended (rather unsuccessfully) to discourage. Civic philanthropy in Protestant countries tended to take the place of ecclesiastical 'good works'. The elect would engage in good works, the Westminster Confession (see below) said, as 'the fruits and evidence of a true and lively faith'.

*   *   *

Protestantism and Political Dissent

Greater perhaps than the social significance of Protestant sectarianism was its impact upon political developments. The emphasis on active endeavour also has its political phase. As Calvinist synods became larger or representative of greater numbers, they grew in power and assertiveness, uniting their adherents, taking sides on all kinds of issues, influencing public opinion, and yet speaking, though in the name of the sovereign God, as delegates of the faithful. Representative and responsible government thus became associated with Calvinism in an age which ordinarily took for granted a close union between church and ruler and in which religious nonconformity, tantamount to political subversion, was often punished as disloyalty to the ruler in his capacity of leader in the national religious organization. In fact, in Lutheran monarchies, as also in England, the ruler formally became the supreme head of the church, thus burnishing the image of monarchy. Even in Calvinist countries presbyteries, consistories, and synods sometimes tried to dictate in civil affairs as well as theology and church matters. And yet in most states, whether Lutheran, Calvinist, or Roman, a monolithic church structure was a thing of the past. Though (with a few previously designated exceptions) intolerant of one another and of dissent within their own ranks, the various sects by seeking religious toleration for themselves became actively engaged in the struggle for freedom of conscience, political liberty, and civil rights. Even persecution indirectly served the cause of toleration, for the enforced emigration of nonconformists spread fragments of sects through much of Europe, notably the enlightened province of Holland, and to a few of the English settlements in the New World, where they gradually acquired the right to worship as they pleased.

Toleration came to the United Provinces only after a tragic political struggle. Once victorious there, Calvinism developed a schism in which political issues merged with doctrinal disputes, centring upon the divergent views of predestination held by two theologians of the University of Leyden, Franciscus Gomarus and Jacobus Arminius. The Gomarists, representing most of the preachers and Reformed congregations, stood for a strict interpretation of predestination; the Arminians (later called Remonstrants, after the 'Remonstrance' in which, in 1610, they defended their position) advocated a liberal interpretation. The Remonstrants demanded a national synod to be convoked under the authority of the States General, but the Gomarists insisted upon submitting the dispute for decision to a church synod only. The Remonstrants thus became Erastians (i.e. followers of the view, somewhat erroneously attributed to a late Swiss scientist and theologian, Thomas Erastus, to the effect that the state was dominant in ecclesiastical matters), and the Contra-Remonstrants (or Gomarists) strict Calvinists in both theology and church polity.

The dispute became a matter of personal conflict between the leading statesman of the young Dutch union, John Oldenbarneveldt, advocate of Holland, who sided with the Remonstrants, and Prince Maurice of Nassau, son of William the Silent, stadholder and a foremost general of his time. In 1614, on the initiative of Hugo Grotius, the States General attempted to grant toleration to both sides and to win mutual forbearance. The conflict in the end, however, was resolved by Maurice's military might, and the Gomarist party made captives of its opponents. It assembled a synod of churchmen at Dort (or Dordrecht), which conferred from 1618 to 1619 in a sort of Council of Trent of the Reformed Church. While most of the synod's more than one hundred members were from the Netherlands and it was intended to deal with the Dutch domestic controversy alone, a number of observers came from Switzerland, Germany, Scotland, England, and other areas where Calvinism had taken hold. It adopted the Netherland Confession and the Heidelberg Catechism. Thus orthodox Calvinism became the official faith throughout the United Provinces, and the Dutch Reformed Church set a pattern for other Calvinists. Oldenbarneveldt was executed on a trumped up charge of treason in 1619; his young colleague Hugo Grotius was imprisoned but managed to escape. The Remonstrants won official toleration in 1632, however, and the United Provinces embarked upon an extraordinary record of religious liberty that was to be one of the crowning glories of its 'Golden Age'.

The political import of religious dissent was especially evident in England, where the struggle against the Anglican episcopacy and for presbyterian or congregational government in church affairs contributed to the origin of a rebellion. A principal aim of the rebels was to limit Stuart absolutism by the establishment (or, from the point of view of some of their apologists, the retention) of constitutional government. The 'Solemn League and Covenant' concluded between Scottish Presbyterians and English dissenters in 1643 sealed the doom of Charles I. The resulting Parliamentary government and Cromwellian rule did not last. Nevertheless, the Westminster Assembly (1643–49) drew up the Westminster Confession, which has remained the creed or at the basis of the creed of Presbyterian churches ever since.

With the restoration of the Stuarts, the Anglican episcopacy was restored, and the struggle against the renewed danger of royal absolutism was resumed. After the Glorious Revolution of 1688, no English king dared openly to attempt to rule without Parliament. The Declaration of Rights and the Act of (limited) Toleration, which lifted the penalties that Protestant dissenters had had to incur for non-attendance at Anglican services, both issued within a few months of the Glorious Revolution, indicated that political liberty and religious freedom might be a logical outcome of the Reformation. Still, after the Act of Settlement (1701), none but a Protestant could hope to sit on the British throne; complete abolition of religious disabilities for subjects of the United Kingdom was not to come until the nineteenth century.

Henry IV, made king of France by civil war, assassination, and conversion, was himself assassinated in 1610. In the troubled reign of Louis XIII, Richelieu undertook the destruction of Huguenot independence, which he considered detrimental to the absolute monarchy that he wanted to establish. He succeeded largely because he was willing to use superior force while the Huguenots failed to muster the unity and organization that had made their past successes possible. Among them, as throughout the rest of France, the influence of the nobility had considerably decreased as the bourgeoisie grew in wealth and power. The Huguenot Duc de Rohan tried in vain to win the concerted support of the Huguenot cities in his fight against the threat of royal absolutism. The bourgeoisie, whether Catholic or Protestant, tended to support the king, from whom they expected protection and the promotion of their economic enterprises. The fall of La Rochelle in 1628 enabled Richelieu to take from the Huguenots their armed strength as an *imperium in imperio*, but he left them still a tolerated sect. Louis XIV, on the mistaken assumption that their number had dwindled to negligibility, first tried to force them into conformity and then revoked the Edict of Nantes (1685). The Protestants remained an outlawed sect until Louis XVI granted them toleration once more (1787).

A similar ebbing of numbers and standing came to the Protestants of Transylvania. Despite the legal equality of Catholics, Calvinists, Lutherans, and Unitarians in Transylvania, after the Thirty Years' War Protestantism gradually diminished there and in Royal Hungary. The ambitious ruling families of Transylvania joined with the Habsburgs against the Protestants. They not only got the help of the triumphant Jesuits but also relied upon the sword to root out the threat that Magyar Calvinism presented to their rule. In 1679, an uprising in Royal Hungary led by Imre Thököly revealed not only the union between the Magyar aristocracy and Protestantism but also the readiness of Magyar Protestants to ally with the Catholic king of France and the infidel sultan of Turkey against the Habsburgs. This Magyar rebellion was a phase of the war against Turkey (see Chapter I) that brought King Jan Sobieski of Poland to the relief of Vienna and resulted in a Holy League against the Turks. When the war ended (1699), Royal Hungary was no longer an elective possession of the Habsburgs but had become hereditary; Transylvania and large parts of Turkish Hungary had been annexed to Austrian Hungary; and the Hungarian Protestants were practically defence-less. Religious and political liberty was restored in 1711 only as a result of a Magyar rebellion during Austria's preoccupation with the War of the Spanish

Succession, but the Protestant population was by that time considerably reduced in size.

Other Protestant sects fared equally badly in eastern Europe. The Bohemian Brethren, having spread from Bohemia and Moravia into Poland, barely survived the Thirty Years' War under their bishop Comenius (see Chapter XVI). Unlike the Brethren, the Socinians had little following among the common people, drawing their support mostly from the Szeklar (i.e. Magyar) landowners of Transylvania, where they still survive. In the great Catholic counter-offensive that in the wake of the Thirty Years' War swept Poland, Bohemia, and Hungary under Jesuit leadership, Socinians and Brethren were practically extirpated from eastern Europe. The Socinians who found their way to England helped to found present-day Unitarianism. From England the movement spread to the Anglo-American colonies, and despite efforts to repress it, Unitarianism flourished in the English-speaking lands. In 1774 its adherents opened a chapel in London. The Bohemian Brethren, as we have seen, became the 'Moravians' of America.

*   *   *

Jansenism

Within Catholicism the quest for personal religious identification had political connotations somewhat similar to those implicit in the Protestant emphasis upon individual freedom of conscience. At the bottom of this quest lay a concern with the problem of predestination newly stimulated by Protestant, especially Calvinist, preoccupations with the teachings of the Church Fathers. At the Council of Trent the question of predestination had been touched upon by implication but never fully settled. At the same time that the issue separated Arminians and Gomarists in the United Provinces it became a focal point in a long controversy that raged between the Jesuits, who propagated an orthodox Scholasticism, and a group of theologians at the Belgian University of Louvain who demanded a more mystical approach to religion that they found in the writings of the Church Fathers. Cornelius Jansen, bishop of Ypres, took a prominent part in the controversy and presented his views in a voluminous treatise on St Augustine, in whose theology predestination had played an important part. Jansen's work, entitled *Augustinus*, was published posthumously in 1640. It attacked Jesuit rationalism and formalism, emphasizing inner experience and an active love of God rather than reason and formal devotion as the way to salvation. Love of God could come to man, Jansen held, only through an act of divine grace completely beyond human volition. Jansen's teachings thus gave a new prominence to the doctrine of predestination, softening it, however—as compared to the eternally fixed election of Calvinism—by a belief in conversion, holding forth the hope of attaining election, if God so willed, during one's earthly existence. The Jesuits subscribed to a theology which put greater stress upon freedom of the will. The Jesuit theologian Luis de Molina (1535–

1600) had in 1588 published a work entitled *Concordia Liberi Arbitrii cum Gratiae Donis, Divina Praesentia, Providentia, Praedestinatione et Reprobatione*, which, as the title indicates, undertook to show that the freedom of the human will was compatible with belief in divine grace and predestination. The Jesuits' emphasis upon the Molinist doctrine of free will led them to see in Jansenism a rank heresy, even though the Jansenists did not deny that good works were also a mark of God's grace and were in the keeping of the Catholic Church.

Jansenism spread into France through Jean du Vergier de Hauranne, abbot of St Cyran, and his disciple, Antoine Arnauld, the ablest spokesman of the rapidly growing movement. Together they established a Jansenist centre at Port Royal, site of a Cistercian convent which had been revivified by Arnauld's sister, Abbess Angélique. Dedicated to a life of practical labour and ascetic devotion, the Jansenist colony at Port Royal through its vigorous intellectual activities and its model schools (see Chapter XVI) became a great influence in French literature. Racine was educated there, and writers like Pascal and scholars like Tillemont were among its illustrious members.

Arnauld's book *De la fréquente communion* (1643), which attacked Jesuit confessional practices, was the signal for a long conflict between Jansenism and orthodox Catholicism. It was condemned as heretical by the Sorbonne and eventually by Pope Innocent X. Though never wholly adopting the ascetic life of the Port Royal solitaries, Pascal espoused the cause of Jansenism. In defence of Arnauld, he began his *Lettres écrites . . . à un provincial*, generally known as the *Lettres provinciales* (1656–57), which added to his already secure fame as a scientist (see Chapter XIV) a glorious reputation as a philosopher, moralist, and writer of prose. Before the last of these *Lettres* was published, Arnauld was expelled from the Sorbonne, but the *Lettres provinciales* have remained a quiver of ironic shafts to aim at the Jesuits, especially for their alleged casuistry and 'probabilism' (readiness to accept debatable tenets and practices).

The Jansensists' views on predestination and their advocacy of a personal religion proved welcome to the large number tired of mere dogma and ritual. At the same time, they appealed to Gallican sentiment—that is, the desire for a French national church, independent of Rome—by their refusal to accept the decisions of Rome. Pasquier Quesnel's *Réflexions morales sur le Nouveau Testament* (1671), which was both a commentary on and a translation of New Testament texts, further popularized Jansenism. The clarity with which he explained the Jansenist position made it both an effective appeal to the laity and a prime target of Jesuit theologians and the papacy.

The Jansenists' non-conformism was bound to bring them into disfavour with Louis XIV, who regarded as disloyal those who did not accept his church. Yet for years no official condemnation was forthcoming. Several factors combined to delay drastic repression: the protection of the king's cousin Madame de Longueville, the moderate attitude of Pope Clement IX, the ability of Jansenists (Arnauld above all) to temporize on all decisions by adroit legalistic arguments and manoeuvres, and widespread doubts as to whether the Jansenists were in fact as heretical as the Jesuits claimed. The death of Madame de Longueville in 1679 ended the protection Jansensists had enjoyed at court, and the French king joined hands with the pope to exterminate this new dissent. Arnauld had to go into exile in the Netherlands, followed six years later by Quesnel. The Jansenists nevertheless refused to break with the papacy, contending that 'respectful silence' without interior assent was sufficient to meet papal condemnation. The pope, they argued, might be infallible regarding questions of heresy but was not infallible regarding the 'facts', such as what was in an author's mind when writing a book. Clement issued the bull *Vineam Domini* (1705), denying the sufficiency of 'respectful silence'.

Meanwhile Louis XIV, urged on by the austere Madame de Maintenon, who was now his wife, and his Jesuit advisers, determined to uproot Jansenism as he believed he already had uprooted Calvinism from the soil of France. Port Royal was destroyed in 1709, after the recusant nuns had been forcibly removed. Importuned by the king, Clement issued a second bull, *Unigenitus* (1713), intended to deprive Jansenism of all theological justification. It anathemized one hundred and one propositions contained in Quesnel's *Réflexions* and condemned popular Bible reading, which had become a practice even among devout Catholics. The bull *Unigenitus* was considered by convinced Gallicans a distinct victory of Ultramontanism (i.e. of papal supremacy), and an important segment of French Catholics refused to accept it. Some of them migrated to Utrecht, where a Jansenist church has maintained itself since the early eighteenth century.

*   *   *

Gallicanism and Febronianism

Foremost among the French clergy who refused to accept *Unigenitus* was Cardinal de Noailles, archbishop of Paris and a leading Gallican, to whom a recent edition of Quesnel's book had been dedicated. Gallicanism thus became an ally of Jansenism. The doctrine of 'Gallican Liberties' had been in the air since the Pragmatic Sanction of Bourges (see Chapter III). An aftermath of the Conciliar Movement, it held that the king's temporal authority was not subject to papal approval and that the pope had only limited jurisdiction over French ecclesiastical affairs. With the intensification of absolutism, the Gallican Liberties had become of mounting concern to the French kings.

At the beginning of the seventeenth century, Edmond Richer, a famous Sorbonne theologian, had gone so far as to claim a voice in Gallican Church affairs for the lower clergy as successors to Jesus' disciples. This doctrine, known as 'Richerism', was dangerous, since it combined a political and social philosophy with dogmatic Gallicanism. It had been condemned by

Cardinal Richelieu and was recanted by its author. The classic formulation of Gallicanism was rather a pronunciamento of upper clergymen; it came from Bishop Bossuet in 1682 at a special assembly of the French clergy. A conflict had arisen between Louis XIV and Pope Innocent XI over the king's right to collect the *régale*, the income from vacant ecclesiastical benefices. The pope's unwillingness to permit this unilateral action led Bossuet to draw up a Declaration of Gallican Liberties, which the assembly unanimously accepted. The declaration reasserted, more explicitly than ever before, the independence of temporal sovereigns from the pope, the superiority of a general council to the pope, the powerlessness of the pope to make decisions contrary to the rules of the Gallican Church, and the fallibility of papal decisions not acceptable to an ecumenical council. In the end, Louis' numerous foreign complications obliged him to withdraw the declaration without pressing for a victory. Gallicanism, nevertheless, had served temporarily to revive conciliarism in France against ultramontane pretensions and in support of divine-right absolutism.

Contrary to Louis XIV's intention, the appeal to a general council became a weapon in the Jansenists' fight against the *Unigenitus*. A brief respite in Jansenist persecution ensued after the death of the Grand Monarch, when the indifferent Duc d'Orleans was regent, but was followed by renewed persecution when Louis XV began to reign in his own right. Gallican sentiment was strong, however, and many members of the Parlement of Paris called themselves Jansenist, though more out of political anti-clericalism than religious conviction. In 1730, when Louis XV ordered the *Unigenitus* to be registered as law, the Parlement of Paris refused to comply.

The essence of Gallicanism—that is, the politico-religious struggle against ultramontane supremacy and papal infallibility—spread beyond the borders of France. In the Holy Roman Empire the movement for national independence from Rome appeared as 'Febronianism'. The name is derived from a book entitled *De Statu Ecclesiae et Legitima Potestate Romani Pontificis*, published in 1763 (under the pseudonym Justinus Febronius) by Nikolaus von Hontheim, auxiliary bishop of Trier. Febronianism denied that the church as instituted by Jesus was a monarchy ruled by the pope. The constitution of the Catholic Church, Hontheim contended, rested upon the common episcopacy of all bishops, with the pope merely *primus inter pares*, having the role of coordinator and collaborator. Attacking the False Decretals, upon which he maintained that the pretensions of the papacy were based, Hontheim reasserted the supremacy of a general council over the pope.

Despite almost immediate papal condemnation, Febronianism was very influential in Catholic Germany and in all the Habsburg dominions. It was generally favoured by German bishops, who since the sixteenth century had enjoyed special privileges, and by the so-called 'enlightened despots' of the eighteenth century, whose reform programmes encompassed domination of the church. Devout Catholic though she was, Empress Maria Theresa refused to prohibit Hontheim's work, and Febronian principles guided Emperor Joseph II, her son, in his attempts to reform state and church. From his vigorous support of Febronianism came the name *Josephism*. Josephism relegated papal authority strictly to the domain of dogma and spiritual guidance, reserving to the state all other measures pertaining to the welfare of its subjects and the government of the church. Joseph thus promoted religious tolerance in the interest of internal peace and emphasized the practical work of the secular clergy among the people above the *vita contemplativa* of the regular orders. Hundreds of new parishes—in the emperor's view, centres of social and religious life—were established, hundreds of religious houses and oratories were closed, and theological seminaries were attached to the secular universities as part of his effort to achieve educational and other reforms. Thus the principle of Erastianism became a weapon also for Catholic monarchs seeking to make the national churches a branch of the dynastic service.

*   *   *

Quietism

Despite Jansenism's emphasis upon the intimate relation of man with God, and despite the occasional devotional outbursts and miracle working that it developed under the pressure of persecution, it was not essentially mystical in nature. In the seventeenth century Catholic mysticism took the form of Quietism. The roots of Quietism go back to the devotionalism that, under the influence of Theresa of Avila and John of the Cross, flourished in Spanish Catholicism during the sixteenth century. Both of these mystics, while stressing an essentially passive love of God, had also insisted upon an active life of practical good works and considered the mediation of the church as necessary. In France a profound religious revival followed the wars of religion. Cardinal Pierre de Bérulle (1575–1629) founded the French Oratorians, Vincent de Paul (1576–1660) the Congregation of the Mission (Lazarists) and the Sisters of Charity, and François de Sales (1562–1622) the Order of the Visitation. These men eloquently preached, in sermons and in books, a personal piety through prayer, love of God, charity, and personal service.

A later manifestation of this widespread Catholic piety was the creed known as Quietism, which, in contrast to the earlier movements, rejected the active life and need for a mediator between man and God. It taught, instead, a love of God so complete and unquestioning that self was utterly submerged and, in the highest stage of communion with God, became, without deliberate intention, the recipient of divine inspiration. This experience, attainable only in moments of most passive contemplation, was considered so personal and so far beyond the power of human reason that neither the church nor man's active desires could guide him toward it. Quietism thus carried to its logical conclusion the mystic's repudiation of the mediatorship of the church. It further asserted that supreme oneness with the divine could come only through a selfless love of God and a submission to the divine will so perfect that intentional preoccupation with the merits of good works, even consciousness of sin, must give way to a sublime indifference to all self-interested concerns. These tenets seemed to Quietism's opponents inveterate heresies alarmingly close to Protestantism.

The essence of Quietism is contained in the *Guida Spirituale* (1675) of the Spanish priest Miguel de Molinos. He resided in Italy, where elaborate ecclesiastical ceremonials provoked him to deny the importance of ritual, dogma, and church, and to emphasize 'contemplation' and 'inner peace' instead. His teachings, widely influential in Italy, remained unopposed for years, until they aroused the opposition of Jesuits, ever alert to threats to the ecclesiastical structure. After other attempts at censure had failed, Father François de La Chaise, Jesuit confessor to Louis XIV, persuaded the French king to instruct his ambassador at Rome to insist upon action. A papal bull in 1688 condemned Molinos' teachings, and he himself languished as a prisoner of the Roman Inquisition until he died in 1697.

Meanwhile Molinos' ideas had spread across the borders of Italy. The most ardent advocates of Quietism in France were the wealthy widow Guyon and her confessor, Father Lacombe. Continuing waves of devotionalism had swept France since Bérulle, François de Sales, Vincent de Paul, and others had founded their new religious societies and charitable orders, making it easy for Madame Guyon and Father Lacombe to recruit a considerable following. Both of these Quietist advocates were imprisoned about the time that Molinos was condemned, but Madame Guyon was subsequently freed and introduced by an influential friend into the circle around Madame de Maintenon. During a brief period of prominence in court society the devout widow won over the famed archbishop of Cambrai, Fénelon (1651–1715). Her writings and proselytizing in Madame de Maintenon's school at St Cyr aroused the disapproval of Bossuet, who on three separate occasions condemned Madame Guyon's teachings and attempted to silence her. Finally, after imprisonment in the Bastille, she went into exile at Blois, devoting her remaining years to piety and philanthropy.

Meanwhile Fénelon had risen in her defence and in his *Maximes des saints* (1697) undertook to explain the Quietist position of disinterested love of God. He insisted that the Quietist doctrine of the love of God required a serene passivity that might become the sole basis of a truly personal religious experience. To his opponents Quietism implied an abandonment of self so complete that the individual might become absolutely indifferent even to his own salvation. Bossuet meanwhile was producing his *Instruction sur les états d'oraison* in defence of an active, personal desire for salvation, and a prolonged and bitter controversy began between the two bishops. Eventually Fénelon's teachings were officially condemned by Pope Innocent XII, and Fénelon submitted, without, however, formally retracting his writings. His submission and exile from the court, Madame Guyon's arrest and exile, and

Louis XIV's support of Bossuet heralded the end of Quietism as a significant movement.

*   *   *

Pietism

The quest for the 'inner light' of a personal religion found more lasting form as a Protestant movement. Whereas the Catholic hierarchy was able to reassert its doctrinal supremacy over Jansensists, Quietists, and other dissidents, Protestant theology as it became formalized in its several established churches was more defenceless. One reaction against established Protestant orthodoxy took the form of Pietism, which exerted an impact upon both Calvinist and Lutheran Protestantism.

Calvinist Pietism spread from the Netherlands into the Reformed territories of Germany. Under the leadership of Jodocus van Lodenstein the first organized sect of Pietist leanings was formed within the established Calvinist church as a protest against the materialism that prosperity had brought to Holland. More radical, Jean de Labadie, a former Jesuit aspirant converted to French Calvinism, founded a religious community that was intended to constitute a 'pure church'. German Pietism merged the less shocking tenets of the Labadists with Quietist and Jansenist ideas, the mysticism of Jacob Boehme, and the poetic spirit of Friedrich von Spee, the Jesuit opponent of witch-hunting.

Phillip Jakob Spener, the founder of Lutheran Pietism as a distinct movement, became convinced through Labadie's sermons and the writings of Boehme of the necessity of reforming the Lutheran Church. In 1675 he published his *Pia Desideria*, which presented the basic tenets of Pietist devotion. His major premise was Luther's concept of the universal priesthood of all Christians, which assigned an important function to the laity. The personal religious experience that alone could give meaning to this priesthood, he taught, was a living, active Christianity, which could be achieved only through the application of Christian principles to everyday life; the essential Christian principles could be grasped only through a loving familiarity with Scripture. To combat the doctrinal inflexibility that held sway over Lutheran theology, he directed the Lutherans back to the foundation of their creed, the Bible.

Perhaps the most lasting achievement of Pietism was that it liberated the study of the Bible from the theologians and placed it in the homes of the laity. Spener advocated the formation of private devotional and study groups such as the *collegia pietatis* (which he initiated in his own house), and the *collegia philobiblica*, seminars for students of the Bible. Such groups and seminars, he held, should lead ministers as well as laity from deadening doctrinal preoccupations toward a practical devotional life, which was the outward manifestation of spiritual regeneration. Congregational singing also became an important phase of lay participation in Pietist religious activity, and Paul Gerhardt, one of the most prolific of Protestant hymn writers, provided Lutheran Pietism with some enduring hymnal expressions of religious devotion.

The University of Halle, founded in 1694 under the patronage of Frederick III, elector of Brandenburg, became a centre of Pietist learning through Spener's influence and the efforts of August Hermann Francke and Christian Thomasius (see Chapter XVI). Lectures on Scripture were made the basis for the training of ministers, who were to be practising Christians rather than orthodox doctrinaires and whose sermons were to inspire rather than to expound. Francke was called upon to help train the missionaries whom Frederick IV of Denmark proposed to send to the Danish possessions in India. Pietism thus became a factor in the Protestant missionary movement, and under Pietist influence (for Zinzendorf was a godson of Spener and an ardent Pietist), missionary work formed an important aspect of the activities of the Bohemian Brethren (see Chapter V).

Pietism was not intended by its founders to be a separatist movement and did not long outlast Spener and Francke (d. 1727) as such. Nevertheless, spiritual pietism—i.e. the call for personal devotion and a living Christianity, the emphasis upon direct communion between the individual and God, and the reliance upon feeling rather than intellect as the way to achieve this communion—continued in pious circles. Distrust of organized religion prevented effective coordination among the Pietist congregations, leaving room for the accusation that their *ecclesiolae in ecclesia* disrupted the unity of the Lutheran Church. On the whole, however, Pietism reasserted the importance of the laity, thitherto rendered almost negligible through the hardening of Lutheran orthodoxy at the hands of the clergy.

Despite its stress upon the intuitive and the sentimental in religious devotion, the very individualism of Pietism was a foretaste of the Enlightenment. The opposition to dogma and to rigid church organization as well as the emphasis upon freedom of conscience and upon personal independence provided a common ground for both Pietism and enlightened philosophy. Though closely identified with Pietism, Thomasius was also an influential exponent of enlightened ideas. In his studies of natural law, he tried to define the role of state and religion in the society of men, and echoing Spee, he attacked the persecution of heretics and the trial of witches. Where, however, the philosophers of the Enlightenment relied upon Reason, Thomasius was more likely to rely upon Revelation (see Chapter IX).

*   *   *

Freethinkers and Devotees

A great Puritan awakening inspired by Richard Baxter in seventeenth-century England in some ways paralleled the Pietism of Germany. Though relatively free of the mass emotionalism which revivalism acquired in later years, these movements were essentially revivalist. To the concern with Christianity as a personal experience and an active way of life, revivalists added a deep-seated loyalty to what they conceived to be the fundamental teachings of Christianity and a desire to impart that loyalty to the populace.

Their appeal to the masses was in large part a reaction against the several rationalist trends and the rising indifferentism of the seventeenth and eighteenth centuries (see Chapter VII). One of the rationalist trends was Latitudinarianism, an effort of English clergymen, like the Cambridge Platonists, to find a common ground upon which Protestant Christians could unite despite their doctrinal differences. Another was Deism, which developed in England and France in the seventeenth century. Deism was a 'natural' religion, free of dogma and church, in which the Deity became First Cause and little more. Some went in that direction only so far as to seek a rational Christianity; others, like Lord Herbert of Cherbury, laid the basis for the rationalist, natural, free-thinking religion of the eighteenth century.

A still more sceptical trend was that of the coterie of French poets of the seventeenth century known to their enemies as 'Libertines'. They were free-thinking, unconventional, even atheistic writers, of whom one of the most prominent was Théophile de Viau (d. 1626). They rejected, along with traditional religion, much of the faith in man, his morality, and secular authority, thus appearing to the devout in the midst of the contemporary revival in France of a prayerful, active Christianity, to be in conspiracy against God, man, and government. The state, egged on by the Jesuits, took vengeance on Viau; after a lengthy trial (1623–25), he was sentenced to exile. 'Libertinage' did not disappear, however; it merely resorted to subtleties. New writers came to be charged with it, Cyrano de Bergerac (d. 1655) among them—composers of light verse, risqué or even obscene poems, irreligious burlesques, and broad satires. Claude Le Petit was executed in 1662 for 'divine and human lèse-majesté'. Still the movement persisted until, in the eighteenth century, literary 'libertinage' merged with the Enlightenment (see Chapters IX and XV).

Revivalism was not the only reaction to the extensive corrosion worked by these rationalist trends upon orthodox theology and the minds of the un-schooled. In Catholic France, with the connivance of influential nobles, officials, and prelates, the Duc de Ventadour in 1629 founded the Compagnie du Saint-Sacrement de l'Autel, a pious, secret society. It was intended not only to combat libertines, Protestants, the less devout workers' organizations (*compagnonages*), the more arbitrary employers, the poverty and paganism of the rural districts, and other threats to orthodoxy but also to bring pressure to bear upon lax or hesitant authorities. The Compagnie operated, with great secrecy but with conspicuous success, through branches in Paris, Lyons, Marseille, and other cities, even abducting and imprisoning arbitrarily women who had incurred its displeasure. In 1660, angered by its usurpations, the government arranged to have the Parlement of Paris suppress unauthor-ized societies, but the well organized 'conspiracy of the devout' continued, sometimes under other names, reaching even into Louis XIV's cabinet.

At the beginning of the eighteenth century, in Protestant England a mass attack on irreligion began. Charles Wesley, John Wesley, and George Whitefield were among a number of Oxford students who were induced by reaction against Latitudinarianism, Deism, and other contemporary religious innovations to study Anglicanism systematically. Their derisive fellow students called them 'Methodists'. John Wesley's concern led him to visit Herrnhut and the Bohemian Brethren, and eventually to become convinced of full salvation by faith in Jesus. Although the two Wesley brothers died (Charles in 1788 and John in 1791) as Anglican ministers, and Whitefield, breaking from the Anglican Church, died a Presbyterian (1770), they were in part responsible for the founding of a new evangelical sect. Wesley lived to see the Wesleyan Methodist Church arise in England, and the Methodist Episcopal Church in the United States. Whitefield's followers had meanwhile organized the Calvinist Methodists, especially strong in Wales. During their lifetime they travelled as evangelists in Europe and America hundreds of thousands of miles, wrote thousands of hymns, and preached scores of thousands of sermons to huge spontaneous congregations in open fields, barns, and specially constructed tabernacles, calling upon their hearers to repent their sins and to revive their faith in salvation. Anglo-America proved to be the land *par excellence* of religious revivals (see Chapter V).[62]

NOTES TO CHAPTER IV

1. Professor A. Dupront points out that the proliferation of indulgences, and in particular, towards the end of the medieval period, the development of indulgences applicable to the dead, is attributable not merely to the inventive cupidity of the Roman Curia but also to a firmly-anchored religious desire to guarantee, by all means available during this life, the life of the future, that is to say, eternity.

2. Professor A. Dupront believes that for modern France a vital consequence of the Concordat was the integration of the church into the growing apparatus of absolutism, the arrogation to royal power of larger material wealth, and also, as a consequence of the system of benefices, that other form of the power of the nobility represented in the seventeenth and eighteenth centuries by the aristocratization of the church. As for the formal aspect, the concordat settlement of 1516 provided a definition of co-operation between the two powers which, while restating but abating the authority of the 'Christian body', in fact served to disintegrate it.

3. Professor A. Dupront feels that here a fundamental aspect has been left aside, the central consciousness of a *philosophia Christi*—a grandiose attempt at a Christology immanent to the century, which, while adamantly refusing all pagan ambiguity, rediscovered the dual discipline of a rhetoric and a σοφια. And again, without trying to multiply Erasmism as the French school in particular has done, there existed in the Nordic and German world, centred around the person of the young emperor, an almost eschatological hope of an imperial, secular, and Christian rule, animating for a few years certain circles among the high authorities at court, in the chancelleries of princes and nobles as well as in the cities. Erasmism was also an attempted synthesis of the two powers in the order and administration of the Empire, just as the *philosophia Christi* was the profoundly religious union of the two halves of history—Classical and Christian.

4. *Works of Martin Luther*, ed. Henry Eyster Jacobs (Philadelphia, 1915), I, p. 33.

5. To Professor A. Dupront this point might be amplified as follows: A 'linear' account of facts does not seem sufficient to convey the extraordinary correspondence existing between Luther's religious crisis and the sudden repercussions of the Ninety-Five Theses and their rapid translation into the vernacular—theses which, moreover, go far beyond a denunciation of the exploitation of indulgences. The traditional historiographer sees no more than a relatively banal causality, whereas there is, in fact, a conjunction between a 'case' of religious exigency, powerful and entirely unbridled, and the reactive spirit of the German nation, temporarily roused against the *gravamina*. That these two should have coalesced, mutually fortifying one another, is no reason to confuse them, or yet to fail to distinguish them sufficiently. For the case of Luther, see Lucien Fèbvre: *Un destin: Martin Luther* (Paris, 1945), and more particularly a work remarkable for its spiritual penetration: Joseph Lortz: *Die Reformation in Deutschland* (2nd ed., Freiburg, 1941).

On the state of mind of Germany during the second decade of the sixteenth century, see Maurice Gravier: *Luther et l'opinion publique. Essai sur la littérature satirique et polémique en langue allemande pendant les années décisives de la Réforme (1520–30)* (Paris, 1942).

Moreover, is it possible to describe Catholic doctrine to the point of saying that 'the salvation of Christians depended largely upon the clergy as the ordained administrators of the sacraments?'

Such extra-temporal schematism seems to forget that the sacramentary doctrine of the church had, in fact, been perfectly proclaimed only in the canons of the Council of Florence, just over a half a century before Luther. On the other hand there exists a theology of the church, linked with the actual history of the church, and there has never been any question but that Christ gave to Peter and the Apostles power to bind and unbind. See Matthew XIX, 18: 'Whatsoever thou shalt bind on earth shall be bound in heaven; and whatsoever thou shalt loose on earth shall be loosed in heaven.'

6. 'A Treatise on Christian Liberty', Luther, *Works*, II, p. 312.

7. *Ibid.*, p. 331.

8. Quoted in James MacKinnon, *Luther and the Reformation*, 4 vols. (London, 1925–29), II, pp. 237–38.

9. *Ibid.*, p. 277.

10. Luther, *Works*, II, p. 84.

11. *Ibid.*, pp. 70–1.

12. Professor A. Dupront stresses that Hutten's interest in the Augustine monks dates only from after his excommunication. All that went before was for him mere clerical squabbling, and the occasion one for championing Germanic liberties in the face of the essentially Roman antichrist, whereas Luther's struggle was for the essential freedom of the Christian.

13. Quoted in J. S. Schapiro, *Social Reform and the Reformation* (New York, 1909), p. 139.

14. Luther, *Works*, IV, p. 249.

15. Quoted in E. W. Zeeden, *The Legacy of Luther* (Newman Press, Md., 1954), p. 15.

16. Professor A. Dupront agrees that, from the point of view of formal classification, the heresy represented by certain major aspects of Lutheranism is still medieval. The new phenomenon is that the heresy became the church. The *Loci Communes* is already a church book. On modern heresy, reference may be made to A. Dupront, 'Reflexions sur l'hérésie moderne', *Archives de Sociologie des Religions*, No. 14 (1962), pp. 17–25.

Moreover, is it justifiable to reproach Luther for a certain decline in humanism and the proliferation of theological controversies? The truth would seem to be that
(1) the fate of humanism was of very little interest to Luther and his followers, who were profoundly religious men;
(2) Lutheran attitude and dogma faced modern religious experience with the problem of direct relations between man and God, outside all church institutions, that is to say, forced into the open the whole drama of Divine Grace.

17. Quoted in Leopold von Ranke, *Deutsche Geschichte in Zeitalter der Reformation* (Munich, 1925), II, pp. 289–90.

18. Oskar Farner, *Zwingli the Reformer*, translated by D. G. Sear (New York, 1952), p. 24.

19. G. W. Bromley, ed., *Zwingli and Bullinger*, Vol. XXIV of the 'Library of Christian Classics' (London, 1953), p. 275.

20. *Institutes of the Christian Religion*, translated by John Allen (6th American ed., Philadelphia, n.d.), II, p. 142 (bk. III, ch. XXI, par. 1).

21. *Ibid.*, p. 634 (bk. IV, ch. XX, par. 2).

22. Two aspects of the demands of Calvinism, quite properly treated in this context, could with advantage be further clarified. One is the ethical demand: to the Calvinist ethics are a style, that is to say a matter for the individual. In practice they became stereotyped: good actions and good works becoming susceptible of reconciliation. This, however, was not a fundamental religious attitude but a social mechanization. It is certain, on the other hand, that a spiritual discipline distinguishing works from faith can spread its teaching only by means of ethical rules more or less stamped with values conforming to the society concerned.

The other aspect is the sharp distinction between the two powers, rapidly obliterated by the Geneva experience. This distinction, lucidly formulated by the reformer, perhaps as a lesson of the Lutheran development, is essential to modern religion. But in this Calvin is more a deliberate clarifier than an innovator: dualism was implicit in the rule so often invoked by canonists from the fourteenth century onwards: 'Render therefore unto Caesar the things which are Caesar's; and unto God the things that are God's.' Matthew XXII, 21. (Alphonse Dupront).

23. *Institutes*, p. 645 (IV, ch. XX, par. 10).

24. For the recent literature on this controversy see George Sarton, 'Deux Centenaires: Servet et Chateillon', *Journal of World History*, II (1954), pp. 140–41.

25. Professor A. Dupront points out that the Genevan theocrat was much more political than is suggested by the traditional image, lit by the flames which consumed Servetus; the man himself was more sensitive than is generally supposed, particularly in his often tender reverence for God, and he was a closer follower of Christ than a blind servitor of a severe and powerful deity.

His genius for organization deserves special emphasis. As regards the teaching of the doctrine contained in the *Institution*, the training of pastors, the foundation of churches, this theologian was a man of action and a first-class educator. Far more than Lutheranism, Calvinism was, down to the last detail, the work of its founder. See André Bieler, *La pensée économique et sociale de Calvin* (Geneva, 1959), which is an indispensable guide on this subject.

26. To Professor A. Dupront behind all these events and actions which mark the progress of Henry VIII's appropriation of the English church, lies the policy of Thomas Cromwell. In 1536, Henry appointed him his vice-gerent in 'spirituals', thus providing complete confirmation of the spiritual omnipotence of the sovereign.

27. Quoted in *Cambridge Modern History* (Cambridge, 1934), II, p. 446.

28. *The Second Prayer-book of King Edward VI (1552), reprinted from a copy in the British Museum* (London, n.d.), pp. 169 and 172. (The spelling of the quoted words has been modernized above.)

29. Professor A. Dupront stresses in this context the originality of the Anglican tradition as it appeared in the middle of the sixteenth century. As a national church and as an essential tool of Tudor absolutism, the Church of England was 'administrative' by definition, that is by secular authority and by Acts of Uniformity. Whether the source of its dogma was traditional or derived from continental heresy, it constitutes the first experiment in the history of the modern Western world of a state church, administering spiritual affairs. If we compare the small number of men who created it, highly situated as these were in the state hierarchy, with its historical success—despite, as the present authors aptly remark, the rest of the reign of Mary Tudor—it must be recognized that this

collective form corresponded to the needs of insular society, 'dissent' finding expression later in the proliferation of religious sects.

30. To Professor A. Dupront the fact that there were no theologians was one of the anomalies of Anabaptism, which we must accustom ourselves to treating as a religion of panic, and thus wholly different from modern religions or at least established modern religions. All the more panic-stricken for its pretension to lucidity particularly in regard to adult baptism and the idea of a church of 'Saints' in which childhood had no part.

31. Quoted in Paul Wappler, *Inquisition und Ketzerprozesse in Zwickau zur Reformationzeit* (Leipzig, 1908), p. 56.

32. To Professor A. Dupront the verdict of history, even more brutal than the collection of reasons here judiciously advanced, was the intense violence of the repression, a clear avowal of panic fear. Did panic breed panic? The root of the matter seems to be—we shall find it again in very different forms in Jansenism—the absolute refusal of the other eschatological, divine, utopian, democratic society, the true City of God, which the Anabaptist preachers proclaimed and worked for, with every sort of revolutionary threat. The fact that the Tyrol became the refuge of the Anabaptists as persecution grew, right up to the end of the century, reveals, besides the obvious protection afforded by the mountains, the demand for a primitive religion, which, if not peasant, was at least non-urban. Naturally the sign of the kingdom was to be the conquest of the cities. Hence the New Jerusalem announced by the Anabaptists in their eschatological sermons.

33. P. Wappler, *Inquisition und Ketzerprozesse in Zwickau zur Reformationzeit*, p. 58.

34. *Ibid.*, p. 62.

35. Quoted in Georg Tumbült, *Die Wiedertaüfer* (Bielefeld & Leipzig, 1899), p. 63. For Calvin's attitude see George Huntston Williams, *The Radical Reformation* (Philadelphia, 1962), pp. 580–614.

36. At the age of forty, Menno Simons, until then a Frisian priest, began a wandering life in the course of which he was to show himself a remarkable and wise organizer of Anabaptists in northern Europe. (Alphonse Dupront.)

37. Quoted in Roland H. Bainton, *The Reformation of the Sixteenth Century* (The Beacon Press, Boston, 1952), p. 129.

38. Professor A. Dupront points out that it has rightly been remarked that Anti-Trinitarianism developed essentially on the fringes of Europe under the influence of men exiled from their native lands, where such beliefs had little hold. In the wake of Servetus, itinerant Italians or Spaniards, doctors or humanists, benefitting from the complicity of Calvinist communities, were to establish in Poland and Transylvania this 'pre-rationalist' doctrine, non-violent in character, deeply imbued with human sensitivity, but, on account of certain analogies with Anabaptism, often anarchic at least in regard to established authority.

   On the subject of this complex group in which men, milieux, and ideas are inextricably tangled, two authoritative studies are by Delio Cantimori, *Per la storia degli eretici italiani del secolo XVI in Europa* (Rome, 1937) and *Eretici italiani del cinquecento, ricerche storiche* (Florence, 1939).

39. To Professor A. Dupront Adrian VI was a northerner and servitor of Charles V, and like other members of the imperial circle, particularly the Erasmians, he believed in the utility of a confession of Roman sins before the Diet. Once Rome admitted the *gravamina* anything was possible. This is the explanation of the quite extraordinary mission of the nuncio Chiergati to the Diet of Nüremberg in 1523, as was underlined by Fra Paolo Sarpi, earliest historian of the Council of Trent, a man of penetrating mind, well informed, and unlikely to be guilty of complaisance towards the papacy.

40. Professor A. Dupront adds two observations which may throw some light on the evolution and meaning of this story. One is the leitmotiv of the convocation of a council. As long as it was demanded with some instance of sincerity, it is clear that there was as yet no split in the 'seamless robe', a fact of the utmost importance for the subsequent general evolution of the process of separation. The other is the 'phenomenological' aspect of the Augsburg Confession: an improvised document, skilfully negotiated and to some

extent determined by the threat of more radical confessions, it came to be the very definition of Lutheranism. With the *Loci Communes* and the *Confessio Augustana*, Melanchthon assumed the role of a wise father of the church.

41. Professor Dupront notes that the scene of negotiations between emperor and pope was Bologna, where the coronation of Charles V also took place: equally sincere, neither protagonist was duped.

42. To Professor A. Dupront the facts presented here (each perfectly correct in itself) suggest, when considered collectively, a 'wait and see' policy on the part of Charles V, completely resolved to resort to force. The emperor was too religious a man, in the most traditional sense of the term, not to do his duty as an extirpator of heresy, but it cannot be established that he accepted and encouraged for at least ten years the effort of religious *colloquia*, which were to culminate in the immense hope inspired at Ratisbon in 1541, followed by failure. It is easier to appreciate at its just value the historical role of Charles V if he is judged not by events, but in relation to his genius, his complexity, his faith, his concept of his duty and of Empire. For recent studies, putting forward different hypotheses, see 'Charles-Quint et son temps,' *Colloque du Centre National de la Recherche Scientifique* (Paris, 1959) and José Antonio Maravall, *Carlos V y el pensamiento politico del Renacimiento* (Madrid, 1960).

43. Language was another important element in Norwegian resistance: the Bible was in Danish, the only official language. (Alphonse Dupront.)

44. Professor A. Dupront notes that we are today revolted by what was normal in a world still permeated by the *habitus* of holy war. The reigning pope, Gregory XIII, a Jesuit from Bologna, was far from resembling his predecessor Pius V. And the rites of thanksgiving and commemorative medal were not innovations, any more than was the special jubilee, prescribed by the bull of September 1572. It is, moreover, clear that the Massacre of St Bartholomew seemed to serve the policy of the Holy League in the crusade against the Turks, which the former pope had been endeavouring with some difficulty to continue after the glories of Lepanto, less than a year before.

45. Professor A. Dupront stresses that in his opinion the Edict of Nantes was, of course, an edict of religious tolerance guaranteed by law. But also and above all it was a basic act of absolutism. As guarantor of religious peace, the state became the supreme power and religion a part of the order of the state. This was well understood at the time, by contemporaries invoking the peace and unity of the 'kingdom'. During the wars of religion the concept of kingdom remained the foremost collective value.

46. To this picture of the religious proselytism of Philip II should be added the specific attempt at 'caesaro-popism' which he never ceased to pursue, often fiercely against Rome. He felt that he was upholding the church within the framework of traditional orthodoxy. (Alphonse Dupront.)

47. The text here sometimes seems to adopt an outdated position: that of a *reformatio* defined as the result of the evolution of the Protestant Reformation, i.e. as a Counter-Reform. In point of fact the demand for reform was much older, the normal act of a healthy, living organism. This is proved by the interior dialogue of the *reformatio* which, during the first half of the sixteenth century was to oscillate between *reformatio in capite* and *reformatio in membris* without coming to any final choice, or, what was more serious, any actual fulfilment. In line with the genius of the Roman Catholic Church, Catholic reform was more an adjustment brought about by a series of successive gestures and without major incitations than a 'Reform' with all the apparent radicalism that this word implies. (Alponse Dupront.)

    The authors wish to call the reader's attention to the initial section of this chapter entitled 'Demands within the Catholic Church for Reform' (pp. 222–25) *and to like passages passim.*

48. Professor A. Dupront notes that besides Erasmism—a recent historiographical concept, perhaps in need of revision—another fact, clearly brought out by Delio Cantimori, is worth underlining: namely that the new ideas penetrating into Italy from across the Alps circulated in Italy in almost all milieux, perhaps not with enthusiasm but at least received with great readiness and persistent sympathy.

Among the towns which were centres of Protestantism, Vicenza, in the Venetian 'terra firma', should be mentioned. As Cantimori has observed, while the new ideas circulated freely all over the peninsula without any compartmentation by state or diocese, the capital of Anabaptism and Anti-Trinitarianism was Venice. Naples, on the other hand, was the city of the Valdesians, that is to say the disciples of Juan de Valdès.

Among the Valdesians should be remembered Ochino, the Capuchin general, who became Anabaptist. The whole movement, difficult to circumscribe, was characterized by its aristocratic clientèle, almost exclusively Italian, and from the spiritual point of view, by its platonizing tendencies. The only man in contact with the masses was Ochino, and, as far as the nostalgia for Platonism was concerned, one has only to follow the career of Vittoria Colonna, her exaltations with the aging Michaelangelo, her relations with Reginald Pole and his group at Viterbo, to understand what 'chiaroscuro' powers they encountered in these circles marked by a spiritual quest which neither Aristotelianism nor Thomism could satisfy.

49. Professor A. Dupront indicates that the Oratorio del Divino Amore was organized under the influence of Saint Catherine of Genoa. Destined to serve as a model, it nevertheless takes its place as part of a movement for the foundation of charitable brotherhoods in many Italian cities at the end of the fifteenth and beginning of the sixteenth centuries. The aim of these brotherhoods founded for charitable purposes, was a communal spiritual life among its members. Their main inspiration was secular, and at the Oratorio itself, in the beginning, the number of priests was limited: a clear indication of a strong current of religious spirituality in peninsular life before the Reform. Contemporary Italian historiography is in process of discovering this at the same time as it emphasizes the wide influence of certain important figures such as Paolo Giustiniani, and the role of certain prelates also pre-reformers in their respective dioceses even before Gianmatteo Giberti in Verona, a model of Catholic reform prior to the Council of Trent.

50. Quoted in Leopold von Ranke, *Die romischen Päpste in den letzten vier Jahrhunderten* (2 vols.; Hamburg, n.d.), I, pp. 89–90.

51. To Professor A. Dupront von Ranke's interpretation needs supplementation: the Consilium was essentially a repertory of abuses, the important factor being its drafting by a commission of cardinals, thus representing an act of *reformatio in capite*. Its fundamental rule, however, was in no way new: true reform—the return to 'the old sublimity' meant the application of canon law; i.e. the reinstatement of church order. Sadeleto's letter to the Genevans marks the end of a whole series of epistolary attempts on the part of the Bishop of Carpentras, among them the famous letters to Melanchthon (June 1537) and to Sturm (July 1518), perhaps a doomed but sincere aspect of a 'pre-irenic' tendency.

52. Professor A. Dupront feels that the effective participation in the Diet of Ratisbon is here somewhat obscured. The Protestant protagonists were Melanchthon and Sturm: Luther was in safe custody in the hands of the Elector of Saxony, who was opposed to the conciliation.

53. The bull *Licet ab initio*, foundation of the future Holy Office, should not be considered as establishing a Spanish-type inquisition. In point of fact it arose, in conjunction with certain panic reflexes against the contagion of heresy, from a need for centralization, establishing Roman authority throughout the peninsula to counteract the weaknesses of diocesan officialdom. It is true that Gian-Pietro Caraffa succeeded in appropriating the institution from the very beginning. (Alphonse Dupront.)

54. Professor A. Dupront thinks that it is not desirable to place on the same plane all the religious families born of the so-called Catholic Reform. For example, the foundation and early development of the Capuchin order was typically medieval as was also their habit of seeking to establish themselves in the countryside, in hermitages, in fulfilment of their original vocation of being, in the actual terms of their Constitution of 1629, '*Fratres Minores Vitae Eventuticae*'. The other congregations of the Catholic reform were, by their very nature, urban.

55. Professor A. Dupront finds that more characteristic of most of their founders are the imprint of advanced spirituality, a kind of spiritual aristocracy, and, in almost every case, the influence of a female mystic, vowed to sainthood. Their precipitate appearance during

the first half of the cinquecento confirms the latent desire for spirituality fermenting in Italian society since the end of the fifteenth century, and even more deeply felt at the time of the foreign occupation of the peninsula.

Filippo Neri, though Florentine in origin, the Roman saint *par excellence*, constitutes a case apart. In founding the Oratorio he sought to create a centre of total religious life, intimately bound up with the life of the city—on the borderline of the regular and the secular—inspired by the desire to incarnate a 'Christian humanism'. An experiment lasting for two generations at the most, but serving to attract a number of noble and attractive non-Oratorian personalities, such as Agostino Valiero, bishop of Verona.

56. To Professor A. Dupront the historical figure of St Carlo Borroméo is here presented somewhat hagiographically. Did he really exercise so great an influence in the Roman Curia, even during the pontificate of his uncle Pius IV, who was in no way a religious character? As for his retirement in Milan, it is certain that there was no further place for him in Rome during the pontificate of Pius V, while at Milan he found his family and also a diocese in which to carry out his apostolic and defensive action against the Spanish power and the authority and liberties of the church. An ascetic, but, aside from certain Spanish influences, little inclined to mystic meditation. Regrettably the great Lombard prelate, destined after the Council of Trent to become the 'good bishop', has not yet found the biographer demanded by what is still the enigma of his personality and his historical importance.

Must we accept the authors' suggestion as to a new type of saint of the Catholic reform? The social tendency is evident, and there are no more martyrs. What is most striking about the cohort of saints borne upon the altars during the first decade of the seventeenth century is the great diversity of 'mortals'—bishops, founders of orders—represented, indicating a demand on the part of different milieux for a renewal of exemplary images. The canonization of founders of orders in particular was for each of the new orders a final consecration of their power and of their virtue of collective sanctification.

57. These figures are taken from a study prepared for this volume by the Spanish National Commission for UNESCO through the mediation of Professor Joaquin Perez Villanueva.

58. Hubert Jedin, 'Conciles généraux', *loc. cit.*, discusses the literature dealing with the Conciliar Movement and the Council of Trent.

59. The decrees of the twenty-third *sessio*, *The Canons and Decrees of the . . . Council of Trent*, translated by J. Waterworth (London, 1848), pp. 172–74.

60. Ranke, *Deutsche Geschichte im Zeitalter der Reformation*, V, p. 108.

61. For a recent discussion of this controversy and its bibliography, see Sidney A. Burrell, "Calvinism, Capitalism, and the Middle Classes: Some Afterthoughts on an Old Problem', *Journal of Modern History*, XXXII (1960), pp. 129–41.

62. *In the course of printing this volume, the distances between the publishers (London), the editors (Paris), and the author-editor (Chicago) prevented the inclusion of the author's rejoinders to Professor Dupront's comments (except the one in n. 47 above). A general remark, therefore, seems called for. While the authors are indebted to Professor Depront for the details he has provided, they do not think that their interpretation of the reform spirit within the Catholic Church before, during, and after the rise of Protestantism differs markedly from his. Nor, despite their emphasis at times upon political considerations and his on religious convictions, do they find themselves differing widely from him, or he from them, even in those regards—as other chapters of this volume will make still clearer.*

CHAPTER V

OTHER RELIGIOUS EVENTS (1500–1775)

CHRISTIANITY OUTSIDE EUROPE

WITH varying degrees of success, Christianity accompanied Europe's explorers and settlers to Africa, Asia, and the Americas (Map I). The Spanish and Portuguese kings, looking upon their new lands east and west as papal grants, felt under special obligation to spread the Christian gospel among them.[1] Cardinal Ximenes in 1516 required every expedition to the Indies to carry missionaries, and famous missionaries sometimes accompanied famous conquistadores. The first effective group of missionaries were twelve Franciscans, who were solemnly welcomed to New Spain by Hernan Cortes in 1524; others reinforced them soon. By 1531 the Franciscans claimed to have baptized about 1,000,000 natives. The Dominicans followed shortly after the Franciscans, and among the Dominicans was Bartolomé de Las Casas, champion of the Indian slave, who for a time was bishop of Chiapa in Guatemala. The Augustinians went out in smaller numbers. And after the Jesuit order was founded, it became the most active of all. Within a century the Spanish-American patriarchate included six archbishropics, thirty-two bishoprics, and two abbeys. In 1676, the archbishopric of Brazil was created, with its seat at Bahia; Portuguese America comprised nine bishoprics at the close of the eighteenth century.

In 1568 Philip II called a Junta Magna to consider the problems of the clergy in the new Spanish lands. This congress proposed the establishment of a patriarchate in New Spain. To the question whether the colonial clergy was responsible to pope or to king it answered largely in favour of the king: a bishop was to be named by the Holy See only on presentation by the king, and a colonial bishop was to name his subordinates only after presentation to the royal provincial representative. In the Antilles dioceses tended to coincide with the royal boundaries; in Mexico they tended to correspond with the missions.

The Junta Magna also limited the missions in America to four orders—Franciscans, Dominicans, Augustinians, and Jesuits, although others already engaged in missionary work nevertheless stayed on. The Franciscans after 1682 established a special missionary branch of their order, of whom Junipero Serra (1713–84) was perhaps the most celebrated; some of the important cities of modern California owe their beginnings at least partly to him. The Dominicans carried on their work mostly in already founded missions and cities. The Jesuits began with the coast settlements of Brazil but spread from there to Mexico, Peru, and elsewhere. Among their Brazilian missionaries José de Anchieta (1530?–97), founder of São Paulo, was probably the most successful. At first they worked within settlements but eventually undertook to establish new missions on the frontiers, especially among the Guarani and Araucanian Indians. Missionaries also worked among the *encomendados*, for the *encomendero* was required to provide instruction in the Christian religion. As the *encomienda* disappeared (see Chapter I), the state, regarding the Indians as its wards, assumed responsibility for continuing their religious education.

Some of the clergy made a special effort to protect the Indian from exploitation. Hence the Indian sometimes received privileges that the Negro rarely enjoyed—in education and office-holding, for example. In Pedro Claver, Jesuit missionary to the Negro slaves, the Negro, too, found a champion, as had the Indian in Las Casas. Over a period of forty years, Claver baptized and befriended around 300,000 of the slaves who arrived on the monthly slave ship at Cartagena. The Inquisition was introduced into Spanish America in 1569 but was not permitted to try Indians, since they were regarded as incapable of valid judgments. Hence many local customs were allowed to enter into the Indians' Christian ritual.

The work of the missionaries necessarily led them toward educational efforts. They studied and wrote books upon local ethnology. They learned the native language and customs, and prepared dictionaries and grammars. They founded schools and universities, such as the technical college of Santa Cruz in Mexico and the College of San Andrés in Quito. They encouraged local artistic talents in the building and maintenance of their churches and cathedrals. To a considerable extent, the eighteenth-century idea of 'the noble savage' was an outcome of their reports, particularly of Las Casas's, upon their experiences with the Indians. Without their investigations and writings, knowledge of the history and culture of antecedent Amerindian societies would have been largely lost.

Perhaps the most celebrated missionary effort in Spanish America involved the Jesuit *reducciones* (settlements of converted Indians) in Paraguay, begun early in the seventeenth century. At their highest point, the 1730's, there were thirty of them, estimated to have about 140,000 inhabitants. Fantastic stories arose about the rich Jesuit kingdoms in Paraguay, and Brazilian slave raiders made attacks upon them, forcing them to move to areas farther south, with consequent interruption of their prosperity. They also suffered from the frequent defensive wars that they had to fight with the warlike, unconverted tribes, who martyred a number of Jesuit fathers. In 1750 seven of the Paraguay *reducciones* were required by treaty to transfer bodily to a part of Uruguay under Portuguese control, but the Jesuits and their wards resisted in the War of the Seven Reductions, yielding only in 1756. When the Society of Jesus was suppressed in Spanish America (1767), the remaining *reducciones* in Paraguay were placed under the Franciscans, but they soon deteriorated and eventually disappeared. The Portuguese annexed much of the territory previously controlled by the Jesuits.

* * *

Catholics and Protestants in North America

In North America, the first Christian settlement that lasted was founded by the Spanish at St Augustine, Florida, in 1565. Whether it could survive as a Spanish Catholic community was at first doubtful, for a French Huguenot settlement was about the same time established at Fort Caroline, Florida. The Spanish admiral Pedro Menéndez de Avilés wiped out the male population of the French colony, however, and shortly afterward slaughtered the Huguenot admiral Jean Ribault and his crews, shipwrecked in an effort to attack Menéndez by sea. Even though a French force two years later retaliated by massacring the Spanish garrison left at Fort Caroline, Florida remained relatively safe for Catholicism until the eighteenth century.

The English soldier James Edward Oglethorpe founded Georgia in 1733 largely in order to keep the area north of Florida out of Spanish hands. Then he took the offensive against the Spanish in Florida, but his siege of St Augustine in 1740 was futile. Florida later fell to the English by the Treaty of Paris (1763), which ended the Seven Years' War, but in 1783 it was returned, still Spanish and Catholic. Hundreds of the French Catholic loyalists of Acadia, which was surrendered to the British in 1713 and renamed Nova Scotia, were in 1755 deported to Georgia, but they soon voluntarily went elsewhere. Georgia, along with North and South Carolina, excluded 'papists' from office until well past our period. On the other hand, these colonies gave full rights to French Huguenots, Moravian Brethren, and other Protestant refugees from Europe.

The other Anglo-American colonies in North America, with the exception for a time of Maryland, were even more exclusively dominated by Protestants. The Protestants came after the Reformation was clearly irreversible in England and at a time when in England feudal obligations were essentially a thing of the past and the individual was relatively free to move about. They brought with them notions of freedom of movement and of conscience (at least for themselves) that probably were less familiar in other parts of Europe and that were bound to become more firmly entrenched among frontiersmen as they tamed a wilderness. Some things the wilderness did for them that Europe could not well do; it cracked the cake of custom, it thinned the influence of overseas authorities and institutions, and it offered them room to go elsewhere if they disagreed with their neighbours.

And disagree they did. The colonists who settled Virginia accepted the Church of England. So did the settlers of the other English colonies eventually established south of Virginia. The Pilgrims who settled in Massachusetts in 1620 were Separatists—i.e. Congregationalists—and other Puritan critics of the established church of England. The Mayflower Compact which they drew up on board ship to serve as their fundamental law was perhaps the first example of 'a social contract' that was expressly written down as such and actually adopted by all those it was intended to govern. Plymouth was the first of several Separatist settlements in Massachusetts. Massachusetts was a strict Puritan state, but the rest of Anglo-America tended toward greater religious flexibility. Strict Calvinism forced Roger Williams and others of a more Arminian view out of Massachusetts and led to the establishment of new colonies in Rhode Island, Connecticut, and New Hampshire—colonies of individualists who not only insisted upon free popular consent as the basis of government but also were ready to extend to other Protestants a greater degree of toleration than they themselves had enjoyed in Massachusetts. New York was built upon the basis of the Dutch colony of New Amsterdam, captured (1664) at a time when Dutch toleration had permitted peoples of many tongues and of various religions (including Jews) to live there. Under King James II it even had a Catholic governor for a time, but Catholicism was all but stamped out after the 'Glorious Revolution.' Pennsylvania and Delaware were the proprietary colonies of William Penn and his descendants, who were Quakers, pacifists, friends of the Indians, advocates of tolerance, and opponents of slavery. Not only Mennonites and Moravians but also Jews and Catholics received asylum there.

Except for Maryland during its early history, Catholics nowhere dominated any of the Anglo-American colonies, and even in Maryland they were not the majority. Maryland was founded by George Calvert (afterward Lord Baltimore), a recent convert to Catholicism. It was politically controlled by Catholics until the English Civil War, when the Puritans ousted the proprietor and seized control of the government (1652). Religious liberty had, however, been permitted from the start and was formally proclaimed in 1649. Terminated by the Puritans, it was restored in 1658. The Baltimores retained their proprietary rights until after the 'Glorious Revolution' and the reign of William and Mary. In 1692 Maryland became a royal colony with the Church of England as its established church, and in 1713 the Baltimores became Protestant. In 1718 Catholics were disenfranchised, and in 1754 the property of the Catholic clergy was confiscated. Catholics continued, however, to live in Maryland unmolested, and Irish immigrants were numerous. The accepted estimate of the number of Catholics in the Anglo-American colonies on the eve of the American Revolution is 25,000, mostly in Pennsylvania and Maryland. Philadelphia had the first and largest organized parish. North Carolina tolerated Catholics but excluded them from office.

As already noted (Chapter IV), the Protestants of Anglo-America were particularly susceptible to religious revivalism. Among the sparse populations of frontier settlements a man was likely to be measured by what he could do rather than by his religious preferences. The indifferentism thus imposed was fundamentally incompatible with orthodoxy, which was strictly enforced only in New England under Calvinist influences, and New England's Calvinists themselves were vulnerable to the appeal of Arminianism, with its liberal view of predestination and forgiveness of sin. To counteract Arminianism and sin, Jonathan Edwards (1703–58), Congregationalist minister of Northampton, Massachusetts, began a series of fiery sermons that started a wave of religious revivals. It spread from 1734 to 1740 throughout New England, culminating in the 'Great Awakening', a chain of devotional meetings and movements that after 1740 moved from New England over the entire Atlantic seaboard, greatly aided by the powerful sermons of the strictly Calvinist George Whitefield.

The Great Awakening was characterized by mass conversions on an unprecedented scale. In the process it was constrained to adapt itself to large numbers of men of different persuasions, especially in the frontier towns, whose inhabitants flocked to hear the revivalists. The message and eloquence of an Edwards or a Whitefield could fill the churches, but sermons such as Edwards' famous *Sinners in the Hands of an Angry God* (1741) and books such as his *Freedom of the Will* (1754) painted too lurid a picture of man's depravity, placed election too far beyond human endeavour, and painted too deterministic a philosophy to satisfy the religious needs of frontiersmen conscious of their own worth and will power. Many a man who had been indifferent or had belonged to the older Puritan creeds joined the Baptist Church, equally evangelical and more Arminian, or the Methodist Church. Edwards himself paid dearly for his inflexibility, since his insistence upon admitting to holy communion only the truly converted led to his dismissal from the congregation which his labours had revitalized and increased. He went out as a missionary to the Indians.

The Great Awakening had implications beyond the realm of theology. For one thing, it made the nonconformist sects of Anglo-America conscious of their strength, and it gave them reason to question the supremacy in America of the established Church of England. For another, it led to the increase in the number of colleges and academies in America (see Chapter XVI). In addition, it had a significant impact upon the literary development of a colonial people. Edwards was the first notable American writer to deal philosophically with the problems of mind, will, and virtue. An upsurge of sermons and other edifying prose and of pious poetry and hymns revealed the spread and intensity of religious emotion, the overpowering joy of a personal faith. Edwards had himself given the cue in a sermon in 1734: 'There is such a thing as a Spiritual and Divine Light, immediately imparted to the Soul by God, of a different nature from any that is obtained by natural means'.[2] The Great Awakening thus helped to articulate the hopefulness and self-reliance that were important ingredients of an American political creed that was contemporaneously taking hold. The spirit of self-determination in the religious sphere was to be translated into the political language of anti-colonialism when the occasion arose (see Chapter IX).

★   ★   ★

Missions to the Eskimos and Indians

Danish missionaries, especially Hans Egede (1686–1758) and his son Paul (1708–89), carried the Gospel to the Greenland Eskimos, and the various Protestant sects that peopled the colonies of England in America carried on missionary work among the Indians. Presbyterians, Anglicans, and Moravians were particularly conspicuous among them. Nevertheless, although 'the propagation of the Gospel' had been declared to be 'first' of the 'Principal and Maine Endes' of the Virginia Company (founded 1606), few North American Indians were converted out of their 'almost invincible ignorance'[3] by the English-speaking colonists. One of the outstanding English missionaries was John Eliot, who preached to the Massachusetts Indians in their own tongue and translated the Bible (1661–63) and other sacred literature for them. On his initiative Parliament incorporated the Society for the Propagation of the Gospel in New England (1649), and before his death he and his helpers converted several thousand Indians.

Large-scale conversion of North American Indians, however, was rather the work of the Catholic missionaries of New France. A few Recollects (Franciscans) arrived in 1615, and in 1623 Champlain sought the assistance of the Jesuits. Until Richelieu founded the company known as the Hundred Associates (1627), little progress was made even by the French; the Associates were pledged to bring the natives instruction in the 'Catholic, Apostolic, Roman religion'. The British capture of Quebec (1629) temporarily delayed their efforts, but after it was returned to the French (1632), the Jesuits began missionary work in earnest (1635). Subsequently (1664) the Recollects returned, but the conversion of large numbers of Hurons and some Iroquois was mostly the work of Jesuit martyrs like Father Bréboeuf and Father Jogues, massacred by the Iroquois in the Iroquois-Huron wars (1646 and 1649 respectively) because the Iroquois considered them allies of the Hurons. In part as a missionary to the Indians Father Marquette canoed down the Mississippi in 1682 and made the vast valley of that river a French Catholic area (except for a brief Spanish occupancy) until the nineteenth century.

When the British won Canada (1763), they allowed its French population to retain the Catholic religion and hierarchy under the bishop of Quebec. Indeed, in 1774, by the Quebec Act, they even widened Quebec's boundaries to the south in order to keep the Ohio valley from settlement by rebellious Protestant English-speaking colonists. Quebec thus remained French-speaking and Catholic even though Jesuits and Franciscans were suppressed.

In Spanish America the missionary frequently preceded the conqueror into the wilderness. While missionaries often were the agents of the conquerors, they also did much to counteract the cruelty of *conquistadores*, slavers, and exploiters. Las Casas held that 'the way to bring into the bosom of the Christian faith and religion men who are outside the church must be a method which persuades their understanding and which moves, exhorts and gently attracts the will'.4

The adaptability of the Amerindian combined with his lack of doctrine and systematic theology to make his conversion relatively easy. Thus, by missionary work as well as by white settlement, the Western Hemisphere became Christian. The Jesuit missions alone are sometimes credited with having brought to Catholicism in the course of time probably more souls in America than were lost to Protestantism in Europe.

*   *   *

Catholic Missions in Asia

Christian missionary activity in Asia in modern times began with the arrival of the Portuguese in India in the 1490's and was extended by the Spanish occupation of the Philippines in the 1560's and 1570's. This work was in the hands of the monastic orders, which functioned under the patronage of the Portuguese and Spanish kings, although a secular clerical hierarchy was also set up to minister to Europeans. Archbishoprics were ultimately established at Goa and Manila. Of the missionary orders the Jesuits soon became the most important in the Portuguese area; in the Philippines they shared the field with Augustinians, Franciscans, and Dominicans. Among the missionaries patronized by Spain, Spaniards probably predominated, but among those who acted under Portuguese patronage after Francis Xavier, Italians were for a long time the most influential if not the most numerous.

Franciscans undertook the first serious Catholic missionary work in India, but from the time of the arrival of Xavier in 1542 the Jesuits rapidly assumed the lead. From India and Ceylon Xavier went to Malacca and Amboina in 1545–46; in 1549 he inaugurated missionary work in Japan; and in 1552 he died on an island off the coast of China in a vain effort to plant a mission there. Most influential in developing the Jesuit mission and shaping its policies was Alessandro Valignani (1539–1606), whose activities as visitor (i.e. superior) of the Society (1574–1606) ranged from Mozambique and India through the Indies to Japan and China. During the 1580's Matteo Ricci was the chief figure of the Jesuit mission in China (see Chapter XIV). He mastered the Chinese language. His scientific instruments and knowledge roused the Chinese interest in Europe, and his reports home excited Europeans toward greater missionary effort in China. The Jesuit College at the University of Coimbra became the principal training centre for Jesuits going to the East. During the course of two centuries it sent out about 1,650 missionaries.

After 1622, with the formation of the Sacra Congregatio de Propaganda Fide, commonly referred to as the Propaganda, the papacy took a more direct hand in promoting missions. The Propaganda maintained a college for educating missionaries to and nationals from foreign lands, it kept a formidable printing establishment busy, and it showed a keen interest in training native clergy. The papacy began to assert its authority over the missions through vicars apostolic and bishops and thereby came into conflict with the Portuguese, for the king of Portugal claimed the *padroado*, or right to promote Christianity and control appointments in the East, conferred by earlier papal bulls. The papacy respected the rights of the Portuguese in areas under their immediate administrative control but asserted its own rights elsewhere, while the Portuguese claimed jurisdiction over all the East.

The missionary spirit spread eastward rapidly. In the seventeenth century Germans and other central Europeans began to appear in increasing numbers among the missionaries of the various orders. The Société des Missions Étrangères was formed in Paris in 1663, and then the French moved into the field in increasing numbers. The Paris missionary society sought lay support and put its emphasis upon the secular clergy as missionaries. It called particularly for the training and establishment of an indigenous secular clergy in foreign lands. François Pallu, a leader in founding this society, was himself an active missionary in Siam and Indo-China. By 1700 the societe had sent out 119 priests, and 198 by 1800. The Capuchin order also increasdy its missionary work.

In the East the missionaries encountered difficulties that did not arise in the New World. In Asia the Europeans did not have political control, Islam was a successful competitor, and, above all, highly developed civilizations were well entrenched, each with its own refined systems of religion, thought, and values, expounded and defended by an established learned class. Hinduism, Buddhism, and Confucianism could meet Christianity on its own intellectual level. Only in Malaya, the East Indies, the Philippines, and, to a certain extent, Japan did the lack of sufficient commitment to an existing system offer good conditions for proselytizing. Islam, already politically dominant in India and actively engaged in spreading its political control in the Indies, was more amenable to the extensive cultural adaptations needed to win the uncommitted than was Christianity. Furthermore, partly because of the very lack of theological and moral sophistication on the part of the East Indians, the Jesuits considered them poor prospects and chose to make their major efforts elsewhere. In the long run Catholicism made effective progress only among the relatively uncommitted peoples who came also under European political control.

The high level of the Eastern civilizations posed a problem of missionary policy. The Jesuits quickly realized that their success might depend upon a sympathetic hearing from the political and intellectual guardians of the established systems and that to get such a hearing Christianity must not appear antithetical to the established order. Under the tolerant leadership of some Italian humanists they therefore adopted a programme of cultural accommodation, based on the postulate that any culture might develop its own Christian forms. They allowed Christian converts to continue in those beliefs and practices which they deemed not positively contradictory to the essential doctrines of Catholicism, while the missionaries themselves studied the local languages, literature, and ideas and attempted to become as much a part of the local culture as possible. They also attempted to make themselves more acceptable by expounding the new science of the West, which seemed to appeal to many Eastern intellectuals. Most of the other missionary groups, however, taking their cue from the unbending Iberian conquistadores, insisted on Europeanizing their converts. In this difference of approach lay the seeds of ultimate controversy.

The two methods reinforced each other at first. Readiness to adapt, aided by favourable political conditions, enabled the Jesuits to make surprising progress during the late-sixteenth and early-seventeenth centuries in Hindu and Mogul India, Japan, and China—all areas outside Iberian political control. The other missionary orders met with their major successes where Spanish and Portuguese political power was strong. By 1600 the number of Christians in the East probably exceeded 1,250,000. The largest single group, if the Syrian Christians, many of whom had come under Catholic leadership, be counted, were in the Portuguese-dominated areas along the Malabar coast and in Ceylon, but Japan and the Spanish Philippines each counted about 300,000 converts. The Christians of the East Indies (found especially in the Spice Islands) probably numbered fewer than 100,000. The successes of the Christian missionaries in China were just beginning.

Modest though these figures were in proportion to the total population, they appeared to indicate great possibilities until some setbacks occurred. In Japan, unification under the Tokugawa shogunate led in 1613–14 to the prohibition of Christianity as potentially inimical to national traditions and the ruling authority. This reversal proved especially disastrous when the prohibitory decrees were followed by savage persecutions, which ultimately wiped out all but a few thousand secret practitioners of Christianity. After the middle of the century the Catholics lost further ground to the Dutch Protestants in Ceylon and the Indies, and about the same time in India the policies of Aurangzīb and internal strife (see below) created conditions unfavourable to Christian missionary activity.

Several propitious developments counterbalanced these losses. Shortly after 1600 the Jesuit Robert de Nobili began a relatively successful mission among the Hindus of south India by adapting Christianity to the caste system.5 A growing stream of devoted men from France reinforced the missionaries in India and elsewhere and initiated new activities in Siam (1662–64). Missionaries banished from Japan met with some success in Cochin-China and Annam. Rapid progress was recorded also in the Philippines. In China, the scientific activity of Ricci was duplicated first by Adam Schall and then by Ferdinand Verbiest (see Chapter XIV), winning for the

Jesuits the toleration of many officials, the patronage of the newly established Manchu emperors, and acceptance of their missionary activity, which culminated in a general edict of toleration for Christianity in 1692. The high water mark of this early period of Christian missionary activity in the East was probably reached about 1700, when the total number of converts was in the neighbourhood of 3,000,000—mostly Catholics. Over 1,000,000 lived in India and perhaps 600,000 (partly Protestant) in Ceylon, 800,000 in the Philippines, 300,000 in China, and 100,000 each (partly Protestant) in Indo-China and the Indies.

Thereafter the vitality of Christian missions in the East, Catholic and Protestant alike, declined, probably reaching its nadir about 1775. The total number of Christians at that time was perhaps as great as in 1700, but the China mission was practically dead, and little expansion had taken place elsewhere, while the morale of the missionaries was generally low. The reasons for this demoralization were numerous. To a certain extent the scepticism that accompanied the Enlightenment in Europe discouraged enthusiasm for missionary activity. More important, however, was the decline of Catholic Portugal and Spain and the concomitant rise of Protestant Holland and Britain as commercial and colonial powers in the East. In a some-times unedifying competition Dutch Protestant missionaries vied with Catholics in Ceylon and replaced them in the Indies, where in addition Islam was busy establishing its hold. In India's constant internal strife, Hindu Maratha nationalists and ardent Muslim princes (like Tipu Sultan) also victimized Christians and destroyed their churches. Jurisdictional rivalries among Portugal, Spain, and the papacy and among the various religious orders and societies further weakened the Catholic effort. These rivalries led to a notorious controversy over ritual that perhaps did more damage to Catholic missionary activity in the eighteenth century than any other single circumstance.

This 'Rites Controversy' resulted from the Jesuits' efforts to make Christianity acceptable to the inhabitants of China, Japan, and India. In India their readiness to accommodate local customs and practices led to the continuation by some of the converts of caste rules and procedures. In China it amounted to the toleration of certain aspects of ancestor worship and permitted Confucian scholars and officials who had become Christians to perform the prescribed rites honouring Confucius. The Christian opponents of the Jesuits were especially shocked that the latter also accepted *T'ien* (*Heaven*) or *Shang-ti* as translations for *God* along with the unobjectionable *T'ien-chu* (*Lord of Heaven*). As early as 1623 the papacy had given a guarded approval of the Jesuit practices in India (the so-called Malabar rites), which were later attacked by the French Capuchins, but the complicated nature of the problem delayed a definitive decision. When Franciscans and Dominicans under Spanish patronage entered China from the Philippines in the 1630's, they immediately found fault with Jesuit latitudinarianism and insisted that their rivals were compromising the basic doctrines of Christianity. The Dominican missionary and world-traveller Domingo de Navarrete (1618–86), among his careful notes on the memorabilia he encountered, told of these controversies, and through him and other correspondents in China, Europe kept well informed not only of Chinese cultural achievements but also of the Jesuits' evangelical 'accommodation' to Confucion rites. A prolonged and bitter conflict ensued, spreading from the Far East to Europe and involving the whole Catholic world, lay as well as clerical.[6]

The Jesuits solicited the K'ang-hsi emperor's opinion, which was naturally in favour of the Chinese rites. On the other hand, in 1704, the papacy finally ruled against the Jesuits, forbidding ancestor worship, participation in the rites honouring Confucius, and the use of T'ien as the name of the Divine. A papal legate, Maillard de Tournon, was sent out to enforce the papal decree and to pacify the Chinese emperor. In India he ruled against the Jesuits' Malabar rites. In China the imperial wrath descended upon him when, in 1706, the papal position became known, and the emperor in effect ordered the banishment of those missionaries who did not accept the Jesuit position. Though Maillard de Tournon ordered the missionaries, on pain of excommunication, to conform with the papal decision, the Portuguese-appointed hierarchy in the East refused to recognize the legate's jurisdiction. As a consequence, many Jesuits' chose to remain in China, while members of other orders were forced to leave. Later efforts to work out a settlement came to nothing, since neither the emperor nor the pope would change his position.

This turn of events encouraged hostile Confucian officials to denounce Christians vehemently. Consequently the Yung-cheng emperor in 1724 banished all missionaries except those retained in his service, ordered converts to give up Christianity, and directed that churches be turned into public places. Although this and later anti-Christian decrees were not rigorously enforced, the mission in China rapidly declined. Since the papacy, with minor modifications, upheld the legate's decision regarding the Malabar rites, the Jesuit mission in south India was also handicapped at this crucial juncture. In part, the ill-will engendered toward the Jesuits by the Rites Controversy reflected the increasing opposition for other reasons to the Society of Jesus in Europe. It was banished from the Portuguese domains in 1759, suppressed in France in 1764 and in the Spanish possessions in 1767, and formally dissolved by the pope in 1773. Thus the major Catholic missionary organization in the East ended (at least until the Jesuit order was again officially restored in 1814), and the Lazarists, who tended to take over in its stead, were not prepared to carry on its far-flung activities.

*   *   *

Protestant and Orthodox Missions

Protestant missionaries received feebler support from governments than did the Catholic missionaries and made less headway, but it was a notable headway still, not only in Dutch, Danish, and British America but also in the East Indies. In 1705 the first Protestant mission in India was established by German Pietists at Tranquebar with the aid of the Danish king Frederick IV and of August Hermann Francke. The Moravian Brethren, with little but their faith to sustain them, went out as missionaries to Greenland and Surinam, to Algeria and the Cape of Good Hope, to Ceylon and other distant points, and even sent a mission to the Hottentots (1737). Except, however, for the ancient Coptic Christians of Ethiopia and Egypt and the newer Calvinist Boers of South Africa, Africa felt little Christian influence, Catholic or Protestant, until the nineteenth century, and although Christian Friedrich Schwarz (1726-98), a Pietist missionary, encountered considerable success at Tranquebar in India, Protestant missionary activity by the end of our period had made little progress in Asia.

In the early-seventeenth century Dutch Calvinists were active in Batavia, Amboina, the Spice Islands, the Timor area, Talaur, the Sangi Islands, and Formosa (where the Dutch had an establishment between 1624 and 1661). The Dutch East India Company supported the missionaries and subjected them to regulation, but the Dutch church examined those to be sent out and maintained correspondence with them. In the areas actually under the company's administration, Dutch missionary policy was at first little better than forceful conversion. The Dutch gave considerable attention to translating the Bible. They made the New Testament available in Portuguese in the Indies in 1682; they put out the complete Bible in Malay in Latin script in 1734 and in Arabic script in 1759; and in Ceylon they published the whole of the New Testament in Tamil and parts of it in Singhalese. Their work was handicapped by language difficulties, shortage of religious personnel, their rigidly assimilative and puritanical policies, and the competition of Islam.

The Dutch missions made greatest progress among those natives who had already been converted to Catholicism. Even among these, however, resistance was encountered—for example, in Ceylon, where missionary work was begun in 1642. After 1658, when the Dutch had completed the conquest of a considerable portion of the island from the Portuguese, they used inducements of every sort to convert non-Christians and to force Catholic natives to become Protestant. Effective resistance among the Catholics was organized by Joseph Vaz (1651-1711), a converted Brahman from the Bombay area. Meanwhile a revived Buddhism under the kings of Kandy competed with both Protestants and Catholics. Dutch missionary activity declined in the eighteenth century along with the financial well-being of the Dutch East India Company. About 1775 the number of Protestants in the Indies was probably under 200,000, and the estimated number in Ceylon, which was 425,000 in 1722, was only 342,000 in 1801.

Other Protestant missions were still less impressive. As indicated in Chapter IV, Pietists from Germany, especially Halle, undertook some missionary work. Under the patronage of King Frederick IV of Denmark and with financial support also from Germany and England, they began (1706) at the Danish settlement of Tranquebar in south India and gradually reached out to other colonial enclaves in India. Toward the end of the eighteenth century they claimed some 20,000 converts, principally in Tranquebar, Madras, and nearby towns. Missionaries of this group translated the whole Bible into Telugu and Tamil, and most of it into Hindustani. Schwarz was one of the Tamil translators. He won the friendship of the raja of Tanjore, who, without turning Christian himself, aided him in his missionary endeavours. In 1760 the Moravians, too, came to Tranquebar, but they were regarded as interlopers, and their efforts to plant missions, chiefly in connection with Danish trading establishments, all ended in failure by 1803. The British East India Company showed no interest in missionary activity, although it provided chaplains at its own settlements.

The Orthodox clergy benefitted from the Russian overland advance eastward. They penetrated Siberia and established a permanent residence in Peking. They went to China, however, as students of the language and as priests to the Russian colony at its capital rather than as missionaries.

*   *   *

Two-way Results of European Missionary Efforts

The net religious effect of Christian missionary activity in the East until 1775 was not very profound. At that date the total number of Christians in southern and eastern Asia, which, we have noted, could not have much exceeded 3,000,000 (and was probably less), constituted only a small fraction of the area's teeming population. The northern Philippines and Goa and other Portuguese possessions in India were and have continued Catholic, and size-able groups in other parts of India, the Spice Islands, Vietnam, and Ceylon were Christian. Yet many of the converts retained animistic beliefs, the vast majority of eastern Asians remained untouched, and the promising beginnings in Japan and China had ended in ruins. Very few Asian intellectuals had been lastingly impressed by either Christianity or the culture it represented. In India most converts to Catholicism and Protestantism were from among either the Syrian Christians[7] or the lowly and the outcast, and in China and Japan most converts had been from poverty-stricken classes not fully committed to Confucianism or Buddhism. In Vietnam, the Indies, and the Philippines the big Christian successes had been among people uncommitted to any other highly developed religious or philosophical system.

Experience thus demonstrated that cultural assimilation, or Europeanization, when not backed by Western state power was ineffective in southern and eastern Asia, and the failure of Jesuit probabilism left little hope that a policy of accommodation to local culture would be much more successful. The two countries that for a time had shown the greatest interest in the science, technology, and geographical knowledge which the missionaries had to offer decided to reject these suspect advantages (see Chapter XIV). Fear of political and cultural ties with Christianity caused Japan to close her doors to almost all of the outside world, and China to intensify her xenophobia.

In the reverse direction, however, the Christian missionaries promoted a trend that possibly exceeded anything they had intended. They provided the Western world with a large body of literature dealing with the geography, languages, literature, arts, manners, customs, and ideas of the East that enriched Europe and unquestionably affected European thought and institutions of the eighteenth century. To this intellectual trend must be added the effect on the economic and political life of Europe produced by its trade and colonial enterprises in the East. These trends, already mentioned in Chapter I, will receive fuller attention in some of the chapters that follow.

THE ORTHODOX CHRISTIANS

The story of the Orthodox Christians in the Polish orbit has been told in Chapter IV, and the beginnings of Orthodox missionary effects in China have been touched upon above. Here we shall deal with Orthodox Christians in Turkey and Russia.

The Turkish sultans who followed Bayezid I (d. 1403, after defeat and capture by Timur) were even more lenient than he toward the Christians of their empire. Following the ancient Islamic code, they allowed their non-Muslim subjects one of three choices—the sword (for obstinate rebels), the Koran (for sincere converts), and tribute (for peaceful unbelievers). In Turkish Europe most Christians, known under the designation *rā'iya*, availed themselves of the third choice, paying a head tax which was not oppressive. The levies on trade and industry, most of which were in Christian hands, were also not oppressive. The submissive among the Christian population, and also among the Jews (as had been true in Muslim Spain), were economically no worse off under Turkish rule than they had been under the Byzantine emperors.

With the fall of Constantinople and the firm establishment of Sultan Mehmet II's rule (1453–81), Eastern Christians had still more reason to feel that the Turkish yoke was comparatively light. The sultan had the leader of the anti-Romanists elected to the patriarchate of Constantinople. To be sure, this patriarch and his successors were kept under close control, and by their nomination of bishops maintained an indirect Turkish restraint upon the several dioceses. Everywhere, however, the bishops were recognized as the heads of the Christian communities, in civil as well as in religious affairs, and the subject populations enjoyed a kind of local self-government. Thus the astute sultan was able to fashion the Orthodox Church into a valuable instrument for stable government. Internal dissensions were left to the patriarch, and the sultan's government not only was relieved of much administrative detail but besides derived considerable income from the sale of the patriarchate to ambitious clergymen.

The sultans also exploited the military and administrative potentialities of their Christian subjects. We have already indicated (Chapter I) that the 'blood tax' created an elite. Christian boys, selected when young, were brought up in the Muslim faith and trained for governmental or military service in schools of Spartan discipline. Some became civil officials or members of the palace guard. The hardiest were enrolled at twenty-five in the famous Janissary corps of shock troops. In Mehmet II's time this corps numbered about twelve thousand. Inured to a régime of absolute obedience and expected to abstain from marriage and luxury, these Christian-born lads, without families or other loyalties, were for centuries considered the most effective warriors of European Islam.

As the Constantinople patriarchate became a tool of the sultans and the Ipek patriarchate of Bulgaria dwindled away, Russia profited by the Turkish conquests. The fall of Constantinople to the Turks made Moscow the virtual capital of the independent Orthodox world—'the third Rome', as a Russian ecclesiastic expressed it. Eventually (1589) the metropolitan see of Moscow was raised to a patriarchate. The Orthodox religion was one of the main bonds of union among the Russians during 'the Time of Troubles' (*Smuta*) that followed. The Jesuits and the Poles on the one hand and the Swedes on the other supported rival pretenders to the Russian throne, but against them the Orthodox religion stood as both a symbol and a reason for resistance to foreign domination. Finally the national Sobor of 1613 chose Michael Romanov to be the new tsar. He was a compromise candidate, one who was related to the old dynasty of the Ivans and upon whom the clergy as well as cossacks, boyars, and merchants could agree, partly at least because these influential groups anticipated from his youth and weak character that they would have little to fear. They reckoned without Michael's father, who was formally enthroned as the Patriarch Philaret in 1619. Before his death (1633), the patriarch inaugurated a policy that eventually enabled the Romanovs to establish a state in which loyalty to the tsar was a compound of patriotic sentiment for 'Mother Russia' and pious devotion to 'Holy Russia'.

Under Michael's son Alexis the Russian national church underwent an internal crisis. The patriarch of that day was Nikon (1605–81), who tried unsuccessfully to make the church strong and independent of the state. Without intending to effect serious reform of ritual or dogma, Nikon introduced changes in the service that were meant to be in keeping with recent scholarship and with the practice of other Orthodox churches. Such apparently trivial things, however, as the Russian spelling of the name Jesus or the number of fingers used in crossing oneself became major issues, and the Russian clergy soon split between those who favoured Nikon's changes of ikons and liturgy and those who opposed them. The opponents of Nikon created a schism (*Raskol*) and were called *Raskolniki* (*Schismatics*). At first their programme was one of liturgical conservatism as against Nikon's minor reforms. Unsupported by the tsar, who resented the patriarch's efforts to divorce the church from the state, Nikon was tried by a synod in 1667 and confined to a monastery.

The Raskolniki were not appeased, however, and the Raskol spread. Peasant discontents that had added fuel to the social seethings in the 'time of troubles' had not yet been assuaged, and, in fact, they grew more bitter with the legal hardening of Russian serfdom under the new Romanovs. Many of the peasants readily identified themselves with the defence of the 'Old Belief' (i.e. with the *Raskolniki*) in their struggle against the landlords. Thus, ironically, religious conservatism, starting out as non-conformity with ritualistic change, became joined with demands for social reform; an extreme sect of the dissenting Old Believers denied the need of a clergy altogether and became a priestless cult (*Byezpopovtsi*). Religious fanaticism, doubtless confirmed by economic despair, seized large numbers of the *Raskolniki*, and thousands of them committed suicide, often by fire, while others, reinforced by local peasants, fugitives from Stenka (Stefan Timo-feevich) Razin's outlaws, and malcontent townsfolk, fled to distant forests, set up communities of their own, stubbornly resisted the tsars' alternating policies of force and conciliation and, despite internal fragmentation, managed to survive. Estimates of the number of Old Believers in the nineteenth century run as high as 20,000,000.

Peter the Great had meanwhile solved the problem in his own high-handed, rationalist manner. He granted the Raskolniki (along with all but Jews and Jesuits) religious toleration, for he saw no reason why they should be outlawed and thus allowed to avoid taxes and work for the state. In order to make certain that no Nikon would arise to question or share his authority, Peter appointed no successor when the Patriarch Adrian died in 1700 but named an 'exarch' (that is, an officer of lower rank and power) instead. Peter practically nationalized the monasteries in 1701, making the monks salaried officials. By ukase in 1718 he required attendance at church every Sunday and holiday on pain of being ineligible for office, but his motive was political rather than religious—that an illiterate people might learn his will as the priests read his ukases. Finally, in 1721, he created a 'Spiritual Department' to explain dogma, regulate the press, and help him to select bishops. This body was presided over by a procurator, who was a layman, but was completely dominated by the tsar. Eventually it became the Holy Synod, and such it remained, dictating the religious life of Russia, until the Revolution of 1917.

Catherine the Great undertook further measures that demonstrated the subordination of religion to the state's purposes. In a series of steps between 1764 and 1786 church lands were secularized, and about 2,000,000 ecclesiastical serfs became directly dependent on the crown (but under conditions that in some respects worsened rather than bettered their lot). Catherine also took a step that made the Russian ruler more obviously the temporal leader of Eastern orthodoxy; by the Treaty of Kutchuk Kainardja with Turkey (1774) she received certain privileges that in the judgment of the Russian foreign office made the tsars protectors of the Christians in the Ottoman Empire. This claim ran counter, however, to French claims of a similar nature and in the next century further complicated the already complex Near Eastern Question.

ISLAM

In the early sixteenth century a series of important changes occurred in the political circumstances of Islam that deeply affected its religious evolution. Previously Islam as a religion had been the chief binding force of the many Muslim peoples, and the local military states that came and went might well have been looked upon as necessary evils. The pious were commonly urged to have as little to do with them as possible, and the governments in turn interfered only sporadically and on a personal basis in the development of religion. The centrifugal force of politics thus failed to disrupt the common loyalty to Islam. By the middle of the sixteenth century, however, a contrary tendency was visible. The central lands of the Muslim faith were traversing separate paths charted by a series of relatively stable Muslim empires, while Islam in the remoter areas was becoming culturally isolated.

At the start of the sixteenth century, Ismā'īl was the head of the Shī'ite Ṣafawiyya order. He set out to conquer as much of the Dār al-Islām as possible and to force the Sunnī populations to adopt Shī'ism. He succeeded in carving out a lasting empire in Iran—the Ṣafavid Empire. There he insisted that everyone should publicly curse such heroes of early Islam as 'Umar and Abū-bakr and follow the Shī'ite form of the sharī'a. The Sunnī ṭarīqas were suppressed, and many Sunnī were killed; Shī'ite books and teachers were brought in hastily from wherever they could be found; and the autonomous body of Shī'ite mujtahids—authorized leading interpreters of the sharī'a— gained an undisputed ascendancy. The original Shī'ism of the movement had been for the most part the esoteric faith of a ṭarīqa, but gradually the mujtahids imposed a Twelver Shī'ite orthodoxy. In the seventeenth century, Muḥammad-Bāqir al-Majlisī, with the aid of the political authorities, was especially effective in putting the doctrine into definitive form (see Chapter IX). The areas incorporated in the Ṣafavid Empire, whether Persian, Turkish, or Arabic speaking, have been insistently Shī'ite ever since; and the Iranians (and with them most Iraqis) were till modern times divided from their Sunnī neighbours in the west, north, and east by an implacable wall of distrust, each side regarding the other as infidel.

The Shī'a paid for its triumph in Iran by suffering great, and equally definitive, massacres in the expanding Ottoman territories, which became for the most part overwhelmingly Sunnī. From a dynamic frontier state in the Balkans and Anatolia, the Ottomans extended their rule to include most of the Arab countries as well. In the new empire the sharī'a, always rather a personal and social than a constitutional law, was made in principle the guide of state affairs, which in fact became unusually coloured by it. In contrast to earlier periods, the large non-Muslim population now took little part in public life or cultural matters, even though their sons, if converted, had a part in ruling the empire. The old system of juridically and even socially segregating lesser faiths in their own autonomous communities was strictly carried out. The Muslim '*ulamā*' became methodically organized in an unprecedentedly hierarchical manner (which incidentally entailed the supremacy throughout the Ottoman Empire of the Ḥanafites over the Shāfi'ites, already suppressed in Shī'ite Iran). The head of the '*ulamā*', the *shaykh al-Islām*, rose during the sixteenth century to a constitutional position almost on a level with the sultan, by whom, however, he was appointed. The sultan himself eventually came to emphasize his own caliphal character as head of the body of Muslims—a character assumed by many other rulers as well after the fall of the old titular caliphate at Baghdad—and as their representative against the infidels. And so the expansion of the Ottoman Empire, and at the end of our period its reverses, were regarded as those of Islam itself.

The Ottoman power reached as far as Algeria. Beyond lay Morocco, where the Sharīfian dynasty (i.e. a dynasty of *sharīfs*, 'nobles', descendants of Mohammed) now replaced the degenerate Berber dynasties. Morocco maintained not only political but also religious independence. The sharīf was honoured as a holy personage, and adherence to him became the touchstone of the faith. By the end of the sixteenth century much of Muslim western Africa had accepted this allegiance, and parts of it have tended to look to Morocco for religious leadership ever since. The earlier inclination of Morocco to regard the rest of Islam as apostate was confirmed, as the Islamic far west became almost self-sufficient.

In northern India arose a great state, the Mogul Empire, which rivalled in splendour the Ottoman and Ṣafavid Empires. Within this empire, as we shall soon see, Indian Islam went through its own, and an equally distinctive, evolution. Elsewhere, though continuing to advance in a number of areas, Islam confronted obstacles. At the beginning of the sixteenth century, Christians from the West put the Muslims on the defensive in many parts of the Indian Ocean coasts and in Africa, Malaysia, and even Arabia. The Muslims of the north at the same time became relatively isolated. Those of the Volga came under Russian rule, while Turkestan was divided between the long-pagan Kazaks and the culturally not much more stimulating Uzbeg rulers, who were bitterly at war with Shī'ite Iran. Thus the Muslims of China had little opportunity for contact with vital Muslim centres.

The *ṭarīqas* continued almost everywhere, although chiefly on a relatively local basis now. In the Ṣafavid domain they survived only in impoverished circumstances. In Ottoman territories the *ṭarīqas* favoured by the Turks, such as the various branches of the Khalwatiyya, increased in strength and enjoyed greater pomp than others; the heads of the North African orders were the objects of a devotion near to anthropolatry. One or another order was introduced in every corner of Islam. Thus, with the saint 'Abd al-Ra'ūf in the seventeenth century, the Shaṭṭāriyya gave self-confidence to a strong mystic movement in newly converted Malaysia. The orders came to show less originality, however; many of the *ṭarīqas* were wealthy and shot through with popular superstition. Yet among the new branches of *ṭarīqas* now set up there were some devoted to reform. Orthodox *'ulamā'* working within a Ṣūfī framework also sometimes carried out reform, as did Aḥmad Sirhindī at the beginning of the seventeenth century in India (see Chapter VII), and so sometimes did simple and pious mystics. In the eighteenth century there arose in Arabia a reform movement which was radically anti-Ṣūfī—that of the Wahhābīs—and it was to have far-reaching effects in the next century.

*   *   *

The Moguls in India

In 1500 India was divided between Muslims and Hindus. Most of north and central India was under Muslim rule. The Afghan sultans ruled at Delhi; independent Muslim rulers controlled Bengal, Malwa, Gujarat, Kashmir, and Khandesh in the north; and the Bahmani kingdom and its successor states (Berar, Ahmadnager, Bihapur, Golkonda, and Bidar) controlled the Deccan. The Hindu Vijayanagar Empire, which reached its height under Krishnadeva Rāya (1509–29), dominated the south; Hindu rulers controlled Orissa and Rajputana; and Assam and Nepal were independent of Muslim control. Elsewhere, despite continued persecutions and desecrations, inter-penetration of the two cultures was in progress, though slowly and generally unintentionally. In some areas, notably Kashmir, the repeal of the poll tax, the use of Hindu advisers, the patronage of vernacular literature, some relaxation of the restrictions on Hindus, and years of contact had somewhat reduced the conflict between Hindu and Muslim.

In the second quarter of the century the Afghans were displaced in north India by the Moguls, or Mughals, under Bābur (1526–30) and Humāyūn (1530–38 and 1555–56). In the reign of Akbar (1556–1605) Mogul rule spread over Bengal, Orissa, Malwa, Gujarat, Rajputana, Berar, and Khandesh. He improved administration, conciliated the Rajputs, repealed the poll tax and pilgrim tax, used Hindu advisers, patronized Hindu learning, and generally tolerated Hinduism, thus creating an era of rare well-being and good will. Meanwhile, in the south, after the sack of Vijayanagar (1565), Hindu rule declined before the advance of the Muslim kingdoms of the Deccan, and Akbar's successors, Jahāngīr (1605–27) and Shāh Jahān (1627–58), extended Mogul sway into the upper Deccan. Under Aurangzīb (1658–1707) it stretched over all of India except the small southern tip.

The rise of the Mogul Empire brought the widest reach of Muslim political power in India and, with it, the maximum degree of Islamic organization and hence of potential proselytizing power. The head of the Sunnī community in India was the sultan (who, from Akbar on, commonly carried also the title of caliph), an emperor who dealt with the Ṣafavī shāh and the Ottoman sultan on a basis of equality. In 1579, renewing the efforts of certain earlier Delhi emperors to extend control to matters of doctrine, Akbar induced the highest 'ulamā' to accept his interpretation on points of religion when the theologians disagreed and to consider his decrees final when they were not in opposition to the Koran and were of benefit to the people. His immediate successors maintained this position. Below the sultan the organization of the Islamic community included various law officials, such as the chief justice, canon law judges (qaḍis), common law judges ('ādils), and subordinate law officers (muftis); various financial officials (dīwān); various religious officials, such as the sadr (in charge of religious endowments and ecclesiastical affairs), the shaykhs (heads of the mendicant orders), the muḥtasibs (censors of public morals), and the imāms (prayer leaders in charge of the mosques and mosque schools). The highest of these posts were occupied by the 'ulamā'.

The Mogul conquest brought an influx of soldiers, scholars, and fortune hunters into India, and Akbar's fame and tolerant attitude attracted Sunnī scholars and Shī'ite refugees alike. Akbar tolerated Hindus, Christians, Jains, and other religious groups, as well as differing Islamic sects. He not only supported and debated with their scholars at his court but he even permitted Hindus to proselytize. Badāyūnī, an orthodox Muslim chronicler, shocked by Akbar's freethinking and conciliation of Hindus, alleged that Islam died during his reign. To be sure, few famous Islamic missionaries appeared after the fifteenth century; yet it may well be that Akbar's toleration attracted more humble Hindus to Islam than did the militant policies of his great-grandson Aurangzīb. Certainly some of his enlightened policies restricted Muslim zealots, but the charge that Akbar abjured Islam and persecuted Muslims seems extreme.[8] His 'Divine Monotheism' appears to have been not a new dispensation but only an order of devoted courtiers.

Jahāngīr, while continuing some of his father's tolerant measures, promoted Islam more actively. Converts appear to have received daily allowances, and Hindus were discouraged from converting or marrying Muslim women. Jahāngīr also persecuted the Jains and drove many of them from Gujarat into Rajputana. Both he and his son, Shāh Jahān, were zealous builders of mosques and patrons of Islamic religious establishments.

Shāh Jahān was an orthodox Sunnī. During his early years he made some changes in the policy of toleration, but most of them were not enforced after 1638. He did, however, establish a superintendent of converts and permitted compulsory conversion. Moreover, he vigorously promoted Islam, observing festivals, encouraging pilgrimages to Mecca, restoring prerogatives to the 'ulamā', imposing the Islamic moral code upon Muslims, and improving court relations with the orthodox.

Aurangzīb, a strict Sunnī and militant puritan, completely reversed the policy of toleration. In 1669 he ordered provincial governors to destroy

Hindu schools and temples and to put an end to idol worship. Temples were demolished all over the country—two hundred and fifty in Rajputana alone in a single year. Hindu religious festivals and pilgrimages were stopped. The hated poll tax was reintroduced, even for Rajput warriors, who were essential to Mogul military power. Aurangzīb encouraged proselytizing and compulsory conversion, with the result that, while many prominent Hindus were converted to Islam, even more died resisting. He also tried to impose the Sunnī law on all Muslims, and his censors strictly enforced his prohibition of wine, spirits, public music, singing, long beards, and objectionable clothing. Unorthodox Muslims were particularly hounded, and the Shīʻite Muharram (new year's festival) was banned. Aurangzīb had the system of Ḥanafite law prevalent in India compiled into the *Fatāwa-iʻĀlamgīrī*, which became the first standard legal code for the Muslim community.

While Aurangzīb's policies undoubtedly pleased the orthodox, they also aroused bitter opposition, which did not end until the Mogul Empire crumbled. Even before his drastic orders of 1669 rebellion began, under the leadership of Sivājī, among the Marathas, and a struggle with the Sikhs was also in progress. In 1669 the Jāt peasants in the Mathura area also revolted, and in 1678 the Rajputs joined in. The emperor's last years were given to the conquest of the Shīʻite sultanates of the Deccan and to a fruitless struggle against the Marathas. After his death the empire rapidly disintegrated. Provincial governors revolted; the Persians raided Delhi; and the Marathas built a loose confederacy that dominated much of India. These chaotic conditions created an occasion and an opportunity for British and French intervention.

During the period of toleration India became a major intellectual centre of the Islamic world, attracting Muslim scholars from everywhere. At the beginning of the seventeenth century the Ṣūfī order of the Naqshbandiyya was introduced into India, but it never became so popular as the older orders. Several irregular orders also arose. Numerous Ṣūfī, Shīʻite, and freethinking scholars shared honours with the orthodox Sunnī ones. Outstanding among them were the freethinkers Mubārak and his two sons, Faizī and Abu'l Faḍl. Another of the liberal scholar was Dārā Shikūh, a son of Shāh Jahān, whose *Majmaʻ-ul-Baḥrayn* emphasized the similarities between Ṣūfism and Hinduism. He was executed by his uncompromising brother Aurangzīb in the struggle for the throne.

The Shīʻites generally prospered under the more tolerant emperors, and the Imāmiyya, the major Shīʻite subdivision, gained ground throughout India, particularly under Akbar. His guardian, Bairām Khan, belonged to this group, and so did the Persian scholar, Sayyid Nūr-Allāh bin Sharīf al-Ḥusayni al-Marʻashi of Shushtar, whom he appointed chief law officer in Lahore. As such, Nūr-Allāh completed in 1604 the *Majālis-ul-Muʼminīn*, a defence of the Shīʻites, only to be executed for heresy in 1610 by Jahāngīr. Until the time of Aurangzīb, the chief Imāmiyya centres were located in the independent sultanates of the Deccan. In his later years Aurangzīb extinguished these sultanates and persecuted the Shī'ites as heretics, but after his death the ruler of Oudh became a Shī'ite, and in 1732 Lucknow, its capital, became the principal centre of the Imāmiyya.

The most important of the other Shī'ite subdivisions in India was the Ismā'īliyya. Already split into Khojahs and Bohrahs (see Chapter III), it now added several new sub-sects. In the sixteenth century the head of the Tayyibī Ismā'īlī (Bohrahs) came from Yemen to make Gujarat his headquarters. Sometime after his death a split occurred in his sect (1588); one group, known as the Sulaymānī, followed a new head (Sulaymān) in Yemen, but most of the Indians in the sect, accepting a Gujarati leader named Dā'ud, became known as the Dā'udī. The Dā'udī ultimately established headquarters in Surat, while at Boroda a deputy of the Yemen succession led the Sulaymānī group. Still another offshoot of the Ismā'īliyya, the Rōshaniyya, was established in the Northwest Frontier in the sixteenth century. Strongly influenced by Hinduism, its adherents believed in transmigration and the pantheistic nature of God and accepted their leaders as divine manifestations. They submitted to Akbar in 1587 and gradually died out. Aurangzīb appointed Sunnī officials for the Bohrah mosques but failed to extinguish them.

Islam began to move out of the cities and into the rural areas during the Mogul period, probably reaching its maximum strength in the reign of Aurangzīb. Improved organization and instruction, the influence of scholars from various parts of the Islamic world, and continual pilgrimages to Mecca all served to deepen the understanding of Islam among its Indian followers and to eliminate some of the unorthodox or local accretions. During the disorders that followed Aurangzīb's death, when the Hindu Marathas were ascendant, Islam apparently made little further progress.

Even while expanding and deepening, Islam generally underwent some Hindu influences, and sects arose that combined Hindu and Islamic ideas (see below). Although Islam frowned upon castes, many caste rules and practices survived among Hindu converts and subtly exerted their spell upon the whole Islamic community. In the popular mind upper-class Indian Muslims were divided into four main groups; the Sayyids, claiming descent from Mohammed through Fatima; the Shaykhs, claiming pure Arab descent; the Moguls, claiming descent from those who came at the time of the Mogul conquest; and the Pathāns, found particularly in the Northwest Frontier, claiming descent from Afghans. The unreliability of these designations as a key to origins was represented in the popular saying, 'Last year I was a Julāhā [or weaver], this year I am a Shaykh, next year, if prices rise, I shall be a Sayyid'.[9] Since most Hindu converts adopted the Shaykh designation to gain social approbation, the vast majority of Indian Muslims came to belong to this group.

*   *   *

The Spread of Islam in Southeast Asia

Despite the contemporaneous development of Christian influence, Islam spread in Malaya and the East Indies. When the Portuguese captured Malacca (1511), they thereby eliminated one of the most important Islamic centres in the East, but the Grisek-Tuban centre in Java remained, and others quickly developed. Acheh (Achin), in western Sumatra, emerged as a Muslim rival to the Portuguese at Malacca and gradually extended its sway over western Sumatra. The displaced sultans of Malacca established themselves at Johore in south Malaya, threatening Malacca and influencing the nearby areas and western Borneo. From Perak, Kedah, and Patani, Islam penetrated lower Malaya and moved into lands controlled by Buddhist Ayuthia (Siam). From Jambi and Johore it spread to central Sumatra, and from Palembang to southeastern Sumatra and southwestern Borneo. Under Sultan Tranggana (1521–46) Demak emerged as the strongest Islamic power on the north coast of Java, and by 1526 its political and missionary efforts won Bantam and West Java as well. In 1568 Hassan Udin, son of Sunan Guning Jati, the chief missionary in the conversion of Bantam, established there an independent sultanate, which then became in its turn a base for the dissemination of Islam.

Except for Malacca, Islam dominated Malaya and the Malay Archipelago in the sixteenth century. Only in the northern Philippines, after the establishment of the Spanish at Manila (1571), did Christian influence conspicuously turn Islam back. Elsewhere in the area Islamic political control pushed onward from the coastal regions into the interior. Although the actual conversion of the hinterland was a rather slow process, when the Dutch and the English arrived (c. 1600) most of that part of the world was at least nominally Muslim.

The gradual extension of European political control over the Malaysian coasts in the seventeenth and eighteenth centuries did little to shake the hold of Islam. Demak declined, but Mataram rose and by 1601 dominated south and central Java. Under Sunan Agung (1613–45), a fervent Muslim, it conquered the Hindu kingdom of Balambang on the eastern tip of Java and gained control over all of that island but Bantam. Agung crusaded against the Hindu-Buddhist remnants, established close relations with Mecca, brought new Islamic contacts to Java, exerted his influence in southern Borneo, and crossed swords with the Dutch at Batavia. About 1604 a Muslim trader converted the raja of Macassar and thus began the conversion of the Bugis of Celebes. They in turn extended Islam into Borneo and the islands east of Java. From Brunei and the Suli area, Islam spread into Mandanao and the Manila Bay region, where it was stopped by the Spanish conquest. Ternate and Tidore remained Islamic centres for the area of the Moluccas and Banda Islands despite repeated counter-measures of the Portuguese, Spanish, and Dutch.

In this area Islam suffered few defeats. The Europeans succeeded in getting permanent Christian footholds only on Amboina and at some points in the Moluccas and northern Celebes. The Dyaks of central Borneo, the Bataks of west-central Sumatra, and some other isolated tribes were never converted to Islam, the Bataks ultimately becoming nominal Christians. On Bali and Lombak Hindu-Buddhism survived despite all efforts to convert them.

Islam also encountered successes north of Malaya. Sometime after their final conquest by the Annamites (about 1470) the Chams of Cochin-China became Muslim. Intermarriage with Indians introduced some Muslims into the Arakan area of western Burma, while others from Yünnan in China established themselves in northern Burma. But an effort to plant Islam in Cambodia about 1650 failed.

During this expansion Islam underwent a complex process of acculturation, analogous to that of Catholicism in the Latin-American countries. This process resulted in the permanent engraftment upon Islam of numerous native folkways that converts would not give up. In consequence, Indonesian Islam emerged as something different from either Middle Eastern or Indian Islam, although most Indonesians came to consider themselves orthodox Sunnī. Many converts had little understanding of Islam's basic doctrines and looked upon it as a superior form of magic. Others were converted *en masse* upon superficially accepting the faith of a recent conqueror. Still others came in as a result of the work of zealous merchants and mystic *faqīrs*, whose knowledge of Islam was much less impressive than their enthusiasm. The number of missionaries who knew Arabic or Persian and were learned in the Koran and Islamic law was not large.

The seventeenth and eighteenth centuries were a period of purification for East Indian Islam. Some of the more unacceptable native practices were eliminated, and some of the more basic tenets of Islam gained wider currency and deeper understanding or were associated with elements of the native tradition that were too precious to surrender. In this process new teachers and missionaries from India and the Middle East or East Indians who had gone to these areas to study were important agents. Pilgrimages to Mecca also played a part. Many local rulers sent their sons to Mecca, and merchants, nobles, and others who could afford it themselves made the pilgrimage. The mosque schools were also effective media of education, as were the private schools, or *pesantren*, taught by gurus. In rural communities, villagers received elementary instruction in prayer halls from leaders who had received a modicum of training in *pesantrens* (see Chapter XVI).

Gradually a Malaysian Islam emerged which, with local variations, had its own distinctive character. The very form of the mosque was distinct, in some ways resembling a pagoda. The Malaysian's attitude toward the five pillars of faith was far from orthodox. His confession of faith did not convey to his mind the strict denial of other beliefs that it conveyed in original Islam. Daily prayers and purification ceremonies were not rigidly observed, while the giving of alms was transformed largely into the offering of rice on festive occasions, an act generally believed to be efficacious in cleansing away sin. The fast of Ramadān was popular because of the belief that it made up for shortcomings during the rest of the year. The pilgrimage to Mecca (*hajj*) was so generally undertaken when financially possible (although substitutes were often sent) that Malaysian Muslims were reputed for their pilgrim zeal. When Islamic law regarding such things as marriage, succession, and inheritance was in conflict with native customary (*adat*) law, the native custom usually prevailed. Other practices showed marked deviations from orthodox Islam: the high social and legal status of women and the absence of *purdah*; the prevalence of ritual feasts (*slametans*) at times of birth, marriage, conception, death, birthdays, and holy days, at which offerings were made to spirits and ancestors; the use of drums in the call to prayer and of native orchestras (*gamelang*) and dramatic dances (*wayang*); the common substitution of incision for circumcision; the attachment to mosques of a *penghulu*, or religious judge and director of mosque affairs, in addition to the prayer leader and other accepted mosque officials; and the mildness of the restrictions on wine.

★   ★   ★

The Muslims of China

In China, too, the number of Muslims increased, but only slowly. They were to be found particularly in the northern provinces and in Yünnan, most often engaged in cattle, horse, and sheep raising, caravan trading, inn keeping, and mercantile operations, although some were farmers and some served as Chinese officials. They avoided pork, alcohol, and opium and the worship of idols and ancestors. Few made the pilgrimage to Mecca; the Koran was not translated into Chinese; and only a few mosque officials knew Arabic. Except for those in Sinkiang and adjacent regions in northwest China, the Muslims of China tended to become Sinicized. Most of them retained or adopted Chinese names and dress, acquired some Confucian learning, participated in the civil service examination, and approved of the worship of Heaven as identical with Allah. Subject to the same government regulations and restrictions as Buddhists and Taoists, in general they lived in harmony with the other Chinese, but some political disturbances in Yünnan and the northwest were not entirely dissociated from religious questions. Migration into the northwest areas seems to have been considerable in the eighteenth century, and the total number of Muslims in China and Sinkiang possibly exceeded ten million in that century.

HINDUISM

During this period Hinduism experienced several reform movements, unconnected with but, despite marked differences, not wholly unlike the contemporary reform movements of the West. Among them were two important Vishnuite cults, the Vallabhas and the Chaitanyas.

As previously indicated, Vallabha seems to have been the one who effectively developed the Rudra tradition and the system of thought and practice associated with it. He lived somewhere between 1470 and 1533. His activities appear to have centred in Benares and Muttra, although he spent many years travelling and teaching in Vijayanagar and other parts of India. During his travels Krishna is supposed to have come to him and directed him to promulgate the worship of the divine cowherd child.

Vallabha's numerous treatises and theological views will be examined in Chapter VII. Here is will suffice to indicate that he expounded a doctrine in some respects suggestive of, though also widely different from, the idea of divine grace set forth in some European theologies. The Lord, he taught, engendered in some souls the capacity to worship Him for no other reason than that they loved Him passionately and without ulterior motive such as a desire for salvation. The Lord gave such favoured souls a divine body like His and allowed them to dwell eternally in Heaven (*Goloka*). The *Gopīs'* (*milkmaids'*) devotion to the youth Krishna best illustrated this kind of divine love. Those who had received divine favour automatically saw everything in the Lord (while others saw Him as everything); they devoted themselves and their belongings to Him and lost themselves in Him, thus eliminating the mortal obstructions of egoism and possessions. This *pushti-mārga*, or salvation by divine grace, was open to all—women, Sudras (the lowest of the four great castes), criminals, peoples of all creeds—whereas lower levels of bliss, available by *karma* (good works) and *jñāna* (knowledge) were open only to males of the three upper castes. Those who hoped for *pushti-mārga* would normally eschew asceticism and aspire to love the Lord as did the Gopīs; for all souls were essentially feminine and had the Lord as their natural husband. Nevertheless, Vallabha warned, sensualism played no part in the love (*rasa-līlā*) of Krishna and the Gopīs, and worldly matters must be forgotten in the Lord's service.

The Vallabhas were augmented and organized by the missionary efforts of Vallabha's eighty-four principal disciples and two sons. His son Vitthalnātha established the chief Vallabha shrine at Gokul, near Muttra, the scene of Krishna's association with the milkmaids. The sect spread in Rajputana, Malwa, Bijapur, and Gujarat. Vitthalnātha's seven sons, in whom Krishna was said to have been incarnated for five years, exercised authority over separate districts. Vallabha's male descendants controlled the sect as teachers, or *gosāins*, and each took the title of maharaja. During the persecutions by Aurangzīb the most sacred image was transferred from Gokul to Nāthadwār in Rajputana, and the maharaja of that shrine became the head of the sect.

The daily prayer and initiation formula of the sect reflected the founder's spirit of devoted service: 'Krishna is my refuge. I, who suffer the infinite pain and torment of enduring for a thousand years separation from Krishna, consecrate to Krishna my body, senses, life, heart and faculties, my wife, house, family, property, and my own self. I am thy slave, O Krishna.'[10] But in time the noble sentiments of this prayer were perverted by less noble practices. A self-indulgence unfolded that appealed especially to the mercantile classes, but the chief beneficiaries of the idea of submission of body, purse, and spirit to Krishna were his earthly representatives. Like the Renaissance popes, the maharajas became more and more wealthy and powerful, and less and less ascetic. The temples were considered their personal property. Lay members came for instruction and guidance to them, who were looked upon as divine. The sect forgot or largely disregarded the prohibition of caste distinctions and Vallabha's warning against sensuality. Since Krishna was adored particularly as a child, images of the infant Krishna were bathed, fed, and fondled in the maharajah's temples. Many of the sect's hymns and dances were licentious. Women seem to have striven to serve the maharajas as Gopīs and paid established fees for looking at them, touching them, swinging, dancing, sitting, or being closeted with them, washing their feet, drinking the water they had bathed in, or eating food from their mouths. Opposition to the Vallabhas' immorality developed, and in the nineteenth century a new sect arose specifically to oppose them.

*　　*　　*

Chaitanya and the Krishna Sects

The Brahman Chaitanya (1485–1533), a contemporary of Vallabha, founded his Vishnuite *bhakti* cult in Bengal. His sect is said by some to belong to the Rudra tradition, by others to the Nimāvats, and by still others to the Mādhvas. Its Krishna-Rādhā worship is attributed to a Mādhavendra Purī, whose disciple, Ishvara Purī, is in one of the relevant traditions supposed to have transmitted it to Chaitanya, and Ishvara Purī does in fact seem to have been associated with the great change that came over Chaitanya just before he began his ministry. These men and others closely connected with Chaitanya were followers of the Mādhva tradition. The Mādhvas certainly leaned heavily on the *Bhāgavata-purāna*. To be sure, that *purāna*, though it extolled Krishna, did not mention Rādhā, but a Bengali variation by Mālādhar Vasu, called *Shri-Krishna-vijay* (written between 1473 and 1480), had introduced the Rādhā romance. Chaitanya clearly drew upon this Bengal tradition about the love of Krishna and Rādhā and upon other sources that were not related directly to the classical books or the older theology. He was also influenced by the Krishna-Rādhā poetry of Jayadeva (*Gīta Govinda*) and (among more recent poets) of Vidyāpati and Baru Chandīdās (see Chapter X).

Chaitanya was a revivalist, a mystic who swooned at the mention of Krishna, and not a theologian. At the age of seventeen, while on a pilgrimage, he began to show signs of religious ecstasy. At twenty-five he abandoned his family, became a *sannyāsī* ('ascetic') and ultimately settled in Puri near the Jagannath Temple. He toured southern and eastern India, meditating, preaching, and demonstrating his ecstatic worship; apparently thousands flocked to hear him. Swaying, dancing, and gesticulating, he sang hymns or gave theatrical performances. The essence of his teachings was that God (that is, Krishna) was love and must be approached through devotion and self-surrender.

The simple, easy, equalitarian, and emotional nature of Chaitanya's teachings made a profound appeal to the oppressed, and even Brahmans and Muslims were converted. The movement spread rapidly in Bengal, eastern India, and Assam, especially at the expense of Shāktism and through the conversion of disorganized remnants of Buddhism. Chaitanya disregarded such outward religious tokens as caste, rites, ceremonies, and asceticism and extolled such inner graces as honesty, simplicity, and sincerity. Members of his sect were not to covet gain, rank, or esteem and were to refrain from self-aggrandizement, self-indulgences, and jealousy. He favoured marriage, vegetarianism, and teetotalism, and in his theology, the sensual and voracious could not attain salvation. Yet he preached a sensuous devotion to God, which, however, like the love of Rādhā for Krishna, contemplated only the Lord's pleasure and not one's own. He conceived of himself as Rādhā in his devotion.

The philosophy of Chaitanya's sect was essentially that of Nimbārka (see Chapter III). The material world was a manifestation of the Deity, eternally distinct but not separate from Him. The soul was a detached portion of the Deity, yet eternally connected with and dependent on Him. It was deluded by *māyā* and found salvation only through *bhakti*—faith, love, and absolute surrender to the saving grace of Krishna; reason was useless. There were five degrees of devotion: calm meditation, servitude, friendship, love like that of a child for its parents, and the highest love, like that of a woman for her lover, like that of Rādhā for Krishna.

The organization of the sect was largely the work of Chaitanya's disciples. Two of them, Nityānanda and Advaita, and Chaitanya himself were called the three masters (*prabhūs*) and were regarded together as a joint incarnation of Krishna. None of the three wrote anything, but two other disciples, Rūpa Gosvāmī and Sanātana Gosvāmī, who lived at Brindaban (near Muttra) and had at one time accepted Islam, wrote a great deal (see Chapter VII). The sect flourished at Puri and Brindaban and in Bengal. The descendants of the disciples, especially those of Nityānanda, became its teachers, or *gosāins*, and were adored almost as deities. The *gosāins* were nearly all Brahmans.

The sect also had its ascetic orders. They seem to have developed under Nityānanda and his son, who apparently admitted by simple initiation ceremonies groups of wandering ascetics, men and women, remnants of Tantric Buddhism. Out of these unpromising beginnings arose nominally ascetic orders—the Vrikats, who were celibates; the Spashta Dāyakas, whose monks and nuns lived together in the same establishments; the Nerā-Neris, wandering pairs of men and women; and other unregulated groups. The tantric Sahajiya[11] (Way of Nature) cult also became associated with the Chaitanyas; it taught the attainment of salvation through the worship and physical love of a beautiful women regarded as representative of Rādhā.

Despite these associates, the principal sect remained, under the leadership of its *gosāins*, a highly moral, though emotional, group. Adoration of the gurus, singing, repetition of the name of the deity, communal meals, and necklaces and rosaries of *tulasī* beads were prominent in its ritual. Its doctrines were developed by Jīva Gosvāmī and Krishnadās Kavirāja, residents of Brindaban. The latter's biography of Chaitanya in Bengali, the *Chaitanya-charitāmrita* (completed about 1616), became probably its most important work. In the seventeenth century the leader Shrīnivāsa transported the writings of the Brindaban group to Bengal, where they became the sect's chief scripture, replacing the *Chaitanya-bhāgavata*, a biography written in Bengali verse by Vrindāvan Dās shortly before 1550. The new doctrinal treatises stimulated the Bengal-Orissa group to another period of expansion, with leaders from the lower castes, women leaders, and women writers. Later in the seventeenth century Vishvanāth was perhaps the Chaitanyas' foremost figure, and in the early-eighteenth century it was perhaps Baladeva, who wrote an important commentary on the *Vedānta-sūtra* and defended the *gosāins'* sect at a crucial meeting of Vishnuites in Jaipur.

The sensuous elements in the sect's doctrine inevitably conflicted with the moral restraints imposed by the *gosāins*. A controversy arose over Rādhā's relationship to Krishna, the *gosāins* maintaining that she was his wife but others preferring to consider her his mistress and advocating the practice of spontaneous love (*rāga-mārga*). In the early-eighteenth century, the *gosāins'* control weakened, while the Sahajiyās and similar groups that concentrated on the erotic side of Rādhā worship asserted themselves. Women other than wives became companions in the course of *sādhana* (training and discipline), in which the pastimes of Krishna and Rādhā were resumed. The advocates of spontaneous love also abandoned vegetarianism and other restrictive practices, and caste distinctions tended to creep back. The Bauls, a sect of musicians and singers who considered the sex act the most appropriate form of worship, became associated with the Chaitanyas, and the Vrikat celibates appear to have yielded to the sensuous persuasion. In the seventeenth century alleged followers of the mystic Chaitanya started a stream of erotic poetry that rose to a flood in the eighteenth. Nevertheless, the main body of the laity continued under the leadership of the gosāins as a morally restrained sect.

Chaitanya's creed had a certain appeal for Muslims; one of his disciples, Haridās, was a poor Muslim. Although direct ministration to Muslims by gurus gradually ended, a cult called the Kartābhajas, to which both Hindus and Muslims belonged, seems to have developed out of the Chaitanyas in Bengal. The cult's founder, Rām Smaran Pāl (born about 1700), taught that there was only one God, Who was incarnated in the *kartā*, or head of the sect. The *kartā* claimed to be the owner of his followers' bodies and extracted rent for the soul's use of the body. Later *kartās* came from the descendants of the founder. The Kartābhajas recognized no distinction of caste or creed, forbade meat and wine, sang or chanted *mantras* five times daily, and regarded Friday as a holy day.

Other Krishna sects were closely related to the Chaitanyas. The Mahā-purushīyas of Assam were founded by Shankar Deb (died *c.* 1569), whose relationship to the Chaitanya movement is uncertain. He preached the worship of Krishna but not of Rādhā and denounced caste, idolatry, sacrifices, and the eating of meat. His successor, Mādhab Deb, rejected these practices even more completely, and his writings became the scriptures of the sect. The Mahāpurushīyas movement was at first opposed by the Shākta Brahmans and was persecuted by the king of Ahom. It continued to grow, however, and even to put out offshoots, such as the monastic Bamunia and the tribal, politically revolutionary Moamarias.

The Haridāsīs were founded at Brindaban by Haridās (fl. *c.* 1600). His teachings were very close to those of the Chaitanyas. A Hindi poet of merit, he also wrote in Sanskrit. Many of his successors as head of the sect were also gifted poets, some of whom expressed devotional views in erotic verse.

Two other Krishna sects of the period, the Rādhā-Vallabhīs and the Sakhi-bhāvas, are often associated with the tradition of Nimbārka. Both concentrated their adoration on Rādhā rather than Krishna, and their practices were tied up with the idea that mankind should cultivate a female love for Krishna, who was the only male. The Rādhā-Vallabhīs were founded by Harivamsha at Brindaban about 1585. He wrote, in both Sanskrit and Hindi, poems that were notoriously erotic, as did later members of the sect as well. In secret ceremonies adherents of the sect were said to dress as women. The Sakhi-bhāvas definitely imitated feminine dress, habits, and functions, and considered themselves female attendants of Rādhā.

* * *

The Vishnuite Sects

A tendency to counteract the flood of Krishnaite sensualism developed within Vishnuism. For one thing, the worship of Rāma was greatly strengthened by the didactic poetry of Tulsī Dās (1532–1623) of Benares. His masterpiece, the *Rāmacaritamānasa* (*Lake of the Deeds of Rāma*), popularly known as the *Rāmāyana*, was but one of his several poems exalting Rāma (see Chapter XI). It became the Bible of the people of north India. Hindu in theology and imagery, it expressed a noble theism and a rare standard of ethics. It depicted Rāma as an omnipotent but kind and tender saviour of all, regardless of caste or position; faith, love of God, and devotion to Him constituted the road to happiness; but the love between the soul and God was no form of sexual passion, nor was salvation mere absorption into the Divine.

The Rāmats continued strong in north India, and several new Rāma sects were formed. Of these the Malūkdāsīs, founded by Malūk Dās (of Allahabad) during the reign of Arangzīb, was perhaps the most important. Malūk Dās was a trader, and in his sect, although monasteries were established, the teachers were laymen and not ascetics. Rāma worshippers generally held aloof from the sensuality of the Krishnaites, but in one of their orders, the Bairāgī, monks and nuns adopted the practice of living as couples.

In the Maratha country, Krishna worship continued, centring around the Pandharpur shrine of Vitthobā (Vishnu), but it was a restrained and elevated creed. Ekanātha (sixteenth century) and Tukārām (1607–49) carried on the devotional, anti-ceremonial, anti-theological tradition of Nāmdev. Tukārām's hymns in Marathi were extraordinarily popular and played a part in the later national revolt under Sivājī. He taught that the way to God was through neither asceticism nor sensual passion but through purity and dedication.

About 1650 Rāmdās (1608–81), the spiritual preceptor of Sivājī, established the Rāmdāsīs sect. His devotion to God and to the equality of all men before Him, expressed in his *Dashabodha* and demonstrated in his monastic foundations, helped to promote Maratha nationalism. The sect flourished especially during the rise and expansion of the Maratha empire. It was devoted to Rāma, accepted the absolute monistic philosophy of Shankara, and taught that faith (*bhakti*), knowledge, and works were necessary to salvation.

Another Vishnuite sect, the Shrī-Vishnuites, while continuing to prosper throughout south India, became further fragmented. After the death of Vedānta Deshika's son, the Vadagalais (or Northerners) tended to separate into autonomous congregations. In the attempt to combat this tendency Ādi Vana-Shathakopa (Shrīnivāsa, died *c.* 1559) established various temples and *maths*, including the famous Ahobhila Monastery, gave privileges to the lower castes in the temples, and endeavoured to unite the northern and southern groups. His attempt failed; though the largest group of the Vadagalais accepted his successors as leaders, other groups, known as the Munitraya-sampradāya, remained independent under local gurus. The Tengalais (or Southerners) continued to expand, especially among non-Brahmans, and became the strongest of the Shrī-Vishnuites. No changes of importance seem to have occurred among other Vishnuite sects.

* * *

Shivaism and Shāktism

Nor in general did Shivaism undergo major modifications. The Pāshupatas shrank to a negligible number, but Southern Shivaism remained strong, and its philosophy (see Chapter VII) and literature were developed by a significant group of writers, including the poet Rāmalinga. The devotional aspect of Shivaism reached its zenith in the Tamil songs of the Sittars (Siddhas), or Perfect Ones. Despite their anti-Brahmanism and anti-sacerdotalism, their hymns are held in reverence still by the southern Shivaites. They reflected severe monotheism, contempt for the *Vedas, shastras*, images, and priests, disbelief in transmigration, and interest in alchemy. Perhaps influenced by Islamic Ṣūfism, they breathed a mystical devotion to a personal deity. The Lingāyat creed continued and apparently was the religion of the viceroys of

Bednūr (Keladi, Ikkeri), who carved an independent kingdom (1550–1763) out of the Vijayanagar Empire. Although the Lingāyats gradually established centres at Kadur, Ujjeri, Benares, Shrisailam, and Kedarnāth in the Himalayas, they seem to have had little strength in north India. In general, Shivaism, patronized by the upper castes and non-sectarian ascetics, despite its pronounced *bhakti* features did not develop the sensuous tendencies of Krishnaism.

Shāktism, having gathered great strength in Bihar, Bengal, and Assam, was expanding its influence there when our period ended. As an organized group it was not strong in other parts of India. The Shāktas appear to have suffered from the competition of Chaitanyaism and to have lost ground during the sixteenth and seventeenth centuries. Conflict and recrimination were frequent between the two creeds. In the eighteenth century, however, as the Chaitanya movement declined or became infected with elements of Shāktism, the Shāktas experienced an upsurge, which correlated also with the economic and political chaos that accompanied the disintegration of the Mogul Empire and the rise of British power in India.

A good deal of Tantric literature devoted to the Shaktis was produced in the centuries under consideration in this chapter. Compilers of the *tantra* digest were especially active in Bengal, their work perhaps reaching its culmination in the *Āgama-tattva-vilāsa* (c. 1687) of Raghunātha Tarka-vāgīsha. New *tantras* were composed, among them the sixteenth-century *Yogini*, clearly connected with the well-known Shakti shrine at Kāmarūpa, which, having been destroyed by the Muslims, was rebuilt (somewhere between 1550 and 1565) with dedicatory ceremonies at which one hundred and forty men were said to have been sacrificed. In the seventeenth century the flow of Tantric literature was reduced, but in the eighteenth perhaps the greatest of the *tantras*, the *Mahānirvāna*, or *Tantra of the Great Liberation*, appeared. In many ways it resembled the *purānas*. Shiva declared in it that Shakti was the mother of the universe and made the worship of her as the creator, preserver, and destroyer necessary for salvation. It also contained hymns to Kali, instructions for the householder, ceremonials, *mantras*, high ethical precepts, and instructions for the erotic circle worship. Many Shākta poets, too, wrote in praise of the goddesses (see Chapter XI).

* * *

Nānak and the Sikhs

During this period Sikhism emerged and ultimately failed as an effort to unite Hindu and Muslim. Its founder, Nānak, was born (1469) a Hindu but at some point in his career came under Muslim influence. Attracted by Kabīr's mixture of Hinduism and Islam, he did not at first aim to establish a new sect but travelled around India appealing to both Hindus and Muslims. He described his followers as Sikhs, or disciples. His teachings and rituals were more Islamic in tone than were Kabīr's, but they included some elements of

Vedāntism also. He believed that there was only one God, the Creator, called Hari, who ruled the world; that God had made the illusions (*māyā*), such as desire, passion, and self-assertion, which condemned souls to be born again and again; but that He was also gracious, and salvation (blissful union with God) could be attained through His grace by those who loved, feared, served, and believed in Him and practised righteousness. Moderation, temperance, honesty, hard work, humility, gentleness, patience, and faith were the elements of righteousness. Forms and rituals were useless, and idolatry and inequalities of caste and sex were wrong; all mankind were brothers and equal before God, whose power and mercy were infinite. Nānak's hymns and sayings, collected only after his death (1538), promoted this monotheistic, pacific, and equalitarian creed.

Nānak and the subsequent leaders of the sect were called gurus. Nānak appointed his own successor, and so did the next two gurus. They spread the faith, adopted a common kitchen to eliminate caste, and abolished the seclusion of women. The fourth guru, Rām Dās (1575-81), acquired a tank at Amritsar and began the construction of the Golden Temple in it. From Amritsar he organized associations of disciples in different parts of the country. He appointed his son Arjun (1581-1606) guru, and thereafter the office became hereditary.

Arjun collected tolls from the faithful and completed the organization of the Sikhs into a community governed from Amritsar. He complied the *Ādi Granth*, the original scriptures of the Sikhs, which consisted of hymns, prayers, and sayings by thirty-five authors including Kabīr, Rāmānanda, Nānak, and Arjun. It was written in a special alphabet and contained pieces in different languages, of which Western Hindi, Punjabi, and Marathi were the most important. Arjun's union of temporal with spiritual power aroused the ire of Emperor Jahāngīr, who charged him with harbouring the emperor's rebellious son and had him cast into prison, where he died.

The union of church and state within the Sikh sect, and the persecutions by bigoted emperors from without, gradually transformed the tolerant religion of Nānak into a creed antagonistic to both Muslims and Hindus. Later gurus undertook to make the Sikh's a military community, bringing on internal dissensions and attacks by imperial troops. The ninth guru, Tej Bahādur (1666-75), was martyred by Aurangzīb. In retaliation, Govind Singh (1675-1708), the tenth and last guru, transforming the Sikhs into a military caste called the Khālsā, engaged in almost continuous warfare with the Moguls.

The ideals of the Khālsā were high. A member was expected to be a 'pure one, who did not believe in caste, colour, sex or credal differences; who believed in the oneness of God and the brotherhood of man; who endeavoured to live a life of usefulness, charity and purity; . . . and who dedicated his life to God and the Gurus, to the service of humanity and to the protection of the weak and the oppressed'.[12] Anyone could, in theory, join the Khālsā, and within it all were equal. Their initiation ceremony, resembling baptism, was performed with sugar and water stirred with a double-edged dagger. The initiate vowed not to worship idols, to bow to none except Sikh gurus, and never to turn his back on the enemy. Sikhs were to salute no Hindus and to destroy all Muslims. All men were to carry swords and wear their hair long and their trousers short. To strengthen the order, Govind Singh compiled a supplement to the *Ādi Granth* incorporating his regulations and ideas, and the combined work was known as the *Granth*. He refused to appoint a successor and told the Sikhs thenceforth to consider the *Granth* their guru.

Internal dissensions and the conflict with Aurangzīb and his immediate successors nearly led to the extermination of the Sikhs. But fanatical leadership kept the movement alive, and as the Mogul power declined, that of the Sikhs rose. By the middle of the eighteenth century they were masters of the Punjab.

*   *   *

Other Followers of Kabīr

Other followers of Kabīr remained more loyal to his apcifist and equalitatian philosophy. The Kabīrpanthīs, concentrated in central and west India, drew support mainly from the lower classes. Their centres at Benares and Maghar, where Kabīr had died, were under a *mahant*, or superior, who traced his descent back to Surat Gopāl, an early follower of Kabīr; the *mahant* at Chattisgarh traced his to Dharm Dās, another early follower. At Maghar Hindus and Muslims had different monasteries but followed very similar practices. The *Bījak*, the Kabīrpanthīs' main scripture, was compiled about 1570, and to it were added the *Sukh Nidhan* (attributed to Surat Gopāl but probably written sometime between 1729 and 1750) and the *Amar Mūl* (written perhaps as late as 1800). As these works revealed, the Kabīrpanthīs tended to revert to traditional Hinduism. Although they abjured caste and idols, they identified Kabīr with the Creator, and he became an object of worship whose help was necessary to salvation. They emphasized the doctrine of the Divine Word, or understanding of the essence of God hidden behind the word *Rām*, but pantheistic Vedāntism, somewhat reminiscent of Ṣūfism, also asserted itself.

A number of Kabīr's followers founded sects of their own, and ultimately no fewer than ten traced at least some of their teachings back to him. In the beginning most of the new sects likewise rejected caste and idolatry and were rather rigidly monotheistic, but in time they too tended to revive Vedāntism and caste, though they were generally open to Muslims as well as Hindus. Some used the word *Rām* or *Rāma* to refer to the Supreme Being, while others used different names; some admitted only ascetics; most of them emphasized the importance of gurus and developed a considerable literature in the vernaculars.

*   *   *

Hinduism about 1775

Nānak and Chaitanya take a prominent place alongside the great spiritual leaders of an earlier period such as Rāmānanda and Kabīr as exponents of the higher religious and humanitarian ideals of mankind. For all that, the story of Hinduism from 1300 to 1775 is of a religion on the defensive, giving ground to Islam both in India and farther east. In the East Indies (except Bali) and the Indo-Chinese peninsula it had ceased to exist as an independent force and had been replaced by Islam and Buddhism respectively. In India Islam had superseded it as the dominant religion in the northwest and parts of Bengal, Muslims were to be found everywhere, and Islamic rulers controlled many states. Nevertheless, Hinduism remained the prevalent creed of the Indian peninsula as a whole and even expanded its influence into Assam.

Confronted by Muslim persecution and competition, Hinduism closed its ranks, reorganized, and assumed the offensive. Some of the new Hindu sects, like the followers of Kabīr, borrowed considerably from Islam, particularly from Ṣūfism. To meet persecution and to compete for popular support the *bhakti* element was stressed, and particularly in Vishnuism a large number of new sects arose, splintering Hinduism in a manner that recalls the contemporaneous splintering of Christianity. *Bhakti* Hinduism reached out to encompass many castes and local cults and practices that the older, more aristocratic faith, with its emphasis on knowledge and works, had ignored. It absorbed most of the remnants of Buddhism in India and reduced the ranks of the Jains. The Smārtas (traditionalists) undoubtedly declined somewhat in relative importance, but they remained strong. Despite the fact that the Brahmans' services became much less essential in many of the *bhakti* cults, as a group the Brahmans managed to maintain their status. By amalgamating many local cults with Hinduism and by assuming the leadership of most of the new *bhakti* and Shakti cults, they made their influence much broader than it had been in 1300.

Whether Shivaism or Vishnuism was the stronger about 1775 is impossible to say. Shivaism was less fragmented than Vishnuism but certainly was also less well organized in north India. Shivaism, being more ascetic, less emotional and erotic, and perhaps more intellectual than Vishnuism, was probably more favoured by the learned and tradition-minded. Among the Vishnuites the sects with the highest moral tone worshipped Rāma or older forms of Vishnu, but Krishna-Rādhā and Shakti worship, tending more and more toward emotional escapism, produced perhaps the most significant trend in Hinudism from 1550 to the end of our period. That escapist trend was evident not only in the rise of new sects and adaptations in the practices of old ones but also in the current vernacular literature.

Until beyond our period, however, no new sects or philosophical ideas of major importance appeared after 1550. Despite this apparent decline in creative power, Hinduism of the eighteenth century was nevertheless better organized, more broadly based, and probably more equalitarian than it had been in 1300. At any rate, it was sufficiently cohesive and dynamic to resist the appeal of Islam and Christianity alike.

BUDDHISM

During this period Buddhism lived on as a religious force, moribund in some countries but in general active enough to have a direct effect upon the lives of at least one third of the people of the world.

Hīnayāna Buddhism suffered in the end only slightly from the inroads of Christianity and Islam. Sinhalese Buddhism, which had previously lost considerable ground through the Tamil invasion, was nearly extinguished by the Portuguese but recovered under the Dutch. The Portuguese arrived in 1505, and between them and the various kingdoms of the island a long and bitter struggle for mastery ensued. The Portuguese, gaining control of the coastal areas, undertook to convert the population to Christianity and by financial considerations and torture induced some Sinhalese to accede. In 1560 the invaders got possession of a relic they believed to be the Buddha's tooth. King Bayin Naung of Pegu (Burma) offered to ransom it, but the Portuguese ecclesiastical authorities of Goa rejected his offer, pounded the tooth to bits, burned them, and scattered the ashes over the sea. This blasphemy resulted in a miracle; two teeth appeared, each alleged to be the original. One was purchased by the king of Pegu from the king of Cotta, while the other, two inches long, remained in Ceylon in the hands of the king of Kandy. Though Kandy remained independent, in 1597 large parts of the rest of the island submitted to the Portuguese, but the chiefs successfully insisted that they should be allowed to retain their religion and customs.

Ceylon's Buddhism had sunk to its lowest level when the Dutch appeared (1602). Joining with the king of Kandy, they succeeded by 1658 in expelling the Portuguese. Once masters of a considerable part of the island, they, too, attempted to force Christianity upon it, but their opposition to Catholicism and their desire to court the favour of the Sinhalese rulers led them ultimately to assist local governments to restore Buddhism. Independent Kandy's later kings were patrons of Buddhism. In the seventeenth century, the monastic succession having failed, Kandy sent to Arakan (Burma) for properly ordained monks (theras), but this importation proved inadequate, for King Kittisiri Rājasiha (1748–81) again found no properly ordained monks; many proclaimed themselves as such, to be sure, but had they had families. With the aid of the Dutch he obtained ordained monks from Siam in 1752 and 1755 and reconstituted the order. The new Siamese order, however, was aristocratic and would admit only members of the highest caste.

In Burma Buddhism had a varied career. About 1525 the Shan king of Ava attempted to exterminate the Buddhist monks of his realm, burning their temples, monasteries, and libraries. This policy of persecution did not last long, however, and when King Bayin Naung (1551–81) of Toungoo captured

Ava (1555) and united all Burma, the tide turned. A Buddhist zealot, he constructed and endowed numerous Buddhist establishments, especially in Pegu, and forced the Shans and Muslims in northern Burma to make a formal profession of Buddhism. Until 1752 his successors at Ava acted as patrons of religion and literature, encouraging Pali commentaries upon the *Abhidhamma*, as well as Burmese translations and paraphrases of it. Toward the end of the seventeenth century, as civil conflict rent the country, a dispute divided the monks over whether the monastic robe should be worn upon both shoulders, as was traditional, or whether the right shoulder should be left bare. The Ekamsika, or One-Shouldered, faction found support only in late authorities and Ceylonese practice, but the controversy was so bitter that royal intervention, though twice called upon, failed to settle it.

The unification of Burma by King Alaungpaya (1752–1760), founder of Rangoon, led to something of a religious and national revival. He was popularly considered to be a *bodhisattva*, and his court piously observed the holy *Uposatha* days, but he also failed to settle the controversy between the Ekamsika and the Pārupana (Fully Clad) faction. Since his chaplain, Atula, was a One-Shouldered supporter, he tenatively ordered the monks to leave one shoulder bare but took no measures against the Fully Clad faction. His successor continued this policy; he also persecuted a heretical sect called the Paramats, who objected to the use of shrines and images. Eventually the Fully Clad group won out, and a royal decree in their favour (1784) was generally accepted.

In Siam Buddhism continued as the national religion under the patronage of the kings of Ayuthia. In 1602 marks were discovered on the rocks at Phrabat, north of Ayuthia, which were identified as footprints of Shākyamuni. Siam thus claimed the honour of having been visited by him, and a legend developed that he had died at Praten (north of Phra Pathom). In the late seventeenth century, a Greek adventurer named Constantine Phaulcon gained power at the court of King Narai. Having turned Roman Catholic, Phaulcon allowed French missionaries to carry on their activities and exchanged embassies with Louis XIV's France. He was eventually executed for treason, however, and after King Narai's death a reaction set in against the French. Considerable Buddhist literature was produced in Siamese, particularly the *Pa: thŏmma sŏmphŏthiyan* (*Wheel of the Law*), a popular life of the Buddha. In the 1750's, as already noted, it was to Siam that Ceylon sent for properly ordained monks. In 1767, when the Burmese destroyed Ayuthia, the Buddhists of Siam suffered a grievous blow, but the Siamese, rallied by the able general P'ya Taksin, drove the Burmans out and established a new capital at Bankgok. During the accompanying disorders the church became disorganized and somewhat corrupt, and in the process of reforming it P'ya Taksin asserted such strenuous authority that the monks participated in his overthrow. A new dynasty, established in 1782, was more co-operative with the Buddhist orders.

In Cambodia and Laos, despite hectic political events, Buddhism suffered little change as the national religion during this period. In the late sixteenth century Spanish and Portuguese missionaries entered Cambodia, but in 1603 a king, subservient to Siam, put an end to Christian missionary activity. Rama Thuppdey Chan (1642–59) became a Muslim, but with the help of the Vietnamese he was deposed. Vietnamese aggressions provoked severe retaliation in 1730 when a Laotian, claiming to be inspired by the Buddha, collected bands of fanatics and attempted to massacre all the Vietnamese in Cambodia.

* * *

Buddhism in the Mahāyāna Lands

In the Mahāyāna lands Buddhism revealed less vitality, on the whole, than in the Hīnayāna lands, but, nevertheless, during the late Ming period Chinese Buddhism began to show some signs of a renewed vigour. The Cheng-te emperor (1506–21) was friendly and seems to have somewhat relaxed the restrictions on the number of monks. His successor, more inclined toward Taoism, had the Buddhist images in the Forbidden City destroyed but on several occasions participated all the same in Buddhist ceremonies. The Wan-li emperor (1573–1620) distributed copies of the *Tripitaka* to monasteries, repaired the famous P'u-t'o sanctuary in Chekiang, and in one of his edicts compared Confucianism and Buddhism with the two wings of a bird, each requiring the co-operation of the other. When Christian missionaries issued a number of tracts refuting Buddhism, which they considered their chief competitor, the Buddhist monk Shen Chu-hung put forth replies in its defence. The Ch'an sect, in particular, and various lay societies and brotherhoods connected with the Pure Land sect exhibited new vigour. The lay brotherhood that showed the greatest religious energy was the Wu-wei-chiao, founded about 1620 by Lo-tsu, who claimed to have received a special revelation. It was strictly vegetarian and objected to images, incense, candles, and other ritualistic usages.

The policy of the Manchu, or Ch'ing, dynasty (1644–1911) was much like that of the Ming, although the emperors were not equally friendly to Buddhism. They regulated Buddhism by an administrative board and limited the number of its monasteries and monks. The Shun-chih emperor (1644–61) showed some interest in Buddhism, and though the Sacred Edict of K'ang-hsi (see below) denounced heterodox doctrines including Buddhism, he took no action against it and at times even patronized it, praising some of its doctrines and publishing the Tibetan *Kanjur*, for which he himself wrote a preface. The Yung-cheng emperor (1723–35), although likewise a staunch Confucian, began the publication of the last imperial collection of the *Tripitaka* (1735–37), and the Ch'ien-lung emperor (1736–95) reputedly had it printed in Mongol, Manchu, and Tibetan. He at first proposed to eliminate the unordained secular clergy by requiring them either to enter monasteries or to become laymen, but he later modified this requirement, allowing them to continue under certain conditions. The Manchus tried at first to get along with the lamas of Tibet, but in the end the Ch'ien-lung emperor occupied it, placed a Chinese resident at Lhasa, and regulated the process by which the reincarnations of the grand lama were picked.

The Buddhism of Korea and Annam was certainly more corrupt and moribund than that of China. Yet even in China it lacked originality and power, and tended to decline in discipline and moral tone. Ignorance and laziness too often characterized its monks, while superstition and the search for special advantages infected its lay followers. Ch'an monks, probably the most active during the Ch'ing period as before, are supposed to have published some 230 works.

In Japan also Buddhism tended to deteriorate, despite official support. Its deterioration is part of the story of sixteenth-century feudal strife, which ended in the rise of the great military leaders who united Japan (see Chapter I). These national leaders destroyed the military power of the Buddhist sects with the aid of the provincial lords. In 1571 Oda Nobunaga (1534–82) stormed and demolished the three thousand Tendai monasteries on Mont Hiei at Kyoto, killed thousands of the inmates, and banished the rest. A few years later he routed the Shin forces from Kaga, but he was able to obtain their surrender at Osaka only in 1580. In 1581 he forced the submission of the Shingon monks of Mount Kōya. In 1584–85 his successor, Hideyoshi (ruled 1582–98), routed them from Kii province and destroyed their stronghold at Negoro. Other military establishments were likewise demolished in the culminating feudal struggle. Meanwhile, in Kyushu and the central provinces the Buddhists lost ground to the Jesuits. Nobunaga and many of the lords of Kyushu were friendly to the Jesuits, and although Hideyoshi, after taking Kyushu (1587), formally banned them, he made no real effort to enforce his decree. In 1591, in the same lenient spirit, he permitted Kennyo Shonin of the Shin Buddhists, who had resisted him at Osaka, to rebuild the Hongwanji Monastery at Kyoto.

Subsequent rulers more vigorously favoured Buddhism, now that it was disarmed, as a state religion. Tokugawa Ieyasu (1598–1616), founder of the Tokugawa shogunate, had family connections with the Jōdō (Pure Land) sect, and Tenkai, a Jōdō monk, and Denchōrō, a Zen monk, were among his close advisers. He clearly used Buddhism to advance his political purposes. He formally recognized the Jōdō sect as independent and built for it the Zōjōji Temple in Edo (Tokyo) when he established a new administration there. He weakened the rival Shin sect, dividing it into two main branches by building a second Hongwanji Monastery at Kyoto for one of Kennyo Shonin's sons, and in 1614 he proscribed the most militant branch of the extremist Nichiren sect. In decrees of 1613–14 he also banned Christianity as a menace to the stability of the state and made Buddhism in effect the state religion (without proscribing Shinto, which he identified with Buddhism). These and later decrees provided that every Japanese was to register at the Buddhist temple of his native district, whatever the sect to which that temple might belong, and to receive a certificate of registration as an identification card; thereafter he or she was to attend the parish temple on certain days, particularly the day of an ancestor's death, on pain of forfeiture of the certificate; and every Buddhist was to be buried according to the rites of his parish temple. Those who had no certificates or who wished to change their burial rites were automatically suspect of being Christians. Buddhist priests were held responsible for visiting their parishioners and reporting on suspected Christians. A separate branch of the Tokugawa administration was set up to supervise Buddhist and Shinto temples, shrines, and monasteries; and funds were provided for their support.

The anti-Christian policy continued under the Tokugawa shoguns. Iyemitsu (1623–51), who was especially vindictive against the Christian remnants and inaugurated the isolation policy, was a generous patron of the Buddhists. During his regime the *Tripitaka* was reprinted (1633–51), and he built many Buddhist temples. Tsunayoshi (1681–1709), who believed that the loss of his son and his inability to have another heir were due to his having been guilty of bloodshed in a previous incarnation, issued many decrees protecting animals, especially dogs. Other shoguns, however, were less fanatical in their Buddhist proclivities.

Along with the establishment of Buddhism as the official religion the shoguns promoted the study of Neo-Confucianism among the samurai. Neo-Confucianism led to criticism of Buddhism and to a school of historical studies that promoted the rise of the Shinto nationalists, who, in turn, criticized Buddhism and Confucianism alike as alien influences that had corrupted the pristine purity of native Japan (see below). Ensconced in their official position, however, the Buddhists seem to have accepted this criticism without vigorous response. A new Zen sect, the Ōbaku, was established in 1655, but it was the work of a Chinese monk, Yin-yüan (Ingen), and remained distinctly Chinese in character. The Zen priest Hakuin (1685–1768) was noted for the style and vigour of his sermons, and the Zen monk Bashō (1644–94) was a popular poet, but otherwise the Buddhists produced few outstanding personalities during the seventeenth and eighteenth centuries. The scholarship they exhibited in history, biography, religious tracts, and new editions of the Buddhist literature was respectable but uninspired, and they seem to have produced practically nothing in reaction to the mounting attacks of Confucian philosophers and Shinto propagandists.

* * *

Tantric Buddhism in India, Nepal, and Tibet

In the Tantric Buddhism of India and Nepal some events of only minor importance took place during the centuries here being considered. Traces of Tantric Buddhism crept into Shāktism and Chaitanyaism, while broader elements survived among the Saraks of Orissa and the Dharma cults of

Orissa and Bengal. In Nepal the chief native Buddhist work, the *Svayambhū-purāna*, was probably produced in the sixteenth century, and the Hinduization of Buddhism seems to have been speeded up when the Gurkhas, a Hinduized tribe of Tibetan stock, conquered Nepal in 1769.

For Tibetan Lamaism, however, the period was notable. To begin with, the Mongols were reconverted. The previous conversion had affected mainly the Mongols in China, who, however, when driven back into Mongolia by the Ming, rapidly relapsed. In the 1570's, upon the invitation of the Mongol ruler, Altan Khan, Grand Lama Sodnams (Sö-nam Gya-tso, 1543–86), of the Gelukpa (Yellow) Church, visited Mongolia, and Altan Khan and his tribesman accepted Lamaism in 1577. A lama who was considered a reincarnation of the *bodhisattva* Mañjushri (the personification of thought, wisdom, and meditation) was put in charge of a temple and monastery at Kuku-khoto. When Altan Khan died (1583), the grand lama returned to Mongolia to consolidate his position; and the Ming dynasty, to assure themselves of his support, conferred the same titles on him that Pagspa had received. When Sodnams died, his reincarnation appeared in a new-born child of the Mongol royal house, and when this new grand lama moved to Lhasa (at the age of fourteen), another lama was established at Urga as his vicar and primate of Mongolia. The grand lamas of Mongolia came to be considered the reincarnation of the Tibetan Buddhist historian Tāranātha and through him of the *bodhisattva* Maitreya. The Chinese, however, required that future Mongolian grand lamas should be reborn in Tibet, and this requirement seems to have been followed.

Tibetan Lamaism made some strides in other lands along the Tibeto-Chinese and Tibeto-Indian frontiers. The *Kanjur* was translated into Mongol between 1604 and 1634 and was published in China by the K'ang-hsi emperor. Lamaism spread to the Kirghis and Kālmuks of Russian Turkestan, the Buriats of the Lake Baikal area, and the Mongols and related peoples in Manchuria and Inner Mongolia. It moved southward into Sikkim (c. 1650), and into Bhutan apparently after its conquest by Tibet (c. 1670). The Red Church dominated in these two areas.

Grand Lama Lozang (1617–80) was able, with the aid of the Mongols, to make himself and his successors temporal as well as spiritual rulers of Tibet. A temporal prince of Tibet who was a follower of one of the unreformed sects seized Lhasa about 1630 and threatened to destroy the Yellow Church. Lozang appealed to the Mongols under Gushi Khan, who thereupon seized all of Tibet (c. 1640) and turned it over to Lozang as temporal ruler. The grand lama proceeded to consolidate his position, building an imposing fortress-residence, the Potala Palace, at Lhasa. In 1652–53 he went to Peking, where the newly established Manchu dynasty heaped honours upon him. He retained control of Tibet during a long lifetime, and his successors remained its rulers. They were, however, gradually brought more and more under Chinese control.

The rise of the reformed Yellow Church to both political and ecclesiastical dominance in Tibet did not mean the end of the older sects or of the native Bön religion. The older sects of the Red Church divided into numerous sub-sects or offshoots, the Nying-ma-pa (Old Ones) being particularly strong in eastern Tibet. Most of the Tibetan monasteries were large and well supported, almost every family anxious to have a son in the monkhood. Celibacy was not enforced in most of the monasteries of the Red Church, and the position of abbot was generally filled by hereditary succession. Tantrism, magic, and superstition were more prominent in the Red Church than in the Yellow, while learning, discipline, and moral standards were higher in the Yellow Church.

CONFUCIANISM AND TAOISM

During this period Confucianism continued along the lines laid down under the early Ming dynasts. Neo-Confucianism remained the official philosophy of the state, and all China's emperors, regardless of their personal inclina-tions, publicly acted as its patrons; and so the official cult was meticulously preserved without material change. Popular Confucianism spread into the far recesses of the empire as a code of behaviour and an ethical system; and while continuing as a system of ancestor worship, it tended to slough off its supernatural elements and emphasize its social and ethical precepts. Although some scholars opposed such changes, the Cult of the Scholars became more rationalist, eliminating images from the Confucian temples and abandoning forms and titles which inclined toward the deification of Confucius in favour of those which extolled him as a mortal sage.

In 1530 the scholar Chang Tsung (1475–1539) induced the Chia-ching emperor to sanction a series of reforms. Images were withdrawn from the official Confucian temples and replaced by wooden tablets; the term 'king' was removed from Confucius' title, and instead he was called 'Master K'ung, the Perfectly Holy Teacher of Antiquity'; titles of nobility were eliminated for other Confucians in the temples and replaced by titles meaning 'illustrious' and 'scholar'; several names were removed from the temples and replaced by those of Sung Neo-Confucians; and the ritual was somewhat simplified. Most of these reforms remained permanent, indicating that the rationalist trend was generally sanctioned by the literati. The absence of images from the temples led the Jesuit missionaries of the next century to look upon most Confucian practices as mere civil and family ceremonies honouring great teachers and ancestors rather than as religious rituals.

During the late Ming period a tendency toward syncretism and eclecticism led some Confucians and Buddhists to emphasize the essential similarity of the 'Three Teachings'. Perhaps the most famous of the free-thinking Con-fucians was Li Chih (1527–1602), who ultimately adopted Buddhist garb, rejected Confucius and the classics as standards, and proclaimed the individual as the judge of right and wrong. Many regarded this attitude as personal moral laxness, which they believed had also infected government. In reaction to it emerged the Tung-lin movement, often referred to as the 'Righteous Circles', founded by Ku Hsien-ch'eng in 1604. This movement reasserted the basic ethical values and behaviour patterns of Neo-Confucianism, calling for a scholars' moral crusade to maintain them.[13]

Under the Manchu dynasty, Neo-Confucianism remained the official philosophy. The laws suppressing heresy and limiting Buddhists and Taoists were re-enacted and reinforced, and Confucian ethics received new emphasis as the underpinning of state and society. In fact, the Manchu emperors were more sedulous in promoting the official creed than their native predecessors had been. They fostered the Cult of the Scholars, built many new and beautiful Confucian temples, and honoured Confucius as a great teacher and sage. No ruler did more to support and expand the ethical principles of Confucianism than the enlightened K'ang-hsi emperor. He generally permitted freedom of thought and tolerated not only Christianity (for a time) but also the School of Han Learning, which, although critical of Neo-Confucianism, emphasized the rational and humanistic aspects of the Confucian system. His Sacred Edict (1671), re-issued and elaborated by his successor in 1724, breathed the moral principles of Confucianism, disparaged unorthodox doctrines, and encouraged the reverence of Heaven. It was publicly read twice monthly in cities and towns, and colloquial versions were prepared for circulation among the masses. K'ang-hsi's successors repressed both Christianity and unorthodox Confucian schools.

*　　*　　*

Taoism under Later Ming and Early Manchu

Although the great days of Taoism were past, the creed nevertheless showed some signs of vitality. Under the later Ming rulers, who were more friendly to Taoism than their predecessors had been, this vitality was demonstrated especially in the field of literary publication. During the Cheng-te reign (1506–21) Taoism's enormous canon, after many years of preparation, was published. The Chia-ching emperor (1522–66) appointed some Taoists to high office and instituted a search for their books on immortality. Taoist adepts had ready access to the Wan-li emperor (1573–1619). A supplement to the Taoist canon was published in 1607, and numerous Taoist pamphlets and tracts were piously disseminated during the later Ming (see Chapter XI). The early Christian missionaries testified to the popularity of Taoist lore and practices and to the search for immortality among the court circle and scholars of the late Ming period, but they obviously did not consider Taoism so serious a competitor as Buddhism.

None of the early Manchu rulers seems to have shown any predilection for Taoism, and the creed underwent a decline. As under the Ming, the

Taoists were regulated through an office at the capital with branches in the provinces. Restrictions upon Taoism and Buddhism, many of which had been relaxed during the late Ming, were re-imposed and more rigorously enforced. One of the first acts of the Ch'ien-lung emperor (1735) was to order secular Taoist and Buddhist priests either to return to lay life or to give up their families and enter monasteries; they were not to have pupils, and most of the property controlled by them was to be confiscated. This decree stirred up so much trouble that by 1738 it had been modified in several regards: many of the secular clergy were given certificates without having to enter the cloisters; property administered by them for temples and monasteries was not to be touched; and each priest, after the age of forty, was permitted to have one pupil to train as his successor. The official attitude toward Taoism as an organized religion nevertheless remained unfriendly, and the Taoists diminished in number. A government enumeration of Buddhist and Taoist monasteries and temples in 1667 indicated a total of 79,622 (of which only 12,482 had been established with imperial permission); the Buddhists numbered 110,292 monks and 8,615 nuns, and the Taoist 21,286 monks and no nuns. These figures did not include the secular clergy; between 1736 and 1739 some 340,000 of these received certificates of registration, the far greater part probably being Buddhist. In other words, the total of registered Taoists seems to have been not much over 100,000—an estimate that does not compare favourably with those for earlier centuries.

Although organized Taoism seemed to be on the decline, Taoist lore and practices apparently remained influential among the masses. Secret and semi-secret vegetarian and self-culture societies of laymen, at least partly inspired by Taoism, were numerous. The Tsai-li Chiao, or Rationalistic Religion, organized in the seventeenth century, advocated, among other things, abstention from tobacco, snuff, and alcohol. More sinister groups also masqueraded under the cover of Taoist or Buddhist practices.

Taoism's two main divisions each divided into two sub-sects. The Cheng-i, or orthodox division, which recognized the headship of the Chang family and was dominated by the home *tao-shih*, split into the Fu-lu (Charms) sub-sect, which emphasized exorcism and necromancy and used amulets, spells, cryptic monograms, ouija boards, and other charms for producing spiritual and psychic phenomena, and the K'o-chiao (Ceremonials) sub-sect, which depended more on religious forms and rituals. The Ch'üan-chen division, strongest in the north, stressed monastic organization. It split into the Lien-yang (Hygiene) sub-sect, which counted on physical and mental hygiene, including meditation, yoga, and sexual practice, to strengthen the body and spirit and to prolong life, and the Fu-shih (Diet) sub-sect, which put faith in the power of herbs, medicine, and potions to maintain and restore vigour.

Taoism maintained itself also in Vietnam and Korea, where its forms and ideas were mixed with local practices.

SHINTOISM

During the Tokugawa period several schools or sects, built around certain shrines or growing out of the teachings of certain families, helped to revive and popularize Shintoism. The Yui-itso Shinto of the Urabe priests held its ground, and with Watarai Nobuyoshi (1615-90), of the priestly family in charge of the Outer Shrine at Ise, the Watari (or Outer Shrine) Shinto blossomed as a competitor of Buddhism. Although he attempted to repudiate Buddhism and Confucianism, he borrowed many pantheistic ideas from Buddhism and drew upon Confucianism in formulating his ethical system. Asserting the superiority of the deities, ceremonials, and teachings of the Outer Shrine over all others, he insisted that the Shinto deities were the source of government and of the principles of human conduct. His emphasis on divination, while showing Taoist influence, also brought native Shinto practices to the fore.

New Shinto schools arose in the seventeenth century. The Suiga school was founded by Yamazaki (1618-82) of Kyoto, a student of Buddhism, Chinese science, and Japanese classics and head of an educational institution for young samurai at Edo. His school so openly espoused Confucian ethics and philosophy that a later (Pure Shinto) writer insisted that it was only a scheme to use Japanese classics to promote Confucianism. The word *Suiga* is composed of the last syllables of the words *shinsui* (divine grace) and *myoga* (divine protection). Suiga emphasized the doctrine that divine grace depended upon prayer and divine protection began with uprightness. Yamazaki taught, too, that *kami* (the basic stuff) was the soul of the universe and that Japanese mankind, as descendants of the *kami* (gods), were the god-stuff of the world; ultimate reality was the identity of God and man. According to Yamazaki, the Sun Goddess, Amaterasu, had taught the system he expounded, which must, therefore, be standard for the nation; reverence for its teachings, the goddess, and her imperial descendants was the highest virtue. Out of the Suiga School grew Tsuchimikado Shinto, founded by Tsuchimikado Yasutomi and his family. It gave special emphasis to the interaction of positive and negative principles (as Suiga Shinto had also done) and to the role of divinition in procuring the well-being of the state and people. Hakke (Head Family) Shinto was allegedly derived from the teachings of the Shirakawa family, which for centuries was in charge of the Department of Shinto Affairs, but its principal expounder was the eighteenth-century figure Mori Masatane. It stressed ritual, propriety in human relations, ceremonials for the dead, and the careful expounding of ancient Shinto texts.

Fukko or Pure Shinto (sometimes called Ancient Learning or Renaissance Shinto) was the most important of the new Shinto schools, though it reached its prime only in the eighteenth century. In keeping with the isolation policy of Japan, it sought to throw off alien influences and to return to the un-adulterated Shinto of primitive Japan. An emperor-centred, nationalistic movement, it revived the study of ancient chronicles and other early Shinto documents. It sprang from the ideas of Kada Azumamaro (1669–1736), a member of the priestly family in charge of the Inari Temple near Kyoto, who insisted that the safety of Japan lay in a revival of the ancient 'Way of the Gods'. He, therefore, favoured the study of the ancient language and literature, and denounced interest in Chinese learning.

Kamo-no-Mabuchi (1697–1769), who came from a long line of Shinto priests and was a pupil of Kada for a short time, was the true founder of Pure Shinto. Continuing Kada's linguistic studies, especially of early poetry and the *norito*, or Shinto liturgies, he came to the conclusion that Chinese ways and ideas had corrupted the Japanese. The ancient rulers, he argued, had reverenced their divine ancestress, Amaterasu, and had intuitively ruled with love and benevolence in accordance with her will, while the people, needing no moral code to guide them, had, with matching intuition, avoided corruption. This was the true Way of the Gods. The importation of Chinese political institutions and practices had destroyed these simple mores, separating the divine rulers from the people and destroying their mutual loyalty and self-sacrifice. Nevertheless, Japan, alone having an unbroken line of rulers descendant from the Sun Goddess, possessed a unique national character and polity, and would return to them once corrupting foreign influences were discarded and ancient ways restored.

Mabuchi's work was carried on by Motoori Norinaga (1730–1801). A physician but also trained in letters and one of the most celebrated scholars of his day, Motoori produced about fifty-five separate works and actively propagated his ideas in lectures and tracts. His major opus was an edition (posthumously printed) of the *Kojiki*, Japan's oldest surviving book, which in his opinion set forth the true story of creation. The Japanese, according to him, were a divine race ruled over by the descendants of the Sun Goddess, who had instituted the state and the true Shinto; the chief duty of man was to follow unquestioningly the teachings of the Sun Goddess and her descendants. Moral ideas were implanted by the Gods and resembled instincts; hence the original Japanese had unerringly followed the moral way without special instruction. Motoori was resentful of foreign influences, although he considered them part of the divine plan, for he held that they had corrupted the Japanese: 'That Japan ranks far above all other countries is a natural consequence [of its origin]. No other nation is entitled to equality with her, and all are bound to do homage to the Japanese sovereign and pay tribute to him'[14]. Motoori's philosophy of life—a hopeful one, contrasting sharply with his gloomy picture of life after death—will engage us in Chapter VII.

With the Pure Shinto revival Shinto passed from a religious to a political stage. Japanese independence from and superiority to other peoples now was asserted with religious conviction, and the restoration of the divine emperors to real power was demanded, along with explicit obedience and loyalty to them. The unity of church and state was thus affirmed. Although the movement did not succeed in disestablishing Buddhism during the Tokugawa period, it helped not only to reduce the prestige of Buddhism and Confucianism but also to undermine the foundations of the Tokugawa shogunate.

JUDAISM

The story of the Jews from 1500 to 1775 is one of persistent persecution in western and central Europe and of relatively favourable treatment in Poland (except, as we shall soon note, from Cossack rebels and their allies) and in the Turkish empire. The tolerant stand of Johann Reuchlin and a few other humanists toward them did not pass on to Protestantism. Luther, who had at first attacked the Catholic practice of compulsory conversion and was regarded by the Jews as a champion, later turned against them, holding that 'if the Jews refuse to be converted, we ought not to suffer them or bear with them any longer'.[15] The one great exception to the general rule of intolerance in western European countries was the Low Countries, where many Spanish, Portuguese, and German Jews settled and prospered. The Jewish communities of the southern provinces began to decline at the time of the conflicts with Spain in the sixteenth century, but Dutch Amsterdam continued to be a refuge for Jews comparable in some ways to Turkish Constantinople and Salonika, and yet different too, since Dutch tolerance did not reflect mere indifference to or contempt for infidels. During the seventeenth century the United Provinces set a new standard of toleration for the West. Rembrandt perpetuated the contemporary Jews' features on canvas, and Grotius inaugurated the fight for their rights. Dutch colonies in the New World, like Curaçao, Dutch Guiana, and New Amsterdam, received not only Dutch Jews but Marrano refugees from Spanish and Portuguese America. When, about 1620, the Dutch temporarily conquered some Portuguese settlements in Brazil, about a thousand Marranos openly declared themselves Jews, but their number quickly diminished when the area was reconquered by the Portuguese.

Even the Dutch Jews did not have full toleration. During the controversy between the Gomarists and the Arminians at the beginning of the seventeenth century, the presence of the Jews aroused unfriendly comment, and from 1616 onward they were made subject to certain disabilities. In 1632 all trades not necessary for providing for themselves were closed to them, with certain exceptions such as printing, the sale of drugs, and money-lending.

The insecurity of the Jewish community in Amsterdam explains in part their severity toward two famous heretics in their midst—Acosta and Spinoza. Uriel Acosta (1590–1647), a descendant of a Christianized Portuguese family, became Jewish of his own volition and left Portugal for the Jewish community of Amsterdam. There, his rationalism, his belief in the mortality of the soul, and his criticism of the community led to his being arrested and fined by the civil authorities and excommunicated by the Jewish community.

He recanted but again incurred disfavour and, being again excommunicated and exposed to severe corporal punishment, finally committed suicide. Spinoza's rationalism (of which we shall say more in Chapter VII) was among the factors that led to his excommunication likewise by Amsterdam's Jews. In both instances, not only the excommunicates' unorthodoxy but also the desire to avoid Christian disapproval appear to have been motives behind persecution of Jews by Jews.

Not until the seventeenth century was the Dutch policy of limited toleration of Jews imitated by any other western country. England was the first to follow the Dutch example. Despite the exclusion initiated by Edward I in 1290, some Jewish families seem to have continued to live clandestinely in London, and under Elizabeth I an influx of 'neo-Christians' had taken place. Shortly after coming to power, Cromwell took some cautious steps toward reversing the exclusion policy. He invited the Amsterdam rabbi Menasseh ben Israel to England and allowed other Jews, mostly merchants, to enter openly. The city of London conformed to, without regularizing, the new attitudes, not so much out of Christian charity as out of mundane considerations. The Jewish community of London soon could boast some influential merchants, especially active in the East and West Indies trade, and some outstanding financiers. Their prominence as well as the malaise it caused was indicated in 1697, when the number of Jewish members of the Royal Exchange was limited to twelve. Various legal restrictions also kept professing Jews from holding office under the crown. A Jew Bill passed by Parliament in 1753 proposed to naturalize them as citizens, but popular clamour soon caused its repeal.

Elsewhere in western and central Europe the plight of the Jews was worse than in the United Provinces or England. They were not allowed to live in Spain and were not allowed to leave Portugal—which meant in both instances that they became crypto-Jews, or Marranos, if not completely converted, though in greater numbers in Portugal than in Spain. Guilds did not readily admit them to membership, and so they were rarely found in the crafts. More often they sold things to each other or followed the old clothes trade or (if they had the means) engaged in money-lending and banking or (if they could get licences) practised the learned professions. They frequently had to wear distinctive clothing or badges and to pay special taxes. In the German cities and principalities, *Schutzjuden* (protected Jews) were special wards of government, for which status they paid *Schutzgeld* (protection money). Even Frederick the Great, for all his enlightenment, found *Schutzgeld* too good a source of revenue to abandon. In a *Schutzbrief* issued in 1750, he divided the already strictly limited number of Prussia's *Schutzjuden* into two classes, allowing some (the 'extraordinary *Schutzjuden*') to will their privileged position, each to one and no more than one son, while others (the 'ordinary *Schutzjuden*') could enjoy it only for life. Other Jews, of course, had no special protection at all, but Frederick at least allowed a number to settle in his domains and usually did not permit maltreatment of them. Prussia's extraordinary *Schutzjuden* collectively paid 70,000 thalers in 1763 for the privilege of passing their protection on to second sons. Prussia's Jewish population increased when Prussia annexed her shares of the Polish partitions. Russia, where no Jews had been allowed before 1772, also acquired a large number of Polish Jews after that date.

In Austria Jews were considerably more restricted. Driven out in 1420, many had gone to Poland. Others, however, had stayed behind, sometimes as crypto-Jews, sometimes in hiding. From time to time the climate grew less unfriendly, but they nearly always had to wear distinctive badges, pay special taxes, and stay out of certain economic activities. In 1670 Emperor Leopold I drove them out of Vienna and some other parts of Austria again. About fifty families found refuge in the Great Elector's Prussia. Others went eastward to Poland and Turkey. Some once more risked staying behind, and others returned, especially those who could claim to be 'Turkish' Jews entitled to favoured treatment by the mutual concessions which, by the Treaty of Passarowitz, Austria and the Porte entered into for the reciprocal protection of each other's subjects.

Even before the 1780's, when Emperor Joseph II cancelled some of their special disabilities, the Austrian Jew had gradually regained some standing. The skill that a number of Austrian and German Jews acquired in finance and commerce led to their becoming royal financial advisers and purveyors to the military. Such Jews became known as 'court Jews' and enjoyed great favour and influence, which sometimes remained in the family. Samuel Oppenheimer and Samson Wertheimer were especially well known court Jews in Vienna in the eighteenth century, but others were equally influential both in Vienna and other German capitals. By the end of the eighteenth century the Jews of the German-speaking lands were well started toward that prominence which had been one of the factors of their ruin in fifteenth-century Spain and was to be again in twentieth-century Germany.

Another kind of influence in Jewish and German affairs was achieved by Moses Mendelssohn. As a philosopher, scholar, and man of letters Mendelssohn had come to know and to be admired by many prominent men in the German-speaking world. He therefore was able to intervene, sometimes with good results, on behalf of his co-religionists who were being persecuted. The German dramatist and critic Gotthold Ephraim Lessing (1729–81) was his lifelong friend. In his play *Die Juden* (1749) Lessing held up to scorn the ignorant man who for no reason condemned the Jews, and thirty years later in another play entitled *Nathan der Weise* he had a Jewish sage (whom critics generally recognize as Mendelssohn) plead convincingly for toleration. Mendelssohn's philosophical writings emphasized the common essentials of Judaism and Christianity—one God, immortality, and the law. He translated the Pentateuch (Torah) into German and had the translation printed in Hebrew characters, thus providing, as a sort of Jewish Luther, an avenue leading from the original Hebrew text through Yiddish (which is essentially medieval German written in Hebrew characters) to modern German. Before he died (1786), he had gone far toward identifying the German Jews with Western culture and toward interesting Enlightenment thought in the plight of the Jews.

*   *   *

Jews in the Ottoman Empire and Poland

The favourable treatment that earlier Jewish refugees from the West had received in the Byzantine Empire continued, and even more noticeably, under the Turkish successors of the Byzantine emperors. The careers of several prominent Jews vividly reflected the general situation; they fled from persecution in western Europe to toleration and even honours in the Ottoman Empire. Joseph Nasi (d. 1519) was an especially striking case. Born in Portugal of a wealthy and influential family of Marranos, he migrated with his family to Antwerp, where he continued the family business as a prosperous banker. Resentful of the pseudo-Catholicism he was compelled to practice in Habsburg-ruled Antwerp, he again migrated, first to Venice, which proved little better than Antwerp, and finally to Turkish Constantinople. Here, openly proclaiming his Judaism, he rose to high rank in the sultan's service. As duke and governor of the island of Naxos from 1566 onward, he exercised such profound influence that Christian rulers of the West sought his advice and aid in diplomatic and commercial relations with Constantinople. Among his several plans was a proposal to establish at Tiberias on the Sea of Galilee a settlement of Jews exiled from Italy, but his scheme, perhaps never seriously intended, failed when he fell from power.

Another case in point was Juan Rodrigo de Castel-Branco (1511–68), better known as Amatus Lusitanus. A Portuguese Marrano, he had acquired a distinguished reputation as a physician, scientist, and teacher of medicine. Finding it obnoxious to conceal his religious convictions, he moved first to Holland, then to France, and then to Italy, where in several cities he followed his profession of doctor and scholar. Settling for a time in Rome, he listed among his patients Pope Julius III and his sister. The anti-Jewish measures of Pope Paul IV forced him to migrate once more, and he went to Turkish Salonika, where there was a relatively large and thriving Jewish community. Here, openly avowing his Judaism, he carried on his humanitarian work until he fell victim of the plague.

The strange story of Sabbatai Sebi (1626–76) would hardly have been possible in Christian Europe but was intelligible in the atmosphere of Turkish indifferentism toward religious disputes among non-Muslims. Whether Sabbatai was a charlatan, as some maintain, or a mystic, he believed or pretended to believe that he was the Messiah and—possibly because his father, who had lived in England, knew about the English Millennarians (see Chapter IX)—that the year 1666 was to be the year of salvation. From his birthplace in Smyrna he moved freely about among the Jewish communities in the Ottoman Empire, sometimes urged or forced on by his opponents but always finding willing disciples and a hopeful following. The Jews of Constantinople, Cairo, Jerusalem, Salonika, Smyrna, Buda, and other cities in the Ottoman Empire were electrified but torn between believers in Sabbatai and sceptics. The fame of 'the Messiah' spread to Jewish and Marrano communities everywhere, and many gave away their worldly goods, did penance for their sins, and awaited the Messiah or sought to go to the Holy Land. Early in 1666 Sabbatai started for Constantinople with a band of his followers, only to be arrested by Vizier Aḥmed Köprülü. Imprisoned at Abydos through a large part of the year 1666, he was treated as a martyr by his followers and as a privileged inmate by the government until a Polish rival, Nehemiah-ha-Kohen—whether to test Sabbatai's sincerity or to strike a bargain with him is unknown—came to see him and decided to denounce him as a traitor to the sultan. Sabbatai was thereupon given a choice between Islam and death and chose Islam. So did a number of his followers, and to this day these *Dönmeh* (Turkish: *apostates*) survive, outwardly professing Islam but also practising many Jewish rites and customs.

Sabbateanism did not wholly end with Sabbatai's conversion. His followers had been especially numerous in Poland. In part, he seemed to be the answer to their prayers for a deliverer from the Cossacks, who were massacring Polish Jews (and Catholics) in a prolonged struggle (1648–67) that foreshadowed the ultimate decline of Poland (see Chapter IV). Sabbateanism also appealed to the poor, unlettered, pietistic Jews who found the dry formalism of the rabbis hard to comprehend and discouraging. Nehemiah-ha-Kohen, upon his return to Poland, seems to have been accepted as Messiah by some of the still undaunted Sabbateans until (the sources disagree) he either died or was disgraced and driven out.

Jacob Frank (1726–91), another self-proclaimed prophet, found a following even in the eighteenth century among the Polish Sabbateans, though only a few went along when he preached conversion to Catholicism. Many more turned to the contemporary mystic who was known as Baal-Shem-Tov (Master of the Good Name). This simple man preached a pietistic religion of direct communication with a pantheistic God through fervent prayer, ecstasy, dance, song, and joy, rather than through learning, jejune ritual, and asceticism. His followers, borrowing an ancient name, called themselves Chassidim, and Chassidism remained a live movement among the eastern European Jews thereafter.

Ritual, however, did not lose its force or its effectiveness as a uniting trait among a dispersed people. Safed, near Jerusalem, was a thriving Jewish community, and a group of Hebrew scholars had established themselves there in the sixteenth century around the learned Isaac Luria (1534–72). In 1535 Joseph ben Ephraim Qaro (1488–1575), an exile from Portugal, joined this community. For fifty years he had frequent visions of a heavenly visitor who spoke to him about Talmudic questions. Qaro kept careful notes of these conversations, and from them came two significant studies of Jewish law. *Beth Josef* was a lengthy commentary on the Talmud and on earlier Talmudic authorities; *Shulhan 'Arukh* was a code of rabbinical practice and ritual. For many years the *Shulhan 'Arukh* was disputed among the rabbis of widely scattered communities, but gradually the very disputes made it better known. By the middle of the seventeenth century most rabbis regarded it as authoritative, and in the eighteenth century they considered it the final word on matters of which it spoke. Thus, even as Mendelssohn's emancipation movement in Germany and Baal-Shem-Tov's Chassidic movement in Poland were taking form, rabbinical ritual and Talmudic learning as codified by Qaro in Palestine acquired authoritative standing. The future of Judaism as a religion lay along those three lines.[16]

NOTES TO CHAPTER V

1. The passages on missionary efforts in South and Central America are largely borrowed from a study especially prepared for this volume by the Spanish National Commission for UNESCO.

2. *The Works of President Edwards*, 8 vols. (Worcester, Mass., 1808–09), Sermon XXVII, Vol. VIII, p. 293.

3. Quoted in Alexander Brown (ed.), *The Genesis of the United States* (Boston, 1890), I, p. 339.

4. Quoted in R. P. Beaver 'Recent Literature on overseas missionary movements from 1300 to 1800', *Journal of World History*, I, (1953), p. 148.

5. Professor O. Lacombe points out that the missionary activity of a Nobili or his kindred Jesuits did not rely only on an adaptation of the caste system. They 'divined' the way by which they might penetrate the 'inner' India (J. Monchanin and H. Le Saux, *Ermites du Saccidânanda* [Paris, 1956], p. 40). The Tamil texts of Father Beschi are considered literary monuments of high value in this particularly difficult language.

6. To Professor O. Lacombe the difficulties involved in the question of Chinese, Japanese, Indian, and other 'rites' were due not to the principle itself (according to which the Church might allow the faithful to observe rites of purely human and social significance, uncontaminated by superstition and not contradictory to faith and morality) but to the frequent absence of any clear distinction between 'civil' and 'religious' rites among the peoples to be evangelized. The missionaries therefore found themselves here treading on slippery and shifting ground and the differences of appreciation in individual situations were considerable. See p. 363.

7. The early Indian Christians, the 'Christians of St Thomas' (here called Syrian Christians), enjoyed a high social status; for the new Christians this was far less frequently the case. (Oliver Lacombe.)

8. Sri Ram Sharma, *The Religious Policy of the Mughal Emperors* (London, 1940), pp. 41–60.

9. Quoted from Ja'far Sharif, *Islam in India*, as translated by G. A. Herklots and revised by William Cooke (Oxford, 1921), p. 10.

10. C. N. E. Eliot, *Hinduism and Buddhism, an Historical Sketch*, 3 vols. (London, 1921), II, p. 250.

11. The literal meaning of the Sanskrit word *sahaja* is 'congenital, innate, connatural, natural'. The translation of the neo-Indian word *Sahajiyā* by 'Way of Nature' should not be interpreted in a naturalistic or empirical sense. The expression in question refers principally, if not exclusively, to that deep, metaphysical blessed spontaneity which is innate and immanent in the heart of man. (Oliver Lacombe.)

12. *Cultural Heritage of India*, II, p. 227.

13. Heinrich Busch, 'The Tung-lin Shu-yüan and Its Political Philosophical Significance', *Monumenta Serica*, XIV (1949–55), pp. 1–163; Charles O. Hucker, 'The Tung-lin Movement of the Late Ming Period', *Chinese Thought and Institutions*, ed. John K. Fairbank (University of Chicago Press, Chicago, 1958), pp. 132–62.

14. Ernest Satow, 'The Revival of Pure Shintau', *Transactions of Asiatic Society in Japan*, Appendix to Vol. III (rev. ed., 1883), p. 32.

15. Quoted in H. Graetz, *History of the Jews*, 6 vols. (Philadelphia, 1891–98), Vol. IV, p. 551.

16. For bibliographical detail, see Baron, as cited for Chapter II, n. 18.

CHAPTER VI

THEOLOGY AND METAPHYSICS
(1300–1500)

GENERAL REMARKS

IN this period, as before, Chinese, Hindu, Buddhist, Jewish, Christian, and Muslim thinkers generally based their theological-metaphysical speculations on certain absolute religious values and confirmed them by orthodox systems of dialectic. Aristotelianism in a 'Christianized' form, for example, dominated western European thought with a rigidity that Aristotle himself would perhaps have disapproved. His syllogistic system of logic, dominant first among east Christian, Muslim, and Jewish scholars and later also among west Christians, had brought to all of them the problem of how to use it in order to rationalize their religious dogma. Aristotelianism was followed by an anti-Aristotelian reaction. During the fourteenth and fifteenth centuries, the highly sharpened tools of Scholastic logic were brought to bear on the products of the older Aristotelian logic.

As Aristotelianism waned, Neoplatonism waxed. The Neoplatonism of this age laid special emphasis upon the intuitive, mystical elements in Plato's philosophy, adding the sympathy of an elite to the ancient urge of the un-lettered toward a more irrational mysticism. Mysticism serves, among other things, as an escape for sensitive or troubled souls from the pressure of spiritual or physical hardship, and this was a period of unusual hardship for great numbers of people. Mysticism is also a counterpoise to rationalism. The marked increase of mysticism during the fourteenth and fifteenth centuries coincided with the heated Scholastic rationalistic controversies of the time and in part was a reaction to them. If the mystic was less of a philosopher than the Christian Thomist or the Hindu Advaitist or the Chinese Rationalist, it was not because life presented him with different questions but rather because his method of arriving at answers relied more upon inspiration than upon his own frail intellect.[1] The mystic, whether European or Asian, trusted in intuition, personal revelation, and other highly individualistic inner processes that often ran counter to organized codes of belief and conduct and to conventional ethics. In western Europe the Roman Catholic hierarchy was likely to be suspicious at first of such individualistic mystics, though it eventually sainted some of them.

Rationalistic theological conflict during the fourteenth and fifteenth centuries tended toward ever greater subtleties of logic. Within Islam theological thought ran to systematic compendia of doctrine regarded as settled—except in Ṣūfism, in connection with which a richly imaginative literature elaborated the themes developed in the two preceding centuries. Judaism especially in the West carried on the old disputations with the Gentiles and inwardly was divided over the problems of Aristotle, Maimonides, and Qaballism. China and Japan, perhaps more than any other region, were melting pots of rival theologies and philosophies—Buddhism, Neo-Confucianism, Taoism, and various shades of rationalism and mysticism. Christianity was torn by schisms, heresies, and schools of logic.

And yet in all major civilizations, the period between 1300 and 1500 seems to have been less outstanding than earlier or later ones in producing new and lasting systems of theology. Instead, as a general rule though with notable exceptions, it was marked, in Europe and to a lesser degree elsewhere, by the application of secular logic to bolster the approved answer to the eternal question of man's place in God's scheme. What was the source of knowledge; whether space, time, and matter were finite or infinite; what was the cause of evil; whether body and soul were the same or different; whether man's will was free or predetermined; whether faith alone or faith only if coupled with some variety of good works would save him—such were the theological and metaphysical problems to which mankind all over the world sought solution. Men's problems were similar even though their vocabularies were diverse.

HINDU DEVELOPMENTS

The six traditional systems of Indian philosophy were already highly developed by 1300, and the thinkers of the period seemed to confine themselves to elaborating, developing, refining, or defending them. The apparently derivative nature of their commentaries, expositions, and polemics might lead to the conclusion that little original was produced after 1300, but, in reality, works whose avowed purpose was either to expound or to criticize an old system sometimes set forth what amounted to a new one. Philosophical speculation continued at a high level into the seventeenth century, and only after that did originality disappear and speculation drop to low levels.

By 1300 the six systems of philosophy had become grouped into three pairs. Within two of these pairs the paired systems were for practical purposes syncretized inseparably. These two were the Nyāya-Vaishesika and the Sānkhya-Yoga. The third was the Pūrva-Mīmāmsā, better known simply as the Mīmāmsā system, and the Uttara-Mīmāmsā, better known as the Vedānta system. Some of these systems were themselves divided into several schools.

Although the six systems differed considerably and much of their literature consisted of mutual polemic, they held certain ideas in common. All six respected the authority of the Vedas, although the third pair, the Vedānta and Mīmāmsā systems, were more dependent upon them than the others. All accepted the doctrine of karma and the idea of *mukti* (*moksha*), or final liberation from the chain of rebirths. How to attain this liberation was in fact the central problem of all Indian theological speculation of the period. The theistic schools, of course, found the answer in devotion to a personal, accessible God, while other schools found it in some form of identity of the individual soul with the absolute, impersonal *brahman*. All the systems believed also in the existence of the soul or self, a permanent and pure element which in some way had become entangled in impurities and passions without their forming a real part of it. Each system had different ideas as to the nature of the soul, but all agreed that final release from the earthly form was attained through removal of the impurities, permitting the soul to realize its own essential, unsullied nature. Each system was rather pessimistic in its attitude toward mundane life, yet optimistic in the belief that ultimate enlightenment and release could be attained. Life on earth was but a succession of sorrows and sufferings brought on by ignorance, the search for pleasure, and 'selfness', or self-centredness. All systems agreed upon the general principles of conduct that should be followed, which included control of the passions, non-injury to life, and restraint of the desire for pleasure. The theistic schools found the next and highest step in *bhakti*, or devotion to a personal deity, while the non-theistic schools found it in meditative yoga practices, which also formed a part of *bhakti* devotionalism. While Hindu philosophy was vitally concerned with moral issues, it devoted little speculation (as distinct from religious instruction) to ethics as conceived in the West or China, perhaps because ethical conduct was taken for granted as part of the search for enlightenment. Enlightenment could be fully attained only through a late stage of knowledge (whether acquired by reason or yoga) or of devotion to God.

The Nyāya-Vaishesika system was realistic and pluralistic. It held that the external world was real and that ultimate reality consisted of many eternal entities. Among them were atoms (which combined to form matter), time, space, mind, souls (self), and the supreme soul, or God (Īshvara). God originally had not played a prominent part in the two systems that had paired to form this one, but before 1300 He had come to be regarded as the efficient, if not the material, cause of the universe, as its architect and controller. Release from the consequences of karma came through recognition that the soul was not dependent on body, mind, or external factors. At first, this knowledge was considered attainable through correct thinking and living, moral detachment, and ultimately higher meditation (yoga), but as theistic ideas penetrated the system, the higher states of enlightenment were deemed possible only through the grace of God, who was generally identified with Shiva.

The Vaishesika system was fundamentally a metaphysical atomic philosophy, and the Nyāya was fundamentally a system of logic and dialectics emphasizing the importance of perception, inference, verbal testimony, and comparison in validating knowledge. Gangesha of Mithilā (*c.* 1200) had presented the logical aspects of the Nyāya-Vaishesika system in so masterful fashion that thereafter its logic was emphasized while its metaphysical features were neglected.[2] The Mithilā school of logic and its method of expression spread in Bihar and Bengal and for a time had great influence, especially with the Vedānta philosophers. Among the proponents of the system were Shankara Mishra (variously dated between 1425 and 1650) and Vāsudeva Sarbabhauma (c. 1450–1525). The former was famed for his commentaries on the *Vaishesika-sūtra* (*Upaskāra*) and on Gangesha's work; the latter also wrote a commentary on Gangesha and was the first exponent of the rival Nadia school of Nyāya logicians, which gained strength in Bengal as the Mithilā school declined.

The Sānkhya-Yoga doctrine may be described as a sort of mechanistic dualism.[3] The Sānkhya system as interpreted in the ninth century was essentially atheistic. It was in accord with a few isolated statements of the *Upanishads* but was fundamentally at odds with their dominant concepts in that it posited the eternal existence and separateness both of matter (*pakrti*) and of an infinity of souls or spirits (*purusa*). In this dualistic scheme, matter had the power to evolve, bringing into existence the material world; the mechanical contact of souls with matter produced consciousness, egoism, and striving, and hence the belief (false in this chain of reasoning) that the soul was enmeshed in matter; release from the consequences of karma could come only when knowledge revealed the unreality of the connection between soul and matter.

The Sānkhya posited but did not develop methods for the attainment of this knowledge. They were developed in the Yoga system of Patañjali (fl. c. 150 BC), which outlined meditative practices that would lead to release from karma. It also posited a theistic principle—the existence of a perfect soul or God (Ĭshvara), Which prompted the process of evolution and salvation and Which was not, like ordinary souls, deluded into believing that It was in bondage to matter. The release of ordinary souls could be attained either by knowledge achieved through yoga practices or through devotion to Ĭshvara.[4]

By 1300 this theistic view was most generally accepted by the followers of the Sānkhya-Yoga system. Nevertheless, several books of this period still advocated the atheism of the ancient Sānkhya system. One of the most important was the *Sānkhya-sūtra*, unknown before the fourteenth century and probably compiled only during that century from previous Sānkhya works though attributed to a writer named Kapila. It was first commented on by Aniruddha in the late-fifteenth century. Its philosophy did not differ essentially from that of the early atheistic Sānkhya system, and it attempted refutation of other doctrines. It seems not to have increased the popularity of atheistic Sānkhya at the expense of the theistic Sānkhya-Yoga system.

The Mīmāmsā system (Pūrva Mīmāmsā) was a type of pluralistic realism having much in common with the Nyāya-Vaishesika. It early split into two schools with certain differences of detail. Of these two during our period the Bhatta school, following the teachings of Kumārila Bhatta (c. AD 700), was the more important. Mīmāmsā was a product of the ritualistic features of the Vedas, its object being to provide a proper method for interpreting the Vedas and, in doing so, to posit a philosophical justification for their rituals. It produced no outstanding contribution to metaphysics but propounded a theory of knowledge and a methodology of interpretation that were widely used by other schools, especially the Vedānta. According to Mīmāmsā, knowledge was derived from perception (through the senses, mind, and other internal organs), inference, comparison, presumption or postulation, non-perception, and verbal testimony. All knowledge was considered as self-validating and hence acceptable as soon as cognized, although illusion and error had to be explained away by technical distinctions. This theory of self-evident knowledge was necessary to confirm the testimony of the Vedas, which along with souls, the material world, heavens, hells, and Vedic deities were considered real and eternal: they had never been created and would never be destroyed. Such a system had no place for a supreme God or absolute, since nothing could be superior to the eternal Vedas. Mīmāmsā held that the law of karma governed the world and rebirth arose from the bondage of the soul or self to the body, the senses, and the material world. *Moksha,* or release from rebirth, came when the soul, having destroyed its bad karma by abstaining from deeds left optional or forbidden in the Vedas and by performing those prescribed, recognized that it was in reality separate from material things. Mādhava (*c.* 1350) and Laugāski Bhāskara (after 1400) produced the most significant of the works on the Mīmāmsā philosophy that appeared between 1300 and 1500.

*   *   *

The Advaita School

The Vedānta system (Uttara-Mimāmsā) showed more originality during those centuries than any other of the six systems. Several schools had arisen within it. All of them claimed to follow the *Upanishads,* and specifically the *Brahma-* or *Vedānta-sūtra* traditionally attributed to Bādarāyana, and each, whether absolutistic or theistic, claimed to present the only true interpretation of this ancient *sūtra.*

Though Vedānta also contained several theistic schools that were growing in importance and popularity, particularly during the period covered by this volume, the school of absolute monism—or, perhaps more accurately, non-duality (*Advaita*)—was the most widely known and influential of all Vedānta schools, and many think of it as synonymous with the whole Vedānta system. Based upon the *Upanishads* and the *Vedānta-sūtra,* the Advaita school had been given its classical monistic statement by Shankara in the ninth century and had been expanded by a host of commentators before 1300. It insisted that the absolute, unitary, impersonal *brahman* was the sole reality and was identical also with the *ātman* (*self* or *soul*), which was pure consciousness and bliss. *Brahman* appeared in the form of the manifest universe (*māyā*) and as individual souls (*jīva*). As the manifest universe, the world we know, it was an illusory phenomenon, similar to the illusion that occurs when a rope is mistaken for a snake; as the individual ego or soul it was the real *ātman* but was perceptible only with the modifications that came inevitably from an illusory universe, much like the yellowness of a white conch when viewed through yellow glass or like the reflection of the sun in a pool.

Māyā thus connoted illusion itself, the power to obscure or to create illusion, and the capacity to create a sense of multiplicity where unity was the only reality. It was inherent in *brahman*. When operating in the causal capacity of *māyā*, *brahman* might be personalized as Īshvara (or God), the efficient and material creator of the illusory multiple universe, and as such was known as the lower or qualified *brahman*. God the Creator was thus a super-illusion produced by the reflection of *brahman* through *māyā*. The *jīva* was a further reflection of Īshvara, and the sense of individuality was but a mirage created by ignorance or nescience (*avidyā*), a component of *māyā*. Salvation or escape from rebirth (*moksha*) was to be obtained through true knowledge (*jñāna*), recognition that individuality and multiplicity were unreal and that the individual soul was actually the changeless, eternal *ātman* or *brahman*. To attain *moksha* required the performance of one's ordinary duties in a detached manner without desire for worldly gains and the taking of the steps necessary to acquire *jñāna*. These steps included formal study of the Advaita under a teacher, reflection, and meditation (*yoga*). The enlightened soul would become completely free and be *ātman* when it cast off the physical body, the last trammels of *māyā*, at death.

By 1300 several branches of the Advaitins had arisen. Most writers belonged to either the Vivarana or the Bhāmati branch, but the differences between them were minor. The Advaitins' major controversies were with the theistically inclined Vedāntists or with the adherents of the other systems. Their dialectical skill steadily improved during the period; as already stated, the monists generally accepted the Nyāya method of logical analysis and a theory of knowledge and a methodology of interpretation similar to those of the pluralist Mīmāmsā school.

Among a host of Advaitin exponents prior to 1500 two are especially noteworthy. Rāmādvaya (probably before 1350) was the author of the *Vedānta-kaumudī*, dealing with Shankara's commentary on the *Vedānta-sūtra*. He elaborated the monists' theory of perception and consciousness, defined right knowledge as experience which did not misrepresent its object, and accepted the Mīmāmsā theory of the self-validity of knowledge. Probably the greatest Advaitin figure of the period was Vidyāranya (fl. 1350), generally known as Mādhava (not to be confused with Madhva, founder of the dualist school of the Vedānta). Mādhava was particularly celebrated for his clear, forceful style and excellent diction. He wrote a compendium of the existing systems of thought (*darshana*) entitled the *Sarva-darshana-samgraha*. Although later writings summarized individual systems or commented on various aspects of one or more of them, Mādhava's work has remained probably the outstanding epitome of Indian thought produced by traditional Indian scholarship. In his writings on the Advaita he followed the Vivarana interpretations. His *Pañcadashi* was a popular presentation of the monistic system; his *Vivarana-prameya-samgraha* was a scholarly commentary and exposition of the work of an earlier Vivarana writer; his *Jīvan-mukti-viveka* was a clear exposition of the monists' view of emancipation and of the training and meditation leading to it. As became increasingly characteristic of monist writers, he gave *māyā* almost an independent existence, even though he considered it still a part of *brahman*.

* * *

The Vīrashaiva Philosophy

The theistic Vedānta schools grew out of the religious sects as a reaction to the impersonal monism of Shankara's followers. The monists' transcendent *brahman*, their complete identification of the soul with *brahman*, their doctrine that individual souls and the manifest universe were but illusory phenomena, and their denial of incarnation were essentially incompatible with a personal religion in which God could save the souls of those devoted to him. In the latter view God, individual souls, and matter had to be real and in some way distinct, and God had to be perfect, all-powerful, and immanent.[5] In the twelfth century both Vishnuite and Shivaite philosopher-theologians had worked out systems of thought that, while meeting the needs of the theists, could compete on intellectual grounds with Shankara's monism; Rāmānuja had provided Vishistādvaita, or qualified monism, the Vishnuite system (which we shall examine a little later), and the Shivaite philosopher Shrī-kantha (Nīlakantha) provided another type of qualified monism. In the next century Meykandar (Shvetabana) and Arunandi perfected the philosophy of Southern Shivaism. It reached definitive form shortly after 1300 in the writings of Umāpati (see Chapter X), the most significant philosophical works among them being the *Shivappirakāsham* and the *Pauskar-āgama*.[6] Several important commentaries were written on the works of Arunandi and Umāpati after 1300.

The Shivaite qualified monists accepted the *Upanishads* and the *Vedānta-sūtra* as the fountain of authority but gave them a theistic interpretation compatible with the Shivaite *Purānas* and *Āgamas*. While they maintained that God, souls, and matter were discrete and real, they endeavoured to maintain a monistic position by asserting that souls and matter, though separate, were in fact identical with God. *Pati*, the Lord (that is, Shiva), was identical with *brahman*, although personal. He was pure, eternal, all-powerful, always present, and free. *Pāsha* (matter) was also eternal. *Pashu*, the eternal individual soul, bound by the fetters of matter, had become separated from the Master. The fetters of matter were *ānava* ('inborn impurity' or 'ignorance'), *karma* (which inevitably resulted from *ānava*), and *māyā* ('illusion').

Although all three were binding, they helped the soul through experience to liberate itself by realizing its true identity with Shiva. To make this possible, Shiva carried out His five-fold function of creation, preservation, destruction, concealment, and bestowal of grace. Concealment was necessary in order to make souls active in seeking experience. When, through the long experiences of transmigration, the devoted soul gradually wore away its fetters and began to comprehend its true identity, the stage was set for release through divine grace. The Lord revealed Himself to the soul, instructed and purified it, and led it to full realization of its identity with Him. While the idealistic school of Kashmir held that the released soul merged with Shiva, the majority of Shivaites believed that the released soul both became a Shiva, although dependent on Him, and retained its distinct identity. Shivaite qualified monism is in some regards analogous to Christianity: *ānava* suggests 'original sin', *bhakti* 'faith', *moksha* 'salvation'.7

In the latter half of the fourteenth century Shrīpati Pandita put the philosophy known as Vīrashaivaism into definitive form. His *Shrīkara-bhāsya*, a commentary on the *Vedānta-sūtra*, was perhaps the most original theistic treatise produced by the Shivaite schools. The Vīrashaiva philosophy insisted that God, souls, and the universe were real. God (that is, Shiva) was the physical and spiritual material of the universe; He was pure consciousness and will; He was energy and action; and He had created the universe out of himself as a spider spins a web. *Brahman* was the essence (*sthala*) of Shiva. By its innate power (*shakti*) *sthala* created the *linga*, individual souls, and material objects. The *linga* was Shiva, and because of its divine nature was to be worshipped. The individual soul was *bhakti* (or devotional) and was the worshipper. The devotional soul, with the aid of Shiva as instructor and guide (redeemer), passed through six stages leading from indifference concerning this world to blissful union (without complete loss of individuality) with Shiva. Love of God and moral and spiritual discipline were essential to redemption.

*　　*　　*

The Vishistādvaita School

The Vishnuite Vishistādvaita, the qualified monism of Rāmānuja, also found a number of able propagators and defenders. Few of them, however, adopted the logical methodology of the Mithilā school, and hence they seldom reached the critical heights of the Shankara and Mādhva schools. Their polemical works were directed mainly against those who were not qualified monists. In the Vishistādvaita system, Nārāyana (that is, Vishnu), the personal God, and *brahman* were identified, and both matter and souls were considered the body of *brahman*, which comprised and pervaded everything. Matter and souls were thus not *māyā* but the substance of God, and were distinct and eternal. Salvation was obtainable by good works, knowledge, devotional meditation (*bhakti*), and self-surrender, assisted by the grace of God, and meant a personal blissful existence near Vishnu, partaking of his qualities without being merged with him. God revealed himself not only as the supreme spirit and as the ruler within the soul but also in various manifestations and incarnations (Rāma and Krishna), and in duly consecrated images.

In the fourteenth century some noteworthy followers of Rāmānuja's qualified monism appeared. The earliest of them was Pillai Lokācārya, who was associated with the development of the doctrine of the Tengalai sub-sect (see Chapter III). This doctrine held that salvation was attainable not so much through good works and effort on the part of the individual as through devotion and self-surrender, after which the Lord parentally grasped the soul. It tended to emphasize not only the omniscience of God but also His kindly, merciful, and blissful nature.

The greatest of the qualified monists after Rāmānuja was Venkatanātha (mentioned in Chapter III as Vedānta Deshika). Venkatanātha (or Vedānta Deshika) was a fine poet and a prolific writer. His numerous treatises on religion and philosophy did so much to clarify and expand the ideas of Rāmānuja that the two rank almost equally high as architects of the Vishistādvaita system. In his *Nyāsa-vimshati* Venkatanātha developed the idea, associated with the Vadagalai sub-sect, that successful self-surrender to God must be preceded by good works and individual effort to grasp God for help and protection. His *Nyāya-parishuddhi* expounded the logical principles of the qualified monist school. He accepted the idea of the self-validity of knowledge and explained illusion as the appearance of one thing in the form of another. He recognized only three sources of knowledge—perception, inference, and scriptural testimony; and he described intuitive yoga knowledge, which had been accepted by Rāmānuja, as a form of higher perception, thus dividing perception into three classes, namely God's, the yogi's, and the ordinary man's. He insisted that some propositions must by nature be valid, because if nothing were considered valid, there would be no basis for any reasoning process. The existence of God, nevertheless, could not be established by reason but must be accepted on the basis of scripture. He also (compare the contemporary European nominalists) denied the reality of universals or categorical concepts, maintaining that they arose only out of human perception of similarities in different and specific things. His *Shāta-dūsanī* was devoted principally to refutation of the views of the Shankarites (among others) about the nature of *brahman*, the soul, reality, and emancipation. He denied their doctrine of *māyā* and insisted upon the reality of the world, but he did not accept the atomic theory of the Vaishesikas.

Perhaps Venkatanātha's greatest work was the *Tattva-muktā-kalāpa*, in which he set forth his own version of qualified monism. To him God was everything—the instrumental and material cause of the world, its controller and director. Individual souls and material things were created by God out of Himself to form His body. They were, therefore, a part of God, yet real, distinct, and eternal. Despite the dependence of the individual on God,

Venkatanātha insisted, God gave man freedom to make his own choices. Although *bhakti*, the joyous adoration of God, was essential to salvation, it must be accompanied by deliberate effort on the part of the individual. The emancipated soul participated in the omniscience and bliss of God but did not partake of His power to create and control the world or to emancipate souls. In the late fourteenth century Varadārya and Shrīnivāsadāsa, Venkatanātha's son and pupil respectively, carried on the master's message, and in the fifteenth century Rāmānujadāsa (also called Mahācārya) not only wrote commentaries on Rāmānuja and Venkatanātha but also as an advocate of Vishistādvaita attempted a refutation of the Mādhva dualists, on the one hand, and of the Shankarite monists, on the other.

*   *   *

The Dvaita School

The dualistic (Dvaita) Vedānta school, founded by Madhva in the thirteenth century and elaborated by Jaya-tīrtha in the first half of the fourteenth,[8] was also a reaction to the Shankara system. Jaya-tīrtha wrote many books expounding, defending, and elaborating the rather cryptic writings of Madhva. His two most important works, the *Nyāya-sudhā* and the *Tattva-prakāshikā*, were commentaries on and elaborations of Madhva's principal philosophical works. The former book has sometimes been described as the most masterful commentary in all Sanskrit literature.

The Dvaita school was theist and realist as well as dualist. It developed a distinctive logic and theory of knowledge. Perception, inference, and scriptural testimony were regarded as the sources of valid knowledge, but each, especially perception, was defined in a way peculiar to the Mādhvas. They held certain things to be real and eternal but distinct—God and soul, different souls, God and matter, soul and matter, and variant forms of matter. In sum, however, they conceived of only two kinds of things in the world—independent and dependent. God alone was independent, everything else was dependent on Him. The existence of God could be established only by revelation. He was identified with *brahman* and called Vishnu or Nārāyana, but he might appear in diverse forms. He was the perfect, all-powerful, omniscient, omnipresent, all-merciful controller of the world; He was its efficient but not its material cause. God and souls were considered related as father to son or master to servant, and each soul was real, eternal, unique, and marked by its own ignorance and imperfections. The substance of the manifest universe (including the human body) was matter (*prakrti*), which was controlled and directed by God. The destiny of souls was predetermined—whether to eternal bliss in the presence of Vishnu, to an eternal round of transmigrations, or to an ever downward course of suffering (as in the case of demons and sinners like the monists). The rebirth and the suffering of souls destined for salvation were caused by the ignorance and imperfections adhering to them, which obscured their true nature and prevented them from acquiring the knowledge essential to salvation. Proper living, study of the scriptures, and detached contemplation and meditation were essential to knowledge of self and God, but the final, indispensable step in salvation was a loving devotion (*bhakti*) that grew out of a realization of God's majesty and goodness. Such devotion led to the bestowal of God's grace, without which salvation was impossible. Salvation was a blissful existence, but even saved souls enjoyed bliss in different degrees, depending on the intrinsic worth of each.

A number of subsequent defenders of the dualist position showed great ingenuity and subtlety in elaborating details, but they added little that was fundamental to Jaya-tīrtha's thought. Probably the greatest controversialist of this period was Vyāsa-tīrtha, who seems to have lived in the fifteenth century. His *Nyāyāmrta* took up the arguments of various monists from Shankara on and refuted them, only to be refuted in turn by Madhusūdana in the sixteenth century. Vyāsa-tīrtha attacked the doctrine of the illusory nature of the world (*māyā*) and questioned the monists' conception of *brahman*, knowledge, ignorance, perception, inference, and liberation. He upheld the reality and distinctness of God, souls, and the material world, supported the idea of a personal God as opposed to the absolute *brahman* devoid of all qualities, and insisted that God or *brahman* could not be the material cause of the world but only its instrumental or efficient cause.9

* * *

The Dvaitādvaitamata School

If Nimbārka lived in the fourteenth rather than the twelfth century,10 then, as the founder of the Dvaitādvaitamata, the school of dualistic monism, he was perhaps the most original, although not necessarily the best, of the Indian thinkers who flourished between 1300 and 1500. His ideas were set forth in a commentary, entitled the *Vedānta-pārijāta-saurabha*, on the *Vedānta-sūtra* and in a brief compendium of doctrine, entitled the *Dasha-shlokī*. Like other theists he was dissatisfied with the system of absolute monism, but he could not entirely cast off its spell. He was also committed to an intensely emotional dedication to God. The result was a qualified, pluralistic realism grafted upon a theistic monism. This philosophy borrowed much from Rāmānuja but developed its own distinctive features. Nimbārka's school accepted the self-validity of knowledge and admitted perception, inference, and scriptural testimony as the sources of knowledge but defined them in its own way.

According to Nimbārka the impersonal *brahman* and the personal Krishna (Vishnu) were the same. God was pure being, bliss, and consciousness; He was all-powerful, all-pervading, and all-merciful. He was both the instrumental and the material cause of the world, for, like the familiar spider spinning its web, he had created souls and the material world out of himself without altering. The world and individual souls were thus a part of him, created out of his energy, or *shakti*. They were dependent on him and could not exist without him, but they were also separate, distinct, eternal, and real. Their relationship to him was like that of waves to water; they existed potentially within God and became manifest in a gross form in the phenomenal world. The monistic texts in the scriptures were thus harmonized with the dualistic ones, in that *brahman* was conceived of as at once different from and yet identical with the world of spirit and matter.

Nimbārka preached a doctrine of salvation by enlightenment and faith. Every soul was encumbered with its own ignorance, impurity, and material body, which caused it to act independently, thus suffering pain and misery. Salvation came when the soul realized its true relationship to God, ceased its striving, and found its place as a participant in God's nature and in blissful, devout contemplation of and servitude to Him. This state of enlightenment, however, could come only as a result of the mercy of Krishna, and grace would be bestowed only on those who felt their helplessness and in faith surrendered to Him. Self-surrender, when accompanied by God's grace, engendered an intense love of and devotion (*bhakti*) to God, which made possible carrying on the routine duties of life, studying the scriptures under an enlightened teacher, and meditating on the nature of God in the manner necessary to the attainment of complete enlightenment.

Shrīnivāsa, Nimbārka's pupil, was his immediate successor as head of the sect. He wrote a commentary, known as the *Vedānta-kaustubha*, on the first of Nimbārka's works, and elsewhere expounded and upheld the master's teachings. After Shrīnivāsa dualistic monism found few able expounders, although some of the heads of the sect were reported to have been great scholars and controversialists.

CHINESE AND JAPANESE DEVELOPMENTS

In contrast to the Indian interest in metaphysics, theism, and salvation, Chinese thought was basically practical, moralistic, and secular. Although Chinese concern with metaphysics was conspicuous during this period, it was regularly subordinated to moral and practical considerations. Since neither Taoism nor Buddhism (with the possible exception of certain Ch'anist writers) produced any thinkers of renown, the only significant system of thought was Neo-Confucianism.

Two major schools of thought had developed within Neo-Confucianism during the Sung period. One was noted for its monistic idealism and is generally known as the Hsin-hsüeh, the School of the Mind, or, simply, the Idealistic school. It looked upon the mind (*hsin*) as everything—as principle (*li*), as the source of knowledge, as the ultimate reality; and it placed great stress upon intuition and the 'investigation of mind' (rather than external things) through meditation. In its emphasis upon the mind as the source of concepts of reality, it bore some resemblance to the subjective idealism of Bishop Berkeley in Europe in the eighteenth century (see Chapter VII). It did not obtain many able followers during the Mongol and early Ming periods and was not to be of much importance until later.

The other major school believed in a sort of dualistic idealism, emphasizing the interaction of principle (*li*)—that is, moral law or reason—and substance (*ch'i*)—that is, matter or material force. Since this school considered *li* the determinant factor in this interaction, it was known as the Li-hsüeh, or Rationalistic school. In emphasizing the 'investigation of things' rather than ideas of the mind as the source of truth (but not in much else) it resembled the empiricists of seventeenth- and eighteenth-century Europe.

Despite their differences, both schools subscribed equally to the unity of the universe and the interdependence of all things within it. Both considered the old Confucian ethical term *jen* (denoting goodness, benevolence, love or human reciprocation) fundamental to their thought, but they also gave it a metaphysical quality, making it the source or unifying principle of the universe. The *jen* of heaven was a principle shared by all things, tending to unite them and, in fact, making them one. They conceived of it not only as 'forming one body with the universe' but also as the 'life force' or 'generative principle'. It was likewise 'the character of mind and the principle of love,' comprehending all the virtues and generating in them the spirit that made them 'real, social, and dynamic'.[11]

*   *   *

The Li-hsüeh

Chu Hsi (1130–1200) was regarded as the greatest exponent of Li-hsüeh, and the Confucian books accepted as classical by him, together with his commentaries on them, were made standard for civil-service examinations in 1313 and remained so until the twentieth century. During the Yung-lo period of the Ming the writings of Chu Hsi and the Rationalists were condensed into the *Hsing-li ta-ch'üan*, or Great Philosophy, and this work, along with the classics and Chu's commentaries, became the basis of instruction in the official schools as well as of the examinations. Official support induced every scholar with ambition for office to turn to the study of Rationalistic philosophy. That philosophy taught that governments, too, had their *li* and that bad government arose because the ruler and his officials, not comprehending that *li*, did not follow it as truly enlightened rulers and officials should. The Rationalistic school completely dominated Chinese thought during the Mongol and early Ming periods until the sixteenth century and continued to exert a profound influence into the twentieth.

The Rationalistic dualists maintained that everything was made up of *li* and *ch'i*. The concept of *li* was much like Plato's doctrine of 'ideas' or 'forms'. *Li* was the governing principle or essence of things—abstract, eternal, and without form itself, but determining the nature of all things. It was, in short, abstract truth. *Ch'i* provided the substance of things. Thus, all being had two levels—the one abstract, absolute, eternal, and 'beyond shapes', and the other concrete, destructable, and 'within shapes'. Everything—the world, human nature, bamboo, motion, bricks, government—had its *li* but became embodied in a particular form only when combined with *ch'i*. *Li* was perfect, but *ch'i* varied in quality; and thus when they were combined in forms, the forms were subject to imperfection and evil. *Li* was superior and prior in the sense that the principle of all things had to exist before the things themselves could be embodied in particular forms. *Li* by itself was potential but inactive; *ch'i* possessed the power of movement and action, and in combination with *li* produced particular forms, the nature of which was determined by their *li*. Differences within the same categories were explained as due to varying amounts or qualities of *ch'i*.

For a thing the standard was *li*, and for the universe the standard was the great *li*, or supreme ultimate (*t'ai-chi*), of which all particular *li* were a part. The supreme ultimate thus contained within itself the potential of everything. It was often equated with *tao*, the way, or cosmic moral law. Furthermore, the supreme ultimate, without losing its unity, was present in every separate thing. Creation and destruction, growth and decay were explained in terms of the interaction of *li* and *ch'i*. The *li* of movement or the *li* of quiescence combined with *ch'i* to produce *yang* or *yin* respectively (action or repose, male or female, light or dark, good or evil), and *yang* and *yin* through their interaction produced the five elements (earth, water, fire, wood, and metal) from which the physical universe arose.

The *li* of each individual within the same category was exactly the same. Hence all humans were endowed with the same *li*, or nature, which consisted of the four fundamental virtues: righteousness (*i*), courtesy and propriety (*li*), wisdom (*chih*), and reciprocal goodness or love (*jen*), which, we have seen, was also the bond of cosmic union. The *li* of mind by itself was incapable of thinking, feeling, or having emotions, but combined with *ch'i* it formed mind (*hsin*), which possessed these capacities. Evil in the world and among men arose because of defective *ch'i*, which tarnished the perfect *li* of man's nature. To triumph over evil, man's purpose should be to strive to attain his true nature, which was good, by understanding the perfect *li*, which united him with all things, and thus to recover his 'lost mind'.

Toward this end the Rationalistic school advocated certain spiritual exercises. They included both 'the extension of knowledge through the investigation of things' and 'attentiveness of the mind', or study and meditative thought. The true nature of the great *li* or of oneself was to be discovered first through the investigation of particular things. After long study and careful investigation with the proper 'attentiveness of the mind', complete enlightenment was likely to come rather suddenly. The enlightened person understood his true nature and his oneness with other men and the universe, and was able to follow the *tao* with equanimity and impartiality. The ideal human way was that of the householder who, practising the four fundamental virtues, lived in harmony with man and nature. The Rationalist philosophy was thus essentially optimistic in its outlook; it believed in the moral perfectibility of man (in this regard resembling the *philosophes* of eighteenth-century Europe) and the possibility of approximating the ideal human society ('the heavenly city') that was supposed to have existed under the sage kings of the dim past.

The Mongol and Ming periods produced a number of able commentators on the Rationalistic system, and most scholars and officials parroted its basic principles, but few undertook to expand it. Chu Hsi, like Thomas Aquinas, appeared to have done his work so well that within its own premises the system could not be improved. Probably, too, the fact that it not only was the official philosophy but also tended to look backward to the classics and to a presumed golden age for inspiration had a stultifying effect. For whatever reason, many fell in with the view that since the time of Chu Hsi the truth had been manifest, further exposition was unnecessary, and nothing was left but to practise it. In consequence, later scholars did not fully apply the injunction to 'investigate things', which might have led them toward experimentation in natural science. On the contrary, they tended, far more than Chu Hsi, to disregard the world about them and, like the contemporary Scholastics of Europe, to investigate and expound the 'things' of their classics.

★   ★   ★

The Hsin-hsüeh

Although the Idealistic school accepted the same classics as the Rationalists and shared many of their ideas, it differed from them on certain fundamental points. To the Idealists mind was pure *li*, and they insisted that nature (*li*), mind, and feelings were different aspects of the same thing. For them there was but one realm of being or reality, namely that of the world of time and space, and what was 'above shapes' and what was 'within shapes' constituted a common realm. They accepted the view that the supreme ultimate was present in everything and argued that since it was present in the mind, the mind was everything: 'The universe is my mind, and my mind is the universe.'[12] The mind was at the same time the source of knowledge and of moral perfection, and one should concentrate on the study of one's own mind through introspection and reflection in order to find the principle of things, the *li* or the *tao*, rather than waste time investigating things. Evil arose because the mind was led astray by external things and became attached to desire. These externals must be shut out, and through concentrated, meditative, introspective study the 'lost mind', which held complete knowledge and understanding within itself, must be sought, and it might be recovered in a burst of sudden enlightenment. This conclusion brought the Idealists close to the Buddhists and Taoists, and indeed they were accused by their opponents of being Buddhists in disguise.

The Rationalistic school remained dominant until the sixteenth century. To be sure, compromise with Idealism was sometimes suggested. For example, during the first half of the fourteenth century Wu Ts'ao-lu and Cheng Shih-shan inclined toward a synthesis of the Rationalistic and Idealistic schools. But later Sun Lien (1310–81) and Fang Hsiao-ju (1357–1402) upheld the Rationalistic school against dilution. The Rationalists thereupon enjoyed a sort of renaissance, despite the martyrdom that Fang and all his relatives suffered for protesting, in proper Confucian fashion, against the seizure of the throne by the Yung-lo emperor.

*   *   *

Possible Synthesis of the Two Schools

Ts'ao Tuan (1376–1434) was the leading Rationalist of the early-fifteenth century. He was followed by two younger contemporaries, Hsüeh Hsüan (1392–1464) of Shansi and Wu Yü-pi (1391–1469) of Kiangsi. Actually, neither Hsüeh nor Wu appear to have fully distinguished between Rationalists and Idealists. Both emphasized investigation of things less than attentiveness of mind and hence, while considering themselves followers of Chu Hsi, promoted views which, strictly interpreted, belonged rather to the Idealists. Nevertheless, while the influence of the Idealist school was increasing, Hsüeh's followers, the so-called Hotung school, made strenuous efforts to uphold the Rationalistic position.

On the other hand, Wu's followers tended more and more toward an Idealist position. Wu, a sort of farmer recluse who shunned official position, himself had emphasized self-denial and self-perfection through meditation. One of his pupils, Hu Chü-jen (1434–84), came very close to the Idealistic school on many points but still loyally upheld the idea of investigating things. Another, Lou Liang (1422–91), was virtually Idealistic. Still another, Ch'en Hsien-chang (1428–1500) of Kwangtung, moved completely over to the Idealistic school. He himself described what happened when he failed to get satisfactory results from the method of study taught by Wu:

'Thereupon I cast aside the complexities of his [method], and sought for a simple one of my own, entirely through "quiet sitting". After a long time I finally came to perceive the very structure of my mind, which mysteriously became visible to me, even as if it were a concrete object. . . . Thereupon I came clearly to have trust in myself. . . . Comprehending this [the all-embracing activities of *li*], I find that Heaven and Earth are established by me, their myriad transmutations issue forth from me, and the whole universe lies within myself.'[13]

In this way some of the more original thinkers emancipated themselves from the orthodox Rationalists and paved the way for a great Idealist revival (see Chapter VII).

*   *   *

Theological Developments in Japan

In Japan Zen Buddhist priests introduced Neo-Confucian ideas from China before 1500, but these ideas were to bear fruit there only after that date.

Before 1500 the most original and interesting theological developments took place in connection with the efforts of court officials and Shinto priests to restore the position of the emperor and revive the native Shinto religion. Their thought was eclectic, borrowed from Buddhism, Confucianism, and Taoism. It was also monistic and pantheistic, the Sun Goddess being identified with the absolute from which all else emanated. It helped to provide eventually the metaphysical and ethical foundations for a theocratic and absolute system, although actual political power during the period remained in the hands of independent feudal lords. The ideas of the chief writers, Kitabatake, Ichijo, and Urabe Kanetomo, have been discussed in connection with Shintoism in Chapter III. In addition, Ryōyo Shōgei, of the Pure Land sect of Buddhism, developed the doctrine that salvation did not mean transportation to the Western Paradise (Pure Land) but represented a change of mind and condition here and now.

ISLAMIC DEVELOPMENTS

In Islam, no less than elsewhere, intellectual life was subservient to religion; and philosophy, along with law and the sciences, was held by the pious to be a handmaid of theology. Muslims distinguished sharply between *kalām* and *falsafa*. *Kalām* corresponds somewhat to theology, but it touched all philosophical questions as well, always from a religious-dogmatic point of view; and *falsafa* was in principle totally natural in method, but it sometimes touched upon questions regarding the nature of God. During our period mysticism was more intensively developed than systematic theology, which, however, was now being put into definitive form by commentators. Like other religions, Islam produced radical, moderate, and conservative factions, and probably in greater diversity and with more distinctive sects than Christianity did before 1500.

In contrast to the contemporary trend in Western Christendom and Judaism, the Muslim states of the West brought forth almost no great theologians, but in the rest of Islam theology flourished. The contrast can be explained, at least in part, by the fewness of the Muslim provinces in the West. The career and posthumous reputation of Ibn-al-'Arabī illustrate the fact that the centre of Muslim intellectual life was in the main areas of Muslim population, for this thirteenth-century Spanish-Muslim visionary migrated to Hijāz and Syria. He gave theological expression to the Neoplatonic and pantheistic aspects of Muslim mysticism and laid the philosophical foundations of one sort of monistic Ṣūfism. His influence, momentous in Islam, even made itself felt in Christendom. Some of his work, notably a chapter in the *Futūhāt Makkiyya* that describes a twofold ascent into Paradise, is considered by some scholars a significant source of Dante's *Divine Comedy*, although perhaps Dante merely reflects the mystical tendencies common in the literature of all the religions of those times. Some scholars assert also that

Ibn-al-'Arabī's mystical treatment of womankind inspired Dante's *Banquet*. It is more widely agreed that the Muslim mystic exerted a strong influence on the writings of Ramon Lull, one of the best Arabists of Christian Europe in his day.

Ibn-al-'Arabī's teachings became one of the subjects of controversy in Islam. Muslim theologians had come to terms with Aristotelian rationalism long before Christianity made its great Thomistic compromise with it, and before 1300 Aristotle had been reconciled with the Koran and other Islamic religious writings. Commentaries were compiled under the influence of the rationalism exemplified by Avicenna and Averroes (see Volume III). But Ibn-al-'Arabī's mystic monism became popular, and his writings raised more keenly than the less explicitly philosophical writings of earlier Ṣūfīs a problem that could scarcely be solved through Aristotelian logic—the significance of cosmic unity for personal experience. The controversies that now arose centred on the concept of *waḥdat al-wujūd* (*unity by existence*), which, while some decried it as in effect negating the identity of God, the majority of Ṣūfī philosophers defended.

Many scholars of the fourteenth and fifteenth centuries in Middle Eastern Islam reacted strongly against the scholasticism of the Aristotelians and in favour of the mysticism of the Ṣūfī. Such was the attitude of 'Abd-al-Karīm al-Jīlī (d. 1428), representative of a famous Iraqian family of conservative theologians; he reduced Ibn-al-'Arabī's visions to a consistent doctrine that presented the ideal man as a microcosm realized in mystical experience. An outstanding champion of the Ṣūfīs among the theologians was 'Abd al-Razzāq (d. 1329), a Persian mystic; he engaged in a controversy with Rukn-al-Din 'Alā' al-Dawla, a contemporary writer who attacked the orthodoxy of Ibn-al-'Arabī. A revived Arabian kingdom in the Yemen produced some theologians of note, prominent among whom was al-Yāfi'ī (*c*. 1300–67), a staunch defender of the mystical tendencies of the Ṣūfīs against the reformism of the Syrian Ḥanbalite Ibn-Taymiyya (1263–1328). Ibn-Taymiyya and his disciple Ibn-Qayyim-al-Jawziyya developed an incisive critique of both philosophy and Ṣūfism in favour of a social and historical puritanism which emphasized the responsibilities of man-in-community. They also attacked the orthodox *'ūlamā'*, for like other Ḥanbalīs they rejected the traditionalist limitations of *taqlīd* (binding by legal precedent) and called for what they regarded as a return to primitive Muslim orthodoxy. Their attacks, whether philosophical or social, were largely ignored.

Mysticism's dominance in Islam was manifested likewise by the Maw-lawiyya *ṭarīqa*, the 'whirling dervishes' of the Turkish lands. Organized by the thirteenth-century Persian-born poet, Jalāl-ud-dīn Rūmī, who was a professor at the *madrasa* of Konya, they were merely one of the more spectacular of the numerous Muslim fraternities of practising mystics. Their members helped to give social prestige to monistic philosophical doctrines.

Probably the most vital line of intellectual endeavour, as might be expected, was the development and the critique of Ṣūfī theosophy. At the beginning of this period, the Syrian school of Ibn-Taymiyya was noted for its all-out opposition to Ṣūfism. Most of the Ṣūfīs' positive work, however, was done not in Syria but in Iran, developing both the Ishrāqī metaphysics of light and the cosmic monism associated with Ibn-al-'Arabī. The most prominent presentation of mystical monism was in the writings of poets such as Jāmī in the fifteenth century, who produced prose commentaries on mystical texts and embodied such ideas in his verse (see Chapter X).

JUDAIC DEVELOPMENTS

Judaism inherited from the centuries before 1300 numerous theological controversies that resulted in factions of conservatives, moderates, and radicals in much the same fashion as in other religions. One of the oldest of the controversies concerned the fundamental basis of faith: Should sacrosanctity be restricted to the Pentateuch (Torah) or should it also extend to other holy scriptures such as the Talmud and to oral tradition?

The relationship of Aristotle to orthodox theology, which had become crucial among Judaism's problems in the eleventh and twelfth centuries, was still highly debated in the fourteenth century. Aristotle's logical treatises circulated widely through the Hebrew world, and his ideas were adapted to current philosophical disputes, often with violence to their original meaning. The conservatives of Judaism under the leadership of some of the rabbis opposed Aristotelianism and the rationalization of faith implicit in it. A moderate faction of intellectuals, on the other hand, adopted the Aristotelian ideology associated with the name of the twelfth-century philosopher Maimonides. A third category, comprising Jewish theologians of a still more moderate, even neutral attitude, was probably the majority group. A fourth group, extreme radicals, even sceptics, opposed Maimonidism as vigorously as did the conservatives.

The strict-constructionist role had for centuries been filled by the Karaites, 'children or followers of the Scripture'. They wrote commentaries on the holy books but vigorously rejected the lore and authority of rabbinical works, holding that each man was free to interpret Torah for himself. In this respect they resembled the later Protestants of Christianity, who rejected the doctrines of the Roman Catholic clergy and church fathers, relying solely on the Bible as their religious authority. This resemblance led certain Roman Catholics in the sixteenth century to refer to the Protestants as 'Karae' (i.e. Karaites).

Aaron ben Elijah of Constantinople (1300–69) is often called the 'Maimonides of Karaitism'. Aaron differed with Maimonides, however, in at least one essential; he questioned Maimonides' attempt to reconcile Aristotle with religious orthodoxy. Aaron's *Tree of Life* rejected Aristotelianism in favour of the earlier orthodoxy of Judaism. Along with his other works it stressed the freedom of the human will and the importance of the ancient prophets. He was influential among the Jews in the West as well as the East, but he was the last outstanding Karaite. Karaitism declined during the late Middle Ages, and conservative ideologies, even in the once-great French, Spanish, and North African centres of Jewish theology, were eclipsed by the ever-increasing forces of skepticism and secularism.

During the fourteenth and fifteenth centuries Maimonides' rationalistic approach to religion continued to be attacked from other quarters. Among the most assiduous of the attackers were the mystics—especially in Spain. A sect of mystical extremists, the Qabbalists, had arisen there in the thirteenth century. The first outstanding Qabbalist, a Catalan Jew named Azriel ben Menahem (1160–1238), had adopted an old theory of emanation, adding to it certain Aristotelian ideas concerning the eternity of the world, and the Biblical account of creation. About a century later, a work (attributed to Moses ben Shem-Tob of Leon by modern scholars) entitled *Sépher ha-Zohar* (*Book of Splendour*) synthesized the prevailing mysticism and became the mainstay of Qabbalism. Qabbalism was an amalgam of magic, pseudo-science, and religion. Strange beliefs and practices from Zoroastrianism, Neoplatonism, and ancient Babylonian mythology were mingled with genuine spiritual idealism. At its worst, with its demonology, lore of numbers, and astrological superstitions, it marked a decline in the ancient faith. On the other hand, its high spiritual aspirations encouraged idealists to rise above the legalism and ritualism of rabbinical Judaism. Qabbalism became immensely popular with those moderate Jews who could accept neither the conservative nor the radical extremes of theology and also with those who sought in an extravagant, visionary lore escape from the tribulations of life.

Qabbalism contributed to the waning of Jewish thought after 1300. Even in Spain, where it had once flourished brilliantly under Muslim rule, Judaic theology declined. The decline was due also in part to the restrictions placed upon the Jews by Christian rulers. As the Christians extended their sway over the lands of the south, Jewish scholars often found it safer to restrict themselves to commentaries on the Old Testament and the Talmud. Such commentaries appeared in great numbers, not only in Spain but also in southern France and north Africa, where large colonies of refugees sought safety from Christian persecution. Another indication of the cumulative flight of Jewish scholars from original thought on Judaic subjects was the rise in the number of translations of Latin works into Hebrew.

In southern France and Spain rival groups of radicals and conservatives built up a vast controversial literature, especially concerning the merits and shortcomings of Maimonides. Some of this literature transcended mere pedantry. Joseph Kaspi (1280–1340), a south-French Jew, wrote brilliant treatises quoting extensively from Aristotle (and sometimes from Plato) and defending the moderate rationalism of Maimonides. Kaspi's contemporary,

Levi ben Gerson, sometimes known as Gersonides (1288–1344), one of Judaism's outstanding scholars, wrote a treatise entitled *The Wars of the Lord*, in which he reconciled Judaism with Aristotelianism. In this and his commentaries on Aristotle and other philosophers, he is sometimes considered more logical and certainly was more truly Aristotelian than Maimonides. Naturally he stirred up violent opposition. During his own lifetime he was charged with heresy, and later Jewish scholars attacked both him and Maimonides. Strange to say, although Gerson was an Aristotelian rationalist, he upheld the 'realist' position of medieval thinkers with regard to universals (see below). The leader in the attacks on Maimonides and Gerson was Hasdai ben Abraham Crescas of Barcelona (1340–1410). Crescas' works mark the climax of the anti-Aristotelian movement in Judaism, and his *Light of the Lord* was appealed to also by anti-Aristotelian Christian scholars in their attacks on Thomist rationalism. Attempts (by Simon ben Zemach Duran Joseph ben Shem-Tob, and others) were made to reconcile the Crescas school with the moderate rationalism of the Maimonidans but proved vain.

Italian humanists and neo-Hebraic writers sometimes mutually influenced one another. A fourteenth-century Italian Jew, Immanuel ben Soloman, wrote, though in a lighter vein, a Hebrew poem modelled in part upon the *Divine Comedy* of his friend Dante. In the fifteenth century, many humanists saw a kinship of Jewish and Christian thought in Qabbalism, with its anti-Aristotelian, Neoplatonic bias, and its reliance on individual instinct rather than logic. Pico della Mirandola, the Neoplatonic humanist (see below), was a friend and student of Jewish scholars in Italy, particularly of Elia del Medigo. He earnestly studied the Qabbalist writings with the help of a less scholarly Jew from Constantinople, Jochanon Aleman. In these works he thought he found proofs of the divinity of Jesus and other Christian doctrines, and with these arguments in hand he hoped to convert Jews to Christianity. Furthermore, he endeavoured to achieve a great syncretistic triumph, reconciling Judaism not only with Christianity but also with Islam, Platonism, and even Aristotelianism.

Pico della Mirandola exerted an unmistakable influence on Judah Leon Abravanel, also known as Leo Hebraeus. Judah was the son of Isaac Abravanel, Jewish philosopher and onetime financial adviser to the Spanish throne, who had preferred exile to remaining as a specially privileged Jew in Spain. Judah was a physician. Both men, after the expulsion of 1492, had found refuge in Italy. Judah Abravanel's *Dialogues of Love*, written in Italian and widely read in Italy, combined the stylistic beauty of literary humanism with fanciful erotic imagery. The lover's desire to be absorbed physically and spiritually into his beloved symbolized for him the mystical union of the human intellect with divine intelligence. Ficino and other Hellenophile mystics of the Platonic Academy in Florence (see below) were somewhat less enthusiastic over Qabbalism than Pico, but they too found in it an ally for their Neoplatonism. It gave them ground for their efforts to synthesize various theological and philosophical schools of thought under one all-embracing mystic essence of Divine Truth.

DEVELOPMENTS IN CHRISTIANITY

Volume III has indicated that when, early in the thirteenth century, Aristotle's *Physics* and *Metaphysics*, with Averroes' rationalistic commentaries, reached Paris, Scholasticism (i.e. the logical method of the Schoolmen) entered a new phase. At first, the church tried to prohibit the teaching of any of 'the philosopher's' writings except those on ethics and logic, but when the prohibition proved unenforceable, the Dominican theologian Thomas Aquinas undertook to harmonize Aristotle with orthodox Christianity.[14] His *Summa Theologica*, the principal work in his aim to organize Christian doctrine into a theological system, provided a formidable defence against free thought on the one hand and thoughtless reaction on the other. His brand of Scholasticism came to be generally known as Thomism. It was widely acceped in the schools around 1300, when it was still possible to expect that a tstable society, a common weal based upon the proper admixture of scripture, church tradition, and Aristotelianism could be indefinitely preserved.

Though in a sense the culmination of medieval Scholasticism, Thomism was challenged from several directions. In Thomas's own day, the deductive method in science was winning persuasive adherents; then Schism and Councils lessened the unity of the church; meanwhile, urbanization and commerce gave power and prominence to a bourgeois class that stressed individual initiative, achievement, and worth rather than birth and stability of social status. Thomas's contemporary Roger Bacon, Franciscan friar and scientific empiricist, rebelled violently against Aristotelian authority as 'a fountain of error' and against its Dominican exponents. The Catalan scholar and missionary Raimon Lull (*c.* 1235–1315) attempted to combine mysticism with reason by a Platonic or Pythagorean rather than an Aristotelian scheme for proving the truths of Christianity; he sought to do so by mathematical logic, equations, and diagrams. The conservative branch of the Augustinian order upheld the supremacy of faith in all matters theological.

Conservative Franciscan theology proved more formidable immediately as a foe of Dominican Scholasticism than empiricism or mystic mathematics or Augustinian faith. Thomas's works were charged with containing over two hundred heretical statements, and a French Franciscan corrected more than half of these so-called heresies. Subsequently the Franciscan archbishop of Canterbury formally condemned 'Thomism'. A more philosophical attack came from Duns Scotus (1266–1308), an English Franciscan who had been schooled at Oxford by empiricists like Bacon. Endowed with one of the keenest minds of his day, trained in logic and mathematics, Duns Scotus, a Schoolman himself, attacked Thomist Scholasticism with a paradox: the very acceptance by Thomas of the major premise that God was the omnipotent

Creator indicated the inadequacy of reason and the primacy of faith, since such a premise was not rationally demonstrable and must be accepted on faith. Furthermore, if God is omnipotent, he must be the cause of evil, and freedom of the human will is an illusion; reason unassisted by faith thus would lead logically to what seemed to Scotus a *reductio ad absurdum*—that God is responsible for the choice of evil by some mortals. Similarly Duns Scotus claimed to have reduced to rational absurdity Thomas' argument that man's immortality is proved by his desire for it and by his resistance to death: animals show similar tendencies. Though unprovable by reason, Duns Scotus argued, the justice of God and other Christian dogmas are necessary for man's morality and must be accepted on faith as a practical necessity. Against Thomas' preference for a rationalizing of religion, Duns Scotus maintained the desirability of keeping religion separate from rationalized thought.

Thomist Scholasticism survived the attack. Shortly after Thomas's death (1274) his old master, Albertus Magnus, persuaded the Dominicans to defend Thomism against the charge of heresy. Early in the fourteenth century, Dante also came to Thomas's defence, making him in the *Divine Comedy* one of his guides in the ascent of the highest steps of Paradise. In 1323 Thomas was canonized.

Yet personal vindication did not carry immunity from further criticism. A younger contemporary of Duns Scotus, William of Ockham (*c.* 1300–49), likewise a Franciscan trained at Oxford, continued the attack. Under papal suspicion for a critical commentary on one of the classics of Scholasticism, Peter Lombard's *Sententiae*, and for a defence of the Spiritual Franciscans, Ockham took refuge with a leading political opponent of the Avignon popes, Emperor Louis of Bavaria. The last twenty years of his life were spent in exile under the emperor's protection, and the philosophical dispute of Thomists and Ockhamists thus became merged with the political disputes between pope and emperor. Ockham's extensive writings and rigorously independent thinking brought to a climax the Franciscan attack on Thomism. With Ockham, as with Duns Scotus, it took the form of a markedly sceptical approach to the validity of Thomas' rationalized universals.[15]

Scepticism regarding the validity of universals is known as *nominalism*, since it holds that universals are merely convenient names without reality; belief in the reality of universals is known as logical *realism*. Coming on the heels of Duns Scotus' questioning of the use of reason in theology, Ockham's nominalism resulted in temporary eclipse of the Thomist brand of 'realism'. We shall discuss Ockham's contribution to logic below. Despite his intention to promote faith as a source of theological truth, his nominalism tended to promote descriptive science by pointing an accusing finger at the weaknesses of the deductive method of reasoning and by carefully indicating the limitations of the inductive method.

Ockham's doubt of Thomas's 'realism' infected the University of Paris, birthplace of Thomism. The fame of Jean Buridan (*c.* 1297–*c.* 1358), professor and later rector at Paris, spread Ockhamist nominalism among students not only of France but also of the new universities of Germany. Buridan's contemporary, Nicole Oresme (1323–82), shared his attitude. A major interest of both men was science (see Chapter XIII), and as philosophers and scientists they were both interested also in the works of Aristotle. Buridan wrote commentaries on Aristotelianism and (at the request of his king, Charles V the Wise) produced the first vernacular (French) translation of Aristotle. Scientific studies brought empirical questioning, which in turn induced philosophical nominalism and led Oresme particularly to support the Scotist-Ockhamist attack on Thomism and on those who would impugn faith by argument. Later French intellectuals, notably Chancellor d'Ailly (1350–1420) and Jean Gerson (1363–1429), his student, colleague, and successor as chancellor, adhered to the nominalist tradition of the University of Paris, impelled in part at least by their openly proclaimed concern for papal reform (see Chapter III) in the course of the Conciliar Movement.

Despite the steady drift from medieval religiousness to what we are accustomed to call 'modern' secularism, Thomism persisted through the fourteenth and fifteenth centuries and regained some of its lost prestige during the sixteenth (see Chapter VII). Scholasticism, especially in its Thomist form, continued as a rallying point for believers who were moderate rationalists. Serving as a buffer between Averroist extremists, unyielding advocates of reason, on the one hand, and conservative Augustinians, equally unyielding advocates of faith, on the other, it strove for the reconciliation of faith with reason.

*   *   *

Mysticism

At the time (mid-fourteenth century) when the German emperor Ludwig the Bavarian was providing a refuge from which the Franciscan William of Ockham delivered his assaults on Thomism, Meister Johannes Eckhart, a Dominican of independent spirit, was preaching doctrines that savoured of pantheism (see Chapter III). Although Eckhart seems to have known no Hindu theological works, a modern Hindu has commented that Eckhart's sermons constituted 'an Upanishad of Europe'.[16][17] The analogy brings vividly to mind the similarity of mysticism in all parts of the world, but Eckhart's mysticism was rooted in the Augustinian-Neoplatonic philosophy of the West, in a soil that knew more of Jewish and Muslim than of Hindu mysticism. Some of his doctrines were formally condemned upon his death.

Eckhart's disciples John Tauler and Henry Suso were also Dominicans. Less philosophical than he, they did more to spread mysticism through the Germanies. Preaching, teaching, and writing in the vernacular, Suso in particular gave Eckhart's ideas a poetic, yet practical turn that made them immensely popular, especially in the Rhineland. Doubtless the poetical trend of Suso's mysticism saved him from charges of heresy such as had plagued Meister Eckhart; in the nineteenth century Suso was beatified. The work of these German Dominicans was continued late in the fourteenth century by the 'fathers' of Flemish mysticism, Jan van Ruysbroeck and Gerhard Groot. Both men, and Groot especially, were closely connected with the Brothers of the Common Life at Deventer and gave that order its mystic flavour. Their direct influence on systematic theology was slight, however, except as illustrating the reaction against the rigid Scholasticism of the day.

Mysticism would seem to be rare among scientists, yet one outstanding mystic of the fifteenth century was found among them. Trained at Deventer, Nicholas of Cusa (1401–64) became an ecclesiastical administrator, a reformer during the Conciliar Movement, a Scholastic logician, and a cardinal. Although he attained an enviable reputation in mathematics and other sciences (see Chapter XIII), he was also a Platonic mystic. His loyalty to Scholasticism and mysticism at the same time illustrates the prevailing dilemma of scholarly churchmen of the late Middle Ages. He escaped from the dilemma through his doctrine of intuitive faith. Denying the validity of human reason as a solvent of theological problems, he went so far as to maintain in his *Learned Ignorance* (*De Docta Ignorantia*, 1439–40) that all human knowledge is mere conjecture and that man is wisest who most readily acknowledges his ignorance. This line of reasoning may well lead directly to scepticism or agnosticism, but it led Cusa to a mystical concept of the Divine, which he set forth particularly in *De Visione Dei* (1453). Only by speculative contemplation and intuitive cognition, he held, can one attain God, Who is infinite, in Whom opposites like maxima and minima coincide, and Who is the sum-total of everything. Although these ideas in turn laid Cusa open to the charge of pantheism, he managed to avoid the accusation of heresy. Until his death he served the papacy faithfully.

* * *

The Platonic Revival

During Cusa's lifetime the Platonic abstractionists grew in numbers and influence, reinforced by the humanist revival of Plato. In the Middle Ages Plato's writings, save portions of the *Timaeus* in Latin, were unread in the West. Platonism in its modified, Neoplatonic form, however, had exercised a powerful influence on early medieval theology, especially through Augustine's works. During the centuries of triumphant Aristotelian Scholasticism after Thomas, Neoplatonism persisted vigorously only among mystics such as Eckhart and his disciples, and weakly in a few learned circles where the works of medieval Neoplatonists were studied. Petrarch possessed some of Plato's works but could not read them in the original Greek. Contenting himself with lauding Plato highly, he devoted serious study almost exclusively to the Latin classics. Boccaccio likewise lauded Plato, along with other Greek writers, but made no significant study of Platonism. To both of these fathers of Italian humanism, Plato was little more than a fellow-fighter in the feud with the deadening logic of Scholasticism. Nicholas of Cusa's Neoplatonic strain was tempered by Scholastic logic and given a humanist's touch by his schooling at Deventer.

Neoplatonism might perhaps have disappeared entirely into vague mystic abstractions had it not been for the revival of Plato in the 'Greek Renaissance'. At the end of the fourteenth century the Greek scholar Chrysoloras lectured upon Greek literature and translated some of it into Latin at Florence and other north Italian towns, and Plato's works were prominent in his repertoire. Early in the fifteenth century, one of Chrysoloras' Florentine disciples, Leonardo Bruni, translated several Greek writings including several of Plato's *Dialogues*. A Greek émigré, John Argyropoulos, added to the number of available translations late in the century. Thus Plato's philosophic ideas became known to Westerners at first hand.

Moreover, numerous second-hand interpretations of Plato were made available by fifteenth-century Byzantine émigrés. Notable among them were Gemistos Plethon and his disciple Bessarion, both members of the Byzantine embassy to the Council of Florence of 1439 (see Chapter III). These two scholars made a favourable impression on Cosimo de' Medici; Bessarion remained in Italy, eventually becoming a cardinal in the Roman church. To Italians the two men's knowledge of Greek philosophy was very impressive indeed. Plethon, who had written learned works on both of the great Greek philosophers, leaned strongly toward Platonism, even Neoplatonism. Bessarion was more moderate. Having translated Aristotle's *Metaphysics* into Latin, he endeavoured to mediate between the sometimes unphilosophically violent protagonists of Aristotle and of Plato. When, however, one of the radical Aristotelians, George of Trebizond, vilified both Plato and Plethon, Bessarion wrote a treatise condeming George in turn (*In Calumniatorem Platonis*). The preference for Plato over Aristotle on the part of Plethon and Bessarion seems, in a century when the adherents of Platonism, Aristotelianism, and nominalism were vying for domination, to have turned the intellectual tide in favour of Platonism in Florence and other Italian centres.

Although Bessarion deserted Greek Orthodox Catholicism, Plethon devoted himself for a time to the creation of a system of Neoplatonic theology that he hoped would reinvigorate the Byzantine church and society. In this role he became the rallying point for Greek as well as Italian Platonists in their attacks on Aristotelianism. Aristotle found vigorous defenders not only in George of Trebizond but also in Theodore of Gaza and Gennadios, the first Turkish-appointed patriarch of the Greek Orthodox Church. The feud raged throughout the latter half of the fifteenth century, interrelated with the ill-fated programme of union of the two churches (see Chapter III). Plato, Plethon, and union became confused with one another, for Platonists generally supported union. Platonist Plethon, on the one hand, was excommunicated by Aristotelian Patriarch Gennadios, while, on the other, Aristotelian

George of Trebizond was dismissed from his papal secretaryship because of his violent anti-Platonic propaganda.

Some humanists made a genuine effort to reconcile Platonism and Christianity. Bessarion, after his conversion to Roman Catholicism and his promotion to the cardinalate, emphasized the Christian implications of Platonism. In contrast, Marsilio Ficino (1433–99) carried doubt of revelation so far as to become orthodox in his Platonism. He was interested, among other things, in finding a solution of the problem of the Christian scholar who loved the pagan classics. All religions, he thought, could be reconciled. Encouraged spiritually and subsidized financially by Cosimo de' Medici to translate Plato, he became secretary of the *de luxe* Platonic Academy of Florence.

Under the leadership of Ficino the Academy gave Platonism its greatest vogue in Italy. Immersed in the labours of translating and commenting on Plato and the third-century Neoplatonist Plotinus, Ficino tended to become a worshipful admirer of the great pagan philosopher. Plato became for him a saint whose pronouncements were no less important than the scriptures. His bust of Plato was treated like a holy image, with candles and other ceremonials. He developed the themes of Platonic love and of the contemplative life by which the spirit can eventually attain oneness with God. The immortality of the soul became the central idea of his philosophic synthesis.

Eventually Ficino summarized his blend of Platonism and Christianity in a treatise with the revealing title *Theologia Platonica*. It was a medley of mystical abstractions in which the Renaissance emphasis on the dignity of man served as an underlying theme. This philosophy satisfied the cosmopolitans of the Platonic Academy; it was intelligent and at the same time orthodox, for Ficino was careful not to push his views too far. An individualist such as Pico della Mirandola, another leading figure in the Neoplatonic movement, might stray into the realm of pantheistic, Judaistic, or Islamic speculation (see below), but Ficino and most of the Academists kept clear of heresy. They covered their deviations from strict orthodoxy, such as the pantheistic concept of God and His relation to the soul, with abstract pronouncements, rhetorical embellishments, and tactful compromises. Reconverted in middle life, Ficino took priestly orders and, when he died, he believed that he had reconciled Platonism and Christianity both spiritually and practically, and many poets and humanists of his time agreed with him.

* * *

Stoicism and Epicureanism in Renaissance Italy

The intellectual climate of the Renaissance, which, especially in Italy, was so favourable to the revival of Platonism, was unfavourable to Stoicism. The stern ideals of self-control and uncompromising virtue for which the Stoics stood were suited only to the sturdiest ascetic souls. Had it not been for the Petrarchian cult of Cicero, Stoicism might have had no vogue at all in Renaissance Italy. Petrarch was familiar also with Seneca's letters, which presented a form of Stoicism more in keeping with Petrarch's Christian philosophy than did Cicero's works. Furthermore, Petrarch's humanism rested on a substratum of medieval asceticism, which in his *Secretum* appeared as a Stoic code of virtue, tempered by Ciceronian rationalism. In his literary masterpieces he solved the dilemma of the semi-fictitious Laura as body and soul by resort to a Ciceronian compromise, rejecting Augustine's extreme asceticism in favour of Stoic self-restraint.

In the fifteenth century, Lorenzo Valla's *De Voluptate et Vero Bono* focused attention on both Epicureanism and Stoicism in a spectacular fashion. Epicurean ideals had been anathema throughout the Middle Ages. A philosophy which taught that the external world was only a fortuitous interplay of void and atoms and that pleasure, no matter how simple and restrained, was the highest good was bound to appear heretical to those who held the Neoplatonic ideal of the plenitude of God and shared the Christian eschatology. Conservative clergymen condemned as atheists those who denied the resurrection of the body or quoted Epicurus and Lucretius to justify living solely for enjoyment. Valla was careful to provide his book with an outward orthodoxy but presented Epicurean ethics in a favourable light. Using the literary device of the dialogue, he presented a defence of Epicureanism by Antonio Beccadelli (author of a series of pornographic Latin epigrams), a defence of Stoicism by Leonardo Bruni, and a reconciliation of Christianity and Greek philosophy by Niccolo de' Niccoli. Since God had created human nature, the book argued, natural desires must be good; therefore the instinctive quest for pleasure should be satisfied; chastity was no virtue; courtesans were better for mankind than nuns.

Along with Beccadelli, Valla and his book were condemned. Nevertheless, during the pontificate of Nicholas V he was made papal secretary, worked as a translator in the Vatican Library, and died (1457) as a respectable canon of the Lateran Church. Similarly amazing was the career of the Florentine humanist Carlo Marsuppini (1399–1453), whose admiration for Classical antiquity led him to reject Christianity and to refuse the last sacrament but who, nevertheless, had served as a papal secretary and was buried magnificently in the Church of Santa Croce. Like Valla, many humanists of the Italian upper classes seem to have sought a pleasure-loving life. Yet few traces of systematic hedonism appear in humanistic writings before the sixteenth century, and the scientific implications of Epicurean atomism received no significant attention until the seventeenth century (see Chapter XIV).

*   *   *

The Attack on Aristotelianism

Hard and fast classification of the humanists into philosophical schools is difficult because of both their intense individualism and the wide range of Renaissance thought. The dilettantism of the humanist mentality is perhaps best exemplified in Pico della Mirandola. A wealthy nobleman, widely travelled, he could afford to be eclectic in his interests and ideologies. He studied sympathetically and unsystematically several different philosophies— Christian, Classical, Muslim, and Jewish—appropriating from each whatever he considered worth-while. He found some good even in Scholasticism, to which most humanists from Petrarch onward were hostile, thus providing a striking example of the searcher for compromise between rational scepticism and orthodox tradition. Tolerant of many ideas he had learned about from both Scholastic works and the writings of Jews and Muslims, he attempted to reconcile them with one another as well as with both Platonism and Aristotelianism. He published a list of nine hundred theses, among which some were dangerous, such as that the dogma of eternal punishment was false because inconsistent with the dignity of man and the goodness of God, and he offered to defend them against all comers at his own expense. In the end he retracted those theses which smacked of heresy, and Pope Alexander VI forgave him. A firm believer in the limitless potentialities of mankind and in the inherent power of human mentality, Pico was nevertheless modest about his own accomplishments and generous to others. Having dedicated his fortune to the indigent, he ended his career at thirty-one as a devout Roman Catholic ascetic, a follower of the fervent reformer Savonarola. Such a man cannot easily be classified as Platonist, nominalist, Stoic, Epicurean, Scholastic, or orthodox.

Despite the diversity in their ranks, humanists exhibited a certain unity in their general disapproval of the formal syllogistic logic of the Schoolmen. In fifteenth-century Italy Valla made an effort to simplify and humanize it, and in the sixteenth century the Spanish-born Juan Luis Vives and the Frenchman Petrus Ramus in his *Aristotelicae Animadversiones* were to insist upon the perniciousness of its errors, particularly its indifference whether major premises were consistent with reality so long as the resulting conclusions were logically derived from it. Humanists also objected to the otherworldliness of Scholastic thought, but the common assumption that humanists were necessarily, like Petrarch, sworn enemies of Scholasticism is suspect, since there were notable exceptions to the general rule, and some of its firm critics saw real hope in its logical method even when they disapproved of its premises. In the universities Scholasticism was well entrenched although in several the division between *moderni* (Ochhamist nominalists) and *antiqui* (Thomist 'realists') was intense. The universities of Bologna and Padua were hotbeds of Scholastic conflict between Thomism and a materialistic Averroism taught by a succession of professors who prepared the way for Pomponazzi (see below). Of these Nicoletto Vernia, professor at Padua from 1468 to 1499, maintained that the truth of science was independent of the truth of theology.

The nominalist neo-Scholastics of Oxford and Paris and the mystic Neoplatonists of Florence and elsewhere may have helped dethrone

Aristotelianism, but Aristotle uncrowned continued to be revered and imitated. Some Platonists, conceding that Aristotelianism could not be destroyed, worked, like Bessarion and Pico della Mirandola, to reconcile the two Greek philosophies but with Aristotle in a minor role. Meanwhile Aristotelians, like George of Trebizond and Theodore of Gaza, vigorously defended Aristotle against Plato and wrote commentaries intended to put Aristotle back in the ascendant. Aristotle's works were, in fact, translated into Latin in both camps—by Platonist Bessarion and by Aristotelian Theodore. In 1495 the Aldine Press at Venice began the printing of a Greek edition of Aristotle. Italian scholars joined in the contest, in which, although the Aristotelians were in a minority, they had strong supporters. Among the open admirers of Aristotle were Federigo de Montefeltro, duke of Urbino, the historian Francesco Guicciardini, the physician Girolamo Cardan, and the scholar Ermolao Barbaro. The commentaries of Jacopo Zabarella (1532–89) and the attacks of humanists such as Ortensio Landi and Ramus testify to the persistent influence of Aristotelianism in the sixteenth century.

The career of Pietro Pomponazzi (1462–1525) vividly illustrates the strength of Scholasticism at the climax of the Italian Renaissance. As professor first at Padua and later at Bologna, Pomponazzi lectured on Aristotle, commenting freely on philosophical problems. Citing 'the philosopher', he used Scholastic logic to prove that the soul was not immortal. Since this position had already been condemned by a Lateran council, charges of heresy ensued. Pomponazzi defended his orthodoxy by resorting to the Averroist argument of double truth: as a Christian he accepted the doctrine of the soul's immortality even though he could not accept it philosophically. In similar fashion he denied supernatural healing (he was a trained physician) but accepted Biblical miracles. He also justified the use of edifying myths, false though they might be, as pragmatic methods of controlling man's natural waywardness. Charges and counter-charges resulted, but the professor continued to teach at Bologna for the remainder of his life, with increases in salary obtained because of flattering offers from other universities. In contradistinction, Giordano Bruno (1548–1600), with his strongly Neoplatonic ideas, was to be driven from one university to another before ending his career at the stake (see Chapter VII).

* * *

Ockham, Lull, Oresme, and Cusa

Despite the disputes between Aristotelians and Neoplatonists, orthodox and sceptics, ancients and moderns, realists and nominalists, Averroists and Thomists, Scholastics and humanists, and other conflicting schools of thought—and, indeed, in part because of them—notable contributions were made to the tools of philosophy during the Renaissance. The newness of William of Ockham's logical method lay not in its originality but in its stringent application of old principles to specific theological problems. Aristotelian logic, enthroned by the thirteenth-century Scholastics as a limited monarch, became a self-destroying tyrant in the ensuing period, thanks to the Ockhamists and Scotists. This trend was more pronounced in the north than in Italy, where Petrarchian humanism exerted a restraining influence on the so-called 'logic-choppers.' Duns Scotus' keenly logical synthesis of philosophical problems dealt a heavy blow, possibly not intended, to Thomism. Ockham's rigid application of logic to certain of these problems was so effective that it undermined, although it failed to destroy, the Thomist structure and led in some quarters to something akin to agnosticism. This outcome was certainly not Ockham's intention. He did not consider himself one of the *moderni*; he questioned not the doctrine so much as the method of proof of the doctrine.

The 'new logic' of Ockham's *Summa Totius Logicae* was merely the sharpening of the weapons that had been shaped by northern thinkers in the thirteenth century. Even the famous logical principle which in the eighteenth century came to be known as 'Ockham's razor' had been earlier used in one form or another by other Oxford Franciscans. In the seventeenth-century form now most commonly but not altogether accurately quoted it reads: *Entia non sunt multiplicanda praeter necessitatem* (loosely translated: *work with the fewest entities necessary*), and is now generally known as 'the law of parsimony'; avoid introducing into any explanation unnecessary hypotheses, principles, or laws. The idea of a law of parsimony, in one wording or another, was emphasized again and again in the works of Ockham.[18]

'Ockham's razor' was meant to shave off the expendable details in the Thomist compromises (which to Ockham appeared more elaborate than substantial) between essence and existence, universal and particular, real and nominal. By purging Thomism of generalizations and abstractions that to him seemed not only unproved but needless he meant to expose what he believed to be its logical barrenness. When we consider epistemology below, we shall see that for Ockham 'singular' things might have reality but the words that substitute for them in speech (i.e. generic nouns) were mere symbols; generalizations from such symbols were mere abstractions, but they led in Thomist thought, he claimed, to still more abstract abstractions. His careful analyses and definitions of grammatical terms and his clarification of the variability of the *suppositiones* (the several substitutive meanings) that the same term may have gave a new emphasis to an old semantic problem. He also clarified the understanding of *consequentiae* (antecedent-consequent relationships).[19] Faith, he argued, was an intuitive act of will, not of logic, and belief in God's attributes and moral laws must rest in the end on faith whether or not they are logically demonstrable. For Ockham this was not, as it was to be for Pomponazzi in humanistic Italy, escape by the stratagem of 'double truth'; it was rather an insistence that in theological matters, logic was insufficient and faith was a superior source of truth. He thus also contributed, and probably unintentionally, to the separation of theology from philosophy and thus to the growing secularism of his day.

The emphasis upon precision in the new logic won the support of some of those who were interested in mathematics and the natural sciences. Lull's effort to improve theological reasoning by the rigorous application of mathematical processes, including complicated diagrams, has already been mentioned; with exaggerated optimism he hoped thus to synthesize all knowledge into a verifiable unity. A century and a half later, Oresme provided another example of the inquiring mind, stressing both the importance of precise logical methods and the unity of knowledge—to the point of an Ockhamist disbelief that faith needed to be harnessed to reason. Although he translated certain of Aristotle's works into French, his logic was not Aristotelian; his concern was rather with mathematics and natural science (see Chapter XIII). His *Quodlibeta* was devoted largely to arguing that a resort to a supernatural explanation was often logically less satisfactory than a natural one.

In Nicholas of Cusa, in contrast, a mathematical mind reacted piously against Ockhamist nominalism, reverting to the fundamental aims of thirteenth-century Scholasticism, the reconciliation of reason and faith. Under the mystical influence of his training at Deventer, he made a virtue of the shortcomings of logic. Criticized by the Aristotelians, he replied by glorifying 'learned ignorance'—that is, the learned man's recognition of the inadequacy of his learning and reasoning. In his *De Docta Ignorantia* intellectual intuition, though buttressed by mathematical symbolism, took the place of formal logic.

*   *   *

Epistemology in the Fourteenth and Fifteenth Centuries

Logic may be considered a major methodological tool of the philosopher; an understanding of epistemology and ontology is among his major objectives. Epistemology includes the search for the bases of knowing, and ontology for the bases of being. Until modern times these two objectives were rarely considered separately. In Aristotle's metaphysics they were combined in a joint quest for true *knowledge* of man's *being*. This problem, which he called 'the first philosophy', was an important element of Aristotelian Scholasticism, as revealed in the conflicts of the Schoolmen over essences and universals, nominalism and realism. Aquinas relied upon both human reason or intellect and human will for the solution of the problem of the course of knowledge, thus partly tending toward a nominalist rather than a realist epistemology. His ambivalent position brought him into opposition with the strict Averroist Siger of Brabant (1235–81) and other Paris Averroists. Siger favoured the sacrifice of faith to logic as the source of knowledge, if necessary, where Aquinas subordinated logic to faith. The attitude of the church was unmistakable; it condemned Averroism (1270) and Siger (1277) and canonized Thomas (1323).

Once Averroism was driven underground, the major attack upon the Thomists' epistemology, as upon other aspects of their philosophy, came from a more orthodox quarter, the Franciscans. Duns Scotus's attack upon Thomist epistemology was for reasons exactly opposite to Siger's. Posited upon his denial of the effectiveness of reason to reinforce belief in the Christian creed, Scotus's epistemology was voluntarist rather than intellectualist. God, 'the First Being', Scotus said, is the source of all essences, but He is primarily will, beyond the understanding of man, and so man must rely for true knowledge on faith, not on reason. Scotus' followers became known as 'Duns men'; like him they attempted to place various articles of faith, as realities in the mind of God, beyond the realm of human reason. Their zeal in combating reason gave to the Duns men the reputation, and epithet, of 'Dunces'. Nevertheless, until the humanists brought a new worldliness into philosophy, the Duns men's brand of epistemology prevailed in the schools—to the disparagement of reason as a source of knowledge and to the neglect of philosophy in favour of Christian theology.

The 'modern' epistemology of William of Ockham, also a Franciscan, was a natural reaction to the extreme realism of the Scotists. Ockham revived nominalism. His brand of nominalism is called 'terminism' because of his theory that all human knowledge of universals is based on 'terms' (*termini*), which represent but are not the actual objects: Man's knowledge of universals cannot arise directly from essences or even from the individual objects; it can arise only with the semantic 'terms' that represent them. This theory of universals, grown from Classical roots, differed from the earlier extreme nominalist theory of universals as mere *flatus vocis* ('hollow sounds of the voice'). Ockham's *termini* were meaningful class-names that the mind could use systematically to formulate general propositions.

Despite his insistence on simplifying logic by shaving off expendable concepts, Ockham in fact built a complicated structure of epistemology. He did not reject the Thomist concept of the existence of universals in God's mind (the Platonic *universalia ante res*); he merely insisted upon the difference between God's universals and man's. Man could grasp the essences of things only from the things themselves (the Aristotelian *universalia in rebus*) or, more explicitly, from his names for them. Man's universals were therefore *universalia post res*; they could come only after examination of the 'singulars'. Ockham did not deny that universals existed in the plenitude of God's mind as essences before the individual things took form as existences; he contended, however, that man was able to recognize universals only in a greatly limited fashion; without Revelation he would be ignorant of those related to God, the soul, and the most important problems of ontology.

Although no sceptic himself, Ockham led directly to what has sometimes been called 'fourteenth-century scepticism'. He cast doubt upon man's ability to know any reality—least of all, abstractions like 'substance' and 'cause'. His sceptic tendencies made suspect all Scholastic thinking whether based on faith or derived from reason. As previously indicated, they penetrated the universities, notably Oxford and Paris, and successive generations of students at Paris under Buridan, Ailly, and Gerson were infected by them. Ailly doubted that man could be certain of anything beyond self. Gerson, although himself a nominalist, became troubled over the doubts and logical subtleties that were multiplying among the students of the university as a result of the application of Ockhamist methods to theology. The sceptical movement, nevertheless, developed without formal condemnation until Nicholas d'Autrecourt carried the attack on Scholasticism so far as to propound an anti-Aristotelian atomism and the belief that little was certain (though some things were probable) even in inferences derived from immediate experience and principles derived *ex terminis*. Accused of the heresy of extreme fideism, he was condemned in 1346 and recanted.[20] Ockham's brand of nominalism, however, and the *via moderna* in logic and epistemology held its own in fifteenth-century scholarly centres despite setbacks and the constant opposition of Thomists and Scotists.

The natural scientists of this period developed no particular school of epistemology. They were usually zealous exponents of the use of the human intellect in science, but where they were not Scholastics themselves, they left epistemological problems to their theological colleagues. They clung to the traditional ideas of man's ability to know himself. No significant treatise on scientific method was achieved in the fourteenth and fifteenth centuries. Scientists generally were Aristotelians and considered speculation upon Atistotelian principles superior to experiment as a way to attain knowledge. Experiment, using the hands as well as the head, was still carried on mainly by astrologers and alchemists. Most of the physicians and physicists tended to a conservative realism, believing that empirical observation had definite limits as a means of attaining knowledge and that Revelation and intuition must often be relied upon in arriving at truth. The early humanists, too, in their adoration of the Classical masters, were sometimes indifferent or even hostile to original thought and experiment.

*   *   *

Medieval Christian Ethics

Medieval ethics was in large part a heritage from Hebrew morality and Classical philosophy. The Mosaic commandments gave Christianity a ready-made code presumed to be in conformity with God's law, and Aristotelian ethics reflected the Classical emphasis on wisdom as the source of man's virtue. Aquinas organized Christian morality into an ethical system based on Aristotelian rationalism but not excluding entirely Stoic, Neoplatonic, and Augustinian teachings. In treating the regulation of vice by law, he differentiated between divine law, natural law, and human law. His emphasis on natural law was an inheritance from the Roman philosophers. Through natural law, he said, man participates in God's eternal law as a free intellectual being. God has implanted in man the knowledge of divine law and a disposition to obey it, but since man's choice is subject to the free exercise of his will, mistakes occur that must be corrected by human law.[21]

Aquinas' doctrine of the close relationship of intellect with will, and of the close co-operation of God's determining will with man's free will, was, along with other parts of Thomist doctrine, attacked by the Scotists and the Ockhamists. Duns Scotus, like Aquinas, stressed the importance of man's intellect in moral actions but, rejecting Aquinas' imputed compromises of faith with reason and remaining consistent with his voluntarism, held that moral behaviour depended more on will than on intelligence. Furthermore, since divine will is above and beyond reason, divine law is absolute in matters of morals. William of Ockham likewise argued against reason as a source of principles of morality. The questioning of the rational basis for morality pointed to unreasoning faith as the obvious alternative for orthodox Christians.

The trend of Italian humanist thought from the fourteenth century on was more inclined toward scepticism than faith. The humanistic emphasis on the dignity of man, on the importance of this world, and on the worth of the individual tended to bring speculation upon ethics down from eternal law to earthly practice. Some of the works already considered, such as Petrarch's *Secretum* and Valla's *De Voluptate*, indicated that the more puritanical pagan philosophies like Stoicism were also acceptable to some Italian humanists of the fourteenth and fifteenth centuries.

Though its prevalent climate tended to be less religious than that of the northern regions of Europe, Italy, too, had its exemplars of a mystical ethics. Under the most cynical of the Avignon popes, Italy produced and lauded Catherine of Siena, Bernardino of Siena, and Savonarola of Florence. Careers like theirs reveal deep currents of Italian spirituality that stirred the souls both of the populace and of intellectuals such as Pico della Mirandola. Unlike Catherine and Bernardino, Savonarola failed to achieve sainthood. His passionate temperament and uncompromising attitudes drove him to such extreme demands for purity in private life and sacrifice for public welfare that he alienated the conservative Florentines and induced the easy-going Borgia pope, Alexander VI, to excommunicate him. He was tortured and hanged as a heretic with two of his disciples, and their bodies were burned and thrown into the Arno. He attained sanctity only in the opinion of some of his followers in Florence and some Protestants such as Luther. Yet his violent career marks, better perhaps than those of his Sienese predecessors, how deep the currents of spirituality ran in Renaissance Italy's great worldly centres such as Florence, Siena, and Rome. Alexander VI and Savonarola exemplified the extremes—the cynical, secularist pope and the uncompromising mystic who died resisting the prevailingly secular trend.

Thus, even while scorned by some Italian humanists, the Christian bases of ethics found fervent champions. Humanists might well be the protégés of some 'tyrant', noble, or merchant prince, benefiting from the drift toward absolutism or from the emergence of capitalism. Nonetheless, the sermons of

Bernardino of Siena and Savonarola, the letters of Catherine of Siena, and several treatises of Abrogio Traversari and Giannozzo Manetti bear witness to the presence of genuine Christian ideals in high intellectual circles. Furthermore, the ethical teachings of the church prevailed among the masses of devout believers, who sometimes were at least the short-run victims of the very political and economic changes from which the middle class and nobility benefited. Savonarola's temporary sway over the people of Florence provides dramatic evidence of the strong undercurrent of Christian morality in Renaissance Italy, of the popular reaction to the humanists' outward contempt of the traditional ethical code.

In the north, mysticism exerted a curious, and sometimes contradictory, influence on ethical beliefs and practices. The mystics' personal communion and direct spiritual contact with God tended to undermine mere traditional forms and systems of ethics; it also tended to prevent the formulation of new ethical conventions. Christian mysticism, closely related to Neoplatonism,[22] emphasized contemplation rather than action, ecstatic union with God rather than rational comprehension, intuitive inspiration rather than intelligence. The leaders of German mysticism, predominantly Dominicans, were more often preachers and teachers than philosophers; their writings usually were inspired sermons or treatises unrelated to systematic thought. Meister Eckhart's works, however, reveal a collected effort to form a metaphysical synthesis. His exposition of the close union of the human soul and mind with the soul and mind of God was so metaphoric and ambiguous as to subject him to charges of pantheism. In his opinion, knowledge, though an end in itself, was inferior to love, but both were activities of the soul, to which God revealed Himself once the soul had renounced everything, including self, whereupon the soul returned to the bosom of God; the soul that had become reunited with God was above mere human moral values. It is easy to understand why this brand of mysticism might remind a modern scholar of Indian mysticism.[23]

In keeping with this persuasion, a follower of the mystical revelation could hold that the actions of a sincere Christian were subject to no controls save those of his divinely guided individual judgment. This conviction made possible the moral excesses of certain radical peripheral groups. It also laid all mystics open to charges of immoral, or at least uncontrolled, conduct. Nevertheless, oblivious to external authority, sincere Christian reformers, north and south, chose to obey God rather than men (even where the man was clothed with ecclesiastical authority). Those mystics who acted as dedicated individuals fared better than those who organized for group action or who publicly advanced their aims in formal writings. Catherine of Siena and Bernardino of Siena preached a stern morality and a drastic type of reform even to popes without incurring penalties. If Savonarola was less fortunate, it was largely because he made the mistake of acquiring political power in opposition to a pope and of writing on philosophical subjects. Mysticism was relatively safe so long as the mystic held to the fundamental spirit of individualism and maintained an unassailable standard of personal ethics.

On the materialistic front, Christianity confronted an ethical problem that ultimately proved more urgent than mysticism. In the fourteenth century the economic principles of the church remained essentially the same as in earlier centuries. The increasing secularism of Western civilization had led Aquinas to devote some of his logical ingenuity to the conflict between the Christian ideal of brotherhood and the prevailing practice of private gain. He endeavoured to solve the dilemma by a rational compromise. On the one hand, he reiterated the Aristotelian and Biblical condemnations of usury (the taking of interest), insisting that the private ownership of property was a violation of divine and natural law and that property-holding was a public trust. On the other hand, he, and later Scholastics as well, occasionally tempered their disapproval of profit and interest. For example, the ideal of 'just price' (based originally on labour costs) was allowed an alternative interpretation that was more practical and flexible; it might normally be determined by supply and demand in the market place, and only when the free market brought too high a departure from accustomed prices would it be necessary for public authority to intervene and fix prices by fiat. A specific example of this flexible standard of economic ethics can be found in Bernardino of Siena's writings (c. 1400).[24]

Nevertheless, the church's general economic attitude was one of disapproval of big commercial profit. This attitude encouraged conservative Christian businessmen to invest in land and agricultural activities, in which the ecclesiastical authorities saw less capitalistic evil. The church's own wealth set a good example, for it was largely in landed property. Contemporary economic theorists like Oresme and Gerson made no serious objections to the conservative economic principles still prevalent in Christendom (see Chapter VIII). Even in the face of increasing usury, monopolies, and other kinds of commercial profit-making, until the sixteenth century the clergy fairly consistently condemned acquisitive capitalistic enterprise as unchristian (see Chapter IX). To be sure, merchants meanwhile engaged in various kinds of subterfuge to make an 'unjust' profit or to take interest, but social pressure for a 'just' price and against interest, even if not always respected, remained quite respectable, whereas 'usury' and even mercantile wealth, even if respected, were regarded as not quite the proper thing.

NOTES TO CHAPTER VI

1. For Professor Olivier Lacombe Thomist tradition always advocated the union and harmony of the three wisdoms: philosophical, theological and mystic. Thomas and more than one of his followers actually practised in their lives their teaching on this subject. Nor did Thomas ever sacrifice metaphysical or spiritual intuition to dialectics and logic. Similar remarks should be made concerning the Indian Advaita, due allowance being, of course,

made for the essential differences between Thomism and the Advaita. Any shifts in balance occurring during the fourteenth and succeeding centuries (or earlier) should not cause us to lose sight of these valuable achievements.

The authors feel, however, that 'the text does not imply that the Thomist might not also be a mystic; it does imply that the mystic was not likely to be a philosopher'.

2. M. Hiriyanna, *Essentials of Indian Philosophy* (London, 1949), p. 85.

3. It is, however, distinguished primarily by an alternating dynamism, sometimes evolutive, sometimes involutive in direction. (O. Lacombe.)

4. From the very first the 'non-theist' Vedānta had its own methods of spiritual concentration; only later are these confused with Yoga proper. The alliance between Buddhism and the methods of Yoga—of a re-thought-out Yoga—appears, on the contrary, to be fundamental. (O. Lacombe.)

5. Professor O. Lacombe stresses the extreme delicacy which is necessary in employing the terms 'immanent' and 'transcendant' in connection with the great doctrines of the Far East. See also p. (159), n. 1.

6. Dasgupta, *op. cit.*, V, 19, says that Umāpati was the author of the *Pauskar-āgama*.

7. Professor O. Lacombe points out that the resemblances emphasized in this text between Christianity and Shivaism will be found elsewhere in the religious world of India. These, however, rarely exceed the limits of the most generalized categories distinguished by the science of religions.

8. This dating is based on the assumption that Madhva died about 1276. Jaya-tīrtha is generally given as the fifth pontiff of the sect after Madhva.

9. Dasgupta, IV, 215 and 312–13.

10. See *ibid.*, III, 399–402, and p. 119 above.

11. Chan Wing-tsit, 'The Evolution of the Confucian Concept *Jen*', *Philosophy East and West*, IV (1955), 308–16, especially 314–16.

12. Lu Hsiang-shan, quoted in Fung Yu-lan, *A History of Chinese Philosophy* (Princeton, 1953), II, 573.

13. Ch'en's *Pai-sha-tzü-ch'uan-chi* (Complete Work of [Ch'en] Pai-sha), quoted *ibid.* pp. 594–95.

14. The work of Thomas is not an 'ambivalent compromise' between faith and reason, Christianity and Aristotelism. Quite the contrary, to quote a now famous expression, it 'distinguishes in order to unite'. (O. Lacombe.)

15. As regards universals, Thomism occupies an original position somewhere between realism and nominalism not accurately covered by the label 'realist'. (O. Lacombe.)

16. Ananda Coomaraswamy, *The Transformation of Nature in Art* (Cambridge, Mass., 1935), p. 61.

17. Professor O. Lacombe writes on this point: 'More than one expert has been struck by the affinities between Eckhartian mysticism and certain forms of Indian mysticism. Since any form of direct historical influence is excluded, we are here faced with the deeper problem of the diversity of mystical attitudes. The univocality of the concept of mysticism is too often taken for granted. It is our opinion that while the mysticism of immanence and that of grace are closely analogous, they are also distinguished by certain essential differences. Meister Eckhart presents a difficult case in so far as his Christian faith puts him in the order of grace while certain moments and aspects of his mystical experience seem to belong rather to the order of immanence.'

18. W. N. Thorburn, 'The Myth of Ockham's Razor', *Mind, a Quarterly Review of Psychology and Philosophy*, XVII (1918), 345–53; Mayrick H. Carre, *Realists and Nominalists* (Oxford University Press, London, 1946), p. 107; A. C. Crombie, *Augustine to Galileo, the History of Science*, AD 400–1650 (London, 1952), p. 231. Ockham's own wording of the so-called razor was: '*Pluralitas non est ponenda praeter necessitatem*'.

19. Philotheus Bochner, *Medieval Logic, an Outline of Its Development from 1200 to c. 1400* (Chicago, 1952), pp. 36–44 and 54–8.

20. See Julius Rudolph Weinberg, *Nicolaus of Autrecourt, a Study in 14th Century Thought* (Princeton, 1948), pp. 4–8; G. M. Sauvage, 'Fideism', *The Catholic Encyclopedia*, VI (1909), 68–9.

21. Natural law, as understood by Thomas, is the immanent expression of the transcending divine law, incapable either of entering into conflict with the economy of salvation which culminates in the person of Christ or of leading it to its ruin. (O. Lacombe.)

22. Professor Lacombe emphasizes that the historical relationship between Christian and Neoplatonic mysticism is well known. But for the reasons indicated in previous notes (pp. 159–60, 221, and 412) such historical links do not, in the majority of cases, imply the essential identity of any two mysticisms.

23. See n. 17 and n. 22 above.

24. See Raymond de Roover, 'The Concept of the Just Price; Theory and Economic Policy', *Journal of Economic History*, XVIII (1958), 418–34.

CHAPTER VII

THEOLOGY AND METAPHYSICS
(1500-1775)

METAPHYSICAL SPECULATION WITHIN HINDUISM AND JAINISM

INDIAN thought after 1500, despite some exceptional individual contributions, did not give rise to any radical cosmological or epistemological departures. The metaphysical questions discussed were still the ones that had long bothered mankind everywhere—monism vs. dualism, the nature of cause, the nature of reality, the relation of man to God, and like ancient and mooted problems. The old theistic trends continued to dominate the attempts to answer them, and traditional Indian theistic speculation remained at a relatively high level until well into the seventeenth century. Then it suffered a rather sudden collapse. Among the reasons for the collapse were (1) the decline of Sanskrit as the vernacular literatures displaced it (see Chapter XI) and (2) the disruption of the traditional foundations of society as the Mogul Empire declined, rival European interests in India grew stronger, and warfare accompanied the shifts in the balance of power. During the period 1500-1775 Western influences helped to impede without otherwise modifying Indian philosophical tendencies, and on the whole Hindu philosophers seem to have been immune to Islamic ideas as well.

After 1500 the Nyāya-Vaishesika system showed little originality. Nevertheless, at least two excellent popular manuals of the system were produced —the *Tarkasamgraha* (before 1585) by Annambhatta and the *Kārikāvalī* by Vishvanātha (before 1634), each provided by the author with commentaries. Raghunātha Shiromani (c. 1477-1547), of the Nadia school of logicians, wrote probably the best commentary on Gangesha logic, and it did much to spread the Nyāya system of logic throughout India, but another commentary on Gangesha—this one by Gadādhara Bhattācārya (c. 1650), likewise of the Nadia school, who is often described as the prince of Indian schoolmen— became the standard textbook. Thus, about the time that Francis Bacon was attacking the deductive method of the European Scholastics, in India over-refinement, technical subtleties, formal perfection, and logical quibbling triumphed. The Nadia school was subsidized by Bacon's compatriots, the early British rulers of Bengal.

Of the Sānkhya system of philosophy the chief expounder after 1500 was Vijñāna Bhiksu, an independent thinker of the sixteenth century. He prepared a commentary on the *Sānkhya-sūtra* entitled the *Sānkhya-pravacana-bhāsya*, an excellent gloss on Vyāsa's commentary on the *Yoga-sūtra*, and a commentary on the *Vedānta-sūtra*, which interpreted it along theistic Sānkhya lines. In these works he attempted to harmonize the orthodox schools of Indian philosophy, maintaining that since there were precedents for each school in the Vedas and *Upanishads*, each represented only a different aspect of the same truth. He sought to harmonize the theistic with the absolutistic systems by identifying the personal God with the absolute *brahman*, and to harmonize pluralistic realism with monistic idealism by arguing that the plural elements were both non-existent and yet potential within the absolute, becoming real whem embodied in material form during the process of world development.

Vijñāna Bhiksu's views were not only in general conformity with the theistic Vedānta of Rāmānuja and Nimbārka but delineated the 'dominant view of the Purānas' and of Hindu life and religion in general. He believed in a number of apparent paradoxes:

'the reality of the universe as well as . . . its spirituality, the distinctness of the individual souls as well as . . . their being centres of the manifestation of God, moral freedom and responsibility as well as a spiritual determinism, a personal God as well as . . . impersonal reality, the ultimate spirit in which matter and pre-matter are dissolved into spirituality, . . . the superior value of knowledge as well as of love, . . . [and] the compulsoriness of moral and social duties as well as . . . their abnegation'.[1]

He insisted that although Sānkhya had originally been theistic, its later atheistic system was so rational that it sufficed to explain the universe even without Īshvara. Besides the theistic and *bhakti* elements that he injected into the Sānkhya-Yoga, he contributed several original interpretations—for example, on the reality of the connection between souls and consciousness, and on the independence of the senses in the perceptive process.

During the sixteenth and seventeenth centuries the Bhātta school of the Mīmāmsā system of philosophy popularized its method of logic. The Bhātta logical method was common to Indian reasoning generally. It consisted essentially of five steps—posing a subject for consideration, raising doubts about it, setting forth a prima-facie view, developing a correct decision, and then relating it to other relevant doctrines.[2] Among the more important works dealing with the Bhātta teachings were the sixteenth-century *Māna-meyodaya* (sometimes attributed to Nārāyana Bhatta but more recently regarded as the work of two authors),[3] the seventeenth-century *Bhātta-dīpikā* by Khandadeva, and an independent manual and exposition of the system, the *Mīmāmsā-nyāya-prakāsha*, by Āpadeva, also of the seventeenth century.

During the sixteenth century, many writers popularized, expounded, refined,and defended the Advaita (monistic) system. Nrsimhāshrama Muni, though renowned among contemporaries, added little to earlier ideas. He emphasized the identity of *brahman* with the self and the illusory nature of the apparent world. One of his pupils, Dharmarāja Adhvarīndra (*c.* 1550), perhaps had greater influence, for his *Vedānta-paribhāsā*, a technical and systematic exposition of the Advaita system, especially of its logical and methodological aspects, became a sort of manual for later monists. He continued the growing tendency to treat *māyā* almost as if it were a real and independent substance and in so doing helped to obscure the distinction between monists and dualists.

Of a more original turn of mind was Prakāshānanda, who, in *Siddhānta-muktāvalī* and other works, re-asserted the absolute monistic position by denying that *māyā* was in any sense the real stuff of the world. He was among the first to try to explain Vedānta 'from a purely sensationalistic viewpoint of idealism', denying the objective existence of any matter. The seeming existence of material objects was nothing more, in his scheme, than perception. He preached the extreme view of the Vedānta system, conceding no objectivity whatsoever and maintaining that *māyā* (the illusory world) did not exist, that ideas had no material basis, that self was the only reality, and that there was no causation or creation.4 Prakāshānanda gained many followers and evoked at least one outstanding commentary on his work.

One of the most prolific writers of the sixteenth century was Appaya Dīkshita (1520–92), an indefatigable and able scholar though not an original thinker. He wrote commentaries on the *Vedānta-sūtra* from varying points of view—the Shivaite, the monistic, and the qualified monistic—but he generally supported the monistic system, trying in particular to refute the dualistic position of Madhva. His *Siddhānta-lesha samgraha* was a collection of the contrasting views of various monistic authors without any attempt to harmonize them or to show his own preference. He wrote a commentary, too, on one of the main texts of the Bhāmati branch of the monists, and this work in part inspired the *Ābhoga* of Lakshmīnrsimha (late-seventeenth century), one of the last significant books concerned with the Bhāmatic interpretation.

Probably the best known of the Advaita writers was the polemicist Madhusūdana Sarasvatī, who flourished somewhere between 1500 and 1650. His most important work, the *Advaita-siddhi*, attempted to refute the objections to the monistic position raised by Vyāsā-tīrtha in defence of Madhva's theistic dualism. His *Vedānta-kalpa-latikā* gave brief and often distorted summaries of other systems and contrasted them unfavourably with the monistic. He defended particularly the monistic view of emancipation (*moksha*). Despite his philosophical adherence to monism he was a confirmed promoter of *bhakti* and wrote numerous works supporting the idea of personal devotion to God.

Various writings relative to Southern Shivaism were produced after 1500. Of those in Tamil or other south Indian languages Shivajñāna Munivar's commentary (late-seventeenth century) on the works of Meykandār was perhaps the most important. Of the Shivaite works in Sanskrit the most important was the *Shivārka-mani-dīpikā* of the aforementioned Advaita scholar Appaya Dīkshita, a commentary on the early philosopher Shrīkantha. Although of value in interpreting early Shivaite thought, it was tinged by the author's greater devotion to monism.

About 1500 several prominent writers expounded the qualified monistic (Vishistādvaita) system of Rāmānuja. Shrīnivāsacārya, a pupil of Rāmānuja-dāsa, wrote a clear, simple exposition of that system, in which he upheld the Vadagalai interpretation of the nature of self-surrender to God and repudiated the doctrine of *māyā* and some other propositions of other schools. Shrīshaila Shrīnivāsa wrote many works, of which the *Virodha-nirodha* was perhaps his best philosophical treatise, refuting the arguments of the Shankarites and others; he was particularly interested in upholding *brahman* as the efficient and material cause of the world, the ultimate creator of all, and in refuting the Shankara theory of causality. Kastūri Rangācārya in his *Kāryā-dhikarana-vāda* supported the Tangalai interpretation of salvation and of self-surrender to God; against Venkatanātha's doctrine that emancipation was only temporary if attained through mere self-realization without recognition that self was a part of God, he held that such emancipation was final, although less rich in experience. Later Vishistādvaita defenders were numerous, but none was outstanding as a philosopher.

The Mādhva dualists continued for some time after 1500 as a strong and energetic group. They prepared many commentaries on their earlier literature and many ingenuous and subtle arguments in defence of their system. Perhaps their most illustrious exponent during the period was Rāmācarya, probably a late-sixteenth-century figure, who, in his *Nyāyāmrta-tarangini*, answered the refutations of the well-known monist Madhusūdana. In his attacks upon the monists Rāmācarya covered much the same ground as Vyāsa-tīrtha (see Chapter VI).

As the popularity of Krishna worship spread, the dualistic monism of Nimbārka likewise produced several able supporters. Purusottama Prasāda, who must have lived in the late-sixteenth century, wrote commentaries on most of the works of Nimbārka and Shrīnivāsa. In the *Shruty-anta-sura-druma*, a commentary on Nimbārka's *Shrī-krishna-stava*, he attacked the Shankarites, criticized Rāmānuja for believing that impure material elements were really a part of *brahman*, upbraided Madhva for insisting that the material elements of the world did not exist as potentials within *brahman*, and sustained Nimbārka's view. Since, he maintained, both the monistic and dualistic scriptures were literally true, everything must exist as potentials within *brahman*, although, in the process of creating souls and the material world out of its energy, *brahman's* true nature remained unchanged and what it produced was not identical with it.

Mādhava Mukunda in his polemical *Para-paksa-giri-vajra* covered much the same ground as Purusottama. He attacked *in toto* the monistic scheme of the Shankarites, upholding the reality of the world and the diversity within unity of God, souls, and matter. He expounded the theory of knowledge long held by the Nimivats. Perception, it ran, was of two kinds, internal and external; external perception was of five kinds, each dependent upon one of the senses, while internal perception was of two kinds, ordinary and transcendental; the perception of pleasure and pain was of the ordinary internal variety, while perception of the nature of God was of the transcendental variety; three kinds of inference were valid—from positive instances, from negative instances, and from both positive and negative instances, when both were available.

★   ★   ★

Vallabha, Chaitanya, and Their Followers

Probably the most original religious thinker of this period was Vallabha (see Chapter V), who developed the Shuddhāvaita school of thought, or pure monism. His *Tattvadīpa* with his own commentary on it (the *Prakāsha*), his *Subodhinī*, a commentary on the *Bhāgavata-purāna*, and his *Anubhāsya*, a commentary on the *Vedānta-sūtra*, were his most significant metaphysical works. Although his system was known as pure monism, he was critical of the Shankarites and their idea of *māyā*, and he found a place for a personal god who saved souls. The Supreme Being—that is, Krishna (Vishnu)—was *brahman*; He was possessed of existence (*sat*), knowledge, (*cit*), bliss (*ānanda*) and sentiment (*rasa*); He was complete, perfect, omnipresent, eternal, and personal; He was both doer and enjoyer. In play (sport) He had created the universe with its individual souls out of Himself without undergoing change, and He was thus both the efficient and the material cause of the world, its sustainer and its absorber, and it was part of Him. Hence the material world and souls were real and eternal and not *māyā* in the Shankarite sense, but they differed. The material world had only existence while the soul could feel. It could lack bliss and, because of ignorance of its true nature, suffer from egotism and the idea of possession (mine and thine). The round of rebirths, therefore, would continue until the soul realized its true nature—that the Lord was everything—after which it would be re-absorbed and would attain bliss. But re-absorption might vary in degree or manner depending upon the mode of realization. Those who attained realization through works (*karma*) and knowledge (*jñāna*) were re-absorbed at a lower level of bliss than those who attained it through devotion (*bhakti*), and the highest form of salvation was through *pushti-bhakti*, or divine grace (see Chapter V).

Vallabha, while, like most of the theistic writers, placing great stress upon *bhakti*, denied that it was intellectual in nature. He emphasized it rather as an emotion that expressed itself in a loving devotion and service which produced a sense of oneness with God. (Compare his European contemporary Luther.) Good works and individual effort were not essential to such a state of mind. In manifesting His qualities as the universe without changing Himself, the Lord, according to Vallabha, appeared as Akshara, or the Immutable Brahman, and as time, karma, and nature. Nature was defined as that which produced change. From it arose the twenty-eight long familiar principles or categories (*tattvas*), which were a further unfolding of God. They were purity, activity, inertia, soul (*purusa*), matter, cosmic intelligence, egoism, five subtle elements, five gross elements, five organs of action, five organs of knowledge, and mind (*manas*); and from these a further unfolding of the world took place. Individual souls (*jīvas*) were parts of *purusa*.

Vallabha's son Vitthalanātha (see Chapter V) expounded his father's system in his *Vidyā-mandana*. He affirmed that *avidyā*, or ignorance, which caused the bondage of the individual soul (*jīva*), was an attribute to God. In discussing the nature of the *jīvas*, he made clear how Vallabha's conception differed from that of some other theistic thinkers. Madhva had regarded *jīvas* as parts of God,[5] yet distinct from and not identical with him; Nimbārka had regarded them as different from, yet similar to, God; and Rāmānuja had believed that God held the souls within himself and by his will dominated them; but the pure monist Vallabha held that the *jīvas*, being parts of God, were one with him although certain powers and qualities which belonged to God were obscured from them by ignorance. In his *Bhakti-hetu*, in connection with his discussion of the routes to salvation Vitthalanātha set forth a doctrine of salvation by two methods that are respectively reminiscent of Catholicism and Calvinism. Some, following the *maryādā-mārga*, the route of good deeds, purity of mind, and intellectual endeavour, would ultimately obtain *bhakti* and thus salvation but only because God had so willed it, for God granted His grace with complete freedom and could not be bound or induced to grant it. Others would receive His special grace and automatically follow the *pushti-bhakti* route to salvation (*pushti-mārga*) with or without personal effort.

Another among Vallabha's numerous followers was Purusottama (born *c*. 1670 and not to be confused with Purusottama Prasāda), who was the author of many treatises. His *Prasthāna-ratnākara* discussed Vallabha's concept of *māyā* as contrasted with that of the Shankarites. According to him, *māyā* was a power of *brahman* and thus identical with *brahman*; it was also identical with *avidyā* (ignorance) and with the three categories *sattva* (purity), *rajas* (activity), and *tamas* (interia), and at the same time was their cause. In individual souls *sattva* produced attachment to pleasure and knowledge, *rajas* produced clinging and desire for action, while *tamas* produced a tendency to error, laziness, and sleep. Thus through *māyā* God manifested Himself as manifold and produced ignorance, desire, and confusion, but this manifestation was real and not an illusion, as the Shankarites held. Purusottama discussed at some length also the nature and theory of knowledge. To perception, scriptural testimony, and inference as sources of knowledge he added implication (which he distinguished from inference)—for instance, that an individual is outside the house when he is not found in the house.

Chaitanya, the other great Hindu religious leader of this period (see

Chapter V), did not himself provide a new theistic system, but several of his followers produced works of theological interest. Rūpa Gosvāmī's *Bhakti-rasāmrta-sindhu* (early-sixteenth century), a particularly famous study of the subject, distinguished three stages, each with many sub-stages, of *bhakti*—the performance of the duties of a Vishnuite, the realization of natural attachment to God, and the combination of the sense of possession of God with absolute detachment from other things. *Bhakti* itself was defined as behaviour wholly and exclusively intended to please God; it was the eternal bliss of God and hence could not be created but existed eternally in the heart and could be aroused as an emotion only through the grace of God.

Jīva Gosvāmī, a nephew of Rūpa, was perhaps the most important of the Chaitanya philosophers. His *Sat-sandarbha* (late-sixteenth century) set forth an eclectic philosophy borrowed from all the previous schools. For him *brahman* was a partial manifestation of the total personality of Bhagavān, or Krishna—that is, God. Pure bliss and consciousness were the substance of God, and His other powers were its attributes. Pure consciousness was the true nature of the soul, realizable through *bhakti*, and in realizing it, the soul realized its identity with *brahman*. God manifested Himself as the presiding lord of the totality of souls, as matter, and as the controller within the soul. Through his power of *māyā* God caused different things to have an apparently independent existence, although they were actually one with Him. The material world and the individual soul were neither wholly real nor wholly unreal; they were real in an unmanifested form, just as a jug exists in a lump of clay, but in a manifested form they were a product of God's power of *māyā*. In emancipation all illusory notions about the world vanished, but the world itself remained, for it was not false; emancipation was a subjective reformation, not an objective disappearance of a false world. Jīva's thought, like that of many Vishnuites, was a form of monistic-dualism in which many contradictions were possible because God was conceived as a super-logical, transcendent Being Who could manifest Himself in all kinds of finite forms and yet remain one and identical with His own supreme and unchangeable nature. Jīva assigned to the highest form of *bhakti* six characteristics: it destroyed sin and ignorance; it created happiness through love and friendship; it brought such joy that it left no desire for emancipation; it could be attained only by the grace of God; its joys were superior to those of emancipation through *brahma*-knowledge; and it overwhelmed God so that He was drawn into the service of His devotees.

Another Chaitanya philosopher, Baladeva Vidyābhūsana (still alive in 1764), wrote the *Govinda-bhāsya*, probably the only significant Chaitanya commentary on the *Vedānta-sūtra*. Its train of thought was somewhat different from that of Jīva Gosvāmī: God was everything and controlled everything; yet souls and matter were distinct from Him, although part of Him and completely dependent on Him; the ultimate end of man was to obtain eternal bliss by attaining true knowledge of God, which could be attained only through true knowledge of self, which could be achieved only by the grace of God through *bhakti*; *bhakti* was a species of knowledge by which one turned to God without any ulterior motive, and its practice bound God to the devotee. The soul's ignorance and bondage were more real to Baladeva than to Jīva; in emancipation their destruction was real and the emancipated soul retained its separate individuality. In another work Baladeva attacked the Shankarites' doctrine of absolute monism.

★   ★   ★

Jain Religious Thought

Between 1300 and 1800 the Jains, although a small group, produced a number of active writers. While they added little to earlier Jain doctrine, several of them contributed to the Jain system of logic. Gunaratna (*c.* 1363–*c.* 1439) produced a critique of the Nyāya system of logic. Dharma-bhūsana's *Nyāya-dipika* (*c.* 1600), after taking up the general characteristics of valid knowledge, discussed perception and indirect knowledge, including in the latter category knowledge derived by recollection, recognition, argumentation, inference, and tradition. Yashovijaya Ganī (1608–1688) elaborated Jain logic and dealt with such theological and philosophical questions as the soul, emancipation, substance, time and space, and the nature of knowledge. Having studied at the Brahman schools of logic in Benares, he wrote a detailed criticism of the Mithilā and Nadia logic taught there. Jainism thus continued to assert its own independent tradition.

METAPHYSICAL SPECULATION IN CHINA[6]

In China the dynamic thought of the sixteenth century was dominated by the Idealist interpretation of Neo-Confucianism, although the official schools, the examination system, and the greater part of the scholars and officials still adhered to the Rationalistic interpretation.

Chan Jo-shui (1466–1560), a student and fellow-provincial of Ch'en Hsien-chang (see Chapter VI), founded a new branch of the Idealistic school known as the Chiang-men branch. In his *Explanation of the Diagram of the Mind and of Nature (Hsin-hsing t'u-shuo)*, he maintained that the mind embraced, permeated, and went beyond heaven, earth, and all other things; that nothing was internal or external for the mind; and that those who considered heaven, earth, and other things outside the mind reduced it to something extremely petty. He seems, however, not to have meant to contend that the external world was only a mirage created by the mind; he criticized his contemporary Wang Yang-ming (see below) for teaching that the investigation of things should take place in the mind and insisted that things themselves should be investigated.

For all that, Wang Yang-ming (1472–1529), also known as Wang Shou-jen), was the towering thinker of the Ming period. With him the Idealistic school reached its apogee. He was not only a scholar, teacher, and philosopher but also a successful military leader and statesman. He received the customary training of the Rationalistic school, at one time making himself ill by an almost uninterrupted seven-day investigation of the bamboo in an effort to comprehend its *li*. He also studied both Buddhism and Taoism. In 1508, while in temporary disgrace at a frontier post for having opposed a powerful court eunuch, he experienced enlightenment and realized that 'the task of "investigating things" has to do only with investigating one's own body and mind'.[7]

Wang's ideas were fundamentally similar to those of the earlier Idealists, but he presented them more fully and clearly and added various new concepts. He began with the basic Idealist premise that principle (*li*) and mind (*hsin*) were the same. Along with all Neo-Confucians, he believed that the great principle, or supreme ultimate, was to be found in all things, was their unifying bond, and in fact made them one. He further insisted, with other Idealists, that principle and nature were the same as mind and feelings, that all things were therefore to be found within the human mind, and that moral perfection and complete knowledge thus were potentials within the mind. In addition Wang emphasized *jen*, a sense of unity with and love of all things, which made sages able to live in harmony with the world, 'rectify affairs', and follow the *tao*. All men had this virtue buried deep within their minds or original natures. The recognition and expression of it Wang called 'the extension of intuitive knowledge'. Intuitive knowledge—conscience, the inner light of the mind, the sense of right and wrong—would inevitably produce the right impulse or answer, if not inhibited, since it was the response of the perfect, all-knowing, or 'original mind.'

The unique feature of Wang's doctrine was that the 'extension of intuitive knowledge' was inseparable from practice. He considered the study of one's own mind through introspective meditation and the elimination of selfishness and desire as necessary to the 'extension of intuitive knowledge' but not enough; intuitive knowledge must be put into actual practice, removing any obstacles which prevented its constant application. Knowledge which was not put into practice was in fact not knowledge at all, but practice would make clearer and extend intuitive knowledge, while meditation and flight from the ordinary affairs of life, as taught by the Buddhists and Taoists, would not. 'Investigation of things' (*ko-wu*) Wang interpreted to mean 'rectification of affairs' (righting wrongs, correcting errors, etc.). Morality was no mere metaphysical concept to him; it extended to everyday action. Filial piety, brotherly love, and other virtues could be understood only through practice.

While Wang believed intuitive knowledge to be the best guide of all conduct, he held that it could not be forced. Extremes in either direction (either too much selfishness or too much effort to eliminate selfishness) were equally sources of evil and would obscure or inhibit intuitive knowledge; for such knowledge was the initial heaven-inspired response of the perfect principle of the mind and would be blurred or obscured by ratiocination. The instantaneous alarm and desire to save a child about to fall into a well was an example of intuitive knowledge at work, illustrative of the *jen* of all men. The perfecting of mankind consisted of extending *jen* to the utmost. In a discussion of the classic *Great Learning*, Wang elaborated his ideas:

'The great man is an all-pervading unity with Heaven, Earth, and all things. He regards all beneath Heaven as one family, and the Middle Kingdom as one man. Those who emphasize the distinction of bodily shapes, and thus make cleavage between the self and others, are the small men. The reason that the great man is able to be one with Heaven, Earth, and all things, is not that he is thus for some purpose, but because the *jen* of his mind is naturally so and thus makes possible this union. . . . The mind of the small man is exactly the same, only he himself makes it small.'[8]

Wang perceived in the *Great Learning* 'three major cords' and 'eight minor wires'. The major cords were: to 'manifest the illustrious virtue', to 'love people', and to 'rest in the highest good'. The minor wires were: to extend knowledge, to investigate things (or to rectify affairs), to be sincere in thought, to rectify the mind, to cultivate the self, to regulate the family, to order the state, and to foster peace—all of which were but aspects of the extension of intuitive knowledge. Like other Confucians Wang emphasized that gradations of *jen* were necessary in order to distinguish the more important from the less important. Beginning with parents it should extend outward in decreasing intensity to other relatives, other men, animals, plants, and inanimate things.[9] The obvious equalitarian implications of this ethical doctrine will be considered when we take up the history of political thought (Chapter IX).

In 1514 Wang began to teach his doctrine of 'the extension of intuitive knowledge' exclusively. Among his more important writings were the *Ch'uan-hsi lu* (*Record of Instruction*), *Ta hsüeh wen* (*Questions on the Great Learning*), a preface to the *Complete Works* of Lu Hsiang-shan, and the *Chu-tzu wan-nien ting-lun* (*Doctrine Reached by Master Chu [Hsi] in Later Life*), in which he tried to prove that Chu Hsi ultimately adopted the Idealistic position. He attracted a throng of followers, and after his death his disciples spread his doctrine far and wide. They were especially strong in south China.

The upsurge of the Idealistic school, and especially Wang's argument that Chi Hsi had really become an Idealist, provoked the Rationalistic school to reply. Two writers, Lo Ch'in-shun (1465–1547) in *K'un chih chi* (*Remarks Reached after Hard Study*) and Ch'en Chien (1497–1567) in *Hsüeh-p'ou t'ung-pien* (*Analysis of the Prejudices of Philosophy*), attempted to refute Wang's contentions about Chu Hsi, insisted that mind and principle were not the same thing, and charged the Idealists with preaching Ch'an Buddhist doctrines. Despite these arguments and a certain amount of official opposition, the Idealistic school continued to expand.

Wang's followers were known as the Yao-chiang school, after Wang's native place in Chekiang province. Ch'ien Te-hung (1496–1574) was probably the most prominent of them and certainly the most faithful to Wang's teachings. He was the compiler of Wang's dialogues, or *Record of Instruction*. He emphasized the inseparability of knowledge and practice, thus promoting the most dynamic aspects of the Idealist's teaching. Another prominent disciple was Wang Ken (1483–1540). Some of his ideas and practices on meditation were so close to Ch'anism that he was charged with having gone over to Buddhism, but he seems to have remained essentially true to Wang Yang-ming's emphasis on practice and in some respects foreshadowed the practical Confucians of the next century. He gave special attention to the perfecting of one's own conduct, which, once correct, would inevitably, he thought, promote correction of the world about. His political philosophy will be mentioned in Chapter IX.

Some of Wang Yang-ming's followers went to great lengths in advocating the spontaneous following of intuitive knowledge and the dictates of the perfect mind, insisting that the learning and teachings of former scholars would only obstruct the true way (*tao*). Others displayed extreme forms of subjectivism and distinct Ch'anist tendencies. Lo Nien-an (1504–64) advocated 'having no desire'. Nieh Hsuang-chiang (1487–1563) taught 'retiring into silence'. Wang Chi (1498–1583), an especially popular teacher, preached 'absence of thought' and was to have great influence in the late-sixteenth century. In the search for spontaneity he opposed any effort to discipline or organize the thinking process, insisting that the mind was devoid of both good and evil and hence that thinking, knowledge, and things were equally devoid of good and evil; evil arose only from interference with the spontaneous flow of thought and action by creating consciousness and attachment to existence. Having adopted the Buddhist ideas of Nirvana and transmigration, he held that the spontaneous way would bring freedom from the endless wheel of life and death. For him no essential difference separated Confucianism, Buddhism, and Taoism.

None of Wang Yang-ming's immediate followers was sufficiently intoxicated by the strong wine of intuitive knowledge to carry it to irresponsible extremes. Wang Chi and some others, however, disregarding the master's warning that almost no great men had spontaneously acquired intuitive knowledge, tended to overlook his restraining doctrine that it must be acquired, tested, and expanded through practice. A second generation of Idealists, which flourished around 1600, and especially the followers of Wang Chi and Wang Ken, carried the doctrine of spontaneity to a drastic conclusion. They denounced traditional practices, beliefs, and authority; and right or wrong, good or bad, became relative matters for them. They simultaneously advocated both non-active meditation and activism in following one's impulses, becoming incapable of decisive action or consistent policy in affairs of state. They promoted the merging of Confucianism, Buddhism, and Taoism, and mingled freely with Buddhist and Taoist monks. For these free-thinkers friendship and conviviality as well as eccentricities became supreme virtues, and many lived the lives of knight-errants.

Li Chih (1527–1602) was representative of these free-thinking, individualistic relativists. Despite his respect for Wang Yang-ming, he rejected the authority of the Confucian classics and adopted the garb and habits of a wandering Buddhist monk. As a lecturer he attracted a huge following by teaching that everybody was a potential sage and that even the common man had inborn moral faculties which he could use to become a perfect personality or a Buddha. Long before Adam Smith he upheld self-interest and profit as worthy incentives. He favoured equality of the sexes and marriage by free choice; and he praised politicians regardless of what they stood for, if they succeeded. Advocating spontaneous 'living in the present', he denounced the ancient virtues of loyalty, chastity, filial piety, and righteousness as artificial and foreign to the nature of the 'inner essence'. Accused of heresy, he committed suicide rather than face trial at Peking.[10]

Under Buddhist slogans of 'quiet sitting' and 'seeing one's own mind', many of the later Idealists degenerated. They became 'loafers, irresponsible talkers, and shameless seekers after fame and profit' who had no higher aspirations than 'women, money and wine'.[11] They undoubtedly contributed indirectly to, or at any rate reflected, the decline of the Ming dynasty and its inability to act decisively when faced with the rising threat of the Manchus.

* * *

The Tung-lin Movement

The moral irresponsibility of the later Idealists was combated by the Rationalists and by the Tung-lin movement (see Chapter V), a political and philosophical reaction to the laxity in government and society growing out of the increasing relativism of the Idealists. The Tung-lin disciples—the 'Righteous Circles'—insisted upon return to rigorous traditional training in morality and self-discipline and to social and political responsibility; most of them were politically active; some of them had been connected with the official censorate but had found it too subservient and had left it. Emphasizing virtue rather than enlightenment, they rejected the notion that human nature was neither good nor bad; in their ethics it was basically good but could not rely on its 'inner essence' alone and must be constantly buttressed by conscious moral exertion. They accepted the Idealist phrase 'living in the present' but interpreted it to imply moral effort, the practice of traditional virtues, and insistence on principle. They rejected all compromise with Buddhism and Taoism.

Beyond generally subscribing to these practical precepts, the Tung-lin thinkers lacked philosophical unity. Most of them attempted some sort of fusion of the views of Chi Hsi and Wang Yang-ming. Of these who leaned more in Wang's direction the outstanding ones where Ch'ien I-pen (1547–1617) and Sun Chen-hsing (1565–1636). They rejected Chi Hsi's distinction between ideal human nature (*li*) and material human nature (*li* plus *ch'i*) and accepted Wang's view that there was but one concrete human nature, which was synonymous with mind. They contended, however, that it required conscious cultivation through strict moral discipline.

Ku Hsien-ch'eng (1550–1612), the leader of the group, leaned more to the side of Chu Hsi. While he emphasized the goodness of human nature and favoured Wang's idea of realizing inborn knowledge, he also placed emphasis upon the necessity of investigating things, which he interpreted to include the moral ideas of the classics. He insisted that both Wang's 'extension of knowledge' and Chu's 'investigation of things' required a rigorous morality and practical activity, and amounted to much the same thing.

Kao P'an-lung (1562–1626) was the most original thinker in the Tung-lin movement. For him 'enlightenment' was essential to moral perfection but was of little value without self-discipline. Kao considered himself a follower of Chu Hsi, but he insisted that *li* and *ch'i* were really one and that *ch'i*, as cosmic matter, provided the common unity of all things. Ch'i was 'ultimate reality', 'the complete substance, to whose nature *li* belonged as immanent laws and forms'.[12] While advocating 'quiescence' and 'sitting quietly', Kao, like Ku, held them up as parts of a programme of practical rigorously moral activity.

Liu Tsung-chou (1578–1645) was a friend of Kao but not a regular member of the Tung-lin group, coming rather from the Rationalist school. He was critical of the contemporary trend of the Idealistic school, but many of his doctrines reflected the best of the Idealistic tradition, He developed a theory of the oneness of *ch'i* and *li* similar to that of Kao, giving primacy to *ch'i*.

★   ★   ★

Confucian Opponents of the Manchus

The reaction against the relativism of the later Idealists and the demands for moral uprightness and reforms in political practice did not save the Ming dynasty. China's collapse before the onslaught of the barbarian Manchus produced, after 1644, among a group of critical and pragmatic scholars an earnest endeavour to discover the reasons for the catastrophe that had befallen their country. These men came from no one group or school, and most of them mixed elements of Idealism and Rationalism to form their own eclectic philosophies. They organized no unified philosophic movement, and none of them made significant contributions to philosophy. They were generally united, however, in denouncing the moral laxity and ethical relativism of the later Idealists, the majority attacking also the speculative, metaphysical, and deductive nature of Sung and Ming philosophy. They insisted that Neo-Confucianism, by taking over Buddhist and Taoist ideas, had corrupted the true Confucian doctrine and, by failing to concentrate on practical, down-to-earth moral and political problems, had brought on the disaster. Some of them may have been influenced by the scientific technique of the Jesuits and by the Jesuits' contention that Sung and Ming metaphysics were derived from Buddhism.

Most of these critical, pragmatic scholars refused to serve the Manchus. Among them was Huang Tsung-hsi (1610–95), a disciple of Liu Tsung-chou (who starved himself to death rather than work for the conquerors). Huang, too, steadfastly spurned employment under the Manchus. Although a disciple of Liu, he was an avowed Idealist; yet he advocated the active cultivation of 'native knowledge' and had little regard for meditative speculation. He critically re-evaluated Sung and Ming thought in his *Sung-Yüan hsüeh-an* and *Ming-ju hsüeh-an*, condemning its Buddhist and Taoist elements. In his study of the legitimate grounds for imperial rule he attacked autocracy in government. Supporting the monist position of the Idealists, he advocated a theory very similar to that of his teacher: *li* and *ch'i* were really one, but *ch'i* was prime. Chu Chih-yü (1600–82) was likewise interested in practical reform and denounced the Ming scholars for their empty abstractions. He ultimately settled in Japan and, as we shall soon see, had considerable influence on the development of historical studies there.

Wang Fu-chih (1619–92) was another of the critical, pragmatic group who opposed the Manchus. Attacking particularly the Idealism of Wang Yang-ming, he undertook to perpetuate the better aspects of the Rationalistic school. He elaborated the doctrine of the investigation of things in a practical way but, not wholly avoiding Buddhist idealist monism, favoured knowledge obtained through one's moral nature over that obtained through one's senses. In his *Remarks on Reading the Four Books* (*Tu Ssu-shu ta-ch'üan-shuo*), however, he developed a monistic theory of the unity of principle and matter similar to that of Kao, Lui, and Huang and very near pure materialism:

'Within the universe there are only *li* and *ch'i*. The *ch'i* is the vehicle of *li*, through which it derives its orderliness. . . . When speaking of mind, nature, Heaven, or *li*, it must in every case be on the basis of *ch'i*. If there were no *ch'i*, none of them would exist.[13]

Without *ch'i* as instrument *tao* would be impossible.

Yen Yüan (1635–1704) and his pupil Li Kung were also among the critical, pragmatic Confucians. They, too, attacked the ideas of the Sung and Ming schools as abstract, impractical, and inspired by Buddhist and Taoist doctrine, and called for a return to ancient principles. Yen's ideas were set forth in his *Preservation of Learning* (*Ts'un-hsüeh*) and *Preservation of the Nature* (*Ts'un-hsing*). These works described the ancient principles as contained in 'the three tasks', 'the six treasures', 'the six patterns of conduct', 'the six virtues', and 'the six liberal arts' of Confucius and those whom he had considered model rulers. 'The three tasks' were the rectification by the ruler of the people's virtue, his utilization of the country's resources for their benefit, and his abundant provision for their livelihood. 'The six treasures' were water, fire, metal, wood, earth, and grain. 'The six patterns of conduct' were filial piety, fraternal devotion, friendship, marital constancy, forbearance, and compassion. 'The six virtues' were wisdom, *jen*, sageness, righteousness, loyalty, and harmoniousness. And 'the six liberal arts' were rituals, music, archery, charioteering, writing, and mathematics. Yen insisted that the 'investigation of things' really meant the actual practice of the three tasks and the other ancient principles. He wanted scholars to take up some useful calling and to put their learning into everyday practice. Unhappy over poverty and the inequalities of wealth, he advocated the redistribution of land. He attacked the Rationalists' dual system of principle and matter, denied the distinction between ideal or moral nature and physical nature, and expounded a monistic system in which *li* and *ch'i* were 'amalgamated into a single continuum'. Man's nature, good and bad, was thus one. Evil resulted from 'enticement, delusion, habit and contagion',[14] but good could be cultivated by education and the practice of *jen*. In a *Commentary on the Four Books* (*Chuan-chu wen*) Li Kung (1659–1733) expanded Yen Yüan's ideas. Neither writer had a large following, however.

The critical scholar Ku Yen-wu (1613–82) practised what he preached, befriending the people and refusing to serve the Manchus. In a general way, he belonged to the Rationalists, but his opposition to metaphysical abstractions, his accentuation of the original meaning of the classics, and his insistence on verifiable statements in scholarship helped to undermine their position. He attacked the Idealists also—for engaging in abstract Buddhist talk about mind and human nature, while failing to take action against the evils that corrupted government and oppressed the people. Modern scholarship, he complained, preferred words to deeds:

'Confucius seldom spoke about "human nature", "fate", or "Heaven", but present-day scholars constantly discuss them. Confucius and Mencius constantly discussed practical questions of conduct, but present-day scholars seldom mention them. . . . In my humble opinion the Way of a sage is [in the words of Confucius] to be "widely versed in learning" and "in one's personal conduct to have a sense of moral obligation." . . . One should feel deeply ashamed if he does nothing to alleviate the poverty of the common people'.[15]

The critical scholars—in particular, Ku and a younger contemporary, Yen Jo-ch'ü (1636–1704)—were the fathers of a new school of empirical research, which, becoming clearly differentiated in the eighteenth century, was known as the School of Han Learning. An omnivorous student, Ku observed the most critical canons of scholarship. His writings on phonetics and geography expanded their use as tools for historical and philological research. Yen Jo-ch'ü in an *Inquiry into the Authenticity of the* CLASSIC OF HISTORY *in Ancient Characters* (*Shang-shu ku-wen shu-cheng*) demonstrated that many sections of the *Classic of History* used by all Neo-Confucians were spurious. He stimulated a return to the texts of the classics as known in Han times and their critical study and revaluation (see below).

The more traditional-minded scholars remained either Rationalists or Idealists and have been generally referred to as the Sung school. Most of this school were Rationalist, used the text of the classics as fixed by Chu Hsi, and followed his commentaries and interpretations. They remained the orthodox official school, promoted by the government and the examination system. Many of the more able Rationalists, such as Chu Shih (1665–1736), not surprisingly became high officials. Li Fu (1675–1750) was one of the few Idealists in the Sung school worthy of note. The school produced a number of fair scholars and able officials, but it was uninspired and uncreative.

* * *

Han Learning and Moral Law

The School of Han Learning received its name because it considered the classical texts and commentaries of the Han period (206 BC–AD 9) to be the most authentic. It held that the texts, commentaries, and philosophical points of view of the Sung and Ming periods had been corrupted by Chu Hsi and his followers, and it was suspicious also of texts that claimed to be earlier than the Han dynasty.

Han Learning was basically practical and empirical in its point of view. It insisted on studying the texts of the Han period afresh and on using them as a practical guide to moral and political action, and not in a metaphysical fashion. Its scholars, therefore, worked hard to re-establish the original meaning of the classics and in the process developed a scientific methodology for the study and analysis of texts. Hence the movement produced a large number of distinguished scholars in the fields of textual criticism, philology, classical commentary, history and historical criticism, historical geography, and Confucian ethical and political theory. They denounced what they considered the bias and subjectivism of Sung and Ming scholars and attempted to reappraise the course of Chinese civilization from more authentic documentation.

Only a small number of the scholars of the Han Learning were interested in metaphysics. Among this number was Tai Chen (1724–77, also known as Tai Tung-yüan), the outstanding philosopher of the school. His particular brand of philosophy is often called the Tao-hsüeh, or Moral Law School, because of the importance of the term *tao* in it. Tai, as a critical and empirical scholar, was interested in all aspects of learning including mathematics, astronomy, geography, and technology, and he asked much the same kind of questions as those that disturbed his contemporaries of the European Enlightenment. He wrote or edited about fifty works, the most important for philosophy being *The Nature of Goodness* (*Yüan shan*) and the *General Survey of the Meaning of Mencius* (*Meng-tzu tzu-i shu-cheng*).

Tai was critical of both Chu Hsi and Wang Yang-ming. He advanced an essentially materialistic theory, which, although similar to that of Wang Fu-chih and other monists, went far beyond them in scope and organization. In his system *ch'i*, or substance, was the sole constituent of all things. He meant, not that things did not have *li*, but that *li* was 'simply the *manner* in which their substance is arranged and organized'.[16] Denying the separate existence of body and soul, he attacked the whole concept of *li* as presented by the Sung and Ming thinkers:

'Since the Sung dynasty there has grown up the habit of regarding *li* as if it were a veritable object, received from Heaven and present in the mind. The result is that those who are able to do so regard their mere opinions as being *li*. . . . Where in the six classics or in the books of Confucius or Mencius is it stated that *li* is such an external object, existing apart from man's feelings and desires, and designed sternly to repress them?'[17]

For Tai *li* was not a part of a cosmic absolute implanted by heaven in the minds of men but a principle inherent in the *ch'i*, or the substance of things. It was not something apart from the concrete material world; it did not transcend things but was immanent in them. *Li* was the internal structure or system of a thing—in other words, its governing principle. It could be discovered and understood, not by introspective meditation or sudden enlightenment, but only by 'wide learning, careful investigation, exact thinking, clear reasoning and sincere conduct'.[18] Tai's views were essentially nominalistic as opposed to the realistic position of the earlier Neo-Confucians. Interestingly enough, although he was recognized as a great scholar and employed and favoured by the emperor, he was never able to pass the highest civil-service examination controlled by the orthodox Realistic school.

For Tai's Moral Law school, *tao* was the activity of nature; it was 'movement' and 'the evolutionary operations of the *ch'i*'. '*Yin* and *yang* and the five elements' constituted its true substance. *Tao* was thus immanent in the *ch'i*; in the natural realm it resulted in unending production and reproduction, and in the realm of human affairs, it manifested itself in the relations among men. *Tao* (the proper way of a thing, of the universe, or of human society) was something inherent in things or institutions. It could be discovered and followed by the mind of man, but it was not a substantive entity:

'The unceasing evaluation of the universe constitutes the *tao*. Does not the alternation of the *yin* and *yang* result in production and reproduction? . . . The process of production and reproduction is that of love (*jen*), and never occurs except according to an orderly pattern. In the orderly unfolding of this pattern we find the highest manifestations of propriety (*li*). And in the distinctions that are laid down in the course of this orderly pattern we find the highest manifestations of righteousness (*i*)'.[19]

Really significant differences between *tao* and *li* are hard to detect in Tai's system, but he seems to have wished to give prominence to *tao* because of the abuses he saw in the applications of *li*. In human affairs, he thought, one found *tao* and *li* by studying mankind, by putting oneself in the place of others and considering how one would then like to act toward oneself. Conclusions reached by this process were to be tested, for one thing, by others' opinions (for that which did not win the approval of others was but personal preference) and, for another, by history (for that which had received confirmation over many generations throughout the world was probably a true principle). Tai clearly believed that most of the principles of the human way had been known to the authors of the classics, but he seemed also to leave the road open for change.

Man's nature, Tzi thought, consisted of blood, breath, and mental faculty and was divided into three particular aspects—feelings, desires, and knowledge. Evil arose because defects in the feelings, desires, and knowledge of men created selfishness, one-sidedness, and delusion. But these defects could be overcome by improved knowledge and by socializing and sublimating the desires rather than repressing them. The desires, if properly understood and guided, could be the foundation of the virtues, which were derived from innate human tendencies and could be developed and strengthened by proper training. Selfishness might be eliminated by strengthening altruism, and delusion by study: 'The benevolent [*jen*] man, wishing to live his own life fully, helps others to live their lives to the full'. Government and society should function in a way to make possible the orderly fulfilment and expression of the desires, and thus the development of the great virtues. The *tao* for Tai, as for Confucius and Mencius, was thus 'a way of human cooperation for the good of all'.[20] In like mood, some contemporary Western thinkers were speaking of the natural order as leading, if correctly understood, to the greatest good of the greatest number.

METAPHYSICAL AND ETHICAL SPECULATION IN JAPAN

In Japan metaphysical speculation was more prevalent after 1500 than before. The earlier trend in favour of Shinto accelerated so rapidly that by the end of the eighteenth century Shinto nationalistic thought became the most dynamic intellectual movement of the country. Motoori Norinaga (see Chap. V) was perhaps the outstanding theologian of the Pure Shinto school at its prime. His views were a mixture of a stark predestinarianism with an optimistic faith. Life on earth, he taught, was a constant struggle between virtue and evil, steadily moving in the direction of the higher good and a sort of best-of-all-possible worlds. All men, however, whether good or bad, must upon death go to *yomi* (the land of the dead), which was a dark, foul, and unpleasant place. No amount of rationalizing or retribution could change this destiny, but absolute resignation to the will of the gods would bring peace of mind.

*   *   *

The Teishu School of Neo-Confucianism

Until well into the eighteenth century, however, the thought that was dominant in Japan was not Shintoism but Neo-Confucianism. Neo-Confucianism was a borrowed system, and its advocates showed no great originality, being generally content merely to restate ideas developed in China. Nonetheless it occupied the minds of most Japanese samurai intellectuals and produced a considerable body of literature, some of which unintentionally promoted Shinto nationalism. Though metaphysics appealed to the Japanese mind perhaps even less than to the Chinese, Japanese thinkers repeated the metaphysics of early Neo-Confucianism but tended to emphasize its practical, ethical, social, and authoritarian aspects. They were particularly interested in its accent on duty, loyalty, and obedience to higher authority, utilizing it to rationalize the *Bushido* code. Neo-Confucianism in Japan was also markedly dogmatic and intolerant; the official school (that is, the branch promoted by the shogunate) in particular encouraged the authorities to repress its rivals. Four main branches of Neo-Confucian thought emerged in the seventeenth century.

The Teishu school, the oldest of these four, became the official school, advocating the dualistic Rationalism of Chu Hsi. Its first great figure was Fujiwara Seikwa (1561–1619). Ieyasu, the founder of the Tokugawa shogunate, patronized him and promoted the study of Confucianism as an intellectual prop to the shogunate and as a device for taming the restless samurai. Fijuwara Seikwa began his career as a Zen priest but ultimately abandoned Buddhism for Confucianism. He was more tolerant than most later members of the Teishu school. While he denounced Christianity, he was less critical of Buddhism and was acquainted with the monistic Idealism of Wang Yang-ming. He emphasized the ideas of *jen* and *te* (virtue), maintaining that people should have compassion for one another (*jen*) and that rulers should be possessed of special virtue (*te*). He insisted that Confucianism and Shintoism were similar and identified the Confucian *jen* with the Way of the Gods (Shinto).

Hayashi Razan (1583–1657), a pupil of Fujiwara Seikwa, was not equally tolerant. As Confucian adviser to the shoguns, he became head of the official academy established at Edo in 1633, and that post thereafter was held by his descendants. He vigorously denounced other systems of thought, including the Idealistic school of Wang Yang-ming. His own thinking led him, to be sure, to insist that *li* (*ri*) and *ch'i* (*ki*) could not be separated—a position that was not very far from the Idealists' monism, but he opposed the doctrine of intuitive knowledge. Emphasizing filial piety and loyalty, he tended to identify Confucianism and Shintoism, with the argument that Shinto was loyalty to the sovereign and loyalty to the sovereign was Confucianism.

Perhaps the most interesting of the Teishu school was Kaibara Ekken (1630–1714). Though he considered himself a supporter of Chu Hsi, he seems clearly to have been influenced by seventeenth-century Chinese writers. He did not accept Chu Hsi's distinction between ideal and material human nature, believing rather that *li* and *ch'i* were one and inseparable. Although he expounded the Confucian virtues and maintained that knowledge and practice should go together, he was also loyal to Japanese institutions and opposed efforts to impose the Chinese system on Japan. His last important work, *My Great Doubt*, reveals that he was no slavish follower of any system. He showed a great concern for the happiness of the ordinary man, popularizing Confucian ideas, travelling a good deal to lecture and teach, and writing his many works in simple Japanese rather than Chinese. A work entitled *The Great Learning for Women*, written by his wife, Token, had considerable influence on the education of women, emphasizing the necessity of their obedience to men.

Kinoshita Junan (1621–98) maintained a private school in Kyoto and was the teacher of three famous Teishu figures—Amamori Hōshū (1611–1708), Arai Hakuseki (1656–1726), and Muro Kyūsō (1658–1774). Not entirely orthodox, Amamori argued for the basic unity of Confucianism, Taoism, and Buddhism, and identified the jewel, the sword, and the mirror of Shinto with the *tao* of Confucius. Arai was a rigid follower of Chu Hsi. As an important adviser of the shogun in the early-eighteenth century, he emphasized the Confucian virtues, expanded court ceremonials and etiquette, and made an effort to apply ethical principles to economic problems. Muro, who succeeded as adviser to the shogun, was less rigid in the application of the Confucian virtues and achieved better results. A staunch upholder of Chu Hsi and of the shogunate, he repeatedly laid stress upon the blessings received from parents, lords, and sages. He identified Chu Hsi's Confucianism and Shinto, insisting that the Way of the Gods was that taught by Chu Hsi.

* * *

The Ōyōmei School

A though the Teishu writers tended to identify Confucianism with Shinto, most of them were supporters of the shogunate, and their emphasis on loyalty helped to buttress the shogunate and foster submission to it. In contrast to the Teishu school was another of the four main branches of Japanese Neo-Confucianism, the Ōyōmei followers of Wang Yang-ming; most Ōyōmei Idealists were critical of the shogunate for not doing more than they did for the welfare of the people. Partly for that reason and partly because their doctrine was unorthodox, their teachings were often under ban, and many of them spent some time in not too onerous house-arrest at the headquarters of some feudal lord. Their criticism helped to weaken the shogunate, while a number of their ideas helped to strengthen Shinto nationalism and promote the demand for the restoration of the emperor. They wanted a government that should strengthen the state and better the lot of the people. Some of them showed an interest in Western thought. Their emphasis on intuition and self-control was similar to that of Zen Buddhism, which had earlier appealed to the warrior class, and samurai with an independent turn of mind were attracted to them.

Nakae Tōju (1608–48) was the founder of the Ōyōmei school. He accepted the characteristic Idealistic Confucian doctrine that everything existed within the heaven-bestowed mind and that man's duty was to develop, articulate, and put into practice the intuitive knowledge that existed as principle in that mind. Nakae's thought was monistic and essentially pantheistic, but at times Heaven took on for him something of the aspect of a personal god. He emphasized the idea of *jen* in human relations and argued for the basic equality of all men: 'Emperor, duke, knight and commoner are not the same socially, but in their dignity as men there is no difference at all.'[21] He became an Idealist only during the last years of his short life, but his views were carried on and given new turns by his most distinguished disciple, Kumazawa Banzan (1619–92).

Kumazawa was especially famous as a critic of the shogun's administration and, as a result, spent considerable time in exile or house-arrest. Although a practical man interested in administrative reform, he strongly supported the idea of intuitive knowledge. He argued that Confucianism and Shintoism were in origin one and the same, that in its original form Shinto was best for Japan, but that Idealistic Confucianism also had certain contributions to make. He also argued, however, that many Idealists were lacking in historical knowledge of Confucianism, that Chu Hsi's ideas did not suit the Japanese, and that Wang Yang-ming placed too much emphasis on *jen*. He likewise criticized both Buddhism and Christianity.

Among the numerous eighteenth-century Ōyōmei scholars were Miwa Shitsusai (1669–1744) and Hayashi Shihei (d. 1793). The former prepared an important edition of some of the writings of Wang Yang-ming. He also laid down a tenfold path toward the attainment of perfection: the first step was to fix one's will on perfection; the other nine comprised a sense of shame, filial piety, nourishment of the body, generosity, control of temper, self-examination, development of intuitive knowledge, carefulness in thought, word, and deed, and the golden mean. Hayashi was interested in Western learning and in order to strengthen Japan advocated opening the country to outside contacts. For him intuitive knowledge of good and evil was conscience, and to obey one's conscience was courage. Most of his books were banned, and he died in prison for his criticism of the shogun's policy.

*   *   *

The Kogakuha and the Mito School

A third school of Neo-Confucianism, the Kogakuha (the Ancient or Classical school), arose in seventeenth-century Japan. It was critical of both the Teishu and the Ōyōmei school for their departure from original Confucianism and, like China's slightly earlier critical scholars, insisted on searching the original texts of the Confucian classics for their true message. Also like some of the Chinese scholars, it preached a monistic materialism in which *ch'i* (*ki*) was the absolute substance to which *li* (*ri*) adhered as guiding principle.

Some doubt arises as to who was the founder of the Kogakuha or Classical school. Yamaga Sokō (1622–85) was the earliest of this group. A student and teacher of military tactics, he laid the philosophic foundations for the knightly code of *Bushido*. An ardent nationalist, he also insisted that Japan was the central kingdom of civilization. In presenting his version of what original Confucianism meant, he attacked the other Confucian schools so violently that he was soon in trouble with the authorities. Itō Jinsai (1627–1705) is perhaps more justly considered a founder of the Classical school. Although, exceptionally enough, he was of mercantile origin, as teacher and writer he developed its characteristic philosophical doctrines.

Like philosophers elsewhere, the Kogakuha school debated the true nature of man. Itō Jinsai believed, with the revered Mencius, that human nature was fundamentally good. Tending to emphasize the practical side of early Confucianism, he exalted the four virtues—benevolence (*jen*), righteousness, propriety, and wisdom—of which he considered *jen* the most important. On the other hand, Ogyū Sorai (1666–1728), following the ancient Confucian Hsün Tzu, insisted that human nature was essentially evil but that the ancient sage-kings had given humanity the proper ethical codes for controlling human nature and that by training in and adherence to the proper ceremonials (*li*) mankind's behaviour could be improved. Although he did not have many disciples, this reasoning, providing as it did a philosophical justification of authoritarian government, found considerable support. His views were opposed by Itō Togai (1670–1736), who, carrying on the teachings of his father, Itō Jinsai, had numerous disciples.

The fourth main branch of Japanese Neo-Confucian thought was the Mito school of historical studies, which will be examined in greater detail in Chapter IX. It too contributed to the rising opposition to the shogunate.

THEOLOGICAL TRENDS IN ISLAM

After 1500, Islam continued to a certain extent to form a single society, of which any member might find himself largely in familiar surroundings no matter how far he might wander within it. Even as Islam expanded in size, travelling Ṣūfīs, merchants, and officials might everywhere encounter the *ṭarīqas* that they knew and find themselves protected and regulated by the same *sharī'a*. Nevertheless, forces were at work that were transforming the essentially apolitical Islamic society of the previous centuries into one dominated by three great political powers—the Ottoman, Ṣafavī, and Mogul empires.

By the middle of the sixteenth century each of these empires was making somewhat divergent changes in the common religious heritage while the remoter areas that did not come under their jurisdiction tended to go their separate ways. In the lands that passed under the control of the Ṣafavī dynasty Shīʿite *mujtahids* (independent learned inquirers) promoted an intensely emotional religion centring upon a ritual of mourning for the martyred *imāms* of Twelver Shīʿites and followed the Shīʿite version of the *sharīʿa*. Al-Majlisī was the outstanding Shīʿite legist of the seventeenth century (see Chapter IX). In India the Shīʿite kingdoms of the south fell under the influence of Persian culture and religious inspiration. On the other hand, the Ottoman Empire bitterly repressed Shīʿism and imposed a militant Sunnism upon its official life: the Sunnī version of the *sharīʿa* was incorporated into the constitution; the *'ulamā'*, guardians of the *sharīʿa*, acquired political and hierarchal status; and some of the *ṭarīqas* were officially favoured.

Within the Ottoman Empire the traditions of the Iranian and Arabic cultural zones met. A standard representative of the Arabic-Maghribī tradition of north Africa was al-Sanūsi (d. 1490), a follower of the theologian al-Ashʿari (873–935). Muḥammad Birgewī, a subtle sixteenth-century theologian, whose catechism became very popular, was a good representative of the Persian-Anatolian tradition; he carried on disputations with Abū-l-Suʿūd Khoja Chelebī (d. 1574), the greatest legal mind of the Ottoman Empire, who advocated the adjustment of tradition to new social and religious realities (see Chapter IX). The mysticism of the Syrian poet and commentator Abd-al-Ghanī al-Nābulusū (d. 1731) well illustrates the confluence within the Ottoman Empire of the Maghribī and Persian-Anatolian traditions.

Despite such confluences the tension between Shīʿite Persia and Sunnī Turkey grew and produced a significant effect upon the variant interpretations of the *sharīʿa*. In earlier centuries the Shāfiʿī school had been the most popular in some central Islamic lands. In the Ottoman Empire, however, the Ḥanafī school was given official recognition, while in Persia the Shāfiʿī school was formally forbidden. Shāfiʿīs still flourished, however, at Cairo and in Arabia, and they acquired new centres as Islam expanded in Malaysia and East Africa.

The *ṭarīqas* retained a good deal of their prestige during this period, and their heads were sometimes the recipients of great devotion, having, as in Persia and Morocco, founded or helped to found illustrious dynasties. The great orders spread their influence as Islam spread, and Ṣūfī mysticism and pantheism went with them. Abd al-Raʿuf, a saint of the Shaṭṭāriyya, took his order to Malaysia in the seventeenth century. New orders arose, too, sometimes in protest against the wealth, superstitious practices, and conventional orthodoxy of the older ones, and tried to bring about reform. In the seventeenth century Aḥmad Sirhindī attempted to reintroduce freedom of speculation and discussion into the *ṭarīqas* of India but won a following chiefly because of the great intensity of his mysticism. He launched the doctrine of *waḥdat al-shuhūd* (*unity by witness*) as against that of *waḥdat al-wujūd*(*unity by existence*),thus attempting to reconcile on the metaphysical level the very personal experience of the mystic with an intensely social activism. As the power of Islam declined in India, his followers were among the most zealous in urging Muslims to restore by words and arms the paramountcy of the *sharī'a*.

For all this activity many *ṭarīqas* of this period produced little new or original thought, and the several movements of reform remained isolated within one or another of the great empires. Not until the anti-Ṣūfī Wahhābī at the end of the eighteenth century (see Volume V) did a reform movement attain wide significance in many Islamic areas at once.

Mogul India produced a series of Muslim thinkers who, like Sirhindī, were concerned with the problems of coexistence with Hinduism. Sometimes they were favourably impressed by Hinduism, as in the case of Prince Dārā Shikūh, who argued the identity of Vedānta and Ṣūfism (see Chapter V). More often they engaged in an attempt to reassert, in historical or psychological terms, the superior social value of a dominant Islam, as in the tradition leading from Sirhindī to Shāh Wali-Allāh (eighteenth century) and his many active disciples. This series of thinkers helped to forge the cultural and intellectual tradition which bound Muslims together as an Islamic community in the Indic subcontinent, a tradition without which the geographical anomaly of Pakistan today would be incomprehensible and the passionate advocacy by many Pakistani leaders of Urdu as a pre-eminently Muslim language would seem absurd.

Philosophy in Islam was not only bound up with theology during this period; it was often, besides, in the hands of poets. The essentially monistic, pantheistic mysticism that has persisted in Arabic letters since the time of Ibn al 'Arabi continued. It has been discussed in Chapter V as theology and will be discussed again in Chapter IX as literature. Arabic prose tended increasingly toward commentary upon and monographic elaboration of older works rather than toward creative or broadly scholarly achievement.

During the years 1500–1800 Iran was an influential centre of philosophical thought, the originality of which, however, was restricted to a limited range of investigation. It developed the implications of themes broached before, particularly in Ṣūfī circles, and treated chiefly by the *mutakallimūn*, men who were theologians first of all and philosophers only secondarily. The trend was toward reaffirming the conventional, though the ban on Sunnism after the fifteenth century led to much effort to formulate and popularize Shī'ite doctrines. Nevertheless, as in the Arabic zone, both in Iran and elsewhere in the Persian-speaking zone scholarship tended increasingly to take the form of commentaries and super-commentaries.

Whether under Sunnite or Shī'ite auspices, the most significant religious thought in the Persian zone concerned the problems raised by the mystical doctrines of the divine unity. Two traditions of thought were chiefly influential—the Ishrāqī metaphysics of light and the mystical monism associated with Ibn al-'Arabī. Even after the advent of the Shī'a, Iran continued to be an influential centre of Ṣūfī-oriented philosophical thought. In the seventeenth century arose a more purely philosophical school of mystical speculators, the teachers and students of Mullā Ṣadrā (d. 1640), in whose system monism was pushed to a subtle extreme. He was a disciple of the relatively freethinking Mīr Dāmād (d. 1631) and of Shaykhi-Bahā'ī (d. 1622), both of whom were speculative thinkers with scientific interests as well as theologians and were protected by Shāh 'Abbās, patron of art and learning. Mullā Ṣadrā was more outspoken than his teachers and wrote with comparatively little regard to theological prejudices. He consequently had much trouble at the hands of the other 'ulamā', who accused him of abandoning the faith. It has been suggested that in the school of Mullā Ṣadrā Neoplatonism with its doctrine of emanations was cast off in favour of a much purer Platonism, but it was a Platonism interpreted nonetheless in terms of the Ishrāqī philosophy of light.

Persian philosophical thought of this period was often tied to special Shī'ite problems, as was suitable in newly Shī'ite Iran. The effort to adapt Shī'ism, hitherto the creed of a minority, to the needs of the whole of a large and prosperous society led to a profusion of both theological and philosophical developments. Twelver Shī'ism as an orthodox legal system came to be divided into two major schools—the Uṣūlīs, who predominated, and the Akhbārīs. The Uṣūlīs insisted on constant reference to the first principles (uṣūl) of faith in the settlement of cases in the sharī'a and therefore stressed the role of the independent inquirer, the mujtahid. The Akhbārīs—not altogether unlike the earlier Sunnīs—stressed dependence on akhbār or ḥadith, certified reports of sayings of the imāms. In the late-eighteenth century the shaykhīs formed a third school with particularly strong philosophical interests. Founded by Shaykh Aḥmad al-Aḥsā'ī (d. 1827), they stressed among other things the metaphysical position of the (Shī'ite) imāmate as a means of human access to divine truth, elaborating to this end novel doctrines about time and substance.

THEOLOGICAL AND EPISTEMOLOGICAL SPECULATION IN THE WEST

In Europe, the sixteenth century was a period of intense theological polemic. The Catholic Counter Reformation brought renewed interest in religious disputations and, with them, a reinvigoration of Scholastic logic. Among the works that Cardinal Cajetan wrote as a Dominican scholar when not occupied with affairs of state were commentaries on the Summa Theologica of Aquinas; they are now adjoined to the papal edition of that work. Neo-scholasticism flourished particularly in Spain, where the work of the Dominican Francisco de Vitoria (1480–1546) and the Jesuit Francisco Suàrez (1548–1617), a disciple of Molina (see Chapter IV), bolstered and rivalled the reputation of Aquinas as defenders of Christianized Aristotelianism.

Vitoria, professor of theology at the University of Salamanca, in *Relectiones Theologicae* (1557) expounded a concept of a *ius gentium*, of natural rights and obligations, as based on eternal, divine law and reason and as binding upon all nations. If rationally observed, it would, he taught, rule out war except in self-defence (and therefore he deprecated even religious conversion by force). While it would justify the power of the state, it would lead also to cooperation among the nations and to freedom of movement for individuals from one country to and in another. Vitoria's views seemed to be an apology for Spanish colonization in American and other lands at the same time that it urged moderation—and not merely in religious affairs—upon the colonizers.

Suàrez's *Disputationes Metaphysicae* (1597) became a widely used text of the Jesuits, since it simplified many of the logical problems created by the realism imputed to the Thomists. Abandoning the Scholastic tradition of writing commentaries upon texts from Aristotle, he undertook an original critique of independent issues that he raised, revealing an encyclopaedic knowledge of the relevant sources. Like the Aristotelian professors of Padua (see Chapter VI), though for more orthodox reasons, he separated theology with its supernatural justifications from philosophy, which, avoiding the more abstruse disputes of the Schoolmen, he limited to speculation on the nature of finite things. 'Suàrezianism' was adopted widely in the north also as a Protestant weapon in the conflict with resurgent Catholicism. Suàrez was the last of the great Scholastics. His political theory will engage our attention later (Chapter IX). In his philosophy theology was still queen of the sciences, but her realm had become less ethereal and considerably narrower than before.

The victories of Thomism were defeats for Ockham's brand of Scholasticism, which had to bow not only to Catholic but also to Protestant religiousness and to humanist ridicule as well. In the Rhineland, ever a stronghold of Thomism, in the Italy of the Council of Trent, and in the Spain of the Most Catholic Monarchs, realism defeated nominalism. In France, the philosopher Petrus Ramus, before he embraced Protestantism and fell a victim of the Massacre of St Bartholomew's Day, had in several works vigorously opposed the old Scholasticism in all its branches, working out a humanist 'new logic', based, he claimed, on a truer interpretation of Aristotle and on more rational methods derived from it for the solution of philosophical problems. Ramus's works had a certain vogue in Protestant countries.

The Neoplatonism of Renaissance scholars evoked among western European scholars relative indifference to other schools of Greek philosophy. Both Protestantism and the Counter Reformation especially in northern Europe, proved more favourable to Stoicism than Renaissance Italy had been. At the University of Louvain from 1592 until his death in 1606, Justus Lipsius, a Belgian scholar famous for his edition of Tacitus, lectured to crowded classes on Seneca's moral treatises. In France Michel de Montaigne (1533–92) for a time was an admirer of Seneca and Plutarch, and Guillaume du Vair

(1556–1621) glorified Stoic virtues. And in the early decades of the seventeenth century several Spanish writers, among whom Francesco de Quevedo was perhaps the most eminent, introduced a vogue of neo-Stoicism sometimes designated as Senecism. Stoicism made little progress in Western thought, however, before the end of the seventeenth century, but then and in the next century the Stoic concepts of Virtue, Reason, and Nature moved into and deeply coloured Enlightenment thought (see Chapter IX).

Similarly, few traces of Epicureanism appeared in humanistic writings before the seventeenth century. The fearless and uncompromising Giordano Bruno, who was burned for heresy in 1600, was Lucretian in a way, but he fell far short of the Epicurean theory of an atomistic world. Bruno, one of the boldest of the sixteenth-century thinkers, followed Nicholas of Cusa (whom he called 'the Divine Cusanus') and Neoplatonism rather than Epicurus and Lucretius. He envisaged God as the infinite combination of finite but constantly evolving matter ('monads') and world soul. He was, however, Lucretian in that he held a heretical theory of an infinite universe of innumerable worlds. It was not his philosophy that brought him to the stake; it was, rather, his iconoclastic temperament. Montaigne and Francisco Sanchez (1550–1623) put forward no less sceptical queries about orthodox knowledge than Bruno;[22] and Pierre Gassendi (1592–1655) was more notable as an advocate of the atomistic universe and of Epicurean thought in general. These men, however, were more tactful than Bruno and did not outspokenly attack religion; consequently they escaped condemnation.

Bruno marks an important point in modern thought. With him the scientific method, on which he lectured widely, invaded humanistic philosophy, eventually to put a demand for systematic verification into the loose, individualistic speculation that had prevailed during the Renaissance. We shall speak of him as a scientist later (Chapter XIII).

*   *   *

The Co-existence of Science and Religion

The European sages of the sixteenth and seventeenth centuries, whether Catholic or Protestant, were almost without exception professing, and generally devout, Christians. When Galileo was accused of having upheld the Copernican theory (which, however, the pope had not *ex cathedra* declared heretical), he was also accused of having been a bad Catholic and of having acted deceitfully; he proved willing to 'abjure, curse and detest' his 'errors and heresies and generally every other error, heresy and sect whatsoever contrary to the Holy Church', but he begged not to be made to say either that he was not a good Catholic or that he had ever deceived anyone, and he was not required to say either.[23] In other words, he was unwilling to risk punishment for teaching what he believed to be true, but he was, it seems, prepared to risk punishment, if he had to, rather than admit to being a bad Catholic. Among other Catholic scientists of foremost rank were Vesalius,

Torricelli, and Pascal, all devout men in their separate ways. Sceptics like Vanini and Hobbes were *rarae aves* in the seventeenth century. Later, during the eighteenth century, scepticism was fairly common among the *philosophes*, but with infrequent exceptions they too openly adhered to some form of Christianity, generally paying it at least public deference. They almost never were outright atheists, even though frequently charged with atheism by their opponents.

Protestants were no less zealous than Catholics in the promotion of science (see Chapter XIV). Some historians have maintained that the Calvinist ascetic spirit furthered the development of science: 'The number of sixteenth century botanists in central and northern Europe who were of the reformed faith is indeed remarkable.'[24] Kepler was a Lutheran. Boyle, Newton, Harvey, and Locke were professing Anglicans. Bayle, though he moved from Protestantism to Catholicism and back to Protestantism, was always a devout Christian. Huygens and Leeuwenhoek were members of the Reformed Church. Examples could easily be multiplied of sixteenth- and seventeenth-century scientists and philosophers, both Catholic and Protestant, whose new knowledge and methods did not seriously disturb their faith in their respective Christian creeds.[25] In general, these men were willing to seek knowledge wherever it could be found. 'If we hold the Spirit of God to be the only source of truth', Calvin wrote, 'we will neither reject nor despise this truth wherever it may reveal itself, provided we do not wish to offend the Spirit of God.'[26]

Part of the quarrel between Jansenists (and also the Oratorians) on the one hand and Jesuits on the other was over the nature of science. Far from thinking of science and theology as at war, these devoutly religious groups differed only regarding the exact nature and value of science in God's plan for man's salvation. To the predestinatarian Jansenists scientific achievement could come only as a result of God's grace and could not affect salvation; it was only a *divertissement* (Pascal's word for it), and the method it employed was not prescribed. To the Jesuits, with their Molinist acceptance of free will, science was a means of drawing upon the treasury of good works, though it could be properly studied only within the Aristotelian framework. For both Jansenist and Jesuit, science was an avenue to the better understanding of the manifestations of God, to greater knowledge of God's Truth, and to a stricter avoidance of Error. The divine mind had, according to many of the sixteenth- and seventeenth-century scientists, Protestant and Catholic alike, best manifested itself through the natural world and could best be studied by studying 'the Book of Nature'.

*　　*　　*

The Rise of Empiricism

The attacks upon Scholasticism were in large part due to what its critics believed to be the Scholastic practice of feeding on itself. According to them the Schoolmen turned mentally inward, reasoning circularly within a more or less closed syllogistic system, where major premises might have no reference to reality, rather than going out and studying mentally and manually the Book of Nature. In the sixteenth century a group of Italian anti-Aristotelians had begun to preach that knowledge derived from sensory data was superior to abstract reasoning. Bernardino Telesio (1509–88), though his senses led him to a rather specious theory of wet-cold and dry-warm forces as the basic principles of existence, nevertheless in his *De Natura Rerum Iuxta Propria Principia* (1568) laid a foundation for an empirical philosophy of science. His work had a direct influence upon Francisco Patrizzi (1529–97) and Tommaso Campanella (1568–1639). As a Neoplatonist and a believer in the primacy of space and light, Patrizzi in *Nova de Universis Philosophia* (1591) expressed some doubt about the validity of Telesio's teachings on force, while Campanella in *Philosophia Sensibus Demonstrata* (also 1591) defended Telesio, but both men, in these and other works, lifted the anti-Scholastic banner, championing some method of interaction of the senses with the mind (though they did not agree on what method) as a better source of truth than syllogistic argument.

Francis Bacon also knew of Telesio and, without endorsing his findings, admired him as the *primus novorum virorum*. Bacon's emphasis upon the inductive method was a direct reaction to the speculative methods of the Scholastics and their Aristotelianism. Find new information, he recommended, by investigating nature with a new method (*novum organum*), using your own hands or working in cooperation with those who used theirs; consider no time-honoured ideas sacred, and avoid predispositions to error ('idols'), whether they are the anthropocentric predispositions of mankind in general (idols of the tribe), personal prejudices (idols of the cave), rhetorical inaccuracies (idols of the market place) or conventional philosophies (idols of the theatre); begin rethinking ('the Great Instauration') from first principles, from irreducible and observed 'instances' (or elements of fact); do not despise the knowledge of craftsmen, who know from actual experience much that is worth knowing. In this way, he thought, as old knowledge was discarded, new knowledge would not only be accumulated but its accumulation would redound to the benefit of mankind.

Bacon's point of view was favourable not only to inductive reasoning but also to empirical methods, tools, and terms, and to utilitarian objectives— in all three regards, a departure from the prevalent view of the Scholastics. He was, if anything, somewhat unappreciative of speculative judgment and deductive reasoning, and seemed particularly unaware of the importance of the mathematical process in scientific investigation. This indifference to mathematics was all the more striking because he was a contemporary of Kepler and Galileo, who were concurrently applying speculation and mathematical principles to empirical data.

Bacon had no quarrel with theology in its own sphere—the nature of God, the soul, and morals. But the *novum organum* was for him the only method of deriving truth in the material sphere—abstract truth that could be tested by its usefulness in revealing 'new works and active directions not known before'.[27] At the same time, he struck at both the contemporary theologians, who claimed that the church was the ultimate source of truth, and the Scholastic and the humanist worshippers of Antiquity, who claimed that either Aristotle's 'induction by simple enumeration' or Platonic 'ideas' were all that was needed to derive truth. Instead, he favoured a process of induction that also required a logical process—a process that (1) would consider the 'negative', 'positive', and 'comparative instances' of forms (or physical properties); (2) would then derive from this observation of forms an 'axiom' (i.e. a generalization about their regularities regarded as objective in God's nature); and (3) would move step by step from axiom to axiom toward a new provisional principle. He thought the 'true way' of 'searching into and discovering truth' was the one that 'derives axioms from the senses and particulars, rising by a gradual and unbroken ascent, so that it arrives at the most general axioms last of all'.[28] Eventually truth would be able 'to endow the life of man with infinite commodities',[29] for institutions devoted to scientific research, much like the House of Solomon pictured in his *New Atlantis* (1627), would help to establish man's control of natural forces and promote his betterment.

Bacon died of a bronchitis brought on by experimenting with refrigeration as a means of preventing animal decay. In several ways he was an anomaly, but not least in affording the picture of a lofty personage, a lord chancellor, who believed that men of science working with their hands as well as their heads and in company with craftsmen should strive to increase knowledge and improve the physical lot of man on this earth rather than, without transgressing traditional methods, speculate upon the learning already in the books, the hereafter, and the greater glory of God. For all the residue of Aristotelian terminology in his discourse and for all the self-seeking in his aristocratic career, this was a secular philosopher of a modern cast, even in his overconfidence in the empirical method.[30]

Although once an amanuensis of Bacon, Thomas Hobbes was nevertheless ready to philosophize and to speculate mathematically. Hobbes tried to explain human behaviour in deductive terms—not only in his famous political treatise, *The Leviathan*, but also in *Human Nature* (1650) and other works. He concluded, apparently on little empirical basis, that the ultimate realities in the cosmos were matter and its qualities of extension and motion. This concept he perhaps derived from Galileo, whom he knew personally and greatly admired. While Galileo had applied it only to the physical universe, Hobbes reduced all science to a quest for laws of motion. Politics and ethics as well as physics and mathematics were for him but the application of those laws to their respective subject matter. The inevitable conclusion from this deductive philosophy was favourable to empiricism: the mind as a product of the elemental realities of matter and motion was neither free nor innate. If changes in the mind are only the effects of motion on matter, knowledge and other mental processes must originate from impulses or sensations that come from outside the mind and effect modifications (i.e. motion) within it. Hobbes' philosophy seemed so thoroughly materialistic that he was sometimes accused of being an atheist. Certainly, as his political views showed (see Chapter IX), he was cynical of man's capacity to solve his social problems, and yet he ranks with other English empiricists and the French *philosophes* as the founder of a school of thought which held that human affairs no less than the physical universe might be subject to rational, natural law.

The materialistic implications of Hobbes' epistemology, along with other sources of scepticism (see Chapter IV), met with reaction among other English thinkers. Ralph Cudworth and Henry More became the central figures of a latitudinarian and idealist group known as the Cambridge Platonists, who argued that an incorporeal and eternal spiritual quality—an *anima mundi*, or 'world spirit'—filled space and time and pervaded the matter of the cosmos, predisposing the human mind to reason and morality. Beliefs like this were reinforced by William Gilbert's contention that magnetism was animate and by Isaac Barrow's that space and time were but mathematical manifestations of God. Barrow was a teacher of Isaac Newton.

The capstone was placed in the structure of English empirical reasoning by John Locke's *Essay Concerning Human Understanding* (1690). Addressing himself directly to the by-then hotly disputed question of the origin of human knowledge, he boldly took the side of those who contended, contrary to Descartes (whom we shall presently encounter), that the mind had no innate ideas. It did have, however, certain innate capabilities, he claimed: it could receive sensations from without, whether the stimuli were inherent in the external object—as, for example, shape, motion, and plurality (primary, quantitative, or tactile features)—or could be appreciated only with the aid of the animal physiology—as, for example, taste, colour, and smell (secondary features); it could store these sensations in the memory; and it could observe its own internal operations and reflect upon them. Out of the combination of sensation, memory, and reflection came the ability to compare the results of cognition ('ideas'), approve or disapprove of them, imaginatively reconstruct them, name them, and generalize about them. Thus the mind developed from a *tabula rasa* at birth ('white paper, void of all characters, without any ideas', but ready to receive 'simple ideas')[31] into a mature thinking apparatus capable of 'complex ideas' and of various kinds of abstract reasoning. Locke considered some of these complex ideas as at least partly *negative*—i.e. thought *not* derived from sense-experience but resulting from the mind's *inability* to comprehend them—as, for example, the idea of the finiteness of time and space, whence, he reasoned, came the positive idea of 'infinity'. He also believed that human beings have intuitive knowledge of their own minds and wills, and from such knowledge comes 'demonstrative knowledge' of God.

Obviously Locke was a theist. As other writings more fully show, he accepted Revelation and Resurrection on faith and as 'above reason'. He was not even a full believer in the *tabula rasa*, since a mind equipped with the ability to receive sensations, remember them, and reflect upon them is not 'white paper'. His argument for the existence of God, based as it was on the awareness of our own being and beginning was not far removed from Descartes'. But he departed from Descartes in emphasizing the need to begin with elementary sensations received from the outside and with simple ideas independent of introspection in order to arrive at complex ideas and to proceed thence to other kinds of knowledge. He thus fortified the arguments of those who favoured the inductive method of learning and reasoning from accumulated details through categories to generalizations rather than by the deductive syllogistic method of the Schoolmen or the intuitive rationalist method of the Cartesians.

*   *   *

Doubts on Empiricism

When we come to consider the history of social thought (Chapter IX) and science (Chapter XIV), we shall see that the great British scientists among Locke's contemporaries were not full-fledged empiricists. Newton, for all his contempt in the *Principia* for hypotheses and his admiration of 'reasoning from mechanical principles', nevertheless believed that since God had existed 'always and everywhere', He 'constitutes duration and space'. Thus Newton found a satisfying explanation and foundation for his premiss of absolute time and absolute space, which prevailed until Einstein expounded the theory of relativity. Newton was able to accept, though certainly he had no sensory experience of them, both the theory of an all-pervading ether and the corpuscular theory (see Chapter XIV). Boyle was more definitely mechanistic than Newton in his philosophy and more empirical in his method, and yet he was one of the first to explain the cosmic order as analogous to that of a clock somewhat like the astonishing time-machine in the Cathedral of Strasbourg with God as the clockmaker, Who might occasionally intervene by miracles to modify the regular operations of His machine. Locke and contemporary empiricists seem never to have dreamed of postulating a world without God. Their thinking was, rather, in the opposite direction: In a sensate world what is the place of God?

As we shall see when we reach the discussion of the history of psychology during this period (Chapter XIV), a number of writers who examined the problem of knowledge doubted the validity of Locke's epistemology. George Berkeley (1685–1753) accepted Locke's assumption that ideas formed by finite minds were based upon blendings of sensations, but Berkeley turned it into a weapon against materialism. He argued that the finite mind could not distinguish between primary and secondary qualities, that even primary qualities are ideas and so cannot exist outside a perceiving substance or mind. Hence, he concluded—somewhat like the Hindu qualified monists and the Chinese Idealists (of whom he probably did not know) and like Jonathan Edwards (who probably neither knew of nor was known to him)—that, whether or not matter existed objectively, it could be perceived only by a conscious mind, and such perception and, more especially, perception of a regular order in nature was possible to finite minds only because the mind of God could and did posit it. David Hume (1711–76), as sceptical a philosopher as was to appear in England before the nineteenth century, raised the question whether self, cause, and other generalizations needed for human understanding could be derived from observation, whether the mind ever perceived a real connection among discrete things, and whether causal generalizations did not in fact depend upon customary and regular associations, mere conjunctions, which the mind came to accept as cause-and-effect. Building on Locke's *tabula rasa* and a theory of nervous vibrations borrowed from Newton, David Hartley (1705–57) developed a system of physiological psychology generally designated as 'associationist', which, while a product of the empirical school, was also a departure from it in the direction of analysis of the role of nerves and brain in the thought process (see Chapter XIV).

*   *   *

Cartesianism and Occasionalism

On the Continent strict materialism—i.e. the certitude that matter was the primary stuff of the cosmos and that mind was a derivative of it—did not flourish until the eighteenth century. Before that, Cartesianism, the school of theist naturalism based upon the rational dualism of René Descartes (1596–1650), was dominant.[32] In the Cartesian scheme matter was inert and continuous but had motion, imparted to it by God. The mind was distinct from matter and contained an irreducible, self-evident awareness of its own existence (*Cogito, ergo sum*) and hence of causality and God. The world of matter was mechanical, since all was a single plenum and continuum, and motions in one part produced circular eddies or 'vortices' that caused respondent motions in all the rest. The essential qualities of matter were for Descartes, as for Hobbes, extension and motion. We shall deal with the scientific implications of this mechanical theory elsewhere (Chapter XIV). The theological significance of it centred upon the contention that God's will alone allowed dead matter (*res extensa*), including animal bodies, to bridge the gap to the animate mind (*res cogitans*) by sensations. Thus Descartes lent his formidable authority to a clear-cut philosophy of dualism—matter and mind, body and soul.

Descartes' dualism was quickly attacked on various religious fronts. The rector of the University of Utrecht, Gisbert Voetius, assailed him in the name of the old orthodox philosophy. Gassendi, as befitted one of the small school of seventeenth-century philosophers who preferred the philosophy of the Epicureans, attacked the idea of the continuum moving by vortices, preferring an atomistic universe. Anticipating Locke (who, also with Descartes in mind, repudiated innate ideas), Gassendi contended that *nihil est in intellectu quod non prius fuerit in sensu* and thus, though himself inconsistently admitting the knowledge of God in the intellect, questioned the logic of Descartes' ontological argument.

The Cartesians themselves felt called upon to modify or expand Descartes' epistemology. The dissociation of matter and mind in Descartes' world raised the question how a change in one could bring a change in the other, how a sensation from the material world could cause an effect in the mind, even when both mind and matter are united, as in man. This problem led to the philosophy of Occasionalism, early broached by Sylvain Régis: when a change occurred in the material world God *occasioned* a corresponding change in the mind. Some of the Cartesians were Complete Occasionalists, who believed that no occurrence whatsoever was independent of God's volition. Others were Restricted Occasionalists, who left to the human mind some limited capacity to act of itself. The Oratorian Nicolas Malebranche (1638–1715) was a Complete Occasionalist, and his most noteworthy opponents among the Restricted Occasionalists were Arnold Geulincx (1624–69) and the Jansenist leader Arnault. The Occasionalists thought of God as, so to speak, a sort of clockmaker who had made *two* clocks that he constantly kept synchronized.

*   *   *

Critics of Cartesianism

This explanation of causality went too far for some and not far enough for others. The English philosopher Joseph Glanvill and the French scientist Blaise Pascal (1623–62) doubted that rational speculation on cause could fortify the Christian sense of the belief in God, Who, rather, must be taken on faith, for human understanding was insufficient for the understanding of the Divine. Glanvill became a Cambridge Platonist, Pascal a Jansenist. No theologian but speaking as a student of law and history (see Chapter IX), Giovanni Battista Vico in the *Principii d'una scienza nuova* (1725) questioned the Cartesian assumption that human knowledge came from thinking, or cogitation, and held that it came rather from doing, or action: *verum et factum convertuntur*. Although he had to wait until the nineteenth century for his views to make a wide impression, Vico thus early formulated the school later known as historicism (explanation by historical development) to counteract both rationalism (knowledge from reason) and empiricism (knowledge from experiment).

Dissatisfaction with the Cartesian explanation of knowledge, causality, and God came not only from empiricists and historicists but also from other kinds of rationalists. Although excommunicated by the Jewish community (see Chapter V), Baruch Spinoza (1632–77) had been trained as a youth in the rational tradition of the rabbis, for whom God was 'the space of the world'.33 In exile in Rijnsburg, Spinoza associated with the Mennonites known as *Collegianten,* many of whom were Cartesians, and Spinoza prepared textbooks on some of Descartes' work without wholly sharing his views. He had in fact already begun to develop an epistemology which, after his death, was published in his *Tractatus de Intellectus Emendatione.* His theory of knowledge differed significantly from both the empiricist Bacon and the rationalist Descartes at the same time, for it insisted that the human mind was capable of not only 'opinion', based upon elementary perceptions (or images) derived from the external world, but also of 'reason', based upon conceptions of, or logical connections among, related things, and of 'intuition' (rational cognition) based upon methodically trained insight into nature's universal laws and rules *sub specie aeternitatis.*

Spinoza's epistemology, set forth chiefly in his *Ethica* (first published in 1677), was of a piece with his cosmology, where, too, he repudiated both the materialists and the dualists while building upon the foundations which they had laid. Essentially he was a Western monist, a religious materialist, a Judeo-Christian pantheist. The *continuum-and-plenum* of Descartes, the all-pervading and infinite *extension* of matter of Hobbes, and the ever-present, ever-active Divine Will of the Occasionalists, Spinoza combined in a mystical concept of Substance. Substance was not for him mere matter, as it was for Descartes and Hobbes, nor yet mere idea as, in a sense, it was for Berkeley, but rather that which always had been and always would be, independent of everything else, eternal, infinite, active, from which all other things were in one way or another derived. Hence it was God, or Nature. It was the object of man's 'intuitive' knowledge (for Spinoza, the most highly trained kind of knowledge). This Substance had Attributes, of which the two known to man were matter or extension and spirit or thought, which, while infinite and complete, were not *absolutely* independent and non-derivative as was Substance. Since the two were equally the Attributes of Substance (or God, or Nature), they are at the same time identical with, though independent of, each other, and their connection or correspondence (occasions or causes) can be conceived by human 'reason'. The Attributes, in turn, have Modes (or modifications) that, when finite and temporary, were particular things like individual minds or bodies or events. Of these Modes man could by perception or imagination have 'opinions'.

Spinoza's ethical views were, in turn, also of a piece with his epistemology. Man's higher feelings, for Spinoza, were the 'active' ones, based on conscious desire, and the lower ones were 'passive', based on influences outside himself. The 'passions' are due to 'human bondage' to 'opinion', the lowest, 'inadequate' form of knowledge, and generally cause pain. The 'active' feelings are due to an exercise of 'reason', and because they are the outcome of some form of self-expression, they sometimes are 'adequate' and generally cause pleasure.

If finally the mind by acquiring adequate ideas is attuned to the cosmos and accepts all things as coming from God, it has reached the highest level of insight, the level of 'intuitive' knowledge. Since this *scientia intuitiva* is rare and difficult, in Spinoza's system a political organization was necessary to enable man to avoid the evils that his 'passions' entail and to live a life of reason (see Chapter IX). Despite the enormous reputation of Spinoza in his own day, some of his most important works were published only post-humously and were not widely known until the end of the eighteenth century.

* * *

Leibniz, Wolff, and Optimism

Gottfried Wilhelm Leibniz (1646–1716), expert in mathematics and mechanics and practiced in history and diplomacy, was too busy ever to set forth his philosophy in a systematic exposition. Yet he wrote several essays and many letters of a philosophical nature, for he knew almost every great thinker of his day. He had met Christian Huygens and several other out-standing Cartesians in Paris, when on a diplomatic mission to divert French aggression from Germany to Egypt, and had gone to Holland to talk to Spinoza, with whom he afterwards kept up a steady correspondence. He also had been to London and knew Newton and Boyle. Besides, Leibniz was more concerned with Chinese philosophy than perhaps any other European scholar of his day. As a mathematician, one of the discoverers of the calculus, he approved of the reasoning method of Descartes and Spinoza—in geometric fashion from simple postulates to complex theorems—and tried to carry it a step further by a universal calculus, somewhat like that advocated today by the symbolic logicians—the reduction of the simple, self-evident truths to symbols which could then by equations of identity or non-identity be used to arrive at more complex truths. Universal truth seemed to him capable of comprehension because the universe was the product of a Pre-established Harmony—'a prevenient divine contrivance, which from the beginning has formed each of these substances [the soul and the body] in a way so perfect and regulated with so much accuracy that merely by following laws of its own, received with its being, it nevertheless agrees with the other, just as if there were mutual influence, or as if God in addition to his general cooperation constantly put his hand thereto'.[34]

Leibniz thus seems to have come as close as a theist could to the concept of a regular order of nature in which all things animate and inanimate work according to eternal, universal, and self-operating laws. He bridged the gap not only chronologically but logically between those of the seventeenth century who spiritualized matter and those of the eighteenth century who materialized spirit. His endowment of matter with spirit was explicitly set forth in a letter to Prince Eugene of Savoy (published as *Monadologie* in 1714), but the problem had already been broached in the *Nouveaux essais sur l'entendement humain* (1704), a step by step refutation of Locke's sensational-ism. To Leibnez, student of mechanics, the primitive stuff of the universe was not substance but force. He conceived of force as present in the ele-mentary units of the universe, which he called *monads* (a term he probably borrowed from Bruno). The monads were the atoms of nature, each of which combines the spiritual and the material, and was perpetual and independent of all others. Each monad was a microcosm sharing in varying degrees all the characteristics of the highest monad, God, Who differs from them not only in being the highest of them but also in being able to create and destroy them. Autonomous and self-perpetuating, the monads nevertheless 'vary in perfec-tion like different representations or drawings in perspective of the same town seen from different points'. Hence, though they exercise 'physical action and passion' (i.e. outward force) on one another, none exercises 'metaphysical action or influence' (i.e. cause and effect) on another, 'and what we call causes are . . . only required as concomitants'. Hence no 'vulgar hypothesis of influence' or of 'occasional cause' is needed to explain the union of soul and body. Instead he propounded the hypothesis of concomitance: 'For God has from the beginning so fashioned soul as well as body . . . that from the first constitution or concept itself of either one, everything that happens in one corresponds perfectly to everything that happens in the other.'[35]

In an effort to explain how evil could exist in the Pre-established Harmony, Leibniz wrote an *Essai de théodicée* (1710) and *Principes de la nature et de la grace* (1714). He argued: 'All spirits . . . .entering by virtue of reason and of the eternal truths into a sort of society with God are members of the City of God, . . . where there is . . . as much virtue and happiness as is possible . . . because by virtue of the perfect order established in the universe, everything is done in the best possible way'; yet 'since God is infinite, he cannot be wholly known,' and 'therefore our happiness will never, and ought not, consist in full joy, where there would be nothing further to desire, rendering our mind stupid; but in a perpetual progress to new pleasures and to new perfections.'[36]

This theodicy was the Optimism which Christian Wolff (1679–1754) made into a more thoroughly anthropocentric philosophy and which Voltaire would make sport of in his *Candide* (1759). Wolff modified Leibniz's logic also in a geocentric direction. Leibniz had held that certain propositions are true because they can logically be reduced to identity with their definitions; these were for him universally 'necessary truths'. Other propositions rested in his philosophy upon 'sufficient reason'; they were 'contingent truths'— true enough, that is, though in an incomplete way, for the present world: anyone with sufficient knowledge could account for their being so and not otherwise. Wolff, however, obliterated the difference between necessary and contingent truth and tried to rationalize all truth into necessary truth. Several of his works were entitled *Vernünftige Gedanken von . . .* (*Rational Thoughts upon . . .*). Kant had Wolff (among others) in mind when he wrote his *Kritik der reinen Vernunft* (see Volume V). Incidentally, like Leibniz, Wolff was greatly interested in Chinese thought.

*   *   *

Indifferentism and Deism

All of this speculation on the nature of cause and reason was going on concomitantly with 'the scientific revolution', which we shall describe in Chapters XIII–XV. As we shall then see, the scientists from Copernicus to Lavoisier, even though they rarely intended to question the foundations of religious faith, raised considerable doubt about the literal interpretation of certain passages in scripture, the reliability of Aristotle's physics, the probability of miracles, and the plausibility of other parts of the Christian credo. At the same time, students of philology and history, like Erasmus and the authors of the *Magdeburg Centuries* (see Chapter IX), were querying the credibility, sometimes the very authenticity, of at least parts of significant pieces of Catholic literature. And Protestant scholars were making the Bible so accessible in the numerous vernaculars that any reader might interpret it for himself, with the consequence that Protestant sects split into so many different fragments that the differences among them appeared sometimes picayune and often confusing to outsiders. Meanwhile explorers and missionaries had made the Christian world aware of highly advanced peoples who lived by venerable ethical codes and righteous concepts of Heaven but who knew nothing of Revelation. More's *Utopia*, Campanella's *Civitas Solis* (1613), and several later works of the same genre revealed the readiness of pious minds at least to idealize for rhetorical effect and perhaps to respect, even to envy, such exotic cultures.

The result of the concurrence of these intellectual developments was rarely complete disbelief by the Europeans in the Judeo-Christian story. Rather it was a widening of the spirit of adiaphorism—a feeling that differences in dogma or ritual were unimportant and that therefore no church should have the power to force its creed upon others or induce governments to do so. The contemporary rise of rationalism led, instead, to the belief that a 'natural religion' could count on man's innate sense of right and wrong for moral conduct and genuine piety.

To the champions of established churches and of the several orthodoxies such indifferentism was shocking, and they seldom hesitated to call it 'atheism'. Though the Pyrrhonic *De Immortalitate Animae* (1516) of Pomponazzi was burned, he himself was spared. His pupil Lucilio Vanini (1585–1619) was less fortunate. He was actually tried and found guilty of atheism (though his books reveal, rather, a pantheistic view) and was sentenced to have his tongue cut out and to be strangled at the stake. Often, too, the offended believer called the unorthodox 'libertines'; and we have seen (Chapter IV) how wretchedly Théophile de Viau and Le Petit fared under such a charge.

Indifferentism nevertheless spread, and in the late seventeenth and the eighteenth centuries a brand known as Deism (or, at first, also Theism) won particular prominence. While Deism found early exponents on the Continent, too, it reached maturity in England after the Civil War—the very war that had produced Fifth Monarchy Men and other millenarians, who based their chiliasm upon a literal interpretation of the Bible (see Chapter IX). Deism, because of its very premises, never became an organized movement or created a unified church; some of its adherents never formally left their respective established churches. Some of them believed in the immortality of the soul, which would be punished or rewarded in a hereafter; others carried free thought so far as to come fairly close to atheism. Despite these divergences they all held in common a belief in a First Cause that had set the universe agoing in accordance with universal laws though It subsequently remained relatively indifferent to the ways of man and was inexorable to prayers or ritual, faith or good works.

This common belief made them all antagonists of organized churches. The English philosopher Herbert of Cherbury (1583–1648), the so-called 'father of Deism', believed, with Descartes, that knowledge of God was innate. Upon that knowledge, he concluded, a 'natural religion', more acceptable than the traditional ones, could be based. The Earl of Shaftesbury (1671–1713) argued that morality, like the sense of beauty, was inborn, and that the highest forms of religion needed no theology or church. Other leading Deists were more direct in their attack upon the Christian church. Matthew Tindal (1656–1733) in *Christianity As Old as Creation* (1730) maintained that the validity of the Christian religion lay in its being, and only in so far as it was, an explicit statement of natural religion. John Toland (1670–1722) in *Christianity Not Mysterious* (1696) and other works undertook to divest it of its mysteries and contradictions, leaving a comprehensible and rational residue. Other Deists, with varying degrees of scholarship in comparative theology and history and of persuasiveness in rhetoric and logic, attacked various parts of what they considered the Christian myth. Viscount Bolingbroke (1678–1751) went so far as to suggest (but posthumously) that church organizations were contrived by the clever only for the purpose of keeping the ignorant in subjection.

French Deism had its native seventeenth-century roots, and it was fortified in the eighteenth-century Enlightenment from England. Voltaire and Rousseau were the most prominent among its proponents. Voltaire found it, and particularly the more cynical brand of Bolingbroke, well suited to his own resentment of ecclesiastical power and intolerance and, after his sojourn in England (1726–29), went on to attack the church, particularly the French Catholic Church, as the chief enemy of enlightenment—witness his *Essais sur les Moeurs* (1756)—and to preach the necessity of 'crushing the infamous thing' ('*Ecrasez l'infame!*') along with all other brands of obscurantism. Rousseau's Savoyard Vicar (see Chapter XVI), though much more of a

Christian than Voltaire, nevertheless propounded in *Émile* (1762) a natural religion without church or clergy. Denis Diderot (1713–84) was so little theist that, without complete justification, he was considered an atheist even by some of his more objective contemporaries. Elsewhere in Europe than England and France the influence of Deism was less marked but none the less familiar in high places. Lessing's pleas for tolerance and the educational theories of Basedow (see Chapter XVI) were perhaps due to both men's acceptance of a similar persuasion. In America outstanding leaders of public opinion—notably Franklin, Jefferson, and the international insurgent Thomas Paine—avowedly believed in a God who needed no church or clergy to rule the universe by ascertainable, even self-evident, laws of nature and natural rights of man.

★   ★   ★

The Rise of Materialism and Mechanism

Until the 1730's Cartesian rationalism, with its dualistic emphasis upon innate ideas, and Cartesian science were in almost unquestioned dominance of the Continent. The empirical naturalism of Locke and Newton, however, was popularized from the 1730's on by Voltaire and others. In 1734 the annual prize of the French Academy of Sciences was divided between Johann Bernoulli and his son Daniel, the older man defending the Cartesian system and the younger the Newtonian one. After 1740 no Cartesian won the prize again. In the 1740's Condillac actually went farther than Locke in the direction of monistic sensationalism by imaginatively creating a hypothetical mind within a statue, endowing it with each of the senses in turn. Diderot reinforced the sensationalist argument by his *Letter on the Blind* (1745) and *Letter on Deaf Mutes* (1751); reversing the procedure of Condillac, he both empirically and imaginatively inquired what the effects on the mind might be if human beings were deprived of any of their senses. Maupertuis in his *Accord des différentes lois de la nature* (1744), noting the efficiency with which the universe seemed to operate, propounded the Principle of Least Action: within a dynamic system unaffected by outside forces change takes place only with the least possible value of a mathematical expression of the energy involved, which is known as the 'action'. Expressed in theistic terms (as Maupertuis did express it), this meant that God chose the simplest means to achieve his ends. That principle, while well in keeping with the Neoplatonic concept of the plenitude of God and with the Leibnizian concept of a Pre-established Harmony, was not incompatible with the Deistic concept of God as the efficient clockmaker.

At the end of the seventeenth and the beginning of the eighteenth century, the work of Leeuwenhoek, Bonnet, Trembley, and other microbiologists (see Chapter XIV) seemed to provide proof of a close relationship among the various forms of life. Their readiness to accept such a conclusion had a disturbing effect upon Europe's philosophers. Maupertius' Principle of

Least Action, broadly interpreted, was sufficient perhaps to explain a life history which seemed to have begun with forms so simple as to be almost indistinguishable from inanimate matter and in which some plant forms could easily be confused with animal forms. But what if this process should still be going on? What if, along with the kind of 'perfection' that Leibniz envisaged (which contemplated reaching toward the harmony of God) or that Bacon envisaged (which contemplated a steady accumulation of knowledge) or that the Abbé de St Pierre envisaged (which contemplated a studied improvement of men's institutions), a continuous and undesigned perfectibility of man's physiological and even psychological nature were also possible? And what if the perfectibility of man were, whether by the original plan of God or no, now due merely to the contingencies of nature?

Before 1775 no one had yet fully formulated a notion of biological evolution, but in the middle of the eighteenth century several had begun to query whether in fact God had created man and the other living things whole and by a single act. Julien Offray de Lamettrie argued almost atheistically in *L'homme machine* (1747), *L'homme plante* (1748), and *Systeme d'Epicure* (1750) that the Cartesian distinction between man and lower forms of life (because man alone has a soul while lower forms are but machines) was false, for, Lamettrie claimed, man's mind, a mere function of his brain, dies when his body dies, his soul is not immortal, and God is an unnecessary hypothesis. In 1748 Benoit de Maillet's *Telliamed* (the title is the author's name spelled backward) cast doubt upon the Biblical account of Creation with his suggestion that every land animal has a marine prototype. In 1749, Comte de Buffon (1707–88) published the first three volumes of his *Histoire Naturelle*, reinforcing the belief that a sort of vitalism ruled the world of life and enabled it to dispense with God as First Cause. In remote Massachusetts Cadwallader Colden argued (in *The Principles of Action in Matter*, 1751) that ether was the universal substance and that matter was only sublimated force, and mind only spiritualized matter. In 1754 the French version of Maupertuis' *Système de la nature* (first published as *Dissertatio Inauguralis Metaphysica* in 1751) queried whether 'the multiplication of the most dissimilar species might have resulted from two single individuals'.[37] And in the next decade Jean Battiste Robinet's *De la nature* (1763) and *Considérations philosophiques sur la gradation naturelle des formes de l'être* (1767) presented a theory of an eternally continuous process of Creation.

In 1751 the first volume of Diderot's *Encyclopédie* had appeared. Its formal title was *Dictionnaire raisonné, etc.*, and the reasoning, D'Alembert indicated in the *Discours préliminaire*, would be along the empirical lines laid down by Bacon and not along the rationalist lines of Descartes. Several of its articles spoke of the possibility that lower forms of life had given rise to the higher ones. Diderot in a number of other works, some not published during his lifetime, moved steadily toward a theory of a dynamic life force that enabled organisms to evolve in response to their organic needs.

By that time materialism had left behind almost all pretence of theism. The *Testament* of the Abbé Jean Meslier (1664–1729) was one of the most widely read of the numerous manuscripts that circulated clandestinely in France in order to avoid the censorship authorities; it attacked all religion as false and all churches as impostures and denied even the Deists' premise of a First Cause. Although Baron d'Holbach was careful to observe the Catholic forms in private life, he psuedonymously (in 1770), wrote a *Système de la nature* that is sometimes called 'the Bible of Atheism'. The fundamental stuff of the cosmos, Holbach contended, is materialistic and mechanistic— matter and motion. Soul was to Holbach synonymous with brain, and thought with imperceptible motions in the brain; God was synonymous with the natural order operating in accordance with natural law; man was not free in will, and morality should be but the prescriptions of the state or society to protect itself and its members from injury and to achieve their maximum happiness. Helvétius in *De l'esprit* (1758) and *De l'homme* (1773–74) set forth a strictly sensationalist psychology from which he derived the same kind of utilitarian explanation of morality. The moral sense must be based, he held, upon the desire to avoid pain and to incur pleasure; since esteem is pleasant and contempt is painful, the business of government, which has no purpose other than to advance the happiness of the greatest number, is to provide a system of education and of rewards and punishments that will make bad conduct painful or ill-esteemed and duty pleasant.

Goethe declared that his revulsion upon reading Holbach's *Système de la nature* drove him into the Sturm-und-Drang movement. Several *philosophes* (Diderot, in the posthumously published *Neveu de Rameau*, for example) had been profoundly disturbed by the question why men should be moral if the soul was mortal, and Rousseau had earlier broken with the *philosophes* because of his insistence upon the religious basis for morality. From agreement with Rousseau and Hume on the inadequacy of the empirical method no less than from disagreement with Wolff on the sufficiency of the rationalist method, Kant was moved to examine the limitations of human reason (see Volume V) and to propound his conclusions on the necessity for faith.

NOTES TO CHAPTER VII

1. Dasgupta, *op. cit.*, III, pp. 471–2.
2. A. B. Keith, *A History of Sanskrit Literature* (Oxford, 1928), p. 473.
3. M. Hiriyanna, *Outlines of Indian Philosophy* (London, 1932), p. 302.
4. Dasgupta, II, pp. 221 and 224.
5. Madhva is often considered a radical 'pluralist'. His thought, however, remains difficult to penetrate. It is to be hoped that more light may be forthcoming in an important work now in preparation. (Oliver Lacombe.)

6. In Professor O. Lacombe's opinion, this section has the advantage of stimulating the reader to reflection. Particularly interesting is the contrast between the 'middle way' of Wang Yang-ming in which the best of the multiple Chinese traditions is once more found, and the unbalance which ensued. Many of the great themes of the history of human thought are evoked in the course of these pages: quietism, the goodness or wickedness of human nature, the role of spontaneity, of virtuous discipline, etc.

7. Wang's Complete Works, quoted in H. G. Creel, *Chinese Thought from Confucius to Mao Tsê-tung* (Chicago, 1953), p. 214.

8. This quotation is adapted from the translation given in Fung Yu-lan, *op. cit.*, II, p. 599 and in Fung Yu-lan and Derk Bodde, *A Short History of Chinese Philosophy* (New York, 1948), pp. 310–13.

9. Fung Yu-lan, II, pp. 613–14.

10. Heinrich Busch, *loc. cit.*, pp. 81–3, 86 and 89.

11. Chan Wing-tsit, *Historical Charts of Chinese Philosophy* (New Haven, 1955), chart 5.

12. Busch, *loc. cit.*, pp. 130–31.

13. Adapted from the translation given in Fung Yu-lan, II, pp. 641–42.

14. *Ibid.*, p. 645.

15. Quoted in Creel, p. 222.

16. *Ibid.*, p. 228.

17. Quoted *ibid.*, pp. 230–31.

18. Feng Chao-yang's article on Tai Chen in Arthur W. Hummel, *Eminent Chinese of the Ch'ing Period* (Washington, 1944), II, p. 699.

19. Quoted in Fung Yu-lan, II, p. 654.

20. Quoted in Creel, p. 231.

21. R. C. Armstrong, *Light from the East. Studies in Japanese Confucianism* (Toronto, 1914), p. 138.

22. Professor O. Lacombe, however, wonders to what extent did Montaigne's philosophic scepticism affect the orthodoxy of the Catholic faith which he professed? He suggests that the question seems far from having been resolved in the direction the text appears to indicate.

23. Georgio de Santillana, *The Crime of Galileo* (Chicago, 1955), pp. 311–12 and 322–23.

24. R. Hooykaas, 'Science and Reformation', *Journal of World History*, III, no. 1 (1956).

25. For a lengthy list arranged according to fields of study, see François Russo, 'Role respectif du Catholicisme et du Protestantisme dans le développement des sciences aux XVIe et XVIIe siècles', *ibid.*, no. 4 (1957), pp. 854–80.

26. *Institutes*, III, 2, no. 15, quoted in Hooykaas, *loc. cit.*, p. 128.

27. Quoted in F. H. Anderson, *The Philosophy of Francis Bacon* (Chicago, 1948), pp. 81–2.

28. *Novum Organum*, Book I, Aphorisms 3, 4, and 19.

29. 'Mr. Bacon in Praise of Knowledge,' quoted in James Spedding, *The Letters and the Life of Francis Bacon* (London, 1861), I, p. 123.

30. On this point see Alexander Koyré, 'Influence of Philosophic Trends on the Formulation of Scientific Theories', *Scientific Monthly*, LXXX (1955), pp. 107–11.

31. Book II, Ch. I, p. 2.

32. Professor O. Lacombe raises the question why, in the above pages less than a single one is devoted to the founder of a tradition which still numbers many devotees, whereas his principle disciples, Spinoza and Leibniz, receive more extensive treatment. Without displaying undue partiality for Descartes—one could wish the following points had been treated here: (1) the unity of soul and body, by means of which Descartes seeks to counterbalance his dualism, and (2) the voluntarist aspect of the doctrine and his theory of divine liberty, of which far from negligeable traces are to be found in certain forms of contem-

porary existentialism, their atheistic humanism notwithstanding; and (3) it should also be recalled that, despite his ambition to reconstruct philosophy without reference to its past history, Descartes remains to some extent indebted to scholastic tradition.

The authors wish to indicate that they deal with Descartes, as well as with Spinoza and Leibniz, at some length in several other contexts.

33. Quoted in A. Wolf, *The History of Science, Technology and Philosophy in the 16th and 17th Centuries* (New York, 1935), p. 666.

34. 'A Letter of Leibnitz on His Philosophical Hypothesis . . .' (1696) in T. V. Smith and Marjorie Greene, *From Descartes to Kant, Readings in the Philosophy of the Renaissance and Enlightenment* (Chicago, 1940), p. 344 n.

35. *Opuscules et fragments inédits de Leibniz*, ed. by Louis Couturat (Paris, 1903), quoted *ibid.*, p. 343. See Leibniz *Monadology*, para. 51.

36. *The Philosophical Works of Leibnitz*, tr. by George Martin Duncan (New Haven, Conn., 1890), quoted in Smith and Greene, pp. 368–69.

37. Quoted in Lester G. Crocker, 'Diderot and Eighteenth Century French Transformism' *Forerunners of Darwin: 1745–1859*, ed. Bentley Glass, Owsei Temkin and William L. Straus, Jr. (Baltimore, 1959), p. 127. See also Arthur O. Lovejoy, *The Great Chain of Being* (Cambridge, Mass., 1936), pp. 227–87; R. R. Palmer, *Catholics and Unbelievers in Eighteenth Century France* (Princeton, 1939), pp. 157–77; and Preserved Smith, *A History of Modern Culture*, Vol. II, *The Enlightenment, 1687–1776* (New York, 1934), pp. 187–88.

CHAPTER VIII

POLITICAL AND SOCIAL THOUGHT AND PRACTICE
(c. 1300–c. 1500)

POLITICAL THEORY AND PRACTICE

The Rise of Political Philosophy in Europe

ONE of the most striking characteristics of modern political structure is the sovereign national state. Such a concept was barely recognized in the Middle Ages of western Europe, where pope and emperor claimed dominion in the respective fields of spiritual and temporal matters. In fact, the intellectual spirit of the early Middle Ages had been favourable to no autocracy but theocracy. Until the struggle between church and state came out in the open, the accepted theocratic ruler on earth was the pope, 'servant of the servants of God'. The line of command, according to ecclesiastical theory, was from God by way of the pope (His vicar on earth) to the clergy for spiritual affairs and to emperor, kings, and nobles for temporal affairs.

When the emperors sought to free themselves from papal authority, they resorted to the doctrine of their God-given right to serve as His vicar in temporal affairs. That is, they sought to change the line of command by moving themselves up to a position of equality with the pope, so that God's will in temporal affairs might be assumed to pass from Him to an emperor directly and not by way of the pope. Medieval artists sometimes depicted either Christ simultaneously handing the keys of Heaven to Peter and the standard of the cross to Emperor Constantine or Peter handing the stole to Pope Leo and the standard to Emperor Charlemagne. For all that, at no time in the Middle Ages had temporal autocracy been effectively based on the premise of the divine right of kings.

Nevertheless, the concept of the divine right of kings persisted. Jesus's words, 'Render under Caesar the things that are Caesar's' and the exhortations to obedience by Peter (I Peter 2:13-17) and Paul (Romans 13:1-7 and Titus 3:1), especially the reminder that 'the powers that be are ordained of God' (Romans 13:1), often were quoted, though usually with a disclaimer to the effect that such injunctions did not apply to tyrants. In the fourteenth century, this general line of reasoning won the support of Wycliffe, who in some passages went so far as to assert that man because of his sinful nature must as a Christian duty submit even to tyranny, since the ruler, right or wrong, is God's vicar. A century later, Pope Pius II reiterated the divine-right theory. But not until the sixteenth century was the doctrine widely accepted full-fledged that Christians were bound to obey their rulers absolutely because they were the representatives of God on earth.[1]

If the theory of divine right of kings had to wait longer for full expression, late-medieval scholars found other arguments in favour of autocracy. They found them in Roman law and history. After the revival of Roman civil law (see Volume III), monarchs began to employ as advisers lawyers trained at Bologna and other Italian centres of Roman law. When Philip IV of France clashed with Boniface VIII at the end of the thirteenth century, he had to find some legal justification for his defiance of God's vicar on earth. He used civil lawyers such as Pierre Flotte and Nogaret to formulate and implement his anti-papal propaganda. In a treatise entitled *De Utraque Potestate*, one of Philip's lawyers drew also on ancient history to provide an independent, pre-papal origin for the French monarchy and its royal authority. Another French legalist, Jean de Jandun, argued that whereas God had only one vicar for spiritual affairs (the pope), for temporal affairs He had to have several, including the king of France as well as the emperor. Still another French publicist, Pierre Dubois, in *Supplication. . . . contre le pape Boniface* (1304) asserted the king's right to use force against corrupt popes for the public welfare. Thus Philip's political exigencies, hastening the literary articulation of certain secular views of law, history, and logic, added to their effectiveness in undermining theocratic ideology.

In Italy at this time the interminable conflict of popes and emperors, of Guelfs and Ghibellines, of despots and cities led to a similar secularization of political philosophy. Looking forward to a day of universal peace and justice, Dante in *De Monarchia* cited Roman imperial history, the Bible, Aristotle, Cicero, Aquinas, and other authorities in support of the emperor's right to head a universal empire. Dante claimed that, like the ancient Roman Empire, an ideal universal empire would be in accordance with God's will and should be independent of the papacy. A little later, another Italian, the Pavian lawyer Bartolus de Sassoferrato (1314–57), analysed monarchical government in a more objective fashion. Also citing Christian scripture, classical and Thomist authority, and Roman history and law, he concluded that whereas small states (especially city states) can best be governed by the entire citizenry or by selected representatives, large states need monarchs. For example, he argued, when Rome became an empire it replaced its multiple executive with a single emperor. Since a good monarch's authority was God-given, he had the power to collect taxes, make laws, and engage in other operations necessary for the administration of the state. But even a monarch was subject to limitations: he had no right to deprive individuals of their property unjustly or to serve his own selfish ends, for rulers who exercise power for their own advantage are tyrants, and tyranny is a corruption of government.

Bartolus and other legalists of the period frankly debated the justice of tyrannicide. Some boldly favoured it; others urged caution. In a treatise entitled *De Tyranno*, Bartolus openly asserted that tyrants might be not only resisted and deposed but even killed. The Florentine statesman Coluccio Salutati (1331–1406), although he concurred in the opinion that to kill a tyrant was honourable, urged caution, citing the precedent of Brutus and Cassius; they had killed Julius Caesar unlawfully, he thought, and had justly been relegated to Hell as traitors in Dante's *Divine Comedy*. In a still more cautious vein one of Bartolus' contemporaries argued that a tyrant might not even be deposed legally. The assassination of Louis of Orleans (1407) as a tyrant (see Chapter III) was approved by a French court though tyrannicide was condemned in principle by the Council of Constance.

In time the tendency to defend temporal autocracy increased. Unconditional defence of it was prevalent especially among civil lawyers, naturally intent upon the independence of civil courts and civil law from church courts and canon law. A number of lawyers argued that the people of ancient Rome had irrevocably granted absolute power to their emperors and that when the Roman Empire disintegrated, this power had passed to their successors, the German emperors. Some even asserted that the monarch's will was law and above all other sources of law within his realm. Although it was generally recognized that rulers must not contravene religious and natural law, civil lawyers stressed the practical importance of the state and of strong rulers. Thus the medieval ideal of the king as an agent of God, pope, and people for the fulfilment of the divine purpose slowly gave way to a concept of temporal autocracy. In the process the Thomist ideology of theocracy was steadily undermined. Legalistic politicians might pay lip service to natural law but were inclined to give it a secular, statist interpretation that favoured autocracy. The ideas of these civil legalists paved the way eventually for Luther's support of autocracy as a Christian dogma.

In Italy the growth of an autocratic ideology came less from religious considerations than from political necessity. As despots increased in numbers in the late-fifteenth and the early-sixteenth century, the defence of autocracy became proportionately intense. After the triumph of the revived papacy over the councils, this autocratic trend became unmistakeable. *The Discourses* and *The Prince* of Niccolo Machiavelli (1469–1527), although they reflected his hard-headed reaction to the realistic and frankly cynical quality of the war-torn, conspiratorial politics of his day rather than ambition, ruthlessness, or any other personal characteristic of his own, gave to political philosophy the term 'Machiavellian'. He stands out not only for the originality of his ideas but perhaps even more for the boldness of his exposition, a candid statement that contrasted vividly with the cant and hypocrisy of his day. He proposed, he said in dedicating *The Prince* to Lorenzo the Magnificent, to do for politics what the painter of his day was doing for landscape art—to examine the scene from a good vantage so as to depict the nature of his subject appropriately. As the son of a lawyer, he had learned the practical side of government in the hard school of experience. He had also acquired the humanists' deference to Classical example; the political philosophy of his *Discourses* is based largely on Livy's *History of Rome*. *The Prince*, more famous though merely a by-product, vividly expounded his belief in statism and autocracy as a practicable system of government. With a toughness that shocks modern readers, he stripped the rationale based upon Aristotelian, Christian, and Roman principles from the accepted princely stereotype, leaving the prince little more than a personification of the empirical precept, derived from contemporary Italian wars and turmoil, that might and cunning make right.

Yet Machiavelli was no mere cold-hearted realist. He upheld the ideal of the strong and wise prince who assumes responsibility as he takes power, who protects his subjects against themselves and considers it a duty to use all possible measures for the preservation of law and order. In several pious passages, Machiavelli presented religious faith as a constructive force in government. Man's susceptibility to religion, he proposed, should be encouraged as a means of preventing the disintegration of the state, whether in a republic or in an autocracy. He even lauded republicanism, though he thought it an impractical ideal for contemporary Italy. Beneath the hard surface of his authoritarian programme burned the patriotism of one who was prepared to make great sacrifices of principle for Italian unity and peace, which, for practical purposes and under existing circumstances, seemed to him to require absolute control of the state by the prince.[2]

For sheer realism unrelieved by deference to ethical principles, Machiavelli's contemporary and friend Francesco Guicciardini (1483–1540) surpassed him in both action and theory. As statesman and diplomat Guicciardini practised the cynical 'virtues' with far more consistency than Machiavelli. Although his preferred form of government was aristocracy and he despised the clergy, he served Medici and papal despots throughout most of his public career. In his two histories (of Florence and of Italy) and his political writings (which included a commentary on Machiavelli's *Discourses*) he presented more coldly objective analyses of government and power politics than any of his contemporaries. His estimate of human character was low, and his own private career helped to justify his estimate. Self-interest was for him the chief motive of human beings, and the quest for power the chief impulse of nations. Among the first to write the history of Italy as one people, he was also among the first to speak of a 'balance of power' as a means of preserving a semblance of peace. Better than Machiavelli's, Guicciardini's political theory reflected the disunity, civic unrest, and private demoralization of the Italy of their day.

*   *   *

The Debate on the Limitations of Authority

Unlike Italy, several other states of Europe (see Chapter I) emerged during this period as unified, dynastic realms, England, Spain, France, and Russia being the outstanding examples. The rise of Russia as a huge unified auto-cracy in some ways, despite its peculiar circumstances, illustrates the contemporary process of centralization of governmental power. Practical conditions rather than Machiavellian theories accounted for the central-ization of Russia (as well as of the other above-designated states), and, in addition, its princes—particularly those of Moscow—showed that they were capable of heroic leadership. As Russia recovered from the Tatar ravages and began to struggle in the common cause against the hated alien yoke, its separate rulers tightened their economic and political bonds. Its urban population too, growing in number, power, and prestige, took part in the drama of centralization, playing a particularly prominent role, celebrated in several chronicles and folktales, in an uprising against the Tatar regent (1327). By the end of the fourteenth century Dimitri Donskoi, having behind him the combined strength of several dependent, semi-dependent, and allied states of north-eastern Russia, was able to defeat the once invincible Golden Horde on Kulikovo Plain (see Chapter I). The Russians now had not only a common cause but also a common tradition, almost indispensable factors in unifying a people. In the next century, despite the enmity of the Tatars, Poland, and Lithuania, Dimitri's successors conquered vast stretches to the west, north, and east. As in other centralizing monarchies, all other com-petitors for leadership were overwhelmed—among them the wealthy com-mercial empire of the city-state Novgorod and the powerful principality of Tver—and the prestige of Moscow's major rivals as capital cities was now systematically undermined. After 1480 tribute was refused to the Golden Horde. By 1500 Russia, unlike Italy, was far from a mere geographical expression; among the titles that the Grand Duke Ivan III (the Great) claimed were *samoderzshets* (autocrat) and *gosudar* (sovereign) of all Russia. The cost of Russia's unification was paid not only by the feudal princes, now weakened, and the boyar officialdom, now dependent on the ruler's good will, but also by the peasants, now more thoroughly subjected to their lords. Yet unification had the support of many merchants, artisans, and other town dwellers, and Russia's writers began to talk of Moscow as 'the third Rome'.

Although in Europe absolutism was becoming more firmly entrenched on nearly all sides, it met with a stern opposition. The nobility, following the feudal tradition so well exemplified in the English Magna Carta, as a general rule did not willingly surrender their ancient rights. Even where kings such as Edward I of England and Philip IV of France initiated no new policy but engaged only in furthering the institutions of dynastic control that were already strong when they had inherited them, the aristocratic families defied them and carried on intermittent feudal wars. The clergy likewise, despite periods of ineffective papal leadership such as that of the Avignon papacy and the Schism, resisted royal encroachments on their rights and properties. The burgher element of the third estate, though usually inclined to ally with the king against the nobility, were by no means disinclined on occasion to form alliances with it in order to resist royal encroachments. In the Holy Roman Empire, Bohemia, Hungary, and Poland, where the rulers were elected and, in several notable instances, also were foreigners more interested in promoting their dynastic ambitions than in perfecting internal administration, the nobles were able to obtain Golden Bulls or other charters and concessions from the crown in return for their support. English Parliaments, French Estates, German Electors, Spanish Cortes, and Polish Sejm and Sejmiki during the fourteenth and fifteenth centuries at times displayed a readiness to oppose autocracy actively. Wherever parliamentary or quasi-parliamentary institutions arose, representatives of at least the higher estates claimed and exerted special rights in taxation, tariffs, elections, appointments of ministers, or other governmental affairs.

The theory behind this sort of check upon absolutism was the medieval principle of popular sovereignty, which the theologian Aquinas and the jurist Bracton had set forth in the thirteenth century. Sovereignty, they had said, comes from God and is vested in the people, who delegate it to their rulers; the rulers are not masters but are the subjects of God and law; and if rulers become tyrannical, the people have the right to overthrow them in an orderly and legal manner. Around 1300 this idea, with minor modifications, was well known to Europe's political theorists. In England the works known as *Fleta, The Mirror of Justice,* and *The Method of Holding Parliament* asserted the king's subservience to law and stressed the authority of the people, through the members of the *curia,* to enforce the law if the king transgressed it. For further guaranty of the public welfare, the king was bound by a coronation oath. Some even asserted that parliaments should be held twice a year, not only for granting aids but also for presenting petitions to which the king must give consideration.

Two English kings (Edward II in 1327 and Richard II in 1399) were in fact deposed by Parliament during this period. While fundamentally the conflicts that led to their downfall were the consequence of the rivalry among contemporary noble families and personages for power and the royal ermine, they reflected also a marked degree of popular unrest. Despite Wycliffe's assertion of the duty of Christians to obey their rulers, some of the Lollards, his followers, though primarily concerned with reform of ritual and clerical extravagance, had no trouble finding in his writings justification for condemnation of and rebellion against a sinful king who violated law. Richard II successfully mastered the Peasants' Revolt under Wat Tyler (see Chapter III), but his treachery and ruthlessness in so doing and his other transgressions on the rights of the *populus* account, in part at least, for his ultimate doom. The Lollards approved the open resistance of their new leader, Sir John Oldcastle, to the authority of both church and state. They were persecuted as heretics and condemned by parliamentary statute; Oldcastle was hanged and burned (1417); but the movement survived despite persecution.

A popular uprising in France during this period was rooted almost entirely in political and economic considerations divorced from religion. This was the revolt of Paris under the leadership of its political head (*prévot des marchands*), Etienne Marcel. The defeats of France in the Hundred Years' War not only depleted the ranks of the nobility but required the dauphin (the future King Charles V, acting as regent during the captivity of his father) to raise large sums of money. Both contingencies played into the hands of the middle class. Under Marcel's guidance they exploited their advantages, demanding concessions in return for continued financial support of the war, and the concessions were made in a statute known as the *Great Ordinance* (*Grande Ordonnance*). Unlike earlier royal charters, the Great Ordinance was no mere set of restrictions on the king's power but rather a statement of requirements for good government, and it vested temporary political power in a commission representing all three estates of the realm, commoners as well as clergy and nobles. Power, however, gradually passed to the middle class of Paris and to Marcel, who claimed to represent 'the will of the people'. He also supported and in turn received support from the peasantry, who rose in numerous *jacqueries*.

Marcel exercised his power for only a brief period (1356–58) before he was killed by an opposing faction acting on mere suspicion that he was engaged in treasonable dealings with the English and out of a deep resentment of his espousal of the peasant cause. His death marked the end of this effort to rule France through an Estates General dominated by the Third Estate. The Great Ordinance was repudiated by the captive king in London, and nothing came of Marcel's brief dictatorship save a precedent and the legend of Etienne Marcel as a leader of the people. Contemporary literature reverberated with popular complaints. A French treatise (*Songe du Verger*), though addressed to King Charles V, suggested the principle of popular sovereignty as a corrective of unjust royal levies: the king had the right to extraordinary taxes only for a just cause such as the defence of the realm; if he misapplied revenues he might be deposed. Similar opinions were expressed by contemporary philosophers like Jean Gerson and Pierre d'Ailly.

In Germany likewise the limitation of the royal prerogative was debated. In a treatise (*De Jure Regni et Imperii Romani*), written about 1338, Luipold Bebenburg discussed at length the electoral right of the people. He maintained that, as in the ancient Roman Empire so also in the Holy Roman Empire, the electors represented the *universitas* of the princes and the people. At the close of the fourteenth century, Emperor Wenceslaus was actually deposed by some of the German electors (a small and select body, to be sure, but yet with some claim to represent the whole empire) for his failure to govern in the public interest. Later, Nicholas of Cusa entered the argument; deriving the origin of governments from natural law, he contended that all political authority was based on popular consent.[3]

Perhaps the strongest statement of the theory of popular sovereignty during this period came from the pen of Marsilius of Padua (possibly with the collaboration of Jean de Jandun). His *Defensor Pacis* (*c.* 1324), like the political works of Dante, Petrarch, and other Italians, was coloured by resentment of papalism, and his major theme was the need to keep the peace despite the warmongers, notably popes and emperors. He applied the Thomist formula to the definition of sovereignty, contending that sovereignty extended from God to the people and from them to their government, which, he felt, should remain responsible to them. His *people*, however, were not the *demos* but rather those typified by the bourgeoisie of Italian cities like his native Padua. Using the term *principans* (*one serving as prince*) to denote a ruler, he stressed the view that the collective citizenry (*civium universitas*) had the right to elect and control a ruler. In case the executive transgressed his delegated powers, the people either as a whole or through its upper-class representatives, its better (*valentior*) part, might depose him. He clearly described the representative-legislator as superior to the *principans*, or executive.

Since the *Defensor Pacis* was dedicated to the emperor-designate Ludwig of Bavaria, sworn enemy of the Avignon papacy, Marsilius' programme was perhaps meant to apply more to the popes than to the temporal autocrats. It portrayed the papacy and clergy rather than emperors and princes as the chief offenders against peace, on the ground that the churchmen were the aggressors, encroaching on the jurisdiction of the secular rulers. His proposal for the solution of this clerical transgression was to subject the church to the state (anticipating Wycliffe, Huss, and Luther in this view). His plea in favour of limiting papal powers was forceful. A forerunner of a philosophy that was to become prominent during the period of the Schism and the Councils, he argued that councils rather than popes were the supreme ecclesiastical authority, for councils were representative of the people, both lay and clerical, and should be convoked by the emperor rather than by the pope.[4]

The impact of Marsilius's ideas was due not so much to their originality as to their direct application to the stormy problem of papal government. His practical approach to the threatening political crisis helped to provide a philosophical justification for its removal from the realm of abstraction to the realm of action. Public response to Marsilius' work was prompt and vigorous. The *Defender of the Peace* was translated into the vernacular; it was attacked by some but also, especially at Ludwig's court, championed. This and his other works, along with those of Jean de Jandun, were exploited for arguments in later polemics, especially against the popes of the Renaissance and the Reformation.

Some fourteenth-century writers, of course, questioned the concept of popular sovereignty. William of Ockham was certainly less liberal and perhaps more objective as a reporter of current views than Marsilius. Though also a protégé of Ludwig of Bavaria, William of Ockham presented the argument,

Scholastic in form, nominalistic in philosophy, that any type of universal empire, whether temporal or spiritual, was apparently a violation of reality (nature),5 to which all concepts of sovereignty, popular or other, must bow. This idea was more explicit in Wycliffe, who, as we know, doubted that the people should exercise authority over God's vicar in the person of their monarch. Nevertheless, the Marsilian view persisted in the political theory of western Christendom—the view that the sovereign authority of the people was not only the original source of political power but also a continuing force in government. Those who favoured this view held that during an interregnum or a breakdown of established government authority reverted to the people as a whole. Some writers upheld a theory of contractual relationship between people and ruler and stressed the importance of election as a means of controlling monarchs (see Chapter IX).

Despite prominent exceptions, however, from Aquinas' to comparatively recent times little doubt existed that, except in certain limited areas, the best form of government was some form of effective monarchy. In the sixteenth century, the practical tone that prevailed in Italian political theory tended to justify the autocracy of the Italian 'despot' rather than the republicanism of the city-state. Although Machiavelli admitted the hypothetical appeal of democracy and the superiority of the people as a whole to the nobility, he argued that, inasmuch as man by nature was deceitful, cruel, and corrupt, authoritarianism was a necessary evil. He held God and morality in abeyance, making the ruler responsible only to himself and the necessities of the state.6 Guicciardini, as behoved perhaps the keenest and most cynical mind of his day, recognized the power of the people but put no faith in them either in his own personal activities or in his political theorizing. For him 'the people is a monster, full of confusion and error'.

*   *   *

How Was Arbitrary Power to Be Resisted?

Yet all thinkers on the subject were inclined to favour some fundamental limitations to the power of the monarch.7 The question was: How and by whom was arbitrary royal power to be restricted? The papal claims to the right to do so, as formulated earlier by Pope Gregory VII and put into effect by Innocent III, carried little weight during the era of the Avignonese, Schismatic, and Renaissance popes, for society could hardly expect protection against royal autocracy from popes who themselves manifested marked autocratic tendencies. Furthermore, the papal claims had to compete with several other answers to the same problem. For the aristocracy, the prince was but *primus inter pares*, one who by some historic chance or method of selection had become foremost in fact among them but was no better by right than they and might be held in check by them, not only for their own but also for the people's defence against arbitrary behaviour. For the towns and cities the prince was often the source of privileges and rights, contained in charters of his granting, but he was also a potential threat that the burghers and guild members within their walled towns must resist if he repudiated royal concessions or made harsh demands. Burghers and nobles sometimes united in parliaments, estates, or cortes against the common danger of auto-cracy, and frequently the clergy was on their side, moved not only by humane considerations but also by their self-interest as a corporate body. Yet clergy, nobility, towns, and other corporate or quasi-corporate bodies or estates were on some matters as likely to be opposed to as to be united with each other against the prince's authority. When they were united they could claim to act in the name of the *universitas* or the *natio*. Future events were to render their united action increasingly feasible and so to make more acceptable the idea that the community (*universitas*) of the people was the arbiter of tyranny and the active agent for restraining it (see Chapter IX).

★   ★   ★

Medieval Republicanism

Before the nineteenth century the premise of popular sovereignty rarely was reduced to its logical extreme of republicanism and democracy. Popular sovereignty was in fact absent from government practice except in some Italian and German city-states, some Swiss cantons, and some Netherland provinces, and even in those instances it took the form of aristocratic repub-licanism rather than popular representative government. The humanists' favourable attitude toward the republican form of government was derived from the Renaissance conception of the ancient Roman Republic (*Senatus Populusque Romanus*) and from the actual republics in the Italy of their day, such as Florence and Venice. None of the contemporary republics, however, was a true democracy. Their governments were dominated by groups of aristocrats and plutocrats, who often brought the leaders of the middle-class guilds into their organization. *A fortiori* in other political structures, it was taken for granted that, although according to natural and divine law the *populus* was the arbiter of the form of government, the sinfulness of at least some of the people required that the actual exercise of power be in the hands of either the *valentior pars* of the citizenry or a prince. Even when theorists differed as to whether the people's delegation of authority to a prince was permanent and whether or how a remedy was to be applied in case the delegated power was misused, popular sovereignty was more or less attenu-ated in theory, and in practice almost undetectable. Limitations on royal power, if at all applied, were applicable only by, and usually only for, the upper classes.

The theoretical *Respublica Christiana* of the medieval theologian was no genuine republic but a theocratic monarchy. The example of the Roman Republic, however, kept recurring to political theorists, especially during the centuries when Classical studies were revived and cultivated with an unprecedented and since unequalled enthusiasm. Although some writers like

Dante in *De Monarchia* concentrated attention on the Roman (and German) empires, others like Petrarch waxed enthusiastic over Ciceronian literature with its high-flown passages on the greatness of the Roman Republic. When the medieval citizens of Rome became dissatisfied with papal government, they were likely to turn to ancient Roman republicanism as a historical justification for rebellion. Rienzi as 'dictator' and 'tribune', clad in a senatorial toga, made a vain effort to revive the *Senatus Populusque Romanus*, using its emblems, and proclaimed himself 'illustrious redeemer of the Holy Roman Republic'. Petrarch's pen worked overtime to rouse 'the invincible Roman People' to the defence of Rienzi and the Classical-Christian 'Liberty' he had restored to them. Elsewhere in Italy the persistence of municipal titles such as *consul* and *senator* and of the terms *populus* and *plebs* bore witness to latent Classical republicanism. In fifteenth-century city-states such as Milan, where despotism was well rooted, tyrannicide after the example of Roman Republican heroes became a devout purpose for some extremists. In 1412 Duke Giovanni Maria Visconti was stabbed to death at the doors of the Cathedral of Milan by three patriotic nobles moved by the story of Brutus. Classically inspired legalists, confronted with the conflict between popular sovereignty and imperial autocracy, tried to solve it by a theory of history to the effect that the sovereign *Populus Romanus* of the Republic had delegated its power irrevocably to the Roman emperors. Some of them asserted that the German emperors had inherited this absolute authority; others, with less success, made the papacy its beneficiary. Such historical assumptions did little to fortify republicanism, which fought a losing fight in the fourteenth and fifteenth centuries.

A century after Rienzi and Petrarch, republicanism of a different inspiration manifested itself in northern Italy. An evanescent, three-year 'Ambrosian' Republic was established by the nobles of Milan on the death of a childless Visconti ruler in 1447. Unlike Rienzi's SPQR it was dedicated to a Christian hero, Bishop Ambrose, who in the fourth century had forced the Roman Emperor Theodosius to submit to ecclesiastical authority. In Florence also republicanism drew on Christian sources. When the Medici dynasty was overthrown during the French invasion of 1494, Savonarola already had acquired a weirdly pious influence over the Florentine *populus*. Summoned to join the council of the newly established republic, he soon dominated its policies, primarily with a view to establishing a puritanical theocracy. He was more successful in purging the city of its 'vanities' than of French invaders, and shortly a violent faction, called 'the Mad Dogs' by his supporters, arose in opposition. Savonarola's miniature *Respublica Christiana*, having become obnoxious to the Borgia pope, Alexander VI, and from the outset unsuited to Florentine Renaissance tastes, soon purged itself of its mentor.

Meanwhile, in resplendent contrast to this short-lived, pre-Calvin puritanism and republicanism, Venice (Guicciardini's ideal) continued the long-lived, prosperous regime of its plutocratic aristocracy. The Adriatic city-state

rivalled Constantinople and Genoa for control of the Balkan and Mediterranean trade. It steadily augmented its huge territorial empire on both sides
of the Adriatic until checked by the Turkish upsurge in the Levant in the
fifteenth century, and its commercial and cultural prestige continued even
after its imperial expansion had ceased. Its ambassadors ably took care of
Venetian interests abroad; their fairly regular written reports, inaugurating
what is still a major function of diplomatic corps, remain a mine of information about the events of their day.

★   ★   ★

Hussite Political Philosophy

In northern Europe, an illustrious example of republicanism had religious
rather than commercial or Classic roots. The Hussite revolt was in part a
protest of Bohemian cities, artisans, and craftsmen against imperial, royal,
and clerical autocrats. The Utraquist doctrine, the belief that the communicant should partake of the wine as well as the bread of the sacrament, came
to be a major shibboleth in the fight, for it meant to its adherents not only a
return to scripture and the primitive church but also the elimination of a class
barrier between clergy and laity. In the course of this struggle the Bohemian
nobles on their own initiative in 1415 convened a general assembly to protest
the sacrifice of Huss by Emperor Sigismund and the Council of Constance
(see Chapter III). Four years later, direct action was taken against the anti-
Hussite town council of Prague by a crowd of Hussite demonstrators under
the leadership of Jan Žižka, one of the great military leaders and patriots of
his day. After defenestrating the councillors and killing the unfortunates who
survived this forceful sign of their displeasure, they set up their own municipal
government. King Wenceslas, unable to quell the uprising, died shortly
after, leaving all Bohemia in the hands of the Hussites. Their kingless government consisted of a diet and local councils, and Prague became not only a city
republic but to some extent a democracy.[8]

For a time the Bohemian nation united behind the Four Articles of Prague
(1420)—freedom of preaching, partaking of the wine as well as the bread of
the sacrament, confiscation of church property, and the proper punishment
of sin. In 1421 a National Assembly at Chaslav, specifying fourteen tyrannical
offences of Emperor Sigismund, declared that 'we have never accepted . . .
nor will we accept him' as king, and so set an early example of a declaration
of national independence.[9] The Hussite republic successfully maintained
itself against the German 'crusaders' led by Emperor Sigismund but then
succumbed to its own factional differences. On the one side were the Utraquists or Calixtines—so called because they believed that the communicant
should be passed the *calix* ('chalice') of the Eucharist; they were the new
conservatives led by the nobles, inclined to call a halt to further reform. On
the other side were the Taborites, made up largely of peasants, who were
more radical not only in religious thought, wanting a more thorough return

to the principles of scripture, but also in social philosophy, wanting the abolition of private property, taxes, and feudal obligations. The Taborites were defeated (1434) by a combination of Utraquists and Catholics. Before the Hussite Revolution came to an end, however, it had provided religious, political, and intellectual precedents that made it 'the first in the great chain of European revolutions which helped to shape the character of modern, Western society'.[10]

The fate of both Lollard and Hussite followers of Wycliffe illustrates the general trend of sociopolitical events and thought in the fourteenth and fifteenth centuries. The doctrines of republicanism and popular sovereignty were dangerous if taken seriously by the rank and file of the people, but they were destined not to be put into long-term practice. They were meant rather as pious or Classical themes for academic philosophizing and for justification of the strong (popes, emperors, or princes) in their resistance to each other. Still, so long as that resistance persisted and called for justification, such doctrines were bound to survive and to have a mass impact.

*　　*　　*

Political Thought and Practice in Islam

During the period 1300–1500 Islamic political control spread gradually, taking along with it political philosophies based upon traditional institutions and theology. In the process of expansion political unity became more remote than ever; after 1258, when the Abbasid caliphate collapsed, it could not be envisaged even in ceremonial terms. Within the Dār al-Islām, however, political boundaries were regarded as of little consequence. In fact, the various rulers rarely interfered with the autonomous working of either the local or the international institutions through which Islamic life was chiefly carried on.

The political problems that presented themselves after the Mongol regime had ceased were confronted in two ways. One was the critique of reformers such as Ibn-Taymiyya (see Chapter VII), who insisted on the rights of the sharī'a and its interpreters, the 'ulamā', against the worldly corruptions of the military rulers. The other was the attempt by both 'ulamā' and philosophers to come to terms with the actualities of fragmented and militarized political life. On the part of the 'ulamā' this attempt took the form of an assertion—in effect—that the subjects were not politically responsible for any established ruler, provided he tolerated the private practices of Islam, on the ground that even the most unjust rule was preferable to rebellion and civil war. More commonly, however, an effort was made to distinguish legitimate government (given the name caliphate in this period, no matter how local its power) from government that failed to uphold the sharī'a and was therefore condemned. For philosophers legitimate 'caliphal' government in this sense was grounded in Classical ethics; the Aristotelian ethical tradition (as interpreted by Avicenna) received its definitive Islamic form in Iran by the end of the fifteenth century at the hands of Muḥammad b. Saʿd-al-dīn Dawwānī (1425–1502/3).

Perhaps at no time, however, have Ṣūfīs as a whole come closer to a complete rejection of political involvement. Refusing to compromise with a political situation which went against all Muslim instincts, yet not happy with the rigidity of the more puritan of the ʿulamāʾ, they often forbade all contact with the amīrs. At this time the doctrine of the Quṭb received full popularity: the Quṭb was the mystical head of all the Ṣūfī hierarchies; he invisibly superintended the life of the whole world, and before him any monarch was a mere child.

Ibn-Khaldūn (1332–1406) was Islam's outstanding political thinker during these centuries. He worked out a monumental analysis of the dynamics of the formation of states and of the relation to state power of the development of civilized culture. He made use of Greek concepts of political forms but transformed them in terms of an analysis of effective historical interrelations. After intimate involvement in the political life of the Maghrib, he seems to have developed his unprecedented theories for the guidance not only of the student of history but also of anyone who might suppose himself capable of undertaking political activity in an idealistic effort to improve society. An answer to the problems of political philosophy raised in this period of Islamic history came only with the changed political situation after 1500 (see Chapter IX).

* * *

Hindu Political Theory

Neither political conditions nor the intellectual climate encouraged political speculation among Hindu thinkers, and they rested content with the traditional political theories set forth in the *Dharma-shāstras* (treatises on *dharma*) and *Artha-shāstras* (treatises on the art of government). These included the *Nānava-dharma-shāstra* (Code of Manu), the *Shāntiparvan* section of the *Mahābhārata*, the *Artha-shāstra* of Kautilya, and the last great treatise on government, the *Shrukranīti*, which was probably a thirteenth-century production although small additions may have crept in later. The fourteenth-century philosopher Mādhava, in his commentary on the *Parāshara smriti*, one of the *Dharma-shāstras*, supported the notion that the king was an incarnate deity, but this was not a universal opinion. He also held that the functions of government should be exercised by the Kshatriya, or military caste, alone. In this view he was to be upheld by Nīlakantha, a writer on legal questions of the sixteenth or seventeenth centuries, but Mitramishra, Nīlakantha's contemporary, contended that government was not a monopoly of the Kshatriya caste and that all who ruled were bound by the responsibilities appertaining to kingship.

In general, Hindu political theory accepted the Brahmanical concept of *dharma* (duty, virtue, creed, law, or way of life) as prior and fundamental to government. Monarchy was the accepted form of political organization, and kingship was looked upon as a necessary institution, whether divine or human, for the maintenance of the *dharma*. The fundamental duties of the monarch were to enforce the *dharma* of the various classes and castes, to punish those who violated it, and to protest his subjects in return for his right to tax them. Rulers should normally come from the Kshatriya, whose duty was to rule, but they should appoint Brahmans as religious advisers, be consecrated by Brahmans, and accept Brahman interpretations of the *dharma*. To maintain his legitimate position the king might resort to any sort of device; yet he was also bound by the *dharma*, and writers often laid great emphasis on his duty to promote the well-being of his subjects. Subjects were supposed to be submissive, but some writers emphasized the duty of subjects to resist a king who violated the *dharma* and sanctioned the deposition of bad rulers.

International relations were generally looked upon as a ceaseless struggle between states. The ruler was justified in using any method—alliances, balance of power, conquest, deception, spies, assassination—to protect and promote the interests of his state. Practical manuals on the art of politics, like that of Kautilya, were as cold-blooded as anything in Machiavelli or the writings of the Chinese Legalists. In contrast to the theory of *Realpolitik* in international relations, however, stood the ancient Hindu-Buddhist conception of the *cakravartin*, or divine world-empire—a peaceful, prosperous, and well-ordered universal empire ruled by a god-king. This ideal, while not entirely forgotten in India, was stronger in Buddhist-dominated areas, where the ruler was often conceived as the secular counterpart of the Buddha. The theory of *cakravartin* rule was generally accepted in Burma, Siam, Cambodia, and Majapahit, despite the fact that those kingdoms were neither peaceful and well-ordered nor universal.

*   *   *

Neo-Confucian Political Ideas

In China thought turned much more often to political affairs than in India, although in neither country was political philosophy sharply distinguished from general thought. Since Confucianism was primarily a social and political philosophy, despite the interest of the Neo-Confucians in metaphysics there was no dearth of political commentary in their writings. Nothing essentially new, however, appeared in their political remarks, and no individual writer of the period stands out. Confucian political theory remained authoritarian, patriarchal, and ethical, with vaguely democratic overtones. The state was the family writ large and was to be governed and held together by the same moral, ethical, and cultural ties. The accepted form of government was monarchy, but the monarch was expected to govern the state as a father would his family—through kindness, guidance, virtue, and moral force, backed when necessary with punishment.

The power of the emperor as the agent of Heaven was absolute, but he was expected to exercise it in accordance with Confucian principles. He was to be assisted and guided by a bureaucracy of scholars who knew the Confucian code and whose duty it was to admonish him when he violated it. This duty was specifically assigned to a censorate, which was responsible for denouncing misuse of power and funds by officials in general. In theory, the emperor ruled by virtue of a mandate from Heaven, which might be withdrawn if he did not rule in an enlightened and benevolent way. Plagues, famines, natural disasters, and popular discontent were evidence that the will of Heaven was being violated and were warnings to the ruler that he must mend his ways. Flouting his advisers' words was further indication on the part of a ruler that he was violating the will of Heaven.[11] In the last analysis, however, the will of Heaven was expressed through the acquiescence or non-acquiesence of the ruled, and the right of revolution was recognized.

As indicated in Chapter VI, Neo-Confucian writers, in conformity with their metaphysical concepts, insisted that governments too had a cosmic *li*, or principle, and would prosper if they adhered to it or decline if they departed from it. Consequently traditional Confucian principles of government came to be regarded as expressions of the cosmic principle (*li*). Rulers and many other officials took advantage of this tendency to insist that their acts, however arbitrary, were in conformity with the *li* of government. As a result, the absolutism of the ruler and the authoritarianism of officialdom were strengthened and a static rather than a dynamic concept of government came to dominate. Yet none of the really great Confucian writers sanctioned the growing absolutism, and a number of Confucian scholar-officials were punished, sometimes with death, because they protested against what they considered violations of the proper principles of government.

In China, during this period, no theory of international relations envisaging an association of equal but contending states gained prominence. Confucian theory conceived of the world as a natural unity along patriarchal lines in which China, the Middle Kingdom, was the centre of culture, enlightenment, stability, and authority. Outside peoples were looked upon as younger brothers who naturally wished to emulate China. The emperor was held to be the patriarch of a family of nations to whom the less important rulers looked for guidance and enlightenment. This theory, in essence, denied the inevitable conflict of interest between China and other people and posited a suzerain-vassal relationship in which differences were to be harmonized and sublimated as in a family. The vassals owed to their suzerain respect and homage in the form of tributary missions and were expected to co-operate with China in maintaining peace and order. In return, they received a certain amount of protection and were permitted to trade with and learn from China. The rulers of vassal states were confirmed in their offices by the emperor, and matrimonial alliances sometimes cemented the relationships between suzerain and vassal.

China tended to keep her interference in the internal affairs of vassal states to a minimum, but at times she did not hesitate to intervene when such action seemed to suit her best interests. New peoples were welcomed as vassals, but China never thought of dealing with outside peoples on a basis of equality. During the Yüan and the early Ming period the vassal-state system was greatly expanded in the central Asian, East Indian, and Indian Ocean areas, but after 1435 China made no effort to expand or even maintain the system except with immediately adjacent peoples. Although this scheme held up the ideal of a universal, if hieratic, system of world organization directed toward peace and order, in practice it was a device for protecting China by maintaining peaceful and docile vassals on her borders.

Other countries of the Far East more or less accepted the Confucian political theories. Korea and Vietnam modelled their governments on that of China and fitted themselves into her vassal-state system. In Japan political theories were an amalgam of Confucian ideas, Buddhist cosmic conceptions, and native tribalism. The important political thinkers of the period were the Shinto writers Kitebatake and Ichijō (see Chapter III), who began laying the foundations for the theocratic and absolutistic monarchy of later times. No writer undertook a theoretical justification of Japan's feudal system of the time.

LEGAL THOUGHT AND PRACTICE

Varying Systems of Law in Europe

In Chapter I and elsewhere we have referred to the growth of the ruler's legal and judicial authority in Europe at the expense of the nobility and the church. Concomitant with that growth, and sometimes in close relationship with it, went several other developments in the field of law.

Before the fourteenth century, in accordance with the then prevailing tradition of co-operation between empire and papacy, law was treated as a basically uniform element of all Christian civilization. The natural law of the Roman Empire was thought to have passed, according to Divine Will, to the popes and the emperors. The Respublica Christiana was founded on both the canon and the civil law. During the fourteenth and fifteenth centuries legalists in Europe rivalled theologians in grappling with the debatable issues of ecclesiastical and temporal government. The conclusions of the Thomists were analysed and reinterpreted not only by the Ockhamists with their 'new' logic but also by the canonists and especially by the 'civilians' (as the experts in Roman civil law were called) with highly developed legal techniques. The basic principle, however, of the thirteenth-century theorists remained unchanged; the law of a state was still regarded as the expression of the customs and will of its people and, therefore, binding on all, even the ruler,

This view was considered justifiable on the grounds that positive municipal law was but the earthly counterpart of natural divine law.

For all that, after 1300 and the era marked by Dante's grand plea for politico-religious unity, western Europe grew both more and more diversified and more and more secularized. Civil law eventually eclipsed canon law; national systems of law replaced imperial papal law; pluralism of law as well as of sovereignty became increasingly evident. To be sure, the assumption of a single divine, natural law persisted, and that law was respected as ubiquitous, but whatever authoritative forms it acquired were likely to be different in different states. The people still might on occasion be considered the final arbiter of law, but the people actually operated in diverse ways in England, France, Spain, Germany, Italy, and elsewhere. Through representatives in parliaments, estates general, cortes, diets, and even church councils, they exercised their prerogatives jointly with, or subordinated to, their respective rulers, and the variant customary law of their various regions received varying formal expression and recognition in such representative bodies. In Italy, where no single political head could lead in a single direction, diversification was still more confounding; each city state had its own autonomous system of law. Similar diversification prevailed in the German regions despite the leadership, often only theoretical, of the Holy Roman emperor. And Spain was not one but three 'Spains'.

England was more advanced toward a unified system of law than the continental countries. She had a well developed 'common' law, which was based on practical experience with English institutions of long standing and was unified in a royally controlled legal organization. That is, it was both traditional and royal. Even in England, however, ecclesiastical courts were originally independent of royal control and operated under the regulations of canon law.

During the Middle Ages in all regions of Europe laws were—in theory—made and enforced by the rulers with the tacit or express consent of the people or 'the stronger part' thereof. A growing number of lawyers contributed to the efficiency and prestige of royal governments. After the eleventh-century revival of Roman law in Italy, civil law was studied at the law schools of Bologna, Padua, Pavia, and other cities in Italy, and later in other countries as well, although canon law continued to be stressed, especially at great theological centres such as Paris. From the start of the new trend in legal studies the legalists turned out by the faculties of law at English, French, Spanish, and especially Italian universities readily found employment. Some obtained positions in the governments of their own or foreign countries; some worked at compiling and improving the several systems of national law.

Under the increasing influence of Roman law a new legal philosophy appeared in the fourteenth century, especially in the works of Italian civil lawyers. Since Roman law was contained in books, it was fit for study in universities, and since the arrangement of those books was very disorderly and hard to understand, the jurists who studied them were forced to develop a systematic juristic method. That method was used to systematize the growing body of canon law, too, and later even the treatment of the various customs (i.e. systems of customary law).

Roman law also came to affect the crystallizing rules of law in a number of countries. It had a far-reaching influence—a process known as the 'Reception' —everywhere except in England, the Scandinavian lands, and Switzerland, and even in those countries the law was not entirely unaffected by it. The Reception of Roman law varied greatly in method and in content. In northern France, for instance, the Roman law infiltrated the supposedly German *coutumes*, or unwritten law, steadily from the twelfth to the seventeenth century; Germany on the whole held it off until late in the fifteenth century but then received it suddenly; in the Low Countries an initial infiltration seems to have been succeeded by something in the nature of a catastrophic Reception. Everywhere the Reception was most pronounced in the law of property and obligations (contracts and torts) and in matters of legal technique; hardly anywhere were the rules of family law or the less technical parts of the law of succession altered by Roman law. Indeed, most of the feudal elements in the law survived until the French Revolution and even afterward.

Roman imperial law placed a strong emphasis on the authority of the ruler. The people were still recognized as the ultimate source of law, but they were thought to have delegated authority permanently and irrevocably to the ruler. Thus, in the minds of theorist no less than in actual government, almost everywhere the ruler tended to supplant the people as the supreme lawgiver. Only among a few theologians and political theorists were the ideals of natural law and popular sovereignty upheld with the old vigour.

A great age of legal compilations had passed with the thirteenth-century *partidas* and *specula* and Bracton's summary of English common law; yet in the fourteenth and fifteenth centuries written law took some notable steps in advance. In Italy the school of civil lawyers known as the 'glossators' had by 1300 begun to decline, but their method had led to the *Glossa* of Franciscus Accursius (d. 1263), which was generally regarded as the standard interpretation of the Roman codes. To rival them, there now arose a school of 'commentators', who tried to harmonize Roman law with local customs, applying to their study the methods of the Schoolmen and developing a traditional analytical method of legal exegesis that became known as the *mos italicus*. Since Bartolus de Sassoferato (d. 1357), whom we encountered above as a tempered monarchist, was the outstanding teacher of this method, its practitioners were frequently called 'Bartolists'. Commentaries on Roman law multiplied, as Bartolus, his student Baldus de Ubaldis (1327 ?–1400), and later Italian 'civilians' continued an already venerable tradition of commentaries on civil and canon law. One of the most notable of the Italian commentaries on Roman law was that of Cino de Pistoia (1270–1336), a friend of Dante and Petrarch. Dictionaries of canon and civil law also appeared. Before the sixteenth century nowhere else in Europe did legalists record achievements comparable to those of the Italian 'civilians'.

*　　*　　*

Codifications of National Laws

The concept of a single fundamental law, of a divine law of nature, that dominated legal theory before 1300 was based upon the assumption that Christians, being uniformly subject to divine will and having the same concept of God and nature, were bound by and ready to submit to the same standards and regulations of human behaviour. The existence side by side of multiform codes—feudal law, commercial law, common law, canon law, and Roman civil law—contributed, even in the church-dominated centuries, to the weakening of the monolithic principle implicit in a divine law of nature. After 1300 the gradual breakdown of imperial and papal prestige in western Europe, and the resulting increase of independence for city states and national states, roused recurrent doubt regarding the possibility or acceptability of a uniform interpretation of God's will. This doubt was reflected in further pluralization of law. National monarchs and town councils disregarded or even defied papal and imperial authority with increasing impunity, while legal theorists, both ecclesiastical and civil, explained and justified such actions by reinterpreting natural law.[12]

The heightening competition of the day between rising dynasts and feudal nobility hastened the movement, for it provided nationalizing authorities with an impetus toward separate, centralized codes of law for their separate peoples written in their separate vernaculars. The first such code in Europe appears to have been the *Siete Partidas* formulated by Alfonso X, the learned ruler of Castile, in the thirteenth century. In the mid-fourteenth century the Spanish cardinal Albornoz, while in the service of the Avignon popes (see Chapter III), after restoring papal rule in central Italy, organized it under an effective government code, the *Constitutiones Aegidianae*. In France private compilations of local *coutumes* appeared, and in 1453 Charles VII formally encouraged the systematic preparation of local codes in northern France, the land of the *droit coutumier*. Such codes tended to incorporate principles of Roman law and royal ordinances with local juridical practices and concepts. The process went on until the eighteenth century, eventually providing one of the sources for Napoleon Bonaparte's national system of codes.

Several rulers of eastern Europe also took a lead in this regard. Along with the royal bulls, charters, statutes, constitutions, and other administrative regulations which they more or less willingly conceded, they also tried to systematize the local practices, feudal customs, and royal decrees of their several lands, but they did not hesitate to introduce innovations where they thought desirable—which was usually to court popular support against

aristocratic rivals. Under King Wenceslas (Vaclav) II (1289–1306) the codification of the mining law of Bohemia (known thereafter as the *Ius Regale
Montanorum* or the *Constitutiones Iuris Metallici*) began. It fortified the royal
claims upon the natural resources against the claims of the feudal aristocracy
and so was comparatively more favourable to the workers in the mines
than was usual in contemporary practice. Around 1346 Casimir III (the
Great) codified separately the laws of Great and Little Poland; he revealed a
favourable attitude toward burghers and peasants, but it was successfully
counteracted by the gentry (*szlachta*) of Poland. In Serbia Stephan Dushan
issued his *Zakonik* (*Book of Law*) in 1349. Emperor Charles IV, who was also
king of Bohemia (1346–78), promulgated the *Majestas Carolina* in 1350; it
remained ineffective, however, because of the opposition of the Bohemian
nobles. The enlightened son of Hunyadi, King Matthias Corvinus, crystalized
Hungarian law in a famous code of 1486, but after the suppression of a bitter
peasant uprising, led by György Dozsa, it was overridden by the considerably
less humane code of 1514, never formally promulgated, and the *Tripartitum
Opus Juris Consuetudinarii* (1517), a manual of Hungary's customary law.
Both of these codes were prep⸗ ed by István Verböczy. They not only gave
the Hungarian nobles special privileges *vis-à-vis* their sovereign but also
tightened their hold upon the peasantry. A Russian code of laws (*Sudebnik*),
issued in 1497 by the government of Ivan III, was augmented in 1550 by
that of Ivan IV. It reflected the Muscovite policy of building up autocratic
administrative power in order to counteract feudal decentralization, but at the
same time it improved the economic status of the aristocracy by greatly
restricting the peasants' right to move away to the towns or to freer and newer
lands, thus attaching them still more firmly to their lords.

* * *

Laws Merchant and Town-Laws

The commercial interests of the burgeoning middle class urged them on to
take a leading part in the struggle for more systematic codes of law. Traders
tended to band together against unfair practices among themselves and
against undue exploitation by both the rulers and the nobles of the countries
in which they found themselves. As a general rule, they supported the kings
against the centrifugal tendencies of feudalism. They preferred, however, to
regulate their own commercial affairs by their own common standards,
settling their disputes in courts and by laws that they themselves controlled
rather than submitting to the laws of foreign sovereigns or to codes that
might contain no provision directly applicable to the dispute in hand. Roman
law had embodied some commercial provisions, and despite the decline of
trade during the Middle Ages actual practice had given rise to compilations
of 'the custom of merchants' in several Italian cities, Rhodes, Oléron,
Catalonia, and other maritime centres. With the increase of trade came new

commercial codes, often named after a mercantile town or region. Such were the *Sea Laws of Flanders* (essentially the same as the famous twelfth-century *Roles of Oléron*), the *Sea Laws of Visby* (later elaborated as the *Sea Laws of Lübeck*, which finally became the laws of the Hanseatic League), and Barcelona's *Consulate of the Sea*. By the choice of the litigants themselves suits concerning contracts, partnerships, 'international' payments, and certain other commercial matters were often adjudged in accordance with these 'laws merchant'.

Somewhat similar developments occurred in some of the landlocked cities of Europe. Often for commercial reasons but also because of political conflicts with a feudal lord, a city could attempt to formulate a coherent town-law. Usually this sort of event (occurring since the earlier Middle Age) resulted in a code peculiarly applicable to that city, but the best codes sometimes became models to be adopted or adapted by other cities.

★   ★   ★

The Dawn of International Law

During the fourteenth century the incidence of war mounted, and legalists, During the fourteenth century the incidence of war mounted, and legalists, no less distressed than others by the carnage, began to wonder how to regulate the conduct of war along some lines resembling international law. A work entitled *De Bello*, dedicated to Cardinal Albornoz, achieved some fame, and an earlier essay by the French legalist Pierre Dubois, *De Recuperatione Terrae Sanctae* (1306), seems to have been better known. Dubois argued that if the Holy Lands were ever to be recovered, the European rulers would first have to create peace among themselves, and he thought they could best do so by joining together under the leadership of the French king. He proposed a series of needed reforms to that end, but his appeal—quite understandably—elicited no enthusiastic response among Europe's rulers.

As politically sovereign units proliferated, economic and political philosophies became more secularized, realistic, and dynastic. Increasingly complicated practices called for a mercantilist reinterpretation of the Aristotelian-Christian generalizations on economics. Abstract moral principles were blunted by the concrete realities of prevailing mercantile, diplomatic, and military methods. In governmental administration, law and lawyers were taken farther away from theories in books and brought nearer to earth. Autocratic dynasties, as the actual forces behind law, became masters rather than subjects of it. They and their staffs of middle-class lawyers made or moulded it to serve their own political ends. Finally, at the dawn of the sixteenth century, Machiavelli's frank pen metamorphosed the abstract, theocratic unity of medieval law into the pragmatic, diversified legalism of the sovereign authoritarian state. He was not, however, creating a new system; he was merely giving explicit literary expression to what was by that time fairly common practice. The principle of *raison d'etat* (national self-interest) rather than of international justice was to dominate international affairs in the centuries that followed.

*   *   *

The Sharī'a *and Its Supplements*

Outside Europe the ancient legal codes were likewise highly respected, both at local and wider levels. After 1300 they were interpreted most often in accordance with the views of famous commentators. Hindu law, for instance, was contained in the ancient *Dharma-shāstras*, consisting of many detailed instructions, often based on religious precepts, for the conduct of public as well as personal affairs. The commentaries on these *Dharma-shāstras* served as the basis of Hindu law throughout our period. In the Islamic world the *sharī'a*, the all-embracing legal system established by the Muslim religion, provided a common set of presuppositions which held together the most diverse communities, but it was almost everywhere supplemented by adminis-trative regulations as well as by local custom, both of which were sometimes codified. The great codes of the Ottoman Empire were essentially elabora-tions of the *sunna* (traditions allegedly documented by the Prophet's sayings) adapted to special conditions. One was promulgated in the fifteenth century by Mehmet II and was called the 'Pearl', the other in the sixteenth by Sulaimān the Magnificent and was called the 'Confluence of the Seas' (*Multaqa-al-abhar*). In China the T'ang code provided a model for the codes of later dynasties.

Islam is a civilization of highly sophisticated legal concepts, and various schools of interpretation of the law existed (see Chapter II). Before 1500 the Ḥanbalite school seems already to have lost ground to the other schools, especially to the Ḥanafites and the Shāfi'ites. The Malakites meanwhile consolidated their hold on the Maghrib. Nevertheless, the legal writings of Ibn Taimiyya (see Chapter VI) gave the Ḥanbalite school new life, and his insistence upon freedom from *ṭaqlid* (the unquestioning acceptance of the teachings of the schools) eventually found great favour with the Wahhābīs.

The Muslims permitted other legal systems to survive in the areas under their control. In India the Hindu system operated side by side with that of the Muslims, who were subject to Muslim law, while Hindus were left largely free to apply their own laws to themselves. In many areas in the north a mixed system grew up among Muslim converts in which Hindu customary law and caste rules survived to a large extent. Islamic rulers in the north, guided by the *'ulamā'* and assisted by various law officers, followed the orthodox Sunnī law as set forth by the Ḥanafī school, while non-orthodox Muslims followed so far as possible their own religious law. The Islamic rulers issued various decrees applicable often to Hindus as well as Muslims, but these were not codified before 1500, and no systematic statute law appeared. Generally speaking, the various religious, social, and tribal groups were largely self-governing communities with their own religious and customary law, and royal decrees did not basically affect the system under which they lived.

* * *

Dharma and Its Supplements

Law (as distinct from religious duty and social convention) did not commonly occupy so important a place in the social structure of other eastern lands as in that of Islam or of the western countries. In the non-Islamic East, law did not become a distinctive subject of study or develop a clearly defined philosophy. Civil law (torts, contracts, and other matters having to do with private rights in the West) in particular was left undeveloped, either remaining within the realm of custom and common ethics or being regarded as acts subject to defined penalties. On the other hand, some acts that were considered punishable crimes in the West remained religious or social offences not subject to legal penalties.

Since law in the non-Islamic East did not develop the same specialized characteristics as in Islam or in the West, highly specialized groups of legal officials did not evolve. Although judicial officials generally came from those learned in the lore of their culture—for example, Brahmans in Hindu areas and Confucian literati in China—they usually combined other administrative functions with their judicial activities. Judges frequently acted as both prosecutor and judge, and no distinct group of lawyers developed. As a rule, the judges exercised a great deal of freedom in interpreting and applying laws and custom to individual cases, and the law itself might differ from individual to individual, depending, among other things, upon his religion, profession, caste or class, or tribe. The principle of impersonal law applicable to all alike had at one time found advocates in China but had long since been discredited.

Judicial procedure in the non-Islamic East was likely to be summary and arbitrary, although, in theory, appeals to the sovereign were permitted. It was not codified, and rules of evidence were not highly developed. Both oral and written testimony were permitted, and, as in the West, torture was likely to be used not only upon the accused but also upon witnesses. In general, the accused was considered guilty until proved innocent. The doctrine of collective responsibility, by which a family or clan might be held responsible for acts of a relative, and neighbours, whole villages, or the local headman for the acts of fellow villagers, was widely applied. As elsewhere, punishments were generally harsh, and although sentences of fines, imprisonment, and banishment were also pronounced, corporal punishment of some kind, like whipping, maiming, strangulation, or beheading, was general. Cruel forms of execution were not uncommon, although burning seems not to have been so frequent as in the West. At the local level, tradition and customary law dominated and were administered by village headmen and elders, sometimes assisted, as in Japan, by a representative of a higher authority.

Hindu religious and civil law was generally set forth in the writings relating to *dharma*. Since *dharma* embraced the whole range of life's duties and responsibilities, it cannot be defined as law in any narrow Western sense. The oldest of the writings on *dharma* were the *Dharma-sūtras*, but the later metrical *Dharma-shāstras*, being more detailed and systematic, became the basic law books. Of these many *shāstras* the *Code of Manu*, the *Yājñavalkya-smriti*, and possibly the *Parāshara-smriti* were the most respected. Vijña-neshvara's *Mitāksharā*, an eleventh-century commentary on the *Yājñavalkya*, was in reality an independent juridical treatise, extremely important in north India and the Deccan. The great *shāstras* had all been written before our period, but several distinguished commentaries on the earlier ones appeared. In addition, law digests increased in significance after the twelfth century, and several appeared after 1300.

The *Dharma-shāstras*, although claiming validity for all castes, were written primarily in the interests of the Brahmans. Their extensive sections on the rights and duties of kings contained the most distinctly legal material. They included sections on the duties and responsibilities of the four great classes of Indian society, on principles of government, on domestic law (encompassing legal procedure and what would be civil and criminal law in the West), on rules of caste, and on morality. Under procedural matters, written and verbal evidence and ordeals were discussed. Other sections dealt with such matters as debts, pledges, sales, partnerships, wages, contracts, disputes over boundaries, defamation, assault, theft, adultery, and inheritance. The most widely known commentary of this period on the *shāstras* was that of Kullūka on the *Code of Manu*. It was written in Benares in the fifteenth century but was largely a recapitulation of the twelfth-century commentary of Govindarāja. Bālambhatta Vaidyanāth and his wife Laksmidevi commented on the *Mitāksharā* and emphasized the property rights of women. Mādhava's fourteenth-century commentary on the *Parāshara* contained a good deal of legal material. Among the law digests, the *Dāyabhāga* of Jīmūta-vāhana, variously placed between 1090 and 1400, came to dominate the law of inheritance in Bengal.

In Siam, Burma, Cambodia, Malaya, and the East Indies the *Code of Manu* became widely known and influential. Siam had a code that was based on the *Manu*, although its most ancient legal canons, dating from the time of Rāma Thibodi (1350–69), presented Thai legal principles before Siam was much affected by Hindu ideas. The *Wagaru Dhammathat*, the oldest extant Burmese law book, compiled at the end of the thirteenth century in Pegu, was essentially a digest of *Manu*. Cambodia also had a code based on the *Manu*. Geja Mada (d. 1364), chief minister of Majapahit, had a law book compiled which replaced an earlier adaptation of the *Manu*, the *Kutaramanava*, used in Java. As Islam invaded Malaya and Indonesia, Islamic law began to compete with Hindu *dharma* and local customary law. Generally speaking, however, local customary law dominated the area, although it differed from country to country, from tribe to tribe, and from locality to locality.

* * *

I, Li, Lü, *and Their Supplements*

The Chinese, because of their great political unity and administrative stability, possessed a highly unified legal system, Conduct, however, was supposed to be guided by the Confucian principle of righteousness and proper behaviour (the *i* and the *li*); law was looked upon only as an adjunct to the application of these principles. The public and officials alike tried to avoid resort to law, because its use was a humiliating reminder that the higher principles had been violated. Civil suits were largely avoided, and no codes of civil law developed beyond customary practices administered by local elders. Even when the law came into operation, the magistrates considered the *li* and *i* involved when judging the evidence and applying the penalties prescribed by law. Chinese and all non-Chinese who lived outside the few tribal administrative areas were potentially subject, of course, to the laws of the empire, but tribal peoples and non-Chinese, such as the Muslims and the small Jewish communities, were generally allowed to live in accordance with their own customs and laws.

China's laws fell into three main categories. One of them comprised imperial decrees and decisions, generally issued in response to proposals made by officials, and local orders arising from the discretionary authority of provincial and local officials. Many of these decrees were applicable only to specific areas or particular problems and, once the need which had given rise to them had passed, fell into disuse, unless they were incorporated into the codes or were revived to meet a new situation. A number of the decrees were of an instructive and exhortative nature, and only some of them carried penalties. A second category of laws comprised the decrees relating to administrative organization and procedure, which were periodically collected into administrative codes known as *Hui-tien*, or *Collected Statutes*. Many of the *Collected Statutes* were merely descriptive or procedural in nature, but others carried penalties. The third category of laws was the legal code proper, or *Lü*.

The *Lü*, also organized along administrative lines, set forth the fundamental laws that had arisen out of the experience of the past. The code issued during the reign of the first Ming emperor was based directly on that of the T'ang dynasty. It began with a general section on principles and definitions (including a description of ordinary punishments), treasonable offences, and the conduct of officials. Then came six sections of matters that normally fell respectively within the purview of the six administrative boards of the central government—civil offices, revenue, ritual, military affairs, public works, and punishments. The section relating to punishments was the largest and contained much of what would be considered criminal law in the West.

The code, in fact, made no distinction between administrative, civil, and criminal law, and thus various kinds of actions that in the West would have fallen under the headings of social custom or civil law became penal matters in China. The section on punishments dealt with abusive language, disobedience to parents, quarrelling, slander, treason, homicide, bribery, corruption, forgery, fraud, incest, and adultery. The section on revenue dealt with succession, inheritance, certain aspects of marriage, smuggling, and usury, along with other matters. The code was highly patriarchal, at every turn buttressing the status of the emperor, the officials and literati, those in senior or superior status, and the father as head of the family. Abusive language to a father might, for example, be punished by strangulation, and fathers under certain circumstances had authority of life and death over children. Although severe in many regards, the code was systematic, self-consistent, and consistent with contemporary mores. Penalties were carefully graded according to the seriousness of the offences; they included slicing, decapitation, strangulation, exile, imprisonment, the cangue, beating with large or small bamboo, castration, and fines; in certain cases self-execution was permitted.

Court procedure was based on the assumption that the emperor was the source of justice. Most cases were reviewed by higher tribunals before sentence was carried out. Appeal usually was permissible and, theoretically, in serious cases could be made to the emperor. No execution, except in times of crisis, could be carried out without imperial approval. Trial took into account both facts and circumstances and considered a host of circumstances that might mitigate or compound a crime. They included motive, intent, type of weapon used, status, age, sex, mental condition, religion, and the relationship of the defendant to the injured party. By the doctrine of collective responsibility whole families might suffer from the treason of a single member, a father or a superior might be punished for the acts of a child or a subordinate, and if a woman's paramour killed her father or husband, she was strangled along with her paramour. Confession was necessary for conviction, and this requirement inevitably led to the use of torture to extort confessions.

The *Lü* was supplemented and interpreted from time to time by the *li*, or supplementary statutes, prepared by the Board of Punishment and issued by imperial decree. They arose largely out of judicial experience, since detailed reports on cases went to the Board of Punishments for study and review. Case books were also compiled and circulated for the use and guidance of magistrates and review officials, who invariably considered precedents in their decision of cases.

In other Far Eastern countries Chinese ideas of ethics and law combined with local custom to form the legal system. Korea and Vietnam promulgated codes derived from those of the Chinese. Japan at one time had the *Taiho* code, based on codes of the T'ang dynasty, but, as a result of the rise of feudalism, the old code fell into disuse and was largely replaced by the house laws of the various feudal families. While influenced by Chinese ideas and the older code, these feudal codes also reflected local custom and experience. They were a compound of ethical principles (both Chinese and Buddhist) and administrative, civil, and penal law. They dealt with the duties and responsibilities of members of the feudal hierarchy, the conditions under which land was held and inherited, and the punishments for rebellion, murder, adultery, forgery, removal of land markers, and other offences. The house law of the Hōjō family, issued under the title of *Jōei Shikimoku* in 1232, was widely imitated by other feudal houses and became the basis of feudal law in medieval Japan. Feudal law continued to grow during our period through the precedents and interpretations established by the courts of the shoguns and of the various feudal houses.

ECONOMIC THOUGHT AND PRACTICE

From Aquinas to Oresme

Aquinas had condemned some contemporary commercial practices, which, however, were already helping to transform Christendom from a rural to an urban civilization. In his opinion (and that of the Catholic Church generally) the increasing of a debt by the addition of interest (called 'usury') and certain other financial operations were un-Christian. On the other hand, he defended slavery and serfdom, and the servile status of the worker of the soil tended to harden as Roman law more and more replaced customary law. The writings of Dante, a citizen and official of Florence, the outstanding financial centre of Italy, testify to the general approval of Aquinas' economic views at the beginning of the fourteenth century; the *Inferno* reserved a special horrible place for 'usurers'. Oresme who, among his many claims to distinction, was an outstanding economic theorist, pronounced no serious strictures upon traditional principles. His *De Origine et Natura, Jure et Mutationibus Monetarum* (*c.* 1356), although it offered some penetrating analyses of monetary fluctuation (see below), generally summarized prevailing economic theory with approval. In the succeeding century Gerson maintained that it was contrary to nature for money to breed money.

Yet, despite public contempt and ecclesiastical pronouncements, the times favoured a practical realism in economic affairs. In fact, Scholastic theologians generally approved the *commenda* ('sleeping' partnership) and other true partnerships (and thus endorsed a most important factor in the future development of capitalism), but they quite consistently condemned fictitious partnerships, monopolies, and conspiracies in restraint of trade. Although the church's disapproval of usury gave general direction to medieval economic theory, in actual practice its animus was directed chiefly against 'manifest' usury—that is, against those who were notorious as userers because in their money-lending, pawnbroking, or other transactions they openly increased the principal of their loans. Bankers were seldom regarded as 'manifest' usurers since they did not openly lend money at interest, being careful to operate by forms that had not incurred theological reproach. For instance, the *cambium* (exchange contract) was regarded as a permissible business transaction, since it was thought to involve not a loan but a transfer of money and so to earn a charge for service rather than to extort usury as strictly defined—that is, as an increment in the principal of a loan. In fact, at the close of the fifteenth century the Franciscans of Italy were allowed to collect fees on loans for the overhead expenses of their *monti di pieta* (pawnshops), though they customarily charged the poorest little or almost nothing. Shortly afterward, Pope Leo X formally approved pawnshops, and Cardinal Cajetan, a Dominican and commentator *par excellence* on Aquinas, went along with the other churchmen who regarded taking advantage of the fertility of money as pardonable.

Jews and other non-Christian financiers often assumed the role of unlicensed usurers and pawnbrokers, thus increasing their risks and, therefore, their interest rates and their unpopularity, but most of the European moneylenders of the Middle Ages were Christians and most of the great bankers were Italian. The names of two great money centres, Cohors in southern France and Lombardy in northern Italy, gave to the words *Cahorsin* and *Lombard* a connotation of moneylender or pawnbroker, frequently in a pejorative sense. Even though the outstanding theorists of the fourteenth and fifteenth centuries hesitated to defend interest, conspiracies in restraint of trade, and other profit-making practices of businessmen, it is extremely debatable whether church scruples impeded the march of capitalism (see Chapter I).

The thirteenth century and the first half of the fourteenth were a boom period for financial enterprise. In Italy mercantile operations, like contemporary political organisms, tended to merge into ever larger units; and the largest strove to monopolize business in their respective spheres or regions of operations. Family business firms grew bigger and more daring, took on more costly enterprises, required greater capital, and so evolved into partnerships, with several owners pooling their resources and sharing the profits and losses. Greater capital meant greater enterprise and more efficient organization. With agents in various parts of the world, with systematic and constantly improving methods of accounting, with carefully audited balance sheets, with accumulating statistical data, with newly devised or better administered methods of transporting funds and credit, such companies expanded into distant regions, attempting to monopolize markets, competing for transport facilities, and amassing fabulous profits for eager partners.

Setbacks and bankruptcy nevertheless occurred. In the mid-fourteenth century economic conditions in the West took such a decidedly bad turn (partly a result of the Black Death and the Hundred Years' War) that the next century (1348–1453) has been referred to as a 'depression', and even after that recovery was slow.[13] The labourers of the industrial towns, the peasants, and the lesser nobles, by contrast with the mercantile plutocracy, were truly hard hit, and their discontent was reflected in the vernacular literature of the day. The *Vision of Piers Plowman* (at least partly attributable to William Langland) made a plea for economic justice based on Christian idealism. 'He who commits the sin of usury', cynics said, 'goes to Hell; he who does not, goes to the poor house.' And in England John Ball, released from prison after leading the Peasants' Revolt, preached a sermon on the popular text: 'When Adam delved and Eve span, who was then the gentleman'?[14] But the fourteenth-and-fifteenth-century theorists did little to probe the social discontent of the lower classes, nor did they expound, or in fact seem to realize, the widely prevailing shifts in population, markets, and agricultural production.

The constantly shifting economy, however, did attract the attention of theorists to serious problems of a financial nature—money, credit, and trade, for instance. In fourteenth-century Italy, the Perugian jurist Baldus wrote a number of *consilia* (*consultations*), in which he made detailed comments on the legal aspects of bills of exchange and other such business transactions. Contemporary mathematicians (notably Jacopo of Florence and Paolo Dagomari) wrote treatises in the Italian vernacular concerning interest, exchange, partnerships, and weights and measures. France rivalled Italy in producing specialized financial writings. About 1300 Pierre Dubois commented on the problem of monetary depreciation and inflation. A half-century later, Oresme produced his *De . . . Mutationibus Monetarum* (mentioned above), one of the first comprehensive treatments of monetary theory.

In this work the author re-examined earlier ideas (with special reliance on his older contemporary Buridan) and analysed them dispassionately. Commenting in detail on usury, monetary stability, the ratio of gold to silver, and similar problems of economics, he came to some basic but at that time relatively uncommon conclusions. In the midst of the Hundred Years' War and the fourteenth-century depression, when the value of the *livre tournois* was being changed several times a year to suit the preference of France's ruler, Charles V, Oresme insisted that for a system of coinage to be sound it must be not a set of mere tokens of a value arbitrarily fixed by those in authority but, rather, a popularly acceptable medium of exchange, each piece with a mercantile value of its own and fluctuating in purchasing power with its intrinsic value. His importance lies less in the partial truth of this view than in the fact that, as a theorist, he approached economic problems as subjects of objective study. His treatise was a notable victory for empiricism in economic thought and deserves to rank with Etienne Marcel's contemporaneous political protests as a denial of arbitrary royal authority. It brought, or at least helped to bring, about an ordinance of Charles V that for a generation assured monetary stability.

*   *   *

Banking in Europe

Meanwhile practical business affairs had wrought some radical changes in economic thought and practice. One of these was the amplification of banking. By the beginning of the fourteenth century the importance of the fairs as trading and financial systems was diminishing, and more or less stationary banks were replacing the peripatetic moneylender (see Chapter I). In Germany and wherever banking was inadequate, the fairs still provided the necessary centres of trade and finance, but in the fourteenth and the fifteenth centuries at least eleven cities in Italy, three in France, three in Spain, one in Flanders, and one in England became banking cities. Sometimes, as for the needs of the papal court, they also furnished itinerant banking facilities.

A rich and important merchant-banker might have branch offices or correspondents in several cities. Francesco Datini of Tuscany (c. 1335–1410) established branches in Florence, Pisa, Avignon, Barcelona, Valencia, and Palma de Mallorca; he had correspondents in Bruges, London, and other places; and he had close associations with other banking houses. Branch banking was at first managed by employees called 'factors', who worked for fixed salaries and were given power of attorney, but in the hard times of the fourteenth century a series of bank failures induced Datini, the Medici, and other Florentine banks to adopt an organization by partnerships. Branches abroad were then managed by partners who received no salary but shared in the profits of the branch. Upon his death Datini willed most of his fortune to a charitable foundation, the Ceppo di Poveri, which he had initiated and which still carries on its philanthropic work from the palace in which its founder once lived. Datini thus was a significant pioneer both in international banking and in private philanthropy.

In the course of time banking became a highly diversified activity. The Medici bank invested its moneys in other enterprises like silk and wool manufacturing and so pioneered in commercial and investment banking. Bankers were now regularly charging interest though still concealing their charges—on exchange operations, for example, by manipulating the rate of price of exchange. In the fourteenth and fifteenth centuries exchange banks existed in the major trading centres of Flanders, Spain, and Italy and even in some of the smaller towns of Germany, but in England private money-changing was severely prohibited, foreign coin being under the control of the royal exchanger in the Tower of London (with branches in other ports). Public banks began with the municipal *taula* of Barcelona in 1401 (which in 1853 was absorbed by the Bank of Spain). Double-entry book-keeping and other improvements in accounting made possible the ready transfer of credit; bills of exchange and certain forms of bank money were beginning to be common; and checks, first used in the fourteenth century, were also becoming familiar. Continued depression brought on repeated bank failures in the fifteenth century, but the private transfer banks were the chief victims of the consequent public displeasure, and public banks grew more numerous in the sixteenth century.[15]

* * *

Mercantilism and Free Enterprise

As explained in Chapter I, the prevailing theory of governmental economics in Europe during this period, was that which eventually came to be known as mercantilism. From the economic point of view, it was a programme to allocate a country's resources so as to make it prosperous in time of peace and strong in time of war. From the political point of view, it envisaged a way of putting control of a country's economy in the hands of its ruler and was a fitting economic corollary of political autocracy. It was expressed in practise by the strict regulation of markets, guilds, exports, and imports, by royal monopoly or subsidization of certain industries, and by the grants of monopolies and patents to favourites.

Mercantilism, coupled with canon law and guild regulations, had rendered enterprise considerably less than free in the period before 1300. The development of the non-guild middle man in commerce who bought wholesale from the manufacturer (usually a member of the local guild) and sold retail to the consumer, and the emergence of the 'domestic' or 'putting-out' system of manufacture (see Chapter I) tended to intrude upon the established guild monopolies and royal controls. Guilds and mercantilist theories did not succumb rapidly, however, to these intruders, and before 1500 their intrusions did not make a deep impression.

* * *

The Muslim World and Asia

From 1300 to 1500 the countries outside western Europe produced little that was new in the field of economic thought and practically nothing that could be called substantive economic theory, independent of moral or political philosophy. Scattered ideas relating to India's economic affairs were to be found in the commentaries on the *Dharma-shāstras* and *Artha-shāstras*, in the legal digests of the period, and in decrees issued by rulers. In China the writings of various Confucians and numerous administrative decrees dealt with economic matters, but strictly in accordance with traditional precepts. In Japan economic ideas were represented in the land regulations of feudal lords, in rules governing the guilds (the *za*), and in the efforts of the *za* either to break down customs barriers or gain monopolistic control for themselves. In general, Asia's economic theories and practices, though autochthonous, were much like Europe's—a combination of communal tradition with partly physiocratic and partly mercantilistic concepts.

The most important theoretical discussion of economics in Muslim literature was that of Ibn-Khaldūn. He analysed the nature of money and the effects of government spending and of taxation under varying historical circumstances. He explained how an abundant government revenue under some social conditions might lay no burden on a society while under others the same society might be overwhelmed though the expenses of its government seemed to require far less revenue. Among other things he opposed governmental commercial ventures. Other Muslim writers on economic matters were divided chiefly into two groups. One wrote fiscal manuals for rulers, commonly stressing the importance of fostering agriculture; the other wrote handbooks for merchants. The law and practice of the fisc were highly complex and produced some controversy, varying greatly from area to area.

The Ṣūfī writer Badr-al-Dīn (1358–1416) became enmeshed in a tangle of economic, religious, and political impulses. He himself preached a doctrine of community of property and attracted a large following among the impoverished in the days when Timur was ravaging Anatolia. Upon the death of that conqueror, Sultan Mehmet I undertook to reunite the Ottoman Empire but encountered considerable opposition. In the area around Aidin a serious dervish revolt broke out, led by Bürklüdje Mustafa among others (1416), but it was repressed. Despite grave doubt of Badr-al-Dīn's complicity, he was hanged along with the known leaders of the revolt.

The Islamic land-tenure system in the Middle East had grown increasingly complex over the centuries, reflecting the accumulative effect of ancient tradition, the *sharī'a*, and a number of experiments in high politics. The arrival of the Mongols had caused a major confusion in the system, and when it was again straightened out in this period, important traces of Mongol law (*yāsā*) had been added to the earlier elements. In most areas the net result was to discourage independent peasant effort. Far-sighted attempts on the part of some enlightened viziers in the early-fourteenth century failed to improve the situation basically, and in the fifteenth century unstable political life and a declining economic level seemed to preclude any further serious effort.

In Asia as in Europe and elsewhere agriculture was the basic support of society and state and was run very largely by communal practices. Private ownership of land had evolved more clearly in China than elsewhere. Government regulations and other controls beyond local practices were dictated more by fiscal needs and political ambitions than by economic or social theories. Governments promoted agriculture, their main source of revenue, through water control, irrigation systems, and reclamation projects. In China and the countries under its influence the farmer occupied a high place in the social scale; he was lauded as the foundation of society and was encouraged to be thrifty and hard working.

In Asia (as elsewhere) commerce and industry were not ordinarily favoured as much as agriculture. In India the attitude toward merchants and artisans seems generally to have been one of laissez-faire, although some rulers, especially those in seacoast areas, encouraged merchants and skilled craftsmen. In Malacca and other trading states of the Indies merchants and artisans were encouraged by the rulers and the mercantile aristocracy. Even in feudal Japan the shoguns and some feudal lords engaged in trade and encouraged mercantile activity. In China the artisans, long organized into guilds, were encouraged but to a somewhat lesser degree than farmers. The moralistic Confucian scholar-officials, like the clergy of the West, looked down upon the merchant as a kind of pariah who produced nothing new or useful and made profit at the expense of the rest of society. Merchants were therefore considered fair game for the exactions of officials. The Mongol rulers tended to encourage foreign trade, but the Ming rulers, especially after the Yung-lo emperor (1403–24), tended to discourage it except as a part of the tributary system, in which it could be controlled and milked to the advantage of the government; they even forbade Chinese to go abroad. Many of the gentry and officials from the south-coast provinces of China defied this policy, and illegal trading grew up between the Chinese and the Japanese and, later, the Portuguese. Eventually it developed into piracy, which seriously infested the south coast and weakened the government, particularly during the sixteenth century. The Chinese government also maintained monopolistic control over salt, certain metals, and some other products. Most Asian governments seem to have been, like Western governments, concerned to prevent the outflow and to promote the inflow of precious metals. Japan in particular was anxious to import coins from China.

HISTORICAL THOUGHT

Europe's Historians

European scholarship in the fourteenth century revealed considerably less change in historiography than in economic theory. The typical historiography of the Middle Ages (i.e. annals and chronicles) continued, usually restricted to events in the author's region but sometimes unrestricted in time or place (often covering all the known world from the beginnings to the author's present). As formerly, most chronicles were written by clergymen in the language used by their church and were dominated by religious interest. Generally those of this period were inferior in quality to their predecessors, especially to those of the English-Norman school. The fourteenth-century Latin *Polychronicon* of the English chronicler Ranulf Higdom was a noteworthy example of a clerical history of the world. It was an impersonal chronicle that began with Adam and came down to his own day; it was continued after his death by others. The chronicle (1377) compiled by the monk Lavrientyi of the Suzdal-Niznegorod principality mirrors the contrasting literary tendencies of contemporary Russia. It reflected the continuing cultural influence of Kiev along with the local pride that emerged with the successful outcome of the struggle with the Tatars and the hopeful beginning of the struggle with Moscow. This *Lavrientski Chronicle* opens with the oldest extant text of the Old-Slavonic *Story of the Times*, compiled by the twelfth-century Kievan monk Nestor and his followers. The Nestorian account began with the Deluge and included episodes probably borrowed from the *byliny* (*epic songs*) and the hagiography of Russia. Lavrientyi and his continuators kept Nestor almost up to date until well into the seventeenth century.

Another heritage from preceding centuries was the layman's history in the vernacular, which generally reflected secular interests. In western Europe it had to vie with the Latin chronicles, usually written from a more pious point of view. Inspired by his own crusading experiences, a French nobleman, Jean de Joinville, produced (*c.* 1309) a spirited account of Louis IX's crusading exploits that is generally regarded as a worthy successor to Villehardouin's thirteenth-century account of the Fourth Crusade. Jean le Bel (*c.* 1300–*c.* 1370) and Jean Froissart (*c.* 1337–*c.* 1405) continued the tradition of history in the vernacular. Their work dealt chiefly with the society they knew, that of the French aristocracy. Froissart's *Chronique de France, d'Angleterre, d'Écosse et d'Espagne* dealt largely with countries he had seen and events he had witnessed. In the fifteenth century Georges Chastellain, Jean Molmet, and Olivier de la Marche wrote works that similarly reflected the persistence of feudal aristocratic ideals in France. The same trend in historiography can be found contemporaneously in other regions but to a lesser degree.

In Italy burgher influences were especially strong. The type of history written in the vernacular by a burgher from a burgher point of view is well exemplified in the *Florentine Chronicle* of Giovanni Villani, a friend of Dante. This work was a chronicle of, by, and for townsfolk. Although medieval in its sweep through the centuries from earliest Biblical times to his own day and in its emphasis on religious events, it is a mine of information on everyday urban affairs. It gives statistics on prices, imports, revenues, and school population and other quantitative data that are invaluable to the modern historian.

With the vogue of humanism, vernacular urban historiography in Italy was temporarily eclipsed by Latin classicism. For a long time after Villani, Italian historians tended to follow Roman models and to stress Latin style. This counter-vernacular trend can be traced to Tuscany as clearly as the trend toward the vernacular to thirteenth-century France. The Tuscan Aeneas Sylvius Piccolomini (later Pope Pius II) wrote several works of a historical nature. Although he himself was the author of a history of Bohemia, he regarded 'such a subject as the history of Bohemia or . . . Hungary' as 'wasting time', and held up (1450) Livy and Sallust as historians of 'the first rank',[16] more because of their literary merit than their subject-matter. He spent a good part of his pre-papal career in Germany and Bohemia, and his *Historia Bohemica* is a leading source of our knowledge of the Hussite wars, despite its biases, rhetorical flourishes, and legends. Among his numerous literary productions were his memoirs (*Commentarii Rerum Memorabilium*), a *Cosmographia*, giving his interpretation of universal history, and a series of short biographies of illustrious contemporaries (*De Viris Claris*). Though not printed until the sixteenth century, his writings had a marked influence on humanist historians in Italy, Hungary, and elsewhere in central Europe.

Leonardo Bruni (1370–1444) wrote the history of his native Florence in classical Latin and from a point of view very different from that of Villani. Bruni's history, like Villani's, swept through the centuries but with Roman rather than Biblical history as the underlying theme. His critical handling of sources and his literary ability have led some modern commentators to give him the somewhat debatable title of 'the first modern historian'. Whether he deserves that title or not, Bruni marks a change for the better in European historiography. He exhibited a scholarly scepticism regarding long-accepted documents and insisted upon testing them for authenticity.

Bruni was followed in this scholarly direction by Flavius Biondus and other savants. These men applied the techniques of humanist philology and archaeology as well as common-sense detection of literary and historical anachronism to their documents. Lorenzo Valla (*c.* 1407–47) did not hesitate to criticize even holy scripture. He combined a biting rhetoric with keen critical analysis in several iconoclastic attacks, not only disproving the validity of the so-called Donation of Constantine and of the apostolic authorship of the Apostles' Creed but also ridiculing medieval moral standards and the faulty linguistics of his contemporaries. Nicolas of Cusa, by a strict historical reasoning cast doubt upon the authenticity of some of the so-called Isidoran documents (ninth century), showing that parts of them (now known as the False Decretals) contained anachronisms.

With this new critical spirit, European historiography became something more than a mere chronicling of events or an unquestioning restatement or paraphasing of literary sources. Esteemed as masters of the historical method, Italian humanist historians were employed abroad by kings seeking to glorify their lineage and to justify their own careers. Paulus Aemilius of Verona served as royal historian in France under Charles VIII and Louis XII, and before his death (1529) wrote ten books *De Rebus Gestis Francorum*, and Polydorus Vergilius of Urbino wrote in twenty-six books his *Anglicae Historiae* for King Henry VII. If the purposes of the royal patrons was far from disinterested, nevertheless these writers used a critical method. Vergilius went so far as to raise suspicion regarding the Arthurian legends.

A return to the vernacular language came in the late-fifteenth and early-sixteenth centuries with the works of Guicciardini and Machiavelli. These Florentines wrote detailed factual histories of Florence and Italy, stressing the importance of contemporary politics (see above). Their historical works, displaying the same realistic secularism that characterized their political philosophy, were written in Italian. Speaking of events of their own day and often of their own experience, they applied to the task an analytical keenness and a tough-minded scepticism that has made their writings sometimes disconcerting to modern readers. Guicciardini was perhaps the less gullible and sentimental of the two, but both were far removed from the uncritical readiness of medieval chroniclers to record whatever they heard. Their disillusioned, amoral spirit fortified the dispassionate, unrhetorical impartiality they tried to convey and so moved in the direction of the judicious detachment so highly prized by some of today's historians.

Works of history comparable to the two Florentines' were rare elsewhere in Europe. Philippe de Commines' *Mémoires* portrayed, with clarity and a commendable degree of disinterestedness, the despotic régime of the 'Spider King', Louis XI, and his successor, Charles VIII. Perhaps because he came a generation before Guicciardini and Machiavelli set the tone, he was less disillusioned than they, but he was nevertheless a keen and honest political analyst. North of the Alps and east of the Rhine few European writers of this period can be classified as scholarly historians. Of these several were Poles, and foremost among them was Jan Długosz, known in Latin as Longinus (1415–80). His thirteen-volume study of the geography, ethnology, and history of his country, his *Historia Polonica* (printed in 1614), was completed in 1479, shortly before his death. Drawing on his experience as tutor of King Casimir IV's children, as ambassador, and as archbishop of Lvov for the recent years, he also exploited the archival and literary sources in the several foreign languages at his command (Czech, Hungarian, and German among them) as well as in Polish and Latin. His aim was to make the Polish people proud of their heritage; his heroes were the church and the Polish nobility. Though partisan, he was not uncritical. Długosz corresponded with Aeneas Sylvius, whose eloquent Latin style he greatly admired.

An intriguing work, which may be classified as history but was at the same time something more and less than that, was Afanasiĭ Nikitin's *Journey beyond the Three Seas*. Between 1466 and 1472 the author, a merchant of Tver, had travelled, primarily for commercial and diplomatic purposes, across the Black, Caspian, and Arabian Seas, visiting the lands washed by their waters, including Abyssinia, Anatolia, Persia, and India. He was a sort of latter-day Russian Marco Polo. A quarter of a century before Vasco de Gama would reach India by sailing around Africa, Nikitin, though by a different route, had already been there and had recorded the things he found, giving particular attention to India's commercial products and religious faiths. While convinced of the truth of his own creed, he made a genuine effort to record faithfully what he believed, though occasionally credulously, to be correct.

At the close of the fifteenth century historiography appeared about to enter a distinctly modern state—critical in method, disinterested in spirit, straightforward in style, and secular in purpose. The Reformation, however, was to convert European historiography once more to religious ends and to make it a vehicle of rhetoric and polemic (see Chapter IX).

*   *   *

Hindu and Islamic Historians of India

Among India's historians a distinction must be drawn between those of Hindu and those of Islamic heritage. All during our period Hindu writers remained preoccupied with other-wordly, religious, moral, and metaphysical ideas and rarely found time for mundane historical matters. As a consequence, they left little historical literature worthy of mention. Some of the later *purānas* and *tantras* provided a historical theory involving endless cycles of creation and destruction, of which the Kali age (supposed to last for 432,000 years of progressive deterioration beginning with the death of Krishna in 3102 BC) was the last stage of the current cycle. Known historical events thus paled into insignificance, hardly worthy of systematic notice. A few Sanskrit epic poems (*kāvya*), most of them intended to instruct the reader in moral principles and the power of the gods rather than to give a sober account of historical events, and a few vernacular works were about the only historical literature left by the Hindus of these centuries. Kalhana's twelfth-century *kāvya*, *Rājataraṅginī* (River of Kings [of Kashmir]), which stands up well in comparison with other great historical epics of the world, was continued by Jonaraja, who died in 1459; his pupil Shrīvara, in *Jaina-Rājataraṅginī* covered the period from 1459 to 1486. Later, Prājya Bhatta and his pupil Shuka carried the epic of the Kashmirian kings slightly beyond the annexation of Kashmir by Akbar. In the fourteenth century Sarvānanda's *Jagadū-carita* sang the praises of a Jain merchant who had helped his fellow Gujaratis during a thirteenth-century famine. Several bardic chronicles of the Rajput clans were written in Hindi. The most important were the fourteenth-century *Hammir-rāsā* and *Hammir-kāvya* of Shārang Dhar, which dealt with the house of Ranthambor.

In Islam generally historical scholarship maintained its high position as a record of the prophetically founded community—its rulers, its scholars, and its saints. In contrast to the Hindu writers, the Persian writers at the courts of the Islamic kings of Delhi produced, like Muslim scholars everywhere, numerous chronicles and histories of the world and of the Afghan and Delhi rulers. Most of these works, however, were narrowly conceived accounts of the sultans, marred by sectarian moralizing and by flattery of their royal patrons. Among the more important were the *Ta'rīkh-i Fīrūz-shāhī*, written during the reign of Firūz Shāh (1351–88) by Zīa-ud-dīn Baranī. The author recommended his own work as a record of great kings and conquerors, as a source for the rules of administration, as a fount of admonitions to kings and rulers, and as 'right and true, and worthy of all confidence'.[17] It gave an account of the Delhi kings from Balban (1266–86) to Firūz Shāh, making an eloquent plea for a strong monarchy. The reign of Firūz Shāh was covered also in a work by a contemporary writer, Shams-i-Sirāj 'Afīf, who went into considerable detail regarding administrative matters and social conditions among the common people. The *Ta'rīkh-i Mubārak-shāhī* of Yaḥyā Aḥmad 'Abdullāh Sirhindī, although it dealt also with earlier periods, was especially important for the Tughlaq sultans from Firūz Shāh on and for their Sayyid successors (1414–50), of whom the author was a contemporary.

*   *   *

Islamic Historians Elsewhere

With the spread of Islam went also a certain consciousness of the desirability of objectivity in the writing of history. Numerous areas, such as the Sudan, for the first time began to produce written chronicles, which normally, however, reflected care for dates and facts more than for imaginative interpretation.

In the centres of Islam several new tendencies enriched historical writing. Local history, after a long development, perhaps reached its peak in the Egyptian studies of al-Maqrīzī (fifteenth century), greatest of a remarkable school of historians of the Mamlūks. The Mongol invasions had broadened the historical vision, especially of Persian Muslims. At the beginning of the fourteenth century Rashīd-al-Din Faḍl-Allāh produced the first history that can truly be called universal so far as the northern half of the eastern hemisphere was concerned. Making accurate use of good informants from as far away as Europe and China, his monumental work is at the same time a singular example of breadth of coverage and cautious fair-mindedness. He fostered and inspired a school of historians dedicated to exact work and a broad viewpoint.

In an age of thorough but often uninspired historical work, Ibn-Khaldūn stands out. As in so many other fields, he developed in history, too, the possibilities that Islamic scholarship had ripened. His chronicles are characterized by a consistent interest in illustrating the social forces that lie behind dynastic events. The introduction to his famous universal history does at least three especially noteworthy things: it presents a systematic and enlightening survey of a total civilization as a working unity, including its crafts and sciences; it gives a sociological analysis of the historical dynamics of politics and culture; and it attempts to make a place for the study of history in the Aristotelian philosophical framework. Ibn-Khaldūn's well-known plea for an internal criticism of historical reports, alongside the external criticism which Islamic historiography had long highly cultivated, is merely incidental to his philosophical thesis.

*   *   *

Historiography in China and Its Neighbours

In the countries of southeast Asia historical writing was represented only by some chronicles and poems, which made little effort to distinguish fact from fiction. Of these, the *Pararaton*, or *Book of Kings*, a fourteenth-century Javanese chronicle, and the *Nagarakertagama*, a poem composed about 1365 by Prapanca, head of the Buddhist clergy at Majapahit, were perhaps the most important.

Although the period 1300–1500 was not the most productive in Chinese historiography, the technique of Chinese historians was perhaps at that time more highly developed than any other in the world. A profound knowledge of the past was held to be an essential part of Confucianism, and historical information was considered indispensable for the proper functioning of government and society. The government, therefore, took precautions to see that significant records were preserved and that appropriate historical works and manuals were written. A Historical Bureau maintained the daily records of each reign (known as the *Diaries of Activity and Repose*), and after the death of a monarch a group of historians was designated to prepare from these and other records the *Shih lu*, or *Veritable Records*, of his reign. Together with other available materials, these records were used by an especially appointed historical commission to write the standard history of a dynasty upon its close.

These elaborate dynastic histories had come by the fourteenth century to follow a regular pattern. They were made up of (1) annals of the various reigns; (2) tables of the imperial family and important officials; (3) treatises on the history of subjects important to the administration of government such as astronomy, the calendar, ritual, music, elemental influences, geography, rivers and canals, food and commodities, law and punishment, civil offices, the examination system, chariots and costume, imperial guards, the army, the militia and colonization, and literature; and (4) biographies, which formed the largest single section of each work. Aside from the official dynastic histories, about twenty-five other types of historical works, some of them official but most of them private, were produced. They included general histories of an annalistic or topical nature, accounts of special periods, collections of biographies and documents, treatises on government, historical geography and chronology, historical criticism and historiography, bibliographies, and histories or gazetteers dealing with provinces, prefectures, districts, and cities.

The Chinese historians aiming at high standards of scholarship, emphasized accuracy, objectivity, and the wide use of original materials and developed to a high level the art of textual criticism. In order to maintain objectivity they generally tended to quote extensively from the sources; judgments were usually confined to concluding remarks or summaries (although they entered, of course, into the selection of the material used). When two conflicting sources could not be harmonized, some writers quoted from both, although a tendency prevailed, particularly in general and dynastic histories, to decide which was right and to quote only from the preferred source. A direct and sober style was cultivated, flights of literary imagination being deemed improper in historical writing. Works on historical criticism from Liu Chih-chi's *Historical Perspectives* (*Shih-t'ung*) of 710 to Lu Shen's *Essentials of Historical Perspectives* (*Shih-t'ung hui-yao*), completed about 1515, emphasized the desirability of the widest possible range of sources, of a questioning spirit, of independent, critical judgment, and of support of conclusions by evidence. Historical works, official and other, were systematically reviewed by later scholars, and a large literature accumulated supplementing, correcting, and criticizing earlier works.

Notwithstanding these merits, judged by modern standards traditional Chinese historiography had patent weaknesses. The rather rigid chronological manner of presentation and the practice of quoting extensively discouraged genuine historical synthesis. Conventional conciseness of style and other literary usages helped to create obscurities, and the resulting stylistic conventions led to the omission of illustrative details. Certain types of economic, social, and even literary information were considered unimportant and so were recorded only inadvertently. Events connected with the emperor or the court were emphasized to the exclusion of information about humbler affairs in the provinces. Ethnocentrism was always evident in passages relating to foreign peoples.

Perhaps the greatest weakness of the Chinese historian, despite his tradition of objectivity, was his penchant to regard history as the working-out of certain Confucian moral principles. This moralistic interpretation was tied up with the idea that dynasties ruled by virtue of a mandate from Heaven and, if they abused their position and ruled badly, the mandate would be withdrawn. Thus, the end of a dynasty automatically implied Heaven's disfavour. Almost inevitably subsequent historians would accentuate the shortcomings and wickedness of the terminal rulers and officials of a dynasty, while the defects of its founders were lightly touched upon or entirely passed over. Likewise, since loyalty to superiors and the ruler was a cardinal virtue, unsuccessful rebels were castigated, while those who succeeded in establishing new dynasties were praised for having expressed the will of Heaven. Thus dynasties were made to rise and decline in a fairly uniform cycle. The last ruler of a dynasty was almost bound to be viewed as a 'bad' emperor, and the first one as a 'good' emperor. This tendency was most pronounced in certain general histories produced under the influence of Chu Hsi and the Rationalistic school of Neo-Confucianism. The school's belief that if the proper principles (*li*) were not followed, disaster was bound to result easily led it toward bias. It selected for emphasis those facts of history which showed that the difficulty or failure of particular rulers or dynasties were the result of their having failed to follow the proper *li*.

Such historiographical weaknesses were prominent in several supplements and abridgements of Chu Hsi's *Mirror* and in some shorter general histories published during the Yüan and Ming dynasties. Of these works perhaps the most important was the supplement of Shang Lu (1414–86) and others, covering the Sung and Yüan periods. The dynastic histories for the Sung, Liao, and Chin dynasties, prepared during the 1340's by a commission under the direction of the Mongol T'o T'o, and the *Yüan shih* (*Yüan History*), prepared under the direction of Sung Lien about 1370, suffered from hasty preparation as well as from the effort to trace in history the workings of moral and philosophical ideas. In addition, though based in part on the Mongol *Tobciyan* (see Chapter X), the *Yüan History* reflected the Chinese bias against the Mongol rulers. The omissions, distortions, and discrepancies of these works were not allowed to go unchallenged, and a number of elaborate critical and corrective histories (by Wang K'o-k'uan, Wang Yu-hsüeh, Hsü Chao-wan, and others) also appeared in the fourteenth and fifteenth centuries.

The encyclopedic study was another significant type of Chinese historical literature, and an important work illustrative of this type was produced at the very beginning of our period. It was the *Wen-hsien t'ung-k'ao* of Ma Tuan-li (*c.* 1250–1319), an elaborate encyclopedia of the history of Chinese civilization. It was arranged under twenty-four topics, including taxation, population, currencies, markets, schools, examinations, offices and their functions, ritual, military matters, punishment, geography, astronomy, literature, and frontier regions.

Chinese standards influenced the historiography of neighbouring countries. Koreans and Annamese in general imitated Chinese historiography but succeeded in producing only annalistic compilations of indifferent merit. Historiography was not highly developed in Japan, where most historical writings were the products of Buddhist monks. If one leaves aside various historical novels of the war-romance type and a few indifferent chronicles, perhaps the two most important works were the *Genko-shakusho*, a history of Buddhism, written about 1322, and Kitabatake's *History of the True Succession of the Divine Emperors* (already noted in Chapter III). Kitabatake's aim was to enhance the position of the imperial family. While he expounded history in accordance with current Chinese leanings toward moral and philosophical principles, he failed to measure up to Chinese standards of accuracy and critical judgment.

NOTES TO CHAPTER VIII

1. Explicitly expounded by Gregory the Great, the theory of Divine Right remained very foreign to the thought of the Middle Ages except, indeed, in the case of Wycliffe, where it appeared in the fourteenth century, as also in Spain with the meeting of the Cortes of Olmedo (1445). Thomas Aquinas, to whom it was unknown, justified the right to resist an unjust government. (Raymond Polin.)

2. Professor R. Polin feels that this statement should be amplified since, in his opinion, Machiavelli cannot be said to have propounded or defended an autocratic ideology. Firstly, his whole work runs counter to what would today be called an ideology. He is indeed the first philosopher to make political reality the subject of truly scientific analysis. What he tries to bring to light are the principles of an effective political technique, whether in the service of a prince or of a republican form of government. Moreover, his prince is in no way an autocrat, trying to justify his power by reasons transcending his

person. His is merely a man who has learned the means of achieving power, as well as how and at what price to use these means effectively. He is also a man knowing how to govern, and lucid and courageous enough to apply this knowledge. He seeks justification neither within nor above himself, but in his works alone. And as is rightly said here, the ends accomplished by his works may very well be moral ends, in the sense of conformity with one or other accepted moral code.

The physical violence of his time and his experience as secretary of the Florentine republic, and sometimes as its ambassador, no doubt helped him to discover that politics are calculations, the rational mean of the forces in human groups. Rising superior to the contingencies of his time, he reached the level of universal premises.

Machiavelli is the founder of modern political philosophy; he does not seek to justify a political system. He seeks to study the conditions and means of political action in order to educate and train good 'politicians'. For him, the quality of those who govern is certainly more important than the legitimacy of the regime—more important too, no doubt, than the nature of such regimes.

3. Professor R. Polin stresses that in the fifteenth century Nicholas of Cusa was to defend in his *Concordantia Catholica* the supremacy of law over the prince and to regard the community as the source of law, since law must be made by those whom it constrains. Therefore he does not hesitate to proclaim that all authority stems from a choice determined by an agreement based on free consent. Such choice is, moreover, in conformity with the law of nature and with the order willed by God. If it opts for a monarchical form of government, the monarchy it chooses will be elective. On this condition only can it be held divine in character.

4. Marsilius of Padua often appears a very modern writer. On many points his theory of sovereignty anticipates that of Hobbes. But his theory of sovereignty as issuing from the people by the will of God and his theory of government by the *valentior pars* should not be interpreted as already democratic in perspective. In reality, his whole thought is dominated by the struggle between pope and emperor, church and state. One of the best means of weakening the power of the pope was, of course, to oppose to his authority that of the councils, that is to say of collective organisms involving systems of representation, of election, of voting, which reappeared in the democracies of the future. It so happens that in striving for the pre-eminence of emperor and state, Marsilius opened up modern lines of thought. (Raymond Polin.)

5. William of Ockham, who, for his part, places the origin of authority in God but regards it as transmitted by the people, declares that while the prince is free in regard to laws, he is nonetheless subject to the law of natural equity. His power remains subject to the pursuit of the common good; he makes law, but with the common good in view, and laws made in his own interest would not be valid. Ockham even goes so far as to allow that a prince violating natural law should be deposed by force. (Raymond Polin.)

6. To Professor R. Polin the argument of Machiavelli is the following: 'Since man is capable of wickedness and evil, he who governs must be in a position to assure respect for law. He must therefore dispose of a sufficient force to impose obedience by constraint on those not reasonable enough to obey in response to persuasion. This is a universal argument and valid not only for a despotic government. As the highly liberal Locke will later entirely agree with Machiavelli, the availability of an adequate public force conditions the very existence of a public authority. This means in effect that political constraint is workable only if it includes the possibility of sanction, which does not necessarily rule out the implication of moral components.

Professor Gottschalk sees small difference in essentials between the comments of Professor Raymond Polin and of the late Professor MacKinney except in regard to their respective emphases upon the ideas of authoritarianism and morality in Machiavelli's writings; MacKinney emphasized Machiavelli's authoritarianism, leaving a little room for morality, while Polin leaves a little room for authoritarianism, emphasizing morality in Machiavelli's thought.

7. Professor R. Polin feels that it is indeed remarkable that medieval political thought had quite systematically sought limits to the power of those who govern in divine will, either

in the presence of the church and the authority of the hierarchy in the feudal system or again in the structure of existing firmly established political communities. After the break with medieval tradition, and while the theory and practice of absolute sovereignty were in process of development, those philosophers concerned with liberties were obliged to start afresh from new premises.

8. See F. G. Heymann, 'The Role of the Towns in the Bohemia of the Later Middle Ages', *Journal of World History*, II (1954), 338.

9. F. G. Heymann, *John Žižka and the Hussite Revolution* (Princeton, 1955), p. 233.

10. *Ibid.*, p. 477.

11. Professor R. Polin points out that it may perhaps be useful to remember here that when Confucius was born, in the sixth century before Jesus Christ, the astonishingly stable political traditions on which Chinese life was based were already almost two thousand years old. These traditions being transmitted by learning, it is easy to understand what a source of strength they were for men of letters, that aristocratic élite which assured the administration of the country and, to all intents and purposes, its government.

12. Professor R. Polin believes that it should not be forgotten that a philosopher as important as Thomas Aquinas differentiated very clearly between various sorts of law: the eternal law of divine providence, that is of God himself, and the natural law which specifically governs reasonable beings and which is revealed to them by natural enlightenment. On the other hand, there exists also a divine law expressed in the Scriptures and positive human laws applicable to reputedly immaterial domains. The plurality of positive laws was thus perfectly well understood and accepted. All laws, however, expressed reason and aimed at justice, a unique justice in conformity with the unity of Christian morality. (See also p. 499 and n. 1.)

13. Robert S. Lopez in M. Postan and E. E. Rich (eds.), *The Cambridge Economic History of Europe*, Vol. II (Cambridge, 1952), p. 338 and n., and Robert S. Lopez and H. A. Miskimin, 'The Economic Depression of the Renaissance', *Economic History Review*, 2nd Series, XIV (1962), 408–26.

14. Both English and German versions of this couplet are quoted in Edward P. Cheyney, *The Dawn of a New Era* (New York, 1936), p. 131 and n. 39.

15. For a detailed bibliography, see Raymond de Roover, 'New Interpretations of the History of Banking', *Journal of World History*, II (1954), 38–76.

16. *De Librorum Educatione*, trans. in W. H. Woodward, *Vittorino da Feltre and Other Humanist Educators* (Cambridge, 1921), p. 152.

17. Quoted in E. M. Elliott and John Dowson, *History of India as Told by its own Historians* (London, 1871), III, 94.

CHAPTER IX

POLITICAL AND SOCIAL THOUGHT AND PRACTICE
(1500–1775)

POLITICAL THEORY

Theories of Absolutism in Europe

IN the sixteenth century, as the number and power of Europe's absolute dynasties grew, the tendency toward a theological justification of autocracy kept pace. While Machiavelli's *Prince* remained the best-known literary plea for strong political leadership, writers like Luther and Calvin also supported autocracy. The reformers pleaded for strong governmental leadership on religious ground, finding divine sanction for absolutism in several Biblical texts, such as Jesus' mandate to his followers to render unto Caesar the things that are Caesar's. Luther vigorously advocated the autocracy of German princes (see Chapter IV), thereby providing a religious sanction for the later principle of territorialism—*cuius regio eius religio* (that is, a territory's religion is that of its ruler). In fact, Luther and Calvin went no further than the Scholastics in circumscribing the power of Christian princes.[1] They limited it only by an injunction to respect natural law, which to them was the will of God, leaving somewhat vague what was to be done if a prince transgressed natural law or differed with his subjects regarding the will of God.

Because Calvin held forth in the free Swiss city-state of Geneva and because his strict doctrine of predestination paid no heed to class distinctions, he is sometimes lauded as an exponent of Christian democracy. We shall see below that in Holland and England as well as Switzerland Calvinism indeed tended in that direction. Whereas Luther came to rely on the Christian prince as the instrument of temporal authority, Calvin relied on republican magistrates. But even though he, like Luther, believed that the state was divinely ordained, he held that the church was independent within the sphere of religious activity, and in actual practice he and his fellow clergymen actually came closer to dominating the Genevan city-state than to being dominated by or completely independent of it. Geneva, ruled by an oligarchy even before Calvin, became still more oligarchic under his auspices. Its General Assembly consisted of all the heads of families, the Assembly met infrequently, and real power lay with the Consistory, which Calvin controlled.

To most sixteenth-century minds democratic republicanism seemed in fact a form of government attractive only to the malcontent and subversive.

The persuasion was prevalent that for most of the countries of Europe geographical and historical circumstances made some form of monarchy inevitable. For Machiavelli, historical change rather than fixed religious precepts or prevailing institutions provided the principles of political action. The hereditary, paternalistic monarch of the Bible as exemplified in Italy's despots and the elective head of the Catholic Church both seemed to him obstacles to the unity and expansion of his beloved Italy. Hence he preferred a monarch (or a republican leader) who would rise to power by his own efforts, probably including force and fraud, who would retain it by preserving the confidence of his people (blaming others, if need be, for unpopular measures), and who would use it to defend the life and liberty of his state: 'For where the only safety of the country depends upon the resolution to be taken, no consideration of justice, humanity or cruelty, glory or shame, should be allowed to prevail'.[2] Machiavelli's prince was guided principally if not exclusively by *raison d'état* and *Realpolitik*. Even when elective (as Machiavelli considered desirable), the ruler's power to achieve a programme was limited only by political realities—that is, what his subjects and his fellow-rulers could be made to tolerate.[3]

Machiavelli's *Prince* had little influence during his lifetime. Yet his view of sovereign power was not essentially different from the more prevalent view of divine-right monarchy. In fact, he pointed to the French monarch as the model of the king trusted and unquestioned by his people. The sources and the rationale of the divine-right philosophers, however, were different from Machiavelli's. They leaned on the Biblical precedent of the anointment of Saul by Samuel and on Paul's injunction of obedience to 'the powers that be' because they are 'ordained by God', and their philosophy had little in common with the unabashed philosophy of force and guile which he had derived from his study of history and from his revulsion against the lip-service to morality prevalent in the Italy of his day. The paternalistic responsibility that devolved upon crowned heads from being the anointed of God—a responsibility upheld in western Europe during the Middle Ages and to be maintained by James I of England, Filmer, Louis XIV, Bossuet, and Fénelon in the seventeenth century—was a far cry from the Machiavellian indifference to humane considerations where the safety of the state was involved. Nevertheless, both schools of western European thought believed in a sovereign ruler limited very little, if at all, by other temporal forces, and a Russian monk, Joseph Volotzki (d. 1515), upheld a similar theory for the tsars. The essential difference between the Machiavellians and the divine-right school was that whereas resistance to a Machiavellian prince was political error (his error if rebellion succeeded, the rebels' if it failed), resistance to a divine-right monarch was religious sin (for God alone could rightly rebuke his anointed). The Third Estate in the last Estates General to meet before the French Revolution, that of 1614, went so far as to signify—in opposition to Suàrez and other advocates of popular or papal supremacy—that no power on earth, whether temporal or spiritual, could absolve the king's subjects from their obligation to obey him faithfully, and thus it gave endorsement to the nascent absolutism of the Bourbons.

While this theory of royal absolutism was rounding out, a partly supplementary, partly conflicting theory arose—that of the enlightened royal patriarch, the father of his people. Andrzej Frycz Modrzewski's *De Republica Emendanda* (Cracow, 1551) advocated a concentration of governmental power in the hands of a sovereign king, who, however, should use it to protect the peasantry from abuse occasioned by the nobles' privileges. Later in the same century Jean Bodin wrote *Les six livres de la république* (1576). In this and other works he presented lessons from his study of history that differed from Machiavelli's. To be sure, he still found that legality rested on power: he defined sovereignty as 'supreme power over citizens and subjects, unrestrained by laws',[4] and he found it generally vested in kings; monarchy had originated, he believed, in the primitive family and, after passing through various complicated forms of association and corporation, had matured into the modern state, to which all the other forms had become subordinated. Yet he distinguished between the tyrant and the just king, though both were sovereign. A tyrant made law of his own arbitrary will; a just king felt bound by the laws of God and nature, treaties with other sovereigns, the customs of his people, and the contracts which his predecessors or he himself had made. Hence a royal sovereign who was not a tyrant was bound by many restrictions, but they were moral and not legal restrictions, since by definition he himself made the laws.

Bodin's prince, if he chose, might be no less absolute than Machiavelli's. Although Bodin, too, thought of sovereignty as the prospect of a historical process rather than of divine will, his prince nevertheless was the 'image of almighty God': 'The laws of the prince should bear the stamp of divine laws.'[5] Thus, unlike Machiavelli's prince, who was not bound by moral considerations, or Bossuet's, who was answerable only to God, or Hobbes's, who was subject to no social contract (see below), Bodin's prince was bound all at once by morality (the laws of nature), God (the laws of God), and social contractual obligations (treaties, contracts, customs), though if he wished to act tyrannically, he would also be free from all legal restraint. Bodin's sovereign had the power to be a despot, but he preferred to be enlightened, and not alone out of the fear of God.

A Russian contemporary of Modrzewski and Bodin, Tsar Ivan the Terrible, argued the same way in self-justification. Prince Andrey Mikhaylovich Kurbsky, having first sought safety in flight to Lithuania, engaged in a famous controversy with the tsar, contending that royal whim must be checked by a senate (i.e. an aristocracy) of 'virtuous men'. In prose that has been since regarded as a masterpiece of Old Russian, Ivan replied somewhat along the lines of Volotzki's argument—that the tsar's power should not be limited—and he cited examples from history and his own experience to show that a ruler's sharing power with nobles brought on division, disorder, and bad government, all of which it was the tsar's duty to avoid.

When, in the seventeenth century, rebels succeeded temporarily in destroying the British monarchy, advocates of royal sovereignty were obliged to inquire whether any rebellion, even a successful one, against a royal sovereign might be justified. Thomas Hobbes, while in exile with the defeated Stuarts, argued (1651) that almost never[6] was a rebellion against a sovereign lord rationally or morally justifiable. He resorted neither to Biblical text, or revelation of God's will, nor to 'right reason', or intuition, to make his point but, re-examining the classical idea of social contract, appealed rather to persuasive reasoning from basic premises about the nature of man. As befitted a mechanistic contemporary of the seventeenth-century 'scientific revolution', he meant to be empirical and inductive in conning the laws of nature.

For Hobbes, man in the state of nature was a competitive and violent creature whose life was 'solitary, poor, nasty, brutish, and short'.[7] Guided by self-interest, natural man seeks peace and security, and so slowly reaches a set of understandings with his fellowmen that in the course of time acquire the force of a social contract, by which each gives up his freedom of action in order to create a state, the 'Leviathan', and to establish order where anarchy prevailed before. This contract binds the individual to the community, but the government that results is not bound by it; the subject is thus pledged to irrevocable obedience, while the king, an instrument of the contract but not a part of it, is pledged to nothing. Hence rebellion was ruled out as a method of resolving social disputes and political ills.

Only in a few paragraphs of Hobbes' book did his rational exposition, while still premised upon a hypothetical notion of the origins of society, make concessions to contemporary reality: if a reigning monarch cannot provide that protection against anarchy which was the original purpose of the contract, his subjects have the right to seek another government that can. In fact, Hobbes himself returned to England and made his peace with Cromwell's Commonwealth. Hobbes, in essence, bolstered the old theological argument in favour of absolute monarchy[8] with an additional secular argument, insisting upon the subject's personal inadequacy and moral obligations (the contract) as the justification of royal sovereignty[9] rather than counting, like Machiavelli, upon the ruler's skilfull manipulation of human interests or, like Bodin, upon the ruler's enlightenment.

*   *   *

Opposition to Absolutism

Starting from the same premise as the divine-right monarchists—namely, the will of God, another school of thought was meanwhile coming to a far different conclusion. Among the Protestant sects of the Reformation era the

Anabaptists may perhaps alone be cited as proponents of democracy. The Zwickau 'Prophets', especially Münzer, preaching a mystic doctrine of guidance by 'inner light', questioned the validity of man-made laws, private property, and social organizations, and eventually took up the sword against the 'godless'. Münzer's disciples turned to Anabaptism, but the chiliasm of the Anabaptists was ambivalent in its political implications. They were theocratic and in some ways anti-republican, particularly in the tenet that the good Christian did not participate in government. Yet their communist economy, their devotion to popular leaders, and their political equalitarianism sometimes caused them to be identified as republicans, and their fanaticism and defeat in Europe brought discredit to the republican ideal (although their survival as Mennonites in the Netherlands and America eventually aided it).

The bloody religious conflicts of the sixteenth century led some of the bolder Calvinists to press the premise of the will of God to a more drastic conclusion than Calvin ever had done. They vindicated revolt and even tyrannicide—if it succeeded (for otherwise it could not be the will of God)— as a last resort against rulers who persisted in violating their 'contractual' obligations to God on the one hand and to their peoples on the other. Particularly after the shock of the St Bartholomew Massacre, Huguenot 'monarchomachs' presented arguments of this sort. No king must force his subjects to transgress the law of God, they contended, sometimes appealing to Classical history as well as the Bible for precedents of revolt and tyrannicide. Theodore Beza (1519–1605) in *The Rights of Magistrates over their Subjects*, François Hotman (1524–90) in *Franco-Gallia*, and an anonymous author in *Vindiciae contra Tyrannos* (*Vengeance against Tyrants*, 1579), usually attributed to either Hubert Languet or Philippe du Plessis-Mornay, spoke up against growing royal absolutism and in favour of some sort of limitation on arbitrary power. The idea of a contractual bond between the ruler and his subjects was further elaborated during the Dutch revolt by Johannes Althusius (1557–1638), a German Calvinist. Assuming that states are made up by the federation of communities of sovereign peoples, he argued that a breach of the social contract by the ruler justified secession of parts of the realm or resistance by the 'ephors' (the internal magistrates and assemblies).

About the same time Spanish jurists were seeking to justify Spain's interference in the affairs of England, France, and other countries on behalf of Catholic resistance. Suàrez and the historian Juan de Mariana (1536–1624), both Jesuits, argued in the same vein as the monarchomachs: a tyrant, even when the legitimate ruler, may be resisted to the point of assassination if he violates the law of God, and it is lawful for a neighbouring prince to aid in his overthrow.

The idea of a social contract legally binding a prince was made fairly familiar in England by Bodin's contemporary Richard Hooker. In *The Laws of Ecclesiastical Polity* (of which the first books were published only in 1594) Hooker was primarily concerned with defending the established Anglican

Church against the attack of Presbyterians, and he maintained that the same principles that justified secular government justified ecclesiastical government as well. Essentially those principles were based upon the consent of the governed, expressed in a social contract that could be broken only by consent of the governed: 'Unto me it seemeth almost out of doubt and controversy, that every independent multitude, before any certain form of regiment established, hath, under God's supreme authority, full dominion over itself.' Hooker's contract was mutable. Whether in the religious or in the secular sphere, the contract issued from a mankind endowed by God 'with full power to guide itself, in what kind of societies soever it should choose to live'.[10] Hooker thus raised doubts about royal absolutism even as the Tudors were building it up in England.

The effort of their successors, the Stuart monarchs, to control both state and church and to dominate Parliament were among the factors that led to the Great Rebellion (1642–52) and the Glorious Revolution of 1688. By acts of force the British people showed that the divinity that 'doth hedge a king' was not sacred enough to keep one of their kings from execution, another from exile, and two others from the obligation to accept explicit conditions if they were to be allowed to sit upon their thrones. More or less contemporaneously estates and *Stände* in the United Provinces, France, Sweden, Spain, and elsewhere tried, with more limited success, to acquire a share of the government and to restrict the growing power of their hereditary dynasties.

The Social Contract and 'Enlightened Despotism'

Out of these conflicts, directly or indirectly, came at least three classic discussions of the social contract—Hobbes's, Spinoza's, and Locke's. Hobbes's view has been set forth above as a ratiocination of absolute monarchy: the compact between natural man and society bound the society but not the government. Spinoza gave the controversy lengthy consideration in his *Tractatus Theologico-politicus* (1670). The state, he claimed, like Hobbes, is formed by a social contract and rules by power. Yet the very bases of power work against its abuse, for one base is reason, another the desire to avoid unrest and revolution, and a third the wisdom not to command the impossible. Unlike Bodin and Hobbes, he counted on *both* the enlightenment *and* the self-interest of the ruler for good government. He concluded that representative government within a monarchy was best, since it was the most likely to preserve the natural rights of man.[11] Locke's *Two Treatises of Government*, written before but published after the Glorious Revolution of 1688, attempted to show that the governed shared sovereignty with the king. Controverting Hobbes, he expounded the theory that the government was party to the social contract and thus removable when it failed to perform its contractual obligations to the satisfaction of the other party, the people. He set forth also a theory of division of powers between the legislature, controlled by the people, and the executive and federative, controlled by the king.[12]

These three classic models of the social contract underwent modification in other men's writings in a variety of ways. As early as 1625 Grotius had equated natural law with human reason (see below). In Germany Samuel Pufendorf (1632–94) developed a concept of the social contract that wedded Hobbes' cynical view of man with Grotius' hopeful view of sovereignty— political power limited by rules of reason that would be substantially valid 'even if we should grant . . . that there is no God' (prolegomena to *De Jure*, ¶ 11). Hence Pufendorf's society rested on two contracts, one which the individual made with the community and another which the community made with the government, the community promising obedience and the government promising regard for the general welfare. Some of the German philosophers of the eighteenth century, like Wolff, accepted this view. Borrowing Locke's theory of the division of governmental powers, though without particular attention to the social contract, Montesquieu in the *Esprit des Lois* (1748) set forth a theory of 'mixed governments'. Analysing the British constitution somewhat inaccurately, he found that its strength lay in a tripartite division of government—the distribution of political authority among the king, who had executive power, the aristocracy, who controlled the legislature, and the people, who were defended by the courts from the abuse of power by king or aristocracy.[13] Rousseau gave to the social contract the finishing touch of popular sovereignty (see below).

By the eighteenth century the idea of absolute monarchy, embodied in the Continental rulers, thus was offset by the idea of limited monarchy. The *philosophes* pleaded for enlightened monarchy and praised its exponents, Frederick of Prussia, Catherine of Russia, Joseph of Austria, Charles of Spain, and others. Frederick himself, before becoming king of Prussia, had joined the chorus in a work entitled *Anti-Machiavel* (1739), in which he rejected the idea that states were the property of their rulers and advocated instead that rulers regard themselves as merely the first servants of the state. The theory of 'enlightened despotism' was perhaps best set forth by the Physiocrats, particularly in Mercier de la Rivière's *L'Ordre naturel et essentiel des sociétés politiques*. As we shall note shortly, the Physiocrats were interested more in economic than political justice. Their political argument ran: Since land was the source of wealth (their major premise) and since a landlord would naturally want his income to be as great as possible, the king as the state's chief landlord would inevitably be concerned that his realm should be as productive as possible; hence he would be 'enlightened'—that is, he would rule according to the laws of nature, attempting to discover what they were in fact rather than exercising his own arbitrary whim or misinformed judgment. With the Physiocrats the idea of absolutism came full circle—'divine right' had become a 'natural order' based upon autonomy of the market.

★   ★   ★

Political Theory and Behaviour in Islam and Hindu India

Elsewhere similar political problems were giving rise to responses that were in some ways similar to those advanced in Europe. Islam is the social, even the political, religion *par excellence*. Although since the time of the Medina Caliphate it had been unable to fulfil its goal of a social order in which religious and political aspects would be one, the aspiration could not be laid aside by seriously pious Muslims. The *'ulamā'* never ceased to think of the ideal unity of Islam in terms of a *khalīfa*, a caliph ruling a human empire. The Ṣūfīs made much of a very different sort of *khalīfa*—the Quṭb, the human being who as perfected microcosm is the final end of, and holds limitless sway over, the world of nature and of men together. He is a Muslim and exercises his power largely upon and through Muslims (particularly through the *Abdāl*, lesser figures in the saintly hierarchy), but a recognized place under his care is available for the believers in every faith however crude—not only for peoples of the Book as in the historical caliphate but also for outright pagans. The kings who come and go are but the servants of such a saint, as many beloved anecdotes make clear; no caliph had such power over his governors as the Ṣūfī *shaykhs*, and especially the supreme *shaykh*, the Quṭb of any given time, had over the earth's rulers. That no one really knew who were the Quṭb and the *Abdāl* in his own day only served to make their power the more awesome.

The motion of the Quṭb who, with all the *shaykhs* as his assistants, continuously kept order in the world, is more than a piece of popular superstition; it is also more than a deduction from a subtle cosmology. The stories told of 'Abd al-Qādir—whose foot was on the neck of every other saint—are no doubt in part the result of the ardent loyalty to their *tarīqa* of the Qādiriyya *shaykhs*. That the leader of the Suhrawardiyya in India should be called Makhdūm-i Jahāniyān—'he whom all worldlings serve'—no doubt in part reflects the imperious personality of the man. When the mild and saintly Niẓām al-Dīn Awliyā' told the story of the saint who, flying over a greater saint's *khaniqah*, failed to show respect and so was thrown to the ground by that saint's power, he wanted in part to teach his listeners humility, but the notion that these and similar stories embody—the notion of the invisible hierarchy of the *shaykhs* of the *tarīqas* and their invisible government of the world—is inescapably political. It is as if the Ṣūfī *tarīqas*, in an age when it was no longer feasible for a single conventional government to give unity to the whole of Islam, were able to offer not only a flexible element of social order but also a correspondingly elastic sense of all-Islamic political unity.

Nevertheless, concrete political reality put a major claim on Muslim thought everywhere. After the extreme attenuation of political life in the late Middle Ages, the development of the great empires of early modern times offered a new and more hopeful climate for political thinking. The response was vigorous and varied. In Iran the chief political concern of theologians tended to be the confirmation of the Shī'ite character of the state, whose monarch was held to be essentially the representative of the Hidden Imām, the Shī'ite eschatological figure, who also spoke through the *mujtahids*. Majlisī was able to assert the effective control of the Shī'ite *mujtahids*— perhaps weakening the state through the bigoted way he exploited his success. The responses in India and in the Ottoman Empire, perhaps more interesting as theory, have been dealt with elsewhere (see Chapters VII and below).

Islamic authors in India, generally speaking, upheld the ideal of an absolute monarch ruling over a theocratic state and enforcing the Islamic law as interpreted by the *'ulamā'*. But Akbar in practice, and Abu'l-Faḍl in the preface to his *Ā'īn-i-Akbarī* (*Institutes of Akbar*), developed the ideal of the benevolent, non-sectarian despot. Akbar conceived his function as the promotion of the well-being of all his subjects, Muslim and Hindu alike, and he further considered himself as both political head (sultan) and religious head (caliph) of Islam in India (see Chapter V). Abu'l Faḍl, a contemporary of Jean Bodin, distinguished between the 'true king' and the 'selfish ruler'. The true king is possessed of a divine light communicated directly by God; he endeavours to remove oppression and promote the general welfare, bringing security, health, chastity, justice, good manners, faithfulness, truth, and growing sincerity. He is characterized by paternal love of his subjects without sectarian blemish and by a daily increasing trust in God. He is 'continually attentive to the health of the body politic, and applies remedies to the several diseases thereof'; by 'the warmth of the ray of unanimity and concord, a multitude of people become fused into one body'.[14] This enlightened, non-sectarian concept of kingship was not favoured by the more orthodox Muslims, but it was generally followed by Akbar's immediate successors. Then a more narrow, orthodox, sectarian view was adopted by Aurangzīb, and it contributed to the decline of the Mogul Empire.

Hindu India contributed nothing of importance to formal political theory during this period, but, as elsewhere, religious disputes had political consequences. The reinvigoration of Hinduism in the *bhakti* religious movement stimulated the rise of the Sikhs and the Marathas, contributing to the growth of Hindu nationalism and to democratic and equalitarian ideas in Hindu society generally. In a work entitled *Dashabodh*, the seventeenth-century Maratha writer Rāmdās denounced the Muslims and encouraged political activity, particularly the formation of secret political associations upon a basis of equality among Hindus, and his religious order practised complete equality. The Marathas developed a confederacy rather than a highly centralized monarchical form of government. The Sikhs became complete equalitarians and, under Islamic pressure, developed military communism as a political system.

*   *   *

Political Theory and Behaviour in China

In China of the late Ming period, the growing despotism of government and the Rationalistic philosophy which had, perhaps unintentionally, contributed to it were challenged. A number of writers insisted on a return to 'true' Confucian principles, which, although generally authoritarian, placed certain limitations upon the ruler and his officials and advocated a dynamic benevolent despotism. The Idealistic philosopher and statesman Wang Yang-ming (Chapter VII) in both his writings and his actions resisted despotism and insisted on government for social betterment.[15] His emphasis upon moral intuition, incumbent upon and available to all alike, implied liberation from certain traditional bonds and a moral equality for all. One of his sixteenth-century followers, Wang Ken, in his *Wang tao lun (Treatise on the Kingly Way)* discussed the means of improving government and promoting universal peace. Many of the later Idealistic philosophers, however, gave but passing attention to improvement in government, and only with the rise of the Tung-lin movement (Chapter VII) at the end of the century did significant protests appear. Imperial indifference to governmental affairs, growing official arbitrariness, and popular moral laxness then became the targets of severe criticism.

The fall of the Ming dynasty encouraged a minority group of scholars to attack the abstract and static political thought that had developed along with Neo-Confucian philosophy and to insist upon the more dynamic and practical ideas of government that they thought they found in the original Confucian writings. Most of these critical scholars opposed the Manchu (Ch'ing) dynasty. They denounced autocratic government and insisted that the ruler should be limited and guided by enlightened officials who, heeding the rules established by the sage emperors of antiquity, would be motivated by a true Confucian esteem for the value and worth of every individual. An official, they held, should not be an impractical theorist acting arbitrarily or in accordance with some abstruse philosophy but rather a morally enlightened man of wide learning and practical knowledge of the country's needs. They considered government a sacred trust, reflecting the interests of the people and administered for the people's benefit. Lamenting the inequalities of wealth and power, they proposed the redistribution of land. None of them, however, seems ever to have conceived of any form of government other than patriarchal monarchy. Their ideas were continued into the eighteenth century by the School of Han Learning.

Huang Tsung-hsi, Ku Yen-wu, Fei Mi (1625–1701) and his son, Yen Yüan, Li Kung, and Tai Chen, most of whom have been discussed in Chapter VII, contributed to this critical point of view. In essays on 'Kingship' and 'Law' in his *Ming-i tai-fang lu* (1662), Huang Tsung-hsi developed a theory of the degeneration of kingship into despotism that in some particulars suggests the later theories of Montesquieu. The early sage-kings, he argued, laboured without selfish ambitions, and they established a rule of law that protected and benefited the people. With the establishment of hereditary rule, however, degeneration set in because the ruler came to regard the empire as a personal patrimony and devised laws to promote his own personal interests and his family's at the expense of the people:

'Anciently the people loved and supported the ruler, looking upon him as a father, considered him to be like Heaven, and in fact he was. Nowadays the people resent and hate their ruler, regarding him as a thieving enemy, calling him a 'mere fellow' without any rightful claim to their allegiance, and in fact he is'.[16]

Deterioration, Huang continued, had been especially marked under alien dynasties and had reached new depths with the decay and abolition of the premiership under the first Ming ruler (for the prime minister had previously served as a check upon the autocracy of the ruler); Neo-Confucianism, with its devotion to metaphysical abstractions and its unquestioning loyalty to the ruler, had contributed to the degeneration of government; rulers no longer served as model examples, and officials sought only to please the tyrant and promote their own interests, without regard to the welfare of the people; as a result, the people, taking their cue from those above them, had likewise become selfish and indifferent to the general interest.

Tai Chen was fundamentally more realistic in his ideas, which vaguely anticipate those of Helvétius and Holbach. While he, too, denounced the bad effects of Neo-Confucianism, the tyranny of rulers and officials, and the evils of self-seeking, he recognized that the drives for self-protection and gratification were basic, and he insisted that such drives, if properly chan-nelled, could be turned into virtues rather than vices. The problem of good government was to institutionalize the basic desires and impulses of people into activities that, while satisfying the individual's needs for security, recognition, and satisfaction, would, at the same time, be beneficial to society as a whole.

The views of this group of critics were not widely disseminated and seem to have had little effect. In some ways, to be sure, the K'ang-hsi emperor was a good example of a benevolent despot; Leibniz in the *Latest News from China* (1697) called him 'the Louis XIV of the East'. But in the eighteenth century the Ch'ien-lung emperor turned his back on tolerance, repressed freedom of expression, sought out and destroyed or expurgated the writings of authors who criticized the Manchus, desecrated their physical remains, and persecuted their descendants. Most officials under the Ch'ing dynasty remained loyal to the customary abstract and static Neo-Confucian political philosophy.

*   *   *

Political Theory in Japan

We have already discussed (Chapters V and VII) some of the Confucian writers and Shinto nationalists of this period who made important contributions to Japanese political thought. Practically all the Confucian writers showed nationalistic leanings, advocated strong paternalistic government, and tended to identify native Shinto with Confucianism. The followers of Chu Hsi, such as Hayashi and Arai, generally supported the authority of the shogun and called for unquestioning loyalty to superiors. While they laid stress upon the ceremonial and institutional aspects of government, they also insisted that government should serve the people. The Kogakuha, or Classical, school tended to emphasize the practical and ethical aspects of early Confucian political thought. Ogyū Sorai was more cynical. Arguing (shortly after Hobbes but without knowing about him) that human nature was essentially evil and could be controlled only by an authoritarian enforcement of the ethical and ceremonial regulations established by the ancient sage-kings, he provided a philosophical justification for enlightened absolutism. The Ōyōmei school, to be sure, were followers of the equalitarian tendencies in the moral philosophy of Wang Yang-ming and were critical of the shogunate's failure to look after the well-being of the people, but by emphasizing rigorous self-discipline and devotion to duty, they appealed to the military and encouraged authoritarian ideas.

Kumazawa Banzan, of the Ōyōmei school, was perhaps the most interesting and influential (in long-range terms) of all the Japanese Confucian writers. His *Dai Gaku Wakumon* (*Certain Questions Respecting the Great Learning*), written between 1686 and 1691, was a treatise on government and economics which was highly critical of the shogunate and its policies, insisting that the shogun was only the viceregent of the emperor. He appealed for *jinsei*, or benevolent government: the ruler's first duty was to promote the welfare of the people; he should employ only just and upright officials; he should exploit the resources and products of the land for the people and not as a monopoly for himself or a privileged group. The people, in turn, should assist the lord in securing benevolent government, obey him, and make up for his short-comings. Kumazawa advocated a lengthy programme of social, economic, political, and religious reforms—among other things, fusing the samurai and the farmers, training the younger sons of nobles as teachers and otherwise reforming and extending education, rebuilding forests, constructing flood-basins, increasing the storage of rice to prevent famine, making rice legal tender, re-opening foreign trade, improving defences, reforming Buddhism, and ending the inquisitorial methods used against Christians. He was also intensely nationalistic.

The ideas of the Confucian writers buttressed the philosophy of the Shinto nationalists. Such theorists as Mabuchi and Motoori (see Chapters V and VII) now came forward with a doctrine that was farther advanced toward nationalism than any in the West or elsewhere: the Japanese were a chosen people, ruled over by a divine emperor, who should be restored to full power in order to bring to Japan, and ultimately to the world, the benefits of the unique Japanese polity, which combined people and ruler in one body devoted to carrying out the divine will. The foundations were thus laid for the theocratic, absolutistic monarchy of the next century.

*   *   *

Concepts of Self-Government and Revolution in Europe

In Europe the prevalent and most commonly acceptable form of government during this period, we have noted, also was monarchy—whether despotic or enlightened. Montesquieu advocated monarchy for countries like France, where the king's power should be limited by aristocratic defenders of the fundamental law through their power in the courts. Nevertheless, he believed that despotism was natural in huge countries like Russia, Turkey, and China, where vast expanses and extremes of climate were encountered. Almost no writer of the sixteenth, seventeenth, and eighteenth centuries believed that a country as large and exposed as France (let alone China) could long survive as a republic. The ideal commonwealths of More's *Utopia*, Campanella's *Civitas Solis*, Bacon's *New Atlantis*, and numerous other utopias imagined between 1500 and 1800 were islands or otherwise limited and strategically isolated communities. The history of republics led writers to believe as a general rule that the republican form of government was adaptable only to such communities and that a republic collapsed, as had the Roman Republic according to Montesquieu, when it became a vast and heterogeneous empire. If they were to survive and flourish, republics either must be commercial aristocracies, like Venice and Genoa (both of which, in Montesquieu's day, were conspicuously declining) or, if bourgeois oligarchies, must be bound together into federations, like the Swiss cantons, Dutch provinces, or Hansa cities.

Outside of some parts of Switzerland, democratic government—i.e. by officials chosen by a liberally enfranchised male electorate—though tried several times, endured nowhere but in the small and sparsely settled American colonies of Rhode Island and Connecticut. By special royal charter those colonies elected their own governors and legislative assemblies and did so by a fairly wide franchise. In 1775 the other eleven Anglo-American colonies on the North American mainland were either proprietary colonies, whose governors were named by the proprietor (Maryland, Pennsylvania, and Delaware), or royal colonies, whose governors were named by the crown (Georgia, the two Carolinas, New Jersey, New York, New Hampshire, Massachusetts, and Virginia). Although each of these eleven proprietary or crown colonies had a representative assembly, a property qualification and usually also a religious qualification restricted the number who could vote for its members. Of the eleven only Massachusetts had a property qualification low enough to permit most of the adult male inhabitants to vote, and apparently about half of them actually did. Thus, although experience with representative government was universal in the Anglo-American continental colonies, participation in government was as a rule a prerogative of the propertied conformist and not of the people at large. From these colonies, nevertheless, was to come a great experiment in democracy after 1775.

Other experiments with representative government were made during our period. Calvinist emphasis upon lay participation in the government of the church, acceptance of the electoral principle in both secular and church affairs, and at least theoretical insistence on the independence of the church from the state, all pointed in a democratic direction and (as we have seen) helped to suggest a social-contract theory. Following the pattern of Calvin's Geneva, Reformed consistories tried to exercise political pressure and often exerted a genuine political influence in the name of their congregations. The Brownists (Separatists) of seventeenth-century England went so far as to maintain a strict theory of congregationalism—that is, the complete independence of each congregation from all other forms of control.

Another effort in a democratic direction was that of Oldenbarneveldt as chief civil official (land's advocate) of the province of Holland. Abetted by Hugo Grotius as chief civil official (pensionary) of the city of Rotterdam, he endeavoured to establish the freedom of action of the province of Holland from domination by the Dutch union's stadholder, Maurice of Nassau, William of Orange's son. Maurice was backed by the States-General, whose members were resentful of the predominance of Holland's bourgeoisie. This conflict for political power became merged with a dispute between the mild Calvinists (Arminians), whom Oldenbarneveldt supported, and the believers in a rigid doctrine of predestination (Gomarists), who looked to Maurice for support (see Chapter IV). It ended in the execution of Oldenbarneveldt and the imprisonment and subsequent flight of Grotius. A victory for the Arminians of Holland probably would have advanced the republican cause in the United Provinces, thus making the final outcome of the Dutch War of Independence a decisive republican triumph. Largely in consequence of the Arminian defeat, the Dutch republicans fought a sometimes successful but usually a losing battle against the Orange cause until ultimate failure in the nineteenth century.

The English Civil War and Interregnum, likewise in some of its phases featured by disputes among Calvinist factions, was also ultimately a defeat for republicanism, but it naturally gave rise to several anti-monarchical views. The ideas of the Levellers, as expressed by John Lilburne and his sympathizers, were definitely republican, advocating the sovereignty of at least the propertied people and the responsibility of Parliament to the nation. The Diggers, a more radical wing, of which Gerard Winstanley was the spokesman, insisted also upon economic equality. The Fifth Monarchy Men, an unorganized group of millenarians who read in the Book of Revelation that the Second Coming would take place in 1666, recalled the political and economic views of the Anabaptists.

Cromwell's army, largely Independents in religion, was more of Lilburne's opinion than of the Diggers' or the Fifth Monarchy Men's. Its proposed Agreement of the People was, along with the Dutch Union of Utrecht (1579), one of the earliest written constitutional documents of a republican tinge. It implicitly abolished kingship and the House of Lords by placing in the hands of a unicameral parliament, elected by universal manhood suffrage, a limited political power—limited by a bill of the rights of Englishmen that not even Parliament was permitted to set aside. 'I thinke that the poorest hee that is in England hath a life to live as the greatest hee', one of the Levellers said.[17] Cromwell, less radical than his New Model Army, tried in vain to save the monarchy, but when Charles I was tried and beheaded, a republic called the Commonwealth was created informally, along the lines laid down in the Agreement of the People. With the overthrow of the Commonwealth and the establishment of the Cromwellian Protectorate the instability of the republican form of government seemed once more demonstrated. Yet the Agreement of the People remained a model for Americans and Frenchmen to contemplate in 1776 and 1789. Moreover, the sentencing of a king to death by a commission appointed by a House of Commons that arrogated to itself the power of the people was a brutal fact and no mere metaphysical theory. The world now had a concrete example of the principle that kings could not maintain themselves if they did not have enough support from the governed.

Thus Europe's tradition of social-contract philosophy, going back at least to the Stoics, was time and again reaffirmed during the religious controversies of the sixteenth and seventeenth centuries. Through Voltaire, Montesquieu, and the Anglomania of the eighteenth century, the lesson of the mutual responsibility of governors and governed was impressed deeply into the consciousness of the *philosophes* and their readers. In that century the parlements of France in their intermittent contest with the kings for judicial power issued cogent remonstrances that articulated and gave wide currency to ancient, deep-seated convictions concerning the fundamental laws of the French. The parlements, representing the aristocratic classes, appealed, along with Montesquieu, to custom and historical documents to bolster their case, but most of the other *philosophes* looked rather to 'higher reason' and an intuitional concept of the laws of nature.

Among the *philosophes* the most explicit presentation of higher justice as resting upon a social compact was Rousseau's. His *Contrat Social* (1762) presented a version of the compact that borrowed from both Hobbes and Locke but agreed with neither. Rousseau's natural man, a pre-moral being, was, like Locke's and unlike Hobbes', capable of good (though also of evil). If he surrendered his pristine liberty to form a society, it was only in order to make his natural rights still more secure. He reached that objective by making a social compact that bound him as an individual to the 'general will' of his society. Rousseau, unlike Locke, did not make the government a party to the compact, nor was the government, as in Hobbes' view, above and beyond the compact. On the contrary, the people were sovereign, their general will (which Rousseau somewhat mystically differentiated from majority will) was law, and they could at any time change the form of government or their rulers.[18]

By the end of our period, the right of revolution, the idea that governments might be changed by the will of the people, was rife in many quarters of the Western world.[19] This idea was eventually assumed to mean that 'governments derive their just powers from consent of the governed'. That thought, defiantly proclaimed in the American Declaration of Independence of 1776, had long been maturing as part of the Americans' political credo. It was a credo that had come to them not only by way of the Calvinist doctrine of congregational responsibility, the monarchomachs, the Great Rebellion and the Levellers, the Glorious Revolution and Locke, the contract theory, the popular libertarian *Cato's Letters* (1720–23), and the *philosophes* but also by way of their own experience with representative government.

LEGAL THOUGHT AND PRACTICE

Natural Law and International Law

Natural law has been variously defined. To the Greeks it consisted of the principles of justice to be found in nature itself as divined by reason. During the European Middle Ages the *lex naturalis* was equated with the law of God. The accumulating knowledge about primitive peoples during the Age of Discovery intensified the Europeans' tendency to think of natural law also as the law of men in some 'state of nature', whether 'nature' was the Garden of Eden, Arcadia, or an exotic land. The development of the physical sciences made some construe the law of nature as a set of automatic, mechanistic principles of human conduct and institutions completely independent of supernatural guidance and empirically discernible.[20]

The distinction between municipal law and the principles of divine justice, between decrees enforced by a civil power and axioms of universal reason, was often obscured where positive law was considered merely an effort to attain the truths of eternal nature. When writers like Bodin and Grotius defined sovereignty as supreme political power beyond the veto of other human forces, they not only clarified the actual source of human law, they also reflected the political actuality of their day; in the sixteenth and seventeenth centuries, when national dynasties were maturing into absolute monarchies, a common saying had it that 'as the king wishes, so the law wishes'. But what if sovereign wills were not clear or were in conflict?

For Grotius, author of the work (*De Jure Belli et Pacis*, 1625) that along with Vitoria's *Relectiones* (1557; see Chapter VII) is still regarded as the starting point of international law, natural law was the unalterable, universal, substantive code of reason, sanctioned by the usages of nations (*jus gentium*); it would be valid even if God had no concern for the affairs of men; it might be called upon to fill the gaps left by royal decrees and legislative enactments.

Grotius found more room for natural law in international than in municipal affairs. Among equal sovereigns, he reasoned, mutually binding treaties and commonly accepted practices could be regarded as an indication of their respective wills, and if such treaties and practices were lacking, reason might be applied to discover the relevant laws of nature. Hence sovereigns were, he concluded, as much bound by the *jus gentium* as by their own decrees. His *De Jure Belli et Pacis* attempted to derive from treaties and international practices, as well as from natural law, a set not only of rights but also of duties to guide and control what he called 'the family of nations'.

Subsequent writers on the subject of 'civilized warfare' might disagree with his view that international law was binding in the same sense as municipal law, but their writings likewise advanced the notion of a family of nations modelling their conduct toward one another upon some accepted or acceptable rational bases. Hobbes, Spinoza, and Pufendorf qualified their adherence to this principle somewhat by maintaining that in the *jus gentium* agreements were not binding, since sovereigns could not be bound even by their own treaties and still remain sovereign. But they recognized no fundamental difference between the *jus gentium* and the *jus naturae*, for both were based upon reason, and only reason dictated how sovereigns should act toward one another. Although the analyses of the problems of war and peace by the great legal minds of the seventeenth century became classic, the efforts to prove that international peace and order, no less than domestic peace and order, depended on a basic, substantive law of nature did not have noticeable immediate results.

On the contrary, sovereign states were often conceived of as existing in a state of nature approaching anarchy, warfare being the *ultima ratio regum*. Indeed, the frequent wars of the period made pacifists of some of the most influential writers from Erasmus to Voltaire. The ideal communities of More, Campanella, Bacon, and other utopians engaged in war only for defensive purposes. A few daring men—Sully, minister of Henry IV, the French abbés Eméric Crucé and Saint-Pierre, and the *philosophe* Rousseau— elaborated schemes to assure peace through the creation of greater solidarity and cooperation among the nations. In general, the prevailing atmosphere of rationalism and humanitarianism during the Enlightenment tended to relegate war and conquest to the realm of barbarism or abuse of monarchical sovereignty—an attitude which was old and widespread in China and India no less than Christendom. Everywhere it was equally ineffectual.

*   *   *

The Increase of Law Codes in Europe

In the sixteenth century, leadership in the study of Roman law passed from Italy to France. The *mos italicus* of the Bartolists, who had displaced the glossators (see Chapter VIII), was displaced in turn, by the *mos gallicus*. In lieu of the analytic method by Scholastic exegesis of the Bartolists, French civilians emphasized a philological and historical approach. The new emphasis was taught by Guillaume Budé (1468–1540), French archaeologist, humanist, and jurist, and by Andrea Alciati (1492–1550), who wandered back and forth between Italian and French chairs of law, and it reached its highest point with Jaques Cujas (1522–90). It led not only to the establishment of more authentic texts of the Roman codes, now at last freed from accretions by the glossators and others, but also to a better understanding of their meaning in their own rather than in a Scholastic literary context and historical setting. Hugues Doneau (1527–91), who, like a number of other French jurists, fled from France after the Massacre of St Bartholomew, wrote abroad much of his twenty-eight books of *Commentarii Juris Civilis* and was largely responsible, along with other French and local civilians, for the influence of the *mos gallicus* in Germany, Holland, and elsewhere.

The nascent power of the absolute monarchies had meanwhile led to the crystallization of positive national legal systems. Royal judges brought local seigniorial courts and feudal justice more fully under the control of a royal bureaucracy and made court practices more uniform. The increasing sway of royal justice and of national law was reflected in the large number of codes drawn up during these centuries. Foremost perhaps of the continental criminal codes of the sixteenth century was the imperial *Constitutio Criminalis Carolina* (1532), but during that century came several other legal codes as well. We have already mentioned the Hungarian code of 1514 (see Chapter VIII). Still others were the Spanish *Nueva Recopilación* (1567), the Portuguese *Manuelinas* (1514), the so-called Lithuanian Statutes (1529, 1566, and 1588), the Czech Statute of King Vladislav (first published in 1500 and expanded in several later editions), and the Polish *Correctura Jurium* (1532–34). The Muscovite *Sudebnik* (see Chapter VIII), when revised and extended in 1550, diminished the power of the gentry by giving greater authority in fiscal and civil as well as criminal matters to district (*zemskye*) administrative bodies.

In the seventeenth century, the Cartesian vogue of geometric clarity was added to the political and social pressures for legal uniformity. Among other codes came the Portuguese *Fillippinas* (1603), the Bavarian code (1616), and the Russian *Ulozhenie Tsarya Alexya Mikhailovicha* (1649). In 1683 Denmark received the completed version of the *Danske Løv* from the hands of its absolute monarch Christian V, who in 1687 also replaced the late-medieval Norwegian *Landsløv* with the *Norske Løv*. Sweden waited for her *Sveriges Rikes Lag* until 1734, during a period of parliamentary government. All these Scandinavian codes were intended to cover the whole field of law (except ecclesiastical relations). In contrast, a series of French ordinances (1667–85), including Louis XIV's *Ordonnance civile*, or Code Louis, inspired by Colbert and Guillaume de Lamoignon (1617–77), dealt only with commercial law, criminal law, and civil and criminal procedure. They did not touch civil law, in some ways the very heart of the law. And since the Scandinavian codes were partly casuistical in method and purported mainly to sum up existing practice, they did not resemble modern civil codes either.

Before modern codes could be compiled, a school of national lawyers had to come into existence. They were needed to foster the growth of enlightened absolute monarchies, to convince the enlightened monarchs that codification was in their interest, then to undertake the arduous task of codification, and finally to force their codes through against the opposition of a conservative profession. There were few such lawyers in our period. The only civil code to come into existence before 1775 was the Bavarian Code of 1756, but it was incomplete and designed merely as a supplement to the Roman law in force. Successive drafts of law codes were produced in the reigns of Frederick the Great and Maria Theresa, but the completed Prussian Code dates only from 1794 and the Austrian Civil Code from 1811. In France, efforts at partial codification petered out towards the middle of the eighteenth century, and it needed the cataclysm of the Revolution and the driving force of Napoleon Bonaparte to produce a uniform Civil Code in 1804. Nevertheless, despite their inadequacy, the eighteenth-century measures suffice to show that enlightened rulers sought to place law on a more equitable basis. In addition to the Swedish Code of 1734 and the Bavarian Code of 1756, there came the ordinances (1731–47) of Louis XV, inspired by Chancellor d'Aguesseau (1668–1751) and supplementing those of Louis XIV, the Bohemian criminal code of Emperor Joseph I (1707), the Austrian *Constitutio Criminalis Theresiana* (1768), the Prussian *Codex Fridericianus* (1747), and the beginnings of Frederick's *Allgemeines preussisches Landrecht*.

Royal codes for the most part were based upon the *Corpus Juris Civilis* of the Roman Empire (which in eastern Europe lasted until 1453). Yet each incorporated local differences and national preferences, thus reducing Roman law to a common link among them without creating uniformity of legal practice or institutions. Uniformity was further hindered by the prevalence, in certain areas, of customary law, stemming from the mores of the Teutonic invaders of the Roman Empire, and, in certain others, of common law, based upon the study of precedents. The French *coutumes*, the German *Landrecht*, and the Spanish *fueros* were examples of customary law; English law was the example *par excellence* of the common law. Royal codification, once it included practices sanctioned theretofore only by customary or common law, automatically made them part of the written law. Moreover, some of the customary law of France had been codified as such—that of Paris, for example, in 1510 (thus becoming a model for the French colonies to imitate), that of Orléans in 1560, that of Moulins in 1566, and that of Blois in 1579.

Parts of the customary law stayed outside the written codes, and common law, strictly speaking, never was codified. Besides, it constantly grew as precedents increased. Nevertheless, the tendency toward national uniformity made itself felt even in these uncodified legal systems in the forms of commentaries that acquired at least a semi-official standing by winning the approval of the legal profession and the courts. Beginning with Charles Dumoulin's commentaries on the *coutumes* of Paris (1539) French jurists had tried to build a code based on common usage until Lamoignon and Aguesseau finally attempted, in the ordinances attributed to their influence above, to incorporate the Roman law that prevailed in southern France with the customary law that prevailed in the north. But they had only limited success, and a single code for all of France had to await Napoleon. In English-speaking countries codification was resisted by some legal minds that preferred the elasticity of uncodified practice, but commentaries on English law appeared. Next to Bracton's the most influential has been the *Commentaries on the Laws of England* (1765–69) by William Blackstone, which came in time to serve as a source not only of study for English precedent but of inspiration to codifiers of new state laws in the United States.

Religious law was widely considered outside royal jurisdiction, though its privileged standing was slowly being undermined in Christian states as the power of the churches waned. Canon law gradually became codified in the centuries after Gratian's *Decretum* (*c.* 1140) had first systematized it, and it reached a definite form in 1563, just about the time the Reformation and the growth of national churches weakened the jurisdiction of clerical courts over laymen and even clerics. The decretals, constitutions, and codices approved by various popes and previously available in various forms were published in an edition of 1671 along with the texts of certain decisions of the Council of Trent under the title *Corpus Juris Canonici.*

The Sephardic refugee Joseph Caro (see Chapter V) completed (1555) a similar undertaking for Jewish law. His *Shulhan 'Arukh (Prepared Table)* set forth the duties and obligations, religious and other, of the Jews, derived mostly from the Talmud. When criticized and expanded by the Polish rabbi Moses Isserles (1530–72), the *Shulhan 'Arukh* shortly became acceptable to Ashkenazi (German) Jews as well. It has served ever since as the basis of Jewish laws in ghettoes and other communities where Jews follow orthodox practice. Before the Jewish 'emancipation' of the nineteenth century, this code held good for nearly all but 'baptized' Jews.

* * *

Cruel But Usual Punishments

On the whole, the new law codes breathed the growing spirit of enlightenment. They attempted, for instance, to reduce the number of crimes punishable by death and the special privileges of certain kinds of individuals (mostly clerics and nobles) in the courts. Nevertheless, torture of wilfully mute prisoners was not unknown, the *peine forte et dure* being abolished in England only in the reign of George III. In other countries torture even of witnesses, whether or not prisoners, was permitted in the courts. The *ordonnances* of Louis XIV gave the practice royal sanction, and it underwent no serious change until the *question préparatoire* (torture to elicit information not essential to the continuation of a trial) was abolished (1780), although the *question préalable* (torture to elicit essential information) continued until the Revolution. The *Constitutio Theresiana* permitted torture, but it was abolished in the Empire in 1776 and all but eliminated in Prussia by the code of Frederick the Great. It disappeared in Denmark under the enlightened minister Struensee in 1771 and in Sweden under Gustavus III in 1772. It was disapproved by Catherine the Great, though not formally forbidden in Russia until her successor's reign.

Severe penalties after conviction remained common, and prisons were usually unspeakable dens, financed at least in part not by the state but by the fees of the prisoners. When John Howard was sheriff of Bedfordshire (1773), he found that a number of prisoners, although innocent or eligible for release, could not get out of filthy, disease-ridden cells, where they had nothing to do all day long, merely because they could not pay the necessary fees to the jailer. Except for such fees, jailers were unpaid, until the House of Commons in 1774 abolished the fee system and provided salaries. Howard's *State of the Prisons in England and Wales* (where the prisons were not the worst) did a great deal to make the world aware of the problem.

Howard was not the first or the foremost in the field of prison and law reform. As early as the 1500's houses of correction or 'bridewells' had been built in England to allow sturdy minor offenders the opportunity to work for pay. Amsterdam opened in 1593 a reformatory for women. Pope Clement XI separated young prisoners from old in the prison of St Michel in Rome. Yet Casanova's description of 'the Leads' in Venice and Latude's of the Bastille in Paris, though they probably exaggerated, did not baselessly malign the jails of the eighteenth century. The continental writer who did the most to awaken the conscience of European rulers to the barbarity of their penal codes and institutions was the Marchese di Beccaria, who in his *Dei delitti e delle pene* (1764) attacked the prevailing system of secret indictments, torture of innocent witnesses, indiscriminate sentences of capital punishment, mutilation, branding, and inhumane prisons.

Enlightenment on criminological matters was a painfully slow process. How unenlightened in some regards one could be who was a beacon in other regards was shown by Blackstone. In his *Commentaries* he wrote:

'To deny the possibility, nay, the actual existence of witchcraft and sorcery, is at once flatly to contradict the revealed Word of God in various passages both of the Old and New Testament; and the thing itself is a truth to which every nation in the world hath in its turn borne testimony'.[21]

This was written over 130 years after the heroic Jesuit poet Friedrich von Spee, who had confessed hundreds of witches condemned to die at the stake had pleaded for an enlightened reconsideration of the subject in his anonymous *Cautio criminalis* (1631). It came about 30 years after the English and Scottish laws against witchcraft were repealed (1738), and almost contemporaneously with Voltaire's, Goldsmith's, and others' ridicule of witchcraft and demonology. Obviously, official cruelty and private superstition did not wholly vanish as enlightenment grew. In the seventeen years (1726–43) alone that Cardinal de Fleury dominated Louis XV's court tens of thousands of *lettres de cachet* were issued, arbitrarily imprisoning those who had incurred official displeasure; in Lisbon the last victim of an auto-da-fe was burned in 1761; in 1771 a Moscow archbishop was lynched when he tried to aid the government during a plague to keep crowds from gathering around an image of the Virgin; a witch was burned in Switzerland as late as 1782, and two in Poland as late as 1793.

★   ★   ★

Muslim, Hindu, and Southeast Asian Law

As already indicated (Chapter VII), a noteworthy shift took place in Muslim legal preferences with the rise of the new Islamic empires. The lands under control of the Ṣafavī dynasty followed the Shīʿite version of the *sharīʿa*, dividing into two major schools, the Usūlīs and the Akhbārīs, while the Ottoman Empire incorporated the Sunnī version into its constitution. The shift in Iran from Shāfiʿī and Ḥanafī law to Twelver Shīʿite law, however, entailed for the most part only minor changes, and the same was true of the extension of Ḥanafī law in the Ottoman Empire (where, in fact, for disputes that did not need to come before a regular court, the parties continued to apply the law ancestorially used in their families). The development of an imperially centralized system in the Ottoman Empire was more important, for it brought with it extensive legal reformulation. Many local legal principles were integrated with the *sharīʿa* system, and both *sharīʿa* and non-*sharīʿa* (*qānūn*) law were subjected to codification of a sort. As indicated in Chapter VII, Majlisī was the outstanding Shīʿite legist of the seventeenth century, and Abū-l-Suʿūd Khoja Chelebī was the greatest legal mind of the Ottoman Empire.

Under Sulaimān Qānūnī (the Lawgiver) Abū-l-Suʿūd was *shaykh-al-Islām* (that is, the highest authority in matters relating to religion and sacred law). He went far toward establishing an elevated but realistically organized position for the *sharīʿa* in the Ottoman Empire, coming nearer than perhaps any other Muslim thinker to establishing effective constitutional principles for a state in harmony with *fiqh* (the recorded fundamentals of traditional Islamic jurisprudence). At the same time, he was a central figure in the process of adjusting Islam to the new conditions that had developed since the time of the Mongols. Heretical groups such as the Yazēdīs and the extreme Ṣūfī *ṭarīqas* by his day had become widespread. Chelebī extended the Ottoman policy of adjustment toward them as well as toward such social innovations as the drinking of coffee.

In India under the Moguls, justice was generally speedy and often arbitrary. The emperors devoted part of at least one day a week to hearing cases directly. Akbar and his immediate successors adjusted the administration of justice so as to allow for the interests of their Hindu subjects. In judging cases involving Hindus Mogul law officers were expected to give attention to Hindu law and custom, though the basic law they administered was, of course, Islamic. Akbar asserted his superiority over the *'ulamā'* in the interpretation of the law, but under Aurangzīb the dominance of the *'ulamā'* was re-established and Hindu interests tended to be disregarded. At the local level the village elders continued to administer justice by traditional procedures, attempting to settle disputes by arbitration and agreement without appeal to law. Civil disputes that went to trial and criminal cases were often heard by traditional *panchāyats*, or village juries, whose findings and recommendations were passed on to higher authorities for final decision. The Moguls developed a more systematic and uniform system of law and legal procedure than had existed under their predecessors. Under Aurangzīb the Ḥanafī legal decisions were compiled into the *Fatāwa-i 'Ālamgīrī*, which became the first standard legal code of Islam in India.

Several Sanskrit digests of Hindu law were produced during this period. The outstanding ones were by Raghunandana (sixteenth century)—twenty-eight treatises (*tattvas*) relating to procedure (including ordeals) and inheritance. Of the seventeenth-century digests Kamalākara's *Nirnayasindhu* was used particularly in the Maratha area, and Nīlakantha's *Bhagavantabhāskara* and Mitramishra's *Viramitrodaya* were widely consulted. Mitramishra also commented on the old juridical treatise, the *Mitākshāra*.

In southeast Asia, few changes took place during this period in the traditional legal ways and codes. In Burma, under King Thalun (d. 1648), the first law book in the Burmese language, the *Manusarashwemin*, was compiled, and under King Alaungpaya (1752–60), founder of a new dynasty, and his immediate successors a good deal of other legal literature appeared. In Malaya and Indonesia, Islamic law of the Shāfi'ite school more completely replaced Hindu law. In areas like the Spanish Philippines and Portuguese Goa, which came under direct European administration, Western systems of law secured a footing.

Legal Codes and Practice in China and Japan

In China, the Manchus rarely made original contributions to Chinese legal institutions. In 1647 the emperor issued the *Ta-Ch'ing lü-li*, the Chinese code best known to the West. It followed with only minor changes the Ming code, which, in turn, had been largely based on that of the T'ang dynasty, but also incorporated modifications made during the Sung and Ming periods. From time to time, later editions were issued which incorporated supplementary statutes and interpretations drawn up by the Board of Punishments. Several compilations of cases were also issued for the guidance of magistrates.

In the philosophy of law Huang Tsung-hsi was the outstanding figure of the period. In a brief essay entitled 'Law', he underlined the principle that law was superior to the will of the monarch, but his concept of law was more that of *li* (traditional behaviour) than that of law in a Western sense. He believed that the only 'laws' of enduring value had come from the sage rulers of great antiquity and characterized the welter issued by later rulers to strengthen their position as the 'rule of illegality'. Ideally, he reasoned, laws should neither hamper officials in fulfilling their responsibilities nor interfere with the people in the proper pursuit of their welfare. Clearly upholding the superiority of Confucian ideas of conduct (*li* and *i*) over laws (*fa, lü, li*) in a narrow legal sense, he maintained that the fewer the laws the better for everyone.

The feudal law of Japan was considerably developed and systematized under the Tokugawas. *The Law of the Military Houses* (*Buke sho-hatto*), issued by Ieyasu in 1615, and the *Code of a Hundred Articles* (*O-sadame-gaki hyakkajō*), like earlier house laws, were combinations of ethical injunctions and legal prohibitions supported by extracts from Chinese and Japanese classics. Aimed at preserving the supremacy of the overlord, basically they merely put into writing certain feudal principles underlying thitherto customary practices. Feudal law was further elaborated by various official pronouncements upon subjects not covered by these codes and by precedents established in the decisions of law officers. Commentaries on basic legislation and case-books setting forth the precedents were issued for the guidance of law officers. Punishments were harsh, and sharp class distinctions made them harsher for commoners than for samurai. Since other feudal houses tended to follow the house law of the Tokugawas, in the end a comparatively unified system emerged. It was not guided, however, by any theory of jurisprudence but developed along empiric lines as specific problems arose. The rationalistic element in the system was furnished by certain ethical principles, the chief of which was the reciprocal loyalty and obligation of superiors and inferiors.

ECONOMIC THOUGHT AND PRACTICE

The Precept of Thrift in Europe

In Europe, Protestant theologians generally did not depart widely from the thirteenth-century Scholastics in their attitude toward economic problems such as just price and usury. Luther, like Aquinas, condemned the taking of interest and inveighed against wicked merchants, and while Calvin permitted the taking of interest, he did not approve taking it from the poor. He also agreed with Luther in emphasizing the 'calling' of every Christian to his particular work as a member of a godly society, thus giving even to menial labour a Christian quality. Calvin's acceptance of the validity, even righteousness, of worldly activities and virtues—and especially, of worldly thrift—has been regarded by some as an inspiration and a mainspring of the capitalistic spirit.[22] Others have seen in the lower-class origin of the Calvinists (especially of the English Puritans) a better explanation of modern preoccupation with business. While the Calvinistic concept of the intramundane ascetic life often seems to have led to thrift, and thrift to a concept of worldly accumulation as a result and visible sign of virtue, this point of view was neither originally nor exclusively Calvinist. Economic activities both in Italian and in Northern towns reveal capitalistic zeal in the period before Luther and Calvin; precepts of thrift appear in pre-Reformation books such as the *Trattato della cura della famiglia* (1431) of Leon Battista Alberti (1404–72). Protestant influence, however, took a prominent place among the new factors favourable to secular endeavour along economic as well as other worldly lines. Discount, for example, developed first in England at the close of the seventeenth century—earlier than in Catholic countries—apparently because of a more lenient Protestant attitude toward 'usury'.

Mercantilism and Its Opponents

Another of the newer economic and political developments was the deliberate policy of governments to promote middle-class enterprise along with the landowners' agriculture. Mercantilism became the prevailing economic theory as changes in certain political and economic conditions became pronounced—as feudalism and barter diminished and political centralization and money increased, as trade with the East sucked Europe's bullion away, as cities rose, as the laws against usury became less stringent, as national dynasties assumed absolute power, and as a rising commercial middle class importuned to be heard. We have already seen (Chapter I) how 'the mercantilist system' issued from the effort to create economic self-sufficiency or superiority in agriculture, manufacture, and trade during an era when markets and raw materials were accessible only by slow means of transportation such as sailing vessels and wagons and when neighbouring realms might frequently be expected to be hostile. The objectives of the system were a confusion of political with economic purposes: it sought both common welfare and royal power; it proposed to achieve an independent and prosperous realm in times of peace and a strong, self-sufficient, well-prepared economy in case of war. Essentially, however, it was a policy for increasing domestic revenue rather than international power. Its results were, on the one hand, government interference in the form of regulation of guilds, supervision of markets, tariff duties, excise taxes, navigation systems, and colonial restrictions and, on the other hand, government aid in the form of paternalism, subsidies, public works, royal industries, monopolies, patents, and charters.

The mercantilists did not form a school and so at times disagreed with one another, and some of them contradicted themselves. Bodin was the unintentional progenitor of the French mercantilists. While he propounded a modern-sounding quantity theory of money, recognizing that money fluctuates in purchasing power and that increase in the amount of money may mean only higher prices rather than greater wealth, in his two *Réponses aux paradoxes de M. Malestroit* (1566 and 1578) and in his better known *République* he advocated an orthodox mercantilist programme of high import duties on manufactured articles and explicit restrictions on the export of raw materials. Bodin's ideas were elaborated by Henry IV's Calvinist controller-general of commerce, Barthélemy de Laffemas, who, in an effort to build up native industry, not only advocated a policy of protection and austerity but also of subsidy for manufactures and inventions, in opposition to the influential minister Sully's agrarian preferences. The French poet Antoine de Mont-chrétien in a *Traité de l'oecomonie politique* (1615), without indulging in monetary theorizing, advocated a thoroughgoing regulatory and protective system for French industry.

An absolute monarch could not easily distinguish between his personal economy and the economy of his realm, and so mercantilism won approval in the era of absolutism as good for the crown and therefore good for the subjects. When, in the 1630's, Thomas Wentworth, later Earl of Strafford, was Charles I's lord-deputy of Ireland, he applied the policy of 'Thorough', a new name for the old policy of high-handed autocracy, which in its economic aspects was mercantilism. He regulated the food trade, encouraged the linen industry, raised the tariffs, suppressed piracy, and developed the country's resources at the same time that, in the interests of the English wool industry, he prohibited trade in Irish wool. Under Louis XIV, Minister Colbert developed mercantilism to so thorough a system that its more advanced application came to be known as Colbertism. He regulated the size and quality of textiles—so much so that a certain kind of lace came to be known as Colbertine. He had roads built, rivers dredged, and canals dug. He policed markets. He manipulated tariffs to the point where, somewhat inaccurately,[23] France's war with the Dutch (1672–78) has sometimes been considered primarily a war over tariff and trade rather than religion and politics. He attempted to unite the domestic markets of France, separated by local *péages* (*tolls*), provincial *douanes* (*customs*), and town *octrois* (*gate taxes*), into a single tariff union, but he succeeded in uniting only twelve of the central provinces, those which profited most by free trade with Paris, into a tariff union (*Les Cinq Grosses Fermes*), within which provincial *douanes* were no longer collected. Even so, inside this union other kinds of duties, and outside it provincial *douanes* as well, were still collected. The mercantilists' anxiety to assure free trade *within* the realm, their hostility to interference by foreign countries, their willingness to promote free exportation, their opposition to the clergy's business scruples, and their other efforts to promote industry and commerce often prompted them to talk of 'freer trade', but they rarely meant freedom from regulation by their own monarchs.[24]

More or less contemporary with the French mercantilists were several from other countries. Antonio Serra, in *Breve trattato . . . d'oro et d'argento* (1613), advocated an industrial as opposed to an agricultural economy and advanced a theory of favourable balance of trade. Gerard de Malynes, in *Maintenance of Free Trade* (1622) and *Consuetudo vel Lex Mercatoria* (1622), attacked dealers in foreign exchange but advocated a favourable balance in bullion. Thomas Mun's subtitle (*Or The Balance of our Forraign Trade is the Rule of our Treasure*) for his *England's Treasure by Forraign Trade* (written *c.* 1630) disclosed its major thesis, and he argued further that a favourable balance was measured by bullion alone. Edward Misselden in *Free Trade or the Means to Make Trade Flourish* (1622) at first recommended regulated rather than joint-stock companies such as the East India Company, which exported bullion in return for Indian goods, even though in *The Circle of Commerce* (1623), in which the term 'balance of trade' seems first to have been used,[25] he reversed this position.

In the states of the Holy Roman Empire, where decentralization tended to retard the development of absolutism, mercantilist thought crystalized only at the end of the seventeenth century. Several Austrian 'cameralists' (i.e. university-trained government officials, administrative experts, and political theorists of an absolutist, mercantilist bent) then wrote extensively on the subject. Wilhelm von Schroeder, who twice visited England, accepted and imported some of Mun's ideas. Philipp Wilhelm von Hornigk's *Oestereich über Alles, wann es nur will* (1684) propounded a policy of strict economic regulation that would, he thought, make Austria not only self-sufficient but also superior to all other countries. Johann Joachim Becher (1625–85) in a *Politischer Discurs* (1688) on the 'real causes' of profit and loss among the states indicated in his very subtitle that he was concerned with the question 'how to make a country populous and prosperous'; his answer was essentially to advocate a monarchical paternalism directed toward the stabilization of economic conditions and, thereby, the increase of population. The economic importance of population growth was given added emphasis in the eighteenth century. J. H. G. von Justi and Joseph von Sonnenfels laid special stress upon demographic factors such as employment, immigration, food supply, and housing as well as exports, imports, and trade balances.

Under the growing absolutism of the Romanovs, mercantilism came to dominate the economic literature of Russia also. The Croatian pan-Slavist Jurij Krizanic (1617–83) preached in Tsar Alexis' Moscow the mercantilist doctrine of enlightened absolutism, stressing, however, the need for state control and support of agriculture no less than of trade. Ivan Tikhonovich Pososhkov's *Kniga o skudosti i bogatstve* (*Book on poverty and wealth*) (1721–24) urged upon Peter the Great a revision of the tax system, combined with a programme of austerity and other reforms calculated to accumulate wealth and improve the peasants' lot. Enlightened officials like the seventeenth-century diplomat Ordyn-Nashchokin and the eighteenth-century historian V. N. Tatishchev not only tried to apply mercantilist principles but also advanced them in their writings. So did the greatest Russian scholar of this period, M. V. Lomonosov (1711–65).

Several of these Austrian and Russian writers, while reflecting a mercantilist preference for royal control of the national economy, are not exclusively classifiable as mercantilists, for they gave attention to government finance, agriculture, industry, labour, and other economic activities as well as or rather than commerce. Some theorists of western Europe similarly mark a deviation from orthodox mercantilism, as the realization dawned that money's purchasing power may fluctuate, regardless of its intrinsic value, with changes in production. William Petty's *Treatise of Taxes and Contributions* (1662) and *Political Arithmetick* (1690) departed from mercantilism sufficiently to consider land and labour as sources of wealth and to advocate that royal tax power be used as a means of securing a more equitable distribution of wealth. Marshal de Vauban, Louis XIV's leading military engineer, in a *Projet d'une dixme royale* (1707), incurred the royal displeasure by arguing even more explicitly for such a distribution, suggesting that the royal tax power be used to collect a tithe on land and alleviate the distress of the poor. Sieur de Boisguilbert in *Le Factum de la France* (1706) advocated an income tax for the same purpose. Without being a genuine free trader, Boisguilbert moved from mercantilism in the direction of *laisser faire*. He contended that wealth consisted of goods and not of money and that hence the interests of an economy were best served not by amassing bullion but by allowing nature and free enterprise to work their own way (*laisser faire la nature et la liberté*).[26]

The growing plea for political liberty which we examined above was being paralleled by, and probably was interrelated with, demands for *laisser faire* in commerce. Such demands took hold best where economic growth made a good domestic market appear more desirable than a favourable balance of trade and made tariffs appear more justified as a way of protecting home industry than of securing an advantage in trade abroad. Early in the seventeenth century, Grotius as an advocate of the Dutch East India Company argued in *De jure praedae* for the freedom of the high seas for all nations against Portuguese (and by implication Spanish, English, and other) claims of commercial and naval control. All during the eighteenth century the Physiocrats of France (Gournay, Cantillon, Quesnay, the elder Mirabeau, Mercier de la Rivière, Turgot, Dupont de Nemours, *et al.*), basing their economic theory on their premise of the exclusive productivity of land, taught the doctrine of *laisser faire*. They maintained that the king as chief landlord should be concerned to achieve the largest possible *produit net* for the entire country (and hence the highest possible revenue from taxes) rather than a favourable balance of trade; he would therefore be best advised not to tax commerce or industry.

In Hume's *Political Discourses* (1752) the mercantilist theory was both summarized and criticized. Hume advanced a quantity theory of money; he considered the stock of money within a country a determinant of prices and of consequent economic behaviour in the short run, even if it might be negligible in its long-run effect. He also pointed out the inconsistency between depending on foreign trade for a favourable balance and hoping thereby to achieve national self-sufficiency.

In 1776, as the steam engine began to speed up England's already partly industrialized economy and as the revolt of her American colonies shed doubt upon the wisdom of a programme of tight colonial mercantilism, Adam Smith published his *Wealth of Nations*. Although he conceded that the quest for opulence should take second place to considerations of national defence, he reasoned that a nation's resources were otherwise best exploited by a policy of autonomy in industry and markets: and although he recognized the importance of natural resources (land) in the production of wealth, he insisted upon labour and capital as component factors. He thus laid the foundation of classical economic theory while undermining the hold of old-style mercantilism. The last important work to champion the mercantilist system proved to be James Steward's *An Inquiry into the Principles of Political Oeconomy* (1767).

*   *   *

Trade and Economic Theories of Asia

The steady eastward flow of gold and silver, one of the major reasons for European economic speculation, was a cause for concern to the countries that received it, for the influx of bullion and the Western demands for certain Asian products brought higher prices to the Asians. No full-fledged theory of *laisser faire*, however, appeared outside of Europe during this period, for Asian theorists continued to look to government for correction of public evils. On the whole, they looked in vain. Each of the European trading powers attempted to monopolize as much of the trade of the East as it could, and the eager competition among the Western merchants encouraged local rulers to pursue their traditional policy of attracting precious metals into their domains. In general, the Western countries had little else to exchange that the Eastern peoples wanted, and so in return for spices, silks, and other Eastern commodities an uninterrupted stream of precious metal poured from Europe into India, China, and other countries of Asia. The ruling dynasties there found it profitable to continue much in the old ways to promote agriculture and the native crafts and to pursue traditional fiscal and tax policies.

Trade practices changed somewhat, however, as the Westerners acquired influence. The arrival of the Portuguese broke the Arab control of the spice trade, destroyed the Islamic commercial empire of Malacca, and did some damage to the trading activities of other mercantile peoples in the area. The Portuguese tried unsuccessfully to monopolize the spice trade, but the Dutch, after replacing them in the East Indies, succeeded in doing so. Yet Europeans did not completely dominate the foreign trade of southern and southeastern Asia until the nineteenth century, after the British and the French as well as the Portuguese and Dutch became entrenched there. The Spanish from the beginning of their control of the Philippines managed trade as a royal monopoly, but they encouraged Chinese traders and settlers from Fukien, who supplied them with silks and other Far Eastern products in return for

Spanish dollars. Thus the Mexican dollar was introduced into the Pacific area and came ultimately to be the chief medium of foreign trade in China and southeast Asia.

Some Eastern governments made an effort to assure what in the West was called 'a favourable balance of trade'. Perhaps Japan alone of the Eastern countries, because of her demand for Chinese silks, was a steady loser of precious metals. Besides the Chinese and the Japanese themselves, first the Portuguese and then the Dutch supplied Japan with these wares. In 1637—but not for bullion losses alone (see Chapter V)—Japan began a policy of national isolation and accordingly forbade its own shipping to go abroad and most foreign shipping to come to Japan. The strict limitation of Dutch and Chinese trade thereafter reduced the outflow of precious metals to a trickle. Ming China made similar efforts to forbid Chinese to trade abroad but could not keep them from dealing with Japan, the Philippines, Batavia, and Vietnam. It also tried to restrict 'barbarian' traders to tributary relations but did not prevent the Portuguese from establishing themselves in Macao (near Canton) or the Dutch in Formosa. The Dutch were driven from Formosa in 1661 by a Ming adherent, the famous Koxinga (Cheng Ch'eng-kung), during his struggle to resist the Manchus. Once entrenched in China, the Manchus pursued a somewhat more liberal policy toward foreign trade, although they succeeded in confining it to specified areas under quite rigid controls.

The eighteenth century was a period of peace and prosperity in China. Prosperity increased as the planting of two crops per season became common in south and central China and as new crops such as the sweet potato and maize were introduced from the West. In consequence, a rapid growth of population took place. Commenting on this phenomenon in a brief essay on the 'Reign of Peace', Hung Liang-chi (1746–1809) produced a theory of population somewhat similar to that of Malthus (see Volume V). Hung noted that during times of peace population increased much more rapidly than the food supply and that natural checks such as floods, famines, and epidemics did not eliminate the surplus population. As population grew, wages and the average rate of income declined while prices rose, unemployment increased, and the condition of the masses deteriorated. He saw no fundamental solution to this unhappy situation, but instead of leaving the outcome to the chances of an autonomous market, he recommended that government do all that it could to alleviate the problem by encouraging the cultivation of new lands, the better use of old lands, and the improvement of crops, by collecting taxes more equitably, and by enacting legislation to discourage waste and extravagance. In other essays he denounced the belief in fate and speculated on the respective roles of heredity and environment in the ceaseless struggle for existence.

In Japan, despite isolation and the feudal regime of the Tokugawas, a town-centred mercantile economy grew up. As in the West, the increase of commerce was accompanied by an increase in the use of money as a medium of exchange and by price fluctuations, which were damaging especially to the peasants and the samurai. These economic phenomena encouraged the period's most original speculations in the field of economic thought outside Europe. They were in the main a combination of ancient Chinese economic ideas, Confucian moral principles, and practical administrative measures aimed at solving a pressing economic problem.

Shortly after 1710 Arai Hakuseki, as Confucian adviser to the shogun, came forward with a series of proposals for dealing with high prices. In his view rising costs were caused by successive debasements of the coinage, and he proposed as a solution a sound coinage and a great reduction of the amount of money in circulation. He demonstrated a grasp of the quantity theory of money not inferior to that of its exponents in France and England about the same time. His philosophy, dominated by Confucian moral values, did not lead to *laisser faire*. Opposed to luxurious living, he favoured sumptuary legislation and the rigid control of foreign trade in order to limit the importation of luxury items, thereby also restricting the outflow of precious metals.

In 1725, in his *Siden* (*Political Discourses*), Ogyū Sorai, of the Classical School of Confucianism, provided a different analysis of the economic problem. By this time, although some prices had fallen. others still were high. Ogyū argued that the fundamental cause of the rise in prices was not the degradation of gold and silver or the increase in their quantity but the increase of demand for commodities created by the luxurious living habits of the samurai who had deserted the rural area for the cities, of the merchants, and even of the peasantry.[27] The programme he proposed included a return of the samurai to the rural areas, enforcement of simpler modes of life by tightened sumptuary legislation, the cancellation of debts, the restriction of future credits, the limitation of interest charges, some managed inflation, and an increase in the velocity of money circulation by the extensive coinage of copper.

In 1729 Dazai Shun's *Treatise on Political Economy* (*Keizai roku*) reviewed the whole field of economic activity. He gave separate chapters to food and wealth, government, social institutions, defence, music, and religion among other matters. His work was a composite of Chinese economic and moral maxims with Chinese and Japanese economic experience. Though it presented no really coherent economic theory, it compares in some ways with the philosophy of the French Physiocrats, who, in fact, also evinced interest in Chinese institutions. In general, while it fulminated against merchants, extravagance, and luxurious living, it advocated hard work, devotion to agriculture, and a simple natural economy in which great value would be placed on food and the necessities of life rather than on money. An ideal government could conduct a well regulated economy, Dazai felt, but for decadent times like his own he seemed to favour an essentially *laisser faire* policy.

Miura Baien (1723–89), about 1775, wrote a short treatise, *The Origin of Value*. He attributed real value to goods and held that economic trouble arose because of desire for money rather than for goods. He developed a quantity theory of money; its only use was as a medium of exchange, and if it increased without a corresponding increase in production, prices would rise, and idleness and wastefulness would result. He advocated the saving of commodities but not of money, the raising of wages to encourage efficiency, taxation of the rich to discourage idleness, and the use of public works and technical education to increase the production of essential goods. During the eighteenth century, along with these more scholarly works a considerable number of popular writings also appeared dealing with such matters as trade, agriculture, and money.

HISTORICAL THOUGHT

The Development of Historical Method in Europe

Whereas European historiography, it is sometimes said, was the servant of religion and eschatological during the Middle Ages, during the Renaissance it was the servant of classical literature and secularistic. While this generalization is only relatively correct, it is true that Renaissance historical techniques centred considerably more than those of the Middle Ages in the accurate textual criticism of Hebrew, Greek, and Latin classics. Outstanding examples of this pursuit were the application of philological techniques to the authentication and analysis of the False Decretals, particularly the so-called Donation of Constantine (see Chapter VIII).

The religious polemics of the sixteenth century, while re-emphasizing the providential interpretation that characterized medieval historiography, brought out more clearly than ever the necessity for careful textual criticism of venerated documents. The humanists' zeal in the study of Classical manuscripts was diverted by northern scholars to Biblical sources, in which they sought not only religious inspiration but also scholarly assurance. Erasmus cast doubt upon the textual accuracy of the Vulgate, the generally used and only church-approved Latin version of the Bible. Luther, in his search for salvation and for factual knowledge concerning the church, turned to the Bible, the Catholic Church fathers, and early church history. What such searchers believed they found was not always in keeping with what the Catholic Church taught, and Roman Catholic scholars, in turn, combed their church archives for evidence in favour of their side. Thus humanists, Protestant reformers, and Catholic apologists all contributed to a trend back to the original sources in the quest for historical truth.

The history of the Christian church which eventually came to be known as *The Magdeburg Centuries* (so-called because it was prepared at Magdeburg and organized by centuries) constituted a strategic weapon in this battle of the history books. Subsidized by several German Protestant princes and originally published (1559–74) as a seven-volume *Historia Ecclesiae Christianae*, it was a collaborative work by Lutheran scholars, the first church history from the Protestant point of view. Using ancient documentary materials, these Lutheran theologians, headed by Matthias Flacius, questioned the historical justification of some Catholic practices and institutions and vigorously attacked the dogmas and rituals, the persecutions and disciplinary measures of the medieval church, claiming that they were anti-Christian deviations from the pristine church to which the Protestants sought to return.

To counteract the impression *The Magdeburg Centuries* made, Filippo Neri requested one of the members of his Oratory, the learned Cardinal Caesar Baronius (1538–1607), to produce a work worthy of rivalling the Protestant account. The result was Baronius' *Ecclesiastical Annals* (*Annales Ecclesiastici a Christo nato ad annum* 1198), twelve volumes (1588–1607) containing many documents drawn from ecclesiastical archives. Despite numerous and sometimes justifiable criticism, the high level of competence of these two opposing works stands out in contrast to the unrelieved partisanship that characterized most of the polemics in the pamphlet war between Catholics and Protestants. *The Magdeburg Centuries* was the first great collection of original sources for the history of the Christian church, even if not a work of impartial scholarship. Baronius' *Annals* was no more impartial, but it, too, contained a formidable array of rare and useful documents.

The sharpening of history as a weapon in religious controversy led also to improvements in the knowledge of chronology. Joseph Justus Scaliger (1540–1609) found the study of chronology chiefly a listing of events in Greek and Roman history and made it a comparative discipline. A son of the famous philologist Julius Caesar Scaliger, he mistakenly supposed himself a descendant of the ancient Scala family of Verona, a mistake that was to cost him dear. He lived most of his life in France and Holland, recognized as the foremost classicist and critical historian of his day. He edited Classical texts, studied Ancient history, and dated every bit of historical information he could locate in time. By carefully collating Persian, Babylonian, Egyptian, and Jewish chronologies with the Greek and Roman, he provided a *Thesaurus Temporum* (1606), the basis of modern historical chronology. Converted to Protestantism, he ended his career at the University of Leyden, applying his critical abilities to the analysis of many documents that otherwise might have been used in support of Catholic interpretations of history.

Scaliger's most damaging attack was directed at Baronius. He published a twelve-volume work—about equal in size to Baronius' *Annals*—which was not a compilation of competing documents but a devastating analysis of Baronius' use of sources. Although Baronius had made a genuine effort to avoid error, Catholic scholars were never able successfully to refute the major points in Scaliger's case, especially after Isaac Casaubon fortified Scaliger's critique. The Jesuits in particular attempted to defend Baronius, even resorting to a successful refutation of Scaliger's claim of descent from the Scalas. This personal attack perhaps did something to hasten Scaliger's death but little to bolster the reliability of Baronius' conclusions.

Despite rival scholars' doubts regarding each other's methods, a large body of old source materials entered the common domain, encouraging the quest for and preservation of new ones. The preservation of the books and papers of the English monasteries after their dissolution by Henry VIII dictated the establishment (1578) of the State Paper Office (which about three centuries later became the Public Record Office). Similar central state archives were afterward created elsewhere (e.g. Stockholm in 1618). Great libraries were searched for historical records, not least of them the Vatican Library, of which Baronius was director, and assiduous scholars studied the authenticity of the records thus unearthed. Claims of venerability, divine inspiration, or Christian zeal were no longer regarded as sufficient tests, for always the hair-splitting criticism of dubious historians in the opposite camp had to be anticipated.

The Congregation of St Maur won for Catholic scholarship the leading role in establishing tests for the authenticity of historical source materials. The Maurists were a congregation of French Benedictines. Their principal monastery was at St Germain-des-Près in Paris, where they had established a school of historical studies. The writers of this school frequently made use of both unpublished material and printed collections of sources. By the mid-seventeenth century, a good historical library could assemble, in addition to the printed works mentioned above, a compilation of French and Norman writers by André Duchesne and the first volumes of the *Acta Sanctorum* of some Jesuit scholars working under Father John Bolland in Antwerp. With such a library at his disposal the Maurist Jean Mabillon embarked (1668) upon a set of *Acta Sanctorum* limited to Benedictine saints. The authors of this Benedictine work generally applied careful principles of dating, testing, textual comparison, emendation, and editing. When they were criticized by a Bollandist editor for improper exploitation of their sources, Mabillon explicitly expounded their method in *De Re Diplomatica* (1681). He thereby laid the foundations of the disciplines known as 'diplomatics' (the testing of the authenticity of medieval Latin manuscripts) and 'palaeography' (the reading of such manuscripts).

Perhaps the capstone in the scholarly study of medieval documents was the publication of Charles Du Fresne du Cange's *Glossarium ad Scriptores Mediae et Infimae Latinitatis* (Paris, 1678), a dictionary of medieval Latin. In 1688 Du Cange followed this work with a similar dictionary of medieval Greek. Although much medieval literature has been found and published since his day, these glossaries (supplemented from time to time by other scholars) remain the leading guides to the understanding of medieval Latin and Greek as well as early monuments of scholarly lexicography. Shortly thereafter (1708), Bernard de Montfaucon published a *Palaeographica*

Graeca. With the new methods and tools well-trained investigators could detect the general patterns of style, form, idiom, orthography, abbreviation, handwriting, and other characteristics of particular regions at particular times, and so eliminate all but the more clever forgeries and locate the genuine documents in time and place.

By the beginning of the eighteenth century the scholarly application of a series of sciences that historians ethnocentrically call 'auxiliaries to history' had come into being. The sciences of chronology, diplomatics, and palaeography made possible the careful editing of authentic medieval source materials. Epigraphy and archaeology, confined more closely to the field of Classical history, followed the same general lines of evolution. The humanists in their search for Classical manuscripts, coins, sculpture, and other relics of Greece and Rome, laid the foundations of the study of Ancient artifacts (archaeology) and of Ancient inscriptions (epigraphy). When the Roman architect and archaeologist Andrea Palladio (1518–80) published a scholarly study of the Ancient basilicas and other monuments of his city, religious history gained access to Ancient remains as a source of knowledge. By the end of the eighteenth century, national source collections were taking shape —Thomas Rymer's *Foedera*, etc. (1704–35), Dom Bouquet's *Recueil des Historiens de la Gaule et de la France* (1738–1833), L. A. Muratori's *Rerum Italicarum Scriptores* (1723–51), Leibniz's *Scriptores Rerum Brunvicensium* (1707–11), among others.

Parallel with the testing and compiling of original source materials went the progress of bibliographical techniques. In 1492 the learned Benedictine Johann Trithemius compiled a catalogue of church writers (*De Scriptoribus Ecclesiasticis*), a work which was continued about a half-century later by Cardinal Bellarmin. In 1545 Konrad von Gesner (1516–65) began to publish his *Bibliotheca Universalis*, containing bibliographical data on both sacred and secular works in Latin, Greek, and Hebrew. Thenceforth series after series of bibliographical works, especially concerning clerical writers, appeared, usually under the title *Bibliotheca*.

*   *   *

New Subjects of Historical Investigation

Meanwhile, the major themes of historical writing had undergone considerable change. The increasing availability of national collections of historical documents heightened the concentration upon a national and regional historiography imbued with a secular philosophy that assigned a primary role to human designs and character. In addition to his history of Florence, Guicciardini produced a *Storia d'Italia*, the first noteworthy Italian national history. While restricted to events of his own day (1492–1532), it attempted in ten volumes of great—even wearisome—detail to cover the political history of Italy as a whole rather than as a congeries of principalities. Though less famous and less influential than Machiavelli, Guicciardini was (as indicated in Chapter VIII) the more reliable historian; while he had had a hand in many of the events he narrated, his tone was dispassionate and his explanation fair. The Spanish historians Gerónimo de Zurita (1512–80) and Juan de Mariana (1536–1624) told the story of their country—Zurita that of Aragon to the death of Ferdinand, and Mariana that of Spain to the accession of Charles V in 1519. While Mariana was perhaps more patriotic than scholarly, Zurita was a careful student of the original records. The French historians Jacques August de Thou (1553–1617) and Theodore Agrippa d'Aubigné (1552–1630) each wrote a history of his own times, the times of the religious wars in France—de Thou as a moderate Catholic and d'Aubigné as a Protestant. De Thou's excellence lay in his effort to be judicious and to document his statements carefully; d'Aubigné's in his to be circumstantial and lively. Of a scholarly excellence comparable to de Thou's were the historical studies produced by Pufendorf, who was a professor at the University of Lund for a time and at Berlin during his later years. In addition to detailed histories of Sweden from the era of Gustavus Adolphus onward, he wrote scholarly biographies of the rulers of Sweden and Brandenburg.

A rising national spirit was discernible also in the historiography of Russia. Early in the sixteenth century Father Filofei, in epistles addressed to Prince Vasily III, Tsar Ivan III, and others, maintained that after Rome and Constantinople, Moscow was the 'third Rome' and there would never be a fourth. The chronicles of that century (foremost among them the *Chronicle of Nikon*) supplemented the older ones with numerous new official documents, lives of saints, legends, and other kinds of sources. About this time the connected narrative began to supersede the mere chronicle. The *Stepennaya Kniga* (*Book of Generations*), instead of recording events year by year, organized them by generations of tsars, narrating the lives of the metropolitans as well. The *Chronograph* (1512) was an early attempt at universal history from Creation to the fall of Constantinople in 1453 centring on Russia; later additions took it to the election of Michael Romanov as tsar. The *Synopsis* (1674) was the first printed textbook of Russia's history (from the founding of Kiev to the times of Tsar Alexis); it eventually went to thirty editions. Thus when Tatishchev prepared his five-volume *History of Russia* (to 1533), which he presented to the St Petersburg Academy in 1739, he had a considerable quantity of sources to draw upon in addition to the documents that he had himself discovered. Gerhard Friedrich Müller (1705–83), a German member of the St Petersburg Academy, who had been with Behring's expedition, compiled a voluminous collection of documents on Siberian history and prepared other extensive works, either in Russian or in German, on Siberia and Russia. The uncritical methods of these predecessors induced Lomonosov to undertake an *Ancient Russian History*, insisting that an indication of interconnections in the historical process was at least as important as the collection of mere facts, but he never finished his task. By this time Russian historiography was not only nationalist in theme but also secular in outlook.

The renewed interest in church history tended to encourage still another method of historical presentation, namely biography. In the effort to rebut the historical arguments of rival churches, ecclesiastical writers composed biographical works in goodly number. Stage by stage Roman Catholic patrology, hagiology, and martyrology led toward an enormous undertaking that should deal with every Christian saint. A forerunner of this enterprise was Bishop Aloysius Lipomanus's *Sanctorum Priscorum Patrum Vitae* (1551–60), but a Flemish Jesuit, Heribert Rosweyde, author of a *Vitae Patrum* (1615), actually laid out a plan for a more formidable series. Finally, in 1643 Father Bolland began the above-mentioned *Acta Sanctorum Quotquot Toto Orbe Coluntur*, which is still in progress. Some years later (1668) Mabillon began the Maurist *Acta* of Benedictine saints, and rivalry between the two Catholic groups of hagiologists resulted in the criticism that, as earlier indicated, led to his *De Re Diplomatica*.

Even before the Catholic *Acta Sanctorum* had taken shape, John Foxe (1516–87) produced a work that was a Protestant analogue. While in exile at Strasbourg during Mary Tudor's reign, Foxe wrote—in Latin—a *History of Christian Persecutions* (to the year 1500), with special emphasis on Wycliffe and Huss. Eventually (in 1563) this work emerged in English as the famous *Book of Martyrs* under a lengthy title that indicates the book's polemical purpose and its method: *Actes and Monuments of these latter and Perillous Dayes, touching matters of the Church, wherein are comprehended and described the great Persecution and horrible Troubles that have been wrought and practised by Romishe Prelates, speciallye in this Realme of England and Scotland, from the yeare of our Lorde a thousande to the time now present. Gathered and collected according to the true Copies and Wrytinges certificatorie as well as the Parties themselves that suffered as also out of the Bishop's Registers, which were the Doers thereof.* Immensely popular in post-Marian England, Foxe's *Martyrs* was refuted in certain details by Roman Catholic writers and so was corrected and republished. A frankly propagandist work, it was inferior to the *Acta Sanctorum* in scholarly accuracy but nonetheless exerted wide influence during and after the author's lifetime, serving as an ever-ready handbook for zealous Protestants.

Meanwhile the widening geographical horizons brought a new concept of world history, which we have already examined in Chapter VII in connection with its impact on theological thought. The common medieval interpretation of history had been based on Biblical prophesy: after the fall from Paradise man would move through a succession of four terrestrial empires, three of which were already past, until he regained Paradise. In 1566 Bodin in his *Methodus ad Facilem Historiarum Cognitionem* departed from prophesy and sought to explain history rather as a progressive succession of racial cultures. Bishop Bossuet's (1679) was the last significant effort to write a world history based upon Christian teleology. In the next generation Vico suggested substituting the sense of human development and recapitulative experience (a view since sometimes called *historicism*) for providential design as the key to the understanding of history, and though Vico was relatively neglected in his own day, Montesquieu, who independently had arrived at much the same philosophy, was not. Furthermore, as the knowledge of the non-Christian world and the awareness of empires unknown to the prophet Daniel accumulated, Europe's historians were required to take account of empires and cultures they could not help but esteem in the Islamic lands, India, the Far East, and America. Voltaire's *Essais sur les moeurs et l'esprit des nations* (1756) spoke of Japan and Peru as well as of Europe, and Montesquieu sought illustrations for his *Esprit des Lois* (1748) in all parts of the world. From Bodin through Vico and Montesquieu to Burke and Justus Möser interest in law, the arts, literature, science, and other cultural manifestations as genetic and organic institutions and in peoples rather than rulers as the carriers of 'civilization' (a new word in the eighteenth century) deepened, and the co-existence of several peoples with different national spirits and regional cultures became more acceptable as a historical thesis, taking precedence over that of an inevitable succession of universal empires leading toward the ultimate triumph of Christianity.

Thus, in the eighteenth-century Enlightenment the Catholic ideal of a world united into one triumphant Christian empire gave way to the view of history as the common adventure of humanity. At the same time, the decline of the ideal of a 'catholic' empire was reflected in a growing number of national histories. The Earl of Clarendon's *True Historical Narrative of the Rebellion and Civil Wars in England* (1702–04), Ludvig Holberg's *History of the Realm of Denmark* (1732–35), Tatishchev's *History of Russia* (1739), Voltaire's *Siècle de Louis XIV* (1751), Hume's *History of England* (1754–61), and William Robertson's *History of Scotland during the Reigns of Queen Mary and of King James VI* (1759) are among the outstanding examples of histories centred upon a national theme. The number of biographies of the heroes of great nations also grew—among them Pufendorf's of the Great Elector (1695), Voltaire's of Charles XII (1731) and Peter the Great (1759), Robertson's of Charles V (1769).

The contemporary vogue of Neoclassicism in literature (see Chapter XI) and art (see Chapter XII) brought with it a broadened, secularized interpretation of the history of Antiquity. Edward Gibbon in *The Decline and Fall of the Roman Empire*, which began to appear in 1776, gave an account of that empire from Trajan's time through the Middle Ages which focused upon Byzantine affairs and the Islamic cultures rather than upon Rome and the papacy, and was none too friendly to the triumph of Christianity in the West. Johann Joachin Winckelmann in his *Geschichte der Kunst des Altertums* (1764), relying on the recent finds in Herculaneum and Pompeii, emphasized the importance of artifacts along with written sources in an appraisal of ancient cultures, and dealt with Egyptian and Persian as well as Greek and Roman culture. He conceived of art as capable of substantive development independent of the lives or persuasions of artists, and Grecian art was for him far superior to the Christian art of the Middle Ages and the Renaissance. Thus, along with their contemporary Voltaire, Gibbon and Winckelmann in different ways made of history a weapon with which to attack traditional Christian preferences, a spyglass with which to sweep an ever widening theatre of human affairs, and a source of a philosophy of progress unlike any that the concepts of original sin and redemption and of the plenitude of God could have permitted.

*   *   *

Islamic, Hindu, and Southeast Asian Historiography

Throughout the Dār al-Islām historical writing continued abundant, usually dealing with the local or regional Muslim community, its learned men, and its rulers. Significant work was done by a series of perceptive Turkish historians, the most celebrated being ‘Alī Chelebi of the late-sixteenth century, who like many other scholars could write prose without over-affectation despite the heritage of floridity from the waning Middle Ages. Late in this period several Turkish historians attempted to analyse the causes of the gradual decline of the Ottoman administrative and military structure.

The Islamic historians at the Mogul court were particularly prolific, producing several works of first-rate importance, which, however, suffered from the defects noted in the previous chapter—narrowness of conception, sectarian moralizing, and flattery of patrons. The memoirs of the emperors Bābur and Jahāngīr, *Bābar-nāma* and *Tūzak-i Jahāngīrī*, had genuine historical merit, but probably the best contemporary history of the period was Abu’l Faḍl’s *Akbar-nāma*. It included the *A’īn-i-Akbarī* (*Institutes of Akbar*), with invaluable information on economic and institutional matters; its purely historical parts covered the Moguls from Timur’s time to 1602. With breadth of view and eloquence of style, it sang the praise of Akbar. By way of counterbalance, the orthodox writer al-Badā’uni, who also served at Akbar’s court, left a rather critical account of the reign in his *Muntakhab-al-Tawārīkh*. Probably the best general history of Moslem India was the *Ta’rīkhi-i Firishta* of Muḥammad Kāsim Hindu-Shāh Firishta, completed about 1620 at the court of Bijapur. In addition to an introduction dealing with Hindu India, it contained histories of all the Islamic kingdoms of India and concluded with an account of India’s Muslim saints, its climate, and its geography. Among the histories of the reign of Aurangzīb was the *Muntakhab-al-Lubāb* of Muḥammad Hāshim (Khāfi Khān).

During this period Hindu India’s most notable historical works were epic poems. Though not purely Hindu, probably the outstanding one was the *Padumāvatī* (*c.* 1540) of Malik Muḥammad Jāyasi, a Persian scholar at a Rajput court. It dealt in a general way with the siege of Chitor by Emperor Alā-ud-din in 1303. The poet, though a Muslim, had been profoundly influenced by Kabīr and wrote his poem in Hindi, generously embroidering it with details borrowed from Hindu mythology and ending with an allegorical religious interpretation. Many other bardic chronicles were produced in Hindi at the courts of the Rajputs; the *Chhatra Prakāsh* of Lāl Kavi, dealing with the history of the rajas of Bundelkhand to about 1730, was one of the most distinguished of them. The Vijayanāgar emperor Krishnadeva wrote in Telegu a notable epic, the *Āmuktamālyada*, which throws light upon the society and institutions of his reign (1509–29). In the seventeenth century several historical poems on Mysore appeared in Karanese.

The historiography of Southeast Asia consisted of little more than the chronicles and annals of the several kingdoms. Many of them were works of imagination rather than of sober history, and the best of them tended to mix fact with folklore and legend. They were usually defective in chronology, laudatory of their royal patrons, and confined to events connected with the royal courts. The oldest surviving Burmese chronicle, a late-fifteenth-century work by monk Shin Thilawuntha, has a mythological approach that renders it of little historical value. Benna Dala wrote in Talaing (*c.* 1570) a chronicle of Razadarit, king of Pegu (1385–1423). A chronicle written by Mg Kala about 1724 dealt with the Toungoo dynasty, which began in 1486. The *Shwemawdaw Thamaing* was a record kept at the Shwemawdaw pagoda in Pegu over a long period of time. For Siam, the *P'ongsawadan* (or *Chronicles of Ayut'ia*) was compiled about 1680; it is generally more reliable than later accounts. A Pali religious work, the *Jinakalamalini*, put together at Chiengmai about 1516 by the priest Rat'ana Panyayana, dealt with the rulers of the northern Thai area. The oldest extant Cambodian chronicle, completed sometime before 1796, survives in a Siamese edition; it covers about a century beginning in 1346. Laos had its annals, and the *Sejarah Melayu* (*Malay Annals*) dealt with Malacca and the Malay Islamic world. The *Badah Tanah Djawi*, written in Javanese prose, was the principal chronicle for Java. Accounts of Islamic kingdoms in the Philippines were recorded in Moro *Tarsilas* (*Chronicles*).

*   *   *

Historiography in the Far East

Vietnam and Korea compiled annals of a somewhat superior quality, modelled on the *Shih-lu*, the dynastic annals, of China. The *Dai Viêt sur ky* (*Annals of Great Viet*), produced in Vietnam between 1672 and 1675, covered that country's history from the beginning to the seventeenth century. The *Tongkuk Tongham* (*Mirror of the East Country*), which was prepared shortly before 1500, covered Korea's whole history, and the *Yijo Sillok* (*Annals of the Yi Dynasty*, which began in 1392) were regularly prolonged by an account of each reign after its close.

Chinese historical scholarship was probably at its best in the seventeenth and eighteenth centuries Although none of it would rival the historical classics in literary worth, a large body of historical literature of scholarly and critical quality was produced. This quality stood out especially after the critical scholars of the seventeenth century and of the School of Han Learning freed historical scholarship from the biases of Sung Neo-Confucian philosophy. The government continued to patronize the traditional official histories. The *Ming History* (*Ming shih*), compiled between 1678 and 1739 by a group of able historians, was completed under the supervision of Chang T'ing-yü. It was, generally speaking, superior to the Sung and Yüan dynastic histories. The *Shih-lu* of each of the Ch'ing (Manchu) emperors was regularly prepared after his death. Various supplements brought the famous *Comprehensive Mirror* of Ssu-ma Kuang (eleventh century) up to date, those by Hsü Ch'ien-hsüeh (1631–94) and by Pi Yüan (1730–97) being perhaps the best. The *Abridged Comprehensive Mirror* of Chu Hsi was also brought up to date. So were the several encyclopaedic treatises on history and institutions such as the *T'ung-tien* and *T'ung-chih*; Wang Ch'i provided (*c.* 1586) the most important individual effort of this sort. The encyclopaedia was in a sense a Chinese invention, although the Chinese encyclopaedia was more like an anthology than a collection of original essays. The great encyclopaedia of the Ch'ing period, the *Ku-chin t'u-shu chi-ch'eng*, in 10,000 chapters (*chüan*), was compiled during the K'ang-hsi period and published with moveable copper type in 1726.

The most important Chinese historiographical works of the period probably were the shorter monographs by the great critical scholars. These studies challenged the authenticity of early texts, commented upon, supplemented or corrected prior works, or dealt with particular questions within a wide range of subjects such as historical geography, philosophy, government, education, literature, jurisprudence, religion, art, music, politics, agriculture, crafts, currency, folkways, and medicine. Among the writers of such monographs were Huang Tsung-hsi, Ku Yen-wu, and Yen Jo-chü (who have already been considered in Chapter VII or earlier in this chapter). Yao Chiheng (1647–1715) and Ku Tung-kao (1679–1759) challenged the authenticity of early works. Ts'ui Shu (1740–1816) in *K'ao-hsin lu* (*A Record of Beliefs Investigated*) exposed the 'stratified fabrications of ancient history', showing how the myths of certain ancient rulers had been built up by later writers. Chao I (1727–1814) produced critical notes on the twenty-two dynastic histories. Ch'en Ching-yün (1670–1747) discussed mistakes in the 'fundamental elements' of the *Comprehensive Mirror*. And Hang Shih-chün (1696–1773) attempted to distinguish the verified from the doubtful in the dynastic histories.

Chang Hsüeh-ch'eng (1738–1801), a younger contemporary of Gibbon and Voltaire and perhaps the best of China's critical historians of the period, deserves to be ranked with the world's most prominent historiographical theorists, although he was not so recognized during his lifetime. The chief author of several local histories or gazetteers, he also laid down principles intended to improve historical scholarship. He strongly favoured general cultural historiography as affording the best opportunity to show the genetic aspect of history and the manifoldness of the factors that influenced historical development. His ideas on this subject were set forth in his *Fundamental Principles of Cultural History* (*Wen-shih t'ung-i*), while his *Fundamental Principles of Historical Criticism* (*Chiao-ch'ou t'ung-i*) discussed historical method, especially textual criticism. He believed that 'history is normative in that it provides fundamental principles governing humanity and is not merely a collection of records or reports of events'.[28] The historian, he held, must be more than a compiler, must have broad learning, creative ability, insight, and critical judgment and should be free to shape his history as the material dictated. Chang maintained that too great attention to formal patterns of historical writing had led to a decline in the quality of Chinese historiography. He criticized some historians for having insight without learning, others for having learning without method, and still others for having method without insight. He himself never wrote a general history of the type he so firmly upheld, thus in a sense violating his belief that 'knowledge' and 'action' should be inseparable.

In Japan during the Tokugawa period, as a result of the influence of Confucian scholarship, historiography attained a respectable position. Hayashi Razan, exponent of the official Chu Hsi school of philosophy, began a history of Japan, which was finished by his son, Harukatsu, about 1675 under the title *Honchō Tsūgan*. Modelled on the *Abridged Comprehensive Mirror* of Chu Hsi, it became Japan's official history. It betrayed the faults but lacked the general factual accuracy of its Chinese prototype. Arai Hakuseki wrote an autobiography, entitled *Burning Faggots*, and two historical works— *Hankampu* (1701), a history of the *daimyos* from 1600 to 1680, and *Tokushi Yoron* (1712), a general history of Japan. The Shinto nationalists also were active in ferreting out the details of early Japanese history, but they were interested less in accuracy and understanding than in praising what was native and damning what was borrowed from China.

Japan's most important historiographical enterprise was associated with the Historical (or Mito) School of Confucian studies sponsored by Tokugawa Mitsykuni (1628–1700) and his successors as head of the Mito branch of the Tokugawa family. This school of historians was greatly aided, and their scholarship probably rendered more thorough and sound, by Chu Chih-yü and other refugee critical scholars from China. They were, nevertheless, motivated by a nationalistic bias, which caused them to search for things uniquely Japanese and to exalt the imperial institution. Under Mitsukuni's leadership, a chain of scholars, eventually including Kuriyama Sempo (1671–1706), Azaka (1656–1737), and Miyaka Kwanran (1675–1712), began about 1657 the compilation of the *Dai Nihonshi* (*History of Great Japan*). The first part, the imperial chronicles, was completed about 1709, but the whole not until the early twentieth century. It centred attention upon the throne, providing support for the eventually triumphant conviction that the shogunate should be abolished and the emperor restored to his true position.

THE ENLIGHTENMENT AND SOCIAL THOUGHT

For some historians the period of the Enlightenment in Europe began when La Bruyère wrote *Les Caractères* at the close of the seventeenth century.[29] His indignant reproach of the self-satisfied members of society who either themselves oppressed the wretched or were indifferent to oppression by others and his heart-rending descriptions of the misery of the poor may not have initiated but certainly gave eloquent reinforcement to a nascent trend in secular letters—social consciousness. In France a succession of writers took up the plea for greater social justice. It will suffice here to recall a few of those considered elsewhere in other chapters in other contexts. Vauban sought a new system of revenue that would tax the rich in order to alleviate the poor. Fénelon endeavoured to teach pacifism and paternalism to his royal pupil. Meslier's *Testament* combined an exposition of materialism with an attack on the clergy, urging the distribution of church property so as to give land to those who were the recipients of charity. Rousseau lamented that the prying of tax officials obliged the peasants to hide even the little that they had. Mably and Morelly advocated a system of society in which property would be held in common for the mutual benefit of all. In addition, a score or more of hopeful authors from Tyssot de Payot at the close of the seventeenth century to Louis Sebastian Mercier and Restif de la Bretonne at the end of the eighteenth century set forth utopias that steadily progressed from imaginative descriptions of a never-never-land in the direction of blueprints for a planned society.

The age-old hope that society might be so organized as to provide justice for all rather than privilege for the few seemed more than an idle dream or a devout prayer to men like these. For in the eighteenth century it drew not only on the ancient sources of righteous indignation at social injustice and of pious wishes for a nobler world but on the course of modern science as well. Until the middle of the eighteenth century social betterment was counted upon to come not merely through the beneficence of the ruling classes but rather through the accumulation of knowledge and the improvement of human institutions. Francis Bacon at the beginning of the seventeenth century had claimed that the growing accumulation of scientific knowledge would, among other things, lead to the amelioration of society, and at the beginning of the next century the Abbé de Sainte-Pierre wrote several books propagating the conviction that, by the application not only of science but also of reason to human problems, man could perfect his institutions, whether local postal services or councils for collective international action.

Some of the bolder spirits of the eighteenth century went even further along these lines. The growing awareness that outside of Europe there existed societies that were happy and peaceful, while lending support to an older persuasion—that the fundamental nature of man, 'man in the state of nature', is essentially good—pointed to a newer persuasion—that he is also capable of continuous achievement by his own unaided efforts. Some travellers like the Baron La Hontan in America and Louis Antoine de Bougainville in Tahiti, and some, like Raynal, who had never travelled outside of Europe but had picked up hither and yon consoling notions about exotic cultures, made current an exoticism that was perhaps too roseate and sanguine. Certainly the *bon sauvage* rarely seemed to those who knew him personally quite so attractive as he appeared to the devotees of the current vogue in Europe. Yet the Chinese sage seemed astonishingly wise even to those who had seen him in China. Jesuit reports made literate Europeans familiar with the high level of Chinese culture, and the strife over Chinese theological beliefs between Dominicans and Jesuits in the notorious Rites Controversy at the close of the seventeenth century (see Chapter V) drew the attention of the learned world of the West to several striking similarities between the Chinese creeds and Christianity. Deists in England, *philosophes* in France, and philosophers like Leibniz and Wolff in Germany wondered whether truth, goodness, and justice were indeed a European monopoly and whether the answers to questions of ethical conduct, if valid at all, were not valid for humanity as a whole. No matter how the *philosophes* might disagree about European man, they believed that humanity's lowest common denominator was high indeed. Furthermore, although Defoe's Moll Flanders and Prévost's Manon Lescaut did not find the new Americans entirely beyond reproach, American Quakers, Pilgrims, and frontiersmen were often considered object lessons in the beneficial effects of a 'return to nature'.

This sort of speculation on the comparative nature of humanity was but one manifestation of the current interest in what are now called the social sciences. Man's growing curiosity about his inner nature, about human psychology, was betrayed likewise in a flood of searching, introspective memoirs and autobiographies (of which those of St Simon, Rousseau, Boswell, Franklin, and Casanova are perhaps the most famous), written with candour and lengthy detail for all to scan. The concern with the workings of the human mind combined with philosophical, scientific, and educational factors examined elsewhere (see Chapters VIII, XV, and XVI, for example) to send authors in quest of a better understanding of human institutions. Descartes' and Rousseau's indifference[30] to history was counterbalanced by Vico's, Montesquieu's, Burke's, and Justus Möser's insistence that man could best be understood by his place in history, and his institutions by an examination of how they had come to be what they were. This emphasis upon man as a historically determined being, with institutions that were, so to speak, organically derived from their historical context, gave rise, as seen above, to the philosophical attitude later known as 'historicism'. Where the great historians of the sixteenth century had written religious polemic (e.g.

Flacius and Baronius) and those of the seventeenth and early-eighteenth had engaged in accumulating and editing collections of sources (e.g. Mabillon and Muratori), those of the late-eighteenth sought to explain what caused the growth and decline of cultures (Montesquieu, Gibbon, Voltaire). In general, history taught them as historians the same lesson (*vide* Condorcet) that 'natural philosophy' taught them as *philosophes*—the lesson that man was capable of self-propelled progress and was destined to indefinite perfectibility.

The growing middle class of Europe looked upon the *philosophes* as allies. It believed, for the most part, that enlightened monarchy was the best form of government and usually, as we have instanced several times, was on the side of the monarch in his disputes with the privileged classes. Middle-class spokesmen tended to regard with particular favour those *philosophes* who came after Montesquieu but did not support his plea in the *Esprit des Lois* for a *monarchie nobiliaire*—that is, for checking royal authority through an honoured and privileged social class. Even the views of *philosophes* like Bayle and Voltaire on freedom from an established church—views generally unacceptable to other segments of society—were welcome to many of the middle class—not merely to Protestants, Jansenists, and other dissident groups but frequently also to the Catholic bourgeoisie. Indeed, some Catholic churchmen, while favouring a state church and certainly disapproving of Voltaire's campaign against the *infame*, did not oppose toleration of Protestants and objected to the privileges of the upper clergy. Thus, the *philosophes* found a ready audience for their incisive observations upon the favoured position of the nobility, whether it was in the military services, government, church, taxes, society, local economic organization, landholding, or other profitable and honorific institutions and influential posts. In fact, the *philosophes* rarely originated—more often, rather, they only reflected and articulated—the views of the bourgeoisie on the privileged classes. The levelling of privileges was the common and major objective of middle class and *philosophes*; the feudal abuses and social injustices that weighed down the overwhelming majority of Europe's population was for them an important but a subordinate target.

*   *   *

The Artist as Social Critic

The artists joined in the battle for 'enlightenment' to a much more limited extent than the men of letters. Although the art of Poussin and the writings of Félibien in seventeenth-century France upheld the moral purpose of art and were concerned with showing noble figures and actions and, in a sense, a rational, ethical world, they were not greatly concerned with social thought. Jacques Callot's 'Miseries of the War' (1633) depicted pillaging, fires, fighting, and hangings but in a manner that passed no judgment on war or violence; and his series ended with the distribution of rewards by the ruler at his court, making war appear to have been glorious and worth-while. Satires in the form of prints were directed against rulers and popes by various Germans in the early-sixteenth century, and against Louis XIV by the Dutch in the seventeenth, but few of them can be classified as art. Leonardo da Vinci and, in the seventeenth century, Bernini, LeBrun, and others did caricature-like studies of men with animal features revealing their innate temperament and appear to have prepared the tool of caricature for the service of enlightenment, but William Hogarth, who began engraving on copper around 1720, is the only major figure explicitly associated with caricature before 1775. He, too, revealed the temperaments of men through animal-like features. While his 'Marriage à la Mode' and 'The Rake's Progress' seem mere commentaries on human nature with little expectation that loveless marriages and rakes would disappear (Pl. 23), his series on cruelty to animals and against drinking and his 'Gin Lane' appear to be clearly directed toward the improvement of society. To be sure, scenes from contemporary and particularly carnival life were painted or etched with wit and documentary detail by the Tiepolo family and Pietro Longhi in Venice, and in Genoa Alessandro Magnasco, with much greater fantasy and decorative intent, depicted grandiloquent scenes of monastic life, synagogues, and everyday events of the city. In the art of the Italians, however, Hogarth's moral purpose is absent.

Several painters of the eighteenth century revealed the sympathy for human suffering, the *sensibilité*, characteristic of Rousseau and other *philosophes*. Jean-Baptiste Chardin's paintings, usually dealt with everyday, touching, intimate human relations, and Jean-Baptiste Greuze gained fame for the moral messages of his paintings, dealing with subjects like 'A Father's Curse' or 'The Paralytic Tended by his Children', but apparently they fell short of explicit concern for 'social thought'. Portraits in which nobles were depicted as shepherds or gypsies seem to have been conceived in a completely playful spirit. In Spain the imitation of the *majos* and *majas* ('gypsies') by leading members of the court reached an extreme not paralleled elsewhere in Europe, but this fad can only with some straining be interpreted as expressive of democratic leanings on the part of the nobility. In the tapestry series done by Maella, Bayeau, and Goya in the second half of the eighteenth century various scenes from the life of common people are depicted, but they do not seem to have been intended to convey a social message.

The studied use of art as an instrument for the spread of social ideas was just beginning as our period ends. Jacques-Louis David's expositions on civic duty and loyalty came closer to such concerns than the work of his predecessors, but his paintings began at the point where our period ends. When Goya produced the original sketches of his 'Caprichos' (1794), he made clear his purpose—to comment on the foibles of society—as if he had had no predecessors in that regard.

★　　　★　　　★

The 'Enlightened Despots' and the philosophes

The so-called 'enlightened despots' fo the eighteenth century, of course, knew or, at least, knew of the *philosophes* and their writings. Frederick of Prussia, when he was not annoyed by Voltaire as a neighbour, considered him a personal friend. Catherine of Russia invited Diderot, Mercier de la Rivière, and other *philosophes* to visit her court, treated them handsomely, permitted their works to be translated into Russian, and had the libraries of Voltaire and Diderot transported to Russia. German princelings corresponded with Rousseau. And yet, great though the interest of the 'enlightened despots' usually was in French social and political philosophy, they were not exclusively dependent on the French *philosophes* for theoretical formulae. They were usually quite capable of deriving their own formulae from their own traditions and situations, and they had other good minds close at hand. The German Aufklärung had such intellectual lights as Leibniz, Thomasius, Wolff, Lessing, and the Cameralists; the Russians had Tatishchev, Lomonosov, Prince A. D. Kantemir, translator and satirist, Nikolai Ivanovitch Novikov, editor and principal author of two courageous serial publications and publisher of numerous books, and T. A. Tretyakov and S. E. Desnitsky, public-spirited professors at the new (1755) University of Moscow; and the list could well be prolonged for these and other 'enlightened' countries. Nearly all contemporary intellectuals, however, whether crowned heads or middle-class critics, tended at least to pay lip service to and sometimes actually to follow the lead of the French *philosophes*.

Anyway, the 'enlightened despots' did not really need intellectuals and formulae to guide them. Opportunism generally was enough to persuade them to be paternalistic, and it was not necessary for their purpose to subscribe to any rationalist theory of human perfectibility or of natural rights. They usually were induced to undertake their programmes of reform not by theories but by practical considerations—by such arguments as that ecclesiastical and aristocratic privileges were a menace to royal power as well as to national welfare and that hopeful and prosperous subjects made better soldiers, producers, and taxpayers than did the downtrodden. None of these rulers more earnestly attempted paternalistic reform than Emperor Joseph II, who took steps in his Habsburg lands in the direction of emancipation of serfs, redistribution of tax loads, confiscation of church lands, toleration of dissidents and Jews, promotion of commerce, uniformity of justice, and other objectives approved by the *philosophes*; yet Joseph made no secret of the fact that he looked upon kingship as a hard-headed business, and once he deliberately slighted Voltaire. Frederick could not get along with Voltaire in person. Catherine enjoyed talking to Diderot but seems to have considered him somewhat academic, and in her later years, frightened by the Pugachev rebellion and the French Revolution, she sent critics of her regime like Novikov and young Alexander Nikolaevich Radishchev to jail.

If the reforms of the absolute monarchs did not spring full-fledged from the brains of the intellectuals, the 'enlightened despots' nevertheless helped to spread the *philosophes'* ideas. Not only did some of the monarchs befriend the *philosophes* and express admiration for their philosophy but they also gave currency to the *philosophes'* writings, patronized their plays, and promoted the academies, clubs, salons, and *sociétés de pensées* in which their latest views were aired. Most of the *philosophes*, in their turn, were believers in enlightened monarchy. The time was not far off, however, when enlightened monarchy would prove manifestly inadequate to meet the rising demands for reform, and then the more radical ideas of the *philosophes* like popular sovereignty, the abolition of aristocratic privileges, and church disestablishment would come to have an almost irresistible power (see Volume V).

NOTES TO CHAPTER IX

1. In Professor R Polin's opinion Calvin, like Luther, participated in a stronger affirmation of the individual and of individual liberties by developing the doctrine of free right of criticism while at the same time contributing to a reinforcement of the powers of the sovereign by freeing them from the bounds which medieval philosophy had often sought to impose on them. Their influence thus tended both toward individualism and toward a self-critical form of absolutism.

2. *Discourses on Livy*, Book III, ch. xli.

3. While the expression *raison d'état* does not appear in Machiavelli, it is clear that a rational political system such as he elaborated must order the means at its disposal in relation to its aims. Moral considerations and forces are, however, included in such a calculation. 'Human actions are judged by their results.'

   While faith in the divine right of established kings may constitute one such moral force, his theory of power based on understanding of natural necessities and rational calculation of the use of force have no common measure. The 'moralism' of this appeal to divine right may, in his view, be no more than a means of 'propaganda'.

   But nothing in Machiavelli's viewpoint prevents the aim of a policy from being a moral value as, indeed, appears to be the case with his own political concept. (Raymond Polin.)

4. *La République*, Book I, ch. viii.

5. *Ibid.*, ch. x.

6. Professor R. Polin indicates an important exception: when life is threatened by the sovereign the contract is broken and each citizen regains the right to revolt. Not the least paradoxical aspect of the work of Hobbes is the fact that the justification of absolute sovereignty is also the basis of claims to the inalienable rights of the individual.

7. *Leviathan*, Part I, ch. xiii.

8. Professor R. Polin argues that whereas Machiavelli calculates rationally the technical conditions of effective political action, whatever its object, Hobbes, on the other hand, calculates rationally the organization of institutions designed to lead infallibly to peace. For Hobbes, political necessity is based neither on religious bond nor on moral obligation, but on the necessity for rational calculation. For him, too, absolute rationalism leads to the justification of absolute sovereignty. The logical outcome of the system should normally be a reasonable sovereign.

9. Professor R. Polin notes that by this theory of law as by his theory of consent, Hobbes was one of the first to help direct the political thought of the Reformation into the path of liberalism. His influence on Locke is marked.

10. *The Works of That Learned and Judicious Divine, Mr Richard Hooker* (ed. John Keble, Oxford, 1845), III, pp. 343–44.

11. In Professor R. Polin's opinion, starting from the principles of Hobbes Spinoza arrived at very different conclusions, setting limits to the power of the sovereign in order to safeguard the freedom of the citizen. He counts heavily on liberty of expression and the resulting education of both citizens and governments to direct the state into reasonable and liberal paths.

12. Professor R. Polin thinks the following points should be stressed: the *Two Treatises*, written in about 1680–82, were directed at least as much against Filmer as against Hobbes. If not actually designed to justify the revolution of 1688, they at least tended in this direction by insisting on the limits to be imposed on the power of governments, whether these were limits inherent in the nature of human affairs (the law of nature, certain inalienable natural laws, particularly the right to judge for oneself) or limits established by contracts based on free consent. Locke, in fact, distinguished three sorts of power, but he did not consider them as truly separate and is therefore very far removed from a theory of check and balance of power, an idea essentially attributable to Montesquieu. It is the concept of trust and trusteeship which determines the relations between the government and the governed; and in case of breach of contract this trust can be challenged on behalf of the people. In fact, the people, the nation taken as a whole, is considered to be the source of all sovereignty, because, as such, it is reasonable. Thus we find expressed here a liberal and individualist doctrine and a theory of the sovereignty of the people both of which were destined to exert a great influence on the development of ideas and of political regimes in Europe for more than two hundred years.

13. Professor R. Polin points out in addition that Montesquieu above all proposes a theory of political government by demonstrating that the successful functioning of a regime of any kind depends, on the one hand, on the compatibility between the nature of that regime and the sum of natural and social conditions in which it is placed and, on the other hand, on the compatibility, the cohesion, between existing institutions and laws and the nature of the regime and the principle which inspires and sustains it. On this descriptive, quasi-sociological analysis is superimposed an option in favour of the liberal regime most rationally adapted to conditions of political life in Europe. Montesquieu opts for a moderate monarchy and finds in the separation of powers and in their reciprocal balance the means of preserving liberties and of checking the abuses and the arbitrary nature of uncontrolled and unlimited power. (See also above, pp. 514 and 539.)

14. Abu'l Fazl 'Allāmī, *The Ā'īn-i Akbarī* (2nd ed., Calcutta, 1927), Vol. I (tr. H. F. Blockman), pp. 2–9, especially p. 4.

15. Professor R. Polin warns that the greatest circumspection must be exercised in applying western political concepts to the description and interpretation of the political thought of other civilizations. The West itself finds it difficult to attribute to such concepts a well-defined, unequivocal meaning. To use them in relation to other civilizations may well lead to a great deal of approximation and misunderstanding. While reasonably legitimate equivalencies to the political and moral concept of the individual can, for instance, be found in Chinese thought, we meet with scarcely any corresponding concept in any other Asian civilization. (See above, pp. 98–99, n. 2.)

16. Huang, 'Monarchy', in Creel, *Chinese Thought*, p. 223. See also L. K. Tao, 'A Chinese Political Theorist of the Seventeenth Century', *Chinese Social and Political Science Review*, II (1917), pp. 71–82.

17. Quoted in Godfrey Davies, *The Early Stuarts 1603–60* (Oxford, 1945), pp. 149–50.

18. The text here is concerned with Rousseau's idea of social compact. Professor Polin expands on Rousseau as follows:

Rousseau is the century's great originator of ideas and emotions. Natural man, the subject of his study, is man reduced to his absolute essence, to that which makes him human. By nature, man is innocent, this side of good and evil; he is free, each man being in essence the equal of all others; his liberty takes the form of perfectibility, endowing him with the capacity of transforming his nature and of progressing in the course of history.

History is something to which he submits. Induced by penury to associate with other men, he becomes dependent on them and, losing both his liberty and his equality with others, becomes alienated and corrupted.

History is also something he can actively create; by constructing an artificial state on the basis of a contract drawn up as a last free and natural unanimous act by all citizens, conferring on each civil and moral liberty and equality, he can transform the nature of man and deliver him from corruption and alienation, by forging for him a new and artificial nature.

This new man enjoys a new liberty, since by obeying laws he also participates in sovereignty, invested in the people as such, expressing itself in their will, a will which is general both in object—the common weal—and in form—the universal form of reason itself. If each individual decision is taken on the basis of a simple majority by 'the will of all', which is the algebraic sum of the votes of the citizens, it is because the general will, always unanimous and universal, has chosen and established once for all the criterion of the majority.

Thus the sovereignty of the people is founded on the universality of reason and with it, the democracy chosen by Rousseau, for which we would opt with less misgiving were modern man less corrupted and were it possible to establish democratic states in which a limited number of citizens might learn to find happiness and the guarantee of their liberties in a frugal way of life.

19. Professor R. Polin maintains that the philosophers of the seventeenth and eighteenth centuries, Hobbes among them, occasionally advanced the theory of the individual right to rebellion (see above). The greatest of them never advanced a theory of the 'right to revolution' though they sometimes studied revolution as a fact, as 'an appeal to Heaven' as Locke put it, in case of a breach of contract between sovereign and people. They avoided postulating a regime in which revolution would appear as a right. They were generally content to consider various forms of resistance capable of insertion in the legal framework. Only one constitution, moreover, was to inscribe among its principles the right to revolution: the French Constitution of 1793, which was never put into force.

The text defines 'the right of revolution' as 'the idea that governments might be changed by the will of the people'. That idea the authors find not only in Locke but also in the American Declaration of Independence and (if they were to go beyond 1776) in the French Declaration of Rights of 1789, which included 'resistance to oppression' as one of the four 'natural and inalienable rights of men'.

20. The theory of the law of nature, barely outlined in certain rare texts of Plato and Aristotle, was developed by the Stoics, in particular in Rome, as the law expressing the nature of man and constituting an obligation, both in respect of the individual and in relations between men. For them, this law, perceived by reason, was the voice of reason itself. Christian thought was on occasion also to consider it somewhat as the voice of God. And these two traditions continued to mingle with or confront one another right down to the modern era, the rationalist interpretation tending during the seventeenth and eighteenth centuries to dominate the religious interpretation, which, however, remained almost always present in the background. At all events it never ceased to form the basis of an obligation, essentially moral in character. (Raymond Polin.)

21. Quoted in Preserved Smith, *A History of Modern Culture*, Vol. II: *The Enlightenment 1687–1776* (New York, 1934), p. 530.

22. E.g. Max Weber, *Die protestantische Ethik und der Geist des Kapitalismus* in *Gesammelte Aufsätze zur Religionssoziologie* (3 vols.; 1922–23), Vol. I, part 1, translated by Talcott Parsons as *The Protestant Ethic and the Spirit of Capitalism* (New York, 1950); R. H. Tawney, *Religion and the Rise of Capitalism* (London, 1926); and Ernst Troeltsch, *Die Soziallehren der christlichen Kirchen und Gruppen* in *Gesammelte Schriften* (4 vols.; Tübingen, 1912–25), Vol. I, translated by Olive Wyon as *The Social Teaching of the Christian Churches* (2 vols.; London, 1931). For a discussion of the literature on this subject see M. M. Knappen, *Tudor Puritanism, A Chapter in the History of Idealism* (Chicago, 1939), especially pp. 341–53 and 513–14; Robert W. Green (ed.), *Protestantism and Capitalism: the Weber Thesis and Its Critics* (Boston, 1959); and Raymond

de Roover, *L'Evolution de la lettre de change, XIV–XVIIIe siècles* (Paris, 1953), pp. 144–46. See also above, p. 321 n. 61.

23. See Herbert H. Rowen, 'John DeWitt and the Triple Alliance', *Journal of Modern History*, XXVI (1954), p. 14, n. 75.

24. See E. A. J. Johnson, *Predecessors of Adam Smith, the Growth of British Economic Thought* (New York, 1937), pp. 61–69 and 142–57.

25. *Ibid.*, p. 62.

26. Quoted in E. R. A. Seligman, 'Boisguillebert', *Encyclopedia of the Social Sciences* (New York, 1937), II, p. 620.

27. See N. S. Smith, 'An Introduction to Some Japanese Economic Writings of the 18th Century', *Transactions of the Asiatic Society of Japan*, XI (1934), p. 72.

28. Han Yu-shan, *Elements of Chinese Historiography* (Hollywood, 1955), pp. 165–66; see also David S. Nivison, 'The Problem of "Knowledge" and "Action" in Chinese Thought since Wang Yang-ming' in Arthur F. Wright (ed.), *Studies in Chinese Thought* (Chicago, 1953), pp. 126–34.

29. See Philippe Sagnac, *La Formation de la société française moderne* (Paris, 1945), I, pp. 152–53.

30. Professor R. Polin points out that while Rousseau indeed devoted no work to historical science, he was, however, a great reader of history and laid much insistence on the role of history in education. Moreover, his *Discourse on the origin of inequality* is entirely devoted to speculation on the history of humanity. It can even be said to constitute a philosophy of history which is one of the vital sources of the philosophy of history of Kant and Hegel.

    The authors agree, on the whole, with this remark. The implication that Rousseau was indifferent to history is based upon his attitude that where historical experience conflicted with a logical construction, historical experience could be disregarded. This attitude is to be found in the Discourse on Inequality *('Let us begin by getting rid of facts, for they do not touch our question') and the* Social Contract *('How has this change [from freedom at birth to chains] come about. I do not know. What can render it legitimate? I believe I can settle this question'.) Rousseau keeps Emile away from history books until his later teens and then (Book IV) finds little good to teach him in the historians (except for Plutarch).*

CHAPTER X

LITERARY COMMUNICATION AND
BELLES-LETTRES (1300–1500)

MANUSCRIPTS, BOOKS, AND PRINTING

IN the period 1300–1775 literacy and literature, without becoming common possessions, became less exclusively than before the marks of upper-class status. The rise in the rate of book-collection helped to bring on this popularization of literature. The early libraries, to be sure, were generally restricted to clerical, royal, aristocratic, or university establishments. Yet the idea that reading matter should be easily accessible spread, particularly after printing made books cheaper. The growth of literature in the vernacular also increased the number who could and wished to read and therefore often influenced the choice of subject-matter of what was written.

The long-established techniques of producing books by script made great strides in Europe during the fourteenth and fifteenth centuries. Manuscript books were copied in small factories, as well as in monasteries, with improved materials (e.g. bleached and polished parchment and paper), more beautiful and compact (though somewhat less legible) scripts, elaborate coloured illustrations, and ornate bindings. More than one copy could be made by dictation from the manuscript to several scribes at once. Paper, made in Europe in the twelfth century, was common for literary purposes in the fifteenth.

Book collecting and library building gained impetus from the revival of interest in Classical manuscripts. Petrarch's description of his own inspired copying of a Cicero manuscript illustrates the personal zeal of an amateur bibliophile. Half a century later Niccolo de' Niccoli, no less zealous as a bibliophile and perhaps more effective as a collector, bankrupted himself by purchases of manuscripts in centres as far distant as Lübeck and Constantinople. More efficient collecting was carried on by rulers such as Cosimo de' Medici, who could make use of agents to arrange for purchases at home and abroad.[1]

Thus, one of the most famous libraries in the world came into being at Florence. Cosimo de' Medici took over the eight-hundred-volume library of the bankrupt Niccolo de' Niccoli and expanded it through additions by copying and purchase. Cosimo's forty-five professional copyists duplicated two hundred manuscripts in a period of less than two years. Lorenzo de' Medici added to the collection, sometimes giving to other collectors the privilege of copying in his library in return for the privilege of copying in theirs. He also purchased finished works through agents whom he sent far and wide. The Greek scholar Joannes Lascaris acquired for him two hundred such works from one of the monasteries at Mount Athos in Greece. Before Lorenzo died, he had collected well over a thousand books, almost half of them in Greek. Eventually housed in a splendid building planned by Michaelangelo, it now, with later accretions, constitutes the famous Laurentian Library, second only to the Vatican Library in the number and value of its manuscript treasures.

The Vatican Library itself had a similar history. Pope Nicholas V was its founder; Pope Sixtus IV enlarged it, increasing the collection from about a thousand to almost four thousand manuscript volumes. He also opened it to scholars for research. The Medici pope, Leo X, further augmented its holdings. These popes sent clerical agents throughout Europe to search for manuscripts. Church councils sometimes facilitated the task of manuscript collection. Poggio Bracciolini, a papal secretary at the Council of Constance, as a supplementary activity explored monastic libraries at St Gall, Fulda, and Cluny, uncovering neglected treatises of Cicero, Quintilian, Lucretius, and other Latin authors.

The excitement that such finds roused among humanists was equalled in the fifteenth-century quest for Greek manuscripts. Although many Greek manuscripts had been carried from Constantinople to Italy by plunderers during the Crusades, Greek literature received little attention from Italians until late in the fourteenth century. The teaching of Greek in Florence and other Italian centres by the Byzantine émigré Chrysoloras (d. 1415) inspired a revival of interest in Hellenic letters. The great flight of manuscripts from Constantinople to the West began almost a half century before the fall of that city to the Turks. Guarino da Verona stayed in Constantinople for five years (1403–09), returning to Italy with over fifty manuscripts, both Greek and Latin. More profitable still were the trips of Giovanni Aurispa (1413–23), who acquired about two hundred and fifty manuscripts, most of them Greek classics. The Council of Florence (1439) brought five hundred Greeks to Italy, where they charmed western scholars with their Classical knowledge. Plethon and Bessarion (see Chapter VI) contributed to the zeal of western collectors; Bessarion willed his own collection of some five hundred manuscripts in Greek and half as many in Latin to the Republic of Venice, where it now comprises an important section of the Library of San Marco. The conquering Turks continued to sell Greek manuscripts to westerners, although in dwindling quantity and importance.

These collectors and libraries were but outstanding examples of a widespread vogue in the fourteenth and fifteenth centuries. Princes such as Galeazzo Visconti and Federigo of Urbino, scholars such as Petrarch, Salutati, and Bembo, and businessmen such as Vespasiano and Chigi were assiduous collectors; and some of their libraries, now incorporated in larger ones, still carry their names (e.g. the Urbino and Chigi collections at the

Vatican). The private collection of Federigo of Urbino is especially note-worthy for the beauty of its manuscripts, their miniatures, and their bindings, since its owner, scorning the new-fangled technique of making books by machinery (i.e. the printing press), lavished money and learning on his beloved hand-made manuscripts. Before 1500 great manuscript collections were to be found (in addition to those in the monasteries) also in the collegiate libraries of Oxford University and the library (some fifty thousand titles) of King Matthias Corvinus of Hungary.

Impressive libraries, monastic, royal, and private, grew up in other advanced civilizations. In India, the Delhi sultans possessed large libraries, and so did the rulers of the Islamic and Hindu states. Many of the Indian monastic foundations assembled palm leaf manuscripts, and wealthy Brahman families made their own collections of manuscripts, sacred and profane. The rulers of south-east Asia also maintained libraries, and the monasteries of Tibet housed considerable numbers of books. In China the great imperial collections of the Ming dynasty included, in addition to printed books and rare manuscripts, immense files of historical records. The Imperial Library catalogue of 1441 listed 7,350 titles of 42,600 volumes (*ts'e*); the great manu-script Yung-lo encyclopedia alone consisted of 11,095 volumes. One author described 14,907 volumes that he considered to be the most important works produced during the Ming period. Among the most famous private libraries before 1500 was the Wan-chüan-lou of the Fang family. Korean kings and monasteries, too, brought together large libraries, and in Japan the Ashikaga College, near Kamakura, and the Kanazawa, patronized by the Hōjō family, reached sizeable proportions.

The 'Burgherization' of Learning in Europe

The uneven history of printing in the Far East will be sketched below in connection with Far Eastern belles-lettres. An ancient technique in China, printing became known also in the West, though only for pictorial block-prints, long before it triumphed over the handicraft of book making. The 'invention' of printing in the West required more than the use of movable type. For the human scribe to be replaced by a machine other factors were needed as well, such as better ink (since scribal ink was not satisfactory for mechanical purposes) and a durable but cheap substitute for parchment. These needs were slowly satisfied during the first half of the fifteenth century. An early result was an increase in the number of picture books with block prints, on which a few words of explanatory text were carved. Efforts were doubtless made to substitute movable for carved type in the texts of these block prints, perhaps in order that the same picture might be used to illus-trate several texts. Experiments with movable type and one-sheet prints seem to have been tried some time before Johann Gutenberg. Finally, about mid-century the thirty-six and forty-two line Bibles of Gutenberg and Schöffer-Fust were produced.

The new technique was developed by Gutenberg and others in the vicinity of Mainz and was so successful that it spread rapidly. German artisans introduced it into neighbouring countries, and within the half-century that constitutes the 'cradle' (*incunabula*) era of the industry (1450–1500) presses were set up throughout western Europe. Several were established in Italy—at Subiaco in 1465, at Rome in 1467, at Venice in 1469, and at Florence in 1471. Printed books appeared in Bohemia in 1468, in Switzerland probably the same year, in France in 1470, in Spain in 1475, and in Poland about the same time. William Caxton, having learned to print in Cologne and having already printed some books at Bruges, founded a press at Westminster in 1476. Sweden and Portugal put up their first presses during the last two decades of the century. The famous printer Aldus Manutius was a late comer, starting his 'Aldine' press in Venice around 1495 (see Chapter XI).

'Democratization' of learning was not the immediate effect of printing, for illiteracy continued unabated and printed books were not cheap. The effect was, rather, the 'burgherization' of learning, especially humanistic learning. Greek and Latin classics, as well as theological works, turned out in numerous large editions, became widely procurable—particularly in Italy—at much lower prices than manuscript versions of the same works. Since the number of schools was increasing concomitantly (see Chapter XVI), the number of laymen with a fair store of Classical books and knowledge multiplied. The domination by universities over learning was lessened, because the scholarly world was no longer dependent upon the authority of the institution or the professor who commanded the only accessible copy of a text. As philological studies improved (see Chapter IX), printing made available a number of identical copies of the same collated and approved texts in different places at the same time.

With the introduction of printing the manufacture of books ceased to be exclusively a learned profession of writers and scribes for learned readers alone. The technical skill of the artisans who perfected and operated the printing press was now also necessary for the spread of scholarly and literary works. In the sixteenth century one of the printing centres was Switzerland, which Erasmus and the printers of Basel made for a time Europe's head-quarters for scholarly publication. The leading printer of Basel was Joannes Froben, who not only published in numerous copies the books that Erasmus wrote or edited but also employed Hans Holbein to make them and other books more attractive by illustrating them. With the rise of Protestantism, printing was brought still more prominently into the service of literary communication. Not only did Protestant scholars, continuing the work of Gerson, Cusa, Valla, Reuchlin, Erasmus, Ximines, and other Catholic scholars, openly challenge the manuscript tradition of medieval theological scholarship but also public propaganda, whether Protestant or Catholic, became more effective with the printed word. The genteel humanist of the fifteenth century (like Federigo of Urbino) who lamented the passing of

Classical texts into vulgar hands was replaced both by the scholarly editor (like Erasmus) of printed texts for the amateur reader and by the zealous preacher (like Luther) of popular causes through broadsides and pamphlets.

Despite the nascent secular and middle-class attitudes and the new techniques, the clergy and religious preoccupation continued to dominate European literature for a long time. Theological and philosophical discussions persisted among university faculties both orally and in print, and authors produced literature of devotion in increasing amounts, especially in the north of Europe. As the theocratic unity of Christendom broke down, religious writings in the vernacular also increased. The statistics of the first half-century of printing bear convincing evidence of the strength of religion in the fifteenth century. Before the technique of movable type was developed, a majority of the books of block prints were illustrated religious books. About forty-five per cent of the known *incunabula* are also religious books. Even in Italy, where the brilliance of Renaissance heterodoxy tends to blind one's eyes to the fundamental strength of orthodox religion, almost half of the printed books were orthodox. The Bible led the list, but sermon literature, *exempla* (moral anecdotes such as those in the *Gesta Romanorum*), and other, less intellectual types of religious writing were also prevalent. Theology in a sense was still queen of the sciences even if her power was being challenged.

With the expansion of the media of communication, conservative elements, and especially the church, began to feel the need of controls. A formal censorship of printed matter did not come, however, until the Catholic Counter-Reformation set up an *Index Librorum Prohibitorum* (see Chapter IV), which was later supplemented by civil censorship. The early history of printing will be treated in the next chapter. Printing, to be sure, had little direct effect on the illiterate, but its influence seeped down at second hand by means of sermons, lawsuits, meetings, plays, conversations, and other oral media. The height of its influence, however, was far in the future. Before 1500 it was the upper middle-class, the scholars, and the aristocracy who chiefly profited from—or were led astray by—the printed book. The clergy, too, profited but perhaps not enough to compensate for the advantage afforded to the reformers of the sixteenth century by the printed word as a propaganda weapon.

THE DEVELOPMENT OF VERNACULAR LANGUAGES

In many parts of the world during the fourteenth and fifteenth centuries the languages of the common people were slowly replacing the languages of the learned in literary usage. Centuries before 1300 Latin, for example, had ceased to be the common language of western Europe, but it continued to be the language of religion, learning, and literature. Therefore scholars often were bilingual. In England, in fact, they might well be tri-lingual, since Norman–French as the court language had been added to Latin and Anglo–

Saxon after the Norman Conquest. Medieval Latin was an artificial medium laboriously acquired by a minority of the population. Whatever its advantages in the world of scholarship, it well might have been a hindrance to creative writing. Although in western Europe Latin continued for centuries as the medium for the formal exposition of theology, philosophy, law, science, and other branches of learning (considered in other parts of this volume), the greatest creations of poetry, drama, and fiction were in the vernaculars, i.e. English, French, German, Italian, Spanish, etc. Only toward the end of the seventeenth century did the respective vernaculars distinctly begin to displace Latin as the medium for learned works.

In Europe literary creativity in the vernacular tongues synchronized with the emergence of nationalism. With some exceptions such as chronicles or translations from the Latin, no great literature was written down in the vernacular before the twelfth and thirteen centuries, when *chansons de geste*, Icelandic sagas, folklore, and several other kinds of oral literature were put into writing. Some of the most notable of these early written vernacular creations were poetical—e.g. the *Chanson de Roland*, the *Poema del Cid*, and the *Roman de la Rose*.[2] By 1300 the merit and popularity of these works seemed to hold the promise of a vigorous future for the folk languages of several regions.

Before 1300 the vernaculars had developed upon a local rather than a national scale. In the nation that we now think of as France, the *langue d'oil* prevailed in the north, and the *langue d'oc* (a form of Provençal) in the south. In some parts of Spain, Catalan was spoken, in others Castilian, and in still others Portuguese. In the Italies, Lombard Italian, Tuscan Italian, and Sicilian Provençal dominated literary work in north, centre, and south respectively. Different kinds of German were spoken in various parts of central Europe, and different kinds of Russian in various parts of what is now Russia.

Standardization along modern national lines came by various means, largely of a political nature. The north French language expanded during the Crusading era, and the Albigensian Crusade of the thirteenth century paved the way for its triumph over the *langue d'oc*. In England the dialect of London eventually became literary English, thanks to the prestige of the metropolis and of Chaucer, who spoke of the English king as 'lord of this language'. In France, England, Spain, and Russia political centralization helped to bring ultimate victory to the dialect of the ruling dynasties, and London English, Parisian French, Castilian Spanish, and Muscovite Russian became the national tongues. The failure of the German-speaking peoples to form an effective union helps to account for the survival of several different kinds of spoken German to this day—*Plattdeutsch*, Swiss, Austrian, and Alsatian, for example—along with *Hochdeutsch*.

Although Italy was no less disunited than Germany, Tuscan Italian became standard through other than political pressures alone. In the thirteenth century at the Sicilian court of Emperor Frederick II, an Italianized Provençal poetry flourished, but its influence was superseded by the Tuscan dialect of Dante and his contemporaries. Dante not only argued the merits of vernacular Italian in his *De Vulgari Eloquentia* (written in Latin for scholars to read); he also proved its worth in his own poems, notably the *Divina Commedia*. Petrarch's and Boccaccio's earlier writings gave additional prestige to the *stil nuovo*, but by their enthusiasm for classical Latin they unwittingly contributed to a century-long eclipse of the vernacular. Late in the fifteenth century Lorenzo de Medici's Florentine court reversed the trend by a revival of the neglected Italian vernacular, and Tuscan Italian became the language of Tasso, Ariosto, and other great poets of the sixteenth century. The triumph of Dante's dialect was not solely attributable, however, to politics, or to the influence of the Medici court. It achieved world fame because of its own intrinsic musicality also and the preference it won in consequence from several literary geniuses.

The triumphant European languages of modern times have taken over elements of the submerged dialects and have absorbed elements of more distant languages as well. English, basically Germanic, is larded with Latin, Greek, Hebrew, Arabic, and Norman French elements, to say nothing of English dialectal curiosities. Russian, basically Old Bulgarian, adapted many words from Greek, Tatar, Germanic, and western European languages. On the other hand, some ancient languages refused to die. Nourished by church ritual, they remained a subject of study and a part of the living tradition. Old Church Slavonic has persisted in Orthodox Russian liturgy. 'Pure' Greek (*koine*) survived in the churches of the Greek Orthodox, Hebrew in the synagogues, Czech and Gaelic in their respective minority religions and traditions—all to become in later centuries a factor in the national revival of the people who spoke or once had spoken them. Medieval Latin persisted in Catholic church services, learned discourse, and official documents, adopting and Latinizing vernacular expressions wherever desirable.

The fifteenth and sixteenth centuries nevertheless saw the gradual decline of medieval Latin as a literary medium. Though scholars continued to use it for their learned works, creative works in Latin were rarely comparable to the great Latin hymns, poems, or prose of the earlier centuries. The national vernaculars and humanistic classicism combined with the declining prestige of the universal church to diminish the importance of medieval Latin as the *langue de culture* of Europe. Philological studies, inspired by the revival of classical Greek and Latin, were presented in classical rather than medieval Latin. The linguistic diatribes of Petrarch, Valla, and Erasmus suggest something of the prevailing scholarly antipathy to medieval church Latin.

The most general characteristic of the European languages during the formative centuries under consideration was an increasing consciousness of the vernacular tongues as media of communication. With varying degrees of intensity language became a subject of scholarly study and rational or aesthetic concern. Scholars became increasingly aware of the nature of speech, the regularities among languages, and the peculiarities within them. For a variety of reasons, the separate tongues were unified and standardized. Models arose everywhere by which to judge and evaluate usage. Among the literate irregular and arbitrary uses of words, phrases, spelling, and syntax were reduced, and many linguistic areas were subjected to more systematic, often more rational, and in any case more accepted standards. Dialects and local linguistic idiosyncrasies began to give way to the standardized languages, though provincial differences persisted and still persist, particularly in spoken usage. Dictionaries and grammars—the Castilian grammar, dictionary, and orthography of Antonio de Lebrija (better known as Antonius Nebrissensis, 1444–1522) are perhaps the earliest examples—made feasible communication by the educated in a more uniform style. In a few instances a specific authority was set up and formally approved as the arbiter of correct forms of oral expression (see below). Scholars began to discover relationships among groups of languages and were able to relate the peculiarities of a people's language to their general culture. Towards the end of our period various thinkers, such as Vico and Herder, came to consider a people's language as a product and an expression of their collective soul.

Conscious reflection upon language and its manipulation was furthered by a number of factors. Political centralization tended to reinforce standardization. Growing nationalist sentiment (in part itself an outgrowth of greater awareness of the separateness of national languages) helped to focus attention upon the desirability of a common means of expression for those who shared one national feeling over against those who shared another. Intensified contacts with strange peoples and different cultures led to increasing reflection about the resemblances and analogies as well as the contrasts in their languages. In Europe, concern with language, already fashionable among the humanists with their love for 'more humane letters' and graceful communication, was to grow as the religious conflicts of the sixteenth and seventeenth centuries made polemic eloquence and style desirable for mass persuasion.

The force with which the vernacular languages asserted themselves in the West helped to augment the rate of breakdown in the ideal of a great united Christian empire. As the dream of universal empire and church faded and the realities of dynastic statism grew more vivid, the need for common media of communication within local groups became more distinctly felt than the need for a universal language, and languages began to become national. Religious reformers preferred to cultivate the means of communication by which a smaller group might reach all its own members rather than the *langue de culture* of a far-reaching church. Certain serious, though limited, efforts were made to preserve the two leading church languages of Europe, but the general emphasis was not reversed. In western Europe only a decreasing, if still large, minority of intellectuals, clerics, officials, and international-minded aristocrats consciously cultivated Latin. In the east European lands, though Church Slavonic prevailed for a long time as the cultured form of expression, in Russia, the 'third Rome', language reform led to an attack upon it and was finally successful during the late-seventeenth and eighteenth centuries.

However divided it might be into religious sects, Europe from the Russian steppes to the Atlantic shores remained mostly Christian, and the basic book of Christianity continued to be of key importance in its literary development. The Bible probably was the most commonly read (and therefore translated) book even before the outbreak of the Protestant revolt. When Anne, the daughter of Emperor Charles IV, went to England to become King Richard's queen (1383), she took with her a Bible translated into Bohemian and German as well as Latin. Religious protest groups such as the Lollards and the Hussites held the heretic view that the Bible should be accessible in the ordinary language to the ordinary believer without the mediating influence of the clergy. At approximately the same time, the humanists, in their desire to go back to the earliest sources, rendered the attack on the revered Vulgate easier by drawing attention to the Greek and Hebrew originals, as well as to Jerome's mistranslations. Religious and scholarly considerations thus reinforced the rising tide of nationalism in prompting the translation of the Bible into the vernacular tongues.

As Queen Anne's Bible showed, translations appeared even before the Reformation in the areas where these movements were strong. Manuscript versions existed or had existed not only in German and Czech but also in English, Dutch, French, and Spanish, and printed translations were published in German as early as 1466, Italian in 1471, Spanish in 1478, French in 1487, and Bohemian in 1488. The English, one of the first of the great nations of the West to become a nation-state and to begin a national literature, were one of the first to translate the Bible into their vernacular, although they were one of the last to print it. Late in the fourteenth century Wycliffe—or his followers or, possibly, some predecessor—translated the Bible into English, but Tyndall's printed edition did not appear for a century and a half (1526). Translations of the Bible helped to assure the victory of Europe's vernaculars over the international languages preferred by the churches (see Chapter XI).

The Standard Languages of Asia and Africa

The Islamic cultural life of the time can be divided between two geographical zones. The first was the one in which Arabic continued to predominate as the literary tongue; it extended from Iraq and Arabia west to the Atlantic and kept penetrating ever farther south into Africa. The second, and perhaps more populous, zone was the one in which Persian had become the predominant Muslim literary language; it extended from the Balkans east to Turkestan and China and south to southern India. In so far as the Islamic world had a common language, it was Arabic, but Persian was culturally more important in a large area.

In the zone where Arabic was predominant the most productive intellectual centres from the fourteenth to the eighteenth centuries were in Syria and Egypt, but all the other areas took some part in intellectual activity. Among these areas now came to be included the countries of the western Sudan, under Maghribī influence. The learned Sudanese generally used Arabic, and their histories were composed on the model of earlier Arabic works. Gradually Hausa, which they learned to write with Arabic characters, came to be a popular vehicle of Islam in the Sudan. Another area of Arabic influence was Muslim east Africa, which was linked to southern Arabia and western India. Since in both southern Arabia and western India different Shī'ite and other sects maintained a communal importance scarcely known elsewhere, Muslim east Africa became a mosaic of mutually exclusive sectarian groupings. Eventually Swahili (essentially a Bantu language with Arabic admixtures) became a vehicle for carrying the Islamic outlook widely in these parts.

The zone in which the Persian language had become the main vehicle of culture showed far more cultural vitality than the Arabic zone. By the end of the Mongol period, Persian was dominant not only in Iran and Turkestan but also in all those lands to the east and west into which the Turks had brought Islam by conquest. Gradually the areas that did not speak Persian began to develop their own literary languages, based on Persian literary and cultural ideals but with national differentiations—among others, western or Ottoman Turkish, Turki of Turkestan, (somewhat later) the highly cultivated Urdu in India, and finally Malay. For a long time, however, the Persian literature of Iran continued to serve as their literary model, even when Persian itself was not written. Persian religious and philological scholarship, meanwhile, proceeded in a lively manner.

In India, although Sanskrit remained the dominant language of learning, its great days were over, especially in the fields of belles lettres and devotional literature. Its position had never been firmly established in the south, where Tamil and other Dravidian tongues had long produced eminent literature and Sanskrit had always been regarded as an intruder confined to the learned. In the north, where Sanskrit and the vernaculars were more closely related because both had a common ancestor in Indo–Aryan, its dominance as a court language was destroyed by the Islamic conquests, and Persian replaced it at the Muslim courts. Under Islamic rule, and often with the patronage of Muslim courts, many of the north Indian nationalities in this period began to develop their vernaculars as vehicles of an increasingly impressive literary output—usually deeply rooted, however, in the Sanskrit tradition.

In China the use of ideographic characters made it possible for the non-conversational literary language to serve as a type of *langue de culture*. Whether pronounced according to the Peking or the Canton dialect, the written characters had the same meaning and so provided a unified written medium. Among the spoken or colloquial languages that of north, west, and central China was by far predominant. It was spoken by most of the officials and was called Kuan-hua (Mandarin), the speech of officials. It was the basic medium of communication among the learned, and its Peking dialect became the standard. The other main spoken media were the Wu group of southern Kiangsu and Chekiang, Fukienese, and Cantonese. The spoken languages differed somewhat from the written language in vocabulary, idiom, and grammar, and the rise of colloquial literature during our period meant that authors were writing in the spoken idiom rather than in the compressed literary idiom, though their writings might be read with Pekingese, Wu, Fukienese, or Cantonese pronunciation. Because of its wider as well as official use, the Kuan-hua was made the national tongue (Kuo-yü) in the twentieth century and the standard for both written and spoken communication.

POETRY, DRAMA, AND STORY IN EUROPE

In western Europe's literary development the fourteenth and, still more, the fifteenth century are sometimes called (with perhaps too much emphasis) 'the Great Transition'. While medieval forms and subjects persisted and no writer departed completely from earlier models, the period marked the gradual dimming of Latin prosody, troubadour conventions, and courtly traditions in secular letters. As they faded, there grew in brilliance a less imitative style, which had its roots in humbler soil and newer themes that were more individualistic and real. Yet borrowings from the medieval romances, imitations of the *Roman de la Rose*, and other evidences of inspiration from older sources continued (nor have they ever vanished); not even the intensely personal poetry of François Villon (1431–63) was wholly free of medieval influences.[3] Moreover, with the partial eclipse of the learned languages came a more vital use of the vernaculars.

In Italian vernacular poetry, the troubadours' Provençal gave way to the *stil nuovo*. The greatest names in this movement were Dante and Petrarch. It would be tedious and should be unnecessary to list their numerous works (some of which, besides, are mentioned in other connections in this book) as testimony or illustration of contemporary developments. Although Dante's subject matter and spirit were still essentially medieval, his use of rhyme—*terza rima*, sonnets, and other newer rhythmic techniques—whether in the lyrics of the *Vita Nuova* or in the cantos of the *Divina Commedia*, constituted a signal milestone in the evolution of modern poetry. It is commonly agreed that no one ever has excelled Dante's skill with tercets, but his successor Petrarch, before turning his literary talents to the imitating of Cicero's style, perfected the sonnet, first used as a written device by Italian poets of the thirteenth century. The easy grace of Petrarch's verses concerning Laura reflected poetry's liberation from the formalism of the troubadours. With similar informality Boccaccio, before his conversion to Latin classicism, set new standards for Italian prose and poetry in his glorification of Fiammetta and profane love, and his *Filostrato*, a poem in *ottava rima*, tells the tale of

Cressida's infidelity to Troilus with a sensitivity that contrasts with the crassness in some of the prose tales in his fascinating *Decameron*.

No comparable contributions were made to Italian poetic style until the revival of the vernacular late in the fifteenth century. In northern Italy, Boiardo in *Orlando Innamorato* and Ariosto in *Orlando Furioso* reinterpreted the Roland epics in a new Charlemagne cycle suited to the sophisticated tastes of despot courts. Ariosto told how Roland, spurned by his beloved in favour of a pagan paladin, was driven mad by jealousy but recovered through the heroic efforts of his friend Astolpho. Although Ariosto's forty thousand lines of polished verse narrated fantastic adventures, they beautifully and understandingly depicted human frailties and feelings. While also a pastoral poet and a literary critic, Tasso (1544–95) is best known as the last of the brilliant epic poets of the period. His *Gerusalemme liberata* portrayed in Virgilian style the capture of Jerusalem from the Muslims in the First Crusade. Doubtless it was also a reminder of the imminent dangers of his own day, for, like the epic of Boiardo and of Ariosto, Tasso's did not hesitate to make bold allusions to contemporary affairs; against the double menace of Turkish infidels and Protestant heretics, the new Jerusalem needed a champion, and Tasso looked for one in a reformed Catholic Church.

Though no other countries of Europe during these two centuries were so often blessed with genius as Italy, the evolution of poetry in some of them did not lag far behind. In Spain the vernacular had acquired a literary respectability through the efforts of Alfonso X, the Wise, king of Castile and Leon (1252–84), who encouraged translations, compilations, and original composition in Castilian. The first significant Castilian poetry came, however, only in the next century—from the pen of Juan Ruiz. The candour and earthiness of his versified autobiography, *Libro de buen amor*, was nowise inhibited by the circumstance that he was the archpriest of Hita and, probably because of irregularities of thought or conduct, was in jail when he finished it (1343). Intending it to be recited by jongleurs rather than to be read, he borrowed from the *fabliaux*, Aesop, and other predecessors with deftness, painted original characters with vividness, and used metrical innovations with variety and skill.

In the next century or so, as the Moors receded and the Christians advanced and as Spain's cities became the foci of Spanish culture, the place once held by the courtly troubadours was taken by the popular *romanceros*, singers of *romances*—i.e. ballads about El Cid and other medieval heroes of war, love, and religion—in verses of eight trochaic feet chanted to instrumental accompaniment. Usually oral but sometimes contemporaneously written down, these lyric-epics were first collected by Martin Nuncio in 1550 in the *Cancionero de romances* and then in other anthologies (also called *romanceros*). They became veritable storehouses of lengthy epic ballads; some of the *romances* not only were later adapted for the Spanish stage but provided writers in other languages also with favourite themes. In the fifteenth century, too, more aristocratic Spanish poets, frequently under the influence of Dante, Petrarch, and other Italian models, wrote sedate, didactic, lengthy poems. Ausias March (1397–1459) broke with the troubadour tradition in his *Cants d'amor*, abandoning Provençal for Castilian and depicting women as real flesh-and-blood creatures. The *Coplas por la muerte de su padre* of Jorge Manrique (1440?–79), inspired by a genuine filial grief, added to Spanish letters enduring stanzas of elegiac melancholy and resignation that recall his contemporary Villon's best lines in a similar mood. The Marqués de Santillana (1398–1458) composed not only imitative sonnets but *canciones* (lyrics) of Spanish style and theme as well and speculated in prose on the nature of poetry.

In the north the older medieval trends, relatively undisturbed by Classical revivals, carried on through the fourteenth and fifteenth centuries. Perhaps the best-known English poems of the fourteenth century were *Piers Plowman* and *The Pearl*. Both were in alliterative verse; both were allegories; both used the convention of the dream or vision introduced a century earlier by the *Roman de la rose* as a literary device; both were anonymous, and their authorship has long been a matter of learned speculation. A background of orthodox Christian ideology softened their main themes (worldly injustice in the one and death in the other) by holding forth the promise of an ultimate reward in Heaven. In *The Pearl* the vision of Paradise is suggestive of that in the *Divine Comedy*. Several other poems are sometimes attributed to the author of *The Pearl*, among them *Sir Gawain and the Green Knight*, an especially eloquent version of a tale narrating the trial of one of King Arthur's knights for courage and integrity. Poems like these, along with numerous popular ballads and folksongs in the vernacular, evidenced the enlivening of the native English tongue as a literary medium. The lower levels of English society sought self-expression in ballads about Robin Hood, legends about King Arthur, and other folklore generally characterized by a marked persistence of medieval religious views and chivalric moral standards.

English vernacular poetry attained the high level of the better poems in the Romance languages through the genius of Geoffrey Chaucer (1340?–1400), but only late in the fourteenth century. Having travelled in France and Italy, he was influenced by French poets such as Guillaume de Machaut (c. 1300–77) and Italians such as Dante and Boccaccio. His borrowing from Boccaccio for his *Troilus and Criseyde* was easy to detect, but while Boccaccio was primarily concerned with narrative, Chaucer's longer poem portrayed character and emotion as well. Chaucer delineated his subjects as victims of war and of other trying circumstances rather than as the embodiments of good and evil that Shakespeare was later to make of them. In the *Canterbury Tales*, somewhat reminiscent of Boccaccio's prose stories, Chaucer produced a work of poetical brilliance, picturesque vigour, and psychological insight. Although he made a translation of Boethius' *De Consolatione Philosophiae*, his perceptive candour in dealing with contemporary events revealed that his humane spirit was not exclusively a product or a concomitant of his humanistic classicism. Without essential reliance upon Antiquity for theme or inspiration, he acquired and gave expression to an understanding of human behaviour and feelings that compares favourably with that of contemporary Italian men of letters. He used metrical forms like the heroic couplet and the rhyme-royal with previously unmatched skill.

The French poet Machaut, who had some influence upon Chaucer, was also a composer of music (see Chapter XII). He was one of a flourishing school of lyricists, among whom the chronicler Froissart and Eustache Deschamps were likewise outstanding members. These men and their confrères wrote literally thousands of lyrics, long and short, making the *ballade* a common form among French poetasters. They gave good standing as well to several other metrical designs; in fact Deschamps wrote an *ars poetica*, a manual for aspiring versifiers—*L'art de dictier et de fere chançons, balades, virelais et rondeaulx*—presenting poetry almost as a handmaiden to song.[4]

Charles d'Orléans (1391–1465) perhaps best marks the transition in France from the troubadours to Villon. It was no mere coincidence that this poet was a great noble, a duke, who was captured in the Battle of Agincourt, which revealed the obsolescence of the armoured knight, and spent many years in England as a prisoner of war. His poems are polished examples of the pure, precise, allegorical, and conventional style of the passing chivalric tradition. Nor was it mere coincidence that François Villon, hardly a chivalric figure, should have been one of his courtly circle at Blois.

Villon (1413–*c.* 1463) ranks with the greatest poetic geniuses of his day in Italy and England. He revealed, a half-century later than Chaucer, a compassion for human weakness somewhat like that of the English poet. The humane touch in Villon's poetry was apparently derived from the emotional impact of a none too wholesome career upon a sensitive mind rather than from imitation of earlier models. His known literary output was decidedly limited. It consisted of both ballads in underworld slang (known as *le jargon*) and some exquisitely polished lyrics. With tenderness alternating with irony, his poems depicted slices of his own life, the Parisian types he knew, and his preoccupation with death and the vanity of human existence.

German poetry was now also undergoing a transition from the troubadour tradition of courtly love. The German troubadours had been known as *Minnesingers*. With the decline of chivalry the *Minnesang* tended to speak less of love and more of politics and became the *Spruch*; and as the court gave way to the city, the *Spruchdichter* became the *Meistersinger*. Whereas the *Minnesinger* had generally been a lesser nobleman, the *Meistersinger* was usually a city artisan. Organized in clubs resembling guilds, the *Meistersinger* prepared his masterpiece somewhat as the candidate for a mastership in any other craft might prepare his. He went to school, entered competitions, and passed from rank to rank upon the approval of recognized judges, who judged not only the merit of his lyric but also that of the song he had composed to go with it. Naturally this sort of contest required rules, and the rules, set forth in a rules book called a *Tabulatur*, did not encourage originality. The Meistersingers made song-writing a common practice in cities where German was spoken. Their schools flourished not only in Germany (Mainz and Frankfurt, for instance) but also in Alsace (Strasbourg), Bohemia (Prague), and Switzerland (Zürich). The outstanding Meistersinger was a well beloved cobbler of Nuremberg, Hans Sachs (1494–1576), whose poems were numbered in the thousand, the best known one being in praise of Luther, *The Nightingale of Wittenberg*.

Among the more learned, German poetry, like German prose, tended toward the serious aspects of human experience, notably religion. Public stupidity and morals were the major theme of Sebastian Brant's satire, *Das Narrenschiff* (*Ship of Fools*) (*c.* 1500), in which various categories of fools sail under other fools to fools' land. In literary quality and in originality of thought, for all its popularity and its influence on future satires of fools, it was inferior to the best of contemporary poetry in other regions of western Europe; its illustrations made up for the humour it lacked.

Didactic poetry still flourished in Germany and other northern regions. It usually lacked lightness of touch, often making use, like the contemporary morality play, of allegory and the 'dream' technique for public moralizing. Such poems portrayed the tribulations of human existence, the injustices of society, and the struggles between 'Vice' and 'Virtue' in the spiritual life of the Christian pilgrim, sometimes in a heavy satirical vein. Chaucer once referred to his English friend John Gower, who wrote didactic poems of this sort in English, Norman French, and Latin, as 'the moral Gower'.

In Bohemia the use of the Czech vernacular was closely associated with the Hussite movement and its offshoot, the Union of the Bohemian Brethren. Huss preached to the people in a simple vernacular that set a standard for contemporary Czech prose, which Chelčický and the Brethren continued to cultivate. The hymns of the people were likewise in the vernacular. Some Czech scholars were, like Huss, fluent in both Latin and Czech. Latin survived, however, chiefly as the language of the oppressors—the aristocracy, the Roman clergy, and the imperial officialdom.

Russian literature did not prosper under the Tatar yoke, but the decline of the Golden Horde brought a new folk spirit. In the fourteenth century trained performers recited the *bylini*, heroic tales, borrowed sometimes from eastern sources, usually about the largely legendary knights-errant who shared the adventures of the sainted Prince Vladimir of Kiev. Composed in a set literary form—unrhymed, intoned verse—the *bylini* were not yet permanently recorded. In the fifteenth century, many poems celebrated Dimitri's victory on the plain of Kulikovo in 1380 (see Chapter I); the *Zadónshchina* by the priest Sophonia of Ryazan was the richest of them in poetic imagery.

Bulgarian and Serbian monks, fleeing from the conquering Turks, brought legends and other stories of great saints with them, and a fairy-tale fiction grew up about lay heroes' struggles against dragons, devils, and other forces of evil. In the *Legend of Prince Peter of Murom and the Maiden Fevronia*, the wise Fevronia, a peasant woman, is the heroine. These folk legends, though prose, often attained a lofty lyrical quality.

In short, Europe of the fourteenth and fifteenth centuries elaborated several forms of poetry (lyric, epic, narrative, didactic) in the vernacular or near-vernacular. Lyrics were perhaps the most popular in western Europe, for gentlemen composed ballades and sonnets on the spur of the moment; Meistersingers frequently and studiously composed *Bare*, or poems to be set to music; and the spirit, if not the quality, of the thirteenth-century Latin hymn continued in popular sacred songs in the vernacular. Epic ran lyric a close second in popularity by reason of the eminence of the Italian epicists. Ballads and other types of folk poems were still common but were yielding to the verse of the professed rhymster and lyricist.

In addition, the epigram, anthologized by the Greeks and, since Roman times, a medium of folk expression in pithy sayings on tombstones, became a formal poetic device. The Greek Anthology, a collection of short, printed poems of Hellenic origin, had been preserved (sometimes mutilated) by various collectors during the Middle Ages. The last such collection was that of Maximus Planudes in 1320. Joannes Lascaris published the Planudean Anthology in 1494, transforming the epigram, a succinct poem with a well-turned ending, into a respectable poetic form (see Chapter XI). In the fifteenth century, too, Santillana collected the proverbs (*refranes*) of the Spanish folk, and Erasmus's *Adagia* (first edited in 1500) culled thousands of quotable proverbs from Classical sources.

Since Goliards, Minnesingers, and troubadours had already shown the way, Western poetry's trend toward earthy and secular themes continued steady, especially in Italy, where the obvious contrast between Dante's *Divine Comedy* and Ariosto's *Orlando Furioso* provides a pat measure of the trend. Piety and chivalry gave way often to sensuous love and coarse adventure; the Christian legend yielded on occasion to pagan, historical, and contemporary themes; and allegory was sometimes fortified by introspection. In Italian poetry the influence of the despot's court was especially noticeable, not only in the sympathetic portrayal of aristocratic and romantic scenes but also in the generally sincere glorification of not always glorious rulers, sometimes accentuated by the revived interest of Italian intellectuals in Vergil, Horace, and other poets who had glorified the Roman emperors. For all this secular tide, however, the religious spirit of the age did not abate in its poetry, particularly in the north. Even in the sometimes far from pious stories of Chaucer's *Canterbury Tales*, contrasting markedly with the piety of *Piers Plowman* and *The Pearl*, the narrators were pilgrims to a martyr's shrine; and one of Villon's most beautiful poems—rowdy, thief, and murderer though he was—was his prayer to the Virgin 'composed on his mother's request'.

The Rise of Secular Drama

Drama, too, continued to be dominated by religion, though it had moved from the altar to the town square. The theatre had been one of the crowning achievements of Classical civilization, but the glamour of the stage had grown dim during the Middle Ages. It had not only run afoul of the general aversion to pagan thought but had in particular suffered from the incompatibility of some of the essential elements of Classical drama, such as the unmitigated tragedy of death and the inexorable decree of fate, with the Christian view of life. Popular church spectacles had taken the place of the theatre, having developed in connection with the celebration of holy days such as Christmas, Carnival, Passion Week, Easter, Corpus Christi, All Saints' Day, and All Souls' Day; and mystery or miracle plays (sometimes distinguished as dealing respectively with Biblical and post-Biblical subjects) had also become familiar. The Resurrection drama evolved from simple Eastertide dialogues at the altar in the ninth century into the action plays of the fourteenth: characters like the three Marys, the angels, the apostles, and Jesus (represented by the priest) moved down the nave of the church and about the chancel, using 'stage props' such as Mary's 'alabaster box of precious ointment'; they ended with a chorus chanting the *Te Deum*. In similar fashion the Nativity was dramatized at Christmastide with living shepherds, angels, and magi, a puppet Christ-child in a manger, and a guiding star pulled along a wire.

Gradually the religious drama moved outside the church edifice, and, as it did so, laymen took charge, the vernacular displaced Latin, and action became freer and more diversified. Mystery and miracle plays continued to portray Adam and Eve, the Last Judgment (with a 'horrid mouth of Hell'), episodes from the life of Jesus, and miracles of the saints, but under secular influences buffoonery and obscenity invaded the stage so that, as early as the thirteenth century, puritanical bishops forbade Christians to take part in or even to attend some performances. In England the 'Towneley Plays' (or 'the Wakefield Mysteries') reflected this trend toward humour and vivacity; in fact, their anonymous author was a virtual pioneer in the comic drama.[5]

Then came the morality plays, of which *Everyman* is the best-known example. *Everyman* probably was Dutch in origin, but it was widely adapted for other peoples. It portrays the death of Everyman, who, summoned before 'the Fader of Heven', finds that of all his earthly companions—Beauty, Knowledge, Goods, Good Deeds, Strength, Fellowship, Kindred, and similar abstractions—only Good Deeds will accompany him. Despite the secular trends of the day and despite the growing number of laity among playwrights and performers, until late in the fifteenth century religious subjects predominated in the drama, as in painting. They were presented, however, in an increasingly secular fashion.

The rise of secular drama can be traced most clearly in Italy. Travelling dramatic companies gradually developed the *commedia dell'arte all' improvviso*, the more or less improvised plays of the professional actors' guilds. These actors presented farcical scenarios of everyday life in a satirical vein, with stock characters like Harlequin, Scaramouch, and Pierrot in stock situations speaking usually stock speeches but adding impromptu lines *ad lib*. The *commedia dell'arte* was immensely popular until the eighteenth century and has left its imprint on ballet, circus, and drama. In similar fashion, public festivals, with elaborate processions and simple festival poems, evoked enthusiastic approval from all classes. The Italian cities of the Renaissance gave to the ancient Roman *panem et circenses* a new form—the public 'carnival' celebration. For the Florentine Mardi Gras a Lorenzo de' Medici might compose verses and a Leonardo da Vinci might prepare magnificent mechanical displays of floats. During the Renaissance the medieval tournament also took on a refined and expanded form, more or less resembling rehearsed drama. (Pl. 60a, b, c.)

If the tableaux and the *trionfi* of a carnival float were not true drama, a more truly dramatic effect was produced as a result of revived Classical influences. Politian, one of the most brilliant Classical scholars of his day (1454–94) was also a good dramatic stylist, and his *Tournament (Giostra)* dazzled the Medici with its descriptions of the mythological garden of love, of Venus rising from the foam, and of other scenes (subsequently painted by Botticelli) that seem to have been acted out on occasion. His *Orfeo*, retelling the myth of Orpheus and Eurydice, was actually intended as a play and, with a musical accompaniment, was presented on the stage in 1471. It marks the liberation of Italian drama from both medieval liturgy and Latin classicism.

Before 1500, even though Seneca's influence (see Chapter XI) was becoming more pronounced, Classical tragedy did not yet appeal to Italian tastes. The revived comedies of Terence and Plautus were more palatable, and thus more important in the evolution of Italian drama, especially when they were done in Italian translation. Machiavelli's humorously risqué *Mandragola* illustrates the type of theatre that won public acclaim from all classes. It tells the story of a young wife's seduction, in which her mother and her husband connive and which only the gullible wife resists, and she but half-heartedly. Completely secular, unburdened with formal classicism, it reflected the extreme of the Renaissance swing away from medievalism. Coming at a time when the moral tone among both aristocracy and populace was far from puritanical, it set for Italian dramatic subject-matter for a long time a hardly edifying standard.

In other regions of Europe the farcical and the burlesque were not considered the highest type of dramatic production. In the north, religious plays sometimes were humorous without losing their moral fervour. In Spain, Nativity, Passion, and Resurrection remained the dominant themes, whether performed under lay or ecclesiastical auspices. A conspicuous exception to the general rule came in the reign of Ferdinand and Isabella with the *Tragicomedia de Calisto y Melibea*, generally known, after the old bawd who is one of its leading characters, as *La Celestina*. It is a dialogue in twenty-one acts, which tell a story of seduction somewhat like that of *Mandragola* and of frustrated young love somewhat like that of *Romeo and Juliet*. At least part of it was the work of a Spanish Jew named Fernando de Rojas. Although it was apparently never performed, its individualistic treatment of already typical roles had a decided influence on the subsequent development of secular drama and fiction not only in Spain but, translated into several other languages, elsewhere as well. On the whole, however, Europe's dramatic maturity still lay in the future.

The Rise of the Prose Narrative

Before 1300 story-tellers seldom told their stories in writing unless they wrote them in verse. Prose was usually devoted to learned purposes. It was little used as an art form for the expression of aesthetic impulses or as a medium of entertainment. Somewhere either at the end of the thirteenth century or, more likely, in the fourteenth appeared a collection in *media latinitas* of anecdotes and miscellaneous material inappropriately labelled *Gesta Romanorum*. Actually it was a sort of compilation (author unknown) intended to help preachers to point a moral or adorn a sermon. Since it borrowed widely, from outside as well as inside Christendom, it became a treasure house from which later authors were to borrow material for their works in the vernacular. Chaucer and Shakespeare were among these borrowers. The book was enormously popular and was issued in numerous editions, each somewhat revised by variant anecdotes.

One aspect of the development of Western prose, which we have already considered, presented a paradox. It was the humanistic effort to achieve stylistic perfection in the use of Latin by imitating the style of Classical antiquity. This earnest effort, perhaps worthy of success, was nonetheless doomed to failure. After a century of valiant and sometimes astonishingly good attempts, the effort to expound thought in a style and a language that were essentially foreign succumbed to the superior flexibility of the mother tongues as media of self-expression.

Vernacular prose reached a high level in the realm of fiction. A partly imaginative hero-literature survived from the Middle Ages in the *Acta Sanctorum*, which now, however, were more thoroughly authenticated and took on the qualities of biography (see Chapter IX). A more creative prose literature flourished in certain vernacular religious writings of the fourteenth and fifteenth centuries. *The Dance of Death* (*Danse Macabre*), originally a set of vividly imaginative dialogues in German[6] between Death and his retinue, gave rise to poems and plays (not to mention pictures) on an elevated as well as a popular level, particularly in the fourteenth century, when the Black Death made dying familiar.

Indicative of the rising tide of secularism was the *novella*, or prose story, often taken from medieval *fabliaux*. The medieval *fabliau* was generally a tale cut to the popular taste and told by strolling *jongleurs*, who entertained, wherever they could find an audience, with tricks and narratives, sometimes derived from Muslim and other Eastern sources. Good *jongleurs* flourished still in the fourteenth century. Their purpose was entertainment rather than edification. In the fifteenth century a collection of the French *jongleurs'* tales, nearly all distinguished by a certain boisterous humour, appeared under the title *Cent Nouvelles Nouvelles*, frequently attributed to a writer of *novella* named Antoine de La Sale. In his *Decameron*, Boccaccio re-clothed some of the *jongleurs' fabliaux* in vernacular prose. Chaucer preferred verse for his *Canterbury Tales*, but the work attributed to Marguerite d'Angoulême, the *Heptameron* (1558), was avowedly an imitation of Boccaccio's *Decameron* even in its title—seven days of story-telling in contrast to the ten of the *Decameron*, and hence 70 (actually 72) stories in contrast to 100. Fiction in prose comparable to Boccaccio's had to await the fuller development of the novel in the sixteenth century and after (see Chapter XI).[7]

Another distinguished prose work of this period is the full-length heroic tale, or 'romance'. In England Caxton published (1485) the *Morte d'Arthur*, a careful selection from the mass of romances in the Arthurian cycle, which he ascribed to Thomas Malory. Whether originally compiled or translated from the French by Malory, the book pieced together a running account of Arthur and the knights of the Round Table. Another full-length romance of the period was *Amadis de Gaula*. At least the final (fourth) book of this work is generally ascribed to the fifteenth-century Spanish writer Garcia Rodriguez de Montalvo. The work deals with the fantastic adventures of a legendary prince, who, though cast away at sea in his cradle, returned to rule in Gaul.

From such romances to the novel dealing at length with credible characters in a plausible setting was but a step—a step first taken in Spain in the fifteenth century in Jahanot Martorell's long, humorous, ribald adventure story entitled *Libre del valerós e estrenu cavaller Tirant lo Blanch* (Valencia, 1490). This work, pretending to be a translation from English but actually composed in Catalan, has been called 'the very first realistic novel', even though some of the hero's exploits may seem superhuman.[8]

Aristocrat, Bourgeois, and Commoner in Literature

Despite the decline of political, military, and economic feudalism, the literature of chivalry remained popular. Amadis of Gaul and Tirant lo Blanch enjoyed a vogue in Spain similar to that of Roland in Italy, and their adventures were among the stories of a dying chivalry that in the seventeenth century were to drive Don Quixote mad. French cycles of romances and epics were re-written and re-read through the West. The medieval *chansons de geste* were now matched by songs of valour, mixed with love and rollicking mischief—sometimes in a cynical, farcical, and humorous combination but not without appeal to the nobler aspects of the aristocratic tradition. In the realm of historiography (see Chapter VIII) heroic accounts were written, especially in France, for and sometimes by the nobility. Literacy was apparently increasing among the upper classes of the laity. In actual life and in the educational theories of Alberti, Castiglione, and other writers of the period (see Chapter XVI), women of the upper middle-class as well as of the aristocracy still enjoyed great consideration. Dante's Beatrice as the personification of theology in 1300 contrasts with Castiglione's spirited and knowledgeable lady of north-Italian court life two centuries later, but both ladies were gracious and respected ornaments of society. Chivalric gallantry was not yet dead.

In short, the literature dealing with the aristocracy changed in attitude only slowly. The slowness is all the more impressive in view of the increase in the number of works concerning the expanding urban life of the period. Villani's burgher approach to Italian history as contrasted with Froissart's aristocratic approach to French history reflects the priority of the emergence of urban interests in Italy. Soon etiquette books appeared, bearing witness to the social ambitions of the wealthy middle class nearly everywhere, and sober essays lectured the burghers on their civic responsibility. Alberti's *Trattato della cura della famiglia* (1431) is a revealing analysis of the social standards and domestic problems of the new rich in northern Italy, an eloquent plea for respect of parental authority combined with devotion to civic duty, but essayists elsewhere also emphasized civic virtue and social welfare (see Chapter XVI). In the Italian *scuola d'abaco* the techniques of business were the subject of specialized studies dealing with commercial arithmetic, money, and various other aspects of mercantile life. And the lighter but not necessarily carefree side of Italian town life among the privileged citizenry stood out vividly not only in Boccaccio's stories but also in the *Autobiography* of Benvenuto Cellini.

The literature of other countries likewise betrayed a mounting concern with the bourgeois virtues. In the north too the rising bourgeoisie showed awareness of the obligations that went with economic success. The papers published in part as *The Paston Letters*, recording the dealings of a pushing family of Norfolk landowners and lawyers in the troubled times of the War of the Roses, provide ample testimony of the middle-class Englishman's literacy, his litigious knowledge of the law, and his loyalty to family. A nascent bourgeois patriotism is manifest in the Tver merchant Nikitin's *Journey beyond the Three Seas* (see Chapter VIII). Though they did not always seem to realize it, the literature by and about townspeople of the fifteenth century shows them caught up in the incipient waves of the bourgeois future.

In this period workingmen were few in the towns, but in the country they were so many that everywhere they formed a vast majority of the total population. Yet they occupied a minor and passive place in literature. Being generally illiterate, the rural population rarely produced formal works of prose or poetry. In the things written by the clergy, theirs was the role of the humble workers who sweat to support the fighters and the prayers, their military and spiritual protectors. In aristocratic literature the peasant and the city worker alike usually were represented as, and may well have been in fact, stupid and beastly, despised and oppressed, fit only to serve their betters.

Yet occasionally in imaginative literature, though certainly less often than among the political writers (see Chapters VIII and IX), a voice was raised in favour of social justice for the peasant. A William Langland (if he was indeed the author of *Piers Plowman*) might now and then appear to express for them as well as for himself the indignation of the oppressed poor. And Piers Plowman's protests were unmistakable even if mild compared with the rebellious spirit of the Wycliffites. François Villon spoke, in a way, for the proletarian poor, but he was not only exceptional, he was suspect. The *jongleur* often constituted himself a friend of the poor, but he too was likely to be a scamp. True proletarian and peasant protests remained largely unwritten. Folk poetry and ballad, the dramas performed in churchyard and market place, and mouth-to-mouth protests were perhaps the truest sources and reflections of the thought of the common man, but of these we have only faint evidence and few survivals. While social injustice is often their theme (witness the Robin Hood ballads), they do not reveal a steady or strong consciousness of class.[9]

POETRY, STORY, AND FORMAL PROSE IN ISLAM

In Islam, as in Europe, one of the most important general literary developments of the period was the rise of vernacular literature. The development of the Islamic vernacular differed, however, in two regards from the European experience: the classical Islamic languages, Arabic and Persian, did not deteriorate, and Islam did not become more secular-minded as vernacularization went on.

Since Islamic cultural life had come by 1300 to be divided more or less sharply into two geographical zones, the intellectual and cultural life, and therefore the development of the languages, of the two zones can to a certain degree be characterized separately. In Arabia, the Fertile Crescent, Egypt, North Africa, and the Sudanese lands, Arabic continued to predominate as the literary tongue even where it was not the spoken language; Cairo was the intellectual capital of this zone, though there were lesser centres, as in south Arabia and in Spain. East of the Arabic zone, Persian became the standard literary language among Muslims, and with it went a whole tradition of

[IHM]

[IHM]

(b)

(a)

1   *Andrei Rublev*
(a) *'The Trinity of the Old Testament'. Moscow, Tretyakov Gallery.* (b) *Detail*

(a)

[*Alinari*

2 (a) *Giotto, 'The Flight into Egypt'. Padua, Scrovegni (Arena) Chapel*

   (b) *Simone Martini, 'The Annunciation'. Detail. Florence, The Uffizi*

(b)

[*Alinari*

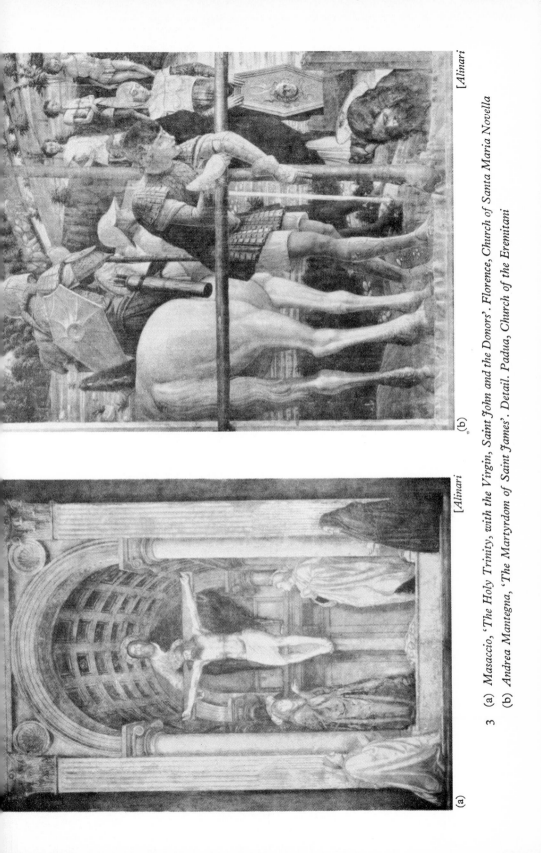

(a)

[Alinari]

(b)

[Alinari]

3   (a)   Masaccio, 'The Holy Trinity, with the Virgin, Saint John and the Donors'. Florence, Church of Santa Maria Novella
     (b)   Andrea Mantegna, 'The Martyrdom of Saint James'. Detail. Padua, Church of the Eremitani

(a)

4 (a) *Fra Angelico, 'The Annunciation'. Florence, Museum of San Marco*
  (b) *Paolo Uccello, 'The Profanation of the Host'. Detail. Urbino, National Gallery*

(b)

5 (a) *Jean Fouquet, 'Etienne Chevalier Worshipping the Madonna'. Miniature. Chantilly, Musée Condé*

(b) *H. and J. Van Eyck, 'The Adoration of the Lamb', 1432. Detail. Ghent*

(a)

[Giraudon

[Giraudon

(a)

6   (a) *Conrad Witz, 'The Miraculous Draught of Fishes'. Geneva, Musée d'Art et d'Histoire*

    (b) *Albrecht Dürer, 'The Passion of Christ—The Ascension'. Munich, Bayerische Staatsbibliothek*

(b)

(a)

7 (a) *Hans Holbein, the Younger,
'Portrait of Bonifacius
Amerbach',* 1519. *Basel,
Oeffentliche Kunstsammlung*

(b) *Lucas Cranach, 'Portrait
of Melanchthon'. Berlin,
Staatlichen Museen*

(b)

[*Gire*

8   *Giorgione, 'The Tempest'. Venice, Accademia*

9 (a) Titian, 'The Assumption of the Virgin'. Venice, S. Maria Gloriosa dei Frari
(b) Titian, 'Emperor Charles V'. Madrid, Prado

(a)

(b)

(a)

[*Giraudon*

(b)

[*Alinari*

19. (a) Leonardo da Vinci 'Madonna of the Rocks' Paris, Musée du Louvre

11 Michelangelo, 'Fall and Expulsion of Adam and Eve'. Rome, Sistine Chapel

Alinari-Giraudon   (b)   [*Alinari*

12   (a)   Tintoretto, 'The Funeral of Saint Marc'. Venice, Palazzo Reale

13   El Greco, 'The Burial of the Count of Orgaz'. Toledo, Church of Saint Thomas

(a)

14   (a)   *Annibale Carracci, 'The Triumph of Bacchus'. Rome, Palazzo Farnese*
       (b)   *Nicolas Poussin, 'The Reign of Flora'. Paris, Musée du Louvre*

(b)

15 (a) *Jan Steen, 'A Terrace Scene with Figures'. London, The National Gallery*

(b) *Pieter de Hooch, 'Interior of a Dutch Home'. London, The National Gallery*

(b)

16 Rembrandt

(a) 'Portrait of a Young Man'.
Paris, Musée du Louvre

(b) 'The Supper at Emmaus'.
Paris, Musée du Louvre

(a)

[Giraudon

(b)

[SMN

17   *Rubens, 'The Rape of the Daughters of Leucippus'. Munich, Alte Pinakothek*

18   Velasquez, 'The Surrender of Breda'. Madrid, Prado

(a)

19 (a) *Giovanni B. Tiepolo, 'Pegasus and Fame'. Venice, Palazzo Labia*

(b) *Francesco Guardi, 'The Lagoon of San Marco'. Venice, The Accademia*

b)

[NG]

[NG]

(b)

(a)

20 (a) *Van Dyck, 'George and Francis Villiers'. London, The National Gallery*

(b) *Thomas Gainsborough, 'The Morning Walk'. London, The National Gallery*

21 (a) *Thomas Gainsborough, 'The Watering Place'. London, The National Gallery*

(b) *Joshua Reynolds, 'The Graces Decorating Hymen'. London, The National Gallery*

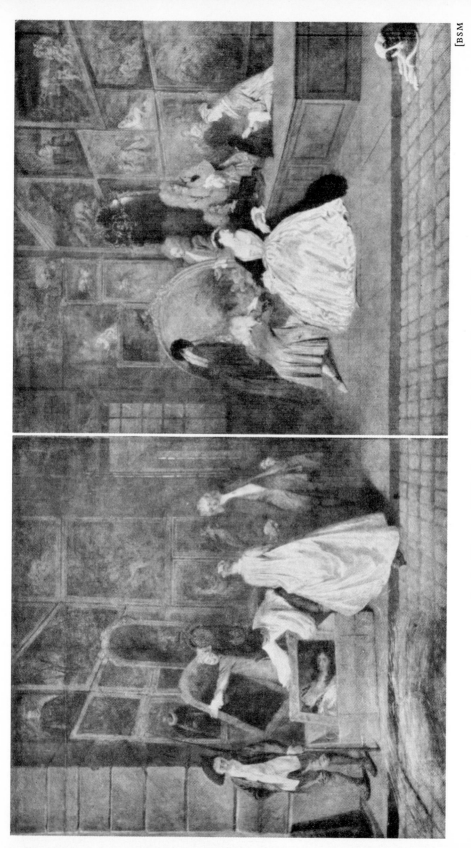

22 *Antoine Watteau, 'L'Enseigne de Gersaint', Berlin Staatlichen Museen*

3 (a) *William Hogarth, 'The Countess's Dressing Room'. London, The National Gallery*

   (b) *Jean-Baptiste Greuze, 'The Village Betrothal'. Paris, Musée du Louvre*

(a)

(b)

24 *Busts of Royalty from the triforium of the Cathedral Saint Vittus in Prague:*

    (a) *Charles IV of Luxemburg, King of Bohemia*

    (b) *Blanche of Valois, Queen of Bohemia*

    (c) *John the Blind, King of Bohemia*

(c)

25   *Moses figure from the Calvary ('The Well of Moses').*
Abbey of Champol near Dijon. Early fifteenth century

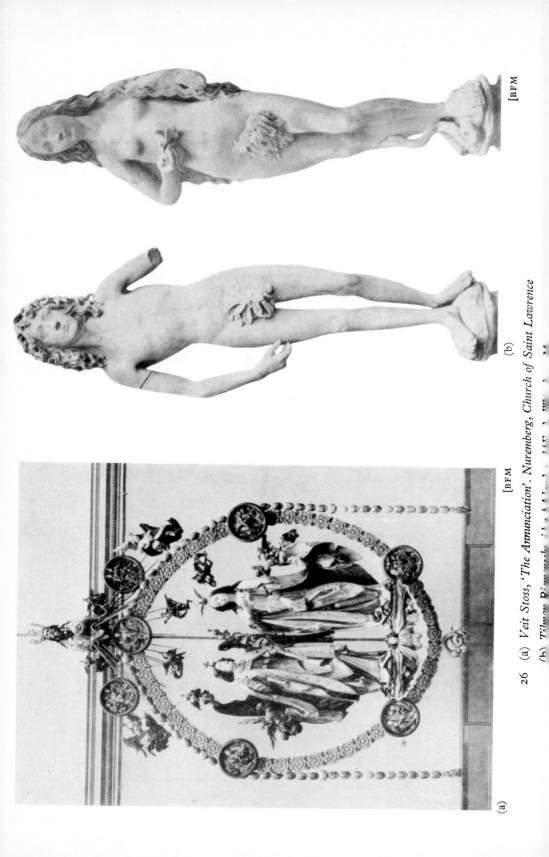

[BFM]

[BFM]

26 (a) *Veit Stoss, 'The Annunciation'. Nuremberg, Church of Saint Lawrence*

(b) *Tilman Riemenschneider, 'Adam' and 'Eve'. Würzburg Museum*

7 (a) *Nicola Pisano, 'The Adoration of the Magi'. Detail from the pulpit of the Baptistry,* 1259, *Pisa*

(b) *Lorenzo Ghiberti, 'The Birth of Eve'—'The Creation'. Detail from a panel of the 'Gates of Paradise'. Florence, bronze doors of the Baptistery*

(a)

28   (a) *Bernt Notkes, 'Saint George and the Dragon'. Stockholm, Church of Saint Nicola*

(b) *Donatello, 'Saint George and the Dragon'. Florence, Church of Orsanmichele*

(b)

(a)

(b)

Alinari

[*Alinari*

29 (a) *Donatello, 'Saint George'. Florence, Museo Nazionale (Bargello)*
(b) *Lorenzo Ghiberti, 'Saint Stephen'. Florence, Church of Orsanmichele*

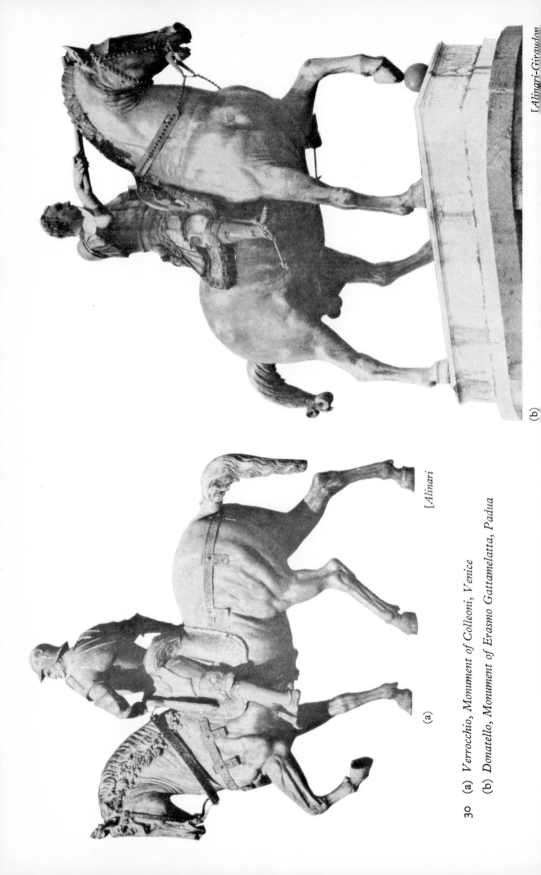

(b)

(a)

30 (a) *Verrocchio, Monument of Colleoni, Venice*

(b) *Donatello, Monument of Erasmo Gattamelatta, Padua*

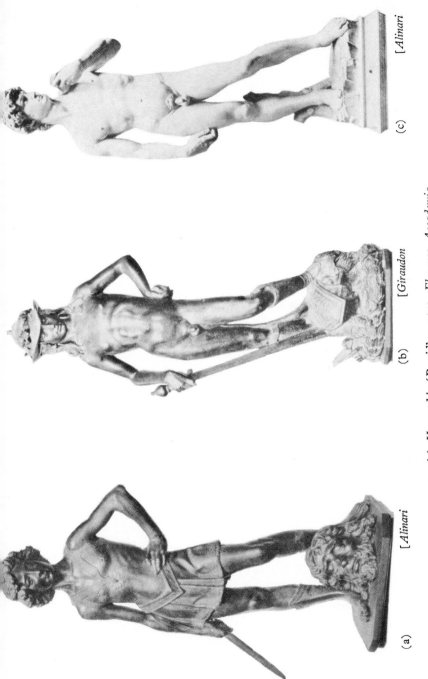

(a)   [Alinari]

(b)   [Giraudon]

(c)   [Alinari]

31 (a) *Verrocchio, 'David', c. 1473. Florence, Accademia*
     (b) *Donatello, 'David'. Florence, Accademia*
     (c) *Michelangelo, 'David'. Florence, Accademia*

(a)

32 (a) *Rossellino, 'Virgin and Child'.*
Tomb of the Cardinal of Portugal,
Florence, S. Miniato. Detail

(b) *Luca della Robbia, 'Virgin and*
Child'. Museo Nazionale (Bargello)

(b)

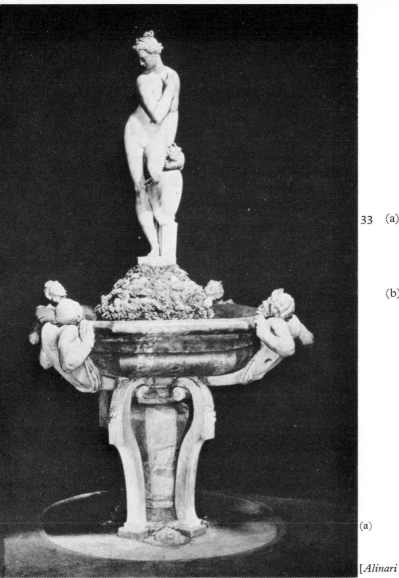

33 (a) *Giovanni da Bologna*
        (Giambologna),
        'Venus'. Florence,
        Buontalenti Grotto,
        Boboli Gardens

    (b) *Jean Goujon, 'Tritons*
        et Néréïdes'

(a)

[*Alinari*

[SMN

34 (a) *Martinez Montañes, 'Saint
          John the Baptist'. Seville,
          Museo Provincial*

    (b) *Gregorio Fernandez, 'Pieta'.
          Valladolid, Museo Provincial*

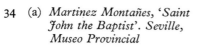

(a)

[*Anderson-Giraudon*

(b)

[SCU

[Alinari]

(a)

[BFM]

(b)

35 (a) Bernini, 'The Ecstasy of Saint Theresa'. Rome, Santa Maria della Vittoria

(b) Egid Quirin Asam, 'The Assumption'. Rohr Abbey Church, The high altar

(a)

Giraudon

36 (a) *A. Coysevox, 'Diana'*
     (Marie-Adélaïde de Savoie,
     duchesse de Bourgogne).
     Paris, Musée du Louvre

   (b) *Houdon, Voltaire, Musée de*
     Versailles

(b)

[SMN

[IHM] (a)

[IHM] (b)

37   (a) *Church of the Transfiguration, 1714. Kizhi*

      (b) *Cathedral of Saint Basil the Blessed, 1555–60. Moscow*

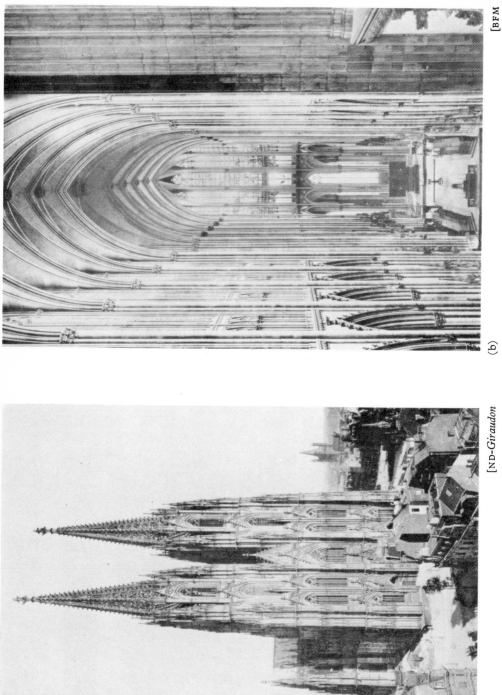

(a)

38 Cologne, the cathedral (1248 onwards)

(b)

(a)　　　　　　　　　　　[BFM]　　　　　　　　　　(b)　　　　　　　　　[BFM]

39　(a)　*Marburg, Saint Elizabeth, c.* 1257–83
　　(b)　*Nuremberg, Saint Lawrence, the interior.* 1439

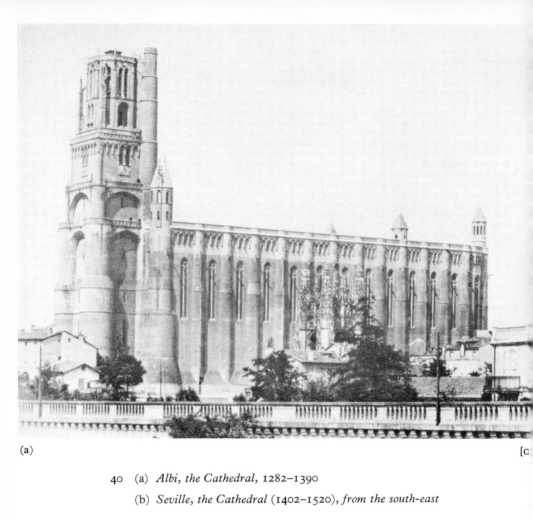

(a)

40   (a) *Albi, the Cathedral,* 1282–1390

        (b) *Seville, the Cathedral* (1402–1520), *from the south-east*

(b)

(b)

(a)

41 *The Cathedral of Gerona*
    (a) *The façade*
    (b) *The nave, 1417–1598*

(a)

(b)

42 Cambridge, King's College
    Chapel, 1446–1515

    (a) *General view*
    (b) *The interior, facing east*

43 (a) *Bourges, The House of Jacques Coeur,* 1442–53

(b) *Venice, Cà d'Oro. Detail of the façade,* 1424–36

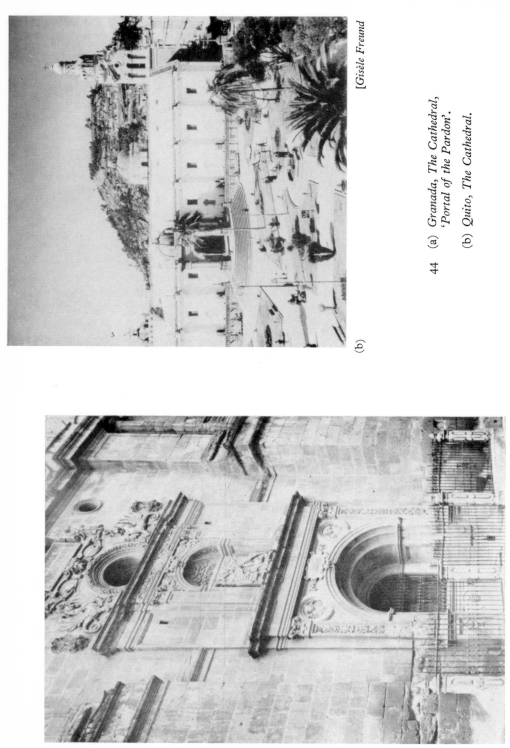

[Gisèle Freund

[BFM

(b)

(a)

44 (a) *Granada, The Cathedral,*
'Portal of the Pardon'.

(b) *Quito, The Cathedral.*

(a)

45 *Mexico City*

    (a) *The Cathedral,* 1563–1667

    (b) *Metropolitan Sanctuary,*
        eighteenth century

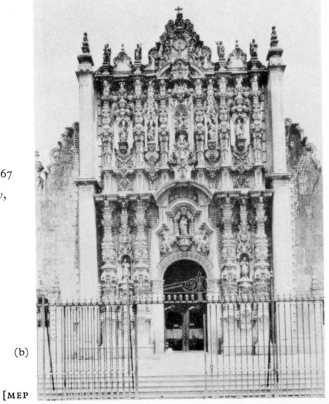

(b)

(a)

46 *Filippo Brunelleschi*

  (a) *Florence, Church of San Lorenzo, 1421–60: the interior*

  (b) *Florence, dome of the Cathedral, 1420–34. In the background the Campanile by Giotto, 1334–59*

(b)

[BFM

47 (a) *Florence, Palazzo Strozzi: the façade, 1489–1539*

(b) *Paris, Hotel (now museum) Carnavalet, c. 1545*

(b)

[CESC

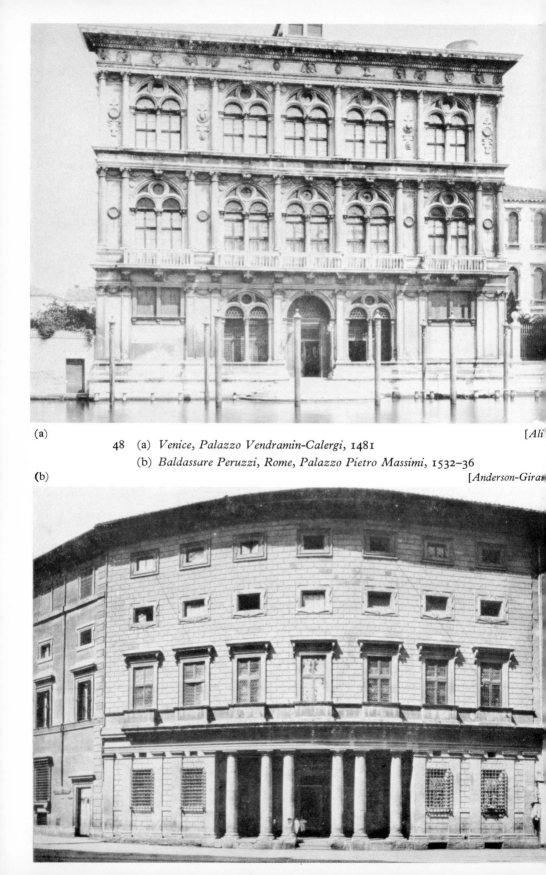

(a)

48   (a) *Venice, Palazzo Vendramin-Calergi, 1481*

      (b) *Baldassare Peruzzi, Rome, Palazzo Pietro Massimi, 1532–36*

(b)

(a)

[*Alinari*

49 *Andrea Palladio*

(a) *Villa Capra (the Rotonda),
    Vicenza,* 1550

(b) *Il Redentore, Venice,
    façade,* 1570

(b)

[*Alinari*

[Ali

50 (a) *Rome: The Capitol (Campidoglio), planned by Michelangelo, c. 1538*

(b) *Rome: Villa Giulia (Villa of Pope Julius III), c. 1555*

[Ali

[*Giraudon et Aéro-Photo*

51 (a) *Louis Levau and André Le Nôtre, Château of Vaux-le-Vicomte, 1657–1661.
     Aerial view*

    (b) *Versailles, the Palace, 1661–1756. Aerial view*

[*Robert Laffont*

52 (a) *J. H. Mansart, Saint Louis des Invalides, Paris*, 1680–91

(b) *Christopher Wren, Saint Paul's Cathedral, London*, 1675–1710

(a)

(b)

[Alinari

53   *The Gesù Church, Rome*, 1568–84
  (a) *The façade* (G. della Porta)
  (b) *the interior* (G. B. Vignola)

[Alinari

54 *Francesco Borromini*

   (a) *Rome, San Carlo alle Quatro Fontane, 1665–67. The façade*

   (b) *Rome, the dome of San Ivo della Sapienza, 1642–59. The interior*

(a)

(b)

55 (a) *Balthasar Neumann,*
Vierzehnheiligen Church,
1744–72: *the nave*

(b) *Die Wies, Bavaria,*
1745–54: *the main altar*

(b)

(a)

56 (a) *Paris, Hôtel de Rohan,* 1705–08

(b) *Versailles, Le Petit Trianon,* 1762–68

(b)

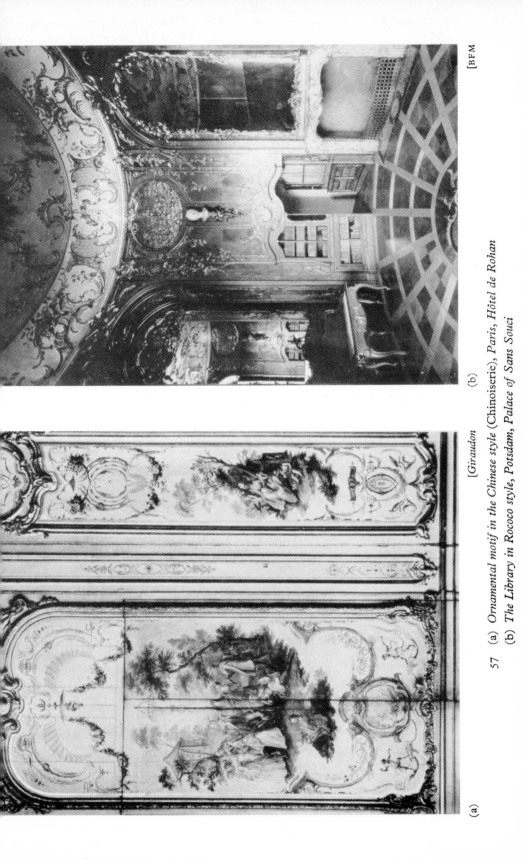

(a)

[Giraudon]

(b)

[BFM]

57 (a) *Ornamental motif in the Chinese style* (Chinoiserie), *Paris, Hôtel de Rohan*
     (b) *The Library in Rococo style, Potsdam, Palace of Sans Souci*

(a)

58 (a) *N. Bataille, 'The Apocalypse', detail of the tapestry designed by Jean Bandol,*
         c. 1375. Angers, Musée des Tapisseries

    (b) *Gobelins tapestry, 'The Visit of Louis XIV to the Gobelins Factory', seventeenth*
         century. Paris, Musée du Louvre

(b)

(a)   [*Giraudon*

59 (a) *Italian Majolica work: plate
from Faenza, fifteenth
century. Paris, Musée Cluny*

      (b) *Bohemian glass,* 1592

(b)

60   Figures from the 'Commedia dell'Arte'

(a) 'Pantalone', Munich, the Nymphemburg, c. 1740. Bayerisches Nationalmuseum, Munich

(b) 'Isabella', Munich, the Nymphemburg, c. 1740. Bayerisches Nationalmuseum, Munich

(c) 'Capitano', Vienna, c. 1760. Museum für Kunsthandwerk, Frankfurt

[BNM]

BNM

[MKF]

(a)

(b)

(c)

(a)   [BFM]   (b)   [IHM]

61   (a) *Granada, The Alhambra, Court of the Lions*

       (b) *Samarkand, The Gur Amir, Mausoleum of Timur, early fifteenth century*

(a)

62 (a) *Riza 'Abbasi,*
painting divided
two parts. Seatt
Seattle Art
Museum, gift of
late Mrs. Donald
E. Frederick

(b) *Muhammad Jafa*
Kashani, tomb co
for Iman Riza,
silkwork of the
sixteenth century.
Cincinnati Art
Museum

(b)

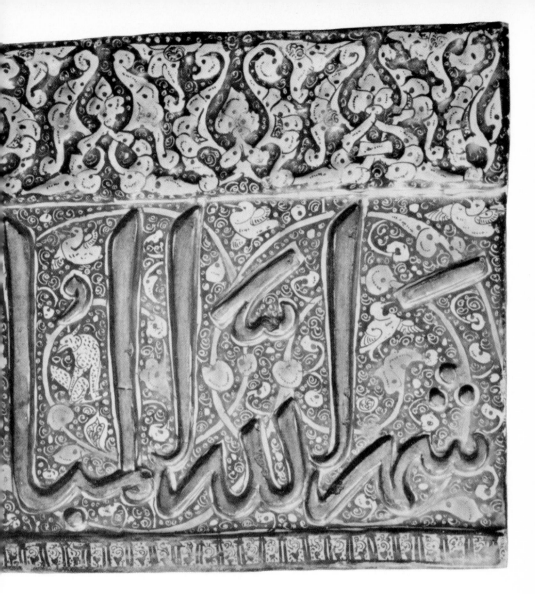

63 (a) *Ceramic tile, Seattle Art Museum, Eugene Fuller Memorial Collection*
      (b) *Kufic inscription on the Taj-Mahal*

(a)

64 (a) *Delhi, The Great Mosque, The 'Alāi Darwāza,* 1310
     (b) *Bijapur, The Ibrahīm Rawda,* 1626–33 (*Ibrahim's II tomb and mosque*)

(b)

(a)

65 (a) *Ahmadabad,*
        The Jāmiʿ Mosque,
        main gate

    (b) *Agra, Jāhāngīrī's*
        Palace, detail of the
        colonnade

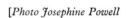

[*Photo Josephine Powell*

(a)

(b)

66 (a) *Fathpūr-Sīkrī,*
The Panch
Mahal

(b) *Fathpūr-Sīkrī,*
The Buland
Darwāza, 160×
02

67   (a) *Delhi, The Palace, the interior of the Diwān-i-Khās*
     (b) *Agra, The Tāj Mahal, 1631–53*

(a) [ASI]

(b) [ICU]

68 (a) Alwar. *Darbar of Jahāngīr*

69 (a) *Trichinapalli, the interior of the Mandapa*

(b) *Shrīrāngam, Ranganātha Temple, columns in the 'Horse Court'*

(b)

(a)

(b)

70 (a) *Hampi, Vitthala
(Vinshu) Temple,
the mandapa*

(b) *Trichinapalli,
Shrīrāngam Temple,
the southern Gopura*

71 (a) *Chao Meng-fu, detail from*
       'Autumn Colours in the
       Ch'iao and Hua Mountains'.
       Taipei, National Palace
       Museum

    (b) *Ni Tsan, 'Jung-hsi Studio',*
       dated 1372. Taipei, National
       Palace Museum

(b)

(a)

72 (a) *Lü Chi, 'Birds in Snowy Landscape'. Taipei,*
        National Palace Museum

     (b) *Shen Chou, 'Night Vigil'. Taipei, National*
        Palace Museum

(b)

73　(a)　*Wang Hui, detail from a landscape, 'Mount Fu-ch'un'. Washington, Freer Gallery of Art, Smithsonian Institution*

　　(b)　*Ch'en Hung-shou, detail from 'Episodes in the Life of T'ao Yüan-ming', dated 1650. Purchase 1954 (Acc. No. 1912.1) Honolulu, Hawaii, Honolulu Academy of Arts*

(a)

(b)

74 (a) *Tao Tchi, after t*
story 'The Peach
Blossom Spring'.
Washington, The
Freer Gallery of
Art, Smithsonian
Institution

(b) *G. Castiglione*
(Lang Shih-Ning
'Ladies-in-Waitin
in the Yüan-Ming
Yüan'. Hamburg,
Museum für
Völkerkunde und
Vorgeschichte

[JCU

[JCU

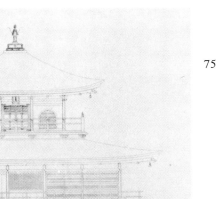

75 (a) *Kon-do (main hall)
of Kwanshin-ji
Temple, Osaka
Prefecture. Early
fourteenth century*

(b) *Kyaku-den (guest
hall) of Kōjō-in
Temple, Shiga
Prefecture*

(c) *Kinkaken (Golden
Pavilion) of Roknon-
ji Temple, Kyoto
(c. 1397)*

[JCU

(a)

76 (a) *The main donjon of Himeji Castle, Hyōgo Prefecture*

    (b) *Hai-den (hall of worship) of Osaki Hachiman Jinja (Shinto shrine), Miyagi Prefecture*

(b)

77 Takashina Takakane, 'The Miracle Record of Kasuga Shinto Shrine', detail from the scroll painting

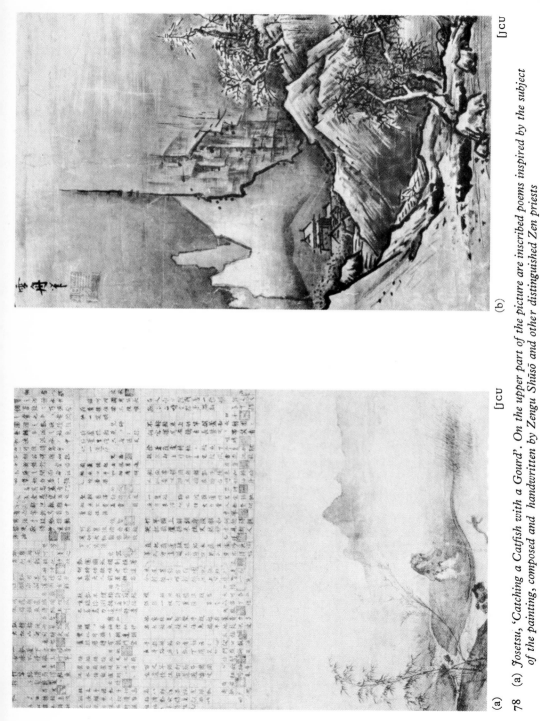

[JCU]

[JCU]

(a)

(b)

78 (a) Josetsu, 'Catching a Catfish with a Gourd'. On the upper part of the picture are inscribed poems inspired by the subject
of the painting, composed and handwritten by Zengu Shūsō and other distinguished Zen priests

79　(a) *Kanō Eitoku, 'Kara-shishi' (an imaginary lion-like animal), six-fold screen*

　　(b) *Ogata Kōrin, 'Red Plum Tree' (screen)*

(b)

[JCU

80   *Suzuki Harunobu*, '*Women on the veranda*' (ukiyoe *print*)

81 *Head of a court official of Benin (sixteenth–eighteenth century) (Collection P. Vérité)*

(a)   [*Giraudon*

82   (a) *The Feathered Serpent, Quetzalcoatl,*
         fourteenth–sixteenth century, Mexico,
         Museo Nacional de Antropologia

     (b) *Chichen-Itza, Yucatan, Mexico. Chao-mool, god of rain*

(b)   [*Roger-Viollet*

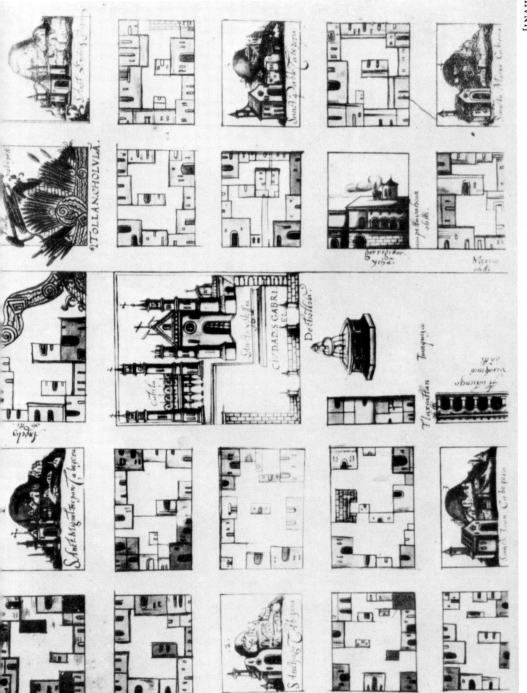

83   *Cholula, México, in 1581, showing pre-Conquest shrines within the colonial grid*

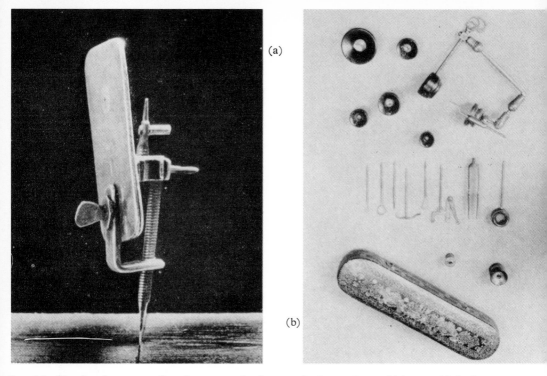

84   (a) *Simple microscope, silver instrument by Leeuwenhoek, c. 1673, which magnified about ×275*
     (b) *Simple microscope with six lenses and various implements for mounting different objects, made*
          by Johan van Musschenbroek, c. 1700
     (c) *Tripod microscope by Edmund Culpeper, c. 1730*
     (d) *Compound microscope by Cuff, c. 1743*   *Leyden, Royal Museum of the History of Scienc*

*(a) and (b) were the best instruments for scientific work; (c) was suitable for amateur work; (d) was
one of the best compound microscopes of the period, but optically it was slightly inferior to (a) and (b)*

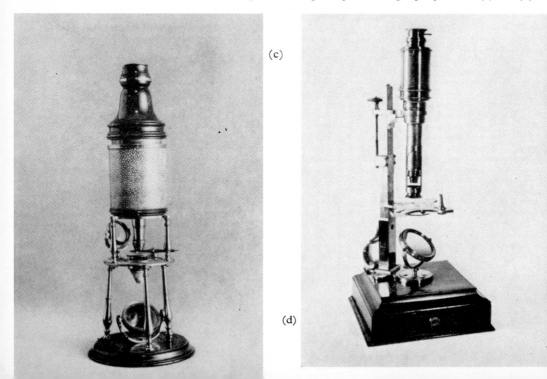

(a)

(b)

85 (a) *First illustration of cells (texture of cork) by Robert Hooke, who called them 'cells or pores', from* Micrographia, 1665

    (b) *Gnat, from Jan Swammerdam,* Biblia Naturae, 1737–38. *Posthumously published.* University Library, Leyden

    (c) *Fresh water micro-organisms on the roots of a duckweed (Hydra Vorticeldia); diatoms and rotaria, observed by Leeuwenhoek, December 25, 1702*

    (d) *Leeuwenhoek-Huygens, spermatozoa of man and dog, sketch made after a drawing of Leeuwenhoek, now lost, March 1678*

Leyden, Royal Museum of the History of Science

(a) i   [*Photo Edmark*

(a) ii   [*Photo Edmark*

86 (a) *English middle Gothic (Y-type) astro-labe, 'The Painswick Astrolabe',* c. 1370–
     i. *Front view*   ii. *Back view*

   (b) *Eastern Islamic spherical astrolabe,* 885 AH (1480/1 AD). *Signed 'Work of Músà. Year 885'. Brass and silver work*

Oxford, Museum of the History of Science

(b)   [*Photo Edmark*

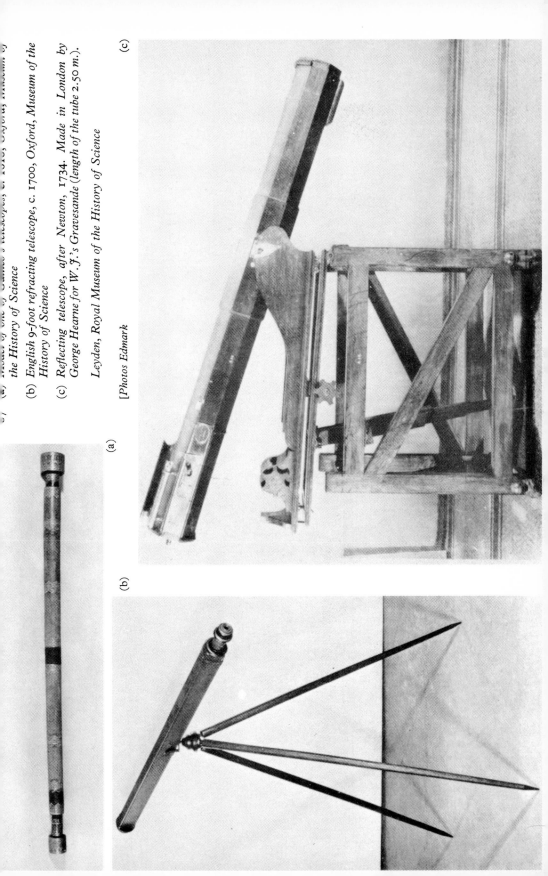

(a) *Model of one of Galileo's telescopes, c. 1610, Oxford, Museum of the History of Science*

(b) *English 9-foot refracting telescope, c. 1700, Oxford, Museum of the History of Science*

(c) *Reflecting telescope, after Newton, 1734. Made in London by George Hearne for W.J.'s Gravesande (length of the tube 2.50 m.).*

Leyden, Royal Museum of the History of Science

[Photos Edmark

88 (a) *Paris, Louis XIV visits the Academy of Sciences. Around the king the courtiers and the academicians. On the horizon can be seen the building of the Royal Observatory*

   (b) *Greenwich, the Royal Observatory in Flamsteed's time showing observers with quadrant and telescope*

(a)

(b)

(a)

89 *The Pendulum clock. Christian Huygens type clock dating from the year of the patent, 1657, made by Salomon Coster*

    (a) *The dial*

    (b) *The mechanism and the pendulum*

Leyden, Royal Museum of the History of Science

(b)

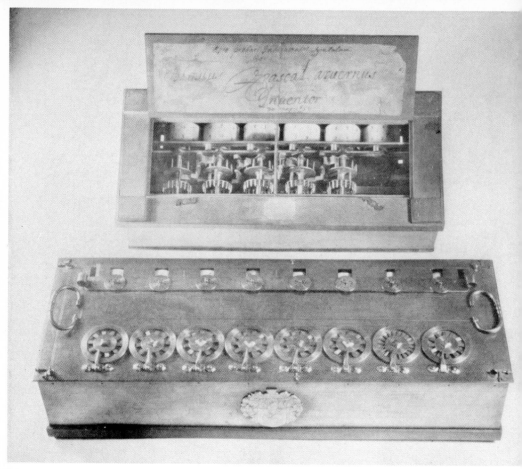

(a)

(b)

90 *Calculating machine of Blaise Pascal,* 164[...] *Paris, Arts et Métier[...]*

   (a) *The machine*

   (b) *The mechanism*

[*Robert Laffont*

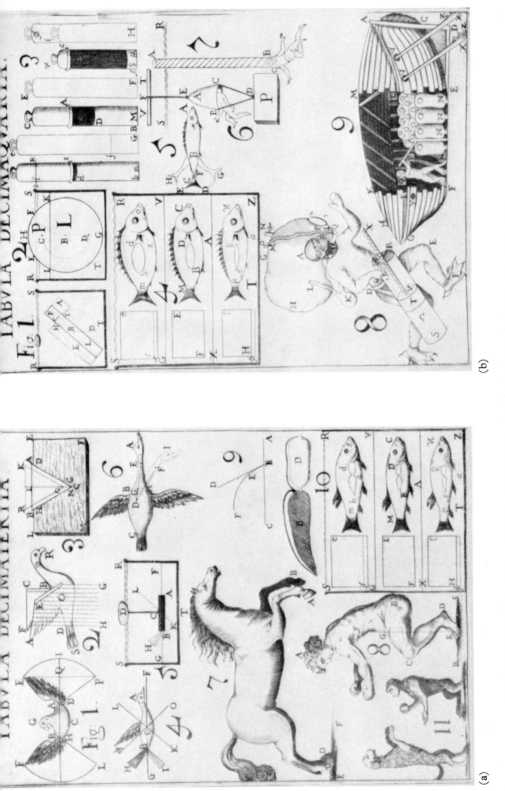

91 *Giovanni Borelli, De motu animalium, Rome, 1680. Plates XIII and XIV. On plate (b) can be seen one of the earliest equipments for underwater exploration*

(a)

(b)

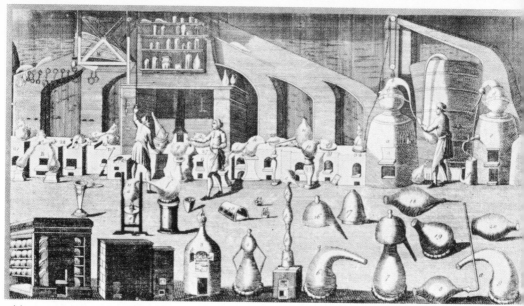

(a)

(b)

92 (a) *An eighteenth-century laboratory* c. 1750

(b) *Jean-Jacques Durameau, 'Saltpetre Factory in Rome', drawing, 1766. Paris, Musé du Louvre, Cabinet des dessins*

[*Louvre*

(b)

93 (a) *The anatomy lesson, from John of Ketham,* Fasciculus Medicinae, *Venice,* 1500
   (b) *Leonardo da Vinci, Anatomical drawings*
   (c) *Vesalius, Anatomical plate from* De Humani Corporis Fabrica, 1543

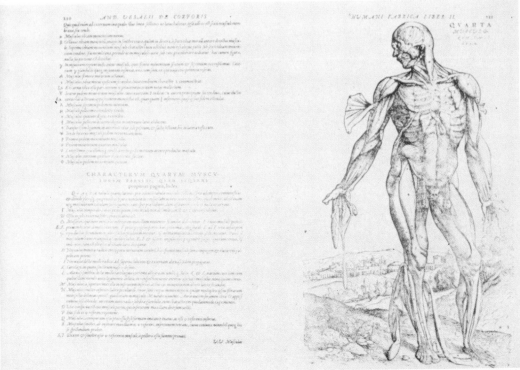

(a)

94 (a) *The main ward in a hospital in the fifteenth century. From a miniature. Paris, Archives de l'Assistance Publique*

(b) *A ward in the Hôpital de la Charité in the seventeenth century. Engraving by Abraham Bosse. Paris, Bibliothèque nationale*

(b)

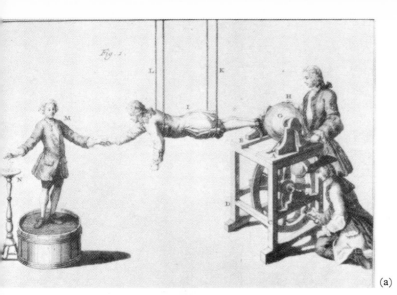

(a)

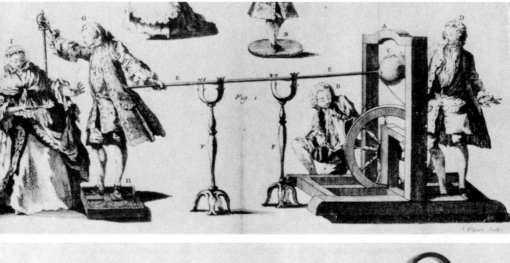

(b)

(c)

95 *Eighteenth-century electricity experiments*
(a) *J. Desaguliers,* De Natuurkunde . . . (*Amsterdam,* 1746)
(b) *Conductivity experiment from W. Watson,* Expériences et observations . . . de l'électricité (*Paris,* 1748)
(c) *Late eighteenth-century electrical machine with electrical chimes and gunner. (Powder was put in the gun which was then closed with a cork. When spark was sent through the powder, the cork came off with a bang and the bells chimed)*

Leyden, Royal Museum of the History of Science

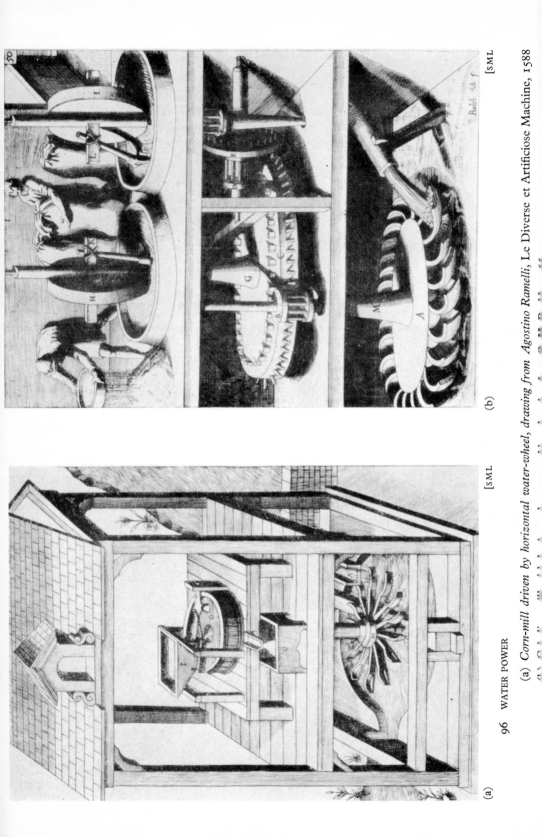

(a) Corn-mill driven by horizontal water-wheel, drawing from Agostino Ramelli, Le Diverse et Artificiose Machine, 1588

[SML]

(b)

[SML]

(a)

Babib Seb f.

(a)

98 (a) *Early wooden bed lathe,*
early eighteenth century

(b) *Rose engine, German,* c. 1750

(b)

(b)

97 WIND POWER

    (a) *Tower mill for grinding corn, from Agostino Ramelli, Le Diverse et Artificiose Machine,* 1588

    (b) *Wind-driven water pump,* c. 1560

(a)

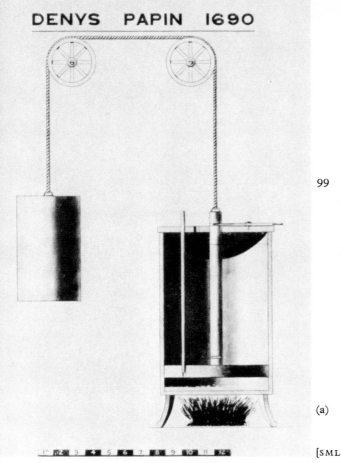

DENYS PAPIN 1690

99　THE STEAM-ENGINE

(a) *Explanatory drawing of
Denis Papin's steam cylinder
apparatus*, 1690

(b) *Engraving of Newcomen's
atmospheric engine, by Sutton
Nicholls*, 1725

(a)

(b)

100   Road building: C. J. Vernet, 'Paysage', Paris, Musée du Louvre

101 *Coalbrookdale cast iron bridge of 1779. Upstream view. This is the first cast iron bridge built by Abraham Darby and John Wilkinson. Photograph made in 1904*

(a)

102 TECHNOLOGY

(a) *Lifting appliance,
from Agricola,*
De Re Metallica,
1556

(b) *Horse-powered
bellows for
ventilating a
mine, from
Agricola,* De Re
Metallica, 1556

(b)

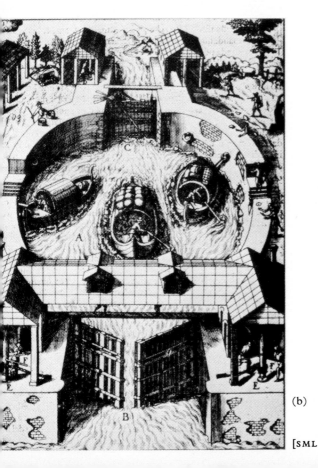

103 CANALS AND PORTS

(a) *Naval yards at St. Petersburg in the eighteenth century*

(b) *Machinery for operating lock-gates, c. 1600*

(b)

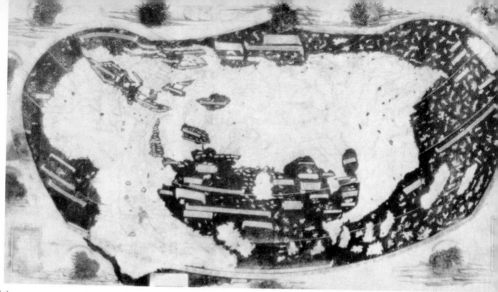

(a)

104   EARLY WORLD CARTOGRAPHY

    (a) *Henricus Martellus, Europe, Africa, Asia and Japan*
    (b) *The Waldseemüller Globe Map of* 1507

(b)

[*Min*

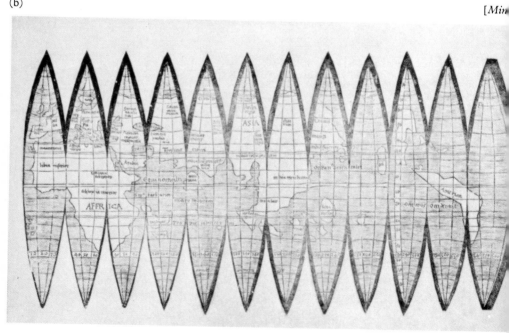

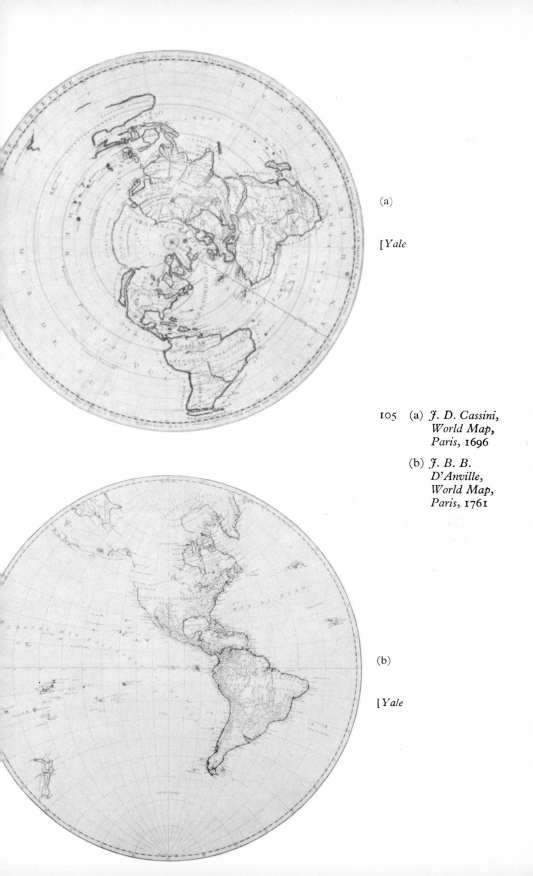

(a)

[*Yale*

105 (a) *J. D. Cassini,*
        World Map,
        Paris, 1696

     (b) *J. B. B.*
        D'Anville,
        World Map,
        Paris, 1761

(b)

⌊*Yale*

(a)

(c)

106 (a) *Model of a Mediterranean sailing ship of the fourteenth century*

(b) *Model of the Santa Maria, Christopher Columbus caravel, 1492*

(c) *Model of a Dutch herring bus, c. 1584*

London, Science Museum

(b)

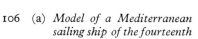

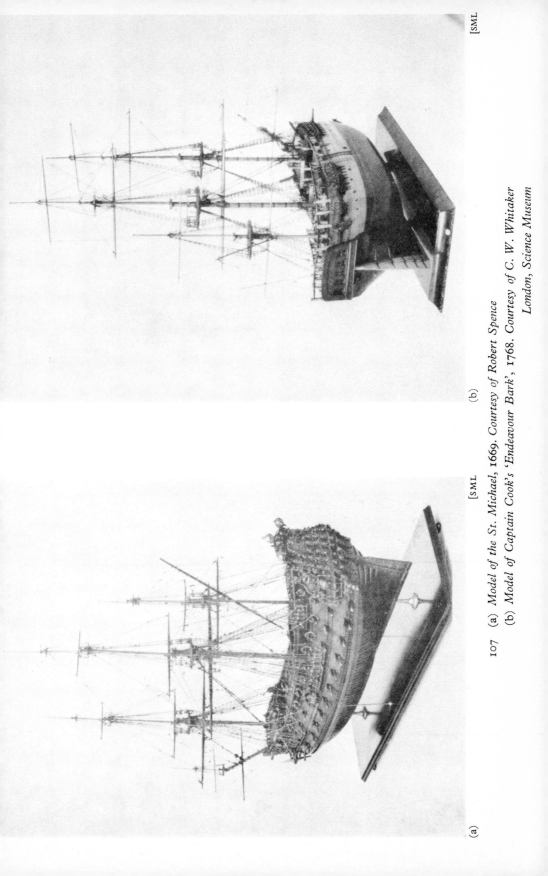

(a)

(b)

107   (a) *Model of the St. Michael, 1669. Courtesy of Robert Spence*
(b) *Model of Captain Cook's 'Endeavour Bark', 1768. Courtesy of C. W. Whitaker*
London, Science Museum

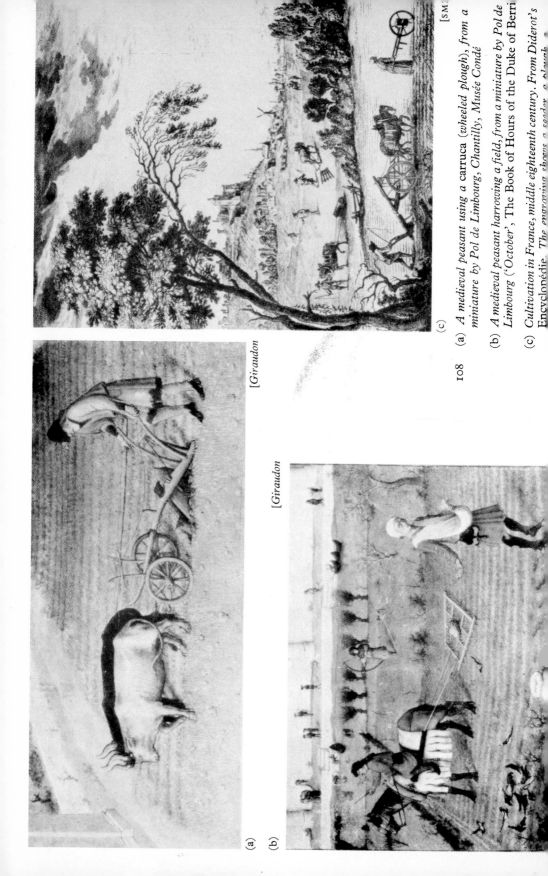

[Giraudon

[Giraudon

(a)

(b)

(c)

108

(a) *A medieval peasant using a carruca (wheeled plough), from a miniature by Pol de Limbourg, Chantilly, Musée Condé*

(b) *A medieval peasant harrowing a field, from a miniature by Pol de Limbourg ('October', The Book of Hours of the Duke of Berri*

(c) *Cultivation in France, middle eighteenth century. From Diderot's Encyclopédie. The engraving shows a seeder, a plough,*

[SM

literary and artistic taste; the seats of cultural life in this zone were legion, especially in Iran.

Nevertheless, the division between Iranic and Arabic civilization was never complete. For instance, it was a Persian of the fourteenth century, Fairūz-ābādī, who composed the nearly definitive Arabic dictionary, the Qāmūs. In an area like Malaysia, both Arabic and Persian influences were prevalent. Arabic was used for certain religious purposes throughout the Dār al-Islām, and in these matters the authors of one zone were read in the other; the Islamic world presented by the *Thousand and One Nights* is one world. At the same time, the Persian zone undoubtedly contained the larger number of Muslims, and the tendency of Persian ways to affect Iraq, Egypt, and the rest of the Arabic zone was very old. The Persian zone was also by and large the more culturally creative.

Many lines of activity, however, took the same turn in both zones. This period (the great controversies having subsided) produced definitive compendia and textbooks of orthodox religious and legal scholarship, which crystallized the points of view accepted by 1500 into statements at once unambiguous and easy of access. Various secondary problems were traced out in the same fields—problems which had escaped the attention of earlier scholars—either in the form of little monographs or of commentaries on earlier writings.

Poetry was the most distinguished medium of literary expression in the Islamic culture of the day. The Arabic zone fell completely behind in this field, for Arabic poetry, though abundant, failed to achieve much novelty or distinction, at least after the fourteenth century. Persian poetry, which had already seen a period of unsurpassed greatness, continued to flourish, and its tradition was now internationalized in many parts of far-flung Islam. To Arabic forms such as the *qaṣīda* (the desert-inspired panegyric ode) and the *ghazal* (love lyric) had been added such Persian forms as the *mathnawī* (historical or romantic epic). In Iran the fourteenth century is that of Ḥāfiẓ of Shīrāz, greatest of all Persian lyric poets. He combined musical grace and technical perfection with an unsurpassed subtlety of esthetic insight in his half-mystical, half-mundane *ghazals*. His nobility of mind was exceptional among the poets. Devoted to the town of Shīrāz, which his verses amply praised, he refused all temptations to seek preferment elsewhere. Contemporary with him was a numerous constellation of talented poets—satirists, lyricists, panegyrists, and mystics. Unlike Ḥāfiẓ they wandered among the many shifting courts of war-torn Iran, seeking princely favour, yet often remaining in relative obscurity in their own time. The practice of writing poetry in Persian was now established outside Iran also. An excellent exponent of this practice was Amīr Khusrav (d. 1324 or 1325) of Delhi, who was the fountainhead of a notable Indian school (see below).

Within Iran in this century the tendency became almost universal for a degree of mysticism to pervade every kind of poetry. Awḥadī inculcated a mystical morality, and Ibn-i Yamīn, using especially the form of *muqaṭṭaʾāt* (fragments), produced ethico-philosophical verse also mystically tinged. With Khwājū, author of romantic-mystical *mathnawīs*, and Salmān of Sāwa, a panegyrist noted for subtle verbal conceits, the Persian poetic tradition became more delicately nuanced. Non-mystical attitudes were represented by the satirist ʿUbayd-i Zākānī, who could also write good eulogies, and the parodist Abū-Isḥāq, who sang of material things like foods. More typically, at the end of the fourteenth century Maghribī wrote pure praises of unity in the Divine, while Kātibī wrote panegyrics at mutually hostile courts till he eventually retired as a Ṣūfī.

The religious trend continued in the fifteenth century. Early in that century there flourished (among others) Niʾmat-Allāh, founder of an influential *ṭariqa*, who was famous for his apocalyptic prophecies, which he alternated with more conventional mystical verse, and Qāsim al-Anwār, who was associated with the Ṣafawiyya order. The foremost poet of the century was Jāmī (1414–92). He wrote not only fine *ghazals* but also a septet of speculative and allegorical *mathnawīs*, the most celebrated of which told the story of the love of Joseph and Zulaykhā (Potiphar's wife), a major theme of Muslim parable. He also wrote good prose, producing not only mystical treatises but serious studies in literary history. The mystical monism embodying a concept of divine unity contemporaneously held by one school of Persian thought (see Chapter VI) was most prominently presented in the works of Jāmī in Iran and several other poets of his persuasion. Jāmī set forth his commentaries on mystical texts in verse as well as in prose. Even ʿAbd al-Karim al-Jīlī, who was the most systematic expositor of this persuasion, thought of himself also as a poet.

Appropriately enough, the internationalization of the Persian poetic tradition was carried out under the aegis of Ṣūfism, but poetry came to be an expression of the regional cultures at least as much as of international Ṣūfism. In Iran itself the golden age had ended. Though poets continued to produce sweet and stately poems in profusion, none could match the giants of the past; some of the greatest of contemporary Persian poets were more appreciated in India and Turkey than at home (and indeed many of them went to live at the Mogul court). In northern India the main vehicle of Islamic verse long continued to be Persian, but in the Deccan by the sixteenth century a Ṣūfī poetry thrived in Urdu, the common language of Muslims in northern and central India. (We shall deal with belles-lettres in India below and in Chapter XI.) In the Ottoman Empire Turkish was most cultivated, for there Arabic, though dialects of it were spoken in much of the empire, played a distinctly secondary role in cultivated life, being treated almost as a dead classical tongue.

Outside the great empires new Islamic literary languages also sprang up. On the east African coast Swahili, which had been developed as the language of the Muslim Bantu, came to possess a sophisticated poetic tradition which could rival Arabic within the region. At the other end of the Indian Ocean a Malay literature eventually grew up under the influence of Persian. It consisted in large part of renderings from Persian and Urdu, but it also took over much from the earlier Malaysian heritage, particularly in poetic forms, only partly Persianized. All of these regional literatures—Arabic, Persian, Turkish (in three forms), Urdu, Swahili, Malay—as well as some lesser Muslim languages which began to be cultivated in this period, used the Arabic alphabet, were infiltrated with Arabic and (in most cases) Persian words, and treated traditional Arabic and Persian themes in their poetry. But of the literature then being produced, Persian alone had an audience among most of the other Muslim language-groups, and even it was little read in the Arabic zone except so far as Turkish rule gave it currency.

Turkish poetry began to develop as early as the fourteenth century, but only in the fifteenth century did it attain mastery, although still essentially modelled on the Persian. Three forms of Turkish emerged—Chaghatai, Azerbaijan, and Ottoman Turkish. Newā'ī (c. 1440–1501), who also wrote and—having a high political position—richly patronized Persian poetry, made of the Chaghatai Turkish of Turkestan a standard language, which was to be used for poetry in the sixteenth century by many even in the Ottoman Empire as well as in Turkestan. Chaghatai Turkish was the vehicle of a prose masterpiece likewise—the memoirs of Bābur, ancestor of the Mogul rulers of India. On the other hand, Fuzūlī of Baghdad (see Chapter XI), who has been called the greatest Turkish poet of all time, was in the sixteenth century to do his best work in the Turkish of Azerbaijan. Moreover, many Ḥurūfī poets—followers of a mystical and esoteric Shī'ite sect of the fifteenth century, especially widespread in the Ottoman domains—used the western or Ottoman form of the language. Nesīmī, killed as a heretic at the beginning of that century, was the ablest of them. Shaykhī and other Persianizing poets of the fifteenth century firmly established this form of Turkish. Subsequently, in the sixteenth century (see Chapter XI), Ottoman Turkish literature was to become the most important of the three.

Arabic poetry, on the other hand, though abundant, failed to achieve much novelty or distinction after the fourteenth century. The old patterns of the qaṣīda and the verbally clever lyric or satire were still repeated, sometimes gracefully but usually with preciosity. As the quality of Arabic poetry declined, Persian poetry improved, although by the seventeenth century both had to yield precedence to Turkish poetry.

Prose as a Medium of Islamic Literature

In the Arab countries the telling or prose stories was a common practice. Story-tellers collected Greek, Indian, Persian, and Arabic tales, and several such collections, often in vernacularized Arabic, had been available in writing for many centuries. One of them, put in final form only around the fourteenth century in Egypt or Syria had a vogue also in the West. This was the *Thousand*

and One Nights, which in the eighteenth century became in translation, first in French and then in other languages, part of the Western literary heritage, too. The device used to effect unity is a single narrator who tells one story each night to her husband, the sultan, in order to keep him distracted from his vow to execute her at daybreak, until he eventually revokes his vow. European merchants and *jongleurs* brought back some of these tales from the Levant, and the oriental tales in Boccaccio and Chaucer probably are borrowed from them.[10] They also seem to have migrated eastward.

As in Europe, prose was not considered in the Muslim countries so appropriate a medium for creative imagination as poetry, and hence prose storytelling was not regarded as one of the major arts. Prose was reserved there, as in the West, rather for history, science, philosophy, and books of travel. Some of the most beautiful pieces of Islamic prose were in Persian, the products of the poet Jāmī. In the *Spring Garden* (1487), part of which was verse, he produced a book-size treatise on ethics illustrated with parables and fables.

In the fourteenth and fifteenth centuries the significant work done in systematizing the information and insight of the past on an encyclopedic level sometimes was in its own way seriously creative. The Egyptian Suyūṭī, in thus bringing together the religious and historical learning of Islam, imposed his own personality on the closely-knit result. Far more important than any other Arabic figure of all this period was Ibn-Khaldūn. In a long work that served as introduction to his historical studies, he made use of the encyclopedic approach—mobilizing the resources both of philosophy and of religious learning—to develop the trenchant analysis of the dynamics of history that we have already encountered (Chapter VIII) and will encounter again (Chapter XIII). He recognized his own time as a time of decline. His new departure was not followed up in the Arabic zone, and truly creative scholarship on a broad scale hardly existed there after Ibn-Khaldūn. A figure like Sha'rānī, a mystical thinker of the sixteenth century who brought a warm personal touch to the older patterns, was exceptional.

In the zone where Persian literary influence prevailed, prose became increasingly afflicted, from the end of Mongol times, with the cultivation of a resplendent but often inappropriate ornateness. Occasional writers preserved a simple style, as did the poet Jāmī in his biographies, but more often desire for an impressive form was allowed to outweigh the need for clarity of matter. This tendency was eventually carried even further perhaps in Turkish and Urdu than in the imitated Persian. In the field of history the masterful fair-mindedness and directness of speech of Rashīd al-Dīn Faḍl-Allāh (see Chapter VIII) set high standards in his vast world history but was less imitated than the elegance of his contemporary Waṣṣāf, who, though he gave much pertinent information, smothered it in skilfully florid verbiage. The many subsequent writers of history and biography in Iran rarely met the standards of either of these masters.

BELLES-LETTRES IN INDIA, SOUTHEAST ASIA, AND SOME
NEIGHBOURING LANDS

Like several other regions considered above or below, during this period India and southeast Asia developed a vernacular literature. In India, various Dravidian and Indo-European tongues emerged to challenge the dominance of Sanskrit as the language of literature and learning. In Burma, Siam, Cambodia, Malaya, and Java the vernaculars had to contend with Pali as well as Sanskrit. In India and southeast Asia, palm leaf provided a cheap writing material, but no system of ready reproduction of the written word had yet come into general use.

Sanskrit had begun to lose its vitality even before the Islamic conquest, and the destruction of seats of learning and monastic centres by the conquerors dealt it a debilitating blow from which it never recovered. Little original and creative work was still being done in the field of *kāvya* literature —i.e. the artificial and ornate verse and prose of the Sanskrit masterpieces. Sanskrit remained dominant, however, in (1) Vedic commentary; (2) theology, philosophy, and *dharma*; (3) grammar, lexicography, and metrics; (4) poetics and literary criticism; (5) politics; and (6) technical or scientific subjects. The growing sectarian character of the literature was evident in the later *purānas* and *tantras* and other theological and philosophical writings (see Chapter VI). Among the eminent traditionalists of the mid-fourteenth century were Mādhava (Vidyāranya), author of the famous manual (see Chapter VI) on the Hindu system of thought, and his brother Sāyana, a notable commentator on the Vedas, both of whom promoted the founding of the Vijayanagar Empire.

In the field of poetics and literary criticism several of the works composed in Sanskrit were still of a high order. Among the books on dramaturgy was Vidyānātha's *Pratāparudra-yashobhūshana* (c. 1300); it included a play which celebrated the glory of the author's patron, the king of Warangal, and which was intended to illustrate the rules of drama. Vishvanātha (fl. in Orissa c. 1350) in his *Sāhityadarpana* covered the whole field of poetics. Bhānudatta (also fourteenth century) in his *Rasamañjarī* and *Rasatarañginī* emphasized the importance of emotion and atmosphere in literature.

Sanskrit poetry itself declined more patently. No great Sanskrit epic was produced after the Islamic conquest. The best Sanskrit poetic achievements of the period were anthologies, but they contained only little of the work of contemporary writers, and that little showed an increasing tendency toward pedantry. Among the anthologies were several collections of lyric poetry— for example, in the fourteenth century, Shāngadhara's *Paddhati* (1363) and Sūrya's *Sūktiratnākara* and, in the fifteenth century, Vallabhadeva's *Subhāshitāvalī* (citing over 350 authors) and Shrīvara's work by the same name (citing more than 380). There were also several collections of Sanskrit gnomic and didactic verse.

Sanskrit prose was not without distinction during the period. The didactic beast fable (usually partly in verse) was represented by a fresh version of the *Pañchatantra*, which in various forms was well known and influential in Europe by 1500. Romantic tales were popular; Vidyāpati's *Purusapariksā* was an early fifteenth-century collection of such tales, and several Jaina collections appeared in the fourteenth and fifteenth centuries. Of the full-scale prose romance, the *Vemabhūpāla-carita* of Vāmana Bhatta Bāna (fl. in south India *c.* 1400) was probably the outstanding example. Drama (combining poetry with prose) was best represented by Gangādhar's *Gangādāsa Pratāpa Vilāsa*, which celebrated the struggle of a prince of Chāmpāner against Muhammed II of Gujarat.

Perhaps the leading literary figure of the period was the early fourteenth-century writer Venkatanātha (or Vedānta Deshika). In addition to writing significantly on religious and philosophical subjects (see Chapters V and VI), he was a distinguished belletrist. Among his Sanskrit works were a lyric in imitation of the illustrious Kālidāsa, an elaborate devotional poem, many shorter devotional and ritualistic poems, a drama in ten acts, and the *Yādavābhyudaya*, an epic on the life of Krishna. He also wrote poems in Tamil. His valiant efforts did not check the decline of Sanskrit in the area of imaginative literature. Nor did the rising vernaculars wholly fill the resulting gap, since they tended to concentrate on religious and devotional, if at times erotic, poetry and disregarded other literary forms as well as secular subjects in general.

Persian and Arabic Letters in India

As Sanskrit drooped in India, one of the two great classical languages of contemporary Islam, Persian, blossomed along with the vernaculars. The rulers of the Muslim kingdoms in north India were for the most part patrons of learning and literature and attracted to their courts numerous Persian and even Arabic writers. Several cities in north India became centres of Persian learning and produced a considerable body of literature in Persian. As indicated above, the most famous Persian-writing literary figure in India of the early-fourteenth century was Amīr Khusrav, who was head of the Imperial Library of Delhi and court poet of Sultan 'Alā-ud-dīn Khaljī (d. 1316). He was prolific in both poetry (reputedly composing Hindi verse also) and prose, writing on music and other subjects. Delhi under 'Alā-ud-dīn was said to be the envy of Baghdad, the rival of Cairo, and the equal of Constantinople because of the scholars and literary figures who came there. Sultan Muḥammad ibn Tughluq (ruled 1325–51) was himself a learned man who wrote with skill in Persian and Arabic, but the leading literary figure of his reign was Maulāna Muaiyyan-ud-dīn-'Umrānī. The long sultanate of Fīrūz Shāh (1351–88) was graced by several memorable literary figures. Sultan Sikandar Lodi (1489–1517) was likewise a poet and patron of literature.

Literature in the Vernaculars of India

The contemporary religious and political situation contributed to the rise of India's vernaculars. For one thing, they were intimately associated with the growth of the theistic religious sects. A sect leader could easily recognize that the use of a newer language would distinguish his sect from the older religious groupings and at the same time make it more readily intelligible to the masses. The Vishnu, Shiva, and Shākta sects exploited this opportunity in whatever tongue seemed best and thus contributed to its development, but Tantric Buddhism also made a contribution to Bengali, and Jainism to Kanarese. The Islamic conquest contributed to the rise of the vernaculars, since it stimulated the religious nationalism of *bhaktism*, furthered the decline of the centres of Sanskrit learning, and weakened the ruling class that used it. Some local Islamic rulers patronized vernacular writers, especially those who used Urdu (or Hindustani), a Persianized form of western Hindi, largely Persian in vocabulary and Hindī in grammar.

Some Persian literary forms slipped into the vernaculars, but Sanskrit left a wide, indelible mark on all of them. They borrowed from it not only words and literary forms but concepts, grammatical structures, and types of meter as well. Moreover, most of the religious ideas in the vernacular literature came from Sanskrit sources, since early sect leaders usually were Brahmans or learned men who had done their own studies in Sanskrit. Many other themes too were drawn from the vast Sanskrit storehouse. Furthermore, and during this period in particular, a considerable portion of vernacular belles-lettres consisted of translations or adaptations of Sanskrit epics and religious works. Most of the early vernacular writings were epic or lyrical poems, largely religiously inspired and, therefore, devotional or didactic in nature, though in small part also historical. The Sanskrit religious and moralistic lyric provided perhaps their richest element, but they tended also to borrow inferior and decadent elements from both Sanskrit and Persian—for example, stereotyped modes and ideas, outworn clichés, minutiae of anatomy, and other forms of eroticism, whether allegorical or not.[11]

In the Dravidian south, Tamil remained the favoured tongue. The Vijay-anagar emperors used Sanskrit and Telugu, but they did not discourage Tamil, and in the far south the Pandya kings gave it deliberate encouragement. Tamil authors were numerous, and they lengthened a productive tradition with a large number of philosophical works, commentaries, *purānas*, and *prabandhas* (grand epics). The new literature was, however, largely imitative and critical rather than creative. A 'somewhat arid scholasticism' pervaded the *maths* (monastic schools) and, as their influence spread in learning and education, infected the entire educational system.[12]

The Tamil authors of the period were mostly Shivaites or Vishnuites but sometimes Jains. Among the Shivaite writers was the fourteenth-century theologian Umāpati, who completed the Tamil canon (see Chapter III). He also wrote the *Koyirpurānum*, dealing with the legends of the Shiva shrine in Chidambaram. The late-fourteenth-century writer Svarūpānanda Dēshikar and his pupil Tattuvarāyar prepared two celebrated anthologies of religious and philosophic poetry. Probably the greatest Shivaite litterateur was Arunagirinātha. He was the author of the *Tiruppugal*, a popular fifteenth-century work containing over 1,360 lyrics in various meters; centring in the God Subrahmanya, it presented much of the sacred lore of Hinduism in vivid imagery. Among the Vishnuite authors were Pillai Lōkācārya and Vedānta Deshika, whose work has been noted several times. A Tamil version of the *Bhāgavatam* appeared at the very end of this period.

Of the more secular Tamil poets at least three should be singled out. Poyyāmoli wrote the *Tañjai-vānan-kōvai*, which dealt with the reign of a Pāndya king who died in 1308. Pugalēndi retold in the *Nalavenbā* (which appears to have been written about this time) the tragic story of Nala and Damayanti from the *Mahābhārata*. Probably the best Tamil secular poem of the period was the *Bharatam* of Villiputtūrar (c. 1400), which dealt with the theme of the *Mahābhārata* in 4,350 well-turned verses, with a profuse admixture of Sanskrit words.

Another of the Dravidian vernaculars was Kanarese (Kannada or Karnātaka). Kanarese literature was not so old as the Tamil, but it, too, had had a considerable period of development prior to 1300, generally dominated by Jaina productions. From 1300 to 1500, under the Vijayanagar Empire, the dominant literature in Kanarese was the religious writings of the Lingāyats or Vīrashaivites (see Chapter II), although Jaina works continued and Vishnuite works began to appear in that language.

A large part of the Vīrashaivite literature was in the form of simple prose tracts (called *vachanas*) or of *purānas* (mostly in six-line stanzas known as *shatpadī*). The *vachanas* expounded religious ideas, and the *purānas* dealt with religious reformers and devotees. Bhīmakavi's *Bāsava-purāna* (1369), a life of Bāsava, founder of the Lingāyats, became one of the sect's main texts and established the supremacy of the *shatpadī* verse-form among Vīrashaivite writers. Another famous life of Bāsava, the *Mahā-Bāsavarāja-charita*, was written by Singirāja about 1500. Chāmarasa's *Prabhulinga-līle*, a life of one of Bāsava's associates, so pleased Emperor Praudha Deva Rāya of Vijayanagar (1419–46) that he had it translated into Telugu and Tamil.

The Jaina works in Kanarese were for the most part *campūs* (that is, mingled poetry and prose), the verse varying in meter and showing marked literary skill. Other pieces generally were *purānas* dealing with the lives of great Jaina religious leaders or patrons. The Jaina writer Nāgarāja's *Punyāshrava* (c. 1331), containing fifty-two tales of puranic heroes, illustrated the duties of a householder. Other Jaina authors were Madhura (c. 1385), court poet of Harihara, whose *Dharmanātha-purāna* narrated the life of a Jaina patriarch, and Bhāskara, whose *Jīvandhara-charita* (1424) dealt with a pious prince who was a favourite subject among Jaina writers of this period.

The chief Vishnuite productions in Kanarese came in the late fifteenth century. They included Kumāra-Vyāsa's *Gadugina-Bhārata* (or *Karnāta Bhārata*), an incomplete version of the *Mahābhārata* (c. 1440), and Kumāra Vālmīki's *Torave Rāmāyana* (c. 1500). The longer Vishnuite poems employed the *shatpadī* form.

The Telugu (or Āndhra) vernacular, also a Dravidian tongue, was spoken in the Warangal area of eastern India reaching from Madras northward. Although it certainly had much earlier beginnings, its budding period extended from the late thirteenth century to about 1500 and was closely associated with Vīrashaivism. From the beginning it had a closer connection with Sanskrit than did Tamil or Kanarese, though its link with Kanarese is also very close. During this period the chief belletristic productions in Telugu were *purānas* and epic and lyric poems adapted from Sanskrit originals and Shivaistic devotional treatises of the puranic type. The Telugu version of the *Mahābhārata*, worked on since the eleventh century, was finally completed by Yerrāpragada (1280–1350), who also produced a version of the *Rāmāyana* (no longer extant) and of the *Harivamsha*, the epilogue to the *Mahābhārata*. In the late-thirteenth and early-fourteenth centuries two classic Telugu versions of the *Rāmāyana* were produced—the *Ranganātha Rāmāyana* of Kona Buddharāja and his son, and the *Bhāskara Rāmāyanam* (in *campū* form) of Hulakki Bhāskara and his son and disciples. Pālkuriki Somanātha, probably of this period, was a Lingāyat pamphleteer, who wrote not only in Telugu but also in Sanskrit and Kanarese. He composed a *Bāsava-purāna* and, in honour of Basava, the first Telugu *shataka*. (A *shataka* consists of a hundred lyric verses addressed to a God, saint, hero, or loved one.) In the early fifteenth century, Vemana, a philosophical poet, wrote *shatakas* that, because of their charm and simplicity, were translated into European and other languages.

The towering figure of Telugu literature in the fifteenth century was Shrīnātha (1365–1440), a staunch Shivaite, who shares with the thirteenth-century Tikkana the reputation of being the best poet in the language. He was patronized by various rajas and the ruler of Vijayanagar. His outstanding work was a majestic translation of Shrīharsha's great epic *Naishadha-carita*. His drama *Krīdābhirāmam*, giving a picture of urban society in Warangal, started a new genre in Telugu—a first-person narrative of the narrator's experiences addressed to a listener. His poem the *Haravilāsamu* contained four stories about Shiva. He may also have been the author of a work on poetics and of the earliest known historical heroic ballad in the literature. His brother-in-law, Bammera Potana (1400–75), in his youth wrote the *Bhōginīdandakam*, a love rhapsody on the king's concubine, the earliest work of this sort in Telugu, and he later translated the *Bhāgavatam* with such smooth diction, vivid description, and spiritual intensity that it became the most popular puranic epic in the Telugu language.

Malayalam is the vernacular of the Malabar coast area. It is a Dravidian dialect, closely related to Tamil, and its literature shows marked dependence on Tamil as well as Sanskrit. It was at first a medium of popular ballads and songs, of some longer metrical works, and of a certain type of ritualistic dance-drama. The earliest extant literary work in Malayalam is an anonymous poem of the fourteenth century telling about the transmission of a love message; it is still considered one of the most exquisite poems in the language. To enrich the ritual of the dance-drama, *campūs* and *prabandhas* were written under the influence of Sanskritists. The prose passages of the *campūs* often were satires upon contemporary usages and personalities. Perhaps the most famous Malayalam composer of this genre was Punam Nambudiri of the fifteenth century, whose masterpiece was the *Rāmāyana-campū*. In the next century Malamangalam Nambudiri in his *Naishadha-campū* pictured puranic scenes with an inspired touch, and the epic poet Cheruśśeri Nambudiri dealt with the life of Krishna in the best-known of his works, *Krishna-gāthā*. The Niranam poets of central Travancore, from the fifteenth century onward, sought to develop a Malayalam style free from Tamil and Sanskrit influences. Among this group were Mādhava Panikkār, author of a translation of the *Gītā*, and his grandson, Rāma Panikkār, author of a number of epics including the *Rāmāyanam*, a *Bhārata-gāthā*, and a *Bhāgavatam*.

In northern India the Indo–Aryan vernaculars won out, and of these the Hindi group was one of the oldest and most important. The several Hindi languages include not only Western and Eastern Hindi but also Rājasthānī and Bihārī, and each of them, in turn, has its own local dialects. Western Hindi was the most important, Hindi can be traced back to the bards of the Rajputs, but it became a language of literary importance only in the late fourteenth and fifteenth centuries with the lyrics of the early *bhakti* poets of Vishnuism, who sang the praises of Rāma and Krishna. The most significant among the several bards of the fourteenth century was Sarang Dhar (see Chapter VIII). Many of the Hindi lyrics of the early *bhakti* poets have been preserved in the *Adi Granth* of the Sikhs and the *Bījak* of the Kabīrpanthīs, which include works of the eminent religious leaders of the fifteenth century such as Rāmānanda, Kabīr, and Nānak (see Chapter VIII). Most of these writers directed their paeans toward Rāma. Kabīr's numerous poems were unpolished, but his telling satire and epigrams and his fascinating rhythm, though rough, gave great power to his poetry. He did more than any other early writer except Mīrā Bāi (see Chapter III) to create and popularize Hindi literature. Nānak wrote in Punjabi as well as Hindi. Although he was not the equal of Kabīr, his pithy verses of praise and prayer (contained in the *Japjī*) were not without poetical merit.

The finest Hindu lyric poets of the period were Vidyāpati Thākur (beginning of the fifteenth century) and Mīrā Bāi. Vidyāpati wrote numerous short songs or sonnets (*pads*) on the love of Rādhā and Krishna in the Maithili dialect of Bihari and so is claimed by Bengali as well as Hindi scholars. He also wrote in Sanskrit, and although his songs about Rādhā's love for Krishna have been interpreted as allegories of the soul's love for God, fundamentally they continue the Sanskrit tradition of Jayadeva's love-poetry. The excellence of his style and diction gave him considerable popularity throughout eastern India. He was the founder of a school of master-singers, which later spread over Bengal, and his songs unquestionably influenced Chaitanya.

The poetess Mīra Bāi, who came from the Muttra area, sacred to Krishnaites, wrote in the Braj Bhāshā dialect of Western Hindi (the dialect of Muttra). A devotee of Krishna from childhood, she expressed her intense love for him in graceful and melodious verses, which also won a wide popular approval. Her poems stimulated the use of the Braj Bhāshā dialect for the lyric poetry of the Krishna cult. Vitthalnātha, son of the founder of the Vallabhas, was reputed to be the author of the *Mandan*, a short prose work in Braj Bhāshā dealing with the story of Rādhā and Krishna.

The literature in Bengali, another of the old Indo–Aryan vernaculars, perhaps showed more originality than that in Hindi. In the fourteenth century the Māgadhī Prakrit language began to assume its Bengali character, which in its literary form (Sādhu-bhāsā) borrowed Sanskrit words freely. A Hindu reaction to Muslim domination led, furthermore, to a sort of classical revival of Sanskrit influence, without, however, obliterating the popular religious pattern.[13] The local folk culture was made up of several elements. The Tantric Buddhism of Bengal had influenced its local cults (of Manasā, Chandi, Dharma, and other folk deities and heroes), whose mythologies took shape during the early centuries of Islamic control, and these cults with their mythologies were, in turn, gradually absorbed into the Krishna-Rādhā and Shākta religious movements, especially from the sixteenth century on. Bengali literature thus eventually derived its major characteristics from five main sources: Tantric Buddhism, local folk cults, Krishna-Rādhā *bhaktism*, Shākta *bhaktism*, and, of course, Sanskrit literature.

The first important body of Bengali literature to survive appeared in the relatively peaceful fifteenth century. The standard element of Bengali poetry, the *payār*, a heroic or rhyming couplet with four feet in each line, had by that time become fully developed. The religious nature of their subject matter led writers to model their narrative poems on the puranas rather than on the great Sanskrit epics and secular works. In their Bengali versions, the grandeur of the Sanskrit epics 'shrank into thin trickles of rustic piety', for 'the most inferior qualities of Sanskrit . . . seem to have had the greatest appeal for Bengali poets.'[14]

This new literature fell into three divisions, which persisted until the nineteenth century. They were (1) translations, (2) Krishna-Rādhā literature, of which the short lyrical devotional and love songs (*pads*) had a distinct literary beauty, and (3) narrative or epic poems setting forth the stories and myths of the local cults. The narrative or epic poems were called either *vijay* ('victory') *kāvya* ('victory' referring to the cruelty with which the deities treated their opponents) or *mangal* ('benevolence') *kāvya* ('benevolence' referring to the kindness which the deities showed toward their followers). Most Bengali poetry was meant to be sung, and the long poems were composed of pieces for semi-musical and semi-dramatic performance by professional and mendicant minstrels or story-tellers.

The earliest cardinal work in Bengali literature has continued to be regarded as a masterpiece; it was the *Rāmāyana* of Krittivās Ojhā, written at Gaur sometime between 1409 and 1414 in *payārs*. Since the author freely modified the original *Rāmāyana* to suit his own religious purpose and to appeal to the common people, the characters were represented as popular, rustic types with little of the heroic spirit. Its simplicity, charm, and ethical qualities have made it the Bible of the Bengal masses. From both the literary and linguistic points of view, however, the *Shrī-Krisna-kīrttan* of Baru Chandīdās (see Chapter III) was the most interesting work of the early-fifteenth century. It was an epic narrating the conquest (*vijay*) of Rādhā by Krishna. Krishna was pictured as the cunning seducer of Rādhā, who, much the most appealing figure in the story, loved him unselfishly and with her whole body and soul, once her resistance had been overcome. Mālādhar Vasu's *Shrī-Krisna-vijay* was a significant version of the *Bhāgavata-purāna*, written between 1473 and 1480. Rādhā had not been mentioned in the original purana, but the theme of Mālādhar's work was Krishna the lover and beloved of Rādhā.

The first of the surviving epics inspired by the local cults was the *Manasā-mangal* of Vijay Gupta, begun in 1494. It told the story of Manasā (here the daughter of Shiva), who, having left her home because of the cruelty of her stepmother Chandī, tried to gain the worship of Chād Sadāgar, a wealthy merchant, in order to avenge herself by taking worshippers away from Shiva and Chandī. It throws much light on contemporary life in Bengal.

A great literary outburst occurred in Bengal under the relatively enlightened rule of Sultan Hussein Shah (1493–1518). One of his officials, Yasorāj Khān, a Hindu turned Muslim, wrote the *Krishna-mangal*. Sanātana and Rūpa Gosvāmī (see Chapters V and VII) also flourished at the sultan's court before they joined the Chaitanya movement. About this time Kavīndra composed his version of the *Mahābhārata*, and Shrīkaran Nandwi his version of a part of it; Shrīdhar produced the earliest rendering of the Sanskrit Vidyā-Sundar story, a tale of a love intrigue between the Princess Vidyā and a disguised foreign prince, Sundar; and Kaviranjan of Shrīkhanda imitated the amatory Rādhā-Krishna lyrics of Vidyāpati so well as to earn the name Minor Vidyāpati.

The literature in other Indo-European vernaculars of north India developed in much the same way as that in Hindi and in Bengali. Marathi literature was noted for its religious mysticism and pure devotionalism. Most of its important writers were religious poets who sang the praises of Vittoba (Vishnu), the deity of the local Pandharpur shrine. The first important Marathi writer was Jñāndeva, who prepared a commentary on the *Bhāgavad-gītā* about 1290; the foremost figure of the period was Nāmdēv (see Chapters II and III). The development of Gujarati literature was closely related to that of Hindi, although it was perhaps more clearly dominated by the Rādhā-Krishna poets.

Many verses of Mīrā Bāi were well known in Gujarati. Narsingh Mehtā wrote (*post* 1450) some noted Gujarati lyrics about the loves of Rādhā and Krishna. The *Pañchatantra* and other Sanskrit stories were translated into that tongue, and at an early date Islamic influences also appeared in it. Punjabi literature was little developed before 1500. Although the Urdu language matured during this period, no literature of any consequence appeared in it. The most prominent writer in Kashmiri was the fourteenth-century ascetic Lallā, whose lyrical songs paid honour to Shiva. In Assam Shāktism and Tantrism were vigorous, and erotic sentiments were prominent in *pads* and longer songs. The foundations for later literary developments in Assamese were laid, probably in the fourteenth century, by Mādhav Kandali's version of the *Rāmāyana*. Mādhav was also the author of the *Devajit*, a more original poem, in praise of Krishna.

The Literatures of Southeast Asia

The literature of the countries of southeast Asia (except Vietnam) fell under profound Pali Buddhist and Sanskrit influences, but the classical sources in those languages were supplemented by native myths and legends. The works of greatest interest and merit were largely inspired by or derived from the Jātaka stories about the life of the Buddha or from the great Sanskrit epics and puranas. Epic and lyric poetry were the chief literary forms, but some stories and native chronicles were recorded in prose, and the dramatic-ballet, employing verse and pantomime accompanied by music, was also a common medium of creative expression. Authors were generally either monks or courtiers.

In the several kingdoms that now make up Burma, though Buddhist religious and philosophical treatises and poems dealing with the story of the Buddha were often written in Pali, in the latter half of the fifteenth century chronicles, law books, and poetry appeared in the vernacular. In the Ava area a group of monkish scholars wrote in both Pali and Burmese. Ariyavamsa (fl. 1450) composed several poems in Burmese; Uttamagyan (b. 1453) used Burmese for a famous poem on the seasons, the *Tawla* (*A Journey through the Forest*); Silavamsa (Thilawunth, 1453–1520) wrote the mythological chronicle *Yazawingyan* as well as other poems in that language; and both Ratthasara (1468–1529) and Aggathamahdi (b. 1479) wrote Burmese poetical versions of the Jātakas. In Pegu the dominant vernacular was that of the Talaing tribe. The oldest surviving law book of the realm is a translation in Talaing. At Toungoo the royal family was celebrated in courtly verses by one of the king's war boat commanders, Thondaunghmu, and in Arakan the court bard Aduminnyo composed an historical poem (*c.* 1430).

The Tibetan dialects are related to Burmese. For a country of so small a population, Tibet produced a considerable literature, primarily of a religious nature. The two canonical collections, the *Kanjur* and the *Tanjur*, reached their definitive form in the early fourteenth century (the *Kanjur* was printed in 1410). Several of the best of the numerous elaborate histories were essentially accounts of Buddhism in Tibet. Among the biographies of religious leaders was Ge-long's of Geden-dub, the first of the great lamas, written about 1494. And the mythological life of Padma-Sambhava, the celebrated founder of Tantric Buddhism in Tibet, probably belongs in this period too. Tibetan authors also produced folktales, accounts of holy places, and poetry, but no poet came forth to compare with Mila, the most celebrated poet of earlier Tibet.

In Siam, except for the Pali Buddhist canon, Pali literature was less influential than in Burma, whereas as early as the fourteenth century various pieces of literature, including several versions of the Jātakas, appeared in the native Thai languages. Thai literature was also strongly influenced by the Sanskrit epics and puranas that came to Siam by way of the Khmer Empire and Java. These works, along with the Jātakas and native traditions, supplied inspiration for popular mythological or semi-historical prose tales and dance-dramas. Versions of the universally beloved *Ramakien* (*Rāmāyana*) were certainly in existence by the fourteenth century, and so probably were many of the other tales that have since been adapted to dance dramas. The well-known historical romance *Inaco*, of Javanese origin, must have been available before 1500. The early versions of the *Maxims of Phra Ruang*, a classic of Siamese moralistic (*nīti*) literature, most likely made their appearance in the fourteenth century, since Phra Ruang, the Thai national hero, probably was Rāma Kamheng, who lived about 1300. Thai literature was especially noted for its short lyric love songs and its *nirats* (extended narrative love poems), in which a traveller addresses his lady love.

Of the literature of Cambodia before the sack of Angkor (1431) by the Thais little is known. Its strong Sanskrit connections are suggested by the Sanskrit elements in Thai and Laotian literature, doubtless imported by way of Cambodia. After the fall of its capital Cambodia had little political or cultural eminence, but its native chronicles and other forms of literature, strongly influenced by the Pali Buddhist tradition as well as the Sanskrit tradition, continued.

Old Javanese, still preserved in Bali as the language of traditional literature, perhaps reached its zenith before the Majapahit period (1293–1415). It prospered until the fifteenth century, heavily dependent on Hindu and Buddhist ideas. Over half the words it used were Sanskrit, and its great classics were adaptations of Sanskrit and Buddhist texts, though thoroughly naturalized. Among them were the *Kāndā* (*Tradition*), *Rāmākavi* (*Rāmāyana*), *Bhārata-yuddha* and *Arjunavivāha* (both from the *Mahābhārata*), *Nītisārakavi* (based on a Hindu work on ethics and religion), and the *Kamahāyānikan* (a Buddhist work expounding Mahāyāna and Tantric ideas). More distinctly native were the chronicles, the romances, the tales of evil spirits, the dance-dramas, and especially the *wayang* (or shadow plays), employing puppets or masked figures. Probably the most admirable original work of the Majapahit period was the *Nagarakertagama*, a poem composed about 1365 by Prapanca, head of the Buddhist clergy, dealing with the life and times of the contemporary ruler Hayam Wuruk. With the rise of Malacca and Islam and the decline of Majapahit, the production of significant literature in Old Javanese ceased, nor was it effectively replaced by works in modern Javanese or the closely related Malay. Malay was written in the Arabic alphabet after the fourteenth century; the literary language since the fifteenth century has undergone little change.

The Filipinos appear to have had before the Spanish conquest a written literature consisting of epic and lyric poetry. Some of it has been preserved and appears in modern times in the form of oral literature and dance dramas. It incorporates local myths, legends, and heroes, and seems to have been influenced also by the great Hindu epics.

BELLES-LETTRES IN THE FAR EAST

In most of the Far East Chinese was the *langue de culture*. The complicated symbolic nature of the Far Eastern writing systems limited the acquirement of reading proficiency to those who had learned the numerous ideographs. A phonetic Mongol script based on the Uigur alphabet developed shortly after 1200, but only a limited amount of Mongol literature appear in it. By 1434 Korea also had a phonetic alphabet, which was used for popular literature and various other purposes, but it did not succeed in replacing literary Chinese for serious writings. Japan had its own *Kana* syllabary in which (sometimes in combination with Chinese characters) its classics were written, and a truly Japanese literature of this type existed, but the period under consideration in this chapter was not one of the great periods of Japanese literary production.

Printing was in general use in China, Korea, Japan, Vietnam, and central Asia throughout our period, facilitating the dissemination and preservation of literature. Moveable type had been used in China since about 1045. The earliest type was made of porcelain, and later examples were of tin and wood (1313). Wooden type of Uigur words dating *c.* 1300 has been found in central Asia. A type mould from which a more durable metal type could be cast was perfected in Korea or China during the fourteenth century. Moveable type seems, however, not to have been widely adopted in China, block printing being generally preferred. The first large book known to have been printed with moveable type in China was a reprint in 1574 of the great *T'ai-ping yü-lan* encyclopedia. In Korea, on the other hand, moveable type was used a great deal in the fifteenth century. The Yi dynasty established a Department of Books charged with casting type and printing, which, beginning actively in 1403, cast many founts, but after 1544 moveable type ceased to be used until revived in 1770. The first book known to have been printed in moveable type in Japan appeared in 1596, but the use of moveable type ended about 1647 in favour of block printing.[15]

Mongol literature was in its infancy during this period. It consisted of native songs and folklore, probably largely unwritten, some annals, and some translations or adaptations of Chinese and Indian works—the Indian works largely indirectly, from Tibetan translations. The so-called *Tobciyan* was a Mongol account of Genghis Khan and his first four successors; it formed the basis of the early parts of the Chinese *Yüan shih* (see Chapter VIII), but it probably had no wide currency among the Mongols themselves. Some of the translations of Chinese and Indian literature were more popular. The *Pañchatantra* tales were among these, as was also the Buddhist classic the *Bodhicaryāvatāra* of Shāntideva, which the translator, the Tibetan monk Čosgi Odsir (early fourteenth century), provided with a commentary. The Mongol version of the Chinese *Classic of Filial Piety* (*Hsiao ching*) was perhaps the finest specimen of this translated literature.[16]

The oldest literary works of Vietnam were not only of Chinese origin but were also written in Chinese, and the earliest native poetry and chronicles were likewise composed in Chinese. In the thirteenth and fourteenth centuries, however, the *chū'-nōm* system of writing developed whereby Vietnamese words were written in modified Chinese characters. Gradually a goodly amount of poetry and tales appeared in this form, along with Vietnamese versions of Chinese dramas, novels, and ethical and philosophical works.

Korean authors also at first wrote in Chinese. A popular work of fiction, the *Adventures of Hong Kil Dong*, by the monk Kasan, probably Korea's most important literary creation of the fourteenth century, was in that language. Both Buddhist and Confucian influences pervaded Korean literature, but after the establishment of the Yi dynasty (1392) Confucian ideas dominated. With the development of the phonetic Korean alphabet, more popular literature, such as folktales, novels, dramas, and adaptations of Chinese classical works, began to appear in pure Korean, while Chinese retained its grip on the more serious literary forms. An upsurge of nationalism and of Confucian idealism under the new dynasty combined with the use of the phonetic script to make the fifteenth century one of the most flourishing in Korean literary history. It culminated in an imposing anthology, the *Tongmun Seon*, prepared by a group of scholars in accordance with a royal order of 1478, which contained selections from about five hundred authors.

Styles of Prose in China

In China the development of the vernacular was somewhat different from elsewhere. The dominance of literary Chinese as the proper language of government documents, learning, and 'true literature' was not seriously challenged, but two new forms of literature, the drama and the novel, emerged, written in *pai-hua*, the colloquial speech. The dramas, having a certain literary elegance, were gradually accepted as literature by the Confucian literati, but the novels, despite their widespread appeal, were not. During our period, however, these 'lower' forms of imaginative letters blossomed and became, despite Confucian purists, the most popular and original.

Some significant work was still produced in the literary language. Prose in that language during our period was of several types—*ku-wen*, *pien-wen*, *fu*, and *pa-ku*. *Ku-wen*, the ancient or loose prose style, was the most used, being employed for most of the *lun* (essays or brief discussions), *hsiao-shuo* (short stories), histories, biographies, and literary criticism. In the Yüan and early Ming periods one of the few well-known essayists was Sung Lien (1310–81), chief author of the *Yüan History*. Short stories in the literary language, once characteristic of the T'ang period, again became popular. They included tales of the marvellous (*ch'uan-ch'i*), fictionized biographies of historical persons, heroic narratives, religious legends, and love stories. The tales of Ch'ü Yu (1341–1427) found in the *Chien-teng lu* and *Chien-teng-hsin-hua* (1378) were widely read. In these and other collections stories of illicit love, verging on the pornographic, predominated. Most of the biographical works were concise, factual, dry, and, while valuable as historical sources, of little literary merit. Among the critics were the early-fourteenth-century scholar Wu Shih-tao, whose *Wu li-pu shih-hua* discussed the principles of poetry, and the late-fifteenth-century statesman Li Tung-yang, whose *Lu-t'ang shih-hua* was critical of poets, past and contemporary.

The other prose styles in the literary language were put to less common use. The complicated *pien-wen* (or parallel-sentence prose) was no longer much needed except in eulogies and formal government documents. The *fu*, originally a rhyming parallel-sentence form of a descriptive or expository nature, had by this time been transformed into the so-called prose *fu*. The *fu* was a genre peculiar to China. It dealt with an assortment of subjects including places, products, animals, scenery, meteorological phenomena, and various emotions such as home-sickness and the sadness of separation. The prose *fu* of our period had a loose structure permitting unpredictable rhymes and parallelisms and allowing considerable freedom but requiring some degree of literary skill to produce anything of distinction. Although many *fu* were written, few, if any, compared with those of earlier periods. The eight-legged essay (*pa-ku*) became the prescribed form for the civil-service examinations, but it promoted a formal and stultified style that did not serve to improve literary standards.

Chinese Poetry

The ability to write poetry was considered one of the accomplishments of the Chinese scholar, and tens of thousands of poems were produced. Most of them were of mediocre quality, and none of the poetry in the traditional style compared favourably with that of the T'ang and Sung periods. It divided into two general groups—the *shih* and the *tz'u*.

The *shih* poems, in turn, were of two general types. The ancient or un-regulated type consisted of lines of four, five, and seven words with no fixed number of lines. The modern or regulated type was popularized during the T'ang period. Its standard form was the *lü-shih*, which consisted of lines of five or seven words each in an eight-line stanza that followed a prescribed rhyme-scheme and observed strict rules of verbal parallelism and tonal sequence in certain lines.[17] A diversification known as the *pai-lü* permitted as many as several hundred lines with variations in the rhyme scheme, and another, the *chüeh-chü*, or broken-off line poem, was of four lines, each consisting of five or seven words—just enough to introduce, develop, embellish, and conclude a theme. These conventions determined that most traditional Chinese poems would be short and, to have any merit, would have to reveal verbal dexterity as well as literary inspiration. The imitators of our period could not match the several original types, among other reasons because linguistic changes had altered tones, making the T'ang rhymes, which they had to follow, sound inaccurate. Liu Chi (1311–75) and Kao Ch'i (1336–74) were perhaps the most distinguished traditional poets of the Mongol period, and of the early Ming period Hsieh Chin (1369–1415), one of the editors of the great Yung-lo encyclopaedia (see Chapter XI), Li Tung-yang (1447–1516), and Li Meng-yang (1472–1529).

The *tz'u* poem, having originated during the T'ang period, had reached its highest level during the Sung period. It was at first a vehicle principally for love lyrics that were intended to be sung. Its lines were of unequal length but with prescribed rhymes and tonal sequences, which occurred in many patterns. Despite its adherence to the literary style it admitted elements of colloquial speech. Gradually it expanded in length, became divorced from music, and developed into purely literary verse dealing with other than lyric subjects. Most of the poets of our period wrote *tz'u* also, but none of them measured up to the Sung masters.

The function of the *tz'u* as song was gradually taken over by the *ch'ü*, or colloquial lyric, designed to be sung to a designated tune by public enter-tainers or sing-song girls. The ancient drum song (*ku-shih*), a rhyming version of the colloquial tale, was similarly meant to be sung or else recited by story-tellers. *The Rhythmic Tales of the Twenty Histories* (*Erh-shih-i shih-t'an ts'u*), by the scholar Yang Shen (1488–1559), presented several drum songs of the Ming period. When taken over and polished by literary men, the *ch'ü* and the *ku-shih* became a new, dynamic poetry. The music, songs, and recitations of the *ch'ü* and *ku-shih* entertainers were combined with the prose tale, whether in the literary or the colloquial language, and with various other popular dramatic forms to create the new drama. *Ch'ü* poetry flourished thenceforth in the theatre, while the drum song, being popular narrative poetry, helped to promote the colloquial prose tale and the novel.

Chinese Drama

Chinese drama reached full maturity during the Yüan period. It appealed
to the Mongol rulers as well as the general public, and many literary men not
employed by the conquerors found an outlet for their talents in writing plays.
The plays they wrote were essentially operatic ballets, employing, along with
both speaking and singing parts, an elaborate system of conventional gestures
with sleeve, hand, arm, foot, leg, waist, or whole body to help explain an
emotion or action. The actors wore elaborate costumes but used little or no
stage setting. They were accompanied by an orchestra, which played music
that exploited popular tunes, for which appropriate *ch'ü* songs were written.
Plots were drawn from history or popular tales and were presented in a
colloquial or semi-colloquial language. Before 1500 Chinese drama was perhaps further advanced than the drama of the West but seems rudimentary
when compared with the best of the Greco-Roman stage or of the later West.

The southern Chinese plays (*nan-hsi* or *hsi-wen*) can be distinguished from
the northern ones (*tsa-chü*). The northern play normally consisted of a
prologue which was an integral part of it and four acts (with an optional fifth).
Only the leading actor sang, and he changed roles from act to act if the leading
role changed. The northern drama had its own distinctive tunes, all of which
in a given act were in the same key. The southern drama was more colloquial
and unconventional. It was generally long and of an irregular number of acts,
and the prologue was not an integral part of it. It employed tunes from south
China, all songs in the same act were not in the same key, and all characters
might sing, often in duets. In the early southern plays tunes from Huei-chou
(Anhwei) and I-chiang (Kiangsi) were especially favoured.

Southern dramatists introduced into their productions lengthy historical
plots as well as Taoist immortals and supernatural elements. They also tended
to emphasize Confucian moral principles. The most noteworthy of the early
southern dramas was the *Tale of a Lute* (*P'i-p'a chi*), written by Kao Tse-
ch'eng probably late in the fourteenth century. It was a melancholy and
highly ethical tale of the responsibilities put upon a young scholar by his
Confucian ideals, especially those of filial piety. It had twenty-four acts and
was clearly not intended to be presented *in toto* at one sitting. Some southern
dramas apparently were already popular in south China before the northern
dramas reached their greatest vogue at Peking, but they were at first disregarded by literary men, and not until the latter part of the Yüan period did
they compete successfully at the capital with the northern dramas.

Most of the early dramas were moralistic in tone, tending to fall within
three general categories—romantic comedies, the 'just official' plays, in which
the hero was an honest and sagacious official, and the warrior-hero or historical plays. Stock characters were customary—the elderly man, the just official,
the military hero, the country bumpkin, the loving mother, the courtesan, the
high-born maiden, the simple country girl. The plots were generally thin,
success depending rather on the popularity of the theme and music and the

ability of the actors than on the literary merit of the play. Dreams and super-natural agencies were often called upon to solve impossible situations. Some of the plays were tragic, but they did not develop the theme of inner conflict characteristic of Greek and later Western tragedy. Chi Chün-hsiang's early-fourteenth-century *Orphan of the House of Chao*, however, suggested it: to save the life of his ward a doctor sacrifices his own son but in the end is rewarded for having discharged his higher duty.

The titles of over 500 northern dramas of the Yüan period have been preserved, and about 132 are still extant. The largest number were preserved in the *Yüan ch'ü hsüan*, compiled during the Ming period. Kuan Han-ch'ing (*c.* 1210–1285), Wang Shih-fu, and Ma Chih-yüan probably were the leading dramatists of the early Yüan period. In Kuan's *Courtesan in Distress* the heroine is rescued from the villain by her true admirer and another courtesan; and in his *Gross Injustice to the Maid T'ou*, a girl is executed for a murder she did not commit, but her father, having become a judge and guided by his dreams, punishes the guilty. Kuan and Wang were joint authors of *The Romance of the West Chamber (Hsi hsiang chi)*, the best-known of the Yüan dramas. It was a sequence of five four-act plays dealing with the 'wing, flowers, snow and moonlight' of a frustrated romance, which worked out in the end, however, to the satisfaction of all concerned. Ma's *Sorrows of Han* dealt with the suicide of a Han princess sent as a concubine to the chief of the Huns in order to save China from attack.

In the later Yüan period, when the southern dramas became popular every-where, the two regional types began to influence each other. In the early Ming period a mixed type developed in which southern tunes predominated and formed the transition to the southern *k'un-ch'ü* drama of the sixteenth century (Chapter XI). *Madame Cassia, or The Tale of a Horse Dealer*, a play in four acts, was a good example of the mixed play. It dealt with the woes of a horse dealer whose children were driven away from home by a vicious step-mother. All are happily re-united in the end, and the villains appropriately punished.

The Short Story and the Novel in China

The short story in the literary language was an old form of belles-lettres in China, but the colloquial tale (*hsiao-shuo*) became popular only during our period. The oldest surviving colloquial tales date from the Sung dynasty or earlier; they survived in story-tellers' prompt books. One of the oldest collections of Sung stories, the *Ch'ing-p'ing-shan t'ang*, was published only between 1522 and 1566; another somewhat better collection, the *Ching-pen t'ung-shu hsiao-shuo*, appears to have come somewhat later. During the Yüan and early Ming periods numerous stories were produced, some 120 of them being published between 1620 and 1628 in three separate collections, known together as the *San-yen (Three Collections)*. The largest group were moralistic tales; others dealt with rewards and punishment, fate, happy reunions of families and lovers, courtesans, talented youths, just officials, immortals, and swindlers; some were of a detective-story nature, with a clever magistrate solving the mystery involved. The oldest collection of tales of historical fiction, the *Completely Illustrated P'ing-hua* (*Ch'uan-hsiang*), can be dated 1321–24.

Out of drum songs, dramas, and colloquial tales grew the longer colloquial prose stories, or novels. These novels were lengthy, repetitious, and rambling, and their plots were weak, but their characterization was often excellent. They represented a vital and dynamic literature-of-the-people. The oldest were historical and picaresque narratives. One of the most notable before 1500 was *The Romance of the Three Kingdoms* (*San-kuo-chih yen-i*), based on the conflict among the three successor states to the Later Han dynasty; its characters were historical figures, and its episodes elaborations of events mentioned in the dynastic histories. It is attributed to Lo Kuan-chung (1328–98), but the novel of 120 chapters which we have today probably is the product of revision and perhaps supplementation by later hands; the oldest surviving printed version dates from about 1522, but its preface indicates that it must have been in print as early as 1494.

The Water Margin (*Shui hu chuan*, translated by Pearl S. Buck in 1933 as *All Men Are Brothers*) was another notable novel of the period before 1500. It was a Chinese Robin Hood story, written in a more colloquial style than *The Romance of the Three Kingdoms*. It dealt with a large band of men forced by hard times and vicious officials to live as robbers in a marsh in Shantung, generally befriending the poor and weak and wreaking vengeance on the oppressors of the people; ultimately pardoned by the emperor and taken into official service, they were gradually destroyed by the machinations of court officials. Some of the characters and many of the incidents were historical but in reality had been widely separated in time and place.

The history of *The Water Margin* may suggest what happened in the course of time to the original texts of other Chinese novels. Its oldest version in 92 chapters was possibly the joint work of Shih Nai-an and Lo Kuan-chung. In the so-called Kuo edition (*c.* 1550) and several other, almost contemporary editions, eight chapters were inserted describing the robbers' campaigns after they had been taken into the emperor's service. In the 1590's a Fukien book-seller brought out an edition, which, though otherwise abbreviated, gave two new campaigns in addition. Li Chih, a champion of vernacular fiction, revised and enlarged the story of the two recently added campaigns and supplied a commentary but followed the Kuo edition in most other respects. This newer version, published in 1614 in 120 chapters, gave the novel its most complete form. Chin Sheng-t'an, a well-known man of letters of the seventeenth century, considered the work of literary value but did not condone its portrayal of robbers as heroes. In 1644 he brought out an edition, with his own prologue and commentary, that eliminated the last fifty chapters, those which narrated the pardon of the robbers and their employment in the imperial service, and substituted an ending in which one of the leaders in a dream sees the whole band put to death. This disinfected version became the standard and is the one usually presented in Western translations and adaptations.[18]

Belles-Lettres in Japan

Japan's classical literature is that of the Heian era, the pre-feudal period (before the end of the twelfth century) when the imperial court flourished at Heian-kyō (or Kyoto). The language of learning of that period, both secular and religious, was Chinese, while that of popular literature was Japanese, in which women excelled. The works in either medium were produced by a relatively small learned class that lived in comparative luxury and idleness around the imperial court. Almost inevitably the quality of courtly learning and literature declined as the rise of the feudal system transferred economic and political power from the imperial court to more vigorous but less learned military men. Furthermore, during the early phases of the feudal period, Buddhist sects grew in popularity, with a corresponding growth in the emphasis upon religious ideas and the influence of monastic learning. Despite the joint impact of feudalism and Buddhism, the decline of courtly literature and secular learning was not abrupt during the Kamakura Shogunate (1185–1333), for central control remained strong in some regards and the court and nobility at Kyoto still enjoyed a relative prosperity.

Hence the Kamakura period was characterized by a mixed literature that reflected the interests of both the declining courtiers and the rising military and religious groups. Poetry, romantic novels, diaries, travel accounts, and miscellanies or jottings, although of inferior quality, continued to be the products of the classical courtly litterateur while military novels and Buddhist tales, both based on historical episodes, reflected the interests of the new dominant groups. Meanwhile, as Buddhism rose in popular estimation, Chinese learning declined. Those who could write in Chinese became so scarce that as early as the thirteenth century a new mixed Sino-Japanese prose style emerged. It was Japanese in grammar and structure, but its vocabulary was rich in Chinese words and Sino-Buddhist terms. This new style was used for both learned and popular literature. As the old, pure Japanese became obsolete and the feudal regime advanced, women gradually disappeared as literary figures.

With the rise of the Ashikaga shoguns after 1333, decentralizing feudalism gradually triumphed and secular learning, the imperial court, and the court nobility declined to their nadir. In the late fifteenth and the early sixteenth century, meritorious literary works almost ceased to be produced, and literary sterility was avoided only by the emergence of new forms that pointed to the great revival of the seventeenth and eighteenth centuries (see Chapter XI). Among the emerging forms were the *renga* (chain-poems), the *otogi-zōshi* (short, fantastic, fairy tales), and the *nō* (lyrical) drama with its *kyōgen* (farcical interludes). All the new forms except the *renga* owed a good deal to Buddhism and other popular concerns. Much of the literature of the period was sombre, reflecting at once the pessimism of the Buddhists and the uncertainties and heroism of a warring and violent age. Yet most writings of the time mirrored the interest in nature, the courtly, lyrical quality, the lightness and grace, the studied avoidance of roughness and vulgarity, the atmosphere of plum-blossoms-and-moonlight, and the slightly effeminate and superficial tone that had been bequeathed by the Heian masters. The interest in nature was reinforced by Zen Buddhism, and the character of the Heian literary heritage as a whole was perpetuated by the triumphant aristocratic, feudal society.

The classical *tanka* (a poem of five lines of 5, 7, 5, 7, and 7 syllables respectively) remained the monopoly of the court poets and those taught by them. The *tanka*'s theme was love or nature, and its tone was one of gentle melancholy. *Tankas* continued to be produced in considerable quantity into the fifteenth century. Five imperial anthologies, containing a total of 8,105 poems, were produced in the thirteenth century; eight of 15,938 in the fourteenth; and one of 2,144, the *New Collection of Ancient and Modern Times Continued* (*Shinzokukokinshu*) in the fifteenth (1433–39). The poetry of the later collections was imitative and uninspired. Its weakness was in all probability accentuated by the development of hereditary lines of court poets, of which the three most prominent (the Nijō, the Kyōgoku, and the Reizei) were descendants of the justly famous Fujiwara Tameie (1198–1275), compiler of two of the imperial anthologies. The Reizei branch was founded by Tamesuke, son of the famous authoress Abutsu, who was the wife or the concubine of Tameie in his old age. It was perhaps more original and vigorous than the others and produced generations of famous poets. It also trained others—for instance, Imagawa Sadoya (Ryōshun, 1324–1420), who was a general of the Ashikagas, and the monk Shōtetsu (1381–1459). The principal compiler of all but three collections of *tankas* after 1144 was a Fujiwara, and the fact that an outsider, Asukai Masayo, was asked to compile the last one probably indicated that the muse was believed to be deserting the Nijō branch of the family. In addition to the imperial anthologies several private collections of *tankas* were compiled; the *Fubokushō* was prepared by Fujiwara Nagakiyo, a pupil of Tamesuke, about 1308–10 and contained over 16,000 poems not included in previous imperial collections.

By the fifteenth century the *tanka* yielded primacy to the *renga* and to poetic forms associated with the *nō* drama. The *renga* was a derivative of the *tanka*. It preserved the syllable arrangement of the *tanka*, but every five-line stanza was the work of two poets. The first composed a seventeen-syllable strophe (5, 7, 5) and the second a fourteen-syllable strophe (7, 7), each taking as his point of departure the immediately preceding strophe.[19] This form gradually developed rigid rules, and a *renga* that happily fulfilled them became the most highly regarded of poetic accomplishments. Its greatest master was the monk Sōgi (1421–1502), who, in 1488, with two disciples composed 100 such linked verses considered the acme of the art.

The *nō* (or lyrical) drama was the pre-eminent literary and artistic product of the Ashikaga period. The great majority of the 235 *nō* dramas contained in a modern collection (*Yōkyoku tsūge*) date from the fifteenth century. Of these the Shinto priest Kwanami Kiyotsuga (1333–84) is credited with 15, and his son Seami Motokiyo (1363–1443) with 93. The *nō* was a dance drama in which a plot of small merit was combined with prose, verse, singing, dancing, and music. Except superficially it had little in common with the Chinese drama and seems not to have been derived from it. On the other hand, it had certain similarities to the Greek drama, including the sparseness of scenery, the use of masks, and a chorus that told the story during the performance.

Nō dramas seem to have originated from a popular form of secular entertainment, a mixture of song and dance known as *sarugaku* (monkey-business). They were probably also influenced by the more religious *dengaku* (field-music) theatricals, associated with harvest and other festivals celebrated at various shrines during the thirteenth and fourteenth centuries. Through the genius of Kwanami and Seami and under the patronage of the Askikaga shoguns at Kyoto, these rustic theatricals were transformed into highly aristocratic and esoteric drama. Each play was performed by a principal dancer, an assistant (generally played by a priest), lesser performers (usually not more than four or five), a chorus, and an orchestra of flutes and drums.

The *nō* play was profoundly influenced by Zen Buddhism both in form and ideas. Its prevailing tone was serious, often tragic. It was rather short. It was symbolic, and its poetry, written in alternating lines of seven and five syllables, was characterized by dramatic and suggestive imagery. The quiet scenes were in prose, but the dramatic episodes were expressed in dances or poems sung to music. *Nō* themes were drawn from Buddhist, Chinese, and Japanese legends and history. The plays generally centred in gods, devils, festivals, warriors, women, or the insane, and echoed sentiments of piety, patriotic and martial fervour, and love of nature. Later, as the *nō* began to be patronized by feudal lords, several schools developed. To break the serious mood and monotony of the *nō*, farces or *kyōgen* (mad-words) were introduced between performances. These *kyōgen* were written in colloquial speech, in contrast to the elegant and flowery court language of the *nō*, and they presented common people such as peasants and priests in skits that often parodied the preceding *nō*.

In practically all Japanese prose literature, verse was liberally interspersed, composed or recited by lovers, officials, warriors, and priests at every turn. Prose stories were usually called *monogatari*, or narratives, whether short or of novel length. The romantic novel had practically ceased to be produced by 1300, and the last historical novel (*rekishi*) of importance was *The Clear Mirror* (*Masu-kagami*), covering the period from the rise of the Kamakura Shogunate to its fall in 1333. The military novel (*gunki* or *senki*) became a favourite form of the early feudal period. It grew out of the historical novel, but it was influenced by the newer and shorter historical and Buddhist tale, and it dealt with military families, especially the Taira and the Minomoto. The most famous, the *Heike monogatari*, which described the decline and fall of the Taira clan, had been written in the early thirteenth century. A number of others followed, the last important one being the *Record of the Great Peace* (*Taiheiki*)—an inappropriate title indeed, since the story was laid in the period (1318–67) of battles and conspiracies that brought the fall of Kamakura, the attempts of the Go-Daigo emperor to regain power, and the rise of the Ashikagas. Pedantic and rhetorical in style, the work bristled with Chinese allusions and Buddhist theological terms and was liberally sprinkled with long poems in alternating lines of five and seven syllables. Its author was probably the Buddhist priest Kojima, who died in 1374.

Of the shorter historical and Buddhist stories, from the fourteenth century on slightly different kinds won special favour. Among these were the *otogi-zōshi*, short tales of fantastic adventure, often much in the nature of fairy tales, and, more or less parallel, the *kōwakamai*, which were recited or chanted (fifteenth and sixteenth centuries). In their archaic grammar and vocabulary they were related to the romantic novels, but in their subject matter they derived, rather, from the historical and military novels and the Buddhist stories.

Some of Japan's best prose went into works of non-fiction. Of the travel diaries, none during our period surpassed the *Izayoi nikki* (*Diary of the Waning Moon*), written in the late thirteenth century by the poetess Abutsu, describing, among other things, her trip from Kyoto to Kamakura. Undoubtedly the finest piece of literature of the period, with the exception perhaps of some *nō* dramas, was the *Grasses of Ennui* (*Tsurezuregusa*), probably written between 1324 and 1331 by the courtier and Buddhist poet Yoshida Kenkō (1283–1350). It was in the *zuihitsu* (jottings) genre, consisting of short sketches, anecdotes, antiquarian notes, and reminiscences interspersed with reflections on life, death, morality, and religion. Somewhat cynical and melancholy in tone and archaic in style, it belonged perhaps, with Abutsu's *Diary*, among the last works of a passing classical age rather than among those pointing to the future.

NOTES TO CHAPTER X

1. The Kings of France—in particular Charles V—and the Dukes of Burgundy—in particular Philip the Good—concerned themselves with the assembly of fine collections of manuscripts, thus effectively encouraging efforts already essentially humanist in character. (Professor Pierre Le Gentil.)

2. In speaking of the contribution of oral literatures, we should not forget the considerable impact of the 'matter of Britain'. It should be added that while epics, romances, and chronicles were at first written in verse form, prose began to flourish as early as the thirteenth century, in particular with the appearance of two masterpieces which played a capital role in the development of the literature of the West: the Lancelot–Grail cycle and the prose Tristan, still appreciated in the fourteenth century. (Pierre Le Gentil.)

3. To Professor Olivier Le Gentil, it would be preferable to say that while Villon's poetry is full of mediaeval themes and reflexes, this traditional aspect of his work in no way detracts from its 'modernity'.

4. In stressing the upsurge of lyricism—above all of the courtly lyric—in the fourteenth and fifteenth centuries, it is necessary to recall that, contrary to what had previously been the case, music and poetry ceased to be indissolubly linked. Not all lyric compositions, even those in set form, were still sung, and when they were, the author of the text was no longer the author of the melody as well.

In the course of the period after Machaut, the last and most famous representative of traditional musical lyricism, the musician figured side by side with the poet, particularly in Spain and France. The taste for allegory and aberrant parody to which this gave rise is worth mentioning. (Pierre Le Gentil.)

5. In the history of the theatre in the West at the end of the Middle Ages, it is impossible not to make mention of the *Miracles de Notre Dame par personnages* (fourteenth century) and, above all, of the great Mystery plays of Mercadé, Greban and J. Michel—all the more since it is in connection with them that arise such questions as the progress of 'mise en scène', of the theatrical troop, not to mention that of the evolution of sensitivity and of religious feeling. Nor should the 'entremets' of the Burgundian court be neglected, for they provide an excellent illustration of the taste for spectacle then playing a more and more determining role in court life and ceremonials. (Olivier Le Gentil.)

6. Professor P. Le Gentil points out that the origin of the 'danse macabre' is still subject to discussion. It should, however, be recalled that the word *macabre* first made its appearance in France in the form of *Macabré*, and that there is an ancient and famous *Danse macabre* (1424–25) in the Cemetery of the Innocents in Paris. Mention should also be made of the Spanish *Danza general de la Muerta*.

7. Professor P. Le Gentil feels that the case of the novella and the romance receives here somewhat summary treatment. Before the *Cent nouvelles nouvelles*, no longer attributed to Antoine de La Sale, mention should have been made of the latter's *Jehan de Saintré*, rightly recognized as a minor masterpiece. It should also be recalled that the court of Burgundy actively promoted the writing of prose versions of the old *chansons de geste* and Breton romances, an activity leading to the production of splendid manuscripts often magnificently illuminated and later proving useful to printers anxious to cater to their clients' persistent taste for the age of chivalry. Something of the mediaeval message thus survived even at the height of the Renaissance. Viewed in this perspective, it is easier to appreciate the role played by writers such as Malory or Montalvo.

8. Dámaso Alonso, 'The Spanish Contribution to the Modern European Novel', *Journal of World History*, VI (1961), 885.

9. Professor P. Le Gentil emphasizes that it is not easy to understand and to convey to others how, during the second half of the fifteenth century, a new age began to take the place of the mediaeval era which, nevertheless, lived on in so many ways, nor yet how such continuity was successfully reconciled with a virtual revolution. Certain signs, however, did herald a change unmarked by any deep or brutal break: a certain taste for the grandiose, expressed in the ambitious attempts of the *Grands Rhétoriqueurs*, or the authors of the Mysteries; a sharpened sense of philology and history leading to the search for Latinity in Cicero rather than in the works of the Schoolmen, and for religious truth in the New Testament itself rather than in the commentaries with which the centuries had overlaid it; a sense of reality which, without rejecting the achievements of a too-chimerical *courtoisie* and *chevalerie*, sought a closer adaptation to life itself, with its carnal needs and positive ambitions, under cover of historical rather than legendary examples or those endorsed by the great civilizations of the past. A combination of contradictory tendencies appeared which associated in a very complex manner sacred and profane; rejection of certain authorities with respect for others; need for material pleasure with the highest aspirations of the mind; nationalism with the search for a new universalism; conservatism with adventure; docility with iconoclasm; objectivity and observation with the most naïve and tendentious remnants of book-learning.

The authors feel, however, that some of the points made in this comment have been, or will be, made quite explicit elsewhere in the volume.

10. H. A. R. Gibbs, 'Literature' in Sir Thomas Arnold and Alfred Guillaume (eds.), *The Legacy of Islam* (Oxford, 1931), pp. 193–4.

11. See J. Chandra Ghosh, 'Vernacular Literatures' in G. T. Garrett (ed.), *The Legacy of India* (Oxford, 1937), p. 378.

12. See K. A. Nilakanta Sastri, *A History of South India* (London, 1955), p. 365.

13. J. C. Ghosh, *Bengali Literature* (London, 1948), p. 11.

14. *Ibid.*, p. 20.

15. T. F. Carter, *The Invention of Printing in China and Its Spread Westward*, by L. Carrington Goodrich (2nd ed., New York, 1955), pp. 211–37.

16. See William Hung, 'The Transmission of the Book Known as *The Secret History of the Mongols*,' *Harvard Journal of Asiatic Studies*, XIV (1951), 433–92. See also the article by Francis Woodman Cleaves, *ibid.*, XVII (1954), 1–129.

17. See James R. Hightower, *Topics in Chinese Literature* (Cambridge, Mass., 1950), p. 65.

18. Richard G. Irwin, *The Evolution of a Chinese Novel* (Cambridge, Mass., 1953), especially pp. 114–16.

19. See Edwin O. Reischauer, 'The Izayoi Nikki', *Harvard Journal of Asiatic Studies*, X (1947), especially pp. 261, 281–82, 293–303, and 383–87.

CHAPTER XI

LITERARY COMMUNICATION AND BELLES-LETTRES (1500–1775)

LANGUAGE AND LINGUISTICS IN EUROPE

The Rise and Spread of the Vernaculars

THE period under consideration in this chapter is well marked in the history of European letters, though far from exclusively, by a concern with the Bible. It opens with Reformation controversies over whether the Bible should be made easily available to all Christians, clerical and lay alike, and, if so, what versions of the Bible, and it closes with Enlightenment controversies over what significance the Bible might have, if it had any at all. The success of the Protestant Reformation greatly hastened the translating of the Bible into a number of the vernaculars, and authorized or generally accepted translations helped to establish literary standards.[1] Perhaps the most spectacular of the translations was Luther's. It was based on the earlier critical studies of the Vulgate that had begun with Valla and on several scholarly editions of parts of the Bible, including Erasmus' revised text of the Greek Testament (see Chapter X). It had the benefit of Luther's acquaintance with earlier translations, his knowledge of philology in general and of the Scriptures in particular, his linguistic verve and vigorous style, his superb feeling for the nuances of German, and his intensive application to the task of translation. He completed his translation of the New Testament while in hiding at the Wartburg.

The first part of Luther's translation appeared in 1522, after revision by Melanchthon and others. For the Old Testament Luther worked with a team of scholars. The translation of the whole Bible was not ready until 1534. Thanks to the quality of his work and the popularity of his cause, Luther's Bible was widely read and became a landmark in the development of a standard German language. Though German unification was long postponed for other reasons, the concept of a common German culture was nevertheless both a cause and an effect of Luther's contribution. About 430 total or partial printings (probably more than 250,000 copies) of his Bible were issued before 1546, the year of his death, each probably exerting an accumulative impact upon the German style of his compatriots.

Before the end of the sixteenth century printed versions of the Bible were available in Danish, Swedish, English, Dutch, German, Italian, Spanish, French, Czech, Polish, Hungarian, Croat, Church Slavonic, and Russian. At the same time, the Vatican, with the Augustinian monk Angelo Rocca (1548–

1620) at the head of its press and as its editor, issued scholarly editions of the Vulgate and the writings of the church fathers. To be sure, in the countries that remained loyal to the Roman Catholic faith the Latin Bible, the Vulgate, even when slightly revised at the Council of Trent, exerted little influence on —might even have interfered with—the developments of the vernacular language, but in several such countries the inhabitants had first joined the Protestant movement, returning to Catholicism only later (e.g. Bohemia, Hungary, and Poland), or had continued thoroughly divided (e.g. Germany), and so had become familiar, if only in part and temporarily, with a vernacular version of the Bible. Quantity-production of the many translations by means of printing helped to broadcast them, even in Catholic countries, and with them went a heightened familiarity with an approved vernacular style. The nationalization of the churches thus tended to promote a nationalization of language and literature.

Popular poetry had a similar effect. The earliest and perhaps most spectacular instances of the power of the poets in this regard had already taken place in Italy and England (see Chapter X). Before 1500 Dante, Petrarch, Boccaccio, Ariosto, and Tasso had gone far toward making their Tuscan dialect Italy's literary language, and Chaucer had made the best English of his day rather than French the language of England's poetry. In the sixteenth century, but perhaps in a less decisive fashion, Francisco Sá de Miranda and Luis Vaz de Camoëns in Portugal, Joachim du Bellay, Pierre de Ronsard, and their associates in the group known as the Pléiade in France, and Garcilaso de la Vega and Fernando de Herrera in Spain had an analogous influence in determining good usage in their respective languages.

Several of the great literary and scholarly lights, sometimes with deliberate intent, helped to crystallize formal speech in their local tongues. In Chapter X we mentioned Lebrija's valiant efforts to standardize good Spanish usage. Calvin's *Institutes* and Montaigne's *Essays*, though less deliberately, set the standard for French prose. The Accademia della Crusca published in 1612 its *Vocabulario*, a dictionary of Italian based on fourteenth-century Tuscan usage, thus giving to the language of Dante a sanction that practically made it the Italian standard and at the same time furnishing a model of lexicography for other languages. The earliest original writer in Polish, Mikotaj Rey (1505–69), and his contemporary Piotr Skarga (1536–1612), the first rector of the Jesuit University of Wilno, provided the models of good composition in Poland. Elizah Bochur contributed to the fuller development of a standard Yiddish during the sixteenth century. Shakespeare's thirty-seven plays (c. 1590–1611), along with his sonnets and other non-dramatic works, were to become second only to the King James version of the Bible (1611) as a continuing influence on the speech of literate Englishmen, and a somewhat analogous influence is sometimes claimed for the approved translations or adaptations of Shakespeare in several other languages. Ludwig Holberg (1684–1754) found Danish a despised tongue and left it a medium of literature.

From the turn of the seventeenth century on, a number of factors made it possible for literary Russian to steer a middle course between the complicated structure of Church Slavonic and the oversimplification of the current vernacular; among them were script reform (which introduced a simpler alphabet than that of Church Slavonic), the western influences nurtured by Peter the Great, and the grammatical works, prose, and poetry of Lomonosov.

Monarchs striving in an age of ascending absolutism to consolidate their realms easily recognized the value of a common language for their purposes. Consequently, political authority was sometimes exerted in a policy to eliminate or at least subordinate the sometimes too free and intractable local patois. France furnished an excellent example of this policy. In 1539 Francis I decreed that all official publications should appear in French, giving precedence to the *langue d'oil* spoken around Paris. Henry IV, in his endeavours to unite his people after the great dissensions of the religious wars, officially commissioned his councillor François de Malherbe in 1605 to purify the French language. Thirty years later a stalwart exponent of centralization, Cardinal Richelieu, won a royal patent for the Académie Française, 'the Forty Immortals', who from their efforts to appraise literature soon passed also to preparing official dictionaries and grammars of their language. The first comprehensive dictionary of the French language appeared from its hands in 1694, during the reign of Louis XIV; a new edition followed in 1718 and again in 1740. By royal decree the Real Academia Española undertook a Spanish dictionary with the like objective of improving the national speech by distinguishing good from bad usage; eventually it published a *Diccionario de autoridades* in six volumes (1726–39), perhaps the most comprehensive dictionary of its day.

In no other cases was equally systematic attention given to language in the interest of political centralization. Royal activity in Portugal and Sweden pointed to a similar effort but to a more limited extent. In Russia too, Peter I, though not given to dealing with esoteric or aesthetic questions, directed some of his energy to the language problem, insisting on the use of the vernacular rather than Church Slavonic; under his influence and Catherine II's, Russian, already filled with Tatar and Polish words, borrowed technical terms freely from Latin and other western languages, particularly German, Dutch, English, and French. The decentralized Low Countries, on the other hand, during our period failed to develop a uniform Dutch, although the province of Holland set the standard in this regard as well as in others. The preparation of a dictionary of the English language 'by which its purity may be preserved' (as Samuel Johnson's *Plan* put it) was left to the initiative of private booksellers and the genius of Johnson; it appeared in two volumes only in 1755.

Grammatical and lexicographical works helped to create criteria of usage and style, furnishing better tools of communication while perhaps unduly restraining the forces that make learning and language a living, adaptable, and spontaneous part of a people's life. Dialects were no longer on an equal footing with the standard national tongue (which had, however, developed from a particular dialect). They nevertheless persisted, and so did several isolated languages like the Celtic tongues of Ireland, Manx, Scotland, Wales, and Brittany, the Basque of northwestern Spain and southwestern France, and the Sorbic of the Wends of East Germany. Elsewhere schoolmasters could teach more systematically an accepted form of expression in terms of which refinement, elegance, and style might be judged.

If a national language strengthened the cohesiveness among the various peoples within a nation, it also tended to become a barrier against communication with other nations. Yet language provided a link as well as a barrier. In contrast to the twentieth century, some cosmopolitan tongue or other continued to be widely used. The learned and cultivated in all west European lands—since scholarship was handed on in Latin, and cultivation of the mind implied the study of the Classics—could usually communicate with one another; they had not only a common language (despite differences of pronunciation) but also a common literary heritage. During the eighteenth century, when the use of Latin had diminished even in such conservative institutions as universities and when French culture asserted a general dominance in Europe, the French language, for a while at least, played a similar role in the discourse of the educated. In addition, the international-minded among the not always learned aristocracy gave French in the eighteenth century a fashionable appeal. It thus provided at least a temporary means of cosmopolitan communication in a civilization steadily growing more nationalistic. Besides, during this period European languages spread to vast territories outside of Europe. Spanish, Portuguese, English, French, Dutch, Danish and Russian conquerors and emigrants carried their language to new lands, thus spreading their literary heritage.

The languages of the immigrants often became modified by the language of the local populations or by the peculiarities of life in new surroundings. New products, institutions, and ways of doing things were reflected in the development of the migrant tongues. Separated from the mother land and from the steadying or altering influences that were there being exerted in linguistic matters, the European languages abroad developed in different directions. Afrikaans became something different from Dutch, Brazilian different from the Portuguese of Lisbon and Coimbra, Argentine and Mexican Spanish different from Castilian, and American different from the king's English. Wherever the products and practices of the wider world became important for Europe itself, they also brought new words to enrich Europe's vocabularies.

The Study of Language

The humanists of the Renaissance, devoted students of good style as they were, willy-nilly contributed to the development of the vernacular tongues. Their scholarly and aesthetic attitude toward the languages and literature of the Ancients was easily transferable to the modern languages, especially since all European languages had already been more or less influenced by Latin and Greek. Though their imitation of Ciceronian Latin may often have been slavish and sterile, discouraging originality and variety of expression, it yet developed an increasing sensitivity to good literary taste. The polemics of pro-Ciceronians and anti-Ciceronians stimulated conscious reflection upon good and bad usage in word construction. The study of a Classical language required a refined understanding of grammar and the structure of speech in general. Ardent teachers, such as Comenius (see Chapter XVI), became concerned about the best ways of teaching languages, and this concern stimulated the search for meaningful regularities and linguistic theories.

A number of linguistic works followed which, though probably not comparable to the flood after 1800, contributed greatly to the development of language tools. The humanists of the fifteenth and early sixteenth centuries compiled adages and other elegant, noteworthy sentiments, taken usually from Latin and Greek authors, who were held up as paramount examples of stylistic excellence. Erasmus's *Adagia* was perhaps the most popular compilation of this kind. Gradually, Classical linguistic interests became more systematic with the work of s⌣.iolars like the Scaligers and the Estiennes. Nonetheless, the Classical languages began in the sixteenth century to give way as subjects of linguistic study before the devoted attention to the vernaculars, and in the case of the French Benedictines of the seventeenth century (most notably represented by Mabillon, Montfaucon, and the lay brother Du Cange) also before medieval Latin and Byzantine Greek, which had been spurned by the humanists as hybrid tongues.

Despite the facts that the study of the grammar, pronunciation, and orthography of several vernaculars had received serious attention since the end of the fifteenth century and that a fair number of authoritative dictionaries were published in the seventeenth and eighteenth centuries, scholarship still was weak on the etymological side. The weakness was due largely to the lack of a comparative Indo-European philology. During our period the scholarly study of comparative linguistics had its beginnings, meagre though they were. Bilingual dictionaries grew in number and precision during and after the Renaissance, and translating became a recognized literary profession. Largely independent of the practical needs of conqueror, administrator, merchant, and missionary, scholars began to investigate the relationships and differences of languages.[2] In 1300 an interest in Greek literature, even though it was one of the sources of Western civilization, was still somewhat rare; by 1500 the study of Greek was respectable and common, but in contrast, students of Hebrew felt called upon to justify their exotic tastes. By 1600 Hebrew had become a common scholarly tool, and Arabic, previously best known among the Christians of Spain, began to be added to the equipment of interested scholars elsewhere in Europe. Gesner in his *Mithridates* (1555) made the first serious attempt to study languages comparatively, but he knew nothing of Sanskrit. Only later did Filippo Sassetti (1540–88), during an extended visit to India, guess from comparable roots and forms that Sanskrit was related to the European languages, a conclusion that was in 1767 with fuller evidence restated by the Jesuit missionary Gaston Laurent Coeurdoux (1691–1779) in a letter to the Académie des Inscriptions. After 1700 Europe's publishers even risked the printing of dictionaries of such languages as Tamil and Algonquin. While Cardinal Ximenez' Polyglot Bible (completed in 1517) had provided texts in only four languages, the polyglot dictionary (*Linguarum Totius Orbis Vocabularis Comparativa*) compiled on the order of Catherine the Great included some 200, the Spanish philologist Lorenzo Hervás y Panduro in his *Catálogo de las lenguas de la naciones conocidas* (1800–1805) was to study 300, and the German philologist Johann Christoph Adelung was to present in his *Mithridates* (1806) samples of 500. Thus, as Europe's separate national languages were replacing the *langues de culture* even for scholars, overseas expansion of Europe's seafaring peoples helped to create an interest in the manifold vehicles of human expression that reached beyond the borders of nations and even of continents.

THE TECHNICAL APPARATUS OF LITERATURE

Bookmaking as a Business

Among the technological factors that fostered the European vernacular languages and literatures, the printing press was the most decisive. Probably, but for the invention of a means of mass publication at the very time that the vernacular tongues were emerging from folk usage to literary usage, they might have remained unacceptable to discriminating readers and writers longer. In terms of quantity and speed of distribution, printing made possible a method of reproducing thought that had never existed before. A writer could now find a wide public in a relatively short time. Thus a thinker or literary artist could within his own lifetime more confidently expect to exert an influence upon his nation or even his entire culture, and a much larger number of men and women could participate in the intellectual and literary life of their age. Since many widely differing ideas could be spread quickly, the printed book became a factor in promoting at the same time both intellectual diversity among the disciples of different writers and intellectual uniformity among the disciples of the same writers.

In an era of rotary presses, binding and cutting machinery, modern paper making, and the ordering of books by telephone and telegraph, the proficiency of the three hundred years between 1500 and 1800 may appear rudimentary indeed. Nevertheless, after the development of printing in Germany and its spread to various regions of the West during the second half of the fifteenth century, the history of printing was a story of amazing technical improvement, entrepreneurial daring, and increase of output. Many printers contributed to these ends. We have already encountered Froben of Basel (see Chapter X); Manutius and Plantin were no less enterprising.

Teobaldo Manuzio, alias Aldus Manutius of Venice (1450–1515), was one of the most productive printers of the sixteenth century. After studying Latin and Greek, and tutoring young aristocrats, Manutius conceived the idea of printing the Greek classics. One of his rich pupils, Alberto Pio, nephew of Pico della Mirandola, proved ready to finance the project, and around 1494 Manutius set up the 'Aldine' publishing house. He chose to do so in Venice, where he could find good libraries, wealthy patrons, wide marketing facilities, and refugee Greeks for editorial tasks. From the handwriting of one of his Cretan assistants, Marcus Musurus, he patterned his Greek type. Paper was obtained from mills in Fabriano (Ancona), famous since the thirteenth century for the excellence of its product. Printing ink was manufactured in Manutius's Venetian establishment, where the binding also was done.

The Aldine press gave to the world some of its first editions of the great classics, sometimes based on the hallowed manuscripts of the Venetian libraries. By 1500 Manutius had published numerous Greek masterpieces, including Hesiod, nine of Aristophanes' plays, and a five-volume Aristotle dedicated to his benefactor Alberto Pio. By the end of his crowded career (1515) he had printed in addition at least some of the works of Thucydides, Herodotus, Xenophon, Plutarch, Sophocles, Euripides, Demosthenes, Pindar, and Plato, to say nothing of a number of Latin works. His editing was a careful scholarly procedure; manuscript versions were collated and texts critically emended. His home was a beehive of scholars engaged in editorial activities. When in 1508 Erasmus's *Adagia* was in the press, the author worked at his final revisions at Manutius' home while Manutius and his proofreader busied themselves with the technical details of editing.

Technologically likewise the 'Aldine' editions were epochmaking. For Latin works Manutius adopted the semi-script type still called *italic*, which was a space-saver. His books were beautifully manufactured in a commendable effort to appease booklovers who resented machine-made products. Their title-pages were adorned with a dolphin-and-anchor emblem, symbolizing speed and stability, and carried the motto *Festina lente*. The volumes were small, a boon to those who actually used books and collected them in libraries. They were remarkably cheap—about two to three dollars a piece in modern currency, much less costly than huge folio tomes or manuscript books. Now, of course, they are collectors' items.

All was not smooth sailing for the new firm. Manutius had labour troubles, problems of distribution, and difficulty with foreign publishers, who 'pirated' his carefully prepared editions. Twice his press had to close because of wars. Meanwhile he had formed a Greek Academy—called *Neacademia*—from his circle of Hellenically inclined humanists. The constitution of the society was drawn up in Greek, Greek was used in its meetings, and most of the members translated or transliterated their names into Greek. Among the honorary foreign members were Erasmus and Thoman Linacre. After Manutius's death in 1515, the Aldine Press carried on under the management of Manutius' relatives and partners until 1597, when his grandson Aldo died. Never a remarkably successful venture from the financial standpoint—Manutius himself died poor and worn out—the Aldine Press was a monument to a practical humanist scholar and his sponsors, who dedicated their energies and fortunes to spreading through the West the literature of ancient Greece and Rome.

In northern Europe the progress of printing was reflected in the career of another great publisher, Christopher Plantin (1514–89) of Antwerp. Plantin started out as a mere bookbinder without much scholarly equipment. He learned to make use of the master engravers of the Netherlands in producing books unsurpassed anywhere for the merit of their illustrations. He printed Latin and Greek classics but is perhaps more famous for various editions of the Bible. One of his Bibles was printed with an exceptionally fine Hebrew type, provided by his partners, the van Bomberghes, descendants of a Dutch Christian, Daniel van Bomberghe, who had specialized in Venice in the printing of works in Hebrew. Another was the famous eight-volume polyglot Bible of Antwerp (c. 1568–71), financed by Philip II, king of Spain and the Netherlands. At the height of Plantin's prosperity his publishing house had somewhere between sixteen and twenty-two presses and between fifty-six and seventy-three pressmen (authorities differ), to say nothing of the staffs and equipment in his branch houses in Paris and Leyden, and Corneille van Bomberghe used a system of cost accounting for its bookkeeping. Today in Antwerp the Musée Plantin, remodelled after his old printing establishment, reveals the remarkable technological progress made by Plantin and other northern printers in the sixteenth century.

During most of that century printers generally used the simple press of the 'incunabula' period. It consisted of an upright frame with a flat, horizontal bed of stone or wood. The type was fitted in the upright frame and the sheets of paper were placed on the horizontal bed. The impression of the type on the paper was obtained by a screw device, which was worked laboriously with a detachable handle in order to apply the proper pressure. When the imprint was made, the pressure of the type-plane on the paper-plane was released by working the same device in reverse. And so on and on, sheet after sheet. With few modifications this sort of press was used till Willem Janszon Blaeu (1571–1638) of Amsterdam produced a better one. The new press, however, merely provided some improvements (which cannot now be exactly determined) in the details of operating the old screw press. Until Charles Stanhope (1753–1816) developed the labour-saving all-iron hand-press, the technical processes of bookmaking retained the cumbersomeness of the inventions of Gutenberg and other fifteenth-century printers.

More appreciable improvements were made in the process of book-illustration. As previously indicated, hand-illustrating of printed books continued during the early decades of printing. In addition, notable examples were provided during the 'incunabula' period of *printed* illustrations. Woodcuts were used, as they had been before the development of movable type—for example, in the *Magdeburg Chronicle*. By the end of the fifteenth century metal engravings had been introduced, though they did not become common until Plantin and other enterprising northern printers adopted them. Etchings came into use still later. From the beginning of printing, colour illustration was employed, done for the most part by hand on black-and-white illustrations that had been printed. Shortly after 1450, however, a remarkable example of multicolour printing appeared in the initial letters and illustrations of a psalter published at Mainz by Fust and Schaffer (1457). More common during this early era were simple initials printed in red and black.

The great printing centre of the fifteenth century was Mainz. During the sixteenth century several other cities achieved fame as printing centres. In addition to Venice with the establishments of Manutius and the Bomberghes, Antwerp with that of Plantin, and Basel with that of Froben, Paris, Leiden, Amsterdam, Leipzig, and Nuremberg (see Chapter XV) also had outstanding printing houses. The proportionally large number of these centres in the Netherlands is a measure of that little country's remarkable progress in the technology of printing as well as in other intellectual activities. Ivan Fedorov was the earliest significant book publisher of Russia. The first work printed in Russian seems to have been an edition (Moscow, 1564) of the Acts of the Apostles by Fedorov and Petr Mstislavets. Among a number of other books published by Federov was the first Russian Bible (Ostrog, 1581).

In its initial half-century the printed book still had to fight an uphill battle against the general humanistic preference for manuscripts. After 1500, however, the printed book almost altogether replaced the work of the scribe and copyist. The volume of printing increased tremendously. A library of machine-produced books was no longer thought of as an odious thing but rather as a mark of culture and learning.

The increase in the quantity of printing after 1500 was tremendous. The Mazarin Bible, one of the earliest printed books, was printed in an edition of 210 copies. Luther's version of the New Testament appeared in an edition of 5,000 copies in 1522 and had to be reprinted in ten weeks. His tract *To the Nobility of the German Nation* sold 4,000 copies in five days—a figure, however, which may be explained in terms of its special situation. In the year 1530 the town of Leipzig, which developed early as one of the book centres of Europe, had forty-six bookdealers. The so-called *Messkataloge* used by the bookdealers and publishers represented at the great fairs in Frankfort listed 256 book titles in 1564, 550 in 1565, 1,211 between 1641 and 1648, and 1,212 between 1649 and 1660; and the bookdealers at Leipzig, which superseded Frankfort by 1700, listed 3,286 titles between 1701 and 1710. Even a sparsely populated area like the nascent United States put out amazing numbers of publications—2,400,000 between 1639 and 1791.

The quality of printing after 1500 varied almost century by century. The sixteenth century was in many ways outstanding in terms of the beauty of the finished product. Manutius in Venice, Froben in Basel, the Estiennes in Paris, and Plantin in Antwerp put out books that were scholarly as well as esthetically pleasing, making good use of the arts of type-making, book-binding, woodcut, and etching. The printers and publishers of the seventeenth century improved the technical quality of the book very little and its artistic quality even less, but editions tended to become larger perhaps, and a few enterprising publishers like the Dutch Elzevir family did much to popularize books further by their economic (and still handsome) editions. During the eighteenth century, printers in England (e.g., William Caslon and John Baskerville), in Italy (e.g. Giambattista Bodoni), and especially in France (where the Imprimerie Royale, established by Richelieu in 1640, and the type designs of Philippe Grandjean set the pace) greatly improved their type and generally succeeded in publishing very attractive and relatively cheap books. As objects of art, the French and the Italian books of the Rococo period were likely to be representative of the contemporary style.

In addition to being a craft, book making was also a business. The gradual trend toward the specialization of labour was in a small way reflected also in printing and publishing between 1450 and 1800. In the beginning the printer had often combined editorial supervision with type-making, printing, illustrating, binding, and selling. Gradually all these functions began to be taken over by specialists with separate establishments and often with competing interests. In general, publishing tended to be a risky business, which seldom resulted in the acquisition of a great fortune. Competition was keen and sometimes unscrupulous. Pirating of texts was fairly common in the absence of copyright laws, the first effective one coming only in 1710 in England. Although the market was considerable, books were by no means cheap,[3] nor could they be produced fast enough for what we would today consider mass consumption. Consequently, publishing tended to concentrate in certain important locations and sometimes depended upon the support of a national government.

The Periodical and Censorship

The speed with which the printed word could reach a large public suggested a new channel for printing. Sometimes printers could exploit a far-reaching crisis, such as a war, a religious struggle, or a political controversy, to sell relatively cheap *gazzettas*, *corantos*, diurnals, newsbooks, or newsletters. The publication of regular newspapers started modestly in the late sixteenth century in Venice with the printing of the *Notizie Scritti* and continued uncertainly in the early seventeenth in Frankfort (*Avisa Relation oder Zeitung*), Antwerp (*Nieuwe Tijdingen*), London (*Weekly Newes*), and other cities. These initial journalistic attempts, despite censorship, bankruptcy, and other hardships, demonstrated that the printing press might be systematically used to satisfy a natural thirst for information on current affairs. The *Frankfurter Postzeitung* started on a long career in 1616, the *Gazette de France* in 1631, and the *Oxford Gazette* (later the *London Gazette*) in 1665. Enduring magazines came somewhat later. The French Academy of Sciences began publication of the *Journal des Sçavans* in 1665, and the same year the *Philosophical Transactions* of the English Royal Society followed. The *Mercure Galant* (subsequently the *Mercure de France*), devoted primarily to literature, first appeared in 1672. Although still limited in circulation and often hampered by governmental taxation and censorship, the new media of communication gained a firm footing. Daily newspapers began to appear only in the eighteenth century. Most of them were ephemeral or collapsed within a few years, but in 1772 the London *Morning Post* and in 1777 the *Journal de Paris* began a long-lived existence. In general, the periodical press tended to be a separate part of the publishing world, providing not only work and profit for a new type of writer, the journalist, but also a vehicle for men who regarded the printing press as an educational and propaganda medium.

The slow but constant growth of literacy in conjunction with the wider spread of the printed word gave literature an increasing persuasive force. Naturally, conservative institutions such as state or church exhibited deep concern, on the one hand, for exploiting the printed word in their own interest and, on the other, for controlling opposing opinions through surveillance of the press. Censorship of literary expression, well known long before 1500, after that date became more systematic in the hands of a still powerful church and an ever more powerful state. The Catholic Church as early as the first decade of the sixteenth century authorized its bishops to keep a watchful eye over the products of printing. In an effort to reinforce its foundations after the Protestant revolt, the papacy firmly institutionalized censorship (see Chapter IV). Though the *Index Librorum Prohibitorum* has never been so restrictive as has sometimes been claimed, it nonetheless was an important and largely successful attempt to limit reading.

The European governments also experimented with various modes of control. Effective use was made by some of them of the 'privilege' or 'license', a permit which the printer was required to get from the central authority before publishing a book and which could easily be revoked. In general, this form of permission was a relatively simple form of prohibition.[4] A publisher, probably a member of the stationers' guild to begin with and, if so, already subject to its regulations, was obliged to proceed at his own risk—the risk being that of subsequent prosecution and loss of license. *Ex post facto* control of this sort cost the state little in bureaucratic machinery, but it also gave controversial writings a good chance to 'slip through'. Preventive censorship, the kind that passed judgment on a manuscript before publication and might forbid its printing, was preferred by some governments to licensing but, because of its bureaucratic cumbersomeness, sometimes gave way to a system of tacit permission. Preventive censorship was abolished in England, for instance, in favour of punitive censorship (1694). A rather common form of censorship, partly because it constituted a source of added revenue, was the taxing of newspapers by means of stamps, which tended to limit circulation by raising the price of papers and pamphlets.

Censorship was the rule in most European countries, but a few allowed unrestricted freedom of publication. Foremost among these few was the United Provinces. Its free press doubtless accounts in part for the intellectual prominence of that small federation during our period. The flood of reading matter emanating from these unrestricted publishing centres in many ways helped to counteract the censorship efforts of other governments. Counting on the great desire of people to say and read what they wished, publishers found many ways of 'bootlegging' literature. One of the favourite ones was to smuggle books into a forbidden area from a free one or merely to falsify the place of publication given on the title page. Occasionally a great public or literary figure openly took up the fight for full freedom of expression, and an eloquent piece of literature like Milton's *Areopagitica* (1644) might result, but most of the time writers battled only with the weapons of wit and satire or with the strategy of evasion by subterfuge and clandestine circulation. That their struggle was neither vain nor personal but was an expression of a general human desire for freedom was perhaps best attested by the universality and force with which freedom of the press was demanded throughout the eighteenth century.

An important outgrowth of the economic possibilities of the printing press and publishing was the growing economic independence of the writer. In former ages writing usually was a luxury which only those could afford who were supported by a wealthy patron or had the economic backing of a powerful institution such as a government, a monastic order, or a university. Some of the writings of the fifteenth-century humanists appear to us in bad taste because they were commissioned works for the glorification of fairly insignificant princes or benefactors, although, of course, many distinguished works also were produced under this sort of patronage. After 1500—the first notable case being Erasmus—the greater market created by the printing press began to make it feasible for a writer to earn a living from the products of his pen. Whether literature improved because writers became less dependent on royal or aristocratic Maecenases and became dependent instead on booksellers will doubtless remain a moot point. Few writers indeed amassed fortunes by relying solely on the income from the sale of their books, and in many cases patrons (among whom the members of the wealthy, book-buying middle class became increasingly consequential) were still assiduously sought. Even so, the man with ideas that did not appeal to the powerful—a radical politician like John Wilkes or an eloquent freethinker like Voltaire—could say what he wished, if he dared, and despite censorship and court penalties could still hope by subterfuge or defiance to find a market and some income.

Libraries and Reference Compendia

The mounting output of books increased the need for storing and in some sense systematizing the written products of the human mind. The number, size, and use of libraries grew tremendously during the period between 1500 and 1775. This growth was both a cause and an effect of the shift in Europe's intellectual life toward secular and temporal influences at the expense of the religious and ecclesiastical. Whereas monasteries or cathedral schools had once provided the great storehouses of manuscripts, the new libraries grew out of the collections of monarchs, rich nobles, universities (which were gradually becoming less and less dominated by clerics and monastic orders), and wealthy members of the middle class. Noteworthy exceptions to this trend were the Vatican Library at Rome and those of the Maurists at Paris and of some Jesuit colleges, where serious scholarly concerns often prevailed. The bigger private collections grew, the more common it became to hand them over eventually to some larger and more public library. The core of many great libraries of our day goes back to such gifts from great collectors. The universities of Europe and, later, the scholarly academics often depended on the contributions of patrons but sometimes were able to accumulate vast bibliographical treasures simply because they could add continually to their collections over a long span of time.

The royal libraries tended to develop into the largest ones. They usually benefited not only from regal munificence but also from the fact that rulers, in their efforts to control publishing, in certain instances created a sort of 'deposit library' to which publishers were required to send one or more copies of the books they published. Especially noteworthy among the new royal foundations of the sixteenth century were Philip II's library at the Escorial Palace near Madrid, the royal Bavarian library at Munich, and the French royal library, which Francis I moved to Fontainebleau, whence later it was returned to Paris, eventually to become part of the Bibliothèque Nationale. Before the end of the sixteenth century other royal collections, destined to be great university or national libraries, had been brought together in Dresden, Vienna, Copenhagen, Cracow, Stockholm, and other capitals. By the early seventeenth century the royal library in Paris had a catalogue of some six thousand volumes.

Other illustrious libraries were instituted during the sixteenth century. Significant book collections had already existed in several universities—e.g. Paris, Salamanca, and Cambridge—and in that century the libraries of some others became the foundations of world-famous collections—e.g. St. Andrews, Glasgow, Aberdeen, Oxford (refounded by Thomas Bodley), Ingolstadt (later removed to Munich), Heidelberg, Basel, Prague, Coimbra, Leyden, Utrecht, and Amsterdam. Municipal libraries became fairly common in urban centres before 1600—e.g. Edinburgh, Angers, Bourges, Carpentras, Clermont-Ferrand, Lyons, Venice, and Modena. The British Museum Library began comparatively late (1700), with the donation of the collection of Robert Bruce Cotton to the nation in 1700. In general, monastic and private collections fell behind in the race, often being absorbed by university or national libraries. Today, in some of Europe's finest libraries the names of some illustrious collection, commemorating a famous private collector such as Chigi, Bessarion, Urbino, Laud, Coislin, Mazarin, and Cotton, give evidence of a voluntary merger by gift or purchase.

The recently settled community of Boston, Massachusetts, created a public library in 1653, but genuinely public libraries, accessible to all comers without fee, did not yet exist in Europe. The Bodleian Library at Oxford, however, had set the precedent for a semi-public library, open to a large if still restricted number of students and other recommended persons, and by the end of the eighteenth century library development had reached a stage that was not far removed from the public libraries of our day; subscription libraries, available to those who paid a regular fee, and book collections of local reading groups (the *sociétés de pensée* of the eighteenth century) filled the needs of a public gradually growing in literacy.

As the sheer bulk of printed materials increased, new tools were developed for the more efficient use of books. Libraries compiled catalogues of their holdings. Scholars and practical bookmen began to publish bibliographies of the available materials on certain subjects. As we have seen, lexicographers made specialized dictionaries of one kind or another. When, in the seventeenth century learned journals began to appear with a certain measure of regularity, they carried sections in which they announced and discussed new publications. Concordances of the Bible and critical editions of basic Classical texts were compiled. This development of special kinds of books for the better use and understanding of other books revealed the mounting significance of books in general.

The accumulating number of encyclopedias also strikingly illustrated the enormous increase in scholarship and literary interest. Compendia of knowledge were known in European antiquity and medieval times and had been still more highly developed in some of the other great cultures, particularly in China (see below). From the thirteenth century on, a good number of compilations of then existing knowledge appeared in Europe. Most of them suffered from the fact that they were the works of a single man. They were usually either ambitious in scope but unreliable or more reliable but limited in scope. One of the more reliable of the one-man compendia was Bayle's *Dictionnaire historique et critique* (1697; English translation, 1710). During the eighteenth century, however, learned men began to work in groups in order to publish encyclopedias that in every sense were worthy predecessors of the great compendia of the modern world. None perhaps ever had greater impact on European intellectual life in its time than the *Encyclopédie* of Diderot and his associates. 'We dare say,' said D'Alembert in the famous *Discours préliminaire* of that work, 'that if the ancients . . . had elaborated such an Encyclopedia and if its manuscript alone had escaped from the fire that destroyed the library of Alexandria, this would have been sufficient to console us for the loss of the rest.'[5]

Libraries outside Europe probably did not arise with equal rapidity, nor did municipal and university libraries for semi-public use develop as fully as in Europe. Nevertheless, in India the great palm-leaf manuscript collections in some monastic and temple schools grew, and the Mogul emperors also collected important manuscript libraries; and in China the libraries of the Manchu emperors exceeded earlier imperial collections. The rate of Chinese book publication rose swiftly; over 15,000 works are estimated to have been published during the K'ang-hsi period alone (1662–1722). Until the middle of the eighteenth century, it has been estimated, China had printed more books than perhaps the rest of the world combined.[6] The enormous *Ssu-k'u ch'uanshu* (*Complete Library of the Four Branches of Literature*), assembled during the Ch'ien-lung period, was an Imperial Manuscript Library of what was regarded as the best among extant books. It contained 3,461 works in over 36,000 volumes (*ts'e*) of 78,000 chapters (*chüan*), and the printed and annotated catalogue (1782) of all the books considered for inclusion contained 10,254 titles in over 171,000 *chüan*. Unfortunately, the editing of this collection was used by the ruler as an opportunity to delete passages or destroy works which criticized the Manchus and other Tatars or otherwise displeased him. Two copies of the yet enormous though purged collection were kept in the Peking area, and others in Jehol, Mukden, Yang-chou, Chin-chiang, and Hang-chou, to make it more accessible to scholars. In China the number of large private library buildings (one of which contained over 100,000 chapters in its founder's day) grew markedly after 1500, more than 500 being famous in the Manchu period. Of these, the T'ien-i-ko of Ningpo, founded in 1550, still survives; it was made of brick and tile without wood, and its staff enforced special rules to prevent fire and other damage. The Yi dynasty of Korea accumulated large libraries at Seoul, and considerable ones arose at Kyoto and Edo in Japan.

POETRY, DRAMA, AND FICTION IN EUROPE

Folk Literature

While brilliant original creative writings immortalized new names between 1500 and 1775, a rich old literature persisted that was nameless and often not dateable. Usually disdained by the educated classes during the first two centuries of our period, it was handed down by oral tradition. Numerous songs, stories, epics, dramas, legends, proverbs, riddles, and fairy tales thus survived many generations, undergoing variations that often further augmented their richness and colour. Some of them were written down by unknown scribes or, on occasion, by writers whose names we sometimes know—e.g. Anders Sprensen Vedel, who in 1591 published a collection of Danish folk-songs, and the Russian Metropolitan Macarius (d. 1563), whose *Chetyi Minei* (*Saints' Calendar*) compiled Holy Scripture, patristic writings, church decrees, lives of saints, and folktales into one huge collection. Sometimes collectors breathed into such folklore their own artistry (see Chapter X), but after 1700 literary-minded persons began to collect it systematically and tried to promote a greater appreciation for the native qualities of its eloquent, if sometimes unrefined, treasures. A great deal of folk literature was then presented to the peoples who had produced it as a part of their respective national heritages. In the late eighteenth and early nineteenth centuries collectors and writers—with a romantic love for tradition, respect for the common people, and belief in the *Volk*—turned to folk-literature as a form of artistic expression fully deserving admiration, study, and even imitation. The vogue of folklore was so pronounced that James Macpherson (1736–96) was able to palm off his own tales as the work of Ossian, legendary bard of the Highlands, until challenged by Dr Johnson and others.

Even though it is quite impossible in most instances to date this folk literature with any accuracy, much of the heritage of song and story either originated or was significantly modified between 1500 and 1775. Identifiable social institutions, moods, and preoccupations, and the impact of particular events are clearly reflected in them. Some German songs were unmistakably associated with the mercenary soldiers (the *Landsknechte*) of the type that flourished roughly from 1450 to 1650. Others reflected the life of the soldier and the horrors of armed conflict in the days of Europe's absolute monarchies. Certain Russian tales centre around the struggle with the 'Golden Horde'; a few disclose the local patriotism of the burghers of Novgorod, Pskov, and other towns subjugated by Moscow or satirize church and state officialdom. Witches, ghosts, and like manifestations of the supernatural were a common theme. Folklore served as a medium by which the unhappy poor released their pent-up feelings against the rich and powerful and by which conquered peoples (e.g. in Mexico, the Balkans, Ireland, and central Europe) managed to preserve some of their 'national' traditions. The unsophisticated stylistic or linguistic characteristics of many of these folk creations, even when poured into a more elegant literary mould by later writers, betrayed their origin as folk literature.

In all likelihood the products of folk literature express to some degree the artistic qualities of the individuals who composed them or gave them their basic formulation, and it would be erroneous to regard them altogether as spontaneous. Nevertheless, this was the literature (rather than the more formal kind soon to be discussed) that thrived among the great masses of people and was most meaningful and accessible to the illiterate. It represented the simple literary tastes of the uncultured and less powerful masses. Its beauty and significance was usually overlooked by the more educated and polished (though they were not entirely free from its pervasive spirit) until the Romantic Movement recognized its intrinsic merit and universal appeal.

New Poetic Forms

The humanists of the Renaissance revived literary forms that had flourished in Antiquity but had been lost or rarely used during the Middle Ages.

Lascaris's publication of *The Greek Anthology* (see Chapter X) was followed by Joseph Scaliger's anthology (1573) of Latin poetry. These anthologies, together with the renditions and translations of Classical poetry by the sixteenth-century French poets Clément Marot and Mellin de Saint-Gelais, gave some of the favourite poetic forms of Antiquity a considerable vogue. For example, the epigram and the ode began to appear frequently in European poetry around 1600.

Other poetic forms usually continued as before, but in some cases, such as the ballade and the sonnet, some refinement took place, so that, for example, the Shakespearean sonnet differed in rhyme pattern from the Italian. Song forms like the Provençal *chanson* and the Italian *canzone* and madrigal (see Chapter XII), frequently written without the intention of musical accompaniment, enjoyed a distinct popularity. Numerous schemes of verse, rhyme, and meter were employed, but the *ottava rima* (eight lines of ten or eleven syllables each) became the accepted stanza of Italian epic poetry after Ariosto and Tasso, Alexandrine verse was almost obligatory for French and other continental epic and tragedy after Ronsard, and Spenser's preference for decasyllabic lines, reinforcing Chaucer's, set the model for English heroic verse. Subsequent epic poets of England—Dryden and Pope, for example—preferred, however, the heroic couplet to the 'Spenserian stanza' (eight decasyllabic iambic lines with a ninth of Alexandrine) of Spenser's *Faërie Queene* (1599–1611). Classical dactylic hexameter was rare before the eighteenth century.

Developments in the Theatre

During this period Classical drama, revived by Renaissance playwrights, merged with Christian spectacle to form the basis of Europe's future dramatic development. The religious play was brought to perhaps its greatest height in the *autos* (*acts*) of the Spanish and the Portuguese dramatists of the late sixteenth and early seventeenth century, of whom Lope de Vega (1562–1635) and Pedro Calderón de la Barca (1600–81) are probably the best known today.[7] The *auto* was usually a one-act spectacle performed outdoors in connection with a church procession and structured around an allegory suitable for the holy day on which it was performed. Such religious dramas were also frequently presented in the Jesuit schools. In general, the religious performances continued longer and flourished more freely in the Catholic and the Lutheran (particularly Scandinavian) areas of Europe than in those dominated by the more iconoclastic Calvinists.

The importance of this kind of religious theatre was greater than the mere number of plays would seem to indicate. It was to a large extent folk drama, enjoyable for all layers of society. It represented a flexible art form (often not even written down), in which improvisation played a good part. It united the common Christian tradition with popular lore. Its patrimony to the professional actors of the *commedia dell'arte* (see Chapter X), which reached its highest elaboration in the sixteenth century, was probably considerable. More important perhaps, the irregular, impromptu dialogue of the religious play and of the *commedia dell'arte* prepared the way for the wider social acceptance of a regular secular theatre. For meanwhile, too, written plays on secular themes (often based on *Schwänke*, *fabliaux*, and historical episodes) had become popular. Of the more than 2,000 dramatic pieces that Lope de Vega is said to have written and the well over 400 of which the text is known, the overwhelming number were on secular themes; and Calderón wrote 120 plays, many of them on secular themes, in addition to numerous *autos*. These two writers (particularly Lope de Vega, whom Calderón often imitated and sometimes, as was a common practice in that day, plagiarized) not only gave form to the Spanish drama but through translations and borrowings also influenced the French and the English stage, both of which frankly exploited their Spanish sources.

Parallel to the rise of the new dramatic literature went a revival of Classical drama—in particular, tragedy. This revival resulted not only in the publication and study of the works of the great Greco-Roman tragedians—Aeschylus, Sophocles, Euripides, and Seneca—but also in a growing awareness of the dramatic theories of Antiquity, particularly Aristotle's. Classical concepts of dramatic form, with the notable exception of the basic role assigned by Ancient writers to the chorus, helped to shape the structure of European drama. Plays were divided into scenes and acts in accordance with Classical conventions. Three acts were used predominantly by Spanish, Portuguese, and Italian writers in imitation of Terence, five by English and French writers in imitation of Seneca. This convention, in turn, influenced the structure and exposition, the climax and denouement of the plot. Meters varied, and the use of rhyme was by no means universal. Toward the close of our period, metric verse was frequently replaced by prose. In general, English and Spanish dramatists developed plays of a freer style than did the French classicists, particularly after a controversy precipitated by Corneille's *Le Cid*. We shall see in greater detail later that the French dramatists attempted to make their plays adhere to fixed rules of dramatic style and form allegedly derived from Aristotle's *Poetics*. Comedy (though more complex because of its association with the looser traditions of farce and burlesque) also was to a certain extent influenced in its formal aspects by the revival of Classical comedy, especially Plautus and Terence (but hardly at all by the greatest comedian of antiquity, Aristophanes).

While religious plays were often performed by amateurs on 'natural' stages (such as the steps of a church), the comedies and tragedies of the modern literary artist called for interpretation by professionals with increasingly elaborate scenery. Repertory theatres with permanent troupes grew up, such as the Globe Theatre, of Shakespearean fame, and the great hall of the Hôtel Bourbon, where Molière's company held forth. More common (and, in a sense, more in keeping with the technical nature of the dramas of a

Racine or a Molière) were the small theatres at royal or princely courts, visited by itinerant companies of professional actors. The Comédie Française founded in 1680, was the first state-supported public theatre. Despite frequent marks of social disapproval the number of theatres, actors, plays, and serious dramatists mounted.

The Ancients versus the Moderns

Great changes in form took place also in prose literature after 1500. While previously prose had, of course, been used extensively in the writing of history, philosophy, and other non-fictional subjects (considered elsewhere in this volume), only rarely was creative writing done in prose. Subsequently a great variety of literary forms employing prose evolved, until literary expression commonly became prose expression. The novelette and the novel emerged as favoured art forms. Collections of short stories, tied together by such simple devices as the single narrator of the *Arabian Nights* or the common audience of Boccaccio's *Decameron*, enjoyed wide popularity. Eighteenth-century novelists frequently used the device of an exchange of letters among their characters to develop their stories. The art of the essay was greatly furthered by such skillful writers as Montaigne and Bayle, Addison and Steele. The increasing number of periodicals, newspapers, and almanacs brought forth a journalistic prose style. Polemic has rarely been more eloquently carried on than in the pamphlets, satires, or letters of Luther, Pascal, Swift, and Voltaire, or memoirs more engagingly narrated than in the autobiographies of Cellini, the *Raskolnik* leader Avvakum, Rousseau, and Franklin. The epigram was nobly employed by La Rochefoucauld and Franklin, homily by the Polish Jesuit Piotr Skarga, the Russian Archbishop Theofan Prokopovich (1681–1736), and the French bishops Jacques Bénigne Bossuet (1627–1704) and Jean Baptiste Massillon (1663–1742), and oratory by Savonarola and Edmund Burke. And under the influence of Classical examples (especially Cicero's) cultivated Europeans, from the humanists through the Russian tsars to the *philosophes*, lifted letter writing to the level of a highly refined art, of which Madame de Sévigné and Lord Chesterfield were perhaps the leading exponents.

In the Western countries, the generations between the Renaissance and the beginning of the Romantic Movement were exceedingly self-conscious about literary criteria. Standards of criticism were explicit in the minds of literary men, in many ways tied up with and analogous to their philological concerns. All in all this period, and especially the decades of 'the Quarrel of the Ancients and the Moderns'—i.e. the battle of the advocates with the opponents of literary neoclassicism—at the close of the seventeenth and the beginning of the eighteenth century were perhaps the most erudite and form-conscious epoch in the history of Western literature.

The Western literary world of these times was torn by the strife between the defenders of free and spontaneous literary form and the advocates of firm models, rules, and standards. On the one side stood those writers who, with qualifications (since literary men can never wholly escape concern with problems of form), were basically preoccupied with saying what they wished to say without serious formal restrictions and those critics who defended the poet's freedom or the artist's right to deviate from rules and preconceived standards of 'good taste'. On that side were found most of the great Spanish poets and dramatists, Shakespeare, and critics like Bernard de Fontenelle (1657–1757) and Charles Perrault (1628–1703); they generally went their own way without much or only amused attention to the literary quarrels around them. These men and their admirers were sometimes referred to as the 'Moderns'. They did not necessarily look down upon literary traditions (Lessing, for example, while holding up Shakespeare as a better model than Racine, respected the authority of Aristotle), but they did feel that modern literature might have merit of its own even when it did not imitate the writings of Antiquity.

On the other side stood the 'Ancients'. They comprised those writers and critics who believed that literature was a disciplined art with an ascertainable hierarchy of forms, each having its particular qualities from which standards could be deduced for firm judgments. They stood for such qualities as edification, clarity, decorum, and symmetry expressed in preferred forms like epigram, epic, and verse tragedy. Foremost among the Ancients in France were Boileau, Racine, and Fénelon—with some assistance, when 'the Quarrel of the Ancients and the Moderns' moved across the Channel, from Swift, Pope, and (ambivalently, because of his admiration for Shakespeare) Dryden. In the eighteenth century, Johnson impugned the dramatic 'unities' (see below) to defend Shakespeare, but in Russia Alexander Petrovich Sumarakov (1718–77), along with Lomonosov, in tragedies based on themes borrowed from Russian history inaugurated a reign of classicism, looking to Boileau, and later Voltaire, as arbiter.

The 'Ancients' were greatly influenced by the revival of Classical literary theories. It was admiration for Classical epigram, epic, and tragedy that led them to the defence of these forms as the most exalted in the literary hierarchy. Under the influence of Classical literary theories, especially those of Aristotle's *Poetics* and Horace's *Ars Poetica*—and these, more particularly, as represented in Boileau's *L'art poétique* (1674) and Pope's *Essay on Criticism* (1711)—they constructed explicit rules for poetry. In drama they upheld with special rigour the rule of the 'three unities'—of action, time, and place— extrapolated in the sixteenth century by Ludovico Castelvetro and other Italian critics from Aristotle's dramatic theory. The 'unities' were followed in Ben Jonson's *Alchemist* (1610), Jean de Mairet's *Sophonisbe* (1634), and Joseph Addison's *Cato* (1713), to cite but a few examples. Even a fairly formalistic dramatist like Corneille at first fell short of the Neoclassicists' doctrines, but after a pamphlet war precipitated by his partial violation of them in *Le Cid* (1636), he conformed to their standards of unity, purity of genre, decorum, and edification. With Racine's *Berenice* (1670), *Phèdre* (1677), *Athalie* (1691), and other tragedies the dramatic unities became a strict convention of the French stage until the time of the Romantics. The works of perhaps the world's greatest writer of tragedies, William Shakespeare, long remained in the Neoclassicists' sight sadly amorphous and sometimes unedifying constructions, and inferior therefore.[8]

Stringent formalism, combined with an esthetic and moralistic aversion to crudities, resulted in comdemnation of some of the memorable literary achievements of Antiquity and ended in such absurdities as the rewriting and purifying of Homer. On the other hand, the intense preoccupation with the formal questions of literature promoted sensitivity to fundamental artistic values and problems. In addition, it gave a mighty impetus to Classical scholarship and to the stylistic vogue in the arts and letters of Neoclassicism. At the close of our period, with the pre-romantics of France and the *Sturm und Drang* of Germany, and most explicitly in the critical writings of Herder, the Classical criteria of literary taste gave way to a preference for greater individuality of form and more spontaneous norms of style and structure.

Varieties of Literary Moods

Like the good literature of all ages, that of 1500–1775 gave expression to universal interests, values, and problems. Love with all its shadings from the basest passion to the feeling of mysterious union with the cosmos; war with its brutal horrors and brave sacrifices; death and disease with their accompanying fears; beauty whether of the female form or of the setting sun; despair, sorrow, and pain; indignation at injustice and the quest for right; hope, joy, laughter, and fun; adulation, contempt, and satire—all the manifold attitudes, experiences, and desires of man found ample and moving articulation in the poetry, drama, and prose of the epoch. It began with the Renaissance humanism of commanding figures like Erasmus, Rabelais, and Machiavelli and ran through the classical period of several national literatures with such peerless masters as Tasso, Cervantes, Shakespeare, and Racine, to the humanitarianism of the Enlightenment, represented by the mature works of Lomonosov, Rousseau, and Voltaire, and the early works of Goethe. At the same time—and this consideration constitutes our basic concern here—this literature also exhibited in its content, themes, and moods the varying peculiarities of the age. So many contemporary movements and problems were somehow reflected in the *belles lettres* of this era of two hundred and seventy-five years (quite apart from its philosophic, polemic, scholarly, and historical prose) that its imaginative literature forms one of the best media for fathoming its changes of temper.

A most troublesome problem of the era was the passionate religious controversy engendered by the Reformation, the Counter Reformation, and the Wars of Religion. The varying character of the numerous Protestant splintergroups (ranging from individualistic pietism to radical social action) can with simple clarity be sensed in their hymns; except for the ubiquitous translations of the Bible, prayer books and hymns were perhaps the most widely influential literary achievement of the Protestants. The deep devotion of the Puritan found more literary expression in John Milton's *Paradise Lost* (1667) and John Bunyan's *Pilgrim's Progress* (1678–84). John Donne (1572–1631) mixed 'metaphysical' profundity with a deep religious conviction in both poems and sermons. Pascal's posthumously published *Pensées* (1670) combined a Jansenist piety, even mysticism, with touches of irony and epigrammatic wisdom. The religious fervour of Spanish poets and mystics like St Theresa of Avila, Fray Luis de Leon (1527–91), and St John of the Cross amply testify to the emotional intensity of the Catholic Counter Reformation.

The Faust and the Don Juan theme illustrate the persistence of traditional concepts of Hell as the terrible, eternal abode of the wicked and worldly. The bohemian Christopher Marlowe, accused by some of his contemporaries of atheism, was, for all that, troubled by the problems of evil and the renunciation of God; the restless scholar who is the central figure in his *Tragical History of Doctor Faustus* (c. 1588), weary of science, bargains away his soul in return for power and pleasure but in the end rues his contract with the Devil. Don Juan's fate, though not the outcome of an explicit bargain, is no kinder. Unmitigated sensualist, seeker after momentary worldly pleasure, enjoying the day and trusting little to the morrow, defying moral and theological principles, Don Juan charmed and seduced for the sheer joy of conquest, but he pays the inescapable penalty in the end. He first appeared in *El burlador de Seville y convidado de piedra* by Fray Gabriel Tellez (pen name, Tirso de Molina, 1584?–1648) and reappeared in Molière's *Le Festin de Pierre* (1660) and other plays before Mozart gave him (1787) operatic immortality.

Nevertheless, the changing mood of early modern man from preoccupation with other-worldliness to skepticism of both heaven and hell and to acceptance of his temporal condition was also easily perceptible in imaginative literature. For one thing, the number of satires on church dignitaries like those in Erasmus's *Praise of Folly* (1509) and in the *Letters of Obscure Men* (1515–17) by Crotus Rubeanus and Ulrich von Hutten increased until the heckling of ecclesiastical obscurantism and *l'infame*, while still risky, ceased to be rare, and passed as a literary heritage to the Enlightenment writers like Voltaire and Diderot. Meanwhile man's conquest of nature through science was eulogized, as in Fontenelle's *Entretiens sur la pluralité des mondes* (1686), and pantheistic nature was glorified, as in James Thomson's *Seasons* (1726–1730). Pagan gods and heroes were more and more substituted in metaphor for saints and angels; Camoëns resorted to this device in *Os Lusiadas* (1572) and Milton, humanist as well as Puritan, in *Comus* (1643) and other poems. The taste for lusty writings like the ubiquitous *facetiae* grew. Marguerite of Angoulême's *Heptameron* and Rabelais' *Gargantua and Pantagruel*, mirroring life in Renaissance France of the sixteenth century, speak candidly of the enjoyment of worldly pleasures, though (as is indicated in other contexts) their authors were greatly concerned with eternal problems and with man's higher nature. The philosophical breadth, not to mention the literary quality, that characterized Rabelais' satire is lacking in some of the libertine writings of the seventeenth and eighteenth century (see Chapter V), but their anti-clerical and pyrrhonist tone is more evident and, if anything, is less jovial and good-natured. Boldness of religious scepticism regarding the Christian tradition culminated with the Enlightenment, and in letters of an imaginative nature (not to rename from Chapter VII the more prosaic titles) it was perhaps most perceptible in Voltaire's *Poème sur le désastre de Lisbonne* (1756), Hume's *Dialogues Concerning Natural Religion*, and Diderot's *Le neveu de Rameau* (the last two published only posthumously).

The Reflection of Current Trends in Literature

The growing consciousness of the inhabitants of the different countries of Europe that they were both heirs and bequeathers of their common culture was enhanced not only by the rise of the vernaculars but by the patriotic trend in poetry, drama, and prose as well. The patriotic spirit manifested itself in the Russian songs and legends celebrating the great victories over Teuton and Tatar, in the Ukrainian *dumy* commemorating the heroic struggles with Tatar, Turk, and Pole, in the plays of Shakespeare about spectacular English kings, in the bitter lamentations of Grimmelshausen's *Simplicissimus* (1669) about a Germany torn by the foreign invasions and internecine strife of the Thirty Years War, in the Alexandrine declamations put by Corneille in the mouths of the patriots of Rome and Spain, and in the dramatizations by Friedrich Gottlieb Klopstock (1724-1803) and Goethe of the lives of German heroic figures.[9]

Polish literature provides a more than typical example of the general literary trend toward national concerns and patriotism. Before 1500 the Polish humanist used the vernacular rarely, perhaps even more rarely than his confreres farther west, but with the Bible translations and the polemics and sermons of the Reformation the foreboding and pride of Polish writers in both camps were often expressed in the vernacular. The Jesuit Father Skarga in his *Parliamentary Sermons* (1547) stirred his hearers and set a standard for Polish prose by his patriotic jeremiads. His lifetime, the turn of the sixteenth century, was also the 'golden age' of Polish poetry. Jan Kochanowski (1530-84) showed convincingly that the vernacular was an excellent vehicle for the Polish muse with his poems *Frazki* (*Trifles*, a collection of proverbs) and *Treny* (*Lamentations*, on the death of his daughter) and with his drama in the Classical vein, *The Dismissal of the Greek Envoys*. His contemporary and successor Simon Szymonowicz (1554-1642) wrote beautiful pastorals, of which *Kolacz* (*The Lake*) may be singled out as perhaps the best and probably the most popular. In the seventeenth century, though Classic (and French) influences still were marked, the intermittent war with the Turks made the patriotic theme more insistent. Woclaw Potocki (1625-96) in *Wojna Chocinska*

(*Chocin Campaign*) and other war epics celebrated the deeds of Sobieski and lesser Polish heroes, reflecting his anxiety about the loss of the ancient Polish virtues. Vespasian Kochowski (1633–1700) also wrote epics of war but is better remembered for his *Polish Psalmody*. The Serbian poet Ivan Gundulić (1588–1638), translator of Tasso and other Latin and Italian poets into Serb, similarly glorified the victory of the Poles over the Turks in his *Osman* (first printed in 1826). If few of the patriotic expressions of this period matched the competitive ardour of nineteenth-century nationalism, they yet reflected the rising national sentiment and at the same time helped to foster it.

Current changes in the political and social order were likewise mirrored in the writings of the day. The general tendency of the patriotic literature was to eulogize princes and dynastic rule, as befitted an era of growing centralization of power. Yet, this tendency was counterbalanced by oft-quoted passages in praise of the republican spirit of Antiquity or in condemnation of the arrogance of rulers in the works of Shakespeare, Corneille, Racine, and Voltaire. Ideals of knighthood, which had strongly coloured the literature of the Middle Ages, were now sometimes treated mockingly as antiquated relics of a no longer viable mode of life; Cervantes' *Don Quixote* (1605 and 1615) gave to literature a new character type—the impractical, simple-minded, visionary but noble knight of the sad countenance, victim of his own illusions, laughable but lovable—*quixotic*, in short. Instead of the knightly ideal writers put forth that of the gentleman, the *honnête homme*, with good manners and good sense, a certain amount of worldly learning and of accomplishment in the arts, a still strongly developed sense of chivalry and honour, and an appreciation of the graciousness of life.

This gentlemanly ideal had been portrayed even before Cervantes made sport of Don Quixote. Alphonse Martinez de Toledo, under the name of the Archpriest of Talavera (as he was), had published as early as 1438 a treatise dealing with worldly love and other questions of common morality and behaviour. Generally known as *El corbacho* (*The Whip*), the book sought to teach more edifying ways, largely through a fictitious misogynist who lashed vice, sin, and bad manners as if they were exclusively feminine weaknesses. Proper behaviour was subsequently held up as an ideal not only in Castiglione's *Il Cortegiano* (1528) and other sixteenth-century writings on education (see Chapter XVI) but also in the seventeenth century in Mme. de Lafayette's novels and Molière's plays, where the crude pretentiousness of the name characters in *Les précieuses ridicules* (1659), *Le bourgeois gentilhomme* (1670), or *Les femmes savantes* (1672) might be set off against the common decency and genuine worth of a lesser character such as Cléante. The gentlemanly hero was thoroughly overdrawn later in Samuel Richardson's *Sir Charles Grandison* (1753) and enveloped in a thick coating of *sensibilité* in the characterization of Wolmar in Rousseau's *Nouvelle Héloïse* (1761)—well-bred, honourable, philanthropic, forgiving, intellectual.

In some ways the counterparts to this urbane ideal were found in the simple heroes of the widespread pastoral literature, who inhabited a blessed never-never-land (Arcadia) where simple shepherds, shepherdesses, and nymphs dwelt in peace and happiness. Their life was rustic but without the harshness of rusticity, for nature was always benevolent and beautiful. The prototypes of this kind of romance are to be found in Greek and Roman literature; but the genre was revived in the *Arcadia* (1504) of Jacopo Sennazaro and was subsequently echoed by Jorge de Montemayor (1521–61), Sir Philip Sidney (1554–86), Spenser, Honoré d'Urfé (1568–1626), Tasso, Cervantes, Milton, and others.

In contrast, the rising bourgeoisie was gaining ground and made its vigour felt. In a way, that vigour was reflected in the 'picaresque' novel, centred in a usually amiable rogue (Spanish, *picaro*), who was sometimes drawn from a historical model. The picaroon was rarely genteel, only occasionally gentle, and nearly always engaged in energetic and merry or exciting frauds and escapades. The first well-known hero of this description was the subject of *La vida de Lazarillo de Tormes y de sus fortunas y adversidades* of unknown authorship but perhaps the work of Diego Hurtado de Mendoza (1503–75). Lazarillo was depicted as a kindly but not very bright beggar boy who serves several masters in turn, not always to his own advantage. His story has been described as the first novel to employ psychological analysis in order to show not only that poverty is not properly a subject of ridicule but also that human character is a mixture of good and bad.[10] It was followed by a number of similar narratives, of which the most famous were Mateo Alemán's *Guzman de Alfarache* (1599), *La Picara Justina* (1605, likewise of disputed authorship), and Quevedo's *Historia y vida del Buscón* (1626). From Spain the vogue spread to the Spanish Netherlands, England, France, and Germany through translation and imitation and eventually found expression at the hands of masters like Daniel Defoe (1661?–1731), Alain René Le Sage (1668–1747), Grimmelshausen, and Henry Fielding (1707–54). Bourgeois vigour appeared to some extent also in the eighteenth-century theatre (for instance, Diderot's realistic plays of 'everyday life' such as *Le Fils Naturel* and Lessing's *burgerliche Trauerspiele* such as *Miss Sara Sampson* and *Emilia Gallotti*). Above all, it was revealed by English novelists of the eighteenth century. Perhaps foremost among their novels of middle-class life were Defoe's *Moll Flanders*, Richardson's *Pamela*, and Fielding's *Tom Jones*.[11]

Middle-class vigour at times took the form of a conscientious concern with social problems like poverty and prostitution. Often combined with a delicate sensitivity to humanitarian and esthetic values (*sensibilité*), this concern led to a characteristic kind of sentimentalism that provided the themes and mood for much of the later literary output of our era, paced by Rousseau's *Nouvelle Héloïse*. The numerous Utopias written between 1500 and 1790 (in part, under the impact of contemporary geographical discoveries) were indirect expressions of social criticism, betraying a troubled awareness that man had not yet achieved the nobler things for which he was meant. Their prominent place in the current vogue of the philosophy of optimism led Voltaire to parody them in the El Dorado of his *Candide, ou l'optimisme* (1759).

The increasing contacts of Europeans with other areas of the world not only stimulated some of the utopian conceits but also induced an adulation of much that was foreign. For example, Leibniz and Wolff exhibited a learned curiosity about China, and Montesquieu and Voltaire, at least for literary purposes, showed a perhaps feigned admiration of Islam. In some instances—e.g. Camoëns' *Os Lusiadas* (1572) and Defoe's *Robinson Crusoe* (1719), to choose widely spaced examples from different genres—writers revealed a keen realization that man had achieved greatness in conquering the oceans and surviving strange encounters. Camoëns' epic built an odyssey around the glamorous story of Vasco da Gama; the hero of Defoe's tale was modelled after an otherwise little known sailor. The supposed simplicity of 'the noble savage' and wisdom of the Eastern sages led to an enthusiasm for strange places and characters in seventeenth and eighteenth-century literature that is sometimes called 'exoticism'. The theme of travel was a common literary device—as in Swift's *Gulliver's Travels* (1726), Le Sage's *Adventures de Robert, dit le chevalier de Beauchesne* (1732) and *Gil Blas* (1735), Voltaire's *Zadig* (1747) and *Candide*, Johnson's *Rasselas* (1759), and Sterne's *Sentimental Journey* (1768)—and the heroine of Defoe's *Moll Flanders* (1721) found, while the hero of Abbé Prévost *Mánon Lescaut* (1731) failed to find, refuge from the woes of Europe in the wilds of America.

The conquest of nature through the sciences likewise formed a recurrent theme in eighteenth-century Europe's literature. Schiller later complained that writers in the eighteenth century described the sun as a gaseous fireball rather than as Hyperion's chariot. The triumphs of a Newton or a Franklin moved Voltaire and lesser poets to verses of praise, and men of letters themselves often engaged in scientific research. Yet the attitude toward science was not always respectful. Swift mocked the learned academies in *Gulliver's Travels*. In Le Sage's novel *Gil Blas*, the picaresque hero at one stage of his career was a quack physician. In the two hundred years between Marlowe and Goethe, only slowly did the half-historical, half-legendary Faust, thirster after new experience and power, change from one whom the Devil ultimately claimed to one whom the angels save from Hell because he had served mankind.

BELLES-LETTRES IN THE ISLAMIC LANDS

The rising trend of Islamic prose after Ibn-Khaldun toward commentary and elaboration rather than toward creative scholarship has already been touched upon (see Chapter VII). Poetry continued abundantly, but in Iran at least it, too, was less notable after the fifteenth century. Jamāl-ud-dīn 'Urfī of Shīrāz (d. 1591) composed stately and traditional verse and was the most famous writer of *quaṣīdas* (elegies, odes, panegyrics) of his day. Like many gifted Persian contemporaries, whether philosophers or poets, he went to the

Mogul court of Delhi to live. He was one of those who were more appreciated in India and Turkey than at home, and the same was true in the next century of Sā'ib of Tabrez (d. 1677), whose influence eclipsed that of earlier poets. The classical tradition represented by these men was continued, although less fruitfully, in the eighteenth century. Alongside it other poetic tendencies appeared, notably the Shī'ite devotional poetry of the *marthiyas* (elegies on the misfortunes of Mohammed's family).

Meanwhile, as pointed out in Chapter X, Ottoman Turkish rose to prominence as a literary language. With the advent of the Uzbeks in Turkestan early in the sixteenth century, Chaghatai Turkish, which had been the most important of the three forms of Turkish in the time of Nevā'ī, tended to languish, though it was still used throughout the north. The best work of Fuzūlī of Baghdad (sixteenth century), perhaps the greatest Turkish poet of all time, was done in the Turkish of Azerbaijan (though he also composed in Persian and Arabic). Nevertheless, the western or Ottoman idiom, modelling itself on the master poet Bāqī of the sixteenth century, came on to lead the field. Ottoman Turkish poetry is generally regarded as superior to contemporary Persian poetry. It abounded in *mathnawīs*, commonly of a mystical tenor. Each *ṭarīqa* had its own poetic tradition.

Turkish poetry continued to feel the influence of contemporary Persian and Indo-Persian poets for a long time, though early in the eighteenth century it developed a greater independence of theme. In Turkish (as in Urdu) the trend toward ornateness, prevalent in the Persian zone, was often carried even further than in Iran itself. By the end of the eighteenth century, Turkish poetry seriously declined. Nonetheless, historical and related fields of learning after 1500 stayed on a high level, as the work of 'Ālī Chelebi demonstrated (see Chapter IX). Travel literature and other sorts of descriptive prose also retained a lofty standard.[12]

Persian literature bloomed in India under the patronage of the Mogul emperors and at the courts of independent Islamic sultans. Abu'l-Faḍl, poet, essayist, critic, and historian as well as vizier of Akbar (see Chapter V), was probably the most distinguished Islamic man of letters in the India of his day, but his brother Fayzī stood well toward the top of the list of contemporary poets. Among Fayzī's conspicuous achievements were his translations of Hindu classics, commissioned by Akbar. At least two of the illustrious poets of Akbar's reign were Persian immigrants. In addition to 'Urfī of Shīrāz, there was Muhammad Husain Nazīrī of Nishāpūr, writer of polished *ghazals*. The courts of Jahāngīr and Shāh Jahān likewise were graced by scholars and belletrists. Probably the most famous literary figure of Shāh Jahān's period was his son, Dārā Shikūh, who was executed in 1657 by his brother Aurangzīb in the struggle for succession. He was a Ṣūfī, well versed in Arabic, Persian, and Sanskrit. He assisted in translating the *Upanishads*, the *Bhāgavad-gītā*, and the *Yoga Vāshishtha Rāmāyana* into Persian. He was also the author of the *Majma'-ul-Baḥrayn*, a work harmonizing Hindu and Ṣūfī theosophies, and of the *Safīnat-ul-Awliyā*, a collection of biographies of the saints of Islam as well as of a separate biography of the saint Mian Mīr. In contrast, Aurang-zīb's religious bigotry led him to discourage art, music, history, and literature, and from his time on, as Islamic control disintegrated, Persian literature in India tended to decline.

A number of ladies of the Mogul court were learned in Persian and Arabic literature and were talented writers. Bābur's daughter, Gulbadan Begam, was the author of a history of Humāyūn's reign. Humāyūn's niece, Salīma Sultāna, composed several poems. The extraordinary woman who was the wife of Jahāngīr, Nūr-Jahān, was also esteemed as a woman of letters. Aurangzīb's daughter Zayb-un-Nisā was a gifted poetess and calligrapher.

Early Urdu literature was largely secular. Although Urdu was extensively used at the court of Akbar, it first developed as a literary language in the Deccan at the end of the sixteenth century under the patronage of the sultans of Bijapur and Golkunda. Urdu poetry generally followed Persian verse forms —*ghazals*, *rubā'īyats*, etc.—and the ornate Persian style. It developed not only traditional Persian themes but also themes taken from the Hindu background. By the eighteenth century Urdu had come to be used likewise in the north and produced masters who were esteemed by certain groups of Hindus as well as by Muslims. The most celebrated poet of the Deccan area was Walī of Aurangabad (b. 1668). His poetry stimulated various eighteenth-century writers—such as Zuhūr-ud-din Hātim (1699–1792) and Khān Ārzū (1689–1756)—who are considered the fathers of Urdu literature in north India and the Punjab. Urdu was ultimately to become the literary language of Pakistan. The disintegration of the Mogul Empire and the decadence of the imperial court fostered the more corrupt aspects of the Persian tradition. The body of the Urdu poetry of the time is said 'to combine a high order of verbal in-genuity and prosodic dexterity with a range of subjects almost exclusively restricted to homosexuality, the cult of the courtesan, and rakish and sadistic cynicism.'[13]

In the other languages spoken by considerable numbers of Muslims the literary achievements of this period were generally of local interest only. Literature in Gujarati remained oriented to the local sects and in good part was translated from Arabic and Persian. Other than the various chronicles mentioned in Chapter IX, modern Javanese and Malay produced little of wide significance. The spread of Islam in Malaysia did not result in conditions conducive to the encouragement of native literature: Islam's literary master-pieces were in Arabic or Persian, and its sacred *Koran* was not to be translated; furthermore, after 1511 it had to compete with Western conquests. The oldest surviving manuscript in Malay seems to date from about 1600. Islamic litera-ture in Javanese and Malay consisted of various adaptations from Arabic, Persian, or Urdu—religious romances, moral exhortations, mystical treatises, and legal works. A more distinctly native tradition endured in proverbs, folktales, and *wayang* (marionette shadow) plays. The Islamic areas of the southern Philippines, which were not conquered by the Spanish, produced, besides some chronicles and law codes, several epic poems celebrating the glories of particular tribes, such as the *Sulayman* of the Moros.

OTHER BELLES-LETTRES IN AND AROUND INDIA (1500–1775)

In eastern Asia during this period printing with movable type had an uneven history, which has already been sketched (Chapter X). In south Asia, printing underwent no significant development except in Vietnam. Even after it was introduced by Westerners, it did not take good hold in India and southeast Asia outside the areas they controlled.

Sanskrit Literature

After a display of renewed vigour in the sixteenth and seventeenth centuries Sanskrit declined rapidly again in the eighteenth as a medium of wide communication. Works continued, however, to appear in Sanskrit. Poets of genuine merit, of course, were rare, here as everywhere. Although epic, lyric, and dramatic poems were produced, at best they were imperfect imitations of older pieces and without beauty of locution or other poetic qualities. Sanskrit verse conveyed the growing interest in *bhakti* devotion, the poems related to the Krishna-Rādhā sects becoming increasingly erotic. While writers in Sanskrit showed greater strength in non-fiction, here too they generally were content to rework the older literature, and the best among them tended to become pedantic and to engage in hair-splitting philosophical discussions.[14]

Among the Sanskrit writers were Appaya Dīkshita (see Chapter VII) and his nephew Nīlakantha Dīkshita. Appaya Dīkshita, a south Indian philosopher and man of letters, was probably the outstanding Indian polymath of his day. He was the author of many devotional poems, two works of literary criticism (the *Citramīmāmsā* and *Lakshanāvalī*), a discussion of figures of speech (the *Kuvalayānanda*), and an analysis of the poetic use of words. He was concerned with the meaning rather than the sound of poetry. Nīlakantha Dīkshita was probably the most accomplished Sanskrit poet of the seventeenth century. His epic *Shiva-līlārnava* sang the praises of Shiva, while his collection of didactic verse, the *Kalividambana*, exposed human weaknesses and pled for a higher code of conduct. In the area of the longer romance, the Sanskrit *campū* (prose and poetry intermingled) became popular in the seventeenth century, and one of the outstanding *campūs* was Nīlakantha Dīkshita's *Nīlakanthavijaya*. It dealt with the ancient story of the churning of the milky sea by the gods, the resulting creation of poison, and Shiva's salvation of the world by consuming the poison.

Jagannātha, of the Mogul court of Shāh Jahān, was the finest critic and literary mind of the period. His *Bhāminivilāsa* was at once an erotic poem, an elegy, and a collection of gnomic sayings. He was most famous for his *Riasagangādhara*, an original treatise on poetics, which re-examined earlier works in the light of his own standards. Differing thoroughly with Appaya Dīkshita, he defined poetry as primarily sound (though it also conveyed meaning), a sort of contemplation that produced transcendental pleasure.

The literary attainments of other authors of the period who wrote in Sanskrit were perhaps less distinguished. Rūpa Gosvāmī (see Chapter VII) was the author of the *Padyāvalī*, which contained many passages of lyric poetry honouring Krishna, and of two religious dramas, the *Vidagdha Mādhava* and the *Lalita Mādhava*. The ingenuity of Sanskrit poets was illustrated in Rāmachandra's sixteenth-century *Rāsikarañjana* (*Delight of Connoisseurs*), which appeared to be, if read in one spirit, a eulogy of asceticism and, if in another, an erotic poem. About 1650 Meghavijaya produced the *Pañchākhyānoddhāra*, modelled upon the *Pañchatantra*; it contained a number of fables that gave evidence of the intercultural connections of India with the West. *Srīvāhāsudhākara*, a *campū* by Nārāyana, described in idyllic fashion the love of Svāhā, the wife of Agni, the god of fire, for the moon.

Tamil, Kanarese, Telegu, and Malayalam Literature

Literature in the Dravidian vernaculars (Tamil, Kanarese, Telegu, and Malayalam) rarely sought inspiration outside Hindu sources. In the Tamil literature of the sixteenth and seventeenth centuries *purānas* dealing with legends relating to famous shrines were particularly popular. In 1,225 easy flowing verses, the *Ariccandira* (1524) of Nallūr Virakavirāyar set forth the trials that the mythological king Harishcandra had to endure because of his devotion to truth. Probably the leading work of this mythological genre was the early seventeenth-century *Tiruvilaiyādal* of Parañjōti, describing the sixty-four sacred sports of Shiva at Madura. Kumāragurupara and Turaimangalam Shivaprakāshar, both of the seventeenth century, were perhaps the best writers in Tamil of the period. The former was the author of many poems honouring Shiva and other deities, of other kinds of devotional and ethical poetry, and of a work on Tamil prosody. The latter, a Vīrashaivite of liberal persuasion, composed poems on the deities of various shrines, a work of ethics, and a refutation of Christianity and translated into Tamil verse various Kanarese and Sanskrit writings on philosophy and Vīrashaivism. The beautiful devotional though anti-Brahman poetry of the Sittars (see Chapter III) preserved in the *Shiva-Vākyāni* probably belongs to this period, but it may have been earlier. In the eighteenth century the most famous scholar of Tamil Shivaism, Shivañānar, compiled, with his pupil Kāñchi Appar, the *Kāñchi-purānam*, which retold the legends of the sacred city of Conjeeveram. Among the more secular writers in Tamil were the Pāndyan king Ativīrarāma (*c.* 1564) and his cousin Varatungarāma Pāndya. The king translated several works from Sanskrit, prepared a small book on morals, and wrote an epic, the *Naidadam*; his cousin produced poems on Shivaite shrines and theology and translated the *Hokhoha*, a Sanskrit work on eroticism; and together they translated the Shivaite *Linga* and *Kūrma purānas*.

After 1500 Vishnuite authors, stimulated by the Chaitanya movement, dominated Kanarese literature, although Vīrashaivite writers remained active and some Jaina works also appeared. The rise of Vishnuite preponderance corresponded with the glorious period of the Vijayanagar Empire under Krishnadeva Rāya (1509–29), who, himself a poet, patronized all learning and literature, especially that in Sanskrit, Kanarese, and Telegu. The blossoming of Vishnuite letters under his patronage betokened a temporary increase in the influence of Brahmanic ideas and Sanskrit literature. Kanarese Vishnuite literature was largely made up of reproductions, in one form or other, of Sanskrit works. In the sixteenth century the Vishnuites produced, besides, a large number of popular songs extolling Vishnu, the most famous of the song writers being Purandaradāsa (d. 1564) and Kanakadadāsa. Kanakadadāsa also wrote the *Mohana-tarangini* (*River of Delight*), consisting of puranic stories about Krishna, and other moral and devotional poems in *shatpadī* verse. Among the Lingāyat contemporaries were Mallanārya of Gubbi, author of the *Vīrashivāmrita* (1530), a popular poetic explanation of the faith; Virūpāk-shapandita, author of the *Channabāsava-purāna*, a most venerated work of the Lingāyats, which dealt with the life of Bāsava's nephew; and Sarvajñamūrti (c. 1600), author of the *Sarvajña-padagalu*, a book of verses frequently on the lips of the common man.

In the late seventeenth and the eighteenth century, after the Vijayanagar Empire was disrupted by the Muslims, Kanarese literature was patronized especially by the rajas of Mysore. Having become independent about 1610 and having given up the Lingāyat faith, they now favoured Vishnuism. Many new versions of Sanskrit writings sacred to the Vishnuites and numerous collections of stories followed, generally in prose but sometimes in verse. King Chikkadēvarāja Odeyar (1672–1704), who persecuted the Jains, was himself an author, and so were several of his ministers and of the ladies at his court. The most eminent Kanarese Vishnuite poet, however, did not have royal patronage. He was Lakshmīsha, author of the *Jaimini Bhārata* (before 1700), the finest and most popular *shatpadī* poem in Kanarese. A very free adaptation of the Sanskrit original, it dealt with an incident from the *Mahābhārata* associated with the horse sacrifice, but its real purpose was to extol Krishna. Among the contemporaneous Lingāyat writers was Shadaksharadēva, who wrote poetry in both Kanarese and Sanskrit. Besides composing *campūs* on Bāsava (1671) and on the sports of Shiva, he elaborated an old story in his principal *campū*, the *Rājashekhara-vilāsa* (1657), which became one of the most highly esteemed poems in Kanarese. After him belles-lettres in Karanese were undistinguished. A new type of popular literature, the *yakshagāna*, emerged, however; it consisted of rude dramas or operatic pieces suited to rustic audiences and possessing neither dramatic skill nor literary merit.

The golden age of Telugu letters fell in the sixteenth century and likewise came under the patronage of Emperor Krishnadeva of Vijayanagar. Vishnuite influence became prominent in it. The principal poetic form was the *pra-*

bandha (grand epic), which like the Sanskrit *mahākāvya* contains descriptions of many things—cities, rivers, mountains, forests, lakes, seasons, sun, moon, travel, politics, battles, birth, marriage, pinings, morals, sex affairs, gambling, and kings. Telugu literature no longer counted so much as previously on translation, and the great *prabandhas* were independent creations, based on some puranic event. Krishnadeva's own epic, the *Āmuktamālyada* (see Chapter IX), is now ranked among the so-called 'five great *prabandhas*' in Telugu for its insight into human nature, its political philosophy, and the light it sheds on the social history and institutions of his reign. It dealt with the life and thought of a Vishnuite saint and the love of his foster daughter for the God Ranganātha.

The 'Eight Elephants' (or pre-eminent poets) of Telugu literature adorned this period. The foremost of them was Allasāni Peddana, the 'grandfather of Telugu poetry', whose simple and dignified *Manucarita* was another of 'the five great *prabandhas*'. It was a puranic story built around the refusal of a Brahman to accept the love of the divine courtesan Varūthinī. Another 'elephant' was Nandi Timmana, author of the *Pārijatāpaharana*, which elaborated in beautiful verse an episode in the life of Krishna, introducing the motif of jealousy in the characterization of Satya, one of Krishna's mistresses. Only three of the remaining 'elephants' were of truly imposing stature. They probably did their work between 1540 and 1590. One of the trio, Pingali Sūranna, was the author of two epics, both of which are sometimes included among 'the great five'. They are the *Kalāpūrnodayam* (*Birth of Kalāpurna*), essentially a novel in verse, which occasionally is regarded as the finest poem in Telugu (and has been compared with Shakespeare's *Comedy of Errors*), and the *Prabhāvatī Pradyumna*, which deals with the marriage of Prabhāvatī and Pradyumna, son of Krishna. Bhattumūrti (or Rāmarajabhushana) was another of the three. His leading poem was the *Vasucaritra* (*c.* 1570), telling a simple story of the love of Prince Vasu and Princess Girika, daughter of a river and a mountain. Tenāli Rāmakrishna (or Rāmalinga), the third of the trio, was the author of the *Pānduranga Māhātmya*, which narrated the rescue of the soul of a dissipated Brahman from the servants of Yama, king of the dead, by those of Vishnu.

With the collapse of Vijayanagar Telugu literature began to deteriorate. The feudatory courts of Nellore, Tanjore, Madura, and other strongholds were the centres of Telugu literature during these centuries of decline. In the seventeenth century Raghunātha Nāyaka, raja of Tanjore, wrote the *Valmīki-caritram*, the first important prose work in Telugu. The great Telugu literary figure of the century was Chāmakūra Venkatakavi, of Raghunātha's court, whose *Vijayavilāsam* was often rated among 'the five great *prabandhas*'. It dealt with the adventures and loves of the semi-divine hero Arjuna. In the eighteenth century Telugu literature reached its nadir, 'the Age of Despair', unrelieved by the number of popular *shatakas*, prose works, and colloquial dramas of the *yakshagāna* variety that it produced but somewhat brightened by Tyāgarāju of Tanjore, perhaps the greatest of Hindu musicians (see Chapter XII).

After Cheruśśeri (see Chapter X) little Malayalam literature was put forth other than local songs and ballads. Tuñcat Rāmānujan Eluttaccan (c. 1700), author of a number of works dealing with Indian mythology, religion, and monistic philosophy, gave shape to the modern speech. He produced Malayalam versions of the *Rāmāyana*, the *Mahābhārata*, and the *Bhāgavata*. Of the popular dance-dramas the *Rāman-āttam* of Kottārakkara Tampurān (perhaps sixteenth century), a work meant to be completed in eight performances, is the oldest extant example. In the seventeenth century the *Shiva-purāna* and the *Brahmānda* were translated into Malayalam.

Hindi Literature

The heyday of Hindi literature was the century (1556–1658) between the beginning of the reign of Akbar and the rise of Aurangzīb. Its glory was a response, in part, to the upsurge of the Vishnuite *bhakti* movements centred on Rāma and Krishna and, in part, to the era of patronage and good will inaugurated by Akbar and continued, though more restrictedly, by his two immediate successors. It took on an artistic and sophisticated character and soared to heights rarely, if ever, attained again. During this period the *Bījak* (c. 1570) and the *Ādi Granth* (1604) were produced and the greatest figures of Hindi literature flourished. Religious devotion was its dominant motivation and supplied its main themes. Lyric poetry retained its prominence, but epics and other poetic forms also thrived.

Many first-rank Hindi writers set an elevated literary tone at Akbar's court, but three towering figures of his reign were not under his direct patronage. Of these the senior was the Krishnaite Sūr Dās (d. c. 1563), 'the blind bard of Agra'. The others were Tulsī Dās and Kēsab Dās. Sūr Dās generally is listed among the eight great Vallabha poets, and he is considered by some to be the greatest Hindi poet (although this honour is generally reserved for Tulsī Dās).[15] He reproduced a large number of episodes and passages from the *Bhāgavata-purāna*; his lyrics relating to Krishna and Rādhā were collected in the *Sūrsagar* and the *Sūrāvalī*. He is said to have written as many as 75,000 verses, noted for the polish, ornament, and variety of their style and for their picturesque images and similes.

Kēsab Dās (1555–1617), of Orchhā in Bundelkhand, was the first significant Hindi writer on poetics. His most admired work, the *Kavi Priyā*, undertook to describe the qualities required of a good poem. Among his other writings were the learned *Rasik Priyā*, dealing with poetical composition, and the *Rām Alankrtmañjarī*, dealing with prosody. Since he illustrated his points with original poems, each of these books constituted also a collection of his own poetry.

Tulsī Dās (d. 1623), of Benares (see Chapter V), is the most celebrated and, as already indicated, is generally considered the best, of the Rāmat writers. His well-known *Rāmāyana* (more moralistic than the original), begun in 1575, is one of the noblest epics ever penned, ranking with *Paradise Lost* among the masterpieces of religious poetry. Written in old Eastern Hindi, which thereafter became the literary language for Rāmats, the poem became household knowledge, revered throughout north India. Tulsī Dās was the author of many other highly moralistic poems, all venerating Rāma. The *Rām Gītāvali* was composed in verses adapted for singing, and the *Vinay Patrikā* was a group of hymns. His *Sāt Sāi*, a discussion of poetics, was illustrated with devotional verses, also on Rāma.

A fourth famous literary figure of the period was Bihārī-Lāl Chaube (c. 1603–63), the most celebrated of many Hindi authorities on the art of poetry. He lived in Muttra and wrote in the Braj Bhāshā dialect. His major opus was a *Sāt Sāi* (1662), a collection of about seven hundred original couplets intended to provide illustrations of various kinds of poems, styles, heroic characters, rhetorical figures, and related subjects. A majority of these verses were in the form of amorous utterances by Rādhā and Krishna, since the author was a Krishnaite. This type of work was quite common, but Bihārī-Lāl's revealed particular skill and excellence of expression.

Of the bardic poems in Hindi, the *Padumāvatī* of Malik Muhammad Jāyasī (see Chapter IX) was easily the most impressive. Its theme, the seige of Chitor by Emperor Alā-ud-dīn (1303), permitted a striking admixture of Hindu and Islamic lore. It was written in a local Hindi dialect of Rajputana in Persian characters with some admixture of Persian words and idioms. Its originality and poetic beauty make it one of the Hindi masterpieces.

Aurangzīb's anti-literary and anti-Hindu policies helped to inaugurate a steady decline of Hindi literature. Civil strife, political and economic disintegration, and the degeneration of the *bhakti* movements prolonged this literary decadence beyond our period. It was characterized by ornateness of style, overattention to form, lack of emotional depth, and increase of eroticism. It was productive of a mounting number of undistinguished translations of the *Rāmāyana*, the *Mahābhārata*, the *Bhāgavad-gītā*, the *Bhāgavata-purāna*, and other Sanskrit classics.

The lesser Hindi authors of the period fall into five groups—court poets and writers, Rāmats, followers of Kabīr, Krishnaites, and bardic chroniclers. Among the first were Rājā Bīrbal, Akbar's poet-laureate, noted for his witty and humorous verses; Ganga Prasād, renowned for his comic style and descriptions of battles; Balbhadra Sanādya Mishra, brother of Kēsab Dās, remembered especially for a *Nakhshikh* (a popular type of poem which described every part of the body of a hero or heroine from toenails to topknot); and Dev Kavi (c. 1673–1745), of whose works thirty are extant, disclosing good form and diction, an ornamental style, striking descriptions of heroines, and patent eroticism. After Tulsī Dās the Rāmat writers were not distinguished; probably the best known was Nābhā Dās, author of the *Bhaktimālā* an account of the lives of Vishnuite devotees. Nor did the followers of Kabīr, although prolific as writers, excel as creative literary lights. The Krishnaite authors were perhaps more memorable; they produced a good deal of poetry of estimable quality, marked by erotic phrasing and sensuous imagery, describing the soul's devotion to the divine as a reflection of Rādhā's surrender to her beloved.[16] Gokulnāth (fl. 1568), author of the *Chaurāsī Vārtā*, a prose work that retold the legends of the Vallabhas, and Hari Dās (fl. 1600) were among the most able of this Krishnaite group. Lāl Kavi (see Chapter IX) was perhaps the best of the numerous eighteenth-century bardic chroniclers.

Literature in Bengali and Other Indo-European Vernaculars

From about 1500 on, the Chaitanya movement and the local Shakta cults dominated Bengali literature, and their joint impact produced the golden age of traditional Bengali literature. After 1650 Shākta influences waxed, as Chaitanyaism waned. The Portuguese had the Christian gospel translated into Bengali and made serious efforts during the seventeenth century to spread it, but the Westerners' Bible seems not to have contributed to the development of Bengali prose before the nineteenth century. The period from 1500 to 1800 is often known as the Nadiyā period, since that city became the centre not only of the Chaitanya movement in particular but of the economic and cultural life of Bengal in general.

Chaitanya poetry was of three kinds: (1) *pads* (short, lyrical, pastoral songs about the love of Krishna and Rādhā), (2) biographies of Chaitanya and other leaders, and (3) expositions of doctrine and practice. Of the last only those disquisitions on *rasa-tattva*, or the cult of love and devotion, were of a belletristic nature. They were based upon the Sanskrit treatises of Rūpa Gosvāmī, and of the disquisitions in Bengali the sixteenth-century *Prem-bhakti-chandrika* by Narottam, who was also an outstanding *pad* writer, was representative. The theological theory they presented, of course, promoted the Krishna-Rādhā love poetry of the *pads*. The standard biographies of Chaitanya by Vrindāvan Dās and Krisnadās Kavirāja have already been mentioned (Chapter V), but numerous poets combined legend and fact in order to present biographies of Chaitanya and other leaders in verse. Pre-eminent among these poetical versions was the eighteenth-century *Bhakti-ratnākar* of Narahari Chakravarttī, which, in addition to its biographical accounts, presented discussions of theology, rhetoric, literature, and related subjects. Narahari also wrote on versification, made a collection of others' *pads*, and was himself an able *pad* writer.

The finest literary products of the Chaitanya movement and perhaps of the whole of Bengali literature were *pads*. More than 3,000 of them by over 150 writers prior to the nineteenth century testify to their popularity. They were greatly influenced by the earlier lyrics of Vidyāpati. Written in a language called Vrajabuli, which was a mixture of Bengali and Maithili, they told of the love of Krishna and Rādhā in lyrics of passionate intensity and undisguised sensuousness, intended to symbolize the love of man for God. They presented the story in its several stages—the dawn of love, the message, the tryst, union, separation, and reunion in spirit; and to heighten their intensity, they introduced an unconventional touch by making Krishna a cowherd and Rādhā a married princess. *Ecstasy* and *emotional madness* were favourite words. The most skilful sixteenth century writer of *pads*, Govindadās Kavirāja, was unrivalled for verbal harmony and alliteration. Among the numerous seventeenth-century writers, both Hindu and Muslim, the Muslim Ālāol stands out, but the general quality of seventeenth-century *pads* was below that of the sixteenth. In the eighteenth century, a further decline in originality took place as numerous anthologies were compiled and the *pad* became more stereotyped.

During these centuries several long narrative poems were produced in Bengali. Among about twenty Bengali versions of the *Rāmāyana*, that by Adbhut Āchārya (seventeenth century) was the most commonly accepted. Of some thirty of the *Mahābhārata*, that of Kāsirām Dās (seventeenth century) was the masterpiece. Of the *mangals* dealing with Krishna, probably the foremost was the *Govinda-mangal* of Kavichandra Chakravarttī (eighteenth century), who was also the author of an excellent version of the *Mahābhārata* and perhaps of a version of the *Rāmāyana*.

A good deal of Bengali literature was inspired by the various local cults, especially those of Shakti (see Chapter V). The outstanding Manasā poem was produced by Ksamānanda (*c.* 1650); it avoided the prolixity and coarseness of much of the other Manasā literature. The praise of Chandī in her genuine character as a local goddess became a common literary theme during the seventeenth century, with accent upon the episodes in which she conferred her favours on a humble male follower, Kālketu, and a female devotee, Khullanā, daughter of a rich merchant. The *Chandī-mangal* of Mukundarām Chakravarttī, written during the late sixteenth century, was peopled with realistic characters. It pictured the harsh life of the Bengal villages and the piratical activity of the Portuguese and appealed to the goddess to better the people's lot. The many Chandī poems of the seventeenth and eighteenth centuries in Bengali did not measure up to it, perhaps because of the competition of the Sanskrit *Mārkandeya-purāna*, which depicted a Brahmanized Chandī, or (as she was more generally known in her Brahmanized form) Durgā, wife of Shiva.

In the seventeenth century the number of poems about Shiva also began to mount, although Durgā often 'stole the show'. The Shiva of Bengal folklore was a rustic plowman or vagabond who ran after low women, but in these poems he was elevated to be the head of a respectable middle-class household, who occasionally got into difficulties as the old husband of a young wife. Dharma, originally the Buddha but now completely distorted by tantric ideas and local lore, was often identified with Shiva. Dharma-cult literature also made its appearance in the seventeenth century, relating the exploits of the hero Lāusen, aided by Dharma. The best of the *mangals* dealing with Dharma was completed by Ghanaram Chakravarttī in 1711, and the *Shiva-samkīrttan* of Rāmesvar Bhattāchārya (eighteenth century) was unsurpassed among the Shivāyan poems.

In the eighteenth century Bengali literature underwent a general deterioration, but with certain redeeming features. Some purely secular poems of merit appeared, of which the elegant love lyrics of Nidhu Bābu decidedly belonged in the drawing-room rather than the village street. Moreover, two of Bengal's ablest poets adorned the century. Ramprasād Sen (*c.* 1718–75), the outstanding song writer of his day, composed and dedicated to the terrible goddess Kālī some simple devotional lyrics that have remained beloved to the present day. In contrast to him, Bhārat-chandra Rāy (1722–60) was a basically secular, courtly writer, whose dexterity has remained unequalled in Bengali poetry. Each of these poets wrote a *Kālikā-mangal*, of which Bāhrat-chandra Rāy's was the more celebrated. It was in reality a trilogy, completed in 1752, of which the Vidya-Sundar love-story (see Chapter X) has particular charm. He contrived to introduce the Goddess Kālī into it, but his absorbing theme was a secular story of illicit love, expounded in sensuous, witty, and elegant phraseology. Although drawn from Sanskrit literature and clearly influenced by Mukundarām Chakravarttī, the poem also showed Islamic influence.

The authors in the other Indo-European vernaculars of India were nearly always religiously inspired. *Bhakti* poetry was a distinct factor in stimulating the Maratha nationalistic movement under Sivājī and his successors (see Chapter V). Ekanātha (d. 1608), Rāmdās (seventeenth century), and especially Tukārām (also seventeenth century) were the foremost Marathi poets of this period. Rāmdās wrote not only a *Rāmāyana* but also two hundred and five verses to the mind. While Gujarati poetry could boast the Krishna poets Nākar and Premānand, Gujarati literature became almost barren in the later seventeenth and eighteenth centuries, except for the lyrics of the Shivaite writer Shivānand (fl. 1750). The ablest examples of Punjabi letters were the poems of Nānak (early sixteenth century) and of other Sikh writers in the *Granth* (see Chapter V).

Literature in Assam, Nepal, Burma, and Siam

Assam, which gallantly maintained an uncertain independence of the Mogul Empire, enjoyed its age of literary glory during the sixteenth and early seventeenth centuries. Assamese literature burst into flower under the Krishna *bhakti* movement led by Shankar Deb and his successor Madhab Deb (d. 1596). Shankar Deb's *Kīrtan-ghosa* was a series of renderings from many puranic sources; he began the use of dramas drawn from the puranas as a means of popular religious instruction. Madhab Deb made translations of Sanskrit ethical and philosophical works and composed devotional songs (*bargīts*) and dramas. Later, Bhattadeva (*c.* 1558–1638) laid the foundation of Assamese prose in the translations of the *Bhāgavata-purāna* and the *Bhāga-*

vad-gītā. After 1650 the Krishna movement declined, and literature, which passed under the patronage of the Shan Ahom kings, grew more secular. Prose then became a commoner literary vehicle, as court poets glorified their kings in prose-and-verse chronicles known as *buranji* (eight of which were written between 1648 and 1742). Biographies of religious leaders (in either prose or verse) shared popularity with romances in *kāvya* style and with Shākta poems in praise of Durgā, Chandī, and Kālī.

Most of the works in the Nepali vernacular were either inspired by or were adaptations of Buddhist and Hindu religious literature, especially *tantras* and puranas. Some independent chronicles or genealogies (*vamshāvalis*) were produced in the seventeenth and eighteenth centuries. Perhaps the most meritorious native literary product was the sixteenth-century *Svayambhū-purāna*, a legendary account of the origins of Nepal under the guidance of the bodhisattva Mañjushrī.

In Burma after 1500 Pali literature remained abundant, but vernacular compositions steadily increased. Translations or adaptations of Pāli philosophical works and of Jātaka tales made up one part of the vernacular output; legal treatises and chronicles made up another; still another comprised *niti* literature (traditional tales illustrative of conduct or dealing with national heroes); and there were poems and dance-dramas, drawn not only from the Jātakas, Indian epics, or puranas but also from native tradition. Several of the Toungoo kings (1531–1752) were patrons of letters and maintained royal chroniclers. Literature bloomed especially under King Bayin Naung (1551–81), when Siamese captives apparently introduced the variety of songs and dances known as *Yodaya* (*Ayuthia*). Zeyyayandameik, a courtier of King Anaukpetlun (1605–28), was the author of a poem entitled *Natshinnaung*, after a Burmese adventurer associated with the Portuguese buccaneer De Brito. In the eighteenth century, under Alaungpaya (see Chapter IX) and his immediate successors, a number of famous poets prospered. Seindakyawthu (1736–71) was especially noted, for his *Kawiletkanathatpon*, a poem in a philosophical vein, and his *Awwadatupyo*, which set forth guiding principles in the pursuit of wisdom.

Most Siamese rulers maintained poets and chroniclers, and kings and other royal personages sometimes were prominent authors. Among the more important of the prose tales, which were popularized through the epic dance-dramas, were new versions of the *Ramakien* and the *Inaco* (see Chapter X). The earliest extant complete version of the *Ramakien* is that of King P'ya Taksin (1767–82); the oldest extant version of the *Inaco* dates only from the nineteenth century. Other tales told of wondrous things—of the origin of mankind from the egg of a sacred goose; of a king who became an ascetic upon contemplating a withered tree; of a princess who was beloved by an elephant; of a princess who was carried off by a crocodile and rescued by her lover; of the love of a dragon princess disguised as a mortal; of a princess betrothed before birth to a giant in return for a piece of fruit her mother wanted;

of a princess guarded by an enchanted spear which fatally stabbed her prince when he climbed to her bower; of the wars of King Mahasot; and of Anuruddha, demi-god grandson of Krishna. Many stories dealt with the life of Buddha, the *Pathomma Somphothiyan* becoming standard by the eighteenth century. Thai literature perhaps found its best expression in its poetry, unrivalled for elegance of diction and musical sound, especially in its *nirats* and shorter love songs. Its *khon* dance-dramas used masked dancers and were usually based on incidents from the *Ramakien*; its *lakon* dance-dramas did not use masks and might be drawn from any source.

BELLES-LETTRES AROUND AND IN CHINA

Literature in Tibet, Mongolia, Manchuria, Vietnam, and Korea

In Tibet the flood of religious literature and folklore went on, particularly in the form of histories of the lamas. Probably the weightiest Tibetan literary achievement of this period, however, was not in Tibetan but in the translation of the *Kanjur* into Mongol (1604–34). From this source there sprang a number of widely accepted religious works in Mongol. Among the Mongolian people the legends of Gesser Khan and Siddhi-kūr (from the Sanskrit) and the Mongol heroic epic *Jangariad* also were favourites. In the seventeenth century Prince Sanang Setzen produced a *History of the Eastern Mongols*, and Saya Pandita devised (1648) an improved alphabet, the Kalmuck, which spread among the western Mongols. In 1748 Čosgi Odsir's rendition of the *Bodhicaryāvatāra* (see Chapter X) was re-edited.

In 1599 the Manchus also had adopted the Mongol script. Some documents, chronicles, and other materials appeared in Manchu, and Dahai began the translation of some Chinese works. Little, however, was done in the way of an independent Manchu literature.

Vietnamese writers continued to use both Chinese and *chũ-nõm* after 1500, but the best expressions of the Vietnamese literary genius were in the native script. Novels and dramas were especially popular. Written shortly after our period ended, the *Kim-vân-kiêu* of Nguyên-du was the best known and best liked Vietnamese *truyên* (narrative in verse); it was inspired by a Chinese novel. The *Cung oan ngam-khuc*, which was purely Vietnamese in origin, was also a favourite. Some missionaries contrived a romanized script, the *quôc-ngũ*, in the seventeenth century; in modified form it gradually supplanted *chũ-nõm* as the written medium and ultimately became the official national script.

In Korea a good literary standard was maintained during the sixteenth and seventeenth centuries, but with the eighteenth a decline in quality if not in quantity set in. Translations and popular renderings of Chinese works kept up, but native ideas also found expression in novelettes, short stories, and works on ceremonies. Conflicts of loyalty were a major theme and provided the plot in two popular novels, the *Chunhyang Jun (Spring Fragrance)*, in which the heroine remained loyal to her lover, and the *Simchung Jun*, in which the heroine remained loyal to her father. After Hideyoshi's invasions began (1592), war too became a common theme. The mid-seventeenth century was dominated by the writings of Song Sol (fl. *c.* 1650). In 1774 an elaborate set of works dealt with the ceremonies of marriage, death, ancestor worship, hospitality, and war.

Chinese Literature in the Traditional Style

In China after 1500 the largest number of writers remained faithful to the traditional literary style and idiom. Their products were perhaps superior to those of the earlier period. Despite the frowns of literati drama, the novel, and other popular forms of literature were more and more generally accepted.

In addition to a supplement of the canon (1607), a number of Taoist works were published during this period. Tung Han-shun, early in the sixteenth century, put out a collection of extracts from Taoist authors, ancient and modern (*Ch'ün-hsien yao-yü*), and in 1566 Yao Ju-hsün issued a popular treatise on Taoism in its modern form (*Chih yu tzu*). In 1640 Hsüeh Ta-hsün published the *Shen-hsien t'ung-chien*, an extensive, illustrated work, giving biographical sketches, largely legendary, of about 800 Taoist immortals, saints, and sages (some of whom were Buddhists). This Taoist *Acta Sanctorum* and its imitations helped to popularize Taoist lore and exerted considerable influence upon Chinese literature and art.

Most of the literary men of the period wrote essays along traditional lines in the involved, elliptical *ku-wên* form. Those of the literary critic Yao Nai (1732–1815) were among the most celebrated. The complicated parallel-sentence prose (see Chapter X) revived somewhat, but it did not seriously threaten the dominance of *ku-wên*. Most of the essays, whether in one form or the other, were more distinguished for elegance of style than for originality of thought. Yüan Mei (1716–98) was a noted practitioner of parallel-sentence prose. His collected works, first published in 1775, contained poetry, *fu*, essays, letters, literary criticism, short stories, and miscellaneous pieces, all fairly representative of contemporaneous literary efforts.

In the late Ming and Ch'ing periods notable anthologies of earlier tales, especially those of the T'ang, were compiled. Original short stories in the literary language also attained a new eminence in the *Strange Stories* (*Liao-chai chih-i*) of P'u Sung-ling (1640–1715). Though his preface was written in 1679, his 431 stories circulated in manuscript until printed in 1766. Their subjects were similar to those of the T'ang tales, but he achieved a new realism in his handling of the supernatural, which he depicted in a distinguished yet simple style. Whereas P'u's stories recited only weird adventures, those of Yüan Mei dealt also with everyday events.

During the centuries here under consideration literary critics were numerous. Yüan Mei and Yao Nai (as already mentioned) were prominent among those who adhered to conventional standards. Other outstanding critics were also of that persuasion. Wu Ching-hsü (early Ch'ing) produced the *Li-tai shih-hua*, a monumental critical review of poets, ancient and modern, and Wang Shih-han completed about 1768 a compendium of critical scholarship relating to the *Wen-hsüan*, an early general collection of prose and poetry. On the other hand, Li Chih,[17] a late-Ming freethinker (see Chapter V), and the eccentric Chin Sheng-t'an (*c.* 1610–61) were less conventional. Both praised more recent literary forms like novels and dramas and were critical of past standards, though they readily conceded enduring glory to some ancient writings and authors. Chin was particularly active. He published an annotated edition of the T'ang poet Tu Fu, of the novel *The Water Margin*, and of the drama *The Romance of the West Chamber* (see Chapter X), an anthology of T'ang poetry, a general anthology, various critical essays, and an original novel. In a fashion, the disagreement of these critics of China parallels the Quarrel of the Ancients and the Moderns in the West.

The poetry written in the literary language developed few new forms, and these centuries were famous rather for monumental collections of earlier verse. An enormous amount of new poetry of a fairly high technical quality was produced, to be sure, but most of it was imitative and uninspired and exploited traditional themes. No *fu* of special distinction was produced, but numerous *shih* writers attained eminence. One was Wang Shih-chen (1526–90), who was also counted among the leading literary critics. Of various *tz'u* writers only the Manchu Na-lan Hsing-te (1655–85) showed exceptional merit; his love poems, which developed new patterns, compared favourably with those of the *tz'u* masters of the Sung. Under the patronage of the Ch'ien-lung emperor (1736–95) several poets achieved a lasting fame but made no new contributions to poetic form.

Drum Song and Drama in China

In vernacular literature, the Chinese exhibited greater talent. Perhaps the best of the various drum songs was the epic *Love in Reincarnations* (*Tsai-sheng yüan*) of the poetess Ch'en Tuan-sheng of the late eighteenth century. It was probably inspired by her unhappiness over the exile of her husband. *Ch'ü* poetry reached new heights in the southern *k'un-ch'ü* dramas. The *k'un-ch'ü* tunes originated in K'un-shan, in the Soochow area of Kiangsu, a province whose economic and cultural prominence attracted many visitors. Soochow sing-song girls came to be widely employed throughout the country and helped spread the popularity of the *k'un-ch'ü* songs and dramas. The musician Wei Liang-fu, of the early sixteenth century, adapted native tunes to operatic scores and enlarged and improved the orchestras (see Chapter XII).

Under Wei's inspiration some dramatists produced polished, elegant texts for the plays, which rose in popularity throughout the sixteenth century. During the Wan-li reign (1573–1620) the *k'un-ch'ü* established its ascendency as the preferred dramatic form of the people, claiming 77 playwrights and over 150 new dramas. Many of these dramas were exceedingly long, running to fifty or sixty acts, and were often intended only to be read, although parts might be performed. They were sometimes more profound and possessed better characterization than earlier drama. The earliest *k'un-ch'ü* dramatist of lasting reputation was Li K'ai-hsien (1501-68). A portion of his *History of a Sword* has survived under the name *Lin Ch'ung Flees by Night*. It deals with a character from the *Shui hu chuan* (*Water Margin*), who, having been unjustly sentenced for murder, escapes. Another dramatist, Liang Ch'en-yü, contributed to the stage success of the *k'un-ch'ü* plays with several romantic plays, among which the *Wash-Girl of the Huan-sha Stream* found special favour. Some playwrights stressed the musical side of the dramas, as did, for example, Shen Ching. Three of his seventeen plays have survived, but his collection of the songs of the time was perhaps an even greater contribution since it served others as a guide. His followers emphasized music and acoustic values. A play by Wang T'ing-no, *The Tale of the Roaring Lioness* (*Shih hou chi*), was a light comedy about shrewish wives, written about the same time as Shakespeare's *The Taming of the Shrew*.

Unquestionably the greatest dramatist of the Wan-li period was T'ang Hsien-tsu (1550-1617), who strove for thoughtful dialogue and interesting plot. *The Romance of the Purple Flute* and *The Peony Pavilion* (*Mu-tan t'ing*) were perhaps his most famous plays. *The Peony Pavilion* was a melodrama of 55 acts, which presented the romance of a prefect's daughter and a young scholar by means of devices involving dreams, supernatural agencies, and resurrection. Some of its scenes had little connection with the main story, and each act had separate titles and could be produced independently. Especially in demand were the scenes entitled 'The Dream Betrothal', 'The Dream Comes True', and 'Spring Perfume Turns the Schoolroom Topsy-Turvy'.

With the fall of the Ming dynasty and the rise of the Ch'ing, scholars undertook to formalize the *k'un-ch'ü*. They encountered the opposition of the leading literary figure of the period, the poet, dramatist, essayist, and fictionist Li Yü (1611-80?). Li was the author of at least sixteen plays, *Feng-cheng wu* (*Tangle of the Kite*) being perhaps the best of them; he also revised several earlier plays; and his *Hsien-ch'ing ou-chi* (1671) was the first Chinese book on dramatic theory. In addition he wrote a number of short stories, and two novels are attributed to him—one of which, *The Flesh Cushion* (*Jou p'u-t'uan*), was later banned because of its eroticism. Li objected to the scholarly formalization of the *k'un-ch'ü*, insisting that the ideal was to express 'profound ideas in plain language, without the least smell of bookishness.'[18] Nevertheless, the language of the plays now became more literary, the style more florid, and the ideas and themes more acceptable to the literati.

The growing academicism of the *k'un-ch'ü* tended to divorce it from its popular roots, threatening it with extinction by competition from more widely accepted forms of drama. It was saved by imperial patronage, which began about 1670 with the K'ang-hsi emperor and continued throughout the eighteenth century under the Ch'ien-lung emperor. Imperial patronage attracted talented poets and writers and encouraged the production of a number of significant plays. The foremost ones were *The Palace of Everlasting Life (Chang-sheng t'ien)* of Hung Sheng (c. 1650–1705) of the north and *The Peach Blossom Fan (T'ao-hua shan)* of K'ung Shang-jen (1648–1708 ?) of the south. *The Palace of Everlasting Life* was based on the actual tragedy of the T'ang emperor Ming-huang and his beautiful concubine Yang Kuei-fei, which culminated in rebellion and the death of Yang. In the play, however, although separated in the twenty-fifth act, the lovers are reunited in the fiftieth. *The Peach Blossom Fan* was more authentic. It dealt with the tragic love of Hou Fang-yüeh, a famous author of the late Ming period, for Li Hsiang-chüng, a celebrated sing-song girl and poetess, and the author contrived no happy ending. Both plays were exceedingly long but were considered literary masterpieces because of their structure, literary quality, and skilful characterization. The principal dramatist of the Ch'ien-lung reign was Chiang Shih-chüan (1725–84), who wrote nine well-known plays, mostly built around historical events of a tragic nature, one being a dramatization of Po Chü-i's famous lyrical poem *The Walking Guitar (P'i-p'a hsing)*. Despite lavish imperial patronage, the *k'un ch'ü* (or 'elegant drama', as it was now called) began to yield to several colloquial forms, which eventually grew into the capital or mandarin drama of the nineteenth century.

Short Story and Novel in China

The popularity of colloquial short stories likewise increased during the late-Ming and Ch'ing periods. Numerous anthologies were issued, of which the *San-yen* collections, published between 1620 and 1628 by Feng Meng-lung (c. 1574–1645), were among the more eminent. Feng, a scholar and minor official of Soochow, was also industrious as an editor, compiler, author, and publisher of novels, anecdotes, and plays as well as of stories in the literary language. His contemporary Ling Meng-ch'u brought out two further collections of stories (1627 and 1632)—some being imitations of *San-yen* stories, others new productions. In the interval between 1633 and 1644 forty stories from these earlier collections appeared in the justly renowned *Strange Tales Ancient and Modern (Chin-ku ch'i-kuan)*, selections from which have become widely known in the West. The detective story also became increasingly popular, and many of them reached short-novel length.

Contemporaneously with a similar development in the West, the Chinese novel reached its full growth during late-Ming and Ch'ing times. Historical and picaresque novels lost none of their general esteem, but the novel of ordinary life also emerged and ultimately became the most noteworthy type. Hundreds of all kinds appeared. Perhaps the best of the numerous historical novels were the *Sui-T'ang yen-i*, dealing with the rise and fall of the Sui and T'ang dynasties, and the *Lieh-kuo chih*, dealing with the period of the Warring States. Five novels are often thought to excel the others of the period: *The Record of a Journey to the West (Hsi yu chi)* belonged to the picaresque group; *A Warning to the Generations Regarding the Destiny of Marriage* (*Hsing-chih yin-yüan chuan*) was of a mixed type; and *The Golden Lotus* (*Chin P'ing Mei*), *The Dream of the Red Chamber* (*Hung-lou meng*) and *The Unofficial History of Officialdom* (*Ju-lin wai-shih*) were realistic novels of everyday affairs.

Several novels were concerned with religion and the supernatural. Of these *The Record of a Journey to the West*, one of the five most esteemed novels just mentioned (written by Wu Ch'eng-en about 1550), had an exceptional vogue. Based on the journey of a Buddhist monk, Hsüan Tsang, to India during the seventh century, it presented allegorically the exploits of supernatural agents, with a strong undercurrent of satire on society and bureaucracy. In solving the superhuman problems confronting him, Hsüan Tsang was aided by an invincible stone monkey, the novel's real hero (hence the title *Monkey* for Arthur Waley's translation). The monkey ultimately brought the journey to a successful end in the Western Paradise. Another work with a supernatural motif was the *List of Canonized Saints* (*Feng-shen jen-i*) of Hsü Chung-lin (c. 1560), a novel despite its unenticing title. It was filled with Taoist mythology and dealt with the founding of the Chou dynasty. Still another was the *Hsi-yang chi* of Lou Meng-ting (c. 1597), which centred on the great voyage of Cheng Ho into the Indian Ocean during the early fifteenth century. In a fashion reminiscent of Dante's *Divina Commedia*, it described a journey through hell, which was discovered to be far to the west of Mecca; both accounts of hell may have drawn on common sources.[19]

A Warning to the Generations Regarding the Destiny of Marriage, another of the five generally preferred novels, was a lengthy work, probably of the early Ch'ing period, often attributed nowadays to the short-story writer P'u Sung-ling. Combining the supernatural with the natural, it consisted of two virtually separate stories: the hero and his concubine, who drove the wife to suicide in the first part, suffered under the abuse of the wife in their second, reincarnated state. The novel turned a glaring light upon lower-middle-class family life.

The Golden Lotus was the first significant novel to be largely divorced from the historical past, legend, the supernatural, and mythology. It was written in the sixteenth century under another title, for its original title (*Chin P'ing Mei*) consists of the names of three of its chief female characters and is untranslatable. An English rendition carried the title *Hsi Men and His Seven Wives*. The novel described the life of a wealthy businessman bent on sensual pleasure and the catastrophes that overtook him and his companions. The author was the first Chinese writer to portray female characters convincingly. Who he was is uncertain. A sequel to the story appeared in the seventeenth century, and various similar erotic novels followed.

The Unofficial History of Officialdom, another of the novels described above as realistic, was by Wu Ching-tzu (1701–54). It might be called 'The Book of Snobs', since it was a satirical attack on the examination system, the literati, and the corruption, inefficiency, and hypocrisy of officialdom by an independent-minded if profligate member of the class he attacked. It lacked plot and was essentially a series of tenuously connected episodes involving different characters. It inspired a series of realistic, satirical, and sometimes salacious works about particular social groups.

Probably the most distinguished of all Chinese novels was the lengthy *Dream of the Red Chamber*, begun by Ts'ao Chan (d. 1763) and completed by Kao O (*c.* 1795). It dealt with the declining fortunes of a once wealthy and powerful official family. The first part apparently was autobiographical, but the semi-happy ending supplied by Kao in the last forty chapters perhaps was not intended by Ts'ao. Despite digressions and sub-plots, it had a better plot than most Chinese novels. While it presented a picture of the life of almost every social group in China in a more realistic fashion than earlier novels, it was in particular an indictment of the great households dominated by women. The story centres upon the search of a sentimental, effeminate, and pampered youth of a scholarly family for affection; because his family prefers another as his wife, his favoured girl combines with her frustrated love a jealousy and self-pity that ultimately destroy her. The author's insight into the psychology of love makes the work unique in Chinese literature.

IMAGINATIVE LITERATURE IN JAPAN[20]

The New and the Traditional in Japanese Literature

Japan's letters of the Tokugawa period mirrored the interests, ideals, and conflicts of the country's two most articulate classes—the samurai and the *chōnin* (the rising middle-class townsmen). The literature reflecting samurai culture was traditionalist, often moralist, and generally without vigour or inspiration. Its chief forms were *nō* drama and poetry and various kinds of prose in the customary Sino-Japanese style. The literature reflecting the *chōnin* culture was new, vigorous, vulgar, erotic, witty, dynamic, often satirical, and critical of traditional ways and values. It was normally written in colloquial language and presented in new forms. This new literature aroused the ire and contempt of the government and hence incurred censorship, regulation, and suppression, but it grew in popularity not only among townsmen but also among samurai and even at the imperial court. It reached full flower during the Genroku period at the end of the seventeenth century. Its major centres were the principal cities of Osaka, Kyoto, and Edo.

The more time-honoured types of literature persisted under the patronage not only of the great courts of the shogun and the emperor but also of the lesser courts of powerful feudal lords (*daimyōs*). Poets at the imperial court and samurai writers continued to turn out *tankas*, while Shinto nationalists deliberately tried to revive and promote traditional Japanese poetic forms. Samurai writers kept on producing uninspired *rengas* (chain-poems) also, while Ieyasu, the founder of the Tokugawa shogunate, and his early successors as earnest patrons fostered the esoteric *nō*. The Confucian moralist Arai Hakuseki persuaded the shogun in 1711 to abandon the *nō* at court banquets in favour of certain kinds of ancient music, but as a traditional art it still won the favour of several *daimyōs* and conservative samurai.

Prose literature was of the most varied types, both new and traditional. Some excellent Japanese prose works of the seventeenth century were the *otogi sōshi*, or children's fables. While this is a type of folk literature familiar in all cultures, such stories as *The Rat's Wedding*, *The Hare's Revenge*, and *The Battle of the Ape and the Crab* have a uniquely Japanese quality. The few traditionalist *monogatari* of the early seventeenth century, such as the *Mokuzu* and the *Usuyuki*, were unimpressive, melodramatic tales of love, passion, intrigue, and revenge. The *Taikōki* (1625), a somewhat legendary biography of Hideyoshi, was of little literary merit. Undoubtedly, the best traditional prose of the period was that of the moral philosophers of the Chinese school. They introduced many new Chinese words, thus greatly enriching the Japanese language, and some of them contributed to the development of a prose that was to meet the needs of modern Japan. Kaibara Ekken's treatises on morals (see Chapter VII) and his books on travel were intentionally written in a simple, semi-colloquial style to appeal to the many.

As traditionalists of a reactionary bent, the Shinto nationalists sought to cultivate the most ancient Japanese forms and ways. In the field of literature Mabuchi and Motoori took a leading part in a deliberate effort to throw off Chinese influence and promote the study of early Japanese. They, too, made a contribution to the modern prose style—in their case, by trying to exclude Chinese words from their vocabularies in favour of the *wabun* (or pure Japanese) style. Furthermore, Motoori laid the foundations of Japanese grammar. One of his many writings, the *Tama Kushige* (*Precious Casket*), giving his views on how a feudal domain should be governed, was written in a simple, straightforward prose suitable to the popular needs of the eighteenth century. Although not a Shinto nationalist, Tokugawa Mitsukuni published in 1678 the *Fusōjiuyoshiu*, an anthology of traditional masterpieces in the pure Japanese style. Shinto nationalists had little in common either psychologically or socially with the rising culture of the middle class, but they were revolutionary in their own way, and they were distinctly modern in their nationalism.

Meanwhile a new urban literature was reaching maturity. It was the literature of the *ukiyo*, the 'floating world' of the theatres, restaurants, brothels, and other merry haunts of the growing towns. Its subjects were actors, dancers, courtesans, wrestlers, singers, and similar inhabitants of a universe of fleeting joys, whose usual patrons were the prosperous bourgeois, the dissolute samurai, and the 'naughty apprentice'.[21] Some of the authors in the new style were samurai, some were *chōnin*, but most were denizens of, or otherwise well acquainted with, the life of 'the nightless city', the amusement area of the towns. Three writers of this school stand out above the rest: the poet Matsuo Bashō (1644–94), the dramatist Chikamatsu Monzayemon (1653–1725), both of whom were samurai, and the novelist and short-story writer Ihara Saikaku (1642–93), who was of lower-class origin.

Poetry and Fiction in Japan

In the sixteenth and seventeenth centuries, in keeping with the new literary freedom, poetic forms became less rigid. The *haikai*, or 'free' chain-poem, tended to replace the older *renga*. Avoiding the formal rules of the *renga*, it loosely employed colloquial or Chinese words and popular, even vulgar, ideas. Its opening verse, which consisted of three lines of 5, 7, and 5 syllables respectively, also developed into an independent genre known as the *haiku*, which, since a *haikai* could not be very successful unless all those participating were of eminent ability, ultimately became the most widely used poetic form. Both forms were imagist poetry, requiring extraordinary skill (even though the *haiku* required less) if they were to come off well. The *haiku* in particular was to influence later Western writers. Saikaku was illustrious in his time as a writer not only of stories but also of *haikus*. A kind of narrative poem known as the *utazaimon*, an often bawdy ballad about contemporary events, was also generally approved during this period, and some of this kind, such as *Osen, the Cooper's Wife* (*Taruya Osen*), dealt with incidents found in some of Saikaku's stories.[22] Another current poetic form was the *kiōka* (mad poetry), a comic, merry, vulgar, and witty variety of the *tanka*. The *senryū*, a type of satirical poem made familiar by Karai Senryū (1718–90), likewise had wide appeal.

Bashō was the pre-eminent poet of the period. A samurai turned Buddhist monk, he travelled a great deal and often joined with local poets in writing *haikai*. His poetry became known throughout the land not only for its cleverness and originality but also for its refinement and purity, in contrast to much of the new poetry. He insisted that the important principles of prosody were change and permanence[23]—change, because style should always be new, fresh, and original; permanence, because the poet should attempt in his own way to solve the eternal problems. Bashō's travel diary, *The Narrow Road of Oku*, contained a number of his poems and sometimes described the circumstances surrounding their composition. His many disciples and imitators dominated the eighteenth century. Though Bashō himself had preferred nature as a subject, his imitators drew their material from 'the floating world'.

Though also a poet and dramatist, Saikaku is best remembered for his colloquial fiction. His novelettes, tales, and sketches marked a departure in Japanese prose, a new type of erotic fiction. While his accounts of contemporary manners and customs were reminiscent of the *monogatari* of the classical period, the social class he described was different; he was concerned in the main with the life, habits, and manners of the nightless city of Osaka.

Harlots, rakes, pederasts, tricky merchants, and even plain middle-class characters who dared to transgress custom or feudal law were prominent in his stories. Women reappeared as notable figures, although they were generally courtesans or daring townswomen rather than highborn ladies. Although some of his plots showed a pronounced inventiveness, he was especially noted for his polished, witty, and realistic pictures of contemporary life. His stories brought out the injustices and inanities of many contemporary practices and pleaded for greater liberty, equality, and humanity.

Saikaku began his career as a writer of fiction with *The Love Rogue* (*Kōshoku ichidai otako*) in 1682, and from that time until his death he turned out a steady stream of best sellers. He has sometimes been compared with Boccaccio; in one of his tales, *The Rise and Fall of Gallantry* (1688), as in one of the *Decameron* stories, an amorous young woman employs an unsuspecting monk to entice a young gallant to her boudoir. His *Five Women Who Loved Love* (1686) dealt with middle-class and lower-class women who risk all for love; four of them lose their lives, not so much because they must pay for their immorality as because they overstep class lines or violate established custom. Saikaku's portrayal of ordinary townswomen as heroines gave rise later, in the middle of the eighteenth century, to a genre employing this device, known as the *yomihon*. His *Tales from the Provinces* (1685) reflected the regionalism of Japan. The *Treasury of Japan* (1688) told how to make and lose a fortune. *A Mirror of the Beauties* (1684) was his only story of suicide for love, of which he disapproved.

Despite the eroticism of Saikaku's works their basic purpose was not pornographic. In fact, his *Tale of Virtuous Conduct* and *Twenty-Four Examples of Unfilial Behaviour* engaged in a moralizing sort of edification. But the same cannot be said of some of his contemporaries. The works of his Edo contemporary Tōrindō Chōmaro and of the Kyoto-Osaka bookseller Jishō (d. 1745) and the latter's collaborator Kiseki (d. 1736) depicted 'the floating world' of Kyoto and Osaka. Though embellished with a good deal of humour, they were largely pornographic. Publishers of this type of literature, known as *sharébon* (or witty books), appeared in the main cities and, despite efforts of the authorities to censor them in 1723 and later, carried on until rather thoroughly suppressed in 1791.

Of course, fiction of a more sedate variety was also produced. The seventeenth-century stories about a hero named Yuriwaka, who, after winning great victories abroad, was abandoned by his evil companions on an isolated island, may possibly reflect Japanese acquaintance with the Ulysses story. A type of historical novel that developed in the eighteenth century dealt with wars and vendettas, some of which revolved around relatively recent personages. One such novel centring on Hideyoshi was a best seller, and the *Ōoka seidan*, recounting the cases of a celebrated judge of the early eighteenth century, was even more so. The *Wasōbē* (1774) was a sort of *Gulliver's Travels* filled with fantastic and impossible adventures.

The Japanese Theatre

Drama was the field of highest literary achievement of the early Tokugawa period. Popular dramatic performances were of two types—the *jōruri* and the *kabuki*. Both types appeared at the beginning of the seventeenth century and reached full maturity by the beginning of the eighteenth. They seem to have grown out of the *nō* with its humorous interludes (*kyōgen*), temple dances and performances, and the chanted or recited metrical romances of the *kōwakamai* variety. The plays that came to be known as *jōruri* (after a legendary princess in one of the favourite pieces) used puppets to enact a story told by a chanter to musical accompaniment. The music was provided by the *samisen* (a three-stringed guitar), after it was introduced (beginning of the eighteenth century) from the Ryukyu Islands. The *jōruri* theatre evolved in Osaka, Kyoto, and Edo. With improvements in the manufacture and manipulation of the puppets, it reached its fullest development at Osaka in the early eighteenth century under Chikamatsu Monzayemon, who also dominated the *kabuki* theatre.

The *kabuki* theatre is believed to have begun in the Kyoto-Osaka area in 1603 with the performances of Okuni, a shrine dancer, who had deserted her temple in Idzumo. It seems certain that the earliest *kabuki* were mostly lascivious, humorous dances and farces put on by prostitutes and their hangers-on to attract customers; in the early stagings women generally played male parts and men often played female parts. From the first, the *Bakufu* (the shogunate) disapproved of these exhibitions and tried, without success, to keep the samurai away from them.[24] It banned women's *kabuki* in 1628, but the ban did not become effective until the 1640's, when the government began to imprison offending theatre managers. Before that date, *kabuki* troupes of boys and young men had appeared, but they, too, soon displeased the authorities, for they seemed to promote homosexuality, especially among the samurai. First female impersonation alone and then (1652) youths' *kabuki* altogether were banned, but afterward male *kabuki* was permitted on condition that female impersonators shaved their forelocks and dressed their hair like men instead of like women.

Both the *jōruri* and the *kabuki* plays rapidly developed into organic dramas of from three to five acts. From Chikamatsu's time on most of them either were historical or dealt with social life and manners. They were full of shocking action, excitement, and melodrama. Edo was noted for actors who specialized in heroics, or 'rough business', and Osaka for actors who depicted the romantic emotions, or 'moist business'.

Most *kabuki* dramas of the seventeenth century were the joint product of the troupe and not the outcome of a single author's effort, but during the eighteenth century several individual authors stood out. None was more imposing than Chikamatsu, even though almost all of his more than fifty plays were written not for *kabuki* but for the puppet (*jōruri*) theatre of Osaka. He defined art as the slender margin between the real and the unreal and considered the puppet theatre best adapted to portray that marginal realm.

Nevertheless, most of his plays were also adapted to the *kabuki*. Like Shakespeare, Chikamatsu wrote both comedies and tragedies, combined poetry with prose, and mixed elegant diction with extreme colloquialism. His characters, however, were not comparable to the English dramatist's.

Most of Chikamatsu's plays were built around some social conflict that resulted in an emotional crisis, and most of them had a highly moralistic tone. The most successful of them was *The Battles of Koxinga* (*Kokusenya kassen*), written in 1715. Its hero was the memorable Chinese pirate and Ming loyalist, Cheng Ch'eng-kung (1624–62), whose mother was Japanese. Two hundred and forty thousand spectators are estimated to have seen it in seventeen months at Osaka. Chikamatsu's *Sagami Lay Monk and the Thousand Dogs* (1714), while ostensibly portraying the last of the Hōjō regents (1303–33), was a political satire on the shogun Tsunayoshi (1681–1709), who, under the influence of Buddhist teachings, had forbidden injury to dogs. Chikamatsu's historical plays were peopled with military and abounded in intrigue, combat, torture, murder, and suicide. His plays of domestic life were about merchants, clerks, prostitutes, and middle-class women who became involved in heroics of the bedchamber, embezzlements, elopements, and suicide for love. He borrowed the themes of several of them from Saikaku's *Five Women*. Perhaps the most familiar one, *The Love-Suicide of Amijima*, told the tragedy of lovers frustrated by the social and class restrictions of their time. While Chikamatsu's plays were not without erotic elements, many other *jōruri* and *kabuki* dramas were more openly lascivious.

Takeda Izumo (d. 1756) was perhaps the most esteemed *kabuki* dramatist of the Edo theatre in the eighteenth century. His best-known play (written with two collaborators and published in 1748) was the *Chūshingura* (*Magazine of Faithful Retainers*). It was based upon an actual vendetta that ended in the suicide of forty-seven *rōnin* ('masterless samurai') involved in a conflict between loyalty to their lord and obedience to the laws of the Bakufu. The story had previously been dealt with by Chikamatsu and was a favourite theme of dramatists and others.

After Takeda's time, Chikamatsu Hanji (c. 1725–83) came to dominate the Japanese stage. His plays emphasized ethical problems, contained little poetry, and made a greater use of dialogue. From his time on, the *jōruri* theatre steadily declined, but the *kabuki* theatre continued to thrive.

NOTES TO CHAPTER XI

1. It must be emphasized, however, that translations of the Bible had very little influence in Italy, France, and Spain. In these countries, the expressive and literary qualities of the national language, the nobility of which was held comparable to that of classical languages, were recognized. An excellent example of this attitude is given by Du Bellay's *Défense et illustration de la langue française* (1549). Literature in the vernacular developed contemporaneously with the existence at court, among the aristocracy and in certain strata of the bourgeoisie, of a reading public for such works. (Raymond Picard.)

2. See G. Bonfante, 'Ideas on the Kinship of European Languages from 1200 to 1800', *Journal of World History*, I (1954), 679–99.

3. For example, a new tragedy by Racine, a small in-16° booklet of 70 pages, cost between 30 sols and 3 livres, or approximately the equivalent of three to six dollars. Volumes of larger format or containing a greater number of pages often cost as much as the equivalent of about 50 dollars. (Raymond Picard.)

4. Professor Raymond Picard notes that the system of 'Privilege', a perfectly normal procedure, implied no particular risk for the publishers and did not necessarily lead to prohibitions. Furthermore if on the one hand it did make preventive censorship possible, since the manuscript to be printed was submitted to the royal censor, on the other hand it guaranteed to the author or his publisher ownership of the work for a certain fixed length of time, within the boundaries of the kingdom. Political and police control was thus accompanied by a form of economic and intellectual protection.

5. *Encyclopédie* (new ed., F. Picavet, Paris, 1894), I, 143.

6. Ping-ti Ho, *The Ladder of Success in Imperial China, Aspects of Social Mobility*, 1368–1911 (New York, 1962), p. 214.

7. Professor Le Gentil notes that Gil Vicenti (c. 1465–1537) should be mentioned in connection with the theatre in the Iberian peninsula. Vicenti has sometimes been called 'the Portuguese Shakespeare'.

8. Professor Raymond Picard points out that the value and use of the unities was not really at issue in this Quarrel. Perrault, champion of the Moderns, never advocated a spontaneous literature freed from all regulations, asserting only that the tragedies of Corneille, for example, were superior, or at any rate equal, to those of Sophocles or Euripides. The elaboration of the system of the unities (1580–1630) dates from well before the beginning of the Quarrel.

    Having considered this opinion, the authors made the following comment: 'The text perhaps overemphasizes the problem of rules and form in "the Quarrel of the Ancients and the Moderns", but the text, when speaking of 'the Quarrel', subsumes it under 'the Western literary world of these times', meaning the years 1500–1775 and not 'the Quarrel' alone. The writers mentioned above lived from the sixteenth to the eighteenth century inclusive and, as the text shows, frequently were interested in forms and rules as well as the relative merits of Classic and modern authors. See Perrault's Parallèles des Anciens et des Modernes (4th Dialogue, part iii), where he argues that "all the arts have been raised in our time to a higher degree of perfection than where they were among the Ancients because time has revealed several secrets in all the arts which, joined to those which the Ancients left us, have rendered them more accomplished, art being nothing other, according to Aristotle himself, than an accumulation of rules (préceptes) for doing well the work which is its objective." Perrault obviously means that the Moderns not only had more but also better rules than the Ancients.'

9. For Professor Raymond Picard the patriotism discernible in the work of Grimmelshausen bears no relation to that of Corneille's heroes. There is no element of French national feeling in the declamations of Horace or Sertorius. Their attitude, like the rhetoric in which it is expressed, derives from the classical texts themselves.

    The authors do not agree with Professor Picard's reading of Corneille. They write: 'Corneille does make Sertorius say: Rome n'est plus dans Rome, elle est toute où je suis. We find it difficult to believe that, writing his best plays under the patronage of Richelieu and during the French participation in the Thirty Years' War, Corneille did not mean his lofty declamations to rouse his hearers' patriotic sentiments as Frenchmen (or that he would have succeeded if he had intended not to do so).'

10. Dámaso Alonso, 'The Spanish Contribution', *loc. cit.*, pp. 888–89.

11. The development of the romanesque novel is one of the great events of the literary history of the eighteenth century. The French tradition of the psychological novel, which derives its scheme from tragedy, produced works remarkable for their unity and truth from *La vie de Marianne* by Marivaux (1731–42) to *Les Liaisons Dangereuses* by Laclos (1782). In his novels written in the form of dialogue, *Le Neveu de Rameau* and *Jacques le Fataliste* (c. 1755–70) Diderot embarked on a bold experiment foreshadowing the modern novel. (Raymond Picard.)

12. Among Turkish poets should also be mentioned Nef'î (d. 1634), one of the great classics, famous for his satirical verve. Mention should also be made of the *Divan* of Nedim (d. 1730), which gives expression to the refined taste of the 'Tulip' period: the stirring songs of Nedim are sung to this day. (Raymond Picard.)

13. J. C. Ghosh, 'Vernacular Literature', in Garratt (ed.), *op. cit.*, p. 380.

14. See C. Lahiri, 'Sanskrit *Kāvya* Literature' in *The Cultural Heritage of India* (Calcutta, 1937), III, 650.

15. See F. E. Keay, *A History of Hindi Literature* (London, 1933), p. 67.

16. See *ibid.*, p. 72.

17. See K. C. Hsiao, 'Li Chih: an Iconoclast of the Sixteenth Century', *T'ien-hsai Monthly*, VI (1938), 317–41.

18. Yao Hsin-nung, 'The Rise and Fall of the K'un Ch'ü', *ibid.*, II (1936), 77.

19. See J. J. L. Duyvendak, 'A Chinese "Divina Commedia"', *T'oung-pao*, XLI (1952), 255–317.

20. This discussion has employed quite freely several papers prepared for the International Commission for a History of the Scientific and Cultural Development of Mankind: Ishida Ichiro, 'The Urban Culture in the Japanese Feudal Age', Richard Lane, 'Saikaku and Boccaccio: the Novella in Japan and Italy', and Donald H. Shively, 'Theater and Government in Tokugawa Japan'.

21. G. B. Sansom, *Japan, a Short Cultural History* (New York, 1943), p. 474.

22. See Richard Lane, 'Saikaku's "Five Women"' in W. T. de Bary's translation of Ihara Saikaku's *Five Women Who Loved Love* (Tokyo, 1956), pp. 236, 244, and 251.

23. See Donald Keene, *Japanese Literature* (London, 1953), p. 38.

24. See Donald H. Shively, 'Bakufu Versus Kabuki', *Harvard Journal of Asiatic Studies*, XVIII (1955), 326–56.

CHAPTER XII

THE VISUAL ARTS AND MUSIC
(1300–1775)

THE FINE ARTS IN EUROPE

ACHIEVEMENT in the visual arts has rarely, if ever, attained a higher level than that of this period in the Western world, which includes the late Gothic, the Renaissance, the Baroque, the Rococo, and the early Neoclassical eras. Many important centres produced works of extraordinary merit, but the major changes in style originated in Italy and, with the late seventeenth century, in France. Innovations leading to Europe's Renaissance and later styles came first in painting early in the Middle Ages (before 1300), and for that reason painting will be given first place in the account below of European developments in the visual arts. It will be followed by a section on sculpture, the art most closely related to painting in Europe of that day, and then by sections on architecture and the decorative arts. A section concerning the changing theories of art and the role of the artist, which were derived in great part from the innovations of practising artists, will conclude our discussion of the visual arts in Europe before we take up music in Europe and the arts in Islam, the Hindu and Buddhist areas, in China, Japan, and neighbouring countries, and in Africa and the Americas.

Painting in the Later Middle Ages

The ancient Hellenistic understanding of plastic form and spatial illusion survived in Byzantine art, but it had become attenuated in the course of time, particularly during the iconoclastic period of the eighth and ninth centuries (see Volume III). After the eleventh century the Byzantine tradition of icon-painting persisted in the churches of Russia—so much so that the word *icon*, when it denotes a representation of a religious subject on panels, has largely lost its original Greek identity and has become closely associated with Russian art. By the end of the fourteenth century the iconostasis, a screen or wall covered with icons and separating the sanctuary from the main part of the church, had become characteristic of the Russian church. The Russian icon-painter for the most part developed a colourful, crowded, two-dimensional, linear style, but artists like Theophanes the Greek (late fourteenth, early fifteenth century) and Andrei Rublev (*c.* 1370–*c.* 1430), probably his disciple, both of whom also painted frescoes on church walls in Novgorod, Vladimir, and Moscow, succeeded in eliminating hieratic non-essentials and in at least suggesting three-dimensional forms. Russian icon-painting sought chiefly, however, to depict a mystical world beyond sense experience and was only incidently concerned with the realities of space and movement. Until late in the seventeenth century when Western standards began to affect Russian art conspicuously, the Russian artist knew little about the ancient Hellenistic tradition. (Pl. 1, a, b.)

Meanwhile, during the centuries here under consideration Western European painting developed a distinctive system of monocular perspective that approximated the homogeneity of the visual world. It was based upon the study of optics and was probably stimulated by literary accounts of spatial illusion in the paintings of Antiquity.

In the early Middle Ages, in contrast to the essentially linear and two-dimensional art of northern Europe, Italian artists had retained the more plastic forms of the Byzantine tradition. There they found reminiscences of Hellenistic modelling, foreshortening, and spatial depth that had been all but lost in the north of Europe. This inclination to seek remnants of the Hellenistic tradition in Byzantine art (and later in the Ancient sources themselves) may have had its origin in a growing desire for concreteness or actuality in representing the events of sacred history. Certainly the somewhat austere symbols and conventional arrangements of the thirteenth century were inadequate to express the Franciscan's desire for a vivid, readily understandable re-enactment of Biblical events. A current belief, based on William of Ockham's philosophy (see Chapter VI)—that reality could best be defined by the particular and individual qualities of things—may have been another stimulus toward more exact detail. Northern European artists, to be sure, often revealed a parallel interest in careful delineation of details, but their more concrete moments were overshadowed by decorative passages of diapered patterns, gold grounds, and ornamental calligraphy. The artists of Tuscany, on the other hand, dedicated themselves to the attainment not only of the actuality of isolated objects but also of spatial unity and homogeneity.

Early in the fourteenth century, Giotto gave clear expression to these aims in the Arena Chapel of Padua and in the Bardi and Peruzzi chapels in Santa Croce of Florence. He gave his forms a convincing life in the round by the use of modelling and by increasing the variety of angles from which to view them. To allow adequate space for his columnar figures, he deepened the platform and rocky ledge used by Byzantine artists and elaborated the small-scale structures that indicated the locale of the sacred event portrayed. His acute depiction of gestures and facial expressions made emotional relationships clear, and aided by the established physical types and by the symbols gradually built up in the Christian world, he encouraged the spectator to participate in the emotions he portrayed. (Pl. 2a.)

Giotto's art pointed the direction that painters of the Renaissance ultimately were to follow, but the artists of the fourteenth century for a time demurred. They tended to develop the genre aspects of Giotto's art rather than his interest in the illusion of solidly modelled figures and clearly defined intervals.

Nevertheless, Duccio da Buoninsegna of Siena, his contemporary, shared some of his spatial and psychological interests, and in the middle of the fourteenth century the Sienese artists Ambrosio and Pietro Lorenzetti painted interiors of remarkable spaciousness (notably Pietro's 'Birth of the Virgin') as well as panoramic views of the city and its countryside (i.e. the 'Allegories of Good and Bad Government'). Furthermore, the dim interiors and extensive landscapes of the anonymous painter known as the Master of the Heures du Maréchal de Boucicaut in the late fourteenth century and the miniatures of the Limbourg brothers in the early fifteenth reveal that the development of pictorial space was occurring also in the French miniature tradition.

In most of the rest of Europe this interest in pictorial space was supplanted by an emphasis on decorative rhythms. The calligraphic art of Simone Martini, developed from the curvilinear grace of Duccio and the French miniaturists, spread over the Continent during the latter half of the fourteenth century, and it continued in many centres until the middle of the fifteenth century. (Pl. 2b.) This vogue was the last flowering of Gothic art, called 'the International Style'. It was characterized by courtly elegance of figures, preciousness of detail, and rhythmic vitality in the cursive line. From the relative homogeneity of this style, distinctive schools of painting emerged in Flanders, Germany, Poland, Bohemia, Hungary, Venice, and elsewhere.[1]

Florentine and Flemish Painting in the Fifteenth Century

Meanwhile, in the early fifteenth century Florentine painting had become distinguished by a new system of spatial construction, now called 'artificial perspective', demonstrated by Filippo Brunelleschi in 1419 and systematized by Leon Battista Alberti in 1435. It made possible the illusion of a continuous space of measurable depth in which all objects were scaled according to their distance from a point symbolizing the spectator's eye and shaped according to their position above, below, or on the level with that point and to the right or left of it. It was a highly intellectual system and not readily understandable to contemporaries. It demanded a new training of the eye to retain the perceptual image, to enable the spectator to interpret the spatial significance of the varying shapes, and to grasp the spatial relations of things in a complex painted scene. It created a new association of viewer to painting—one that aided the immediacy and vividness of the viewer's participation in the event depicted.

Gothic painters had arranged pictorial symbols according to conventions that had little to do with their way of seeing, but now painters faced the varied problems of designing in depth. Their concern for a convincing illusion of space also led to a preference for a rectangular format composed of the vertical and horizontal co-ordinates on which perspective is constructed. Such a self-contained visual world, gathered around its own centre, was more naturally enclosed within the architectural framework of a wall or large 'easel' painting than on manuscripts or chests or within the decorative frames and small panels of retables.

The paintings of Brunelleschi's young contemporary Masaccio in Florence, in contrast to the decorative poetry of the International Style, were severe essays in modelling and spatial construction. Masaccio rejected bright colours, stamping, gilding, undulating lines, and precious details in order to model clearly shaped figures that occupy space and possess weight. He painted the human body not simply as a sum of parts but as a volumetric unit, firmly held together by broad passages of light and shade and, in so doing, strongly intensified Giotto's use of light and re-affirmed his predecessor's emphasis on the block-like totality of figures existing in the round. The fresco the 'Trinity', painted by Masaccio in Santa Maria Novella in 1425, was a major step in the realization of the spatial unity of artificial perspective. (Pl. 3a.)

Painters who followed Masaccio employed this 'scientific' system for creating the illusion of pictorial space without diminishing the individuality of their art. Witness Fra Angelico's delicately but firmly modelled volumes, clear colours, and exquisite detail, Paolo Uccello's foreshortened silhouettes and decorative colour areas, Piero della Francesca's breadth and dignity, and Andrea Mantegna's minutely defined surfaces and sculpturesque shapes. (Pl. 4a, b.) For less creative artists of the period Brunelleschi's artificial perspective provided a secure basis within which their decorative talents might thrive. French illuminators of the fifteenth century, like Jean Fouquet, sometimes expressed sympathy with the new spatial order by reserving for each miniature a whole page free from lettering. (Pl. 5a). These departures from the purely ornamental role of illumination signal the surrender of the Gothic tradition to the new Tuscan ideals.

In the second half of the fifteenth century, the knowledge of the structure and appearance of natural forms was markedly refined. Followers of Masaccio tended to avoid his strong contrasts of light and dark, which disturbed the clarity of colour areas, but they sought to achieve the appearance of roundness that he gave to his figures. An ingenious pictorial solution was suggested by the 'modelling line' introduced around the middle of the century by Donatello in sculptural reliefs. Andrea del Castagno, Antonio Pollaiuolo, and Andrea Verrocchio developed this contour line to give the impression of three dimensions, while Domenico Veneziano, Paolo Uccello, and Sandro Botticelli explored its decorative possibilities. Unlike strong light, line as a dominant modelling agent did not disturb the colour area and was readily adjusted to the ambiguity of its actual life on the surface and its illusory life in depth. Furthermore, the Renaissance predilection for the human body, particularly the nude, as the major subject of painting gained from a growing knowledge of it. Pollaiuolo, Verrocchio, and Leonardo da Vinci studied not only the anatomical structure and mechanism of the body but also the way in which its parts were reshaped by movement and bodily tension. Their figures in motion provided another affirmation of the depth and continuity of pictorial space.

Movement was also intimately related to the Renaissance interest in depicting the 'mind of man'; Leonardo's well-defined descriptions of the histrionic attitudes associated with basic emotional states lived on in the academies of Europe into the eighteenth century. Other observations made during the fifteenth century contributed to a still more convincing representation of space. Some of them centred on 'aerial perspective', or the effect of atmospheric haze on the clarity of outline and the vividness of colour in distant objects. The intimate link between discoveries in optics and innovations in pictorial form became a central feature of Western art and the basis for an unparalleled rapidity of change in the formal aspects of painting.

During this period, the Italian artist also attained but temporarily put aside a space construction that the Baroque artist was enthusiastically to develop later. Andrea Mantegna, in his mid-fifteenth century frescoes of the life of Saint James in Padua's Eremitani Chapel, used eccentric angles and a perspective point that fell beneath the lower edge of the scene. (Pl. 3b.) In his frescoed ceiling in the Ducal Palace in Mantua, he delineated a circular opening with a sharply foreshortened parapet over which leaning figures looked down, with a blue sky above them. Correggio in the early sixteenth century was to realize fully the illusional possibilities of this use of perspective in his frescoes on the domes of the Cathedral and of San Giovanni Evangelista in Parma, but it was avoided by most Renaissance artists in central Italy, who were inclined to respect the surface on which they worked as the beginning plane of a world like that of the spectator but not as one continuous with it.

Shortly before Brunelleschi and Masaccio demonstrated artificial perspective to fellow Tuscans, Hubert and Jan van Eyck in Flanders developed a pictorial form characterized by great spatial depth and most exacting natural detail. This art form was derived from the French illuminations, particularly those of the Limbourg brothers, in which, as already mentioned, some of the illusional possibilities of the Tuscan tradition had been developed. The Van Eycks' Ghent altar-piece, finished in 1432, shows an encyclopedic interest and a marvellous attention to infinitesimal details—in floor tiles, individual leaves on distant trees, and precious stones on the crown of the Father. (Pl. 5b.)

One marvels not only at the Van Eycks' infinite observations and patience but also at their skill in ordering this multiplicity. They were enabled to achieve this effect by means of a new oil technique. 'Tempera' was the technique then used in most areas of Europe including Italy; it was earth or mineral pigment moistened with water and mixed with an oily, fatty, or resinous substance to make an emulsion. The Tuscans commonly made use of egg yolk to bind the ingredients. The resulting surface had a somewhat chalky and opaque appearance, which was counteracted usually by a coat of warm-coloured varnish. Some artists of northern Europe, omitting the egg yolk, had been experimenting with boiled or sun-thickened oils. The Van Eycks adopted this oil technique. It produced sticky substances that facilitated the minute touches, heightened the suggestions of texture, and made transparent films of colour ('glazes'), which gave unity to a multitude of small parts. In contrast to the rationally and quantitatively constructed space of Tuscan art, that of the Van Eycks was a qualitative one, depending on the delicate nuances of colour, fused and flowing within the broad tones of the glazes.

This subtle artistry had little immediate following. It was overshadowed by the more vigorous and dramatic style of the painter known as the Master of Flemalle (probably Robert Campin) and of Rogier van der Weyden, which appears to stem from a monumental art like that of the sculptor Claus Sluter (see below) rather than from the illuminated manuscript tradition. The accentuated individualities and intense expressions of sorrow and pain of the Master of Flemalle's figures were continued in the work of Rogier van der Weyden, but Rogier's art is distinguished by a strong, rhythmic line that organized his panels in large-scale, diagrammatic patterns. In his large 'Deposition' in the Prado (1438), the long curving contour lines of the limp body of Jesus and the lines that describe the garments and sorrowful contortions of the Magdalene reveal his full mastery of the style. Various aspects of his art continued in the Low Countries (in Hans Memling, for example), in other areas where the Gothic style had left a special preference for line (such as Germany, Spain, and France), and even in north Italian artists like Cosimo Tura. Jerome Bosch's imaginative fantasies and, in the mid-sixteenth century, Pieter Bruegel the Elder's landscape and genre scenes were based on northern traditions, but the art of others, such as Quentin Matsys and Jan Mabuse (Gossart), reveals that the pictorial concepts of central Italy were by their time being accepted in the Low Countries.[2]

German Painting, Woodcut, and Engraving

The German School, which in a short life produced works of great emotional intensity and realism of detail, was based in the fifteenth century on contemporary Flemish art and was later influenced by fifteenth-century Italian art. In spite of its affinity with the earlier Flemish and Tuscan schools, German painting boasted several varied art forms. Conrad Witz's Geneva altar-piece exhibits amazing clarity in the depth of its space and in its full volumes. (Pl. 6a.) Martin Schongauer's style is represented by his delicately executed 'Virgin of the Rose Arbor'. Mathias Grünewald ranges in his Isenheim altar-piece from a realistic portrayal of a writhing, brutally beaten Jesus on the cross to a visionary image of the resurrected Christ suffused with white light within an aureole of rainbow colours. Albrecht Altdorfer placed Biblical events in verdant and moody landscapes. Albrecht Dürer's draftsmanship imparted powerful volumes and emotional intensity to his figures. (Pl. 6b.) Hans Holbein the younger executed exactly observed and precisely delineated portraits; he obtained an international reputation, carrying out commissions throughout Europe and leaving a strong impression on the art of sixteenth century England. With the painting of Holbein and Lucas Cranach (Pl. 7a.), this imposing display of German talent ended, never to regain a comparable place in European painting. (Pl. 7b.)

Schongauer, Dürer, Holbein, and other leading German (as well as Italian) painters did some of their most significant work in woodcuts and after 1460 engraving on copperplate. The origin of these techniques is conjectural, but by the early fifteenth century woodcuts were already used for printing sacred images and playing cards and, by the middle of the century, for illustrating popular legends such as the 'Dance of Death'—for which Holbein later did a famous set—and printed books. Print-making spread rapidly, and many capable though frequently anonymous artisans were at work, particularly in Germany, where the special feeling for line and texture was readily expressed by this new pictorial process.3 Variations (such as dry point and, by the sixteenth century, etching) on the earlier intaglio process of engraving revealed considerable technical inventiveness and produced an increasing variety of effects. These media were widely used to copy paintings, and by way of prints many motives, figures types, and compositions were rapidly diffused. With Schongauer, engraving and, with Dürer, woodcut attained the stature of independent art forms. In several of Dürer's woodcut series— e.g. the 'Passion of Christ' and the 'Life of Mary'—and in his individual engravings—e.g. 'The Knight, Death and the Devil' and 'Saint Jerome in His Study'—both media reached a technical and esthetic level never attained again. While admired all over Europe, Dürer's prints were especially praised in Florence during the early sixteenth century, particularly by artists like Andrea del Sarto and Jacopo da Pontormo, who were prominent in the formation of the so-called Mannerist style (see below). Thus German woodcut and engraving, along with German portraiture, had greater international repercussions than other spheres of German art. Perhaps the most important result of the invention of print-making was the acceleration of the interchange of artistic ideas among the leading centres of Europe.

The Venetian Form and Technique

Venetian painters meanwhile had been spurred by their contact with Tuscan art to create a pictorial form that was to be studied through the centuries by artists from all parts of Europe. The sejourn of Jacopo Bellini and his sons in Padua in the mid-fifteenth century, bringing them in contact with the sculpturesque art of Mantegna, led to their fusion of the sumptuous colour of Venice with the clear spatial order of Tuscan painting adopted by the Paduan school. To the Venetians, colour was not simply, as it was in Florentine art, an addition to the basic structure of the drawing; it was the principle element in the shaping of parts and in the achievement of pictorial unity. The new kind of painting was most impressively demonstrated by Giorgione, a creative follower of the Bellini, in his 'Tempest' and 'Fête Champêtre'. (Pl. 8.) Idyllic landscapes (as settings for arcadian adventures) and reclining nudes became popular subjects in Venice and eventually in all of Europe; Titian, while developing still further the bucolic and sensuous aspects of Giorgione's art, emphasized dramatic action rather than poetic reverie. The vigorous, spiralling movement of his Virgin of the 'Assumption' in the Frari Church in Venice (1516) brought a new vitality of movement into the art of Venice. (Pl. 9a.) Giorgione's half-length portraits of moody and self-conscious youths, which recall the intimate aspects of Flemish portraits, were transformed in the hands of Titian into the dignified three-quarter or full-length portraits that became the 'official portrait' type of Europe for the next one hundred and fifty years. Titian's equestrian portrait of Charles V (Pl. 9b.) was also to serve as a model for Baroque painters such as Rubens, Van Dyck, and Velasquez (see below Pl. 17, 18, 20a). Although the Bellini and Giorgione had learned to paint with the more successful oil techniques of Flanders and Germany, Titian was among the first to use oils not simply as a variation on tempera but with a feeling for the substance of the pigment. His rich variety of heavy impasto strokes, the web-like intermingling of the trails of his brush, and the transparency of his glazes, in which subtle details could be laid one upon another, developed oil painting beyond anything attained by the Flemish. The Venetians, using raw oil rather than the sticky sun-thickened or boiled oil of the Flemish, achieved a broader, more fluid kind of brushwork, which became a vehicle as characteristic as handwriting for the expression of the artist's personality.

Painting in the Sixteenth Century

Rome in the early sixteenth century became the art metropolis of central Italy, attracting artists from various local schools. The resulting style, dominated by Tuscan traditions, has been called 'High Renaissance' to indicate its maturity and fullness of realization. In a sense it resolved the many conflicting ideals that earlier generations of the Renaissance had created, attaining an admirable balance of surface and deep-space design, integrating the modelling roles of light and line, and subduing the decorative colour areas in favour of more sculptural aims. Completely in command of the devices that create the illusion of space and volume and lend anatomical vitality to the figures, Leonardo da Vinci, Michelangelo, and Raphael enriched scientific spatial construction with a new rhythmic articulation of space. No longer treating figures and objects as isolated guardians or markers of space, they began to harmonize movements, silhouettes, and volumes so that individual figures fused into groups of three or five or more. These groups, in turn, were so disposed that they formed a flow of masses guiding the viewer's eye along a rhythmic path through the depth of the painting. At the same time the subordination of decoration or descriptive details to the large, simple shapes of the figural and architectural parts brought a new monumentality to the art of Italy. (Pl. 10a, b.) As a result the total configuration of huge paintings composed of many figures (like Raphael's in the Stanza della Signatura) can be seen with an immediacy unequalled in the earlier Renaissance. Leonardo, Michelangelo (particularly in the Sistine Ceiling), and Raphael created, besides, ideal physical types, a 'new race of men', handsome beyond any creation of Nature. While in some ways the fruition of the fifteenth-century artists' study of optics and the natural world, the painting of the High Renaissance became a new art, more decorative and beautiful than the visual world. (Pl. 11.)

Contemporary artists were apparently overwhelmed by these perfect physical types and adroit pictorial arrangements. They tended to avoid the imperfections of nature and to depend directly on painting and engraving after the masters they admired. Yet none of the followers of Michelangelo could successfully imitate his particular rhetoric, lacking the tragic intensity that sustained his figures. The imitative followers of Raphael and Michelangelo are called 'Mannerists'. Although their complex artifice and 'attitudinizing' are often disturbing, they nevertheless made original contributions by new adjustments of surface and space design less dependent on artificial perspective and more dependent on the new ideal of rhythmic or ornamental relationship. The Florentine Mannerists Pontormo, Bronzino, and Il Rosso, together with Parmigianino of the Parma school, frequently attained an elegance in their figures, a refined sensuousness in their surfaces, and a subtle, minor-key colour harmony unequalled in the High Renaissance. Theirs was an art whose form and often obscure allegorical subject-matter appealed to subtle intellects and tastes. It was this style and not that of the High Renaissance which was successfully transplanted to Fontainebleau in France, and the subtleties, elegance, and refined sensuousness of the Tuscan Mannerists have since remained fairly characteristic of French art.

Venice, under the guidance of Titian and the superb decorator Paolo Veronese, remained relatively independent of Mannerism. The style of Tintoretto, in the second half of the sixteenth century, while different in some aspects from that of his Venetian contemporaries, was equally far from that of the Mannerists. He did not merely follow the elongated and contorted figures of Michelangelo but within the broad tones of the Venetian tradition, achieved an intense dynamism of flickering light, which gave his figures and deep space a striking vitality.[4] (Pl. 12a.)

El Greco (d. 1614) was a kindred spirit. After a period of study in Venice and Rome, he found a stimulating atmosphere in the intensely devout Toledo of Spain. There he acquired a unique style, characterized by an ecstatic energy that absorbed and reshaped his figures, and by a new palette of fierce, sulphurous colours that are both icy and vivid at the same time. (Pl. 13.) His austere and vibrant art has much in common with the flame-like figures of the earlier Toledan sculptor Alonso Berruguete but contrasts with the equally vibrant but voluptuous art of Correggio, Federigo Barocci, and later Baroque artists.

Painting in the Seventeeth Century

The style of art known as Baroque is conventionally said to have begun in Italy in the late sixteenth century. It developed further through two strikingly different departures by opponents of the Mannerist style. The first, initiated in Bologna by Lodovico Carracci and his nephews, Agostino and Annibale Carracci, was carried by Annibale to Rome in 1595; the second was largely a Roman development initiated by Caravaggio.[5]

The Carracci, though diverse in style, had much in common. They all admired the drawing of Raphael and his ideal but still natural figures, the warmth of Venetian colour, and the art of Antiquity. Lodovico's more painterly manner, based on colour and light effects, inspired the Baroque style of Guido Reni and Guercino, while Annibale's vigorous, sculptural, and Classicist tendencies influenced Domenichino, Francesco Albani, and the French painter Nicholas Poussin. (Pl. 14a.) Pictorial form still rested, as it had in the Renaissance, on the arrangement of modelled volumes in the illusory depths of the painting, but Baroque space was more dependent on nuances of light, colour, and atmospheric effects than on linear perspective, and in addition provided the spectator with more eccentric and diagonal points of view. The Tuscan insistence on drawing as the basis of painting was not completely abandoned, but momentary, accidental light became during the Baroque period the vital element in the definition of shapes.

These formal changes from Renaissance painting contributed to the success of a pictorial marvel of the seventeenth century in Italy—the illusory frescoes that opened the vaults of a room onto a spectacle attended by heavenly hosts floating freely in an infinite expanse of blue sky. Pietro da Cortona's fresco of the 1630's in the Palazzo Barberini, glorifying the magnificence, virtue, and wisdom of Pope Urban VIII, is filled with hundreds of robust and vigorous figures. Massed and entangled, all are possessed by a common state of excitement; each silhouette and surface is restless and vibrant. This suggestion of energy does not depend on a convincing portrayal of anatomical movement but rather on a fluid and all-pervading dynamism which unites many complex parts into one vision of ecstatic intensity. As mentioned previously, Correggio had pioneered in this kind of illusion a century earlier, and Cortona's fresco is a panoramic extension of Correggio's frescoes in Parma. In the late seventeenth century, Andrea Pozzo's frescoed vault in the Church of San Ignazio in Rome continued the rise of the wall by means of painted architecture creating the illusion of a space twice as high as it actually is. Beyond, one sees Saint Ignatius in glory, while allegorical figures representing the four parts of the earth pay homage. Exalted themes and grandiose ensembles like these represent the climax of the Baroque style in Catholic countries and have few analogies in Protestant areas.

In Rome Poussin was imbued with Annibale Carracci's fondness for Classic and High Renaissance models, firm contours, and Venetian colour. The mature Poussin with the dignified rhetoric of his ideal types, the sculptural clarity of his figures, and the calculated and rhythmic arrangement of his groups more completely realized the art of Raphael than did any other painter in the seventeenth century. Poussin's was an unusually restrained, even stoic, and noble utterance, perfectly sustained. For him Biblical events required a deliberate classicism characterized by geometric shaping and arrangements of parts, while subjects like 'The Reign of Flora' called for softer and more sensuous treatment of flesh and more delight in colour. (Pl. 14b.)

Although he did not form a 'school' of followers, Poussin's calm, reasoned, tectonic art with its noble and moral content appealed to Charles LeBrun, leader of the new Royal Academy of Painting and Sculpture in Paris. Chapter XVI will describe the rise and influence of Europe's academies of art. None of them made a more serious effort to mould national standards than the French academy. It gave a firm direction to the training of artists and to the formation of a French school of painting. Poussin's art, as interpreted by the Academicians, became the basis for the 'Grande Manière' of the French tradition.[6]

Landscape painting of several different kinds also flourished in Rome in the early seventeenth century. Annibale Carracci brought the idyllic, arcadian landscape of northern Italy. Paul Brill was representative of the rich Flemish tradition, which boasts the extensive, detailed and delightfully varied terrains of such a master as Joachim Patinir. Adam Elsheimer depicted nocturnal landscapes with the exuberant vegetation typical of the German school. Drawing on Italian traditions, Poussin constructed magnificent landscapes.[7] His compatriot in Rome, Claude Lorrain, developed subtle tonalities on far-reaching views of the Roman countryside broken by an occasional ruin or of a harbour bordered by grandiose palaces; Lorrain's landscapes conveyed a special mood by captivating light effects, particularly the warm glow and low angle of twilight.

While the art of the Carracci initiated one significant direction in European art, Caravaggio was the originator of another. (Pl. 12b.) Most late sixteenth-century opponents of Caravaggio's painting objected to his 'artless' naturalism and his ordinary rather than ideal physical types. The most influential aspect of his work, however, was not this realism but his use of chiaroscuro. The unusually harsh contrast of his light and dark causes the contours of his objects to be almost lost in broad passages of impenetrable darkness. His denial of the Tuscan-Roman belief in clear drawing as the basic element of painting was more in accord with Lombard and Venetian art. The strong contrast of light and dark found in Giorgionesque night scenes, particularly those of Correggio, and the monochromatic tonalities and the sometimes violent light and dark of the later Titian and Tintoretto provided possible models for Caravaggio's use of 'artificial' light.

Even before Caravaggio, several artists, particularly when endowing the

Nativity with a mystic light, had shown great skill in the use of chiaroscuro. In Spain Navarrete had worked in the tenebrist manner of the Venetians at the Escorial near Madrid, and his follower Francisco Ribalta had carried that manner to Valencia. There José Ribera received his early training; then, after acquiring the realism and the more intense chiaroscuro of Caravaggio, he formed a style of painting in Naples that was followed through the seventeenth century.

Most of Europe came to know Caravaggio's style through his followers Saraceni and Orazio Gentileschi and various Dutch artists in Rome rather than from his own paintings. These painters emphasized 'cellar' lighting effects, tavern or street scenes, and ignoble physical types, overlooking Caravaggio's profound understanding of mental states and human relations. Many also failed to duplicate his clear structure of space and the volumes within it. A provincial French follower, Georges de la Tour, however, succeeded in developing a highly personal style in which a warm light appears to glide out of utter darkness onto the smooth surfaces of extremely simplified shapes of silent and humbly devout people. Valentin de Boulogne, who spent most of his life in Rome, followed Caravaggio's art less creatively. Simon Vouet, after an initial attraction to tenebrism, found himself—as did most Frenchmen—more in accord with the Carracci current than with the harsh realism of Caravaggio.

The Dutch Baroque style meanwhile also departed markedly from the exalted manner of Italy. Dutch artists were now deeply rooted in fifteenth century Flemish realism and in the genre art initiated in the sixteenth century by Pieter Brueghel. Hence they readily accepted the ordinary faces and everyday events of the 'Caravaggisti'. Jan Steen executed rowdy scenes like Brueghel's; Pieter de Hooch presented the unspectacular life of that class of Dutch homes in which women tended their own children and quietly performed household chores; Gerard Terborg as well as Honthorst depicted a more genteel, elegantly dressed set politely conversing or playing musical instruments.[8] Paintings of such unimportant, easily recognizable subjects provide a more complete pictorial record of Dutch life than those left by any other cultural area. (Pl. 15a, b.) The relative calm of the figures and the adjustment of the main wall planes to parallel the surface of the painting contrast with the dramatic events, dynamic figures, and diagonal movement of space in the Italian Grand Manner. In further contrast with contemporary Italian painting, the patiently recorded patterns of floor tiles and of multi-coloured carpets, and the minute details of the maps hanging on the walls were all kept firmly in place within the varied lighting of the interior by the perfection of each colour within its tonal area. Less tenebrist and anecdotic than most Dutch painters, Jan Vermeer carefully adjusted delicately varied colours to subtle areas of tone without dimming the beauty and clarity of the individual colour.

In the sixteenth and particularly the seventeenth century two subjects, formerly subordinate to the primarily narrative purpose of painting, gained a new independence. They were the non-figural landscape and the still-life. Both were given a more prominent place in Dutch painting than in that of any other cultural area of Europe. Pieter Claesz' and Willem Kalf's pictures of abandoned dinner tables laden with the torn and nibbled left-overs of a meal, although accidental in appearance, are most skilfully contrived; the luscious, tempting colours and textures of food scattered among shining silver, pewter, and glass reveal the epicurean side of Dutch upper-class life. Views of the sea, cities, and open country, independent of any narrative, were aspects of the Dutchman's biography which he apparently enjoyed contemplating in pictorial reproduction. The landscapes of Jacob van Ruysdael and his pupil Myndaert Hobbema not only recorded the topographical peculiarities of Holland but also expressed the dynamic character of nature; billowing clouds, patches of shadow across a field, and vigorous vegetation revealed an interest in growth and change that was characteristic of Baroque painting.

Rembrandt, the giant among the Dutch painters of this golden age, did some of his most memorable work as portraits. Portraits had become an important art form among the Flemish and the Italians of the fifteenth century. The Flemish patiently depicted every detail of face and costume, and the Italians tended to glorify the beauty, dignity and even grandeur of Man. In contrast, Rembrandt subordinated much of the setting and the costume in a warm umber spaciousness, defining selected details with crisp touches of impasto. Usually presenting Man as humble and contemplative or seriously and frankly concerned with life, he seems to glimpse into the inmost mind of the portrayed. (Pl. 16a.) The laughing eyes and animated spirits of Frans Hals' extroverts or the carefully composed mien of Valezquez's regal personages do not so cogently invite exploration of the psyche.

While Rembrandt also did some mythological paintings and landscapes, his favoured subject (if his etchings, drawings, and paintings are all considered) was the Biblical event. (Pl. 16b.) After a period in which he followed the rhetorical gestures of the Italian tradition, he tended to concentrate increasingly on the inner reactions of the participants. His art represents the ultimate potential of Caravaggio's chiaroscuro as a means of creating space and placing figures within it, but Rembrandt's light and dark are less harshly separated than Caravaggio's, and his light is more intimately fused with warm, earthy colour tonalities (sometimes accented with brilliant colour, in keeping with his admiration for Venetian painting).

Rembrandt's relatively sombre paintings in Protestant Holland contrasted dramatically with the predominately light-filled and vivid colour of the Catholic painter Peter Paul Rubens in nearby Flanders. Although Rubens' special sensibility to varied textures and light-reflecting qualities has deep roots in Flemish art, his opulent colour was derived from Venetian painting, and his grand rhythmic movements, his groupings of figures, and their rhetorical gestures draw upon the Tuscan-Roman tradition and, perhaps, the ecstatic dynamism of Correggio and Barocci. Rich and vivid in hues, his 'Rape of the Daughters of Leucippus' in Munich reveals his unique characteristics; the soft and heavy white bodies of the women contrast with the hardened, sun-tanned skin of the men, the turbulence of their twisting bodies magnified by a vitality that permeates all the canvas. (Pl. 17.) The same pictorial qualities with which he portrayed indulgences of the flesh contributed fervour to his depiction of a triumph of faith or an apotheosis of a saint. In him and Pietro da Cortona in Rome the Grand Manner of the seventeenth century reached its zenith.

Technical ability also reached its zenith about the same time. In the handling of oil paint, Rubens stands out along with Rembrandt and Velasquez, the heirs of Titian, as a most accomplished technician. The variety of ways in which pigment can be smeared, trailed, touched, or glazed over the surface—and endure—has remained unexcelled, and the manipulation of pigment as a vehicle of individuality was brought to its highest pitch, remaining a model for painters to this day. Rembrandt also raised etching to a technical and aesthetic level never equalled for variety of texture and tone.

The national school of Spain in the seventeenth century provided not only her golden age in painting but also the clearest and most austere pictorial statement of the Counter-Reformation in Europe. The mature Velasquez, to be sure, was a court painter, particularly noted for the magnificence and mastery of his portraits in the Venetian tradition and for the colour and aerial perspective of his historical paintings (e.g. the 'Surrender of Breda').[9] (Pl. 18.) Other Spanish painters, however, received most of their commissions from the church. Francisco Zurbarán created a non-sensuous world of quiet surfaces and clear shapes that effectively conveyed the chaste life or the intense visions of the white-habited monks whose life he portrayed. Valdes Leal's disturbing reminders of the death of the body and the eternal life of the spirit emphasized the ephemeral nature of matter by the insistent actuality of the physical substance he depicted. Murillo, while creating an unrivalled representation of the Immaculate Conception and tender images of the Holy Family, developed an atmospheric spaciousness that gently merged the physical world and the celestial vision, effectively portraying the intimate relation between the material and the spiritual in Spanish Catholicism.

Painting in the Eighteenth Century

In the early seventeenth century, Europe had become a cosmos of richly varied national styles. By the eighteenth century, however, the Flemish, Dutch, and Spanish schools had lost their creative vigour, leaving Venice rivalled for leadership only by England and, more particularly, France. Throughout the seventeenth century the artists of Europe continued to make the pilgrimage to Venice to learn the colour secrets of Titian and Veronese. In the eighteenth century, the superb Venetian colourist and decorator

Giovanni Battista Tiepolo won international fame and was called upon to carry out huge frescoed ceilings in the illusional tradition of Italy not only in his own country but in Würzburg and Madrid. (Pl 19a.) Antonio Canaletto's and Francesco Guardi's views of the piazzas and canals of Venice, memorable for the shimmering blues and greens of water and sky and the warm rose and tan of buildings, were painted in response to a steady demand from tourists, particularly English, who flocked to Venice. (Pl. 19b.)

England during the eighteenth century was not only a good market for landscapes but, for the first time, could boast a native group of painters who ranked among the major figures of European art. In the seventeenth century some brilliant pupils or followers of Rubens—Anthony Van Dyck, Peter Lely, and Godfrey Kneller—had gone to England from the Continent. Van Dyck was the most influential of them. His manner was facile but less vigorous and sensuous than Rubens', and his figures were more dignified and elegant. (Pl. 20a.) These immigrant artists provided England with a basic type for its portrait school. Joshua Reynolds and Thomas Gainsborough followed that type (Pl. 20b), and George Romney helped to carry the tradition into the nineteenth century. Gainsborough also painted hastily executed and sparkling landscapes that recall Rubens (as well as Watteau) in their vibrancy and Hobbema and the Dutch school in the dynamic and irregular character of the nature they portray and in their lack of historical or narrative reference. (Pl. 21a.) Reynolds appears to have adapted the landscapes of Claude Lorrain to the role of background for his fashionable portraits. (Pl. 21b.) In the eighteenth century, watercolour became a prominent medium for landscapes and views of towns in the skilful and sensitive hands of Paul Sandby and John Robert Cozens. One of the most insistently 'English' painters of the period, William Hogarth, painted and engraved shrewd commentaries on contemporary morals and customs (see Chapter IX and Pl. 23a).

In France the exalted and domineering voice of the Royal Academy had not gone unchallenged. The latter half of the seventeenth century was characterized by arguments between the 'Rubensists', who emphasized colour, and the Classicists of the Academy, identified as 'Poussinists', who emphasized drawing. By the early eighteenth century the argument had lost its significance, because the important place claimed for colour by the Rubensists was accepted, and a leader of that group, Antoine Watteau, was a member of the Academy.

Watteau, although essentially a colourist like Rubens, is notably different. His paintings tend to be quite small in contrast to Rubens' monumentality, and unlike Rubens' full, rich colour, Watteau's tends to be subtle, delicate, and iridescent. (Pl. 22.) Watteau's 'well-groomed wilderness,' peopled for the day by dreamy, fragile youths and maidens of the leisure classes, glitters with the bright sheen of silk against the soft, misty hues of the woodlands. His loose brush reveals great facility in the Rubens tradition, but the present deteriorated state of his works testifies to a less exacting craftsmanship. The vagueness of the events in Watteau's 'fêtes galantes' and their aspect of reverie as well as their blond tonality recall the pastorals of Giorgione's followers in Venice, but the French scenes have more of a touch of languor or nostalgia shading their participants' pleasure.

By its variety, delicacy, elegance, feminine grace, and emphasis on genteel and sensuous pleasures, Watteau's art gave direction to the 'Rococo' style in early eighteenth-century painting. Lesser artists, such as Jean Baptiste Pater and Nicholas Lancret, repeated Watteau's subjects, and Jean Honoré Fragonard and Madame de Pompadour's favourite, François Boucher, continued his love themes. The works of Fragonard revealed more tenderness and genuine voluptuousness than the calculated, erotic works of Boucher. While Boucher and Fragonard followed Watteau's colour and sensuousness, they looked also to Italian artists of the decorative tradition, such as Tiepolo, for models for their mural designs in the intimate salons and boudoirs of the Rococo hôtel. Nicholas Largillière's portraits were ornamental and flattering versions of the Van Dyck portrait, while Maurice Quentin de la Tour and Jean-Etienne Liotard executed more intimate portraits in pastel, a delicate medium permitting the most gentle transitions and subtle nuances of colour, and thus particularly pleasing to the Rococo taste.

In striking contrast with this group, Chardin painted middle-class life and (more memorably) still-lifes. His paintings contain no obviously contrived or complicated arrangements but a careful ordering of simple shapes, rich, low-key colours, and homespun textures. In this way he pointed toward a kind of 'pure painting' that remains an ideal in French art to the present day. Greuze's paintings also mirrored the village life of his day, reflecting more than Chardin the contemporary vogue of *sensibilité* (see Chapter IX and Pl. 23b).

About the mid-eighteenth century, a new burst of admiration for the Greco-Roman world was set off by some extraordinary archaeological excavations, particularly at Herculaneum and Pompeii. The archaeologist Comte de Caylus, Anton Raphael Mengs, painter and director of the Vatican Academy of Art, and the art historian Winckelmann urged the study of Ancient art not only for its form and appeal to the senses but also for its appeal to virtue and the elevated emotions (see Chapter IX). It was not, however, the bourgeois morality of a Greuze that the lovers of Antiquity had in mind. The noble ideals envisioned by these Neoclassicists were to be exemplified rather in the last quarter of the century by the tales of civic virtue, courage, and patriotism painted by Jacques Louis David.

Although the Europeans faced many of the same problems in the depiction of space encountered centuries before by Chinese artists, the solutions the West found suggest no awareness of the Far Eastern tradition. When Europeans finally came in contact with the Chinese pictorial form, they were so completely conditioned by the homogeneous space of their perspective system that the Eastern space devices appeared to them simply naïve. On the other hand, the most insistent efforts of religious orders such as the Jesuits to teach

Western painting in China and Japan won a number of apt pupils but brought no general disturbance to the continuity of the Eastern tradition. The Chinese were not inclined to base their paintings on natural science or to subordinate pictorial arrangement to discoveries in optics (see below).

Sculpture in France, the Germanies, and Northern Europe (c. 1300–1500)

European sculpture underwent style changes similar to those of painting but with some important differences. Unlike northern miniature painters, who reacted early in the fourteenth century to the illusional spatial depth of Sienese and Florentine painting, northern sculptors remained relatively unaffected by Italian sculptural developments until late in the fifteenth century. In certain areas, indeed, the Gothic tradition of polychrome wood sculpture, in opposition to the unadorned bronze and marble statuary of central Italy, persisted until the late eighteenth century.

In the medieval tradition, sculpture was associated predominantly with cult images, altar retables, church façades and portals, and tombs. During the thirteenth and early fourteenth centuries the main portals of cathedrals were profusely decorated with sculptured figures and scenes sacred to the church. Carved on archivolts and tympanums from the stone with which the cathedral was built, sculpture was scaled and aligned like an architectural feature. Many of the great portals had been completed by the fourteenth century, but important sculptural programmes were still under way on the cathedrals of Strasbourg, Lyon, and Rouen in France, Exeter in England, and Augsburg, Nuremberg, Gmünd, and Ulm in Germany. Sculptors of this period tended to free portal figures from their somewhat columnar compactness by permitting the arms to move out and the drapery to fall more freely from the body. In the fourteenth century an 'S' curve, rising through these figures and released by the tilt of the heads, lent a gracefulness that relieved the earlier rigidity. The tendency toward grace and ease was accentuated when the artist, now rarely called upon for monumental stone sculpture, instead did small devotional images in ivory, silver, alabaster, marble, or polychrome wood.

Leadership in setting style passed during the fourteenth century from the Île-de-France to several new centres. While the style of the French centre continued (and even reasserted itself in the Loire valley during the so-called 'Détente' of the late fifteenth and early sixteenth centuries), Prague, the Low Countries, Burgundy, and Germany became hubs of more realistic styles that contrasted with the idealized types, simple shapes, and gentle dignity of the Île-de-France. The Parler family, radiating from Prague, formed a style characterized by weighty volumes and realistic surface details like those of the bust portraits in the triforium of the Prague Cathedral. (Pl. 24a, b, c.) Patrons all over Europe ordered many works from Dutch and Flemish centres, but wholesale destruction of sculpture in the Low Countries during the religious strife of the sixteenth century makes difficult an estimate of the amount of work done there. During the last third of the fourteenth century, the Flemish André Beauneveu, particularly renowned for the realism of his effigies, carried out some important sepulchral commissions around Paris, notably those for King Charles V and King Philippe VI in Saint-Denis.

The major figure of the Burgundian school, Claus Sluter, is believed to have come from Holland during the last decade of the fourteenth century to complete the work initiated by Jean Marville for the Carthusian monastery at Champmol near Dijon. His effigies of the duke and duchess of Burgundy (placed with their attendant saints on brackets on either side of paired façade portals) adore the Virgin and Child located between the two portals; larger than life-size, fully round, and animated by vigorously swirling draperies, these figures are more independent of their architectural setting than any in the Île-de-France Gothic tradition. Sluter's ponderous and energetic prophets, carved around a base for a huge calvary in the same monastery's cloisters, suggest that this calvary was probably the most impressive sculptural monument in the Europe of 1400. The magnificent drapery arrangements with the deep, shadowed recesses of their folds, the realism of detail, and the fierce alertness of the prophets' faces impart a physical forcefulness and a dramatic intensity equalled only by Donatello in the following century. (Pl. 25.)

The sculptural production of Germany during the fifteenth and sixteenth centuries is better preserved than that of the Low Countries. In sculptural form northwest Germany was close to the Low Countries, while southern and eastern Germany created more original styles. Most German sculptors worked predominantly in wood. One of the best preserved works of the Franconian Veit Stoss is the huge retable of polychrome wood begun around 1477 in Cracow. The definition of his figures, in contrast to those by Sluter or the sculptors of the Île-de-France tradition, depends on applied colour and on the light and shade and suggestion of line created by abrupt changes of surface and by deep undercutting in the draperies. These 'pictorial' characteristics of his sculpture, particularly his angular drapery patterns, and the dramatic intensity of his figures call to mind the paintings of Rogier van der Weyden. German technical mastery of wood is exemplified by Stoss's 'Annunciation', carved within a rosary and suspended over the choir of Saint Lawrence in Nuremberg (Pl. 26a); its small, delicate parts and its many perforations lend an immaterial, visionary aspect to the scene. Tilman Riemenschneider, though also a Franconian, reflected the lyric and melancholy spirit of Swabian sculptors rather than the vigorous and dramatic character of Stoss. Although most of Riemenschneider's work is in wood, his nude statues of Adam and Eve are stone. (Pl. 26b, c.) Their simple shapes and somewhat stiff appearance disclose that his knowledge of anatomy was more limited than that of contemporary Italians (see below). Bernt Notke's decorative Saint George killing a fierce and fanciful dragon, made for the Church of Saint Nicola in Stockholm in 1489, displays a rearing horse that recalls Leonardo's designs for the Trivulzio monument, but it suggests none of the Italian's understanding of the anatomy of a body in motion. (Pl. 28a.) Peter Vischer excelled in bronze casting. His technical proficiency in that medium stemmed from a long German tradition in metal work, but some of his isolated motifs show a growing awareness of the classical vocabulary of Italy. Such were the putti and the leaf forms among the slim shapes and lively silhouettes of his early sixteenth century shrine of Saint Sebald in Nuremberg.

Sculpture in Italy (c. 1250–1600)

In medieval Italy the lingering of the Romanesque style and the relatively slow acceptance of Gothic forms reflected the continued vitality of the Classical tradition there. Striking references to ancient sculpture were also to be found in French works, notably the 'Visitation' on the façade of the Cathedral of Reims, but they were isolated instances. In Italy such references were less exotic. In the middle of the thirteenth century, when the Gothic style was spreading to all of Europe, Emperor Frederick II in southern Italy commissioned artists to copy ancient sculpture in an effort to enhance his imperial status by reminders of the Roman Empire. Nicola Pisano's reliefs on the pulpit of the Baptistry of Pisa (completed in 1259) indicated a careful study of Classical models. (Pl. 27a.) Giotto's paintings of well-rounded figures disposed in a clearly defined interval were an added stimulus in the direction indicated by Nicola Pisano. Although Giovanni Pisano, his son, turned to northern Gothic models, Andrea Pisano followed the more Classical tradition of Giotto and Nicola in his bronze reliefs for the early fourteenth-century door of the Florence Baptistry and in his stone reliefs for the Cathedral tower.[10]

During the early fifteenth century, much sculptural work went on in Florence. More-than-life-size statues of saints and apostles were commissioned for the Cathedral and the Oratory of San Michele, and reliefs in marble and bronze for the Baptistry, the Cathedral, and the Oratory. Florentine sculptors were stimulated by the desire, which they shared with contemporary painters, to regain the perfection of Ancient art. Donatello and Ghiberti, the leading sculptors of the period, collected and studied Ancient bronzes and marbles (probably small or fragmentary pieces) and also Ancient gems and coins. Furthermore, the keen observation of nature that was transforming painting was also changing sculpture. The bronze panels depicting 'The Sacrifice of Isaac' submitted by Brunelleschi and by Ghiberti in the competition in 1401 for the Baptistry doors reveal attempts to create the pictorial illusion of adequate and convincing space.

About 1417, Donatello carved the marble relief of 'Saint George and the Dragon' for the base of his Statue of Saint George for the Orsanmichele Church. (Pl. 28b.) It ranged from half-round figures in the foreground to very low relief in the background to create another version of the pictorial relief. Delicate variations of light give to the subtly bevelled surfaces of the background an almost atmospheric softness and distance that contrast with the effect created by the broader expanses of light on the strong relief of the figures in the foreground. In making these suggestions of depth, Donatello was 'painting with light' on marble, a technique which the sixteenth-century art historian Giorgio Vasari said he had learned from Ancient gems.

In the square reliefs for his 'Gates of Paradise' (as Michelangelo is supposed to have called the Baptistry doors) Ghiberti incorporated some of Donatello's subtle devices. He was able to create a homogeneous space that continues from the almost free-standing figures in the foreground into the low relief and illusional depths of the panel. (Pl. 27b.) The twisting life of Ghiberti's figures can be seen from a variety of angles, and their more natural scale in relation to their architectural setting contribute pictorial effects that compare favourably with contemporary painting. The association of sculptural relief with the spatial illusion of painting continued as a dominant attitude until recent times. The detail and surface refinements of Ghiberti's reliefs surpassed the work of the most accomplished heirs of Germany's long tradition of bronze casting. As early as 1414 he had successfully cast an eight-foot bronze statue in one piece—a technical feat seldom accomplished in Europe since Antiquity, though contemporary bronze-casting traditions to compare with those of Florence and Germany were to be found, we shall soon see, in China, Japan, India, and Benin.

Donatello's over-life-size figures in marble for the tower of the Cathedral and the exterior of the Orsanmichele Church were formed with a non-ornamental, 'scientific' purpose comparable to those later painted by Masaccio. The clear volumes that compose his statue of Saint George are confined by undisturbed surfaces, simplified for the sculptural effect of lights. (Pl. 29a.) Its forceful modelling and its compactness suggest density and weight and lend to the figure an appearance of physical energy, enhanced by its broad stance, which braces it against the pull of gravity. This clear interdependence of bodily parts within an organic unit distinguishes Donatello's sculpture and that of the later Renaissance. Another characteristic of Donatello's sculpture is the careful control of the contours of the silhouette to form rhythmic continuities that make a precisely frontal view the most harmonious and satisfying. This frontality reflects the influence of *disegno* ('drawing'), which was considered by Florentines to be fundamental to both painting and sculpture. Donatello's severe monolithic statues contrast with the fluidity and subtlety of surfaces, the looping folds, and the gracefully meandering edges of the draperies—vestiges of the International Style—in Ghiberti's figures of Saint John the Baptist and Saint Stephen on the Orsanmichele Church. (Pl. 29b.)

On the other hand, Donatello shares with Ghiberti a sensitivity to the adjustment of a figure in height and volume to its niche. Both sought to place their statuary in such a way that it was neither overwhelmed by a huge cavity nor cramped by inadequate space. Their suggestion of the complementary nature of solid and void, within the homogeneity of figure and space, tended to a close balance comparable to that sought in contemporary painting. Sculptors also shared the contemporary painters' concern for the optical effect of foreshortening, on occasion noticeably enlarging the upper part of a figure placed on high in order to counteract the illusory diminution of size.

One of the most stimulating problems of the fifteenth century was that of free-standing sculpture, unrelated to the architectural background and visible from all sides. The columnar female figures rising freely from the parapet of the fountain begun about 1414 by Jacopo della Quercia for the main square of Siena and the bronze 'David' (1430–40) made by Donatello in the court of the Medici Palace in Florence are the first free-standing nude statues known to have been erected since Antiquity. (Pl. 31b.) Although in-the-round figures, they were clearly designed to be most informative and most esthetically satisfying from the front view. Even the famous equestrian monument of Gattamelatta in Padua was intended to be seen from the two profile views. (Pl. 30b.) When, however, the triangular base for Donatello's bronze 'Judith and Holofernes' was completed (c. 1455) for the Medici Gardens, it indicated a plurifacial concept of sculpture; the limbs of the dead Holofernes hanging beyond the base form a departure from the earlier compactness of marble sculpture around its own core and prepared for a more lively interchange between the free-standing figure and space. Bodily parts were flung even more vigorously beyond the sculptural core in Pollaiuolo's triangular based statuette of 'Hercules Strangling Anteus'.

The boldest step in the plurifacial concept of sculpture came with Verrocchio. His bronze putto posed on tiptoe and affectionately clutching a dolphin was completed (c. 1470) for the gardens of the Villa Careggi. The later installation of this statue in the court of the Palazzo Vecchio in Florence probably re-emphasized its original plurifacial aims since it was made to resolve, constantly presenting a new angle, by the pressure of water that passes through the figure and out through the mouth of the dolphin. The placement of Verrochio's equestrian statue of Colleoni (Pl. 30a) in 1489 in the square of Saint Giovanni e Paolo in Venice reflected a similar consciousness of multiple views, in this case obtained from the five or six entries into the square. Nevertheless, both of these statues have readily recognizable primary views more satisfying than the several secondary ones.

The vigour of the free-standing figures by Pollaiuolo and Verrocchio was made still more convincing by the sculptors' increased knowledge of anatomy. Though only about thirty years separated Verrocchio's bronze 'David' (1460) from Donatello's, Verrocchio's showed more advanced anatomical knowledge. (Pl. 31a.) Growing knowledge freed the artist of the late fifteenth century from the limited repertory of poses used during the Middle Ages and enabled him to present the human body persuasively in any action or arrangement he chose. Leonardo's 'Rider on a Rearing Horse,' delineated in his plans (1511–12) for the Trivulzio monument, presented not only a new intensity of action but in addition a rotary kind of movement; his curvilinear silhouette forced the eye to return to the core of the statue.[12] This revival of compactness of sculptural form and of balanced stability of parts without sacrifice of the ease or vigour of the figure in space was to become characteristic of the High Renaissance.

During the quattrocento several other notable accomplishments were recorded. Desiderio de Settignano and the Rossellini brothers translated the subtle surfaces and light effects of Ghiberti's bronzes into marble and attained a refinement in the treatment of marble surfaces that was to be equalled only by Bernini and, eventually, by the French sculptors of the eighteenth century. This refinement together with the careful study of human anatomy at various ages enabled this group to fashion sculpture (portrait busts of women, a youthful Saint John, a child Jesus) with amazing delicacy of structure and apparent softness of surface. (Pl. 32a.) Donatello, Verrocchio, and Benedetto da Maiano did male busts of a more vigorous and harshly detailed character but with the aim in each case to suggest a living presence. The Rossellini brothers and Desiderio also formed a favoured sepulchral type composed of an elaborately carved sarcophagus and an effigy of the deceased, both enclosed within a symbolic triumphal arch. In the second quarter of the fifteenth century Luca della Robbia initiated glazed terra cotta sculpture. (Pl. 32b.) While Luca restricted the use of blue, lavender, or green glazes for details on the predominantly white surfaces of his sculpture, more elaborate colour schemes are characteristic of his followers. The school founded by Luca represents the major continuity of polychrome statuary in central Italy.

While sculptors in Lombardy and Emilia produced impressive works, Florentine sculptors attracted to the papal court preserved the main tradition in Rome. The fullness of volumes, the heroic types, and the easy grace of the early sixteenth century are exemplified by Michelangelo's 'Pieta' in Saint Peter's in Rome and his gigantic 'David' in Florence and by Andrea Sansovino's 'Virtues' in the niches of the triumphal-arch tombs in Santa Maria del Popolo in Rome. (Pl. 31c.) These figures reveal the confidence with which sculptors of the High Renaissance employed the technical skills, the anatomical knowledge, and the standards of beauty developed during the fifteenth century. Andrea's favoured pupil, Jacopo Sansovino, continuing the master's sculptural types, emphasized the graceful and even elegant aspects of the human figure in such works as the 'Apollo' and the 'Mercury' of the Loggetta in Venice. Michelangelo, on the other hand, created a new sense of spiritual tension, which he enhanced by arranging the limbs so as to seem to compress rather than release the energy pent up in his figures. His 'Saint Matthew', his so-called 'Slaves' (initiated for the ambitious tomb planned for Julius II), and his figures sculptured for the Medici tombs are accommodated to rhythmic configurations essentially different from the natural positions designed by fifteenth-century sculptors.[13] His figural inventions were much admired and accepted as models by painters and sculptors during the cinquecento.

How to relate a statue to surrounding space and how to design it so as to allow an advantageous view from many angles persisted as sculptural problems. Michelangelo's youthful, inebriated 'Bacchus' lifting his wine cup into space, Jacopo Sansovino's 'Bacchus' with even more extended limbs, and Benvenuto Cellini's 'Perseus' holding forth the head of Medusa are examples both of the often abrupt extension from the central core and of the invitation to secondary views. Tribolo, Pierino da Vinci, and Bartolomeo Ammannati, in sculpture planned for garden and fountain settings, made notable contributions to the development of statues in contorted Michelangelesque positions placed precariously on the edge of a fountain pedestal or a basin. Cellini, in arguing the superiority of sculpture over painting and the greater difficulties faced by the sculptor, claimed that the sculptor was not concerned simply with one but with 'forty angles of view,' all of which must be painstakingly designed and adjusted to one another. Despite the advocacy of a plurifacial ideal, Cellini and other cinquecentists generally remained under the spell of a primary, frontal view.

Cellini's aim was realized most fully by Giovanni da Bologna. A Fleming by birth, he came from a sculptural tradition less under the compulsion of a primary view. Out of the Verrocchio-Leonardo-Michelangelo tradition, he developed a *figura serpentinata* that spiralled about a stable central axis, encouraging the continual movement of the spectator around it by presenting no view that was in itself completely satisfying. His bronze 'Mercury' (1564), balanced on tiptoe on one leg with arms and the other leg flung into space, his small marble 'Venus' in the Grotto of the Boboli Gardens, covering her nakedness with her arms, while turning to look at the satyrs peeping over the edge of the basin, and particularly the three struggling figures of his 'Rape of the Sabines' demonstrate a rhythmic spiraling of forms within a column of space. (Pl. 33a.) This organization of figures maintained the autonomy and composure of the free-standing figure, releasing the sculptured limbs in an easy interplay with space, and provided a maximum number of pleasing views with easy passage from one to another.

Spread of Italian Sculptural Ideals

Italian sculptural ideals of the Renaissance penetrated into other parts of Europe to varying degrees. Reacting only little to Italian developments, England for the most part continued her own rich decorative vocabulary, evolved during the late Middle Ages. Among the earliest and most accomplished sculptors outside Italy to follow the Renaissance manner were certain Spaniards. Bartolomé Ordóñez, Diego Siloé, and Damián Forment revealed a clear grasp of Renaissance forms, and so sometimes did the anonymous sculptors of arabesque ornaments in the highly ornamental Spanish architectural style known as the 'Plateresque'. Nevertheless, polychrome wood sculpture and a less Classical aim became dominant among Spanish sculptors (see below).

Germany's political and religious disturbances, reinforcing her strong Gothic tradition, seem to have limited her participation in the elaboration of Classical ideals, but Germans readily followed Italian interest in bronze statuettes and plaques, with an excellence of workmanship in metal work drawn from their medieval technical tradition. By the end of the sixteenth and the beginning of the seventeenth century, Giovanni da Bologna's spiralling figures were adopted in Germany and the Low Countries. Notable among his followers were Hubert Gerhard, who cast bronze figures for fountains in Augsburg and Munich, Andriaen de Vries, who worked in The Hague and Augsburg, and Jacques du Broeucq, who took Bologna's type of sculpture to the Low Countries after a period of study in Italy. The decorative vocabulary of arabesques and other Classical motifs diffused more readily on the Continent than most other aspects of Italian Renaissance sculpture. In Protestant lands, however, nothing significant was contributed to the development of Italian sculptural forms.

Italy's principles of sculpture were transferred more successfully to France than elsewhere. Various Italian sculptors—Leonardo da Vinci, Francesco Laurana, Rustici, Cellini, several members of the Fontainebleau School, and other lesser lights—worked in France during the late fifteenth and the early sixteenth century[14] So little of their work has been preserved or identified that it is difficult to reconstruct the nature of the stimuli they provided. Major French sculptors of this period, such as Michel Colombe and Jean Goujon, are known to us only by way of a few mature pieces, which clearly reveal their awareness of Italian Renaissance and Ancient art, but the formation of their artistic personalities also remains conjectural. Colombe, probably trained in the calm and idealized forms of the 'Détente', readily responded to the motifs and sculptural attitudes of the Italians. His free-standing marble tomb for Duke Francis II of Brittany in the Cathedral of Nantes followed French sepulchral types, but he employed medallions and apostles in niches, framed by half-round arches, elaborately carved pilasters, and Classical mouldings that reflect the clear geometric shapes and minute goldsmith detail of the Tuscan-Lombard tradition. His four 'Virtues', arranged as guardians at the corners of the sepulchre, were carved in the round, attaining a stability of balanced weight, an anatomical 'correctness' of bodily parts, and a fall of draperies that reveal the fusion of Italian ideals with those of the 'Détente'. Goujon worked in co-operation with the outstanding architect Pierre Lescot (see below). Goujon's often low reliefs of decorative and elegant nymphs and allegorical figures, made in the 1540's to ornament the façade of the Louvre, the court of the Hôtel Carnavalet, and his Fountain of the Innocents, employ the elongated figure types and the contrived and subtly sensuous poses of the Italian Mannerists. (Pl. 33b.)

On the other hand, Pierre Bontempts' contemporary work suggests no admiration for such decorative figural inventions. He did much of his work in conjunction with another major architect of the period, Philibert de l'Orme (see below). The tomb of Francis I in Saint Denis, surmounted by precisely finished and boldly shaped bronze effigies of the royal family, is a foremost example of their sober and accomplished workmanship.

After the 1560's the prominence of Catherine de Medici, widow of King Henry II, and her Italian superintendent of art, Primaticcio, encouraged French inclinations to follow Renaissance models. Germain Pilon received commissions from Primaticcio and probably carried out plans designed by him. Pilon was famous for effigies and allegorical figures for sepulchres, and for carefully observed and meticulously executed bronze busts, such as that of Jean de Morvillier, in the Museum of Orleans. Although most of his sculpture is generally quite static, several religious works of the 1580's, particularly his terra-cotta 'Virgin of Sorrows' in the Louvre and his 'Saint Francis in Ecstacy', attain a surprising emotional intensity not only in the expression and gestures of the personages but in undulating surfaces and linear complications. Sculptors in France were rarely called upon to do figures completely free of architectural or sepulchral settings, but, in the late sixteenth century and after, statues of the kings, frequently equestrian, were erected in the centre of the Place Royale of several cities. Although some of these statues were destroyed during the French Revolution as 'monuments of feudalism and idolatry', surviving examples and engravings make it evident that these free-standing equestrian statues depended on Italian models. Pierre Francheville and others continued Giovanni da Bologna's sculptural types into the seventeenth century. Particularly notable is the bronze figure of 'Fame' (modelled on Giovanni's 'Mercury') originally mounted over the tomb of the Duc d'Épernon. French sculptors of the sixteenth century are less important for innovations than for the absorption of Italian and then Ancient ideals into the French tradition, thus giving a Classical direction to the country which was to become the leading art centre of Europe during the late seventeenth and eighteenth centuries.

Polychrome Wood Sculpture

In Spain and Germany while some native sculptors were accomplished in Renaissance forms and Italians were invited to court centres, the Italian Renaissance influence was opposed by those who continued the Gothic tradition of polychrome wood sculpture. Statues of cold marble and bronze may have served the esthetic needs of those who judged by standards of correctness and beauty, but they did not convey the warmth and the impression of actual presence demanded by devout Germans and Spaniards. In the polychrome statuary of the sixteenth and seventeenth centuries, the great variation of physical types, emotional expression, formal arrangement, and treatment of colour testify not simply to a lingering of the medieval tradition but to its prolonged vitality.

Customarily, in this tradition, one artist carved the figure; another completed the costumes, often enriched by designs scratched through upper layers of colour to reveal threads of the gold leaf beneath; and a third did the flesh. The full volumes, the realism in details, and the clarity of local colour in the 'Entombment' of Juan de Juni in Valladolid, completed in the mid-sixteenth century, remind one of the similar groups favoured in France and northern Italy a century earlier. The many figures of Berruguete's huge retable, now in the Museum of Valladolid, have something of the sublime and tragic intensity of Michelangelo's but augmented to a frantic state and absorbed by a flame-like energy. Early-seventeenth-century polychrome sculptors, particularly Gregorio Fernandez in Valladolid and Martínez Montañez in Sevilla (Pl. 34a), employed more limited and subdued colour over figures of greater calm and monumentality. Fernandez' 'Pieta' displays some of the realism for which Spanish and Latin American sculptors of this period are famous: Jesus' deep wounds and open mouth with carefully carved teeth and tongue accentuate his last painful breath. (Pl. 34b.) Although the polychrome sculpture of Germany in the late sixteenth and the early seventeenth century did not match earlier German accomplishments, the works of Ignaz Günther and the Asam brothers in the eighteenth century betokened a renewal of vitality.

Bernini and the Baroque Style

During the seventeenth century, the Classical tradition of Italian sculpture was transformed into the Baroque style largely by the emotional exuberance of Giovanni Lorenzo Bernini, a Neapolitan sculptor who worked chiefly in Rome. Although much of his sculpture was carried out in marble, his technical mastery permitted him to shape and finish his figures as if they were made of wax. In his early busts, such as those of Cardinal Scipione Borghese and of Costanza Bonarelli, he surpassed the effect of living presence in the Renaissance portrait through his startling ability to translate into stone not only the physical structure, softness, and texture of skin and hair but also the state of mind of an alert individual caught in an unguarded moment. His 'Santa Teresa in Ecstasy' is an unexcelled example of the Baroque effort to penetrate the psychology of the persons represented; it portrays the saint's emotion at the moment of spiritual union with Christ, recalling the ecstasies painted by Correggio and Baroccio or the excited sculptures of Berruguete and Stoss. (Pl. 35a.) Like the Gothic sculpture of Germany, Bernini's pieces are often described as 'pictorial': his subtle and fluid surfaces dissolve the hardness, weight, and even bulk of the marble; his gradations of light and shade are the result of studied concern; and his works in architectural settings, like the Santa Teresa and the equestrian statue of Constantine in the narthex of St Peter's, were usually conceived from a primary view. Yet his soft and discontinuous contours do not confine his sculpture so firmly within a primary view as the more precise and coherent contours of Renaissance sculptors confined theirs, and as a result the figures and objects of Bernini's fountains, tombs, and free-standing groups present multiple views and intermingle freely with surrounding space.[15]

Another major seventeenth-century figure in Rome was Alessandro Algardi. He showed greater faithfulness than Bernini to the Classical tradition in his clear opposition of sculptural volume to spatial voids and in the greater restraint of his emotional display. The relatively static forms of Algardi's tomb for Leo XI and the fluid energy of Bernini's tomb for Urban VIII, both in Saint Peter's in Rome, reveal the fundamental difference in their art.

Bernini's art was greatly admired by contemporaries, but few of his followers matched his emotional gusto or his sensibility to the textural and colouring possibilities of light and shade in sculpture. Jacques Sarazin adopted certain aspects of Bernini's style, but most French sculptors working in Rome and the influential François Duquesnoy, a Fleming, were closer in spirit to Algardi. Most Berninesque among the sculptors in France was Pierre Puget; his marble statue of Milo of Crotona attacked by a lion, carved originally for the gardens of Versailles in the 1670's, reveals a comparable technical facility, particularly in the suggestion of the softness of the flesh rent by the lion's claws. In the Low Countries and in Germany during the seventeenth and eighteenth centuries, sculptors more readily adopted, even intensified, the turbulence of Bernini's draperies and the excitement of his figures and frequently equalled his marvellous technique. Among the most lavish sculptural works in these northern areas, and particularly the Low Countries, were church confessionals and pulpits. The confessional in the Church of Ninove by Theodore Verhaegen, the pulpit in Saint Andrew's in Antwerp by Jan van Greel and Jan van Hool, and that in Saint-Gudule in Brussels by Henri François Verbruggen are among the most impressive Dutch and Flemish examples. Andreas Schluter's equestrian statue of the Great Elector in Berlin, Balthasar Permoser's sculptural decoration on the pavilions of the Zwinger in Dresden, and Egid Quirin Assam's excited figures of the 'Assumption of the Virgin' in the Convent Church of Rohr, exemplify the continuity of the Bernini style in eighteenth-century Germany. (Pl. 35b.)

The Classical and the Rococo

Except for Puget, French sculptors, under the watchful eye of the Royal Academy of Painting and Sculpture, rarely approached the emotional and pictorial tendencies of Bernini. In the early seventeenth century, academicians shifted from Italian Renaissance to Ancient models and thus gained a degree of independence from Italian sculptural developments. When Bernini, as leader of the new Italian Baroque style, presented his exuberant bust and equestrian statue of King Louis XIV in Paris in 1665, French sculptors found that they lacked the dignity and restraint appropriate to the person of the king. The Classical ideals of the French Academy were revealed by the sculpture commissioned for the palace and gardens of Versailles and by the many copies of ancient marbles made by French students in Rome and installed in Versailles in the 1680's. The sculpture of Versailles, dedicated to the glorification of the Sun-King, formed a rich, planned concentration of sculptural work equalled only by the Gothic cathedral.

François Girardon was the leading sculptor during the period in which LeBrun directed the art of Versailles. The heroic, idealized figures of Girardon's 'Rape of Proserpine', although in violent poses, are transfixed by the calm and hard surfaces that enclose the figural volumes, with no suggestion of fleshly softness or vitality comparable to Bernini's surfaces. Even Girardon's somewhat pictorial group of 'Apollo and the Nymphs', an allegorical reference to Louis XIV, aimed at the statuesque clarity of bodily parts rather than the sense of breathing life sought by Baroque sculptors in Italy.

The later, more spirited, and less monumental work of Charles Antoine Coysevox, probably stimulated by Puget and other Baroque artists, introduced the Rococo style in sculpture. This style spread rapidly to other court circles in Europe, but the voices of Classicism were never stilled, and throughout the eighteenth century in much of Europe conflict raged between these contrasting points of view. The Rococo style fostered by Coysevox was carried on with an unusual constancy into the nineteenth century by a sequence of sculptors, who were frequently related not only by sculptural traditions but by family ties. Guillaume and Nicolas Coustou, nephews of Coysevox, trained Jean-Baptiste Lemoyne, whose son, Jean-Louis Lemoyne, became the teacher of such important Rococo sculptors as Jean-Baptiste Pigalle and Etienne-Maurice Falconet.

This style was well suited to the portrayal of intimate, playful, or tender moments of life but was less effective in subjects of a heroic nature. Coysevox's sprightly figure of the Duchess of Burgundy as 'Diana', made originally (1710) for the Château of Marly, and Falconet's small and charming 'Bather' (1757) are examples of the special talent of the Rococo sculptor for the portrayal of the softness, delicacy, and grace of the feminine figure. (Pl. 36a.) Pigalle's children in playful activities and his 'Mercury Attaching His Sandals' are examples of the small scale and the light and often trivial subjects of Rococo works. The statuettes by Clodion (Claude Michel) of nymphs and satyrs reveal the joyful and sensuous inclinations of this style. The departure from the monumentality and grandeur of French Classicism is further emphasized by the ceramic figurines, popular items of ornament during the eighteenth century in Europe, for which many Rococo sculptors designed pieces. Perhaps the sculptural acme of the Rococo group was reached with their highly individualized, life-size busts, which projected emotional warmth, intellectual alertness, and love of life in a manner that transformed the momentary character of Bernini's portraits into a peculiarly Rococo, and French, vivaciousness. Coysevox's 'Self-portrait' and his bust of Robert de Cotte are examples of this type. It culminated during the late eighteenth century in the lively and penetrating portraits of Jean-Antoine Houdon. (Pl. 36b.)

During the seventeenth and eighteenth centuries sculpture usually attempted to attain effects associated with painting. Girardon's marble relief 'Nymphs Bathing' recalls the Donatellesque tradition of utilizing subtle surface variations and delicate linear passages to represent an atmospheric spaciousness behind the half-round of the forward figures. This type of relief sculpture developed fragile pieces of virtuosity and pictorial effect such as the 'Horses of the Sun', carved by Le Lorrain over the entrance to the stables of the Hôtel de Rohan. The Rococo style also entered more monumental statuary. Such works as the 'Horse Tamers of Marly', carried out by Guillaume Coustou in 1740 and now on the Place de la Concorde in Paris, reveals the sensibility to fragile projections and the lively variations of surface and silhouette characteristic of Rococo.

The soft contours and the vitality of small Rococo sculpture enhanced the suggestion of life-in-the-round, but monumental works showed a marked tendency toward a preferred, most informative viewing point. Although European sculpture had been freed from subservience to architecture, large-scale, free-standing statues and monuments continued to be affected by the overall sense of order which spatial complexes such as courts, gardens, and public squares imposed. With the acceptance of axial principles of architectural planning in most parts of Europe in the seventeenth century, the sculptor was somewhat released from demands for an infinite number of views imposed during the Renaissance by centripetal placement. Rococo sculptors usually planned a major and several secondary views, on the assumption that the spectator would follow the axial paths planned by the architect.

Monumental and profusely sculptured tombs afforded a major opportunity to French sculptors. During the late seventeenth century the traditional praying attitude of the sepulchral effigy was transformed into one in which the deceased offers himself to the Deity. Early examples are the figure of Colbert on his tomb in Saint-Eustache and that of Mazarin, both by Coysevox. Among the most elaborate allegorical tombs of the period were those made by Pigalle for the Comte d'Harcourt in Notre Dame in Paris and for the Comte de Saxe in Strasbourg, both of which employ the shrouded skeleton, a medieval symbol of death, and figures that plead or weep for the dead.

Eighteenth-century sculptors all over Europe by the excellence of their workmanship and the suggestion of a living presence in their sculpture revealed their indebtedness not only to the strict standards and philosophical principles of the French Academy but also to the keen observations and formal inventions of the artists of the earlier Tuscan-Roman tradition. The lively, pictorial quality of Rococo sculpture was increasingly opposed during the third quarter of the eighteenth century by Neoclassic standards of statuesque calm and by idealized figure types modelled on ancient Greek works. The Neoclassic style was to be most fully realized in sculpture during the last years of the eighteenth century by the Italian Canova and the Dane Thorwaldsen.

Architecture in Pre-Petrine Scandinavia and Russia

In regions where timber was easily available, a style of architecture had arisen in the Middle Ages that combined function with both the limitations and the flexibility of wood as a building material. Few examples of the stave church of the Scandinavian countries and the timber church of northern Russia survive in their original form because of the combustibility and the perishability of wood. Yet some of them have been preserved in some state of repair or restoration.

The wooden church of Russia revealed certain features that may be Byzantine, Tatar, or Gothic, but it remained essentially Russian. The octagonal central space and the pyramidal exterior, traceable to the eleventh-century Cathedral of Sancta Sophia in Kiev, was probably derived from the need to adapt the Greek-cross plan to the most ample practical arrangement to which a log structure could aspire. The tall roof, resembling a tent and frequently called a tent roof, built of planks laid on vertical rafters, is known by the Tatar name of 'shater'. The high vertical reach (obtained by a shater resting on an octagonal drum and topped by a spired, bulbous cupola) may suggest that Gothic influence came into northern Russia from German and Polish contacts with the merchant city of Novgorod even before the arrival of Italian craftsmen at the court of Ivan III in the fifteenth century. But the octagonal drum, the shater, and the cupola, characteristics of the Russian church, probably were themselves the answer of the Russian carpenter-builder to the problem of adapting his materials to his objectives, as were also the *bochki* ('barrels'), or omega-shaped broken arches, with which he decorated the exterior of his churches. One of the best examples of the carpenter-builder's craft, though sometimes considered too extravagant, was the Church of the Transfiguration at Kizhi, built in 1714, with twenty-three cupolas and numerous bochki. (Pl. 37b.)

Russian masonry churches followed the same general structure. They were essentially octagonal, pyramidal, tent churches on the cross plan even when stone permitted, if desired, a greater variety of ornamentation, subsidiary chapels, and more massive dimensions. The Cathedral of St Basil the Blessed, built by Ivan IV in 1555–60 and noted today because it dominates the square outside the walls enclosing the congeries of buildings known as the Moscow Kremlin, is perhaps the outstanding example of the Russian masonry church. Its nine towers are each topped with a polychrome cupola. Built (notwithstanding a persistent legend to the contrary) by the Russian architects Postnik and Barma, it remains, despite or perhaps because of its exuberance, one of the most celebrated landmarks of pre-Petrine architecture. (Pl. 37a.)

Gothic Architecture

The Gothic style, characteristic of most of Western and Central Europe's architecture in 1300, had likewise been developed primarily in the design of churches and cathedrals. Neither belief nor ceremony had been static, and builders had been called upon to shape interior spaces to meet the changing demands of the cult. A search for a greater structural and stylistic unity of architectural elements also favoured change. The Classical rules for the arrangement of architectural elements had been in part lost and, more significant, in part invalidated by an architectural inclination unknown to Greek and Roman architects—the Christian aspiration to create a vast interior reaching toward unprecedented heights. The Île-de-France cathedral was accepted as a model by most of the Continent, but by 1300 adjustments to varying local traditions resulted in several distinct styles.

A Gothic church was a stone skeleton composed of rib-vaults supported by piers and sustained against the outward thrust of the vaults by buttresses. In the second half of the thirteenth century, piers became slimmer and taller, articulated by shafts that continued directly into the ribs of the vaults; arches became more sharply pointed; and all parts seem to have been shaped by a wish to attain an ever higher interior. The huge cathedrals (Reims, Amiens, Cologne, Beauvais, and Troyes) on which work continued during the fourteenth century present dramatic evidence of local devotion and civic pride in their tremendous interior height. (Pl. 38a, b.) In 1284, however, when the vaults of the Cathedral of Beauvais crashed from the unprecedented height of 157 feet, cathedral-builders apparently recognized that they had reached the limit of their structural technique.

The vast, tall interior unity of the Christian cathedral, essentially founded on the technological and esthetic development of the rib-vault, had no parallel outside Europe. It differed strikingly, for example, from the low, horizontal compartments of the hypostyle Islamic mosque. With every step inside his mosque the Muslim experiences change along severely channelled aisles in a space shattered in all directions by a forest of columns, inducing him to draw within himself to pray. The Christian, upon entering his cathedral, becomes part of a continuous space that expands into the light-filled upper reaches of a central nave, inducing him to feel united with the rest of the congregation and the main altar.

Although few cathedrals were initiated in the fourteenth and fifteenth centuries and activity centred around parish or monastery churches and secular buildings, the ideal of expansive space continued to dominate their interiors. In Germany architects formed a great unity of space and light by raising the side aisles and eliminating the independent reaches of the transept. In this new type of church, the 'hall' church, the unbroken rise of the slim shafts of the piers into the vaults gave a new emphasis to the overhead as the final gathering place of the structure's linear energy. Unity in width as well as height was gained by interweaving ribs and intermediary mouldings to form an ornamental web that spanned the full length and breadth of the interior. Outstanding examples (1200–1500) of the German 'hall' church are Saint Elizabeth's in Marburg, the choir of Saint Lawrence's in Nuremberg, Saint Stephen's in Vienna, and Saint Lawrence's in Landshut. (Pl. 39a, b.)

An altogether different sense of spatial unity was characteristic of southern France and Catalonia. The Cathedral of Albi, completed in 1380, provided an interior space dominated by a vast single nave, evenly lighted by tall lancet windows, well suited to the bright sun of the south, and covered by vaults of exceptional spans. The fortress-like exterior is characterized by a taut alternation of half-round buttresses with shallow rectangular chapels surrounding the nave. Its impressiveness is accented by a tower that forms the single western entry. (Pl. 40a.) Another striking example of this type, the Cathedral of Gerona in Catalonia, is covered by a vault with an amazing span of 73 feet—an engineering miracle of the early fifteenth century that drew upon the combined knowledge of architects from all over Europe. (Pl. 41a, b.)

The Hispanization of the Île-de-France cathedral can be followed from its faithful reproduction in the Cathedral of Léon through its variations in the cathedrals of Burgos and Toledo to the uniquely Spanish form of the Cathedral of Seville. The Cathedral of Seville was begun in 1401 with the famous resolution—expressive of the grandiloquent aspiration which continued to motivate Gothic Europe—to build 'such a church that those who see it will take us for mad' to have begun it.[16] It completely covers the 250 feet by 400 feet rectangle originally occupied by the main Muslim mosque and thus has a rectangular plan, five aisles wide and nine bays long. (Pl. 40b.) This aspect of the ground plan, the block-like clarity of the exterior parts, and the acceptance of the old minaret as the cathedral's bell-tower were frank admissions of the Islamic heritage, which, moreover, lived on in the art of Christian Spain. Like Germany and England, Spain preserved an amazingly creative vitality within the forms of the Gothic style. In Spain it lasted until well into the sixteenth century.

Maintaining a marked degree of architectural independence until the seventeenth century England initiated a late phase of Gothic architecture, which subsequently took root also on the Continent. English architects began to move toward a frankly decorative treatment of vaults and window traceries in the early fourteenth century. The names given to English architecture during this period—'decorated' or 'curvilinear'—are clues to its ornamental and lively nature. Small-scale motifs were spread over the surfaces of spandrels and tympanums of cusped, mixtilinear, and, occasionally, ogee arches, but the main areas of innovation were the vaults, where the various ribs rising from the piers were elaborated by intermediary and interlocking ribs in such a way that complicated 'star-like' patterns were created. The spectacular stellar vaults of the cathedrals of Gloucester, Canterbury, Wells, Ely, and Exeter have spatial implications; they seem to be ornamental webs that merge all the individual bays into a continuous decorative unit. Architects in nearby

Normandy appear to have taken over the ogee arch and the curvilinear rhythms to form the French 'flamboyant' style, which was readily diffused over most of the Continent.[17] The exuberant, if no longer transcendental, energy of this style rises through the fragile pentagonal porch of Saint-Maclou in Rouen (1434) and the north portal of the Cathedral of Strasbourg (1495).

Meanwhile, England had abandoned the 'curvilinear' style and, in the late fourteenth century, had initiated a new one called 'perpendicular' or 'rectilinear'. Exceptional fifteenth-century examples of this kind of ornament are the lantern over the crossing of the Cathedral of Ely, the chapels of Eton College and King's College in Cambridge, and, not completed until the next century, the Saint George Chapel of Windsor Castle. (Pl. 42a, b.) The terms 'fan', 'palm', or 'conoidal', used to describe their vaults, suggest spreading, curving surfaces that rise directly from the walls or piers to form the vaults.

Surfaces had been of secondary importance in the Gothic style of the thirteenth century, but in the fifteenth century they became the main realm of decorative invention, a major factor in the unity of interior space, and the conqueror of the linear skeleton that had previously characterized Gothic architecture. This sensibility to the concreteness of the decorative surface was the common denominator of the architectural styles of many parts of fifteenth-century Europe. The 'Isabeline' in Spain, the 'Manueline' in Portugal, and the 'Florid Gothic' in Venice have an opulence of decoration and an excellence of craftsmanship comparable to contemporary works in England, France, and Germany.

In keeping with the general trend toward secularization, this style was most successful in the secular architecture of the late Gothic period. It was adopted for city halls like that of Compiègne in France and of Lübeck and Stralsund in Germany, for châteaux like that of Josselin in Brittany, for bourgeois mansions like Jacques Coeur's in Bourges, and for English manor houses. (Pl. 43a.) Perhaps the outstanding example was the Palais de Justice in Rouen, begun in 1493. Its windows and portals assume ornamental shapes; its walls terminate in a fragile arcade along the roofline; the piers sectioning its façade gradually diminish into delicately carved finials; and the lace-like frames of the dormer windows join with these features to carry its wall decoratively into the steep rise of a tall roof. Among the most exceptional of the many Gothic merchant palaces of Europe was Marino Contarini's Ca' d'Oro on the Grand Canal in Venice. (Pl. 43b.) Its several stages of galleries are supported by elaborately carved and ornamentally shaped arcades, and the preciousness of its white marble and pale rose-coloured walls is lavishly enriched with gold and the flicker of light reflected from the canal.

The Beginnings of Italian Renaissance Architecture

While Tuscan painters had long been stirred by a new ideal, Tuscan architects continued to build in the Italian Gothic style until the fifteenth century.

By 1420, however, Brunelleschi established an essentially different architectural 'vocabulary' and 'syntax' based on his understanding of ancient Roman architecture. In a spirit that paralleled that of his contemporaries in Florence who waxed enthusiastic about the ancient forms in literature or the visual arts, he and his followers believed that Greco-Roman architectural forms were superior to the 'unmeasured and mixtilinear' forms of the Gothic, which they attributed to Germanic 'barbarians'. In pursuit of their aim, they gave unprecedented deference to the rules of architecture laid down in a treatise by Vitruvius in the first century BC and eagerly studied the architectural and decorative vocabulary of Roman ruins. Where the lessons learned from the actual monuments did not coincide with the advice given by Vitruvius the motifs or solutions found in Roman ruins won out, along with those derived from Early Christian, Byzantine, or Romanesque buildings believed to reflect ancient forms. In this way, the architects of Tuscany conjured up an image of Roman architecture that was amazingly complete. Brunelleschi's churches (San Lorenzo and Santo Spirito) in Florence gave a new architectural ideal to Italy and eventually to the whole of Europe and America. (Pl. 46a.) The models for his supports and ceilings were not provided by the local Gothic churches; rather the columns and half-round arches, the flat ceilings, and the boxlike nave and transepts were fashioned on the Romanesque Church of SS. Apostoli, which, his contemporaries believed, was built by Charlemagne.

The architectural vocabulary which Brunelleschi used was based on the ornate 'Corinthian order', composed of a pedestal, round shaft, capital, abacus, and entablature (made up of a lower moulding or architrave, a frieze, and a top cornice). Each of the ancient orders, however, whether Corinthian, Doric, or Ionic, came to be defined by rules for the shape, the scale, and the sequence of its parts, and practice allowed only a limited variation in specifications. The parts of Brunelleschi's order were held together as a continuous system by the contrast of the grey stone of which they were made with the white plaster of the walls; and the careful ratios of parts within the order were reflected in the simple 1:2 and 3:5 ratios that determined the length, width, and height of nave, crossing dome, arms, and chapels. Visual awareness of these ratios adds to the harmony and coherence of structure and interior space.

In Brunelleschi's Latin-cross plan the dome at the intersection, especially the large dome he designed for the Cathedral of Florence, provided a central core to which all parts referred. (Fig. 1; Pl. 46b.) This ordered stability, based upon a building's central vertical axis, is more readily seen in his early Pazzi chapel and most impressively developed in his last work, the unfinished Church of Santa Maria degli Angeli in Florence. Derived from the domed rotunda-with-ambulatory of late Antiquity, this architectural type is characterized by massive piers and chapels arranged around a rotunda dominated by a dome.[18]

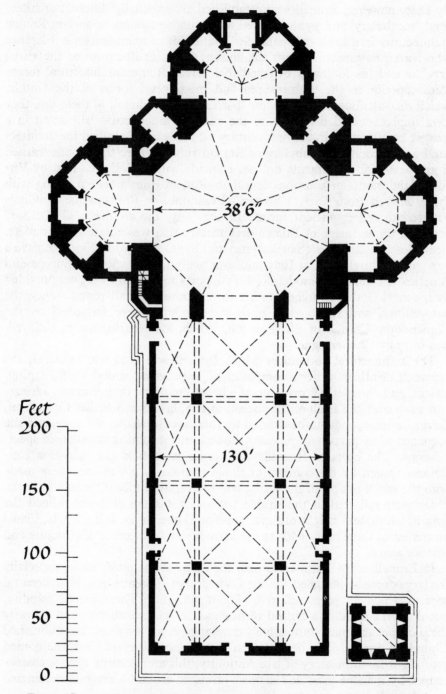

FIG. 1. Ground-plan of Santa Maria delle Fiori, Florence (after Fletcher).

Alberti, the leading theorist of the fifteenth century, defined the essence of Brunelleschi's architectural form as the proportional harmony of all parts to the whole.[19] He also fostered the idea that the noble orders served to decorate the wall, dramatizing its inherent strength and proportions. Furthermore, he held that new forms could be created by merging several ancient models or

FIG. 2. Plan of Palmanova

by combining an ancient form with a Christian one. This merging was particularly evident in the variety of basilican church façades that he devised from the triumphal arch and the pedimented temple façade of the Romans. Alberti, like most of the architects of the fifteenth century, looked upon the basilican church with its high central aisle and its lower side aisles as an unfortunate historical accident, which should be corrected even at that late date. His effort at correction in the barrel-vaulted church of Sant' Andrea in

Mantua was particularly ingenious but was not generally followed until, shortly after the middle of the sixteenth century, it was taken as a model for the Gesu, the mother church of the Jesuit Order. On the other hand, his church of San Sebastiano in Mantua, planned in 1460 and apparently based on the domed, Greek-cross churches of the Byzantine tradition, did gain a wide following.[20]

During the late fifteenth century and the early sixteenth, several architects contributed to the formation of compactly ordered central churches. The designs of Antonio Averlino, called il Filarete, and the exploratory sketches of Leonardo da Vinci were especially significant. Contemporaries extolled Santa Maria delle Carceri in Prato, Santa Maria della Consolazione in Todi, and San Biagio in Montepulciano, outstanding examples of this central type, as the most perfect expression of cosmic order and thus appropriate symbolically, if not ceremonially, for Christian worship. So convinced were they of the superiority of the central plan that even Saint Peter's in Rome, the most revered basilican church in the Christian world of that day, fell victim to their criticism, and a domed Greek-cross church, the largest in the Western world, arose in its place (with the religious and political repercussions examined in Chapter IV). The new Saint Peter's was planned and initiated by Donato Bramante but was continued according to a revision by Michelangelo and was completed only in the early seventeenth century merely to be redesigned again (see below). The central church, in its clear reciprocal relation of exterior to interior and its careful balance of spaces around the central cavity of the dome, was the ultimate statement of an architectural order stabilized around its own centre.

Centrally ordered architecture was set up as the ideal in secular enterprises as well. Its formal aim led to the square, block-design palace with façades of three graduated stages and an arcaded central court, of which the Palazzo Riccardi-Medici, planned during the second quarter of the fifteenth century, and the Palazzo Strozzi are magnificent illustrations. (Pl. 47a.) Central symmetry, being considered practical for defence purposes, was also accepted for the overall plan of a city. Filarete and Francesco di Giorgio in the late fifteenth century fostered this type of city plan, and its long life is evidenced by Scamozzi's design for Palmanova in 1593 (Fig. 2), Christopher Wren's for the centre of London in 1666, and L'Enfant's for Washington in 1791. The rectangular grid-plan, however, proved a more practical, if less ornamental, basis for the organization or expansion of a city. In south and Central America Spanish architects planned the most impressive examples of this type. (Pl. 83.)

Further Developments (from the Sixteenth to the Eighteenth Century)

Some aspects of the Florentine style were accepted in Milan and Urbino, and in these secondary centres Bramante, the leading architect of the early sixteenth century, acquired his training and carried out his first works.

Although he developed a more severe and monumental architectural style in Rome after 1500, his early works in Lombardy reflected the local admiration for rich terra cotta and plaster decoration. The most profusely ornamented of these is the façade of the Certosa of Pavia, which was more admired by visitors from the rest of Europe than the more restrained architecture of Tuscany; its relatively clear framework in horizontals and verticals is charged with a multitude of small figures, geometric inlays, and vegetal courses in a variety of colourful marbles and in varying degrees of relief. Lombardy and, to a lesser degree, Naples, probably because of their geographic positions, became the centres in which most of Europe encountered the new architectural style. The French and the Spanish who came to Italy in the late fifteenth and early sixteenth century as conquerors were impressed by the architectural wonders they saw and, within the next few decades, deferred to Italian Renaissance forms.

Until the middle of the sixteenth century, the advance of the Renaissance in France was fostered mainly by its kings, Charles VIII and Francis I. They imported works of art, designs, engravings, and even artists to make the royal palaces and chateaux appropriately sumptuous. In his enthusiasm Francis I initiated many works, but he was dependent on architects and masons for whom Italian Renaissance forms meant an abrupt disturbance of the accustomed way. The large, block-design palace with a square central court designed by Pierre Lescot for the Louvre in the middle of the sixteenth century merged the French tradition of pavilion-and-corridor architecture with the central plan of Italy. In this work and that of the more traditional Hôtel Carnavalet, Lescot (working, as we have seen, with the sculptor Goujon) created elegantly proportioned and richly sculptured façades that reveal a tendency toward 'correctness' in the proportions of the orders, a tendency which France (in contrast with Italy) was to intensify during the seventeenth century. (Pl. 47b.) Sebastiano Serlio's designs and his 'model books' on architecture, though more inventive and less 'correct' than the growing awareness of France would tolerate, were nevertheless important steps in the formation of her Renaissance ideals. De l'Orme in the third quarter of the sixteenth century ran more parallel to contemporary works in Italy in the fullness of his forms, the use of rustication, and the aim of monumentality, but he used Italian models along with traditional French types in a completely sovereign way.

During the first half of the sixteenth century, Spain was even more prolific than France as a follower of the Lombard Renaissance. The Spanish 'Plateresque' style is characterized by profuse and small-scale decorative motifs carved as textural patterns within the confines of pilasters, pedestals, friezes, window frames, and parapets along the roofline. The 'Puerta del Pardon' of the Cathedral in Granada (Pl. 44a) and the City Hall in Seville are its foremost representatives. It was not limited to secular structures and ornamental portals because, unlike France, Spain had to provide impressive cathedrals—

not only for the major cities of Andalusia, recently re-won from Islam, but also for the new cities of the New World. (Pl. 44b; 45a, b.)

Juan de Herrera, following the trend of which Serlio was an outstanding exponent, formed an architectural style of unprecedented gravity that contrasted sharply with the Plateresque. As architect to the king, Herrera was able to impose his style on Spain and the New World (see below). His gigantic square palace of the Escorial with its twelve courts, church, monastery, palace, and royal residence was considered by contemporaries to surpass anything built in ancient times. The majesty and sobriety which characterize his architecture were still more magnificently revealed in his design for the Cathedral of Valladolid, which, enhancing the traditional rectangular ground plan of the Cathedral of Seville with four corner towers, he made into a centrally ordered rectangle of most impressive dimensions and grandeur.

Next to France and Spain, the most significant architectural development outside central Italy occurred in the Venetian Republic. Venice also had encountered the Tuscan forms clothed in the ornate and polychrome vestments of Lombardy, but, in the last years of the fifteenth century, a Venetian, Mauro Coducci, brought a clearer understanding of the Albertian concept of architecture. Coducci's Palazzo-Corner Spinelli and Palazzo Vendramin-Calergi provided a Colosseum-like façade, divided into several stages by entablatures, supported by piers and arcades and constructed not of the light and bright materials of the Ca'd'Oro but of grey stone. (Pl. 48a.) Jacopo Sansovino in Venice and Michele Sanmichele in Verona designed successively more monumental versions of the stylar façades introduced by Alberti in the Rucellai Palace in Florence and by Bramante in the 'House of Raphael' in Rome. In so doing, however, Venetians put aside a palatial type ideally suited to the watery setting of their city.

In the third quarter of the sixteenth century Andrea Palladio emerged from this sober Classical atmosphere. He demonstrated again the fruitfulness of the centripetal principle of arrangement in his Villa Rotonda near Vincenza. (Pl. 49a.) Perhaps the most influential feature of this villa, particularly upon English country houses during the seventeenth and eighteenth centuries, was the temple-like façade with which he faced its four sides. In the church façades of San Giorgio and Il Redentore in Venice, Palladio furthermore made the most important innovation in the temple-type façade since it was initiated by Alberti. (Pl. 49b.) The Ancient temple façade, fundamentally a colonnade surmounted by a triangular pediment, had caused embarrassment to those who attempted to use it to front the tall centre and lower sides of the Christian basilica, but Palladio solved the formal difficulty by interpenetrating two pedimented temple façades, a broad one on the lower level of the side chapels under a tall one with two-stage columns rising to the height of the centre nave. This solution was used in many variations for the next two hundred years.

Palladio's architecture was put aside by most of Catholic Europe in favour of the sixteenth-century idiom of central Italy, but it won a limited favour in England when it was introduced by Inigo Jones in the Banqueting House at Whitehall, London, in 1619, and it gained more general recognition when fostered by Richard Boyle in the early eighteenth century. England, her colonies, and Protestant countries generally continued the Palladian tradition of Renaissance architecture in opposition to the exuberant Baroque of Catholic Europe and America.

Meanwhile, in central Italy a movement paralleling Mannerism in painting had taken place in architecture. Most Renaissance designers had accepted the separate existence of the plane of the wall and its openings behind the self-sufficient grid of horizontals and verticals that comprise the architectural orders, but in the second quarter of the sixteenth century architects sought a greater decorative coherence of wall and order. To this end, the self-sufficiency of the architectural order was violated. Parts were made to overlap, interlink, or participate in patterns of rhythmic intervals, textures, colours, or shapes, so that the elements of the order and of the wall were brought into a decorative relationship to each other. Giulio Romano's house and his Palazzo del Te in Mantua, Baldassare Peruzzi's Palazzo Massimi in Rome (Pl. 48b), Serlio's published designs, and Vignola's Palazzo Farnese in Caprarola reflected this new attitude toward the treatment of the wall.

Michelangelo, recognized as an early leader of the revolt against Vitruvian rules, had initiated the new approach in his designs (1519) for the façade of Brunelleschi's Church of San Lorenzo and had further developed it in the Laurentian Library and the Medici Chapel of Florence. The style requires a sculptural organization of shapes so as to make them seem to react to one another, with no individual part autonomous and all equal before the modelling force of light. Starting with a completely traditional form, such as his original design for the wall niches alongside the Medici tombs, Michelangelo gradually caused the interaction of adjacent shapes, and the compressing and interlinking of parts, until he transformed the whole into something quite unique in its inherent order. The arrangement of parts was no longer dependent on Alberti's sense for an anthropomorphic balance of weights and supports but rather on a sense of decorative unity; and the size of architectural elements was no longer scaled in relation to man. They became gigantic, scaled to pilasters or columns that rose through several stages, like those on the Palace of the Conservatori on the Capitoline Hill (1536) or on the apse of St Peter's in Rome (1546). The new attitude tended to make the solution of each architectural problem unique and, thus, to a degree not known before, transformed architecture into a medium for personal expression. Few contemporary architects outside central Italy grasped the significance of this attitude, and even in Italy few were able to act as arbiters of architectural form with the self-confidence of Michelangelo.

*   *   *

Another important change in the architecture of central Italy (and eventually much of the rest of Europe) was the displacement of the Renaissance preference for a centripetal order by a new axial continuity along an ideal line of vision or movement. This inclination had been expressed as early as the fifteenth century in the relation of Tuscan villas to surrounding gardens. Bramante provided an important preparation for the new inclination in his early-sixteenth-century design for the great complex of levels in the Vatican's Belvedere Court, which he ordered along a longitudinal axis of view, if not of movement. A dramatic instance of the transformation of the centrally ordered palace occurred in the modifications planned in 1546 by Michelangelo for the traditional block-type Palazzo Farnese in Rome. Here he planned a longitudinal continuity that, starting in a carefully ordered piazza in front of the palace, passed through an open loggia at the rear of the court into the gardens and finally, by means of a projected bridge across the Tiber, to the Villa Farnesina on the other side. Michelangelo also designed the Piazza of the Campidoglio in Rome along axial schemes of movement[22] (Pl. 50a), Ammannati transformed the Pitti Palace in Florence, and Vignola provided a more complex axial order for the Villa Giulia outside Rome. (Pl. 50b.) This axial scheme was favoured in the seventeenth century. The ideal building no longer turned introspectively toward its own centre but opened expansively to become part of a larger plan.

The growing interest in movement and in long continuities gave unprecedented importance to staircases as dramatic elements of an architectural complex. Among the first products of this development was the monumental stair planned by Bramante to connect the several levels of the Belvedere Court. More imposing examples followed in the seventeenth and eighteenth centuries. The axial stairway (enhanced by watercourses and fountains) that serves to relate the elevated Villa d'Este to its lower gardens, and the ornamental Spanish Steps constructed on the steep slope before the Church of the Trinity in Rome were among the most spectacular. Interior staircases also became important as decorative ensembles in most of Europe. The main staircases of the Escorial in Spain, the Scala Regia leading from the vestibule of Saint Peter's to the Vatican apartments of the pope, the Staircase of the Ambassadors at Versailles (destroyed in the eighteenth century), and the grand staircase of the Archbishop's Palace in Würzburg served as models until modern times.

Grand-scale planning was most impressively developed in France. Early efforts were the palace and town built by Jacques Lemercier for Vicomte Richelieu (1631) and the château Vaux-le-Vicomte (1657), begun by Louis Levau and completed with gardens by Le Nôtre. (Pl. 51a.) These architects and others had a hand in designing the Palace of Versailles, begun in 1627 as a château, enlarged in the 1660's as the royal residence of Louis XIV, and elaborated until well into the eighteenth century. (Pl. 51b.) It was built not only to house the ten thousand people who made up Louis' court and the embassies sent by the other governments of Europe but also to impress the world with visual attributes of his political power and patronage in the form of decorative marvels and to serve as the focus and pinnacle of European aristocratic society. Portions of the interior such as Jules Hardouin Mansard's Hall of Mirrors, rich in glass, multicoloured marbles, gilding, fabrics, painting, and sculpture, flaunted a magnificence unrivalled in Europe. The interior decoration depended less on the finish of individual parts than on the grandeur of the ensemble. Derived from Annibale Carracci's interiors in the Palazzo Farnese in Rome, it also recalled the Gallery of Francis I at Fontainebleau, carried out by Florentine artists a century earlier. The most impressive evidence of the Sun King's power was the very scale on which the palace and its dependencies were planned. With its approaching roads, huge cour d'honneur, wide-spreading wings, terraces, pools, fountains, geometric gardens (by Lenôtre), radial avenues, play villages, and parks, all arranged on an axial plan, the palace dominates the landscape as far as the eye can see.

Versailles became a model of grand-scale architecture for all of Europe. German princelings built impressive palaces of the Versailles type such as the Palace of Pommersfelden in Franconia and the episcopal residence at Würzburg. The palaces of La Granja and Aranjuez in Spain, Peter the Great's Peterhof, Frederick the Great's Sans Souci, and Maria Theresa's Schönbrunn clearly follow the same model. Even relatively conservative English architects designed large Palladian complexes, such as Blenheim Palace in Oxfordshire and Castle Howard in Yorkshire, both by John Vanbrugh. For all their grandeur, however, these European projects do not surpass the extensive architectural complexes of northern India or Peking (see below).

The Baroque Style in Architecture

In central Italy in the sixteenth century the central church was transformed by the same axial order that re-shaped the plans of palaces and city squares. The church that gathered around a circular dome was superseded by the oval church, which produced the effect of a dynamic interior space guiding the entrant along the longitudinal axis from the entry to the altar and expanding into an oval dome that lent unity to the enclosing surfaces. Two of the most important examples of this type were Vignola's churches of San Giacomo degli Incurabili and Santa Anna dei Palafrenieri in Rome. Among the most impressive variations of the oval plan in the seventeenth century are Borromini's San Carlo alle Quattro Fontane and Bernini's Sant' Andrea al Quirinale in Rome and, in the early eighteenth century, Fischer von Erlach's Karlskirche in Vienna. The domed Greek-cross church of the Renaissance lived on into the seventeenth century in other longitudinal variations. Examples are Levau's church of the Collège des Quatre Nations (now the

Palais de l'Institut), Mansart's huge Saint Louis des Invalides (Pl. 52a) in Paris, Wren's Saint Paul's in London (Pl. 52b), and Fischer von Erlach's University Church in Salzburg.

The most influential type of church of the post-Tridentine world, however, was the one designed in 1568 by Vignola for the new order of the Jesuits in Rome. Commissioned, in the new reform spirit, to build an inexpensive church with a single vaulted nave and side chapels but to follow the rules of good architecture, Vignola apparently took as his model the Church of Sant' Andrea in Mantua, designed in 1471 by Alberti. The resulting edifice, the compact Latin-cross Gesù with barrel-vaulted nave and arms and a tall crossing dome, became the church most often imitated in the next two hundred and fifty years. (Fig. 3; Pl. 53a, b.) Even Michelangelo's central church of Saint Peter's in Rome was redesigned in 1606 by Carlo Maderno to become a gigantic three-aisled version of the Gesù. Architects in France and in Spain and her colonies enthusiastically followed the Gesù plan until the middle of the eighteenth century. The Gesù façade designed by Giacomo della Porta was equally influential. Following a façade type invented by Alberti for Santa Maria Novella in Florence in the use of the scroll to bind the lower sides to the higher centre, he attained a greater compactness of form around the centre axis, anticipating the Baroque architects' more dramatic culmination along the centreline. In façades such as that of the Saint Gervais in Paris, France produced some of the most impressive variations on the Gesù. The Jesuit order, in its faithfulness to the plan and the façade of the Gesù, played an important role in the spread of Baroque architecture.

Although Italian architects of the late sixteenth century departed notably from Renaissance models in the basic order of their ground plan and in their organization of façades, they tended, under the leadership of Carlo Maderno, to return to the more 'Classic' and more robust architectural elements of the High Renaissance, abandoning the ambiguously interlinked and interacting shapes of the Mannerists of the mid-sixteenth century. To be sure, Bernini and Pietro da Cortona lent excitement to their structures by utilizing multi-coloured marbles and strongly shadowed intervals between parts, and their curving walls and ornamental ground plans brought a ponderous vitality to their architecture, but the separate parts were relatively static and dense volumes that participated in a system of burdens and supports not unlike that of the Renaissance.[23]

In France, where the Royal Academy of Architecture (founded 1670) more strictly maintained the rules of the orders, proximity to the Renaissance was even greater. In addition, French architects tended in their arrangements of the orders to avoid the more lively groupings and curvatures and the interruptive shadows employed by the Italians. The more rational and staid character of French architectural ideals is evident in the rejection of the curving façades planned by Bernini for the Louvre in 1665. England, Holland, and much of northern Europe, inclined toward a free Palladianism, main-

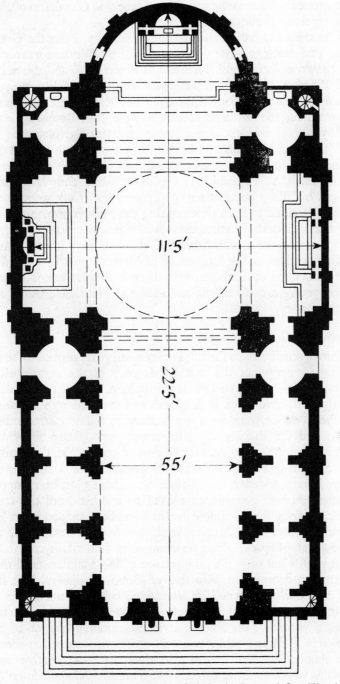

FIG. 3. Ground-plan of the Church of Il Gesù, Rome (after Fletcher).

tained an attitude closer to the refined and reserved Classicism of France than the more vigorous Baroque of Italy.

When, in the early half of the eighteenth century, Peter the Great and his successors undertook to build on marshy land the Western metropolis which today is known as Leningrad (formerly St Petersburg) and the neighbouring town of Pushkin (formerly Tsarskoye Selo), they deliberately imported Western architects and adopted Baroque and Rococo architectural models. Foremost among the Western architects were Jean-Baptiste-Alexandre Le Blond (1679–1719) and his young Italian assistant Bartolommeo Francesco Rastrelli (1700–71), who arrived in Russia in 1715. With the aid of Russian labour and Russian architects such as Mikhail Grigorieivch Zemtsov (1688–1743) they made St Petersburg a capital of stone churches, palaces, and government buildings contrasting vividly with the many wooden structures of Moscow, destined to burn down during the French invasion of 1812. The Baroque trend in both Russian cities was checked when, in 1757, Tsarina Elizabeth decreed the establishment of the Academy of Fine Arts, which became independent of the University of Moscow only in 1763. Its regulations were modelled upon those of the French Academy, and like its model it prodded young artistic talents to follow the Neoclassic trend of the late eighteenth century.

The Rococo Style in Architecture

Borromini's sensibility to the fluid unity of all parts proved to be the initial step in the formation of the graceful Rococo of the eighteenth century. Exponents of Classicism like Claude Perrault in France, the theatrical Vanbrugh and the flexible Wren in England, and even the most vigorous of the Italians, Pietro da Cortona, were not inclined to follow Borromini's unusual attitude toward the shaping of architectural parts. Borromini's method of designing of the 1630's is evident in the ground plan of San Carlo alle Quattro Fontane in Rome. (Pl. 54a.) Commissioned to make a church, refectory, dormitory,.library, cloister, and garden on a small plot, he compressed the parts, causing one to accommodate itself to another until the church had completely departed from a simple oval and had been shaped into a lobed oval with membrane-like walls. Architectural parts became flexible and malleable before the action of space, taking on some of its fluid vitality. In this respect, Borromini recalls not only the architecture of the Mannerists of the middle of the sixteenth century but also that of Gothic designers. The important façade of San Carlo, animated by alternating concave and convex surfaces, presents the first monumental example since late Antiquity of the undulated wall, a basic feature of the Rococo style. Borromini's Church of Sant' Ivo della Sapienza in Rome achieves a still more intricate interpenetration of geometric shapes; a stellar ground plan gives rise to alternative convex and concave walls, which continue directly into a uniquely shaped dome. (Pl. 54b.) The style of Borromini, not directly but as modified and elaborated by his followers Guarino Guarini and Filippe Juvara, passed to France, Portugal, Germany, Austria, and Bohemia as well as to Spain and Latin America, where it reinforced the Churrigueresque style—i.e. the style named after the exuberantly adorned architecture of Jose Churriguera (1650–1725).

In France the new Italian style was refined by a sense for the delicate, subtle, and harmonious. The architecture that resulted was truly one of 'youthfulness and spirit', as Louis XIV described the art that pleased him. The Rococo continued the vivaciousness and voluptuousness of the Baroque but called for more subtle variations of colour, shape, texture, and rhythm, and a lighter and more playful mood. The best examples of Rococo are found in the residences of the wealthy bourgeoisie and nobility of the city-centred court in the seventeenth and eighteenth centuries. Absenting themselves from their grand châteaux in the country, the nobles tended to build *hôtels*, more intimate and less palatial dwellings, in Paris and Versailles. (Pl. 56a.)

Since the fifteenth century, in houses such as that of Jacques Coeur in Bourges, the hôtel had maintained a fairly standard form. Although frequently building on irregularly shaped lots, seventeenth century architects attempted to arrange the hôtel along a longitudinal axis. A typical plan, such as that for the Hôtel de Bretonvilliers in Paris, provided a cour d'honneur screened from the street by a one-storey wall, flanked by offices and stables in wings to the right and left, and terminating with a corps de logis, with other private rooms facing the gardens to the rear. Among the more famous seventeenth-century examples are François Mansart's Hôtel de la Vrilliere (now the Bank of France) and Levau's Hôtel Lambert in Paris. The Petit Trianon, the week-end house in the gardens of Versailles designed for Madame de Pompadour in 1762 by Jacques Ange Gabriel, was most influential. (Pl. 56b.) This elegant structure, and particularly its west façade, served as an architectural model for several generations.

Many of the interiors of these buildings were decorated in the Rococo style. The intimate atmosphere of the eighteenth-century salon encouraged the Rococo artist to create his liveliest and most exquisite works. Although the delicate motifs in some French interiors tend to follow the rectilinear panelling of the room, the oval Hall of Princes in the Hôtel de Soubise in Paris, decorated by Germain Boffrand in the 1730's, is characterized by a more fluid passage of the wall into the vault. *Chinoiserie*, borrowings from Chinese and other Eastern works of art, played a prominent role in the mid-century wall paintings of the Hôtel de Rohan in Paris and appeared frequently in the wall paper, ornamental motifs, and furnishings of the houses of the well-to-do. (Pl. 57a.) Beyond this decorative vogue in the West and the influence of the Chinese garden in Western landscape architecture, Europe's intensified contact with the Far East produced no fundamental effect upon the architecture of either cultural area.

In Austria and southern Germany the new style won enthusiastic approval. The interiors of the palaces of Nymphenburg, Würzburg, and Potsdam

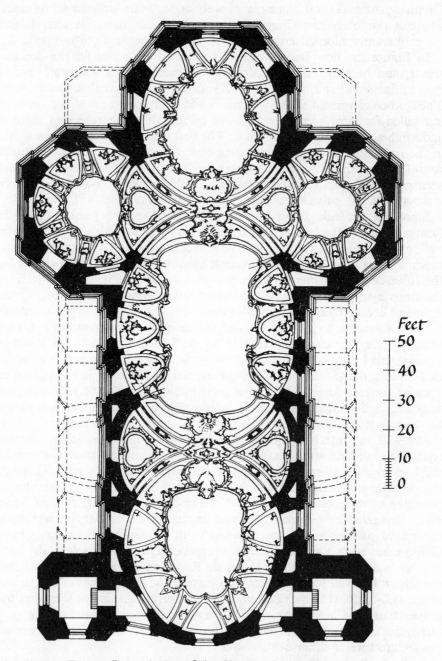

Fᴵɢ. 4. Ground-plan of the Church of Vierzehnheiligen
(after Fletcher).

(Sans Souci) were enriched with equally delicate but more exuberant decoration. (Pl. 57b.) All their surfaces and architectural courses undulate gracefully, avoiding the strength of straight lines and geometric shapes, and depending on a fluid and lively continuity to unify the many small parts into a decorative ensemble. German and Austrian architects extended the Rococo style to religious architecture, creating the most impassioned and visually exciting churches on the Continent. The luminous interiors of the Vierzehn-heiligen in Franconia by Johann Balthasar Neumann (Fig. 4; Pl. 55a), the Benedictine abbey of Ottobeuren by Johann Michael Fischer, and the pilgrimage church of the Wies (Pl. 55b) in Bavaria are characterized by a fluidity of space within a diaphanous white structure, gilded and frescoed to evoke an emotional exhilaration which contrasts strikingly with the intellectual curiosity summoned by the spatial complications of Guarini in Italy. Decorators of elaborate altars and restless surfaces, such as the Asam brothers and the stucco-workers of Wessobrunn, played unusually important roles in Rococo architecture. A major feature of these south German churches was the frescoed ceiling toward which all parts of the interior rose in excited curvilinear movements. Fully populated with a multitude of active figures, seen from below against a delicate blue sky in the Italian and particularly the Tiepolo manner, the vaults served as avenues for the final release of emotional fervour. (Pl. 19a.) The only other works in Christendom to compare with these exuberant Germanic creations were made in Spain and Portugal and their colonies in America.

England remained relatively aloof from the decorative excitement of Rococo style on the Continent. The bold architectural types of Wren and Vanbrugh continued in its churches, city squares, and country houses. The most original English architectural contribution of the period was the English landscape garden, which, in its irregularities and picturesqueness, makes a pleasing contrast to the formality of 'Georgian' architecture (the English adaptation of the Palladian style) and directly opposes the geometric patterns of French or Italian gardens. Probably the landscapes of Claude Lorrain were leading incentives toward this new ideal, and probably also it reflects English admiration for the Chinese garden not only by ornamental pagodas and bridges but also by the nascent Romantic sense of irregularity and freedom with which the elements of nature were arranged. These Romantic inclinations expressed themselves also in a mid-century interest in Gothic forms.

Yet the main direction of English architecture was along more Classic lines. Richard Boyle actively marked out this direction by sponsoring the English publications of Vitruvius, Alberti, and Palladio and also of model-books of the works of Inigo Jones and John Webb, the seventeenth-century architects who had first introduced England to the Palladian style. The Society of Dilettanti, founded in 1732, and chiefly interested in Classical archaeology, sent James Stuart and Nicholas Revett to Greece in 1750 to make measured drawings, which were eventually published in 1762 under the title *Antiquities of Athens*.

Illustrated publications on the ruins of Palmyra, Baalbek, and Herculaneum also appeared about this time, and the first systematic excavation of Pompeii was undertaken in 1763. In this atmosphere Robert Adam and his contemporaries in the third quarter of the eighteenth century led the way to a more direct dependence on Greco-Roman architectural models.

A similar Classical tendency meanwhile had been initiated in Paris. In 1732 the Palladian design of the Italian-born Jean Nicholas Servandoni won a competition among the plans submitted for the façade of the Church of Saint-Sulpice. By the 1760's the even more Classic forms of Gabriel's Petit Trianon at Versailles and Jacques Germain Soufflot's Church of Saint Geneviève (today the Panthéon) signalled the rise of Neoclassicism and the decline of Rococo on the Continent.

THE DECORATIVE ARTS IN EUROPE

The gradual separation of the decorative (the so-called 'minor') arts from the fine (the so-called 'major') arts of painting, sculpture, and architecture was a phenomenon peculiar to Europe during this period. Artists of medieval Europe, the Far East, Islam, and apparently also pre-Columbian America did not make any such distinction. Although many artists of this period in Europe worked in the decorative as well as the fine arts, and some objects occupy a position between the two, the distinction, nevertheless, has some justification. Artisans who made furniture, textiles, pottery, metalware, and glassware or who carved, painted, or inlaid designs on art objects did not have the same claim to scientific knowledge or intellectual accomplishment that enabled Renaissance painters, sculptors, and architects to demand successfully the status of liberal arts for their media. The making of utilitarian objects, the shape of which was largely determined by custom and by the purpose for which they were used, and the distribution of decorative motifs over the surface of such objects were believed to be less complicated and difficult formal problems than those faced in the major arts. Painting, sculpture, and architecture were also considered to be more capable of embodying the profound and elevated truths of science, philosophy, and Christianity, which the Western artists sought to represent in art. Some decorative motifs —emblems, for example—had specific meanings or associations, but from around 1500 many motifs were more generally used as ornament than as meaningful symbols. Decorative motifs from Antiquity, Islam, and the Far East were incorporated into the European repertory with little regard to their meaning. For all these reasons, when the minor arts were not actually small versions of the major arts, their content was considerably less coherent or less profound.[24]

Ornament and Decoration

The decorative tradition of Christian Europe during this period was not so homogeneous or so stable and independent as that of Islam or of China. Among the most widely used of decorative motifs were the architectural elements employed in contemporary buildings. Cusped and mixtilinear arches, interlaced or simply applied to a surface as blind arcades, were favoured during the Middle Ages. The Gothic triforium was enriched by ornamental arcades. Arcuated forms were effectively accommodated to the wheel-like tracery of the rose window. Late Gothic designers gave much attention to the invention of decorative treatments for architectural surfaces and thus created an increasingly rich repertory of decorative motifs. Reliquaries and shrines of wood or metal took on the structure of miniature Gothic edifices. Architectural motifs were used for the ornament of tombs, chests, and ecclesiastical furniture such as choir stalls, altar canopies, and frames for retables.

During the Renaissance architectural motifs continued to be the leading decorative elements, but the unique vocabulary of the Gothic style was replaced by the orders of Antiquity. For a period during the late fifteenth and early sixteenth centuries, the motifs of the Flamboyant and the Renaissance styles were decoratively merged in most areas of Europe outside central Italy. The autonomy, clarity, and static character of Renaissance motifs and designs contrasted with the lively and fluid shapes and rhythmic continuities of the Flamboyant elements, but some magnificent hybrid forms were created. The ancient architectural vocabulary, although not so flexible or readily combined in a rhythmic or ornamental way as the Gothic elements, gradually took over the traditional decorative functions of architectural elements. The severely tectonic arrangement of architectural orders used by decorators in the Renaissance was replaced by the less restrained, more dynamic combinations of architectural elements employed by Baroque designers. During the early eighteenth century freely varied shapes and asymmetrical rhythms departed from the tectonic ideals of the Renaissance. By the third quarter of the eighteenth century Neoclassic architects led the return to the ancient orders, then clarified by a growing archaeological knowledge.

Personal emblems and coats of arms were prominent decorative elements inherited from the Middle Ages. They were used on banners, shields, clothes, tapestries, armour, silver plate, illuminated manuscripts, bookbindings, furniture, fireplaces, portals, and façades. As the social significance of the coat of arms waned, it was transformed into the completely decorative 'cartouche', an elaborately scrolled oblong frame with a decorative or even blank centre. Mottoes, sometimes revised to commemorate important events, together with personal initials, ornamentally shaped and intertwined, became favourite motifs in the late fourteenth and the fifteenth century.[25]

Plant motifs comprise another special category of European ornament. The intensified study of plant life (see Chapter XIII) led to a naturalism that contrasted strikingly with the stylized forms of Islam. Flowers and leaves were favoured during the fourteenth and fifteenth centuries in the delicately and elaborately designed borders painted around manuscript miniatures and woven into the borders of tapestries. In some tapestries, known as 'verdures', the entire background behind the large figures is a flat floral and foliate pattern. Plant motifs were also embroidered in cloth, worked on leather, engraved in metal objects, and carved on ecclesiastical furniture and on architectural elements such as brackets, capitals, and frames of windows and doors. The Flamboyant Style readily accommodated the naturalism of these motifs to its fanciful and curvilinear inclinations. Plants, as well as the older repertory of animals, were readily exchanged for designs modelled upon the ancient Roman 'grotteschi' (so called because the first examples were found in grottoes under the Palatine in Rome), which are composed of fanciful hybrid creatures formed of vegetable, animal, and human parts and joined in continuous arabesques. 'Grotteschi' were widely used during the sixteenth and seventeenth centuries on pilasters, friezes, panelled sections of walls and ceilings, borders of bookplates, and parts of armour. Natural plant motifs, however, were never abandoned.

Perhaps the most unique tendency of European decoration was the ever-increasing use of painting and sculpture to ornament surfaces. Gems, metal cups, furniture, and the walls of rooms often provided surfaces for sculptural reliefs. Pottery was frequently ornamented with scenes comparable to contemporary painting in the illusion they created of depth. When ornament is literally sculpture or painting, it often evidences little sensitivity to the continuity of the surfaces, and hence the basic shape, of the object decorated. As a result, a new ornamental entity, composed of actual and illusional shapes, is created.

Tapestries, stained glass windows, and intarsia (inlay in wood), which are essentially two dimensional in character, became subdivisions of painting. Tapestry technique permits the insertion of many short pieces of yarn and, thus, a great variety of subtle changes of colour. During the fourteenth and fifteenth centuries the hunt, courtly love, the Crusades, and Ancient or sacred history provided subjects for Flemish tapestries. Later Raphael's 'Acts of the Apostles', designed for the Sistine Chapel and made in Brussels, revealed the degree to which tapestries aspired to look like paintings. The sixteenth-century painters Bernard van Orley, Lucas van Leyden, and Jan Mabuse frequently provided cartoons for Flemish tapestries. The Gobelin factory at Paris and the factories at Beauvais and Aubusson, all of which became prominent during the last third of the seventeenth century, increased the variety of colours and tones in the threads to attain the subtle suggestions of modelling and the atmospheric effects characteristic of contemporary painting. Toward the same end, the small pieces of stained glass which created the mosaic-like splendour of medieval windows were replaced by larger pieces of painted glass creating the illusion of modelled figures and deep space. Intarsia often replaced painting as a decorative treatment for furniture.[26] In the early fifteenth century, contrasting woods formed various two-dimensional geometric designs, probably indicative of the Islamic origins of the craft. As the century advanced, historical events or landscapes and still-life subjects were represented. Very small pieces of wood together with new methods of staining half-tones with oils and acids created many subtle variations of golden tans, browns, and greens and enabled intarsia workers to approximate the effects of painting.[27]

*   *   *

The decorative objects of the period 1300–1775 in Europe are conveniently grouped under the materials from which they were made—yarn, clay, glass, metal, gems, and wood. Moreover, this arrangement helps to emphasize two developments that the decorative arts conspicuously illustrate—the alliance of art and technology, and intercultural borrowing.

Textiles and tapestries

The yarn from which the most elaborately woven and decorative textiles were made was silk. Before the thirteenth century Europe had imported practically all its silks from the Middle and the Far East to serve as church vestments, burial robes, and court costumes. Although Hispano-Islamic centres continued to produce magnificent fabrics, the supply of silks was rendered unsteady in the thirteenth century because of the Mongol invasion of the Near East and the decline of silk factories in Sicily. Muslim silk weavers were thereupon invited or even forced to bring their skill to Christian Europe. Lucca, Florence, and Venice in Italy, Lyons in France, and Bruges in Flanders early became important centres of the European silk industry. Luxurious brocades were made also in Russia, Bulgaria, and Greece as well as Turkey and Persia. Western Europe, however, having reached a technical skill comparable to that of Islam and the Far East, began to supply most of its own needs.

Italian weavers had long been famous for fine woollen cloth, but silk soon won favour also. It was not readily destroyed by pests, took dyes beautifully, and folded luxuriously. In the fourteenth century Italian silk designers borrowed generously from the Islamic lands and the Far East, but their inclination toward naturalism greatly enlarged their decorative repertory and resulted in novel compositions. They adopted the animal and bird motifs that Islamic artists had inherited from the Sassanian-Byzantine tradition but often abandoned the heraldic aspect of confronted positions and frequently removed the animals and birds from the confines of the interlaced roundels so charac-teristic of Islam to dispose them more freely in diagonal rows. The tendril and other plant motifs were more naturally· varied and, once released, along with the animals and birds, from the stylized forms of Islam, gained vitality. Fourteenth-century Italian textiles were often more directly copied from Chinese gold-brocaded satins of the thirteenth century. Lotus tendrils, flaming rays, phoenixes, pheasants, cranes, and other Chinese motifs were used in Italian silks, particularly those made in Lucca, although sometimes transformed to resemble the flora and fauna of Europe. A pseudo-Kufic script, inspired by Persian or Hispano-Islamic textiles, became fashionable in the mid-fourteenth century, and in the fifteenth the pine cone, or so-called pomegranate, pattern. Italian textile designers avoided the pictorial inclinations that transformed several other decorative arts. They showed a tendency to eliminate small tendrils and delicate irregularities in order to attain greater scale and boldness of contour. With this interest in bolder designs, velvet came to the fore, particularly the polychrome velvet made in Florence and later in Genoa.

The most decorative use of the fine woollen cloth produced by European weavers was in tapestries. Scaled to the huge interiors of castles, palaces, and churches, tapestries were monumental mural-like fabrics that served not only to decorate but to keep out cold. (Pl. 58a.) Arras, Tournai, and Paris were most important for tapestry production until the fifteenth century, when Brussels and Bruges became the major producers. French factories, particularly the one created by the Gobelin family near Paris, were foremost during the late seventeenth and the eighteenth century as royal enterprises, but most of their early weavers were Flemish. (Pl. 58b.) At Savonnerie about 1590, the French opened a rug factory, where the knotted technique and the floral designs of Persia were imitated, but Europe never learned to produce rugs comparable to those of the Near and Far East and continued to import its finer rugs.

Lace, the most fragile fabric made of yarn, consists of delicate threads of flax, cotton, and silk intertwined. Good lace requires great skill and patience. Lacemaking may have evolved from the *reticella* work of the Ionian Islands during the late fifteenth century, but it became a peculiarly west European art, centred at first in Venice, Milan, and Genoa but shifting to France and Belgium during the late seventeenth century. It was used as trim on women's clothing, men's shirts, bedspreads, altar cloths, and church vestments. Rose point, flat point, and grounded point were among the lace techniques that the rest of Europe learned from Venice. The 'point d'Alençon', built upon the firm base of a fine net and enriched with 'cordonnet' ridges buttonholed over horsehair, was a French invention that heralded the leadership of France in lacemaking. Argentan, Le Puy, Chantilly, and Valenciennes became famous for fine lace. So did Barcelona in Spain, and Brussels and Malines in the Low Countries.

Plain cloth was frequently decorated by means of embroidery. Gradually Europe had become conscious of the richly embroidered textiles of Persia, Morocco, Turkey, India, China, and Japan. In Europe, England became particularly famous from the fourteenth century on for its embroidery, known then as *opus anglicanum* and widely used for church vestments, court finery, and (in later centuries) upholstery. This art was one of the few not restricted by the requirements of skill to professionals; gentle ladies occupied themselves with the embroidery of domestic articles and clothing.

The stamped, printed, and resist-dyed cottons and silks of India stimulated one of the major textile industries of Europe. Marco Polo in the thirteenth century and Portuguese adventurers in the fifteenth noted that stained and printed cottons were highly prized fabrics in India, and in the sixteenth century England and the Low Countries began to import Indian palampores in great quantities. Although Europeans admired this type of textile and used it for clothes, curtains, and furniture covers, they were not satisfied with the Indian designs, and English craftsmen were sent to teach Indian printmakers the designs preferred by Europeans. The demand for these prints became so great that England, Holland, and France decided to produce them. Among French textiles 'toile de Jouy' became particularly famous. The changes in weaving methods during the late seventeenth and the eighteenth century (connected with 'the Industrial Revolution', which we shall consider in Chapter XV) reduced costs, regularized patterns and assured more uniform colours but diminished the quality of Europe's prints and chintzes.

Ceramics

Potter's clay provided another good medium for decorative expression. Several Spanish regions had borrowed from the Moors the low-fire process of baking the glaze with moderate heat, and it moved from Spain to other Christian areas. Majorca in the twelfth century, Malaga in the fourteenth, and Manises near Valencia in the fifteenth became famous for a gold and ruby lustreware decorated with plant life, Kufic script, animals, concentric circles, and European coats of arms, in brown, violet, and cobalt blue, frequently modelled in low relief to give emphasis to the main part of the design. Italy at first imported this ware from Spain, but by the late fourteenth century Faenza (whence the word *faience*) began to make it, and in the fifteenth century Urbino, Gubbio, and other Italian towns followed suit. The Spanish-Italian ware was called *majolica*. Italian potters were attracted to the low-fire treatment not so much by the lustre it gave as by the greater range of colours it permitted than the high-fire treatment that European potters commonly used. They adorned their plates and bowls, predominantly blue and yellow and often very large, with pictorial effects that contrasted with the two-dimensional motifs of Islamic potters. (Pl. 59a.)

Increased contact with the Far East provided an impetus that elevated ceramics to one of the leading decorative arts—and industries (see Chapter XV)—of eighteenth-century Europe. European potters attempted to make a ware comparable to Chinese and Japanese porcelain. The handsome wares of Delft, Rouen and Sèvres approached the thin translucence and delicate qualities of Far Eastern porcelain. The ware developed at Meissen near Dresden shortly after 1709 was accepted as the equal of Chinese porcelain. Ansbach, Vienna, Capodimonte near Naples, and Buen Retiro near Madrid were other centres established during the eighteenth century. The porcelain factories of Germany and France produced colourful and delicately fashioned figurines depicting playful activities. (Pl. 60.) Although some English ware such as Lowestoft was hard-paste porcelain, the pottery made at Chelsea, Staffordshire, and most other English centres was soft-paste porcelain. Wedgwood ware, characterized by white cameo-like figures in relief on blue, rose, green, and tan grounds, is still numbered among England's most distinctive products.

Glass

Glassware was one of the decorative arts in which Europe excelled even during the Middle Ages. Stained and leaded glass windows reveal the feeling of medieval Europe for the splendour of light-filled and colourful materials. Those of Saint-Nazaire in Carcassone exemplify the tiered arrangement of figures and events, the larger pieces of glass, and the greater array of colours and tonal variations characteristic of fourteenth-century windows in contrast to earlier ones. These tendencies were furthered during the fifteenth and sixteenth centuries by the more widespread acceptance of paintings as models for stained-glass windows.[28] Unevenly coloured glass provided the suggestion of shading in figures and draperies, and transparent enamels applied with a brush enabled the artist to come closer to pictorial effects. The strong two-dimensional design of the leads and the armatures was eliminated whenever possible to create an illusory depth, constructed by means of the devices used to give perspective in painting. In the first decade of the sixteenth century Guglielmo de Marcillat created some of the earliest examples of frankly pictorial stained-glass windows for churches in Arezzo and Cortena. Pictorial aims continued to dominate through the seventeenth and eighteenth centuries.

The craftsmen of medieval Venice, heirs to the Byzantine tradition of glassmaking, improved their processes under a cloak of secrecy and remained unsurpassed if not unrivalled as producers of fine glass until the eighteenth century. Glass goblets, cups, vases, dishes, table decorations, and beads (the mainstay of the Venetian industry) were made in great variety. Among the most famous of Venetian glassware are 'crackled', 'marble', and 'millefiori' glass, and glass with goldleaf either on the surface or worked in. 'Lace' glass, characterized by opaque white lines that create delicate patterns, and glass of the *reticella* ('net') type, with bubbles of air enclosed at the intersections of a network of white lines, were other marvels of technical skill. The *avanturine* type, an amber-coloured glass speckled with myriads of burnished-copper flecks, was the result of a process invented in the early seventeenth century and effectively guarded for two hundred years. The Low Countries, the British Isles, Germany, Bohemia, and France originally made glass on Venetian models and then gradually developed decorative types of their own (see Chapter XV). Gold ruby glass, invented in the late seventeenth century in Potsdam, and cut glass, which appeared also in the seventeenth century (see Chapter XV), were among the innovations that caused the decline of the Venetian market. (Pl. 59b.)

Metal works

Metal provided still another medium of decoration. Near Eastern and Hispanic centres of Islam had gained fame in Europe during the medieval period for steel swords ornamented with inlays of brass and silver. Armour became impractical for military use after the invention of gunpowder but was maintained for ceremonial purposes, and swords, too, became increasingly ceremonial. Ceremonial swords not only were made of precious metals but also were often beautifully adorned and studded with jewels. Ceremonial weapons and armour presented an unusually good opportunity to decorative artists and became more and more elaborate. Designs were frequently etched or inlaid with contrasting metals into the armour plate, and sculptural reliefs of figures or *grotteschi* often embellished breast-plates and helmets.

The metal objects required for the Christian service were numerous. Insistence on rare and costly materials and on elaborate workmanship for ceremonial objects led to some of Europe's most unique and decorative forms. Reliquaries, monstrances, processional crosses, candlesticks, croziers, chalices, patens, and alms dishes were made of gold and silver. These metals, rich in colour and light-reflecting properties, were decoratively pierced, chased, or worked in filigree or repoussé, and often enriched with enamel, carved ivory, and precious stones.

Brass, bronze, and copper objects were frequently enriched with enamels. Medieval Europe continued an enamel technique known as *champlevé*, which had been practised by the ancient Romans: enamel, in the form of powder or paste, was laid into cells which had been engraved into or scooped from the metal surface, and then was fired to attain a glass-like quality. The enamels in the European *champlevé* technique were usually opaque, in contrast to the translucent enamels used by Byzantine craftsmen over a gold base to produce an opalescent effect. During the fifteenth century the technique of painting with enamel on a copper base became prevalent in Europe. Like so many other kinds of decorative artists in Europe, enamel artists attempted to duplicate the effects of contemporary painting.

In the sixteenth century, secular, and particularly domestic, items became an increasingly important part of the goldsmith's work in Europe. Goblets, standing salts, basins, and plates were made of gold or silver. By the sixteenth century, huge collections of silver plate had been amassed by the dukes of Burgundy and the kings of England, France, and Spain. Guilds, colleges, town halls, and wealthy families owned silver plate especially designed for them. The desire to display silver service made the sideboard, and later the buffet, increasingly important. During the fifteenth and sixteenth centuries France, Italy, and particularly Augsburg and Nuremberg in Germany became prominent centres of the goldsmith's and silversmith's craft. Silver service complemented tableware of fine porcelain. French silversmiths at Bordeaux, Strasbourg, Lille, and Paris made table service treasured all over Europe. The introduction of coffee and tea to Europe resulted in the late seventeenth and the eighteenth century in decoratively shaped and richly ornamented silver coffee pots and teapots, as well as cream pitchers and sugar bowls. The silver of Holland and of England and her American colonies, while somewhat more sturdy and less ornamental in shape and surface than contemporary French and German work, nevertheless furnished notable examples of the silversmith's art.

Designs were enamelled, engraved, chased or carried out in repoussé on the gold or silver surface. Some works, like the large salt cellar made by Cellini for Francis I, were fashioned as miniature works of sculpture. Reliquaries and standing cups were occasionally carved of rock crystal, amber, agate, or coconut shells and set in gilded silver or in gold. Renaissance artists also made commemorative medals in bronze, silver, and gold. Although major painters and sculptors such as Pisanello and Cellini occasionally prepared designs for medals, some, particularly in Germany, France, and Italy, devoted themselves primarily to the making of medals.

Jewellery

Jewellery engaged not only the goldsmith or silversmith, but also the lapidary. In Europe, pendants, often worn on the forehead, rings, brooches and necklaces were favoured. Table-cut emeralds and rubies, gems with carved reliefs in the manner of the Ancients, enamel insets, and pearls were given fanciful settings of foliate and *grotteschi* forms in gold and silver. The jewellery of France during the late sixteenth and the seventeenth century was greatly admired, and the designs of Jacques Androust Ducerceau, Etienne Delaune, and Pierre Woeriot of Lorraine were copied in all parts of Europe. Paste, textured and coloured to look like gems, was introduced in the seventeenth century along with other shams of mass-produced jewellery. The aigrette, a cluster of precious stones set in enamelled gold and mounted on movable stalks, and sprays of leaves and flowers with knotted and flowing ribbons were among the most delicate and precious works of eighteenth-century craftsmanship. The magnificent jewellery of the Far East and the Islamic countries (see below) appears to have begun to impress European artisans in the late seventeenth century.

Woodwork

Wood as a medium of decorative art was used in Europe most elaborately in the making of furniture. The Christian church required many wooden objects—retables, altars, canopies, pulpits, and huge choir stalls. These furnishings demanded not only appropriate symbolic references but also richness in materials and workmanship. Domestic furniture during the

Middle Ages was, on the other hand, made of plain, sturdy oak wood, though frequently ingeniously built to serve several purposes. It was restricted to trestle tables, benches, beds, and chests, which were rigid and box-like with only occasional carved panels or arcade motifs. With the Renaissance more attention was given to the decoration of domestic furniture, and more varied types of furnishings were developed. Bureaux with drawers, tables, chairs, *cassoni* (or marriage chests), wall cupboards (or credences), and (later) sideboards were elaborately ornamented. The painting of panels, intarsia (particularly on *cassoni* and cupboards), and the carving of table and chair legs were favoured methods of decoration. During the sixteenth century the boxlike shapes and the relatively flat surfaces of Gothic furniture were replaced by more bulbous and vigorous shapes, which nevertheless retained a compact structural aspect. Robustly shaped caryatids, allegorical figures, medallions, *grotteschi*, garlands, emblems, coats of arms, and (later) *cartouche* frames were frequently carved in the wood or plastered on it in relief. Architectural elements such as columns, entablatures, pediments, mouldings, and brackets often enhanced the tectonic appearance of Renaissance and Baroque furniture in Italy.

During the sixteenth and seventeenth centuries, French furniture gradually gained prominence in Europe. French *armoires* (or cabinets), desks, tables, chairs with leather or cane seats, and reclining couches became elaborate. As the seventeenth century advanced, novelty and magnificence became more and more conspicuously the aims of decoration. Marquetry (as intarsia was called in the north) was carried out not only by inlays in wood, preferably rare woods, but also by incrustations of mother-of-pearl, metal, and ivory. Chairs and couches were upholstered in the late seventeenth century and onward with multicoloured fabrics such as tapestries, needlepoint, embroideries, velvets, and brocades. Colbert established the royal manufactory of furniture in 1667 and brought artisans from all parts of Europe to teach French workmen. New designs and decorative treatments of furniture were readily available to artisans by means of engravings in model books. The engravings of De l'Orme and Ducerceau in the sixteenth century and Jean Lepautré in the seventeenth were among the most influential. Although the richly ornamented pieces of the wood carvers of Augsburg and Nuremberg were widely admired and although England maintained an independent style favouring traditional motifs such as the linen-fold design and turned or spindle supports with 'melon-bulb' protuberances, French furniture designers eventually provided the models for all of Europe.

Those English and French designers who worked within the dominant Rococo style of the eighteenth century not only created more varied, comfortable, and luxurious furnishings but they also elevated their craft to a highly personal art. Furniture was relieved of its earlier tectonic heaviness and bulkiness. The rhythmic curvatures of slim supports and the undulation of surfaces produced a lighter appearance and more ornamental shapes. Surfaces reached an ultimate refinement with inlays of rare woods, porcelains, ivory, tortoise shell, and brass and with veneers of mahogany, rosewood, satinwood, and walnut. Lacquered surfaces, imitating the technique developed in Japan and known in France as *vernis Martin*, had reached a high point of elegance early in the seventeenth century. Soft colours and gilding further enhanced the look of delicacy in this Rococo furniture. Decorative handles, corner mountings, and gilded-bronze supports were added to chests and tables. The contrasts of these various materials and textures resulted in an exceptionally rich and sensuous effect unequalled by earlier European furniture.

The variety and value of the materials, the excellence of the craftsmanship, and the ornamental purpose of Rococo interiors encouraged talented artists to occupy themselves with the making of furniture. Jean Baptiste Pillement and Philippe de Lassalle were foremost among the designers who gained fame for their upholstery fabrics during the latter half of the eighteenth century. By means of the shaping, scaling, finishing, and arranging of parts, eighteenth-century designers frequently impressed a readily identified personal style on their furniture. André-Charles Boulle employed a type of tortoise-shell-and-brass inlay which came to be known as 'buhl' or 'buhlwork'. Thomas Chippendale, drawing upon French predecessors, published an illustrated furniture book, *The Gentleman and Cabinet Maker's Director*, in 1754 and thereby initiated a series of influential English furniture styles. George Heppelwhite and Thomas Sheraton during the late eighteenth century brought England to a foremost place in furniture fashions.

THEORIES OF ART AND THE ROLE OF THE ARTIST

The universe of art in which the European artist of 1775 was educated not only was infinitely more complex than that of his counterpart in 1300 but also offered a much greater freedom for his orientation within it.[29] The status of the European practitioner of the arts changed between 1300 and 1775 from that of a relatively nameless 'artisan' to that of an 'artist'. In the early fifteenth century he became a friend of humanists, philosophers, mathematicians, and poets, and as a result, he freed himself from the control of the guild. Except for an occasional autodidact the artist received his professional training in ateliers and, by the seventeenth century, in academies (see Chapter XVI).

A significant stimulant to change in the prestige of the artist during this period was his role in establishing and clarifying the theory that art is an imitation of nature. Renaissance writers occasionally noted the importance of fancy or imagination and, while generally upholding the intellectual nature and didactic purposes of art, recognized also that sensuous pleasure was to be derived from it. They never succeeded in synthesizing the various ideas derived from the Ancients or inherited from the Middle Ages, but among those ideas the principle of imitation was most influential.

While previously art theory had been written predominantly by philosophers and theologians, that of the Renaissance was primarily the creation of practicing artists who began to theorize about the nature of their practice. Concerned with the imitation of natural forms, they studied optics, developing a linear system of monocular perspective and devices for aerial perspective that in painting and in relief sculpture approximated the visual experience of figures and objects in space. Optics and perspective became a central subject of theoretical notebooks on art, notably those by Alberti, Ghiberti, Piero della Francesca, Leonardo, Jean Pélerin, and Dürer. The foremost object of study, however, not only by painters and sculptors but also by architects, was the human body. An understanding of its anatomical structure, its laws of movement, and the proportional norms on which its beauty depends became an essential part of artistic training in the Western tradition. Leonardo and Dürer stated the proportions of beauty in arithmetical fractions (as the Ancients had) in contrast to the geometric schemes prevalent in the Middle Ages. Leonardo, in the notes and drawings for his encyclopedic treatise on art, epitomized the fifteenth-century concept of art as a demonstration of the artist's knowledge of optics and of nature and its underlying laws. Ghiberti, Alberti, and Leonardo, insisting that the artist deal exclusively with what he saw, abjured metaphysical explanations of the origin of art. An interest in the physical facts of man and nature remained characteristic of Western art and caused Europeans to concentrate their attention upon the corporeal aspects of man's existence rather than the spiritual or religious.

At the same time that early Renaissance artists attempted to approximate the physical appearance of objective natural forms, they saw in the physical world a revelation of the beauty, harmony, and order of the Deity, and they imitated the 'best' parts of nature in creating their own forms. This 'best' came to mean a criterion of perfection. It led Raphael and Michelangelo to shape human figures of a beauty far superior to that of the average human being, and they disposed limbs and grouped figures so as to present rhythmic intervals between the solids and the voids that gave natural forms and events a decorative or artful arrangement. Raphael achieved a subtle balance between approximation and superiority to Nature, but Michelangelo moved farther toward the decorative and away from verisimilitude in the colour, shape, and arrangement of the human figure. Contemporaries accepted the art of Raphael and Michelangelo as revelations of beauty greater than those of natural forms and referred to the revealers of this beauty as 'the divine ones'.

The followers of 'the divine ones' were the Mannerists. They probed the subjective realm of fantasy, depending on what was called the *idea interna* more than on visual experience for the forms of their art. For the Mannerists art was no longer a vehicle for the demonstration of objective knowledge of the world and man but the revelation of a highly subjective sense of perfection or truth. This mystic attitude, probably nourished by Neoplatonic ideas of the visual arts and poetry, accepted the sensible form of art as a means by which the soul could be awakened to intellectual beauty and led to Ultimate Beauty, which is God. Various aspects of the Mannerist idea of art and the artist were codified by Vincenzo Danti in 1567, Giovanni Paolo Lomazzo and Giovanni Battista Armenini in the 1580's, and Frederico Zuccari in 1607. Although the significance of the artists' creativity in this connection appears to have been only vaguely appreciated, they were considered revealers of truth, often independent of the clergy, who were the guardians of Christian Truth. The Council of Trent recognized this invasion of ecclesiastical functions by stating, in effect, that what pertained to theology belonged to the theologians and what pertained to poetic invention to the artists (see below). That dictum, however, did not end the association of artists with the revelation of truths of a mystic or spiritual nature. On the contrary, the association persisted and gathered strength.

The Attitude of the Churches toward Art

While the church remained the dominant patron during the Renaissance (even for profane subjects in painting and sculpture for the palaces and villas of the clergy), its previously overwhelming control of commissions began to diminish.[30] Gradually the earlier restrictions of the artist to works that were useful in the Christian ritual or in perpetuating the faith began to loosen. Yet probably at least 75 per cent of the works commissioned in the Renaissance were still of a religious nature, and that percentage continued into the seventeenth century in Catholic countries.

To Protestant minds, on the other hand, art became something a church could do without—mere ornamentation, which detracted from spiritual growth rather than aided it. Protestants stripped the old churches they had taken over and tended in the new ones they built to avoid images, objects of beauty, and distracting ornament. The visual arts in Germany, vigorous and inventive until the sixteenth century, declined by the middle of that century. Cranach may have intended to convey a Lutheran point of view (as opposed to the Anabaptists) in his scenes of Christ surrounded by little children ('Suffer the little children to come unto me'), but most of his paintings until his death in 1553 were of secular subjects. England's foremost position in architecture and decoration appears to have been relinquished upon departure from the Roman church. The only Protestant country that achieved an art of international importance before the eighteenth century was Holland during the seventeenth century, her golden age. Most Dutch artists devoted themselves, however, exclusively to secular subjects—interiors, tavern scenes, still-lifes, landscapes, and portraits. Rembrandt's depiction of Biblical scenes is unusual for Holland; apparently most of them were not commissioned but were motivated by a personal inclination to probe the significance of sacred legends by means of pictorial realizations of them.

Catholic art of the late sixteenth and seventeenth centuries reflected the split in the Christian community. The twenty-fifth *sessio* of the Council of Trent (December 4, 1563) affirmed that art was the handmaiden of the church and instructed members of the clergy at all levels to take responsibility for the 'correctness' of the images on display in their areas. Innovation was curtailed so far as to require all ecclesiastics to submit any 'unusual' images to the bishop for approval. Gilio da Fabriano in 1564, Carlo Borromeo in 1572, and Gabriel Paleotti in 1582 wrote treatises that defined 'correctness' in greater detail than had the Council of Trent, but they followed the council's affirmation that painters and sculptors were poets and not priests by praising those who subordinated their art to Truth rather than allowed Truth to be distorted for the purposes of art. These writers explained that the matter deserved great attention because images are more impressive than words, and they reminded the artist of his responsibility.[31] Nudity was specifically restricted by the Council of Trent as not conducive to pious thought on the part of the beholder.

The official attitude of the church toward art had prompt effects. Daniele da Volterra, an artist otherwise well worthy of respect, became notorious as *il braghettone* ('the pants maker') by painting clothes on the figures of Michelangelo's 'Last Judgment' by the order of Pope Paul IV. Ammannati in a letter to the Accademia di San Lucca in 1582 expressed his regret for having sculptured nudes, and he disavowed the view that the beauty of the human body was a channel for the realization of the beauty of the Deity. Veronese, when asked by the Inquisition in 1573 to explain the 'extra' figures and distracting events that he had placed prominently in his 'Feast in the House of Simon', now in the Accademia in Venice, was less penitent but apologetic still.

The church's policy on art had visible if more subtle and less frank effects upon subject matter and style. Post-Tridentine Catholic artists favoured themes that sustained beliefs disputed by Protestants—for example, the God-given role of the pope as head of Christendom, the belief in saints as intercessors, the efficacy of prayer and penitence in the attainment of salvation, and the validity of visions as revelations of Christian truth. Events of sacred history were no longer simply narrated by clearly identifying persons and establishing the emotional relations among them, as had been done from Giotto's time through the early sixteenth century. Rather, they were interpreted with a Counter-Reformation emphasis. For some subjects, such as the Immaculate Conception of Mary, a new image was developed to connote the context without direct references to the event itself. Catholic artists tended to depict scenes from sacred history, and in the Grand Manner of the Renaissance, rather than ordinary types and realistic actions, which Protestant artists preferred. If seventeenth-century Spanish and Neapolitan artists employed realism, it was in order to emphasize the low and transient nature of the physical world in contrast to that of the spiritual.

Architecture also reflected the new spirit of the Counter-Reformation. The cosmic order represented in the central church was put aside by Borromeo, and architects were advised to abandon that pagan form. Because preaching had again become important, particularly among the Jesuits, they laid down requirements in 1568 for their mother-church, the Gesù at Rome, as a single nave and vaulted structure, which was readily accepted elsewhere as a compact setting suitable for a sermon. (Pl. 54b; Fig. 3.) The increasing importance of the sermon led also to the elaboration of the pulpit in the seventeenth and eighteenth centuries until in some churches it became the most ornate part.

The Rise of Art Criticism

By the late seventeenth century the judgment of art was subject to the influence of writers and critics, most of whom were not artists. While Italians and some Spaniards continued to exalt fancy or imagination, the most influential works of criticism were published in Cartesian France. There theorists attempted to systematize the more concrete ideas put forth earlier in Italy in order to attain a more objective basis for the judgment of art. The Renaissance categories of primary emotional states[32] (codified by Leonardo and emphasized by artists from Donatello to Poussin) were further clarified by Descartes' *Traité des Passions* and then finally conventionalized by Le Brun and the Académie Royale.[33] Art subjects also were graded—according to the talents they required and the nobility of expression inherent in them. The Renaissance idea persisted that the artist's most worthy subject was man in the act of expressing his most noble emotions, and in consequence the most respected themes were those derived from the dramatic episodes of history, both sacred and profane. Portraiture, animals, landscapes, and still-lifes ranked afterward in respectability in that order. André Félibien (1619–95) and Roger de Piles (1635–1709), outstanding historians and critics of art, fostered a simple, flexible, and, they believed, objective method for judging relative perfection in art by separating and scoring a work's various aspects, such as drawing, colour, composition, expression, and invention, and then totalling the score. This quantitative approach to the quality of art aimed at universal validity by recognizing that weakness in one regard might be compensated by excellence in another. The separate aspects were not considered mutually exclusive, the greatest artists, such as Raphael, being ranked very high in all categories. Some critics were inclined to consider excellence in drawing more important than excellence in colour. The argument between the 'Rubensists', who held that colour was the life of painting and the 'Poussinists', who maintained that drawing was its essential element, became an important part of the literary 'Quarrel of the Ancients and the Moderns' (see Chapter XI), which in art became a quarrel between advocates of the Classical and of the Baroque. It was settled in the last decade of the seventeenth century, when colour and drawing were given equal status.

During the seventeenth century, theorists began to recognize a variety of art categories (in addition to classes of subjects), each with its own aims and conditions of judgment. Frederico Zuccari in 1607 distinguished three kinds of art—natural, artificial, and fantastic. Poussin described several 'modes' of arrangement, each appropriate to a different emotion evoked by a particular kind of event, and (according to Félibien) tried to understand the reasons for various kinds of beauty. The faculty of 'Taste' was first referred to by the Spaniard Baltasar Gracian in 1642, and it was accepted into the domain of esthetics by La Bruyère in 1688. It was, however, too indeterminate for most French theorists, intent as they were on establishing an intellectual basis for judgment.

The expansion of art categories was probably stimulated by the increased range of art forms known to the seventeenth and eighteenth centuries; in any event, the several categories provided a more specific framework for judgments of taste than did the vague but apparently single and absolute norm of 'perfection' by which works had been gauged in the Renaissance. Thinking within these categories, critics became more concerned with relative 'quality' than with 'perfection'.

In the eighteenth century, when writers were especially prone to put order into nature's variety by grouping things into categories, the idea developed of 'species of art', as Hume called them. Giovanni Gravina (1718) inferred that the laws of judgment were as numerous as the things to be judged. Jonathan Richardson (1719) suggested that a work of art was most appropriately judged within the setting of the local school or historical period to which it belonged. Edmund Burke (1756) distinguished two categories of art, the sublime and the beautiful. Raphael Mengs (1762) defined three additional ones—the expressive, the graceful, and the natural. Each of the five was accepted as a kind in which varying degrees of perfection could be reached, but the most noble was generally believed to be that classified as beautiful.

The Debate over the Criteria of Feeling and of Reason

Much attention was given during the eighteenth century to the nature of art and, particularly, of the experience to be derived from viewing works of art. Some of the most interesting and novel observations were made in respect to the non-rational associations with art—the imagination and the feelings. These observations threatened the major premise on which art theory had been based since the beginning of the Renaissance. Although Italian Mannerists had expressed admiration for the elusive quality of *grazia* and Charles Alphone Dufresney (1611–65) and De Piles had given great stress to the factor of 'genius', art was generally regarded as primarily an intellectual activity that could be learned and understood by reason.

Among the eighteenth-century critics of pure rationalism, especially the British, this manner of thinking lost ground. Joseph Addison claimed that imagination combined with reason to produce the wonders of art. Francis Hutcheson suggested that beauty was understood by an 'inner sense' and could not be perceived by reason. David Hume contended that the role of reason was to distinguish truth from falsehood and such a distinction was not basic to the discernment of beauty. Nevertheless, a large group of other

English theorists, although they likewise tended to associate art with non-rational faculties, also assumed that the more disorderly forces might be guided during the creative act by reason. They believed that the attraction of beauty was somehow related to man's God-given sense of pleasure by his preference for order, uniformity, and regularity. They held also that good taste could be taught and that reason paved the way for pleasure in art. In this way, after some foraging into the unexplored areas of the imagination, the English empiricists before the end of the century returned to a rational basis for the understanding of art.

Meanwhile on the Continent the same argument was going on. In Italy Vico, as early as 1725 and without qualifications, had claimed that imagination, not reason, was the essential faculty of the artist. In France Jean Baptiste Dubos (1719) and Charles Batteux (1746) were leading figures in a school of thought that tended to regard engaging the emotions as the chief aim of art, but Batteux still expected to find a clear and distinct idea at the base of the arts and wanted 'to clear away the mists and establish the precepts'.[34] In Germany, Alexander Gottlieb Baumgarten (who in 1735 was the first to use the word *aesthetic* for the science of art) likewise observed that the material of art was not precisely intellectual, and Johann Georg Sulzer (1774) described the aesthetic idea as not sufficiently distinct to be cognitive. These men suggested that the basis for art was not learning, science, or rules but feeling and imagination. These ideas, however, were not synthesized sufficiently to withstand the clear expositions of the rationalists. Diderot, leader among the rationalists, rejected Hutcheson's 'inner sense' and assured his readers that ideas of order, unity, symmetry, and proportion, on which beauty was based, were as 'positive, distinct and real'[35] as the length, breadth, and thickness of things.

Neoclassicism reflected in art the rationalism of the eighteenth century. It was a most effective and widespread theory reaffirming the rules, the ideal types, and the intellectual basis of art. During the third quarter of the century, Caylus, Winckelmann, C. L. Hagerdorn, Mengs, and Lessing eulogized Greek works of art as the most perfect creations of Man. Reynolds also pointed to Greek models, though along with Italian masters as well. His suggestions that the artist observe, digest, compare, and systematize his visual experience reflected the rational approach of Italian and French theorists also. Even Hogarth, who ridiculed rule-ridden academicians, expressed admiration for Greek art and established a law of his own to the effect that beauty is based on a 'precise serpentine line' (probably echoing the claim of the sixteenth-century historian-painter Giovanni Paolo Lomazzo that Michelangelo considered it 'the line of beauty'). These Neoclassicists admired the majesty and repose of the ideal but 'natural' figure, in contrast to the 'affections' of the Rococo, and pointed out that perfection in contour was the chief characteristic of Greek art. Neoclassicists were basically different from Renaissance theorists, although both found inspiration in Antiquity. For one thing, the artists of the eighteenth century looked to Classical Greek art and those of the fifteenth century to Hellenistic Roman art as the acme of Ancient achievement; for another, the more exact archaeological knowledge of the Neoclassicists gave them a better idea of Antiquity than that which Renaissance artists had formed from scattered comments by Ancient writers and from the few fragments of Ancient art known to them.

The pre-eminent speculative genius of the late eighteenth century, Immanuel Kant, attempted to establish intellectual principles of judgment in opposition to the concept of 'taste', but a new attitude fostered by the 'Sturm und Drang' school promised to dislodge the belief that art is an intellectual activity subject to rational judgments. This group, in art as in letters (see Chapter XI), demanded originality rather than correctness and elegance, and intensity of feeling rather than adherence to rules. It accepted the senses as the source of art and lauded creative activity as the most exalted occupation of man. Even Diderot and particularly Rousseau fostered some of these ideas, and thus gave expression to the movement that later was to be known as 'Romantic'.

The Rise of Art History

In contrast to the artist of the early eighteenth century, the artist of 1300 had been relatively unaware of historical change in art forms. Artists began to be conscious, however, of being part of a historical process during the fourteenth century, when Dante, Boccaccio, Petrarch, and Villani described three major phases of art history—that of the great Ancients, the 'barbaric' art of the 'Dark Ages', and the revival evident in their own time. Ghiberti and Alberti continued these historical divisions and expressed confidence that they were about to regain the 'good arts' of Antiquity. Ghiberti interpreted the history of Ancient art and that of his own period as a series of pictorial and sculptural inventions or innovations which gradually would bring art to perfection, or an approximation of nature. Vasari in the mid-sixteenth century thought that his contemporaries, particularly Michelangelo and Raphael, had surpassed not only the Ancients but nature itself, bringing the continuous progress since Giotto and Nicola Pisano to its climax.[36]

Whereas Renaissance artists had been stimulated by the idea of contributing to this progress toward perfection, after the late sixteenth century changes were thought of more as differences of manner brought about by leading artists than as evidence of progress. Few critics in the seventeenth or eighteenth centuries believed that any of their contemporaries had surpassed Raphael; on the contrary they frequently looked back to his art as the most nearly perfect. Although Félibien, De Piles, Richardson, C. H. von Heineken, Hagedorn, and other critics affirmed a greater interest in the style and method of the best artists than in anecdotes about them, the history of art remained an account of the men whose distinctive manners had changed its course. Thus, during most of this period, artists associated change and innovation with the genius of individuals.

Historians of the eighteenth century introduced some new attitudes which gradually altered the artist's view of his place in history. The influence of local cultural differences on art had been recognized earlier, but Johann Friedrich Christ (1726) and A. J. Dezaillier d'Argensville (1754) emphasized the importance of an artist's national art tradition to his style, and Caylus dramatized the persistence of national characteristics by describing chronological changes within the art of a country simply as gradations of tone within one colour continuity. The artist of the 1750's began to think of his national origin as something affecting him, perhaps even inescapable. About the same time Caylus and Winckelmann, presenting a new concept of the history of art, emphasized another historical force acting on the artist. They conceived of art forms as having lives and destinies of their own, and therefore of artists as actors in, rather than creators of, their development. The artist's accomplishment was thus held to be determined at least in part· by the people among whom, and the time at which, he was born.

The Development of Art as a Profession

Another important change which occurred between 1300 and 1750 was the new evaluation of a work of art as a collector's item. Independent of its ritual or decorative function, an art object came to be looked upon primarily as evidence of the artistry of the man who had made it. Early collectors, such as Federigo of Urbino, Cosimo de' Medici, Isabella and Alfonso d'Este, Francis I, Charles V, and Federigo Gonzaga, at times expressed the desire to have 'a work by the hand of' a specified artist. Some of these works were selected to give pleasure or edification or to provide models for local artists, but whatever the reason, they suggested that the designated work was believed to have an intrinsic aesthetic value. Collections gathered on this basis were different from church treasuries—the only 'collections' of the Middle Ages. They also tended to become more specialized than the collections of gems, odd stones, coins, relics, and occasional works of art housed in the fifteenth-century 'Wunderkammer', or 'room of marvels'. During the Renaissance the palace court, the villa garden, or the 'studiolo' became display areas for private collections of paintings, drawings, engravings, and sculpture. Princely collectors vied with the clergy for the artist's services. Artists themselves collected—at first, generally pieces to serve as models in their workshops but by the late sixteenth century works reflecting more interest in connoisseurship than in practical use. Art academies formed collections of winners in their competitions or of examples submitted for election to membership. These collections, as well as many private ones, were available to the artist for study, and toward the mid-eighteenth century some of the larger ones, having been taken over by the national governments, were opened also to the public. By the end of the century the artist had begun to look to the collector and the museum as patrons. When the new British Museum failed to buy contemporary English works, Hogarth led an attack on those British who purchased the art of the Continent or of the past exclusively.

Not only had the artist become accustomed to thinking of his art as eventually belonging to a collection and displayed as a self-sufficient work in a gallery but he had begun to depend on exhibitions also as a means of reaching the public and patrons. Since 1663 the Académie des Beaux Arts in Paris had displayed the works of its members. Although they were available for purchase, only about a dozen are recorded to have been sold during the last third of the seventeenth century. By that time, however, the artist was beginning to think of his creation less in relation to a particular use or decorative purpose and more as an independent memorial to his genius, permanently housed in an art collection. Before the seventeenth century artists had rarely undertaken work that was not ordered for some specific purpose. The patronage of collectors and museums, as well as the artist's own concept of his product as primarily an embodiment of his artistry, induced painters, with growing frequency, to initiate pieces that were not commissioned. During the seventeenth century, painters, particularly those of Holland, began to place their landscapes and still-lifes in the hands of dealers, who sought purchasers for them. (Pl. 22.) Sculptors and architects, however, because of the costly nature of their materials and technical processes, were less likely to undertake works that were not commissioned.

Freedom from the taste of a specific patron and from the requirements imposed by a specified assignment allowed an artist like Rembrandt to regard an uncommissioned painting as an avenue of unrestricted intercourse with his genius and conscience. But frequently lesser men found themselves at the mercy of untrained bourgeois tastes. As the artist became increasingly dependent on the patronage of a broader segment of the public, he attempted to improve the general level of taste. Academicians and Neoclassicists alike became concerned with the instruction of manufacturers and craftsmen in the minor arts. Artists and theorists extended their roles as creators and educators of taste from their original concern with the princely patron and other artists to the European public as a whole.

By the end of our period, as a result of both the changes noted above and the influence of the schools and academies to be noted in Chapter XVI, the European artist had ceased to be a humble artisan. He had gained a dignified professional status; he had become a man of recognized intellect and creative genius; he was accepted as a director of the public taste. An artist now tended to think of his works as self-sufficient objects, as expressions of his personality, and as enduring evidence of his genius. Technical facility was, to be sure, an aspect of his art in which he still took pride, but he regarded it as only a means of releasing his particular sensibilities and sense of form, which were for him the most important constituents of his art. Art, which had once been essentially a collective effort by a community of artisans in the service of the church had now become largely an expression of individual creativeness.

THE DANCE AND MUSIC IN EUROPE

In Europe before 1300 dancing was usually under explicit religious controls. The Roman Catholic clergy discouraged processional dancing inside the church edifice and discountenanced Maypole dances elsewhere as an unbecoming pagan practice. Still, in Spain, the region *par excellence* of the western European dance, they were unable to eliminate religious processional dancing. To the present day, Easter processions in Seville, with elaborately adorned images of the Virgin, retain much of their primitive emotionalism. In more subdued form, controlled, rhythmical movement survives in the processional, recessional, and canon of the Roman Catholic mass and in other ritualistic acts, such as the swinging of the censers.

Before 1300 dancing was rarely encountered as a conscious and avowed form of amusement except among the peasantry. Nevertheless, rustic folk dances, sometimes violent and even ribald, were being adapted, refined, and embellished for the entertainment of all classes in town and country. A famous instance was the 'morris dances' of England. Though linked to the Robin Hood legend, they were probably originally called 'Moorish dances' and imported from Spain. Whatever their origin, they were modified to fit English preferences and were early associated with the medieval May Day celebration and Maypole dance, with its varied foreign embellishments.

Pantomime and procession were important features of primitive and rustic dances. When knights and noble ladies took to dancing, the peasants' freedom of movement was denied them by their courtly tradition and dress, which lent themselves rather to stateliness. The two forms nevertheless developed side by side, and as court dances evolved in the fourteenth and fifteenth centuries, they readily borrowed from the more vigorous and less seemly rustic dances. Gradually the 'dancing master' acquired professional standing, thus widening the distance between the dances he supervised and those of the folk, without destroying the possibility of mutual borrowing.

The custom soon arose of alternating slow dances with fast ones. Such couplings of dances remained fashionable under different names to the end of the sixteenth century. Most of the fourteenth century dances were carried over into the fifteenth century, when little was added to the dance-repertory except the *gaillarde* and the *basse danse*. The latter derived its name from the 'low' (walking) steps of the dancers, which contrasted with the 'high' (jumping) steps of the *danses hautes*, such as the *gaillarde* and the *tourdion*. Later, some of these dances were replaced by various *branles* (English, *brawles*), which became so popular that they figured prominently in all kinds of social entertainment.

After 1500, Spanish and Italian dances, modified by the sophistication demanded of royal entertainment, were performed at various courts. Aided by the patronage of the Bourbon kings, French modifications and nomenclature eventually triumphed. Today the names of the courtly dances of this period are commonly French, although the dances themselves are sometimes not French in origin—for example, *sarabande*, *pavane*, and *gaillarde*. So great was the social prestige of Louis XIV's court that France was able to take the local dances of other peoples, refine them, and then export them as French cultural influences to all the rest of western Europe. Dances of peasant origin, some of them ages old, developed into polite, mincing steps suitable to aristocratic tastes—e.g. the formalized *minuet*, the *gavotte*, the *bourrée*, and the *passepied*. Series of such stylized dances figured in the new *ballets de cour*.

The ballet began in Italy and France. At occasional festivities in the late fifteenth and early sixteenth centuries costumed dancers would perform for royal guests amid sumptuous scenery and to musical accompaniment.37 In the second half of the seventeenth century the French ballet attained a high degree of excellence and passed from the court to the theatrical stage. Professional dancers were now trained by ballet-masters, and the best contemporary talent wrote much of the music to which they performed. Jean-Baptiste Lully (1633–87), the foremost composer of the period, though born in Italy, had a spectacular career at the court of Louis XIV, rising from a simple violinist in the royal orchestra and *baladin* ('dancer') to the rank of plenipotentiary director of the Paris opera. He not only provided fine music for the *ballets de cour* but also introduced formal ballets into his operas. Moreover, in co-operation with Molière he created the *comédie-ballet*, a combination of theatre and dance, exemplified in *Le Bourgeois Gentilhomme*. By that time the *ballet de cour* was so popular that princes, princesses, and courtiers often took part in them. Louis XIV himself sometimes consented to strut in ballets written to commemorate his greatness. One of these was Lully's 'Ballet de la Nuit' (1653), in which the king took the part of the *roi soleil*, a role that gave him a lasting sobriquet.

In Lully's time ballet-music became an art-form, and theatrical dancing an art in its own right. Subsequently, the ballet was so much in demand that it remained an indispensable part of operatic work well into the eighteenth century. That a ballet presented in several acts could successfully fill an entire evening was proven by Lully's illustrious successor, Jean Philippe Rameau (1683–1764). In the eighteenth century several dancers of both sexes became famous performers, and several treatises on the art of the dance appeared, Jean Georges Noverre's *Lettres sur la danse et les ballets* (1760), being perhaps the most notable of them.

While the *ballet de cour* flourished in France, England developed its own version of courtly and aristocratic entertainment in the masque. Introduced into England from Italy and France, the masque inherited certain characteristics, such as mythological plots and lavish settings, but it also developed its own distinctive features; stereotyped formal dances performed by aristocratic maskers often were interspersed with dialogues and songs performed by professional actors. That the English masque became a sophisticated art-form is due in great part to the co-operation of such eminent literary men as Ben Jonson, Thomas Campion, and Milton, who supplied the texts, and to artists like Inigo Jones, who designed the masks and stage-settings. The decline of the masque began with intrusion of comic and grotesque scenes and dances, called antimasques.

By the end of our period, the dance had become a profession for the vurtuoso as well as a pastime for the amateur, and it was no longer necessarily an expression of religious devotion or of rustic merriment. From Europe it passed to the European colonies in the Western Hemisphere, where it both enriched and was enriched by the tribal dances of the American Indian and possibly also of the African slave.

The Ars Nova of the Fourteenth Century

The history of the dance is in large part also the history of music. Although spontaneous, unrecorded folksongs and dances never lost their appeal, before 1300 the cultivated music of the Western world consisted almost entirely of church hymnology. In its earliest phases Catholic Church music was represented by the pure, unaccompanied (monophonic) Gregorian chant. The gradual addition of melodic lines to the unalterable Gregorian chant (i.e. to the so-called cantus firmus) marked a signal advancement, and from the twelfth century on, contrapuntal or polyphonic (many-voiced) vocal compositions became increasingly customary. By 1300 primitive counterpoint, which set note against note (point counter point) had progressed to the organum and discantus of the Notre Dame School, and musical composition had become fairly complex.

The church looked with disfavour upon the 'deterioration' of the Gregorian chant. In 1324 a papal bull laid down severe restrictions upon innovations. Nevertheless, ecclesiastical displeasure could neither check the growth of the polyphonic style nor prevent the increasing infiltration of secular elements into religious music. The trend was well illustrated by the development of the motet, the representative musical form of the 'Gothic' period. It was originally a three-part contrapuntal composition sung to sacred Latin texts, with the leading Gregorian melody, the cantus firmus, in the tenor; the added voices were called duplum and triplum. When a text was assigned also to the second voice (usually a paraphrase of the fundamental thought expressed in the tenor) it was called motetus (i.e. 'worded part'), and this term eventually was attached to the entire composition. From the fourteenth century on, the motet was adopted also outside the church. Sometimes contrasting melodies and texts were combined in the same motet, and sometimes, too, the liturgical tenor melody was replaced by worldly tunes. The French folk melody 'L'homme armé' became famous because between the fifteenth and the seventeenth century more than thirty motets based on it were written by outstanding French, Flemish, and Italian masters.

The amalgamation of sacred and secular elements led to the emergence of the *ars nova*, so named by the fourteenth-century musician-poet Philippe de Vitry to distinguish it from the *ars antiqua*, the style of the previous century. The composers of the *ars nova* tried to break away from the *ars antiqua*, which in their opinion was characterized by stiffness. They strove for greater rhythmic-melodic freedom and, above all, for a greater liberty of expression. With them, a new spirit came into music—a spirit that paralleled the lyric quality and the rebellion against rigidity that was expressed in the poems of Dante and Petrarch and in the frescoes of Giotto and Fra Angelico. Nevertheless, the contrapuntal technique dominant in church music continued to influence the construction also of worldly music. Under this influence emerged the secular motet and the catch (or canon), a more or less elaborate part-song in which the voices fell in one after the other, imitating and trying to 'catch' each other. The earliest example of this kind of song is the famous canon (or round) 'Sumer is icumen in', attributed to the English monk John of Fornsete (thirteenth century).

Machaut (see Chapter X) and Francesco Landino (*c.* 1325–97) were the ranking masters of the *ars nova*. Being poets as well as musicians, both put inventiveness and charm into their works. Machaut, born in Champagne, excelled in *ballades*, *rondeaux*, and *virelais*, subtle, sophisticated songs and dances that had sprung up in France. Landino was a master of the Italian *ballata* and the early madrigal, in which a few stanzas sung by a sole voice alternated with instrumental sections. Educated amateurs all over Europe enthusiastically performed the new French and Italian art-forms, and probably for that reason music found an established place in the cultured secular society of the epoch.

In church music the organ was the principal instrument. While of imposing size and tone-power in many a cathedral, it also came in smaller form, such as the 'positive', a stationary chamber-organ, and the picturesque organetto, a small portable instrument carried by a shoulder-strap, the right hand manipulating the keys and the left the bellows. Many other instruments were in use, however; Machaut himself mentions thirty-six kinds. When the wandering musicians of Paris founded a Confrérie et Corporation des Ménestrels (Minstrel's Guild) in 1321, an applicant for membership was expected to play no less than nine different instruments. The strings of the time included various fiddles, which were bowed; harps, zithers, psalteries, and lutes, which were plucked; and the dulcimer, which was beaten. Woodwinds took forms such as the bombarde, the cromorne (from *Krummhorn*, i.e. 'curved horn'), and the shawm or other ancestor of the oboe family. Other wind instruments were the slide-trumpet (not unlike the modern trombone) and the bagpipe. Several types of drums were also used. During the fifteenth and sixteenth centuries some of these instruments became obsolete, others refined. Many of them appear in contemporary paintings and sculptures and survive in the collections and museums of our own day.

The 'Netherlands School' and Modern Notation

In the fifteenth century the seat of musical activity shifted to England and the Low Countries. During the first decades the leading role fell to England's foremost composer John Dunstable (d. 1453), renowned also as a mathematician and an astrologer. Although steeped in the traditional polyphonic style, he transcended it in the free, melodic imagination with which he adorned the *cantus firmus* and in the distinctive euphony of his masses and motets. Thereby he greatly influenced the musical language of his disciples, among whom were Guillaume Dufay and Gilles Binchois, who were to become known as the founders of the Burgundian School of music.

On the Continent musical leadership had already begun to pass from Italy and France to the Low Countries. In Italy, though popular music still flourished, the higher musical art-forms lagged in the competition for talent, with the result that music fell far behind the visual arts, while in France the trials of the Hundred Years' War had temporarily brought exhaustion. About the same time, the Low Countries entered a period of economic and cultural prosperity, and many outstanding French musicians migrated to Flemish Burgundy. Together with talented natives of those parts like Dufay and Binchois they founded the Burgundian School of music, the initial phase of the great grouping usually but inaccurately called the Netherlands School, which comprised three generations of late medieval and early Renaissance composers.

The leader of the Burgundian School was Dufay. Born around 1400 in the county of Hainaut in the borderland between France and the Low Countries, he started out as a choirboy at the Cathedral of Cambrai and died in 1470 as one of its canons. The enterprising Duke Charles (the Bold) of Burgundy made Flanders a centre of musical attainment, and the cathedral school of Cambrai became a seat of musical education. Dufay also spent some years in Rome, where he was exposed to the 'anti-Gothic' spirit of the Italian Renaissance. On the one hand, this spirit modified Dufay's 'Gothic' musical construction; on the other, his solid contrapuntal style decidedly affected Italian music.

Dufay's influence in Italy was reinforced by the great masters of the second generation of the Netherlands School (1460–1500), best represented by the Flemish Johannes Ockeghem (1430–95), Dufay's outstanding disciple, and the Dutch Jacob Obrecht (1430–1505). Ockeghem dominated the second half of the fifteenth century as the creator of exalted religious works in the so-called neo-Gothic style and also as the teacher of practically all the famous composers of the next generation. His name and that of Obrecht are linked to a momentous change in musical thinking that took place in the course of the fifteenth century.

In its early stages polyphonic composition had been primarily the inter-weaving of strands of melodic voices—without much concern, however, whether the harmonies (chords) resulting from the coincidence of different melodic lines clashed or blended. The old contrapuntal practice was, figura-tively speaking, 'horizontal' (each part having its own melodic design), the 'vertical' (or chordal) aspect being more or less unplanned. The incidence of clashing sounds was somewhat diminished by the limited *tessitura* (i.e. the prevailing, average pitch) of the participating voices. Combinations of melody and harmony, already successfully attempted in the secular music of the fourteenth-century *ars nova*, had developed more fully in the worldly French *chanson* of the fifteenth, but in learned church music Ockeghem and Obrecht were the first masters to base intricate polyphony and expanded *tessitura* on a groundwork of firm harmonic structure—a principle that still is valid in contrapuntal composition.

A third generation of 'Netherlanders' arose at the end of the fifteenth century. Some of them, now the heirs to a highly developed contrapuntal tech-nique, put a finishing touch on it by writing mammoth canons, sometimes for more than thirty separate voices, or by devising part-songs that could be per-formed forward and backward (the so-called crab-canons). Others underwent a southern harmonic influence, which gained momentum with the growing migration of Flemish musicians to Italy. Both developments were summed up in Josquin Des Prés (1450–1521), who fully attained the art of combining expressive voice-parts with ordered, meaningful harmonies. Born in France, he became Ockeghem's pupil in Paris, lived in Italy for thirty years, and got to be as celebrated for his music—both sacred and secular—as Leonardo and Raphael for their paintings.

Josquin was the first great master in a true musical Renaissance. His mature works reflect the ideals of balance, clarity, and symmetry of form dear to Renaissance artists. He not only could command the styles and techniques of the time, he also is credited with introducing the method of composition by which a musical work is unified through 'imitation'—i.e. the reiteration of the same motif as it passes from voice to voice. This device, which still is used in polyphonic music, is known as continual imitation (*durchimitierender Stil*). Josquin's masses, motets, and chansons remained the model for two genera-tions of composers all over Europe. His influence was made all the more pervasive by the contemporary development of the printing press and its adaptation to music.

Unlike the products of the visual arts, musical composition comes to life only through actual performance, and performance requires a system of notation. The music of the Middle Ages had been couched in manifold, involved notations, but with the accumulating innovations in music, com-posers had slowly and laboriously been elaborating a modern scheme of representing musical sounds and idiom. By 1500 musical notation had moved decisively from the medieval toward the modern script, and thenceforth the steady accumulation of printed scores hastened the dissemination and cultivation of music. In the course of the next few centuries the medieval script gradually fell into disuse, and for a long time modern musicians were unable to read and hence to perform the music of the Middle Ages. Only a few decades ago musicologists began to decipher it and to reconstruct its performing practices. Thanks to their efforts, combined with those of dedicated artists and recording companies, the gap has now been largely filled.

Music of the High Renaissance

In the sixteenth century leadership in music was on the wane in the north, and it passed to Italy. The music of the Italian Renaissance developed along two main lines: it attained an unsurpassed level in vocal polyphony, and it began a new polyphonic instrumental style. Vocal part-music reached a summit in the secular chanson and madrigal, and an unexcelled perfection in the masses of Pierluigi Palestrina (1525-94).

Palestrina, chapel master of St Peter's in Rome and honorary *maestro compositore* to the pope, was no innovator; he was, rather, the crowning figure of a long historic evolution. His popular fame rests on a now disproved legend. The pure, dignified style of his masses is supposed to have convinced a group of musical judges (appointed by Pope Pius IV in keeping with a resolution of the Council of Trent) that polyphonic music had a rightful place in the church and thus to have averted the reinstatement of the monophonic Gregorian chant. Though not by any such direct route the saviour of Catholic music, Palestrina was the greatest composer of sacred music within the Catholic Church. The serene spirituality of his masses, motets, and other religious compositions sets him apart even from the few contemporary masters who approximated the perfection of his blending of counterpoint with harmony.

Though they are overshadowed in historical importance by the majesty of his church music, Palestrina also wrote numerous secular pieces. The principal secular songs of the day were the chanson and the madrigal. The chanson, of French origin, was a finely wrought part-song for several voices with the leading melody in the treble. It was written to short poetic texts, and whether the poems were lyrical, contemplative, humorous, or frankly frivolous, they usually dealt with love in all its aspects. Some composers—Palestrina's contemporary Clément Jannequin conspicuous among them—delighted also in chansons of a descriptive character—e.g., 'La Guerre', 'Le Chant des Oyseaux', and 'Le Caquet des Femmes'.

The Italian counterpart of the chanson was the sixteenth-century madrigal (not to be confused with its fourteenth-century predecessor). Like the French chanson, it was a kind of vocal chamber music, written for four, five, or six unaccompanied voices. The madrigalists of the High Renaissance tried to translate the varying moods and ideas of the underlying poem into an equally varying flow of musical invention, adapting meter and rhythm, mode and harmony to the nuances of the text. Thereby they often succeeded in adding variety, flexibility, and finesse to the polyphonic style. Among the musically most advanced madrigals, in addition to those by Palestrina, there must be counted some composed by Giovanni Giacomo Gastoldi (c. 1550–c. 1610), Luca Marenzio (c. 1560–90), and Don Carlos Gesualdo, prince of Venosa (c. 1560–1613). Full of dramatic suspense and bold chromatic inflections, the works of Gesualdo were modernist in their own time and still sound modernist. The musical versatility of both men and women of Italy's patrician circles enabled them to perform this elegant sort of vocal polyphony sitting around a table with their part-books in front of them.

From Italy the madrigal spread to Germany and to England. In England it flourished for four decades of the Elizabethan and Jacobean era in a vital, 'naturalized' form. The foremost composers of those decades were Thomas Tallis, Orlando Gibbons, William Byrd, Thomas Morley, and John Dowland. Their madrigals, songs, and anthems still delight music lovers everywhere.

Palestrina's great Continental contemporaries were the Flemings Roland de Lassus (c. 1525–94) and Philippe de Monte (1525–1603), the Spaniards Cristobal Morales (c. 1500–53) and Tomás Luis de Victoria (c. 1540–c. 1613), who was known as 'the Spanish Palestrina', and the Venetians Andrea and Giovanni Gabrieli (1510–86 and 1557–1612 respectively). Lassus stands out as the most versatile composer of the century. Unlike Palestrina, who hardly ever left Rome, he lived and worked in many countries and spent the last decades of his life in Munich, at the ducal court of Bavaria. He produced some 2000 works and excelled in many different styles, including masses, Latin motets and psalms, French chansons, Italian madrigals, and German part-songs. A truly cosmopolitan figure, he embodied the spirit of the late Renaissance. On the other hand, the Spanish priest Victoria wrote sacred music of a kind that imparts the passionate spirit of the dawning Baroque era. Likewise, the works of the two Gabrielis bear the marks of the early Baroque in their predilection for double and multiple choirs with colourful orchestral accompaniments that suggest the splendour of contemporary painting. Their providing for the participation of instruments in their church music, however, was not a complete innovation. Though previous centuries had been dominated by purely vocal church music, instruments had often been used to support or supplant vocal parts, and as early as 1526 Erasmus had complained that churches reverberated with the sound of flutes, pipes, trumpets, and trombones.

Music in the Baroque Era

At the close of the sixteenth century the musical stiaution was exceedingly complex. On the one hand, the vocal polyphonic style, which had taken about four hundred years to mature, was at its peak, and, on the other hand, new trends held forth the promise of fresh achievements in the future. At that juncture music entered the stage of development known as the Baroque, which was to close some one hundred and fifty years later with the death of

Johann Sebastian Bach (1685–1750) and George Frederick Handel (1685–1759). Their most important German forerunners were Johann Hermann Schein (1586–1630), Samuel Scheidt (1587–1654), and Henrich Schütz (1585–1672). With the works of these three masters, particularly with the oratorios and passions of Schütz (who was in a sense a runner-up to Bach as much as his forerunner), Protestant Germany rose to the rank of a full-fledged partner in the musical development of the Western nations.

Until then, German music had been remarkably slow in asserting its individual quality. To be sure, the country's native folksong had flourished at all times, and the Meistersingers had produced a widespread, petty bourgeois musical practice (see Chapter X), but the cross-currents of northern ('Netherlands') and southern (Italian) cultural influences had to be absorbed before German music could reach its height. From the sixteenth century to the end of our period (and beyond), it remained ascendant.

The earliest known examples of polyphonic music based on German folk-songs appear in the so-called *Lochamer Liederbuch* (c. 1450). Germany's subsequent contribution to the evolution of music coincided with the rise of Protestantism. Luther was a talented and trained musician, and in the seventeenth century the Pietist musician Paul Gerhardt wrote some of Germany's finest hymns (see Chapter IV). Reared in the musical traditions of the Roman Catholic Church, Luther became familiar with the great polyphonic works—secular as well as religious—of the masters of his time, Josquin being his favourite. He is credited (though not uncontestedly) with the authorship of the so-called battle-hymn of the Reformation ('A Mighty Fortress is Our God') and other religious songs. At any rate, as the founder and organizer of a new liturgy he based the musical part of the service on the chorale—i.e. on simple metrical hymn-tunes with devotional German texts. They were sung in unison by the congregation—first without, and later with, organ accompaniment. The chorale, in turn, gave rise to the chorale-prelude, the chorale-fantasy, and the chorale-variation, art-forms that permitted organist-composers to display their instrumental and contrapuntal skill.

The chorale also found its way in Protestant Germany into larger forms of music, the most important being the cantata, the oratorio, and the passion. These were religious but non-liturgical compositions, characterized by the blending of traditional polyphonic technique with new, dramatic elements. The first German master to achieve this blending was Schütz. He introduced into his oratorios and passions not only the new Italian monody and recitative (soon to be described) but also the alternation of accompanied solo voices and massive choral sections which he had learned to compose in Venice under Gabrieli. The monumentality and the eloquence of Schütz's choral compositions guarantee him a place among the first great figures of the Baroque era.

The century and a half of Baroque music corresponds roughly to the Baroque period in the visual arts and to the so-called scientific revolution. The name *Baroque* when applied to music tends to associate it with some of the characteristics of Baroque art—the mixture of worldliness and piety, the quest for complexity within unity, the monumentality of Baroque architecture. It may suggest association also with some aspects of the scientific spirit of the day—a quest for precision, a restraint of self-expression, a growing knowledge of acoustics (see Chapter XIV), an improvement of techniques and instruments, and a respect for regularity of form.

Early in the Baroque period instrumental music, hitherto secondary, emerged into the foreground. In the sixteenth century, to be sure, *toccatas* ('touch-pieces') and *ricercari* (complex musical designs) had been expressly written for the organ, and dances and all sorts of transcriptions for the lute, the all-purpose instrument of the day. Nevertheless, most compositions still bore the instruction *da cantare o suonare* (to be sung or played), without specifying a particular instrument. Only in the seventeenth century did composers begin to show interest in writing music to be performed on a specific instrument. They invented more and more musical designs and patterns to suit the nature of the chosen medium, bringing out in each instrument its characteristic potentials. In Italy and the northern countries the organ, in Spain the lute, in England the virginal each acquired its own repertory. The organists of the time—even Girolamo Frescobaldi (1583–1643), the greatest among them—perhaps because of the traditional prestige of the organ as the church instrument par excellence, clung more or less loyally to forms inherited from the preceding century. In contrast, the Elizabethan composers created a music that effectively exhibited the merits of a newer and simpler keyboard instrument, the harpsichord. In their so-called 'grounds' (variations written to a recurrent bass-figure) and particularly in the free-and-easy variations on popular songs (some of which were prescribed by Shakespeare for use as incidental music in his plays) Morley, Gibbons, Giles Farnaby, and others plumbed all the resources that the keyboard offered—swift scale and chord passages, trills, and the like.

The harpsichord served also as the favourite medium for another important art-form of the Baroque, the dance-suite. From the great wealth of seventeenth-century dance-forms emerged the German *allemande*, the French *courante*, the Spanish *sarabanda*, and the English *jig* as standard movements. Around 1700 the harpsichord suite was enriched by the inclusion of optional numbers, such as the gavotte, the bourrée, and the minuet, all of which figured also in the ballets and operas of Lully, Purcell, and Rameau. The eighteenth-century dance-suite was to reach its ultimate perfection in Bach's clavier-suites and partitas, as well as in his suites for orchestra.

The fuller development of literature for bowed instruments began in the seventeenth century, coinciding with the great period of violin craftsmanship at Cremona in Italy. The making of the best violins began about 1630 and lasted well into the eighteenth century. Its most famous and still unsurpassed masters were Nicolo Amati (d. 1684) and his pupil Antonio Stradivarius (1644–1737). The German composers of the time stressed the virtuoso rather than the expressive side of violin playing, whereas the Italians used the 'singing' quality of the violin tone to full advantage. In the violin sonata and the sonata da camera (both with an accompanying harpsichord) and in the Baroque solo-concerto and the concerto grosso for string orchestra the Italian masters Archangelo Corelli (1653–1713) and Antonio Vivaldi (1680–1743) created novel art-forms for the violin-family. Guiseppe Tartini (1692–1770), a brilliant violinist as well as a composer, developed a virtuoso style for its dominating member, the violin.

On the whole, the evolution of instrumental music in the seventeenth century was but a diversified continuation of earlier developments. The only relatively unprecedented event was the rise of the *dramma per musica*. The new Italian music-drama owed its existence to the scientists, literati, and musicians who gathered around 1600 in the drawing rooms (the *camerata*) of the Florentine music lover Count Bardi. Tired of polyphony, which, in fact, obscures the text of vocal music, they believed that the future of music lay in the rebirth of the Greek music drama and the adoption of a monodic, declamatory style for its singers. Monody—i.e. the accompanied solo (*monos*) song—was no novelty in itself; it had long been practiced by folk singers and amateurs. Polyphony, however, still enjoyed undisputed hegemony, and the introduction of the monodic style into dramatic art-music marked a turning point in the development of music because it challenged that hegemony. So as to accentuate diction, the composers of the camerata employed the *recitative*, a kind of musical recitation accompanied by sparse chords. The resulting declamatory style inevitably involved a certain dryness and monotony. Hence Claudio Monteverdi (1567–1643), the ranking figure and the only man of genius in the group, interspersed lyrical *ariosos* in his *recitativos*, thereby enriching the scope of the new style. The effort to represent in this fashion the personality of the characters of a musical drama was given the name *stile rappresentative*. With the rise of the monodic style a new kind of notation came into use—the *basso continuo* or figured bass, which is a method of indicating an accompanying part by the bass notes, together with figures indicating the chords and intervals to be played above the bass. This practice lapsed with the passing of the Baroque era; in the eighteenth century the modern system of notation became common and was generally used for all types of music.

The somewhat experimental music drama of the early Baroque was soon superseded by the Italian opera, which had begun its triumphal march in the 1630's. The first permanent opera house was opened in Venice in 1637. When Rome, Naples, Paris, Vienna, and other cities followed suit, opera became an international concern. Dramatic action was no longer placed in the foreground; from the words to be set to music, the emphasis shifted to the music itself, and above all to the arias. In its typical form, perfected by Alessandro Scarlatti (1659?–1725), the leader of the Neapolitan school, the so-called *da-capo aria* became the main vehicle for lyrical expression, while the *coloratura aria* gave the singers an opportunity to show their virtuosity. How highly the art of *bel canto* was thought of (and paid for) in the seventeenth and eighteenth centuries is perhaps correctly measured by the fame and wealth of the *castrati*, for whom roles were specially composed that would reveal their brilliant soprano and contralto voices.

France was somewhat late in producing an operatic style that could match the dramatic art of Corneille and Racine or of its highly developed courtly ballet. In Lully (whose ballets we have already considered) French opera had its first worthy representative. A first-rate theatrical composer, he adapted his music to the classicist style of the libretti he chose, occasionally with Molière's advice. Some of Lully's operas and ballets remained on the French repertoire for almost a century.

In Germany opera was a product of the late Baroque. From humble beginnings in the popular *Singspiel* there evolved the *opera seria*, Italian in style but with German libretti. It attained a certain eminence under a few composers affiliated with the Hamburg Opera, founded in 1678. Their leader, Reinhold Keiser (1674–1739), was much admired; even Handel borrowed from him for some of his own forty operatic works, written between 1711 and 1741. After a span of fifty-odd years, however, most of the German opera houses either closed down or were taken over by Italians and Italian or Italian-style opera, as was true all over the Continent. Not until the advent of Christoph Willibald Gluck (1714–87) was Germany to produce its next great opera-composer.

If the German-born Handel is not counted as English, England produced only one distinguished opera-composer—Henry Purcell (1659–95)—perhaps, at least in part, for the reason that it possessed its home-grown version of the musical drama in the masque. Purcell's 'Dido and Aeneas' is a masterpiece ranking with his many pieces for harpsichord and chamber music, his incidental music (incidental, that is, to spoken dramas), and the anthems and hymns he wrote as organist at Westminster Abbey and the Chapel Royal.

With the works of the generation after Purcell the music of the Baroque reached its height. François Couperin (1668–1733) and Rameau in France, Vivaldi and Domenico Scarlatti (1685–1757) in Italy, Bach in Germany, and Handel in Germany and England were the leading masters of the period. Couperin and Rameau excelled in music for the harpsichord. Rameau also wrote operas and ballets. Some of them were written to traditional Classic, mythological, or allegorical plots; others featured the current interest in the exotic (e.g. 'Les Indes Galantes'). Though Rameau's musical innovations brought on several bitter controversies with Rousseau and other influential contemporaries, he was perhaps more significant as a musical theorist. In an epochal work, the *Traité de l'harmonie* (1722), he laid down the principles of harmonic functions in musical phraseology. This treatise had a far-reaching influence upon generations of composers and still is not obsolete.

While Italy continued to make important contributions to instrumental music, opera, and oratorio, in the first half of the eighteenth century musical leadership fell to Germany. That period is often called 'the Age of Bach and Handel', and with good reason. The works of those giants transformed the various national styles of the period into a higher unity, a perfect fusion of Italian, French—and, in Handel's case, English—elements with a fundamentally German background. Moreover, although both spoke the complex musical idiom of their day, the personal characteristics of their art outweighed the typical Baroque features they had in common.

Handel was at his best in large, dramatic forms. After having written a great number of successful operas during his 'Italian' period, he settled down in London and turned definitely to the composition of oratorios, of which he wrote more than thirty. Most of them depicted heroic episodes derived from the Old Testament (e.g. 'Saul', 'Israel in Egypt', 'Esther', 'Judas Maccabeus'), with pathos, grandeur, and dramatic eloquence. They took England by storm and won vast audiences abroad. The secret of the strong emotional impact that Handel's oratorios have always exerted lies partly in their melodic appeal but mainly in their mighty choruses. Yet it was not the forceful spirit of his Biblical 'chorus dramas' that made Handel world-famous. It was 'The Messiah', the only oratorio from his hand in which lyric and contemplative elements predominate. With 'The Messiah', Handel became a national figure in his adopted country. The work itself came to be considered all over Europe as the archetype not only of the Handelian oratorio but of 'the oratorio' in general. Handel made generous contributions to almost all branches of instrumental music also, and the organ concerto with orchestra was his specific addition to that genre. Since, however, in one or another kind of instrumental music Bach or some other contemporary master may occasionally have overshadowed him, his glory rests on the oratorio, in which he was unsurpassed.

Handel was a man of the world; his was the grand Baroque manner, reflected equally in his life and in his work. Bach's spiritual attitude was entirely different. His cantatas and passions were a musical embodiment of Protestant piety, and his numerous instrumental compositions mark the acme of musical architecture, logic, and inspired craftsmanship. An organist, choirmaster, and church-composer in central Germany, he led the simple, well-regulated life of a hard-working middle-class citizen. In the toil of creative fulfilment Bach knew no bounds. While some of Handel's large-scale works show traces of improvisation here and there, Bach's compositions, whether conceived on a large or a small scale, bear the imprint of his genius to the last detail. This quality holds true for his didactic works—such as the *Inventions*, the forty-eight preludes and fugues assembled in the *Well-tempered Clavier* (that is, for the clavier tuned in the equal temperament universally used today) and *The Art of the Fugue*, which is an exegesis of polyphonic composition—and it holds just as true for the many musical works in which he gave free rein to his imagination. In his organ-fantasias and organ-toccatas,

'Chromatic Fantasy and Fugue' for clavier, 'Chaconne' for solo-violin, and certain mystic-symbolic cantatas—to give but a few examples—Bach is widely believed to have surpassed all his contemporaries, including Handel.

Bach and Handel appeared at a time when the polyphonic and the monodic style had reached a high degree of integration. Bach, essentially a contrapuntist, leaned more to the former style; Handel, essentially a dramatist, to the latter. Bach's and Handel's monumental works sum up a long musical evolution. Yet, whereas some of Handel's works (e.g. 'The Messiah') never ceased to be performed (particularly in England, where he spent most of his life), Bach's music was wellnigh forgotten after his death and had to wait for revival until twenty-year-old Felix Mendelssohn performed the 'Passion after St Matthew' in 1829—exactly a hundred years after it was written.

From Bach to 'the Viennese Classics'

In the generation after Bach the feeling prevailed that the grandiose, complicated contrapuntal style had outlived its day. The reaction against the musical tradition asserted itself, on the one hand, in the so-called 'style galant' —an echo in music of the Rococo in architecture—and, on the other, in a new emotionalism (*Empfindsamkeit, sensibilité*), which stressed the milder, more intimate feelings or 'affects'. The slogan of the innovators of the latter persuasion was 'back to nature', and in music at least, this urge can be correctly associated with Rousseau. Once again new esthetic needs led to the quest for new art-forms. It found vent in a movement that paved the way for the compositional technique of those paragons who were to become known as the 'Viennese Classics', Franz Joseph Haydn, Wolfgang Amadeus Mozart, and Ludwig van Beethoven. Three of Bach's sons were pioneers in this movement.

These pioneers inaugurated the sonata-form. The merit of the new form lies in its 'dialectic' nature—i.e. in the opposition of contrasting themes within a single movement, a signal change from the 'monothematic' construction that prevailed in the instrumental music of the Baroque period. Although experimental and frail in its incipient stages, the new form proved to be viable. As finally brought to perfection under Haydn, it was integrated with two or three independent movements in what is generally known as the 'classical sonata at large'. In its broader acceptance, the term *sonata* now covers any large-scale work written on this basic plan, whether for a single instrument (e.g. the piano), a larger group of players (e.g. a string quartet), or an orchestra (in which case it is called a symphony.)

A favourite medium of the post-Baroque composers was the pianoforte. This new keyboard-instrument, first designed by Bartolommeo Cristofori in 1709, superseded the competing harpsichord in a period which valued the expression of tenderness and delicacy. On the harpsichord only the most skilful player could produce anything but abrupt contrasts of 'forte' and 'piano'; on the new instruments, which even then possessed the complicated lever-action of our modern piano, the tone could be modulated by the mere pressure of the fingers. Thus allowing many shadings of intensity, the pianoforte lent itself admirably to the requirements of the new style.

The pioneering endeavours of Bach's sons and their followers were paralleled by the innovations in orchestral music and performance cultivated by the so-called Mannheim School, connected with one of the German ducal courts. Here a group of conductors and composers were brought together, largely from Austria (e.g. Ignaz Holzbauer) and Bohemia (e.g. Franz Xaver Richter and Johann W. A. Stamitz). They laid the foundation for the modern orchestra (the celebrated orchestra of the Mannheim court had a goodly number of wind and string instruments, aided occasionally by drummers) as well as for the symphonic style of the Viennese Classics. They enriched the tonal palette of orchestral performance by introducing unexpected dynamic accents, sudden pauses, extended crescendos, and other hitherto little used or unused devices, which were eagerly taken over by Haydn, Mozart, and particularly Beethoven.

In the operatic field the striving for 'true, natural feelings' found its champion in Gluck. His 'reform-operas' (as he called them) reveal not only an outstanding composer but also a man of profound esthetic principles. Like Monteverdi a century and a half earlier, he stressed the organic unity in opera of text, acting, and music—a principle that was to find its greatest champion in Richard Wagner a hundred years later. Consequently, Gluck banned coloratura arias from his operas, which were all written around plots taken from Classical literature, and allowed ballets only if they did not retard the action. An ideological and literary battle ensued between the Gluckists, his adherents, and the Piccinnists, adherents of Niccola Piccinni, the leading composer in the traditional Italian operatic style. Queen Marie Antoinette, for political rather than aesthetic reasons (Gluck too was Austrian), supported Gluck, and Rousseau, consistent with his avowed opposition to artifice, likewise sided with him. Posterity also seems to have vindicated Gluck. Piccinni's music fell into oblivion while some of Gluck's works still form part of the operatic repertoire.

In the eighteenth century, the three classical masters, Haydn, Mozart, and Beethoven, made of Vienna the musical capital of Europe. Haydn, chronologically the first of the three (1732–1809), had by 1775 composed a number of his finest symphonies and sonatas, helping to perfect those musical types. He also wrote oratorios, masses, and songs, and an astonishing number of string quartets and other kinds of chamber music. Many of his best compositions, however, were to come after 1775. Mozart was only nineteen years old in that year. Having begun to compose when he was five, he had already written a number of operas and symphonies and a good deal of church music as well as sonatas and concertos for his favourite instrument, the piano. All of these early compositions show his extraordinary, if yet not fully matured, gift for melody and harmony and his amazing ability to see a projected composition at once and whole as a mental picture.

The culmination of Haydn's career, the full development of Mozart's genius, and the whole of Beethoven's contribution belongs to the period of Volume V. As if to put a finishing touch upon our period, in 1776 Charles Burney and John Hawkins each began to publish a lengthy history of music, without which much of the knowledge of early music would have been lost. Both of these works are now considered classics in their field.

Music as a Profession

Since the fourteenth century the musician had changed his status considerably. The eighteenth-century musician of reputation might still be a choirmaster, like Bach, or connected in some other way with religious services, but he was not necessarily a functionary of a church, particularly in Protestant countries. More commonly now he was also or entirely in the service of a prince or a bourgeois patron. He might even be a private entrepreneur like Handel, who made and lost fortunes in producing operas and oratorios in England, or like Haydn and Mozart, who composed on commission for special occasions. Purcell, Lully, Bach, Handel, Haydn, and others were happy enough to have royal patrons. Since copyright did not exist and borrowing others' work was common, a royal patron was an especially good asset, for such patrons not only could reward handsomely but also might grant privileges amounting to copyright by placing restrictions upon competitors. With *concerts spirituels* (initiated in Paris in 1725) and operas as well as public concerts becoming regular events in a number of European countries, the works of contemporary composers reached ever widening audiences on more and more social levels. Music in Europe was now not only an art but a secular, even a competitive, profession as well.

THE ARTS OF ISLAM

Architecture

Among the visual arts in the civilization of Islam, architecture remained supreme. Islam perhaps owed much more than the West to the Chinese in the decorative arts, but it was largely exempt from Chinese influence in architecture. After the Mongol invasions the lands of the Persian-using zone (largely under Turkish rule) excelled in architecture, but it continued to be very fruitfully cultivated likewise in the Arabic countries (some of them also Turkish-ruled), especially before 1500. The greatest monuments still were religious buildings—mosques, khānaqāhs (Ṣūfī meeting-places), madrasas (schools for 'ulama'), and great mausoleums often with mosques attached. Care was taken also with secular buildings, such as fortresses, caravanserais, and especially palaces, as well as with the homes of the wealthy.

In the Arabic lands the fourteenth and fifteenth centuries were the great age for the building of madrasas. In Egypt and Syria a madrasa was associated with the mausoleum-mosque of its founder; it was commonly cruciform, allowing classes to meet, according to the hour or the need, in each of the arms of the cross. This complex pattern was broken up toward the end of our period as social needs changed; in later centuries separate portions—such as a school centred on a fountain—were built as individual foundations. The most noticeable monuments that survive from Mamlūk Egypt are its many mosques with their delicately silhouetted minarets and luxuriant use of geometric interlacings. Farther west the tradition of the solidly square minaret was maintained, and the numerous *madrasas* were built more simply. In contrast to the Gothic cathedral, the mosque was hypostyle, many columns breaking it up visually into horizontal compartments (see above). Palace architecture persisted in the rich strength represented by the Alhambra, the fourteenth century palace-citadel of the kings of Granada. (Pl. 61a.)

In Iran and Turkestan the Mongols took readily to buildings in the old Islamic manner, with even increased magnificence. The tombs of rulers were built with an especially massive majesty, usually culminating in a high dome, such as was cultivated also in India. Early in the fourteenth century the tomb of Uljaitu (d. 1316) at Sultaniya helped set this pattern; the blue and gold mausoleum of Timur in Samarkand, erected a century later, is its most impressive example. (Pl. 61b.) Mosques in Iran also emphasized the great high dome, displaying the brightly coloured tiles distinctive of Iran, but they retained the open court as the main body of the prayer space. After 1500, in the Ṣafavid Empire, Iranian architecture was represented at its best in the magnificence of the imperial city of Isfahan, with its garden boulevards and open, landscaped palaces set off by the impressive use of columns. The floral type of decoration was enriched by numerous kinds of ornamental forms, some based on motifs borrowed from Europe and China. A high level of elegance was maintained till the end of the seventeenth century, when political catastrophes put an end to the great age of building. To Julfa, a suburb of Isfahan, Shah Abbas in 1603 transferred a number of Armenian Christian families, whose cathedral, decorated inside with murals depicting scenes of Christian martyrdom painted by Italian journeymen artists, was made externally to look like a mosque.

In the Turkish countries in the fourteenth and especially the fifteenth century there was introduced, perhaps after the Byzantine pattern, a form of mosque in which the main prayer room was placed under the dome instead of in an open court. In the Blue Mosque of Tabriz of the later fifteenth century, the main prayer room was so placed. In the design of some sixteenth century mosques Muslim architects partly adopted the Hagia Sophia in Istanbul as a model, using half-domes to buttress the great central dome. Sinān, the famous Albanian architect of the Sulaymāniyya and other Istanbul mosques, created imposing variations of this central form, originating a fully new and integrated type. With Ottoman domination after 1500, the domed mosque of this general type spread widely in the Arab countries,[38] where otherwise, however, architecture was largely static or even declined. In the eighteenth century in the Turkish provinces of the Ottoman Empire, an Italianate style, modelled on Western Renaissance architecture, came into favour for palaces and homes.

Miniature painting

The best Muslim painting was of miniatures. After 1300 Muslim miniature painting was confined chiefly to the zone, from the Balkans through India, where the Iranian tradition predominated. A sound foundation had been laid for it before Mongol times by both Arab and Persian miniaturists, who stressed colour and pattern, but Chinese influences became strong in the Mongol era, and with them developed the brilliant schools of Islamic painting admired today. This kind of art reached its peak in book illustration, which sometimes affected mural painting. Eventually separate sheets were collected, as individual artists (from the fifteenth century on) received recognition as such. Painting was closely connected with the development of Persian calligraphy, in the *nasta'līq* style (see below), into a cascade of harmoniously flowing lines. In such centres of royal patronage as Samarkand and Herat the Chinese impulse was gradually absorbed, until a new form of aesthetic imagination was produced. At the end of the fifteenth century the miniaturist Bihzād of Herat (1450–*post* 1520) exemplified the establishment of an independent art, relatively more realistic within what was still a largely stylized decorative form. He was the master of the long-lived and varied Tabriz school. Early in the seventeenth century the school of Isfahan, latter-day capital of the Ṣafavids, found its outstanding master in Riza 'Abbāsī, who excelled in portraits and in genre scenes, in which he showed a subtle sense of humour. (Pl. 62a.) He was not altogether uninfluenced by Western painting.

In the eighteenth century the art of miniature painting declined in Iran and imitations of Western as well as of Indian art failed to revive it. The miniatures of the Ottoman Empire, where painting was vigorously frowned on by religious puritans (as was even more the case by then in Arab countries), were abundant but are not thought to have achieved such high distinction as those of Iran and Turkestan. In India (see below) a distinct and vigorous school developed at the Mogul court and influenced non-Muslim art as well.

Decorative arts

In the decorative arts, Islamic craftsmen lent much to and borrowed little from their European colleagues. They borrowed more from the craftsmanship of cultures farther east, but in some crafts—pottery, for example—lent to them also. In the visual arts of all kinds, after the Mongol invasions Iran and the other countries where Muslims used the Persian language were in the forefront, the Arabic countries gradually, especially under Turkish rule, learning to follow their patterns. Iran continued to set the tone for carpets of all sorts, which, like pottery and other types of decorative pieces for regular use, achieved in the Ṣafavid period an unsurpassed refinement of craftsmanship and elegance of design. In all these objects the Chinese influence had become, since the Mongol invasions, unmistakably strong in motifs and even in manner.

The luxurious rugs of the Near East (and of the Far East, too) were made predominantly of wool-and-silk yarn. The technique of rugmaking, which originated in China or the Near East and spread through the Mediterranean area with the expansion of Islam, changed little with respect to the materials, dyes, or implements used. The pile of the rug was built simply by knotting variously coloured yarns, tuft by tuft, to a warp stretched across a frame. After 1300 Persian rugs, particularly those made in Kurdistan, Khorasan, Kerman, and Feraghan during the sixteenth and seventeenth centuries, are generally considered the finest. The best ones are solidly made, having as many as four hundred knots to the square inch. In these rugs a complicated tracery—for instance, of meandering tendrils—constantly varied in colour plays over larger divisions or motifs. Ṣafavid rug makers daringly introduced overall patterns from book bindings and even from miniatures; the manner in which certain major motifs appear—particularly huge medallions, geometric compartments or borders, and floral or animal forms—frequently enables the connoisseur to place and date a rug. Turkish rugs tend to have a pile that is longer, looser, and softer than those of Persia. Many, like those of Ghiordez, employed the motifs of the 'praying dome' and the bejewelled lamp found on prayer rugs as a basic design over which delicate tendrils intertwine. Caucasian rugs are frequently smaller and narrower than Persian or Turkish rugs. Some of the most distinctive designs are those composed of small geometric shapes infinitely varied to create engaging decorative complications.

Unlike the Far Eastern and the American Indian artists, who were apparently concerned with symbolism in almost all their art forms, Muslim artists were little concerned with the meaning of the symbols they adopted. Islam was averse to the presentation of doctrine by any means other than the spoken word, and this aversion permitted Islamic artists to incorporate into their eclectic repertory the motifs of various cultural areas with little concern for the ideas originally associated with them, whereas the more self-contained and continuous traditions of the Far Eastern artists preserved the meanings of their motifs and, even in a decorative context, used them with a sense of propriety.

This lack of concern of Muslim artists with symbolism helps to explain why the most purely decorative or non-representational tradition for the enrichment of surfaces was that of Islam. Far-flung expansion had resulted in an eclectic decorative vocabulary, which was gradually chastened by the non-representational tendency of the Muslim religion. So, by the fourteenth century, Islam's decorative repertory reached a fair degree of homogeneity. The decorative treatment of the surfaces of objects or of the walls of buildings depended on the rhythmic intertwining of plant motifs or the rational inter-lacing of bands and geometric motifs. Plant motifs were more frequently used for pottery and textile designs, and geometric motifs for the surfaces of archi-tecture or furniture, but they were also combined. This limited decorative vocabulary, although subject to infinite variations in detail and colour, was usually arranged according to a few simple schemes. Motifs were repeated or alternated along a scrolling stem, or a strap interlace was continued in a band or extended endlessly in all directions to form a trellis-like structure. Another favourite arrangement on a two-dimensional surface centred around a 'star of fruition' from which strap-like projections extended and interlaced, creating geometric areas between them.

The expansive surfaces that make up the geometric shapes of Islamic architecture, as well as the poor building materials, invited decorative treat-ment. Bricks were frequently carved or combined with stone and arranged in lattice patterns. Mosaics and glazed tiles together with carved, inlaid and polychromed panels of wood or marble were applied over the rubble walls and the wooden framework. Far western Islam tended to emphasize geometric motifs and the complication and multiplication of uniformly small motifs to create a sense of decorative profusion rarely approached by any other orna-mental tradition, as the lavish fourteenth-century decorations of the Alhambra Palace in Granada and the mosque in Tlemcen illustrate. In Persia, partly under Arabic influence, more freely flowing plant motifs and less mechanically extended geometric designs were favoured, as in the early-fourteenth-century mosques of Veramin, Yezd, and Riza. In Cairo the mosque of the Sultan Barkūk (1384), placed amid the domed 'tombs of the caliphs', and in Con-stantinople the mosque of Suleiman (seventeenth century) testify to their architects' skill with tracery.

The technical and decorative traditions of Islam were continued in Spain by Muslim architects who remained after the Christian reconquests as Mudé-jares. They constructed palaces, castles, towers, gates, and churches whose exteriors were enriched by combinations of brick, stone, and tile long used to decorate Muslim buildings. Inside, walls, ceilings, and door and window frames were embellished with geometric motifs (sometimes combined with Christian emblems) carved in plaster or inlaid in wood and then articulated by colour. The patio of the Doncellas and that of the Muñecas in the Alcazar in Seville are prominent examples of Mudéjar decoration completed in the fourteenth century. Even as late as the sixteenth century Christian designers modelled the *cimborios*, or crossing vaults, of the Burgos Cathedral and La Seo of Zaragosa on the parallel-rib constructions of Islamic architecture.

The resourceful, universal use of calligraphic design was the most distinc-tive triumph of Islamic art. Styles of writing were cultivated for every possible purpose. *Kūfic* lettering was employed for stateliness or for masculine vigour, *naskhī* for an evenly smooth rhythm, *nasta'līq* for a flowing and some-times almost ethereal elegance. Fine books were inscribed in rich materials by calligraphers, normally accorded a higher regard than miniaturists. Sometimes a few lines, marvellously refined, sufficed for a page. In religious architecture the most significant formulas of the faith were given monumental form in various styles of kūfic and naskhī lettering, which were blended with and counterpoised to the surrounding arabesque. (Pl. 63a,b.)

The furnishing of Muslim homes displayed a luxury and richness of taste that had greatly impressed the Crusaders, who came from European homes which before 1300 were much drabber than they were later to become. Tables and chests were the chief home furnishings which Islamic artisans were called upon to make of wood, for the Muslim used fewer articles of furniture than the Christian. These tables and chests were beautifully carved and inlaid and went along with luxurious rugs and ornamental panels for the doors and shutters. The *minbar*, or pulpit, was the outstanding piece of elaborately decorated furniture needed in the hypostyle mosque. While metal objects were also less common in mosque than in church, Mosul in Mesopotamia was famous for bronze lamps and ceremonial vessels handsomely decorated with silver inlay.

Vases and bowls might give finishing touches to a Muslim interior. Among the most decorative pottery types of our period was the lustreware of Islam. It was characterized by a metallic sheen obtained by coating the already decorated surface with a glaze containing gold, silver, or copper and then firing the glaze with moderate heat. Perhaps the technique was developed originally in Egypt and Syria, but during the late Middle Ages Persia and Turkey were its most important Middle Eastern centres. Multicoloured and lustrous bowls, dishes, pear-shaped bottles, tiles, and mosque lamps were ornamented with narrative scenes or with plant, flower, and bird motifs. The quality of the enamelled glass made in the Near East declined during the fifteenth century, but excellent pots and bottles of blue and green glass were still made in Persia from the sixteenth to the eighteenth century.

The Muslim lady or gentleman was likely to be strikingly clothed and bejewelled. While Europe had learned to make good silk, during the sixteenth and seventeenth centuries some of the Asian countries regained an important place even in the European textile market. Persian weavers, under the patronage of the Ṣafavid dynasty, produced brocades, damasks, and other rich fabrics of the finest quality at Yezd, Kashan, and Isfahan. (Pl. 62b.) Stained and printed cottons were highly prized fabrics, imported from India. Striking jewellery was worn by Muslims in at least the sixteenth century. Earrings, rings, belt plaques, diadems, and turban pieces were made in silver filigree, enamelled or set with precious stones—pearls, torquoises, rubies, cats-eyes, and carnelians.

Indo-Muslim architecture

The Muslim conquests in India brought about the development of a type of Islamic art best described as Indo-Muslim. It flourished under the patronage of Islamic rulers, and from the Mogul period on, it dominated the palaces, villas, mosques, temples, tombs, towers, fortresses, schools, and other buildings of most of India. It was produced largely by Hindu craftsmen and artists, who, naturally imparting to their works some of their own artistic tradition, gave them a subtle Hindu quality not found in other Islamic art. This Indo-Muslim style produced some excellent painting and some of the world's most beautiful architecture.

The earliest buildings of the Muslim conquerors were laid out according to traditional Islamic requirements, but the Hindu builders, being unacquainted with the pointed arch and other features of Islamic architecture, often achieved the desired effect by an adaptation of Hindu architectural principles. Also, in many cases, parts of Hindu buildings were bodily incorporated into mosques, or decorated stones from demolished Hindu temples were, with some re-working, fitted into Islamic structures. The Hindu builders were expert sculptors, and they inevitably introduced sculpturesque qualities into their columns, capitals, beams, and decorative designs, joining Hindu with Islamic decorative motifs. Thus Hindu and Islamic architectural features gradually were fused into a composite style.

Several features of this architecture reveal its Indo-Muslim ancestry. They include (1) a dome which was basically Muslim in style but often employed Indian structural features, especially an octagonal arrangement of the supporting pillars; (2) pointed arches of the Persian variety, topped by a true keystone but also often formed by the Indian pyramid technique of successive inward-projecting layers of masonry; (3) stone lintels and bracketed capitals of the Indian type; (4) slender turrets, decorative kiosks in an Indian style, and minarets; (5) halls, arcades, and colonnades supported by decorated columns reflecting the influence of Indian sculpture; (6) an Indo-Saracenic gate in the form of a large semi-dome located in the front wall though the actual opening was a small door under the arch; (7) open courts surrounded by buildings or colonnades, which were characteristic of both Hindu and Islamic architecture, but with spacious and better lighted interiors in a distinctly Muslim fashion; (8) enamel tiles, mosaics, and inlays of both Saracenic and Indian design; and (9) considerable, often sculpturesque, decoration in the form of surface design or low relief in which traditional Islamic geometric figures, calligraphic lettering, arabesques, and conventional foliage patterns were fused with Jain and Hindu flowers, wreaths, baskets, and (sometimes) animals to give a much more exuberant and exotic appearance than was characteristic of purely Islamic decoration. Formal gardens, laid out in geometric patterns with pavilions, fountains, canals, terraces, walks, flowers, and trees, were a distinctly Islamic contribution to the Indian scene.

The sultans of Delhi built some magnificent structures. 'Alā-ud-dīn (1296–1316), of the Khaljī dynasty, was especially active, his greatest triumph being the 'Alāi Darwāza at the Quṭb Minār (the south gateway to the Great Mosque of Delhi), erected in 1310 and renowned for its exquisite proportions and surface decorations. (Pl. 64a.) 'Alā-ud-dīn's own tomb stands out for its calligraphic ornamentation. The architecture of the succeeding dynasty, the Tughluqs (1320–1414), was prosaic and formal and had a 'deadening effect'.[39] Its massive severity was typified in the tomb of Ghiyās-ud-dīn, an austere sandstone structure with marble dome, and in the citadel-like Kalan Mosque with its domed bastions, completed in 1387. The Sayyids (1414–51) and the Lodis (1451–1526) attempted to revive the splendour of the Khaljīs. The domes and tombs of the Sayyids were distinguished by their Hindu features.

While the architecture of Delhi set the prevailing tone, several of the finest works of the period were in somewhat variant provincial styles. In the fifteenth century Jaunpur developed an architecture well illustrated in the Jāmi' Mosque (1438–78); it was characterized by high platforms, massive sloping walls, square pillars, lofty gates in front of vaulted porches, storied cloisters, and mosques with minarets of an unconventional type—features that were for the most part distinctly Hindu. (Pl. 65a.) Bengal produced a unique architecture that is well represented at Gaur and in the many-domed Ādina Mosque at Pāndu; it used brick with subsidiary stone, pointed arches on short bracketed columns, curved cornices, roofs reflecting the influence of northern Hindu curvilinear temple towers, and carved Hindu symbols such as the lotus. A beautiful type of architecture flourished in Gujarat, where the indigenous Hindu and Jain styles prevailed, using predominantly Hindu wood-carvings and delicate stone lattices and Indian arches and domes, although the Muslim pointed arch was also in evidence. The capital city of Gujarat, Ahmadabad, was famed for its palaces, its Jāmi' Mosque (begun in 1411 with two hundred and sixty pillars supporting fifteen stone domes constructed of projecting courses of stone in the Hindu style), the Mosque of Mahafiz Khan (built toward the end of the fifteenth century), and the tomb of Abū Turab (built a century later). In nearby Māndū, the capital of Malwa, Muslim tradition dominated, with massive fifteenth-century marble and sandstone mosques, palaces, and tombs, such as that of Hüshing Shāh (1405–35). In the Deccan, the Bahmani kings (1347–1527) and their successors were great builders, and their fortresses, mosques, and tombs showed direct Indian, Turkish, Egyptian, and Persian influences. Notable among several older structures was the Jāmi' Mosque at Gulbarga, built by a Persian architect. In the sixteenth century Bijāpur emerged as the architectural centre of the Deccan, and Hindu architects and craftsmen strongly reasserted themselves. Purely ornamental minarets, rich cornices, and lotus domes distinguished their style, seen in the unique Rawda Mosque of Ibrāhīm II (d. 1626). (Pl. 64b.) The stately Gūl Gumbaz, or tomb of Muḥammad (d. 1673), was unique for its Chinese-pagoda-like turrets at the four corners. The Golconda (1512–1687) style, as illustrated in the tomb of Quli Quṭb Shāh, erected in 1625, was identifiable by its lofty windows, its bulbous domes reminiscent of Russian churches, and the plaster decorations on its minarets.

The Indo-Muslim style became more homogeneous, if perhaps slightly more Muslim, under the Moguls. Although neither Bābur nor Humāyun were in India long enough to leave monuments of special note, they definitely encouraged Persian influences and may also have introduced Ottoman ideas through pupils of Sinān. The Afghan reign of Sher Shāh (1538–45) is commemorated by two distinguished monuments—the Qil'a-i Kuhna Mosque near Delhi, with recessed portals and small minarets around the dome, and his own dignified mausoleum, built on a high terrace in a lake at Sasarām in Bihar.

Under the patronage of Akbar and his immediate successors Hindu and Muslim architects, builders, and artists worked in harmony to perfect the Indo-Muslim style, and it reached its apogee during the century 1556–1667. White marble and coloured sandstone were favourite building materials, and relief carving, mosaic, inlay, and glazed enamel tile were highly cultivated as decorative devices. Persian influence was strong at the beginning, as illustrated in the tomb of Humāyūn at Delhi (1569), but Hindu ideas, especially in decoration, reasserted themselves as Akbar's reign advanced. At Allahābād the Palace of Forty Pillars had a projecting veranda-roof supported by rows of Hindu pillars. At Agra the Jāhāngīrī Palace with its square pillars and bracketed capitals revealed rows of Hindu arches (Pl. 65b), and the Great Mosque (Jāmi' Masjid) was reared in red sandstone, rose stone, and white marble, with three large bulbous domes, ornamental minarets, and Jain-like cupolas. Akbar's greatest architectural triumph was his capital city of Fathpūr-Sīkrī (near Agra), 'a romance in stone', largely constructed between 1569 and 1574 (now partly in ruins). Its numerous carved and ornamented buildings represented an almost perfect fusion of the Iranian and Hindu styles. Among the most salient structures were the Emperor's Office (of Hindu design, with a projecting veranda roof over a colonnade), the Panch Mahal (Pl. 66a) (a five-storied pavilion, each storey smaller than the one below, on the style of the Buddhist *vihāra*, or assembly hall), the Great Mosque (with its sanctuary copied from an Iranian model but constructed of white marble), and the massive Buland Darwāza (a triumphal arch, 176 feet in height, built in 1601–2 of white marble and pink sandstone to memorialize Akbar's conquest of Gujarat). (Pl. 66b.)

Two magnificent buildings were erected during Jahāngīr's reign. Akbar's Mausoleum at Sikandara, designed during his lifetime but complete in 1613, was a fitting resting place for a great emperor. Constructed of polychrome stone and marble, it had five superimposed terraces, impressive balustrades and kiosks, and a pyramid of buildings, 'which some have thought fit to compare with certain Buddhist *vihāras*'.[40] The tomb of I'timād-ud-daulah at Agra was built in white marble by his daughter, the Empress Nūr Jahān in 1628. It was one of the earliest Indo-Muslim buildings to employ *pietra dura* inlay as decoration. Subsequently, under Jahāngīr's successor, Shāh Jahān, inlay tended to supersede mosaic.

With Shāh Jahān Indo-Muslim architecture experienced a new wave of Iranian influence, attaining a certain feminine elegance that has led to its being described as 'jewellery on a bigger scale'. The tomb of Jahāngīr at Shāhdara, Lahore, with high pagoda-like towers at the four corners and with kiosks at the top, went up early in the reign. The palace at Delhi, begun in 1638, included the majestic and highly decorated Halls for Public and Private Audience. In the white marble galleries of the Private Hall (Diwān-i-Khās), Shāh Jahān's 'paradise on earth', the ceilings were of silver, and the pillars, arches, and ribs were encrusted with Persian designs of jaspar, onyx, and cornelian. (Pl. 67a.) In it stood the famous Peacock Throne with a glittering array of rubies, pearls, and diamonds, the most celebrated creation of the Indian lapidaries' and jewellers' skill. The Great Mosque of Delhi, designed on the outside 'to attract the eye of the faithful from afar and proclaim the glory of Islam',[41] had an austere and simple interior. The Moti Masjid (or Pearl Mosque) of Agra, put up between 1646 and 1693, was perfect in simplicity and proportion. And the Tāj Mahal of Agra (1631–53) arose in all its exalting majesty in order that beneath its marble dome, amidst gardens of incomparable magnificence, Shāh Jahān's beloved empress, Mumtāz Mahal, might sleep in eternal peace. (Pl. 67b.) The Tāj seems to have been the joint product of Muslim, Hindu, and possibly even European designers, but the master architect probably was the Turk Ustād 'Isā.

With Aurangzīb the architecture of Mogul India began to decline. His intolerance and puritanical scruples discouraged Muslim art and led to the destruction of Hindu temples and statues. The best of his few buildings, the Lahore Mosque, completed in 1674, though having a distinct merit of its own, did not match earlier masterpieces. The comparative good will, however, that had prevailed from the reign of Akbar through that of Shāh Jahān had facilitated the spread of the Indo-Muslim style among the Hindus. It was noticeable in secular architecture such as Rajput palaces and civil buildings from Madras south to Tanjore and Madura. It was even accepted by Hindu temple builders in the north, where the Jugat Kishor at Brindāban (1629) and the Jain temples of Sonogarth in Bundelkhand testify to its vigour in the seventeenth century, and Bengal temples in the eighteenth. In fact, by 1775 a decaying Indo-Muslim style was in use almost everywhere; only Hindu temple architecture in the extreme south escaped its influence.

Indo-Muslim painting

Since Islam definitely discouraged sculpture and was not unconditionally favourable to painting, those arts did not flourish in Islamic India before the sixteenth century. Nonetheless, with the Timurids and their successors after the Mongol conquest there emerged the Persian school of painting, of which we have already noted that probably the greatest representative was Bihzād of Herat. Under the patronage of the early Mogul emperors an Indo-Persian style developed. About 1550, Humāyūn brought to India Mīr Sayyid 'Ali and Khwāja 'Abdus-Samād, at least one of whom was a pupil of Bihzād.

Akbar supported a large group of court painters, both Persian and Hindu, and under his patronage and pressure the Sino-Persian and native Hindu styles gradually blended to create the Indo-Persian-Mogul style. It reached its apogee under the inspiration and patronage of Jahāngīr. The chief characteristics of this style were: (1) calligraphic line, inherited from the Sino-Persian and Jain traditions; (2) brilliant colours, which reflected both the Persian and the Hindu heritage; (3) realism and conformity to nature, borrowed particularly from Hindu portraiture, landscapes, and representations of animals and plants; (4) character portrayal, revealed in a remarkable capacity to bring out the subject's psychological traits; and (5) its courtly nature, attributable to patrons who were sultans and nobles interested in commemorating their exploits on the battlefield, in the hunt, at court, or in the harem. Rembrandt studied Mogul paintings brought to Holland by the Dutch East India Company.[42] The wide gap between his broad chiaroscuro art and the decorative and bright colour areas of Mogul painting suggests why the art of these two areas made little impression at that time on each other.

Persian painting, we have indicated, was associated with calligraphy, book illustration, and miniatures, and in India these media were likewise highly cultivated. Full page (or larger) paintings were done on paper, at first imported from Persia but later manufactured in India. The murals, painted in palaces and tombs, in particular reflected an Indian tradition. Few murals have survived, but many illustrated books and albums have. Despite the realisms of the psychological studies and the excellence of the faces, the human anatomy was not well represented, but from Jahāngīr's time onward other techniques of the painter, such as perspective, foreshortening, modelling, and shading, steadily improved. The subjects of pictures varied—emperors, nobles, ladies, or holy men; landscapes (most often only as backgrounds to portraits or divan, durbar, and hunting episodes); battles and hunting; court life (audiences, receptions, picnics, etc.); love scenes; pastimes and activities in the harem (in which the semi-nudity borrowed by Muslim ladies from the Hindus was often evident); religious and mythological stories; plants and flowers; birds; larger animals like horses, elephants, tigers, and gazelles. (Pl. 68a.)

Akbar's patronage attracted many artists and stimulated the various Hindu schools of painting. A host of artists were employed for many years in decorating the fabulous buildings at Fathpūr-Sīkrī with murals. Of the seventeen most famous painters at Akbar's court, thirteen are said to have been Hindus. Perhaps the two best-known Hindus were students of 'Abdus-Samād — Basavān, who was noted for his portraits and backgrounds (Pl. 68b), and Daswanth (d. 1584), of the palanquin-bearer caste, who won distinction under Akbar for his treatment of Indian subjects in a Persian manner. Three Hindu painters continued as important figures into Jahāngīr's time—Lāl Kesu,

Manohar (honoured for his divan scenes and animals), and the portraitist Bhagvati. Abu'l-Faḍl said of the Hindus: 'Their pictures surpass our conception of things. Few indeed in the whole world are found equal to them.'[43] Among the Persian painters, besides Sayyid 'Ali and 'Abdus-Samād, were Khursau Quli and Jamshed. Farrukh Beg, a Kalmuck, remained prominent during Jahāngīr's reign, especially for his hunting scenes.

Jahāngīr was himself an excellent connoisseur and art critic. He collected the best of Hindu and Islamic paintings, as well as paintings by Italian artists and engravings by Dürer and Holbein. Under his critical eye, the eye of a lover of nature, the Mogul school reached its highest level in the intensity of its three-quarters-portrait studies of character and in the naturalism of its landscapes and plant and animal pictures, which often represented rare specimens. Abul-Ḥasan, whose father was a painter of Herat, was Jahāngīr's favourite portrait painter. Ustād Manṣūr was noted for his animals, birds, and flowers; Muḥammad Murād of Samark for his gazelles; and Shāfī 'Abbāsī of Persia for his flowers. Among the Hindus, Bisham Dās was unequalled as a portraitist.

Shāh Jahān reduced the number of court painters. Among the newer artists realism now began to give way to decorativeness, and innovation to tradition. Muḥammad Nādir, a Samarkandi hold-over from Jahāngīr's time, was an eminent portrait painter. Mīr Muḥammad Hāshim rose to fame with his drawings of Mogul court figures. Shāh Jahān's eldest son, Dārā Shikūh, Aurangzīb's brother and doomed rival, was a liberal patron of Hindu artists and left a priceless album of works dated 1603–34. His preferred portraitist was Anūpchātar.

With Aurangzīb courtly painting, like architecture, declined. He discontinued patronage of painters and probably even had some murals defaced Under Shāh Jahān many artists had already become commercial or had shifted to the patronage of local nobles, some of whom, like Āsaf Khān of Lahore, decorated their villas with murals. Under Aurangzīb and his successors the dispersion of artists to local centres, such as Oudh, Hyderabad, Mysore, Bengal, Lucknow, and Patna, continued. These developments, while popularizing painting, brought with them a decline in quality, but as Mogul painting declined, Rajput painting emerged as the leading school in Hindustan (see below).

Muslim Art in Indonesia

For Indonesian art the coming of Islam spelled deterioration. Islamic opposition to sculpture discouraged native talent, and most of the subsequent Indonesian mosques had little distinction. A few, such as those at Medan in Sumatra, were constructed according to the classic Islamic style, but most of the early ones were more like pagodas, with multiple receding roofs, one above the other. The earliest ones did not have minarets. The minaret of the Koudous Mosque in Java, one of the oldest, was a square tower resting on a raised base. Christian conquest brought no greater additions to the artistic accomplishments of the Indonesians.

HINDU AND BUDDHIST ART

Hindu architecture and sculpture

Traditional Hindu art had passed its zenith before 1300, and telling blows were dealt it in the north by the Muslim conquest. Nevertheless, it continued to produce work of outstanding merit in south India. Hindu architecture was characterized by (1) massiveness, (2) a profusion of sculptured ornamentation, (3) bracketed capitals and huge stone beams and lintels, (4) elaborate pillared porches and entrance verandas (mandapas), and (5) enormous central towers (shikharas), representing the sacred mountains of Hinduism, made of horizontal rows of brick or stone receding inward to reach a peak over the square shrine which housed the god. In the northern style these towers were curvilinear; in the southern or Dravidian style they were in the form of steep, truncated pyramids; and in the Deccan style they were a mixture of the two, employing a barrel roof. In all styles the tower was heavily decorated with sculptured figures and capped with a large knob, or āmalaka, and crowned with further symbolic decorations. Before our period the use of the gopura had already begun in the south; it was a pyramid-like gate tower in the wall that surrounded a temple—a tower so gigantic that it often overshadowed the central shrine. Many of the southern temples consisted of towering gateways and other accumulations erected between 1300 and 1750 about an inconspicuous shrine of great antiquity.

Under the Vijayanagar Empire, south Indian temples became very elaborate, with pillared halls, pillared pavilions, and pillared subordinate structures, frequently added to old temples. Characteristic additions were the kalyāna-mandapa, an ornate pillared pavilion for the reception of the deity and his consort at the annual celebration of their marriage, and the 'thousand-pillared mandapa', a huge hall with rows upon rows of pillars. (Pl. 69a.) The variety and complexity of pillars were perhaps the most striking feature of the Vijayanagar style. Around a pillar's shaft was grouped a vast amount of huge statuary sculptured in the round, the whole carved out of a single block of stone. Often the most conspicuous element of the sculpture would be a furious horse, a rampant hippogryph, or a rearing supernatural animal.[44]

Several now ruined edifices at Vijayanagar City were representative of the style. One of them was the ornate Vitthala (Vishnu) Temple, the major portion of which was constructed in the sixteenth century under Krishnadeva Rāya. (Pl. 70a.) Its most distinctive feature was an immense hall of fifty-six pillars, each twelve feet high and forming a structural group of rearing chargers and fantastic monsters. Facing them was the chariot of the god, with movable wheels, all carved out of a single block of granite. Another representative edifice was the Hazāra Rāma Temple, whose inner walls were decorated in stone relief with scenes from the *Rāmāyana*. Still another was the King's Audience Hall, which had a hundred stone pillars arranged in ten tows of ten each. Elsewhere also—Vellore, Kanchi, or Tādpatri, for example—could be found beautiful reception pavilions, pillars with imaginative groupings of statuary, or exquisitely carved gateways. At Shrīrāngam the Horse-Court of the Ranganātha Temple had a colonnade of fighting chargers, each rearing to a height of about nine feet. (Pl. 69b.)

After the decline of Vijayanagar the Nāyak dynasty of Madura became the chief patrons of the arts, and many of the great surviving shrines of the south were completed during the late sixteenth and the seventeenth century in the so-called Madura style. This style was at the same time a flamboyant extension of the Vijayanagar style and a revival of that of Madura's old Pāndya dynasty. It was illustrated in the temple at Rāmeshvaram, which was laid out on a unitary plan with 3000 feet of pillared corridors. The Nāyaks enlarged the Shrīrāngam temple, already famous for its Horse-Court, increasing its concentric enclosures to seven and thus making its outermost dimensions 2880 feet by 2475; it contained impressive gateway towers, a Hall of a Thousand Pillars, and a golden-domed tower. (Pl. 70b.) The dual temple of Sundareshvara and Mīnākshī at Madura, erected mainly between 1623 and 1659, is perhaps the pre-eminent south Indian temple because of its systematic plan, its Tank of Golden Lilies, and its many-columned corridors, especially its Hall of a Thousand Pillars, whose sculpture is generally regarded as superior to any similar hall's. Its great gateway towers dwarf its central shrines. Outside its walls lies Tirumalai's choultry, a large open hall, the central pillars of which form life-sized statues of the Nāyak kings.

Hindu sculpture, which was done both in relief and in the round, was almost exclusively a feature of temples and public structures. Columns, capitals, cornices, niches, and the outsides of towers were covered with figures, usually of a high sculptural quality, of deities, saints, kings, and animals. During the latter part of our period stucco was used extensively. This sculpture, as well as temple construction, was the work of the superior craftsmen of the Kammālar caste, who claimed equality with the Brahmans. The south Indian bronze (largely copper) work of earlier times also continued. Pieces in the traditional style portrayed Natarāja (the dancing Shiva) and Shivaite saints, Vishnu and Lakshmī, Rāma and the young dancing Krishna, Vishnuite saints, and Kālī and Pārvatī. Life-sized figures of historic characters were also produced, like those of Krishnadeva Rāya and his two wives in the Tirupati Temple. Although highly conventionalized, Hindu sculpture was basically realist, especially in the voluptuousness of the female figures.

Hindu painting

Before the sixteenth century the Hindu tradition of fresco painting and manuscript illumination flourished in various centres. Murals probably often adorned the temples and palaces, but only few, such as the Natarāja frescoes of the Shiva Temple at Ellamānūr, have lasted. The oldest illustrated Jain manuscript of Gujarat is on palm leaf and dates from the thirteenth century, and a number on paper date from the fifteenth century. The most commonly illustrated manuscript was the *Kalpa sūtra*, dealing with the lives of the Jain saints, but a secular *Vasanta Vilāsa*, dated as of 1451, has also survived. These paintings, characterized by calligraphic line and brilliant, jewel-like colouring, preserved an ancient tradition of composition and style without showing any originality, giving elaborate detail and angular forms against a groundwork of red, gold, or yellow clouds (auspicious omens). Individual figures were given a three-quarters profile with long pointed noses and large, protruding eyes.

From the sixteenth to the nineteenth century Hindu painting underwent a renaissance in Rajputana. Under the patronage of Rajput princes, Hindu artists continued the ancient Indian tradition both in murals in the Rajput palaces and in small-scale paintings on paper. Although influenced more and more by Mogul painting as time went on, Rajput art remained distinguishable from that of contemporary artists at the Mogul courts, emphasizing colour rather than line, borrowing the technique and conception of sixth-century Ajantā fresco rather than of miniature, and drawing inspiration primarily from traditional Hindu religion and literature rather than from contemporary court life.[45] Its brilliant reds, yellows, pinks, greens, browns, and purples were relieved by white and velvet blacks (gold appearing only late in Rajput painting). It employed in the background traditional formulas packed with symbolic meaning, such as flowers, trees, plants, birds, animals, hills, moons, clouds, rain, and lightning.

Most of the extant pictures are to be found in albums or sets illustrating some ancient theme. They are generally divided into the Rājasthānī and the Pahārī (Mountain) school. The former flourished in Rajputana and Bundelkhand in the sixteenth century and after; the latter developed in the upper Punjab in the seventeenth century and continued into the nineteenth century. Both schools treated the same basic subjects, among which were: (1) the thirty-six *rāgas* and *rāginīs* (from among the musical modes to be described below) that were associated with seasons, months, days, and hours and depicted emotional situations; (2) the great epics and romances and Rajput chivalry; (3) puranic and tantric texts, especially those relating to Krishna and Rādhā; (4) the 'flavour of love' theme dealing with phases of affection and types of heroes and heroines from classical literature; (5) scenes of popular life; and (6) portraiture emphasizing personality. Both frequently combined realism with romanticism and mysticism, exhibiting *bhakti* qualities, religious eroticism, tender humility, and the sympathetic treatment of animals.

Music and Dance

Music, dance, drama, lyric poetry, and religion were inextricably intertwined in Hindu India. Much of the lyric poetry was meant to be sung; dramas employed singing, music, and dance, many of them in fact being dramatic ballets; and singing, dancing, and dramatic performances were an essential part of religion. Hindu music was highly developed both in theory and practice, both as a fine art and as a folk art. It was melody untouched by harmony, based upon a seven-tone scale with (practically) quarter-tone intervals. The numerous musical *rāgas* (musical 'flavours' or melody patterns) were differentiated by their tonic, their flats and sharps, and the number of tones they used (five, six, or seven).

Although singing and the playing of various musical instruments were popular arts, particular castes specialized in professional singing, playing, and dancing. The variety of string, wind, and percussion instruments was large, differing considerably from north to south. Professional singers, musicians, and dancers were employed in many religious and court ceremonies and entertainments, and musicians were patronized by the various temples and rajas.

The early Mogul rulers and various independent sultans, especially those of Bijapur, were generous patrons of musicians, both Islamic and Hindu. The most illustrious singer at the court of Akbar was Miyan Tānsēn, originally a Hindu of Gwalior. He and the other musicians at court developed new varieties of *rāgas* and a type of northern music that was a mixture of Hindu and Muslim. This Mogul school of music suffered a setback when Aurangzīb placed a ban on music, but it was not destroyed.

After the decline of Vijayanagar, Tanjore became an active centre of Hindu music and contributed considerably to the development of a style called Carnatic. In the seventeenth century Kshetrayya, under the patronage of the raja of Tanjore, wrote numerous erotic religious songs in Telugu. In the eighteenth century Tyāgarāju of Tanjore, though he shunned kings and courts, is said by some to have been the best of Hindu musicians. He wrote many chaste songs in praise of Rāma in Telugu in the Carnatic style.

The dance, occupying the important place it did in religious, court, and folk affairs in Hindu India, is often depicted in Hindu art. Almost all the leading south Indian temples and rulers employed female dancing troupes. The kings of Vijayanagar had special rooms where royal dancers practiced and performed, and the theory, meaning, and symbolism of the dance and music were set forth in elaborate treatises by Brahman pundits. Dancers normally belonged to a particular caste and were trained from childhood by dancing-masters, who knew both the theory and the practice of the dance. In general, dances told some familiar story from the rich lore of Hinduism, and some (for example the *rāsa mandala*, or circle dance of Krishna) expressed a religious eroticism. They usually required relatively little movement of the lower body (some being performed from a sitting position) but a great variety of symbolic hand and upper-body gestures (*mudrās*). Often the performers sang as they danced, richly clad. They generally wore around their ankles strings of bells which provided part of the accompaniment as they moved their feet in time with the music. Dances were commonly performed to honour some deity, ruler, or other dignitary, and consequently they took place at religious festivals, processions, marriages, births, reunions, the dedication of houses or buildings, and court ceremonies. They also played a prominent part in dramatic performances.

Nepalese, Tibetan, and Singhalese Art

Nepalese and Tibetan art grew out of the late Tantric Buddhist art of Bengal but was influenced, especially in architecture, also by Chinese ideas and techniques. Buildings were generally of stone or brick, but wood was frequently used in Nepal—for example, in the five-storey Bahavāni Temple of Bhatgāon, erected about 1703, rising one storey upon the other to form a pyramid. This temple has a projecting roof, supported by brackets and turned up at the eaves and corners in the Chinese style. Such roofs were common. The eighteenth-century temple of Patan in Nepal combined a brick structure with tiers of sloping roofs and elaborate carved-wood decorations. Another type of religious architecture encountered in Tibet and other Buddhist countries was the stupa, or pagoda; in Nepal and Tibet these tower-shrines generally consisted of a square, high base surmounted by a bulbous dome, which was crowned by a square *harmikā*, out of which rise tiers of telescoped umbrellas culminating in a spire; often the all-seeing eye of the supreme Buddha was depicted upon each of the four sides of the *harmikā*. Probably the most distinctive architectural forms of Tibet are its massive, fortress-like monasteries and palaces with inward sloping walls plastered in various colours. The most familiar of these is the seventeenth-century Potala Palace of the grand lamas at Lhasa, but other imposing monasteries are located in Lhasa and Tashilhunpo.

The justly esteemed banners (*tankas*) of Tibet are painted on cotton, canvas, or, sometimes, silk. The older ones rather rigorously perpetuate the ancient style of Bengal, but later ones, especially those of the eighteenth century, show Chinese influences, particularly in the background landscapes. The banners generally show a central figure, like the popular goddess Tārā, surrounded by many lesser figures. The subjects they depict are almost always religious episodes from the life of Shākyamuni, various Buddhas, bodhisattvas, and Shaktis (often in the nude), fierce and threatening beings, Tibetan saints and lamas, famous places, or Bön (pre-Buddhist) themes. Scenes of nativity, damnation, tantric ritual, sorcery, mysticism, magic, terror, and sexuality are common.[46]

Illuminated manuscripts and wood carvings were produced in both Nepal and Tibet, and the arts of the goldsmith and silversmith were highly developed, but perhaps the finest artistic achievements of the two countries were in bronze and brass. In fantastically bedecked figures, large and small, of the deities (often cast in the form of contorted or elongated nudes) as well as in ritual vessels, incense burners, and replicas of animals and lotuses, skilful and ingenious bronze and iron workers reproduced the style of ancient Buddhist Bengal, giving occasional evidence of borrowing also from China.

Ceylon, although its earlier achievements continued to exert an influence on Burma and to some extent Siam, was ravaged by invasions and internal conflicts throughout most of our period and produced scarcely any works of art worthy of special consideration. The chief artistic remains still stand at Kandy, dating from the late eighteenth century, when wood was used a good deal. The Temple of the Tooth Relic is well known, as are also the temples of Lankātilaka (stone and brick) and Gadalādeniya (partly in stone) near Kandy. Very good wood carvings decorate many of the temples.

Art in Southeast Asia

The artistic achievements of the Buddhist countries of the Indo-Chinese peninsula—Burma, Siam, Cambodia, and Laos—clearly reflected ancient Buddhist and Hindu ideas. This influence was evident in their stupas (which took the form of a bell-shaped dome mounted on a raised platform and from which rose a long spire), in their pyramidal *shikharas*, and in their multiple-tiered temples and monasteries with receding roofs. Local background, taste, and technique tended to develop a relatively distinctive style in each country.

The sack and ultimate abandonment of Angkor in the fourteenth century marked the end of the monumental Khmer style of Cambodia. The last significant production of this glorious tradition was the Shivaite sanctuary of Ishvarapura at Bantéai Srei. It consisted of three shrines and two edifices (probably intended as temple libraries) constructed in the early fourteenth century. Its bas-reliefs in stone and its stone sculpture in the round combined naturalism and grace with archaism; it exhibited such a profusion of decorative elements as to give rise to the expression 'Khmer flamboyant style'. The Buddhist pagodas and sculpture of the new Cambodian capitals at Lovek and Phnom Penh were on a more modest and restrained scale and, although possessed of a beauty and charm of their own, were not among the chief masterpieces. Laotian architecture was influenced by Angkor and Siam. One of its foremost examples was the pyramid-type stupa known as That Luong, built at Vien Chang shortly after 1563.

The classic (Pagan) period of Burmese art ended at the close of the thirteenth century with the Mongol and Shan invasions, and during the ensuing period Burmese art took on a folk character, 'typified at once by exuberance and poverty of expression'.[47] Although numerous royal palaces and religious edifices were built at the capitals of Ava and Pegu and elsewhere, most of the religious buildings were indifferent adaptations of two earlier styles typified by the Mingalazedi Stupa (1274) and the Anānda Temple of Pagan. The former was characterized by a square, high, pyramidal-terraced base (with stairways for access, and small stupas at the corners) on top of which was a large bell-shaped stupa tapering off into a long slender spire. The Anānda Temple, although designed as early as 1090, survives largely as a restoration of our period. It was in the form of a Greek cross; successive receding terraces, developed to a great height, gave it a cubical effect and provided space for numerous chapels and galleries, the central part capped by a golden dome-like pinnacle. The whole had the appearance of a huge white mountain. The gilded Shwedagon Pagoda of Rangoon, probably the most striking stupa of the period, generally conformed to the Mingalazedi type, but its elongated spire made it unique; it was raised to 66 feet about 1362 and to 302 by 1472. The large but simple bell-shaped pagoda of Kaunghmudaw, erected during Thalun's reign (1629–48), has no spire. The Mingun Pagoda, which rises to a height of 140 feet, was begun in the eighteenth century and was planned to reach to about three times its present height.

Brick and mortar but little stone were used in the construction of these edifices. They were abundantly decorated with relief work depicting Jātaka and other Buddhist subjects, and decorative details accumulated as time went on, as did the amount of gold, gilt, lacquer work, and elaborate wood carvings. Wood grew in importance as a building material toward the end of the period. Successive receding stories, with roofs turned up at the eaves and corners in the Chinese manner, became increasingly common.

The classic Thai, or Siamese, art of the Ayut'ia period (1350–1767) grew directly out of the Northern or Burmese style of Chiengmai and the Southern or Mon-Khmer style of Sukhotai of the thirteenth and the early fourteenth century. It also underwent Indian and Ceylonese influences, and as time went on, clear evidences of Chinese ideas appeared. In both architecture and sculpture the classic influence moved in the direction of richness of detail rather than of functional structure.[48] Although stone had been used as a structural material earlier, brick, stucco, and wood (especially in the north) were basic. The famous brick and stucco temple, Wat Chet Yot, near Chiengmai (built shortly after 1292), was a copy of the Mahābodhi (Great Temple) of Pagan (itself a copy of the Mahābodhi Temple of Bodh Gayā in India). It was an impressive pyramid on a high square base topped by a long spire. Other principal Northern-style temples were those of the Standing Buddha (P'ra Yün) at Lamp'ūn, built shortly after 1369, and the Royal Pagoda (P'rajedi Luang) at Chiengmai (completed in 1478), which once housed the famous Emerald Buddha.

The ruins at Sukhotai are numerous. The Great Pagoda (Mahā-Tāt) has a huge standing Buddha and assembly hall (*vihāra*), and the Shri Chum a huge seated Buddha and sculptured reliefs of stories from the Jātakas (c. 1350). The Singhalese-type stupa of the Chāng Lom Temple, with its long needle dome, attributed to Rama Khamheng (c. 1293), is located in nearby Sawank'alōk.

The principal ruin of Ayut'ia today is the temple of Shri Sarap'et, dating from the late fifteenth century. Its numerous bell-shaped *prachedi* (or stupas) are characteristic of the Ayut'ia style, showing greater Burmese and Singhalese than Khmer influence. Their bases were formed of a series of diminishing rings leading to a bell-shaped dome, from which rose a long spire formed by diminishing rings. They were shrines for the ashes of Buddhist holy men and Siamese kings. Ayut'ia's wooden structures employed teak columns covered with lacquer and multiple receding roofs, with slightly turned up, ornamental eaves and gables.

Amid the ruins of Ayut'ia are numerous stucco and bronze Buddhas, of which the giant seated bronze P'ra Mangala Pabitra, perhaps of the sixteenth century, is particularly noteworthy. Stucco was common for reliefs, and sculpture in the round was often done in plaster or bronze. A characteristically Siamese Buddhist figure developed, typified by the arched brows, almond eyes, oval face, sharp hooked nose, and small moulded lips of the Chiengmai figures. In the course of time stylization (emphasized by the flame-shaped topknot) set in: the faces became elongated; the figures grew stiffer and more formless; and the bodies were covered with meaningless draperies, often heavily bedecked with gold relief in imitation of embroidery.

Other vestiges of the Siamese art of the period likewise testify to its 'distinction and delicacy'. A few frescoes depicting Jātaka scenes, apparently produced during the Ayut'ia period, and some illustrated manuscripts and temple banners have survived. For a time porcelains, manufactured according to an imported Chinese technique, were produced at Sawank'alōk. In general, Siamese art was less original than that of the Kmer school. It was 'a belated flower of Buddhist art', but it had 'a fragrance of its own, . . . a supremely civilized fragrance'.[49]

Hindu and Buddhist Art in Indonesia

In Indonesia, Hindu and Buddhist art continued during the Majapahit period but showed a growing independence from Indian models and a corresponding reliance upon purely native ideas. It, too, was more ornamental than structural. The Buddhist shrine of Candi Jābung (c. 1354) and the Shivaite temple complex of Panataram (built largely between 1320 and 1370) must be counted among the superior monuments of the period. The former (a circular tower, unique in Java) stood on a high, rectangular, terraced base. The latter consisted of a group of unrelated structures built to house the ashes of the royal family. They were usually in the form of a square, terraced pyramid, supported on a high, square, and narrow base, which was decorated with relief sculpture. Though the sculptors derived their subjects from the *Rāmāyana*, their sculpture and the masks over the doorways were Indonesian in form, showing clear relationship to the puppets of the *wayang* plays. High gateways were also in evidence. This style, modified in various ways, was continued after the decline of Majapahit in Bali, where the Pura ye Ganga Temple, dating from the fourteenth and fifteenth centuries, follows the Panataram style. Later shrines were surrounded by walls with high, pyramid gateways, and the pyramid-pagoda temples were decorated with sculptures of fantastic forms in high relief. As previously remarked, Islam and Christianity brought deterioration rather than betterment to Indonesian art.

Music, Dance, and Ornament in Southeast Asia

Music and the dance were highly regarded throughout Southeast Asia. As in India, they were closely associated with religion and poetry and formed a part of most dramatic performances. Indian influence was everywhere evident, although local history and tradition gave distinctiveness to the music and dances of the several countries. Singing, dancing, and the playing of musical instruments were popular arts, but they reached their highest form in the work of professionals. Strolling bands of musicians and dancers were common, but noble or wealthy families often maintained their own troupes, and musicians, singers, and dancers were patronized by the kings. The royal ballets of Siam, Cambodia, and Java enjoyed a high repute, as did also the village dance troupes of Bali. The themes of their performance were traditional. The music included love-songs, ballads, boat-songs, lullabies, heroic songs commemorating exploits human and divine, and religious chants. The dances fell into two main categories, classic and popular. Popular dances were generally of folk origin, classic dances of Indian origin. The classic dances were usually religious in nature, performed by professional female dancers in gorgeous costumes with symbolic gestures and movements.

Personal adornment in Ceylon, Burma, and Siam was spectacular even though steadfastly traditional. Multiple strings of turquoise or amber beads and pierced pearls were used as necklaces, armlets, and anklets or draped over clothes and turbans. Gold and silver rings set with rubies, sapphires, emeralds diamonds, and pearls were worn in abundance. Turban pieces were enamelled or set with precious stones. The widespread fondness for jewellery in southern Asia resulted in great quantities of sham jewellery and mass-produced trinkets in brass and lesser materials.

*　　*　　*

We shall deal below with Buddhist art in China, Japan, Vietnam, and Korea.

THE ARTS IN CHINA, VIETNAM, AND KOREA

Although China's art of our period cannot be considered the greatest in her history, much of it was of high quality, and the quantity that survives vastly exceeds that for earlier and more illustrious periods. Chinese music has been treated in Chapter X and XI in connection with Chinese drama and will be so treated again below (in conjunction with Japanese music). China's sculptural products (except for ceramic figures) was of little consequence, being few in number and lacking in inspiration and technical perfection. Bronze work and jade and ivory carving were of a high technical proficiency but consciously archaic and imitative. Many architectural remains date from this period, but they were generally imitative of earlier styles, although they possessed a majestic dignity and symmetrical beauty that reflected the power and pomp of the imperial dynasties. Except in the fourteenth century (Yüan period) painters were likewise essentially imitative, although the quality of their work was high and the quantity enormous. Decadence in sculpture and imitativeness in architecture and painting were undoubtedly aggravated by the dominance during the Ming and Ch'ing periods of backward-looking, rationalistic Neo-Confucianism and by a consequent decline in the inspiration provided by the emotionalism, spiritualism, and mysticism of Buddhism and Taoism.

Some artistic achievements of the age, however, are more than imitative of traditional styles. The artists of the Yüan period at least made it one of significant creative painting. Lacquered ware and porcelain reached their apex before 1775. Textiles also attained a high artistic level. Just as sculpture was the great achievement of the pre-T'ang and early T'ang periods, and painting of the T'ang, Sung, and Yüan dynasties, so porcelain was that of the Ming and early Manchu periods; imperial patronage contributed to the perfection of the ceramic arts. And out of painting and printing came, in the sixteenth and seventeenth centuries, the popular art of the colour-print. The expansion of trade and the consequent rise of larger mercantile and artisan classes with money to spend for simple luxuries contributed to the improvement of lacquered ware, porcelain, textiles, and colour-prints. In those arts, moreover, Confucian traditionalism exerted less restraining influence.

Architecture in China

Except for the pagoda, most Chinese architecture was an extension of domestic architecture, consisting essentially of courtyards formed by detached halls. Their sloping, concave, tile roofs, often two in number in public buildings, were held up by wooden pillars, with walls filled in by panelling and brick work. The structures of our period were numerous—domestic buildings, imperial palaces and tombs, ancestral and Confucian temples, official buildings in provincial, prefectural, and district cities, Buddhist and Taoist temples and monasteries, pagodas, relatively open rectangular, round, or polygonal pavilions in numerous gardens, memorial arches, walls, towers, bridges. The vast majority of the buildings were of comparatively light wood-and-brick construction, but stone and brick were used for the more massive edifices.

Two styles of architecture prevailed—the northern and the southern. The northern style may be distinguished from the southern by the degree of roof curvature and the amount of ornamentation on roof ridges, eaves, and pillars. In the simpler northern style, which was dominant, curvature was not extensive and ornamentation was limited. In the southern style (which was not, however, confined to the south), curvature was prolonged until the eaves turned up like horns at the corners, and carving and ornamentation were so profuse as to obscure the line of the roof.

City plans were also distinguishable, perhaps because of the varying nature of the terrain, the relative value of land, and differing defensive needs. Northern cities tended to be more symmetrical and spacious and, because invaders came from the north, were surrounded by higher and more massive walls. Most extant walls date from this period. They were made of clay and faced with brick and were narrower at the top than at the bottom. Storied, pagoda-like watch towers rose at their corners and over their gates. Broad avenues extended across the city from gate to opposite gate. At their intersections in the centre of the city rose three-storied 'drum towers', from which movement through the city was controlled and drums announced the passage of the hours. The walls and gate towers of Sian and Peking are justly admired, but all of north China, especially Shansi province, was dotted with similar walls and gate towers. Much of the Great Wall, as it now stands, with its massive gates and impressive towers, was either constructed anew or rebuilt during the Ming dynasty.

Perhaps the finest edifices of the period were the imperial palaces and temples of the Peking area and the Ming and Ch'ing tombs outside Nanking and Peking. The construction of the present city of Peking, on the remains of the celebrated Mongol capital of Khanbalak (Cambaluc) and earlier cities, was begun by the Yung-lo emperor (1403–24), who gave it its permanent form and character. It consisted essentially of three almost square walled cities, one outside the other, to the south of which another rectangular walled city ultimately developed. The innermost city, the Purple Forbidden City, defended by crenellated walls and a wide moat, contained the ceremonial halls, government offices, and imperial residential quarters, the public buildings separated from the residential quarters by walls. Next came the Imperial City, which housed officials and members of the imperial clans. The outer city was available to others. The basic pattern was similar to earlier Chinese capital cities, and the official buildings also followed tradition, being arranged symmetrically in a series of spacious courts.[50] Designed upon a monumental, although somewhat monotonous, plan for business and ceremonial purposes, they have seldom failed to impress visitors with their dignity, grace, and grandeur.

Most of the large official halls were two-roofed, wooden structures in the northern style, often built on high brick platforms. Following the distinctive Ming style of the fifteenth century, the lower roof was small and the upper roof extended downward in sweeping curves from the ridge on each of the four sides of the building (hipped roof). In later-Ming and Ch'ing structures the lower roof became larger, the upper diminished in importance, the space between the roofs became greater, and, in keeping with an earlier style, only the front and the rear of the upper roof continued uninterrupted to the eaves, while the sides were gable-ended. By the eighteenth century Chinese architecture had become conspicuously ornamental. Porticos, carved pillars and panelling, and marble terraces, staircases, and balustrades added decorativeness, and brilliant paint lent colourfulness, but a building's crowning glory was the yellow, blue, and green of its enamelled-tile roof. Yellow was reserved for the emperor.

Peking is a veritable sea of public monuments and edifices.51 Most of the palace buildings have been restored or rebuilt (generally on the original plan) during the centuries, but the Chih-hua Temple, built in 1444, still clearly illustrates the early Ming style. The famous Wu-men, or south gate, of the Forbidden City (rebuilt in 1647) is topped with an imposing pavilion. The main ceremonial Hall of Supreme Harmony (T'ai-ho-tien, 1627), raised on three white marble terraces, contains the imperial throne. The personal palace of the emperor is the Palace of Cloudless Heaven (Ch'ien-ch'eng-kung), destroyed by fire in 1514 and rebuilt several times. The three last-named structures show the stately hipped-roof style at its best, while the Hall of Classics illustrates the eighteenth-century Ch'ien-lung style. The three-storied Drum Tower, built originally in 1273, was subsequently reconstructed. The tomb of the Yung-lo emperor, northwest of Peking, and those of K'ang-hsi, Yung-cheng, and Ch'ien-lung outside Peking are splendid examples of the tomb temples. The pavilions, galleries, temples, and pagodas around the lake in the Imperial City and at the celebrated Summer Palace outside Peking, built during the seventeenth and eighteenth centuries, were less formal buildings, well adapted to the gardens of China. Modified French styles, introduced by Jesuit architects, were evident in several Summer Palace buildings.52

A number of religious structures complement the majesty of Peking's civil edifices. The imperial Altar of Heaven and Temple of Agriculture in the southern city of Peking date from the Yung-lo period but were later recon-structed. Both were circular, three-level structures in white marble. The three-terraced Altar was open-topped, but the round three-storied Temple rising from the centre of the third terrace has three blue-tile roofs. The Monastery of Glory and Happiness dates from the 1450's, and the Taoist Palace of Shining Light from 1557.

There are renowned masonry structures elsewhere, mainly of Buddhist origin. The K'ai-yüan Monastery at Ch'üan-chou (1389) has unique cary-atids. The Iron Pagoda of Kaifeng (completed in 1383) is a fabulous thirteen-storey polygon faced with enamelled bricks. The Monastery of the Five Towers (Wu-t'ai) was built outside Peking between 1465 and 1488, the Green Jade Cloud Monastery west of Peking between 1520 and 1580, and the great white Dagoba, a Tibetan-type stupa, in 1652. Various Tibetan-type struc-tures were put up at the Manchu summer palace in Jehol, one in frank imitation of the Potala.

Painting in China

China's paintings, mostly on scrolls or screens, gained a three-dimensional illusion of space without the Western device of converging lines. Objects were painted in relative positions to the right or the left of a primary viewpoint or above or below it, leaving the objects isolated and independent. The Chinese artist thereby succeeded in creating an effective impression of wide landscape and panoramic view.

Chinese monochrome ink painting reached its highest point during the fourteenth century. Yüan artists perfected the old techniques and forms, giving painstaking attention to the quality of ink, brush strokes, and drawing, and combining realism with freedom of expression. They also revived the use of colour, thereby not only promoting the trend toward realism but also adding new life to painting, and linked calligraphy with painting more closely than ever before. Most of the Yüan masters, while eschewing the extreme impressionism of their predecessors, the Southern Sung painters, succeeded in recapturing their predecessors' spirit.

The painting of bamboos, plum blossoms, and horses now reached its highest level. Chao Meng-fu (1254–1322) was one of the best-known court painters. Although he continued the traditions of the Sung Academy, he used new techniques to great advantage and became the founder of a school of realistic horse-and-warrior painting. He stood out also for his calligraphy, landscapes, flowers, and bamboos. (Pl. 71a.) Another court painter, Yen Hui, was noted for his hermits and Buddhist figures. The majority of the great fourteenth-century painters, however, were gifted amateurs, men of wealth and learning who painted for themselves and friends and not for the Mongol conquerors. Among them were the so-called Four Masters: Huang Kung-wang (1269–1354), who became a Taoist recluse; a grandson of Chao, Wang Meng (d. 1385), esteemed for his waterfalls, peaks, temples, and pine trees; Wu Chen (d. c. 1354), a Taoist poet and calligrapher, prominent for his bamboo and fishermen; and the best of them, Ni Tsan (1301–74), of Wu-hsi near Soochow. Ni Tsan's simple compositions had power and austerity; by depicting a few trees or flowers, a hut, some hills, and a stretch of water he created landscapes that no one else could successfully copy. (Pl. 71b.) Ni Tsan was a master painter of plum blossoms, as was also Wang Mien. The best of all the painters of bamboo was Li K'an.

The artists of the Ming period for the most part returned to the past and copied old masters. Nevertheless, they produced pictures of marked technical proficiency, elegance, and grace, often much enlivened by colour. The Ming emperors, zealous patrons of the arts, maintained court painters, and the Hsuan-te emperor (1425–35) was himself a painter of some ability. The leading artists of this period too were gifted amateurs, the so-called 'literary-men painters'. They copied the masterpieces of earlier generations and were more interested in the history, theory, and collection of art than in original creation.53 Among the more famous collectors were Hsiang Yüan-pien (1525–90) and Liang Ch'eng-piao (1620–91). Collection promoted the appearance of art criticism, such as *The Treatise on the Paintings and Writings of the Ten Bamboo Studies* (1633), and induced professional artists to cater to the tastes of the wealthy. The mutual interest of collector and artist contributed to the development of the colour-print (see below).

Three schools of painting may be distinguished during the Ming period: (1) a school of bird and flower painters, represented by Lü Chi (fl. 1488–1505) and some landscape painters who followed the Northern Sung Academy (Pl. 72a); (2) the Che school, which followed the impressionistic black-and-white landscapes of Ma Yüan and Hsia Kuei and other traditions of the Southern Sung Academy and was at its best in the works of Tai Chin (fl. 1430–50) and Wu Wei (1459–1508); and (3) the Wu, or Southern school, of the Soochow area, which followed the traditions of the tenth century and the Four Masters of the Yüan period but was notable for use of colour, free expression, and eclecticism.

The Wu school proved to be the most influential of the three. It was founded by the landscape painter Shen Chou (1427–1509), probably the outstanding Ming painter. (Pl. 72b.) He made a striking use of colours—blues, greyish-greens, and reddish tans—but subordinated them to brushwork in his compositions. Others associated with this school were Wen Pi (1470–1559), T'ang Yin, and Ch'iu Ying, painters of landscapes, court scenes, portraits, and pictures centred on women. With Tung Ch'i-ch'ang (1555–1636), who had a telling influence on late Ming and Ch'ing painting, the Wu school became increasingly academic and abstract. He insisted that a landscape painting could not and should not compete with nature but should rather express a landscape's inner realities, which could best be found by analysis of the masters of the past.

Most Ch'ing painters continued the academic tradition of the Wu school. They used a good deal of colour and developed the 'boneless style'—wash without line—in their landscapes, but their compositions lacked originality. The four Wangs, Wu Li (1632–1718), a landscape painter who was a convert to Christianity, and Yün Shou-p'ing, the last eminent flower painter, were generally considered the most gifted of these academic painters. The works of these six became increasingly uniform. Wang Hui (1632–1717), probably the most able of them, painted his own versions of many old masters. (Pl. 73a.)

For all that, several artists of the seventeenth century remained rather independent. Ch'en Hung-shou painted Taoist fairies, elongated women, and illustrations for wood-block prints (Pl. 73b), and Kung Hsien produced blasted and devastated landscapes. Three Buddhist monks—Chu Ta, K'un-ts'an, and Tao-chi (or Shih-ta'o)—were more original; and one of these three, Tao-chi (1630–1707), was probably unsurpassed by any other Ch'ing painter. (Pl. 74a.) Chu Ta's animals appeared to be sullen or enraged; K'un-ts'an's landscapes were sombre; Tao-chi's landscapes were more realistic than those of his contemporaries. Insisting that the spirit but not the style of the ancients should be followed, Tao-chi attacked tradition, emphasizing individualism and originality. 'I paint in my own style,' he said.54 He used colour or ink alone in some pictures and combinations of ink and colour in others.

The Wu tradition continued in the eighteenth century. Father Giuseppi Castiglione (Lang Shih-ning) and other Western court painters introduced a blend of Western naturalism and perspective with pseudo-Chinese techniques (Pl. 74b), but the Wu tradition was only slightly varied thereby; on the whole, Western painting had no appreciable influence on Chinese painters. Figure paintings, portraits, and court scenes became increasingly conspicuous in the Ch'ing period, which was noteworthy also for its collections and its art criticism. Art precepts and theories were set forth in the famous *Mustard Seed Garden Painting Manual (Chieh-tzu yüan-hua chuan)*, a work by many hands, which reached its final form between 1679 and 1701. An *Imperial Encyclopaedia of Calligraphy and Painting* was begun in 1705. The first part of a *Catalogue of the Imperial Collections (Shih ch'ü pao chi)* was completed in 1745. The Ch'ing emperors were not, however, the most competent of art critics, and they often failed to make the best choice of court painters or of collection items.

The most original developments in painting after the creative Yüan period came in the decoration of porcelain and lacquered ware and in colour-prints. These developments reflected a growing commercialism, although colour-prints, despite their Chinese origins, were not popularized to the same extent as in Japan (see below). Wood-block prints in black and white came into use during the Ming period to illustrate books, novels, tales, and scientific works, and as colour technique improved, artists of reputation took more and more to drawing for woodcut illustrations. Ting Yün-p'eng's illustrations in the *Ch'eng shih mo yüan*, printed in 1606, are the oldest known Chinese colour-prints. The technique was perfected in the work of art criticism mentioned above, *The Treatise on ... the Ten Bamboo Studios* (1633), and thereafter various independent albums of colour-prints appeared. Ch'en Hung-shou, who was actively engaged in this kind of work, did the illustrations for a famous novel (*Shui hu chüan*). The art of colour-print mounted in importance in the eighteenth century.

Sculpture in China

Chinese sculpture, when not relief, was carved or cast on the assumption that it would be seen from a primary view or a limited number of views, and it was sculpturally indifferent to the surrounding space. Except for jade, ivory, and wood carvings and the sculpturesque porcelains of Fukien, the only significant Chinese sculptures of this period were the stiff, colossal stone warriors, officials, elephants, camels, and other animals at the Ming tombs near Nanking and Peking, some reliefs in the marble terraces at Peking, and the relief work on the Kü-yung Gate in the Great Wall near Nan-k'ou (1345). The colossal, free-standing statues of animals and men flanking the avenue to the tomb of the Hung-wu emperor, the founder of the Ming dynasty (d. 1398), are rigidly adjusted to the four sides of the original stone slab.

Ceramics in China

Chinese ceramics, the oldest continuous art tradition in the world, was perhaps also the most influential of all Far Eastern arts. During the T'ang and Sung periods the shapes of various types of vessels had been dignified and well-proportioned, and the variety of textures and colours in glaze had been unparalleled. Craftsmen of the Ming period produced some excellent pottery along these traditional lines, but otherwise Ming pottery was predominantly massive, simple in shape, and often broad and vigorous in decorative motif. It was frequently glazed, like Sung pottery, with a single, strong colour such as turquoise blue, dark violet, or yellow, but other prominent types were the 'three-colour vase' and the 'five-colour ware', emphasizing the sustained leaning of Chinese potters toward polychromy. Fine threads of clay standing out in relief framed the various colour areas.

The major development in pottery-making during the Ming period was a change of emphasis from the traditional stoneware to porcelain. Porcelain is produced from a clay that fires to a harder and finer consistency and results in a homogeneous, vitreous pottery. Although porcelain had been known in China since the T'ang period, it had advanced farther in Persia (see Chapter XIII), and the arrival of Persian potters at the Mongol court appears to have stimulated its manufacture among the Chinese.

Particularly good clay for porcelain was found at this time at Ching-te-chen in Kiangsi. The methods of ceramic production were crude and uncertain, but the many craftsmen who participated in them—sculptor, painter, chemist, and factory administrator—were highly organized, and each was specialized in a particular phase of the lengthy process. The translucent porcelain was first coated with a colourless glaze and then, with lead-silicate enamels, decorated in designs similar to those used on silk brocades. Monochrome Sung ware was imitated during the Yüan and much of the Ming period, but its popularity, except perhaps for the celadons, gradually declined as Ching-te-chen wares gained favour.

Under the patronage of the Ming and Ch'ing emperors Ching-te-chen became the greatest porcelain centre in China, operating an imperial porcelain factory and many private establishments besides. The basis of most of its pottery was white porcelain, but it produced a number of fine monochromes (sacrificial red, blue, turquoise, celadon, lustrous black, brown, and the famed egg-shell white of the Yung-lo period) and was distinguished during the Ming period for its blue-and-whites, tri-colours, and multi-coloured enamels. The blue-and-white ware, made by painting designs in cobalt blue on the biscuit before the glaze was applied, was outstanding during the Hsüan-te (1426–35), Cheng-te (1506–21), and Chia-ching (1522–66) periods because of a superior 'Mohammedan blue' imported from the Near East, but other colours such as green, red, and yellow were also sometimes used. The so-called 'three-colour wares' came in fact in more than three colours—dark violet, turquoise, aubergine purple, yellow, and neutral white.[55] Multicoloured enamels were formed by painting designs in liquefied coloured glass on the glaze and fixing them with a light firing. During the Wan-li period (1573–1619) enamel work on top of blue and white became especially popular as 'Wan-li polychrome'.

From China, the art of porcelain-making spread to various parts of the Far East and the Western world. After 1600 the English and the Dutch began to import Chinese porcelain. From the sixteenth century on, royal collections were common in Europe, sometimes including thousands of pieces, and by the end of the seventeenth century every house of any pretensions displayed its 'chinaware'. Chinese pottery specifically designed to please European tastes was staple in a lucrative trade that lasted into the nineteenth century. During the late-Ming and the Ch'ing period several kinds of porcelains were manufactured largely for the export market—the milk-white ware (blanc de Chine) of Te-hua, Fukien, eminent for its sculpturesque figures; the red, buff, and grey stoneware of Yi-hsing, Kiangsu, whose red tea ware influenced European pottery; the colour-glazed stoneware of Shekwan, near Canton. During the Ch'ing period Ching-te-chen porcelain was often decorated and enamelled at Canton for the European market. Chinese designs were traditionally of a floral nature; lotuses, peonies, peach blossoms, and pine trees served as setting for cranes, peacocks, tortoises, and smaller birds or for dragons, the Eight Immortals, the Eight Precious Things of Buddhism, or willowy women. As the export trade grew, however, the traditional Chinese jars, bottles, vases, and bowls were modified to meet the Western taste for teacups, saucers, plates, and the like.

After the disorders accompanying the fall of the Ming dynasty subsided, the Ch'ing emperors became lavish promoters of the Ching-te-chen porcelains, while Western demands for Chinese porcelains mounted. According to Father d'Entrecolles, who wrote from Ching-te-chen in 1712 and 1722 (probably with some exaggeration), it possessed about 3000 furnaces maintained by a community of nearly a million people. The industry involved almost an assembly-line technique, different workers specializing in different aspects of manufacture and decoration.

Able men placed in charge of the imperial kilns at Ching-te-chen developed new techniques and ingenious forms, designs, and colours to please their imperial masters. Ts'ang Ying-hsüan was in charge after 1682, and T'ang Ying, who left several treatises on porcelain manufacture, was the guiding light from 1728 until 1749. The K'ang-hsi period (1662–1722) was noted for its blue-and-white ware (featuring a sapphire blue), its sleek and transparent tri-colour glazes (in green, yellow, and aubergine), and its enamelled ware in soft, vivid greens (*famille verte*) and lustrous blacks (*famille noire*) supported by yellow, coral red, aubergine, and violet. Many of the enamels were painted directly on the unglazed biscuit. Among its more famous monochromes were various reds, peach-blossom pinks, powder-blues, pale lavenders, Mazarin blues, apple greens, and crackled mustard yellows. During the Ch'ien-lung period (1736–95) new coloured enamels were elaborated—among them, the various rose colours (*famille rose*), decorated with delicate, effeminate, miniature-like designs. In monochromes new colours were tea-dust, iron-rust, and bronze. Metals, shells, birds' eggs, grained wood, jade, and ivory were accurately copied. Ingenious forms and intricate lace-work and rice-grain designs were also fashioned. By this time Chinese ceramics had reached its summit of technical perfection, but it had already begun to decline as art: 'At its best the decoration is more ingenious than original, and more pretty than artistic.'[56]

Other Decorative Arts in China

During this period some other Chinese decorative arts, such as cloisonné, silk weaving, and carpet making, likewise attained unprecedented heights. If the extensive decorative repertory of China is one of the most stable in the world, its stability perhaps results from the specific nature of the meanings associated with specific motifs. The plant, animal, bird, and human forms that comprise the greater part of the Chinese repertory were in most instances symbols associated with the emperor or with Buddhist or Taoist beliefs. Some motifs embody several references, and not only the representational motifs but also the relatively abstract ones were meaningful. The symbolic character of Chinese ornament probably contributed to the stabilizing of motifs in a readily identifiable form and certainly restricted their use and governed the way in which they were combined. Chinese motifs are generally asymmetrical and irregular in silhouette and rhythmically linear in form, with little suggestion of the sculptural relief or tectonic stability which at times characterized European ornament.

During the Ming and Ch'ing periods, the decorators of textiles, as well as of pottery, frequently imitated paintings. The basically calligraphic nature of Chinese painting and the relatively episodic treatment of space was not disturbing to the surfaces and shapes of the decorated objects in the way that the light modelled figures and the deep homogeneous space of European painting was. The ground colour was usually maintained in Chinese ornament as a continuous surface on which isolated motifs float like vignettes. None of the arts of China was under the pressure of style changes comparable to those of Europe, and for that reason artists had time to elaborate and refine the traditional techniques, motifs, and arrangements of the decorative arts. During the Ming and particularly the Ch'ing period, they frequently became virtuosos producing *tours de force* unequalled in previous eras.

Luxury in articles of ceremonial or daily use, demanded and supplied in the Sung period beyond anything known in contemporary Europe, continued to be supplied by Ming and Ch'ing craftsmen. After the mid-thirteenth century China produced rugs, for example, that though not so firm as those of Persia, were admired for the especially fine sheen of the long, soft yarn of wool, silk, and camels' hair used for the pile. Unusual geometric shapes in yellow, blue, and red with golden and reddish tans predominating in the ground are characteristic of Chinese rugs. Ming craftsmen (and their contemporaries in Japan) embroidered multicoloured floral designs on ceremonial and ritual robes which are among the finest examples of this art. Ming goldsmiths, among the most accomplished in China's long history, made delicate and elaborate pieces in foliate, floral, animal, or fantastic forms. Chinese filigree silver was equal to any. Precious stones were not faceted as they were in Europe but cut *en cabochon*, or in a rounded form, and strings of jewels were frequently interspersed with plaques of carved jade to form necklaces. Chinese craftsmen continued to make traditional ceremonial vessels, although Ming bronzes are not now so highly regarded as the earlier work on which they were modelled.

Champlevé and painted enamel processes were known to Chinese (and other Asian) craftsmen, and they also developed the technique of cloisonné. In the making of cloisonné, small cells are formed by soldering thin, flat wire on a copper surface and then are filled with enamel powder or paste, which then is fired. Chinese cloisonné was brought to a point of unparalleled refinement by Ming craftsmen, who frequently designed on a dark-blue ground. In Japan, where the technique was introduced only in the seventeenth century, a dark-green background was preferred; and at Jaipur, Pertubghur, and Ratan in India, an opalescent effect was gained from a gold ground.

Art in Vietnam

The art of Vietnam, like other elements of its civilization reflected its close cultural relationship with China. It added something, however, to what it borrowed, and the resulting product had a distinctly national character. The chief Vietnamese achievements were in the field of architecture. Buddhist pagodas and monasteries, Confucian temples, civil buildings, and tombs were constructed of wood. In general, the buildings of Hanoi, Hué, and the few other cities that were among the architectural centres reflected the southern (the more ornate) Chinese style. Perhaps the finest architectural monument was the Confucian temple complex at Hanoi. A good deal of wood carving was fashioned, but painting seems to have been little developed.

Art in Korea

Korea likewise borrowed from China but gave its borrowings a national character. Korea has a long and imposing art history, and during the Yi dynasty (1392–1910), its achievements in architecture, painting, and ceramics were in accord with its tradition. The dominance of Confucianism discouraged Buddhist sculpture and the erection of elaborate monasteries and pagodas. The Floating Stone Monastery (Pu-sŏk-sa) near Yŏngtju (c. 1350) contained some noteworthy mural paintings and was a good example of the wood-style monasteries of Korea, generally constructed in scenic, out of-the-way places. One of the few wooden pagodas was the five-storied Pŏp-tju-sa at Chung-chŏngto (fifteenth century). Of the many stone pagodas the square, marble edifices at Songto and Seoul (each of ten stories counting the three-storey base) were striking examples.

The most laudable achievements of the period, however, were neither monasteries nor pagodas but Confucian temples, royal palaces, and city walls. Generally they followed the northern style of China in their pavilions, two-storied halls, colonnades, gates, and towers. The two-storied, hipped-roof pavilion on the East Gate of Seoul, first built in 1392, was an august and stately structure, while the dignified Confucian temple of Seoul, constructed immediately after the founding of the Yi dynasty and rebuilt in 1601, served as a model on a more splendid scale for many structures in other towns. Within a century of the founding of the dynasty, three royal palaces were constructed at Seoul, upon designs similar to, though less elaborate than, those of Peking. These and many other wooden buildings were destroyed during Hideyoshi's invasion of 1593, but two of them were reconstructed during the seventeenth century. The king's private apartments, the gardens, and the majestic two-storied throne-room of the reconstructed Palace of Ample Virtue (Chang-tŏk-kung) are especially striking.

A large number of gifted artists of the Yi period reflected the trend toward painting in ink and colour. The panels and walls, both inside and outside, of Buddhist temples and monasteries were decorated with Buddhist paintings, and Confucian scholars promoted the Chinese ideal of the literary-man's painting. Wood-block engraving in black and white also engaged some able artists. Pottery and porcelain reached a lofty standard before the invasion of Hideyoshi, when many Korean potters were taken to Japan.

THE ARTS IN JAPAN

Upon casual examination, most Japanese art seems to reveal an enormous indebtedness to China. Yet careful study shows how non-Chinese or, better, how Japanese it is. Although the Japanese have borrowed many of their basic artistic forms, concepts, and techniques from China, they have always altered them in spirit or execution to conform to their own esthetic ideals. In general, Japanese artistic products give the impression of being somewhat more delicate and ornate, somewhat less vast and sublime in conception, than Chinese.

Our period, which covers that part of the feudal epoch which extends from the decline of the Kamakura Shogunate to the beginning of the decline of the Tokugawa Shogunate, was an era of significant productivity. Japanese painting reached its highest plane, the plebeian colour-print rose to prominence, the Japanese garden became famous, Japanese porcelain acquired an independent character, and although religious architecture declined, military and civil architecture burgeoned. During the early part of the epoch the martial spirit dominated, exerting a profound influence on native Japanese art, while intuitive Zen Buddhism arose and spread, introducing Chinese architecture and the impressionistic landscape-painting of the Sung dynasty. Later Japanese art was deeply affected by the middle-class culture that emerged during 'the great peace' inaugurated by the Tokugawas.

Architecture

At the beginning of our period Japanese architects built temples in a native style, predominantly in wood. That style had developed during the Heian period (794–1185) by adaptations of Chinese models. When the Sung Chinese architecture was introduced by Zen Buddhism, it differed from the native style in its general lay-out, in the shape of its pillars, brackets, eaves, doors, and windows, and in its either plain or simple coloured interiors. In general, the Japanese gables of our period are considered to have been much more artistically handled than the Chinese. Thatch was often used instead of tile for roofing.

Zen monasteries were arranged after the Chinese manner in a series of courts facing the main gate to the south. (Fig. 5.) The main halls (Buddha hall, preaching hall, residential halls, etc.), one behind the other, formed the north and south sides of the courts; the lesser halls, belfry, sutra depository, meditation quarters, bath house, and toilet formed the other sides. Inside the main gate came a pond with a stone bridge over it, and then a two-storied gate in front of the first of the main halls. The chief surviving example of the Zen-Chinese style is the two-storied Shari-den of the Engaku-ji Monastery of Kamakura (1282).

In the early fourteenth century appeared a third style, a single-storey (*setchūyō*) hybrid of the other two styles. The main temple of the Kwanshin-ji, Osaka Prefecture, an early Ashikaga structure, is one of its most impressive examples. Low proportions, verandas, graceful curves, and tastefully decorated gables impart to this temple an air of simple dignity. (Pl. 75a.)

During the Ashikaga (or Muromachi) period (1334–1573), when Kyoto, the traditional cultural centre, was once again the political seat of the shoguns, numerous monasteries were built in all three styles, but the Zen-Chinese was perhaps the most common. It was adapted for the three-storied, octagonal pagoda of the Anraku-ji Monastery of Bessho, Nagano Prefecture, and for the Main Hall (1314) of the Eihō-ji Monastery at Tajimi near Nagoya.

In its earlier stages military architecture meant wooden stockades and ramparts, solid gates, and substantial quarters for the guards. The residence of the lord inside the stockade was at first built in a luxurious fashion imitative of the imperial residences at Kyoto, but during the Ashikaga period, in keeping with the rusticity and simplicity of the tea-cult (see below), a more simple yet elegant residential architecture, called the *shoin-zukuri* (*study-style*), emerged.

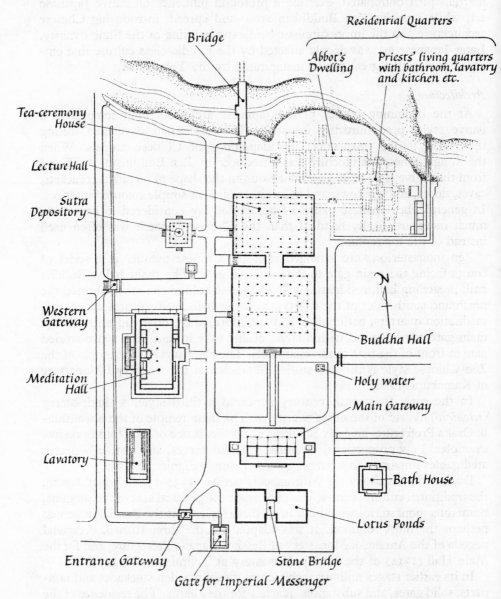

Bridge

Residential Quarters

Abbot's Dwelling

Priests' living quarters with bathroom, lavatory and kitchen etc.

Tea-ceremony House

Lecture Hall

Sutra Depository

N

Western Gateway

Buddha Hall

Meditation Hall

Holy water

Main Gateway

Lavatory

Bath House

Lotus Ponds

Entrance Gateway

Stone Bridge

Gate for Imperial Messenger

FIG. 5. Plan of the Zen Monasteries at Tojoku-ji Temple, Kyoto.

It used sliding panels or screen partitions, decorated with paintings, as walls, the upper part of the outside panels being covered with transparent paper to let in light. (Pl. 75b.) One of its basic features was a low, elevated room (*jōdan-no-ma*) with an alcove (for flowers, incense burner, and a painting), ornamental shelves, and a desk ledge. This room was designed to open up so as to become essentially a part of the garden and thus appropriate for guests, ceremonials, and receptions.

Much elaborated, study-style architecture became the palatial architecture of the nobles of the Momoyama and Tokugawa periods and the prototype for later residential architecture. Another earlier development in residential architecture also reached its culmination in the Momoyama period. That was the *chaseki*, or tea-ceremony room or building. It usually was plain, yet refined, but at times elegant.

The two pre-eminent civil buildings of Kyoto during the Ashikaga period embodied most of the architectural trends of the time. The Golden Pavilion (built *c.* 1397, burned down in 1950, reconstructed in 1955), had three stories, a hipped roof, and a veranda and overlooked a pond in a magnificent garden. (Pl. 75c.) The lowest storey contained living rooms in the old residential style, the second was in a mixed style, and the third was a Zen-styled single room, decorated in gold leaf. The Silver Pavilion (1480) also had a veranda and overlooked a pond in a magnificent garden, but it was two-storied and square and not so ornate, reflecting the simplicity of the tea-cult. The lower storey was in the new study-style architecture, while the second, in the Zen style, was lacquered inside and out and was intended to be overlaid in silver leaf. It was used at first as a retiring place and art treasury by the shogun, but both buildings ultimately became Buddhist temples.

The Momoyama period (1574–1614) is the time of the three great military leaders Nobunaga, Hideyoshi, and Ieyasu. Under Hideyoshi military and civil architecture prevailed over monastic architecture, bringing a flamboyance, gorgeousness of colour, and grandiosity of design that reflected his personality and the expansive mood of the military. Momoyama architecture was characterized by massive castles surrounded by deep moats and stone walls provided with corner and gate towers. Inside the walls on high foundations stood strong, elaborate, storied, wooden residences, built in the study-style, with numerous gables and other decorative features. A high central tower or *donjon* loomed above the other buildings to add to the grandeur and to serve as a look-out.

The first grand castle of this description was that of Adzuchi, no longer extant, erected (1576–79) by Nobunaga on the shores of Lake Biwa. Its central tower was seven stories high, and its rooms were elaborately decorated with paintings and carvings in gilt and gold by the most honoured artists of the day. The largest, strongest, and most elaborate was Hideyoshi's castle at Osaka (1583–85). Destroyed after 1615, it was partly restored in recent times. Hideyoshi also erected (1593) the palatial and highly decorated residential castle of Momoyama at Fushimi, near Kyoto. It, too, was destroyed (in the 1630's), but some of its buildings—superb examples of study-style architecture—were transferred to other places. The Nishi-Hongwan-ji Monastery of Kyoto has six of the halls, including a matchless *jōdan-no-ma* room and a magnificent Karamon Gate, and also the unique Hiun-kaku, a residential pavilion from Hideyoshi's residence at Fushimi. Of the castles of the Momoyama period, that of Himeji, in the Hyōgo Prefecture, with a five-storied *donjon*, alone survives. (P. 76a.)

The monuments of Tokugawa Ieyasu's time (d. 1616) have had a better fate. He completed (1610) one of Japan's noblest castles, that of Nagoya, also with a five-storied *donjon*, constructed under the direction of the warrior-architect Kātō Kiyomasa. (This castle was burned down in an air-raid in World War II; it has since been reconstructed of reinforced concrete on an iron frame.) Ieyasu also built (Kyoto, 1603) the Nijo castle-palace of the shoguns, illustrious for its well-proportioned corner towers and gates, the Karamon Gate, its four great halls (Waiting, Audience, Black, and White), and its garden. (Fig. 6.) The Shōnan-tei of the Sāihō-ji Monastery, Kyoto, a tea-ceremony house, was another notable monument of his day. When, however, Ieyasu established the Tokugawa military capital at Edo (Tokyo), the castle buildings he erected there were uninspired copies of the Momoyama style. Furthermore, Lord Masamune Daté put up at Sendai in 1607 the Shinto shrine of Ōsaki Hachiman, the first fully elaborated example of the ornate *gongen* style, generally used for mausoleums. It involved a complicated system of roofs, much carving and lacquer work, and the joining of the main shrine or mausoleum with the hall of prayer by a lobby. (Pl 76b.)

After Ieyasu, Tokugawa architecture steadily deteriorated. The Tokugawas banned the building of castles, and Buddhism, controlled and declining, showed no creative enthusiasm, repairing or rebuilding numerous monasteries in their original style. A few new monasteries erected under the patronage of the shoguns were in the *gongen* style, which was often used by Buddhists as well as Shintoists. A complete Ming Chinese style was followed in the Mampuku-ji Monastery near Kyoto, an establishment of the new Ōbaku sect of Zen introduced from China in 1655. The most important buildings of the later Tokugawas were the mausoleums of shoguns and great feudal lords, the principal ones being Ieyasu's (1636) and the third shogun's (1653) at Nikko, the second shogun's at Shiba Park (1635, destroyed in an air-raid in 1945), and Lord Daté's at Sendai (1637). The shrine and the five-storied pagoda to Ieyasu erected (*c.* 1639) in Ueno Park, Edo, were good examples of the uninspired style of the time. The more pretentious new structures, especially after the seventeenth century, whether in the *gongen* style or some other, and whether built by shogun, noble, priest, or rich merchant, were overly ornamental and lavish in colour, putting a sort of Rococo end to traditional Japanese architecture. Garden architecture, however, retained its superb qualities throughout the whole of our period.

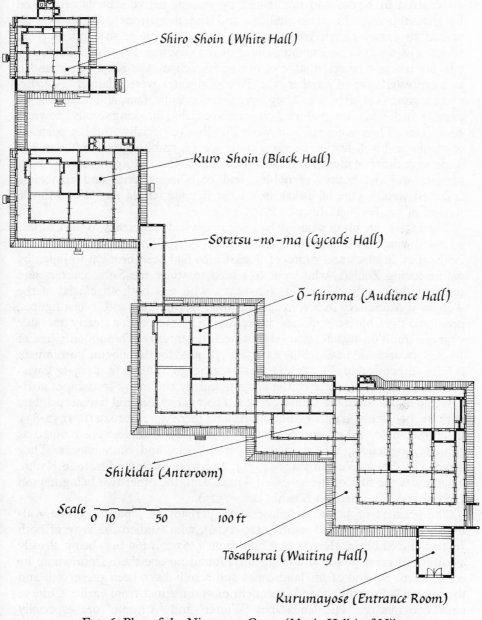

Shiro Shoin (White Hall)

Kuro Shoin (Black Hall)

Sotetsu-no-ma (Cycads Hall)

Ō-hiroma (Audience Hall)

Shikidai (Anteroom)

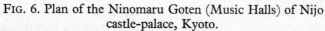

Scale

0 10   50   100 ft

Tōsaburai (Waiting Hall)

Kurumayose (Entrance Room)

FIG. 6. Plan of the Ninomaru Goten (Music Halls) of Nijo
castle-palace, Kyoto.

Painting

At the beginning of the fourteenth century painting in Japan was a courtly art centred in Kyoto and dominated by various native schools patronized by the emperor, the court nobles, and the monasteries. These schools tended to pass on their tradition from father to son or to a gifted pupil adopted as a son. The leading painter of the day was Takashina Takakane, who started as a representative of one native school, the Kasuga, but ended as a representative of another, the Tosa. Paintings were relatively realistic, using a great deal of colour. They were done on walls, fans, and screens or on paper, which was often mounted on panels or rolled into long scrolls known as *emakimono*. Their main subjects were Buddhas (especially Amida), portraits of monks and well-known persons, court scenes, and historical episodes, but some were didactic illustrations of Buddhist doctrines. Murals decorated both temples and the houses of nobles, and both monasteries and aristocrats collected scrolls. One of Takakane's most famous scrolls was 'The Miracle Record of the Kasuga Shrine'. (Pl. 77.)

The native schools of painting had begun to yield supremacy to the Chinese school during the Kamakura period (1185–1333). The impressionistic ink landscapes, in black and white, of Sung China had been brought to Japan by nature-loving Zenists, who went to China to study the Sung masters and imitated their style. Minchō (1352–1431), who was both an official of the Tōfuku-ji Monastery in Kyoto and a painter of Buddhist and Taoist figures, promoted the Chinese landscape style, but the first to begin a clearly traceable Chinese tradition was Josetsu (early fifteenth century). Though only one of Josetsu's works, 'Man Catching a Catfish', painted for the shogun Yoshimitsu, is fully authenticated (Pl. 78a), he was a teacher of Shūbun (c. 1414–65), who became an official painter of the shogun and by the many landscapes attributed to him assured the Chinese school's popularity. Several famous painters of that school studied under Shūbun. Among them were Dasoku (fl. 1452–83), Oguri Sōtan (d. 1481), and Nōami (1397–1476). All three were reputed as painters, gardeners, tea-ceremony experts, poets, and connoisseurs. They served the shogun Yoshimasa (1449–74) and were arbiters of taste in Kyoto. Nōami was the first of the so-called Three Ami, the other two being his son Geiami and his grandson Sōami (1472–1523).

The greatest of Japanese landscapists, perhaps of Japanese painters altogether, was the monk Sesshū (1420–1506), who studied the style of both Josetsu and Shūbun. He was in China from 1467 to 1469 but, being already a painter of great power and originality, found no one there from whom he could learn. Several of his landscapes and scrolls have been preserved, and they reveal a forceful style independent of and distinct from earlier Chinese landscape masters. His landscapes 'Winter' and 'Autumn' are especially impressive. (Pl. 78b.)

Most of the landscapists were monks and not painters by profession, but in the late fifteenth century a group of professional painters, employed by the shoguns and known as the Kanō school arose, and it remained dominant for the next two centuries. It was founded by Kanō Masanobu (1453–90) and developed by his son Kanō Motonobu (1476–1559). While continuing to paint landscapes in the Chinese monochrome style, these masters applied suitable modifications of Chinese techniques to the traditional subjects of the native Tosa school and reintroduced the use of colour. Motonobu, the most illustrious painter of the period after Sesshū, was a master in both ink and colour. Meanwhile an older contemporary, Tosa Mitsunobu (1434–1525), was breathing new life into the Tosa school of imperial painters with the fine colour and design of his historical scrolls, although he also worked in ink. When Motonobu married the daughter of Mitsunobu, the marriage symbolied the union of the traditional Japanese school with the Chinese school.

Certain trends evident in the late Ashikaga period, such as the revival of colour and of native tradition, culminated in the flamboyant art of the Momoyama period. The enthusiasm for colour and bigness went hand in hand with a penchant for gold leaf and a preference for the animated and the heroic. Walls, sliding panels, folding screens, and scrolls were now decorated with huge pictures in resplendent hues on gilt and gold backgrounds and in gold lacquer. For contrast, paintings were done also in black and white. Among the most able masters of the flamboyant art were Kanō Eitoku (1543–90), grandson of Mononobu, and Kanō Sanraku (1559–1635), a favourite of Hideyoshi adopted by the Kanōs. Both of them were employed by Hideyoshi to decorate his castles. Eitoku worked with brilliant tints, a heroic style, and vigorous brush strokes to portray giant pine and plum trees, lions, rocks, mountains, and flowers and to tell Japanese tales. (Pl. 79a.) Sanraku's paintings resembled those of his master Eitoku.

The leadership of the Kanōs, however, was not uncontested. Kaiho Yūshō (1533–1615), who studied under Kanō Eitoku, later founded a school of his own and won distinction particularly for his screens depicting Chinese legends, pine trees in black and white, and fish nets. Hasegawa Tōhaku (1539–1610) also studied under the Kanō school, but then, for a time, he devoted himself to the Sesshū style and, still later, adopted also the Chinese painting styles of the Sung and Yüan dynasties, finally establishing a style of his own. Another distinguished contemporary was Unkoku Tōgan (1547–1618), who contended with Tōhaku for recognition as the rightful successor to Sesshu. Meanwhile Tosa Mitsuyoshi (1539–1613) continued in gold and rich colour the epic tradition of the Tosa school, with detailed pictures of horsemen, battles, and scenes from Buddhist lore.

Honnami Kōetsu (1569–1637), an independent genius, was the first of a new group of 'decorative painters'. They were highly regarded for their lacquer work, especially in gold, for their skill in the several styles of the time, for their use of ink on gold backgrounds, and for the wide range of their subjects. Master of the techniques of pottery, gold lacquer, and calligraphy as well as of painting, Kōetsu was outstanding for his use of lead on lacquered screens and for his portraits of priests. The approximately contemporary artist Sōtatsu further developed the decorative technique of Kōetsu, with boldly conceived screen pictures in colour. His *suiboku* paintings (monochrome, done in *sumi*, or ink) also showed a high degree of specifically Japanese composition and technique, easily distinguishable from those of the Chinese style.

In the early Tokugawa period the Kanō, Tosa, and decorative schools kept up the flamboyant Momoyama style, though on a somewhat moderated scale. A host of Kanō masters were official painters to the shoguns at Edo in the seventeenth century and, as time wore on, they became increasingly bureaucratic. Kanō Tannyū (1602–74) and his two brothers were the best known of them; Tannyū himself was an original genius who modified accepted canons. To suit the Confucian interests of the bureaucracy the Kanō school turned to Chinese subjects such as Confucius, the Seven Wise Men of the Bamboo Grove, Chinese rulers and their loyal subjects, and sacred animals such as dragons, tigers, lions, *ch'i-lins*, cranes, and phoenixes, along with landscapes, trees, and flowers. Kanō Sansetsu (1589–1651), an adopted son of Sanraku, adopted the black and white technique; he established a branch of the school at Kyoto. Kanō Tsunenobu (1636–1713), son of one of Tannyū's brothers, was also an accomplished painter. Meanwhile, Tosa Mitsunari (1583–1638) carried the Tosa classical tradition into the Tokugawa period; later Tosas continued as court painters at Kyoto. The decorative painters could also boast several able exponents, of whom Ogata Kōrin (1658–1716) is sometimes considered the most able because of the exceptional beauty of his decorated screens, figures, landscapes, flowers, and birds; he used gold and silver paste or ink mixed with gold paste to obtain decorative effects. (Pl. 79b.)

Ogata Korin flourished at a time—the Genroku Era (1688–1703)—when the superior elements of the old tradition were being combined with a rising graphic medium, the *ukiyoe* (or genre picture), to create a memorable period in art. The *ukiyoe* prints and pictures had attracted the middle-class townsmen, who demanded a relatively cheap art in large quantities. The artists of this group were the same sort of townsmen and renegade samurai that, turning their backs on the sumarai art of the older schools and looking to the life of the town for inspiration, cultivated *chonin* literature (see Chapter XI). Among their favourite pictorial subjects were courtesans and actors; they leaned toward love scenes, street scenes, scenes of everyday life, and, as time went on, landscapes; and they had a penchant for pictures that poked fun at sacred figures. Some of the *ukiyoe* were painted by hand, others were printed from wood-blocks. The Chinese wood-block print certainly helped to bring on this development, but the colour-print went much further in Japan than in China.

The new genre painting had developed in three stages. It was born in the early Tokugawa period with the works of Iwasa Matahei (1568–1650) of the Tosa school, who was noted for his 'Thirty-six Poets'. During the second stage (*c.* 1650–1740), hand-painted pictures in various colours and black and white prints were characteristic. The chief figures of this stage were Hishi-kawa Moronobu (1688–1703), whose subjects were courtesans, often with a landscape background, and who introduced picture books, and Torii Kiyonobu (1664–1729), founder of the Torii school, who specialized in theatre signs and actors. During the third stage (1740–1843) the genuine colour-print emerged, the combined work of painter, engraver, and printer, in which a basic pink was contrasted with green, yellow, and other colours. Okumura Masanobu (1690–1768) and Ishikawa Toyonobu (1711–85) were pioneers of the colour-print. Masanobu portrayed actors, courtesans, legend-ary scenes, and popular heroes against a background of elegance, luxury, and eroticism. Suzuki Harunobu (1718–70) elaborated the brocade or many-coloured print and was the leading *ukiyoe* master of our period. (Pl. 80.) He painted highly idealized tea-house beauties, daughters of merchants, and lovers, generally with a landscape background.

In the eighteenth century, as the *ukiyoe* won prominence, the aristocratic schools of the old tradition lost vitality. Confucian scholars became interested in the abstract, literary-man's painting exemplified by the Wu or Southern School of China. In Japan they were known as the Nanga School, and Ike-no Taiga (1723–76) was their most eminent representative. On the other hand, Maruyama Ōkyo (1738–95), having been somewhat influenced by a relatively unknown Chinese painter, Shen Nan-p'in, who visited Nagasaki in 1731–33, established a very realistic school of landscape painting, which also became popular among townsmen.

Other arts

During the Tokugawa period, the ceramic arts made noteworthy strides. Their advance was attributable to the growing popularity of the tea-cult and to Hideyoshi's importation of Korean potters. Especially favoured wares were Imari and Arita polychromes along with Hirado whites. Some realistic portraiture in wood of Buddhist monks was still done in the fourteenth century, but sculpture was less emphasized in later centuries than pottery and porcelain. It survived, too, in the decorative arts—in the fashioning of ornaments for the interiors or exteriors of buildings, in the carving of puppets and *nō* masks, and in ivory-carvings. A variety of other decorative arts—among them, tray-landscapes, potted dwarfed trees, fans, dolls, lacquer ware, screens, and flower arrangements—produced masterpieces of their own, and the craftsmanship of Japanese swords and armour won a well deserved repu-tation.

In Japan as in China music and the dance (other than the court music, continued from earlier centuries) were particularly associated with dramatic performances (see Chapter XI). Although Confucian scholars considered music an important means of social control, it was not highly developed as a public art. Composers were unknown as such. In both Japan and China a variety of chants and popular airs grew up in connection with dramatic performances and with entertainment by geishas and sing-song girls, but they were considered lewd (as often they were) by scholars, who favoured only certain kinds of solemn and traditional music associated with sacrifices, coronations, and other important ceremonial occasions.

In both countries likewise, the solemn classical dances associated with religious events and ceremonies were approved by Confucian moralists, while dramatic or popular dances were not, with the exception of those in the symbolic and esoteric *nō* dramas (which were generally regarded, however, as belonging in the classic group). Hence popular dances (other than folk dances) were, like popular music, associated with the dramas and geisha entertainment. Symbolic gestures had to be carefully studied, and some of the military and sword dances required fast movement and extreme dexterity. Gorgeous costuming was essential to all kinds of dancing, which was a much more highly developed art in Japan than in China.

In both countries instrument making had been carefully practiced since an early date. The Chinese had devised a seven-string zither or lute (*ch'in*), other string instruments (*se* and *p'i-p'a*), and various wind instruments (*hsiao, sheng, ti*), around which an abundant lore accumulated. Performers of all classes from scholars to sing-song girls played them, both for private and semi-private entertainment. In the early sixteenth century the Chinese musician Wei Liang-fu adapted native tunes to operatic scores and enlarged and improved the orchestras that accompanied the *k'un-ch'ü* songs and dramas (see Chapter XI). Chinese instrumentation came to include the flute, the guitar, the reed-organ (*sheng*), the drum, and castenets, lending a new emphasis to the musical and acoustical values of *k'un ch'ü* drama. At the beginning of the eighteenth century the Japanese introduced into their *jōruri* plays the three-stringed guitar (*samisen*) of the Ryukyu Islands.

THE ARTS OUTSIDE EURASIA

African Sculpture

Before Eurasian influences began to affect other continents, several peoples of Africa and the Americas had developed an independent art tradition of a high order. In Africa the artists of Benin achieved an impressive type of sculpture free from imitation of contemporary Mediterranean art but perhaps indebted to ancient Greek or oriental art. Before 1500 they had a knowledge of bronze casting that was surpassed only by the better craftsmen of Florence, Germany, India, and the Far East. Benin was the capital of the Beni of the Niger region, one of the most highly organized of the Sudanic peoples of our period. Its culture probably was originally derived from Ifé, the holy city of the nearby Yoruba people. Benin's technical tradition appears to have originated about 1300 and to have reached its climax about the sixteenth century, when Portuguese traders, then establishing trade relationships with that area, were depicted on some of the Beni reliefs.[57] The subtle surfaces of Ifé portraits and the intricate details of Benin masks were magnificently done, even if they did not reach the complexities or the exquisite finish of Florentine workmanship or match the long technical tradition of bronze casting in China and Japan. (Pl. 81.)

The bronze and terra cotta heads of Ifé are unusual in the African tradition both for their naturalism and the material of which they are made. Most other African sculpture was done in wood, usually small and compactly held within the original block. While the human body was the primary subject of Negro sculpture, as it was in European art, animals too were often represented. Also sensitive to the contrast of sculptural volumes and spatial penetrations, the African artist tended to confine his sculpture to the shape of the block, suggesting little concern for the surrounding space or for the viewer's angle of vision.

The Arts in Pre-Columbian America

In the Americas, the most significant art traditions of the fourteenth and fifteenth centuries were those of the Incas in Peru and the Aztecs in Mexico. Highly conventionalized animals, birds, fish, and human figures and various abstract forms not readily identifiable comprise most of the decorative vocabulary. The floral and foliate motifs prominent in the Far East, India, the Middle East, and Europe were noticeably lacking in the Americas. Definite meanings were apparently associated with even such abstract forms as the fret and the wave. Inca and Aztec designs seldom suggest sculptural relief or depth. Most motifs are flat, occupying the same plane as the ground. A tendency toward angular, triangular, and rectangular shaping of parts, particularly characteristic of Inca ornament, may reflect the textile origin of a number of them. The arrival of the Europeans played havoc with the leading decorative arts, but some of them have survived in the form of folk arts.

Before the European conquerors rechannelled the course of the Amerindians' culture, it had developed various architectural traditions. Along the Andean highlands, the Incas built mountain cities and fortified places with cyclopean stones, cut and fitted together without mortar or metal tools but with a precision and skill that evokes admiration to this day. In Central America, numerous and often gigantic pyramidal platforms for small temples with tall, ornamental crests rose slowly from the plains, still causing wonder at the immensity of the planning and labour they required and at the forcefulness and fantasy of the sculpture which covered and enriched them. In the area that was to become the southwest of the United States, the many-celled communal dwellings of the Pueblo Indians clung to the protective ledges of rocky cliffs. The architects of the Amerindians had not discovered a true arch and were therefore limited in their interiors to variations of column and lintel construction (the so-called 'false arch'), attaining only the most meagre, low corridor-space inside their often enormous structures.

Aztec sculpture along with the earlier Mayan, stands out as part of one of the finest pre-Columbian art traditions in the Americas. Mayan sculpture had seen its best days before 1300 (see *History of Mankind*, Vol. III), and the culture which the Spaniards found in Mexico was dominated by the Aztecs. Aztec sculpture, while greatly varied, was often characterized by compactness of form with little interplay between the sculptural mass and the surrounding space. The huge stone Coatlicue, or serpent goddess, now in the Mexican Archaeological Museum, is richly carved on all sides but with reliefs that respect the planes of the original stone block. Occasionally small works such as the spiralled arrangements of the feathered serpent deity, Quetzalcoatl, take on a distinct life-in-the-round, but Aztec sculpture is rarely designed to provide interesting views from all possible angles. (Pl. 82a, b.)

*   *   *

Many areas of the world outside Europe during this period employed a decorative, polychrome sculpture, particularly those areas in which wood was the predominant medium, such as Africa and the islands of Polynesia and Melanesia in the Pacific Ocean. Though in stone, most Aztec sculpture, whether round or in relief, was enriched by vivid areas of colour. The Americas, Africa, and Oceania, however, during this period do not appear to have demanded a great amount or variety of decorative architectural devices or of decorative furniture, whether for ceremonial or for domestic purposes, in the interiors of their structures.

On the other hand, the early Americas produced many unique pieces of ceremonial jewellery. From Peru to Mexico the Spaniards encountered fabulous objects in gold, silver, jadeite, turquoise, shell, and rock crystal. Delicately wrought gold ornaments were sewn on ceremonial robes. The Amerindian goldsmiths fashioned pendants, earrings, oar plugs, pectoral plates, headdresses, bracelets, rings, necklaces. Burial masks, wrought of thin sheets of beaten gold, and other funerary objects were among their most impressive work. Spanish and Portuguese conquerors admired many of these objects, but the ready currency value of the materials apparently overruled admiration for design and workmanship, for many were melted down before they left America. In consequence, European artisans probably saw few products of the American Indian's craftsmanship in jewellery.

Among the Incas of South America a highly ornamental effect was achieved in cloth. During the fourteenth and fifteenth centuries they were the only cultural group in the Americas to make intricately woven and richly decorated textiles of cotton-and-wool yarn. Despite their relatively simple implements, they attained an amazing refinement in the spinning of cotton and wool, and their weaving methods included almost all those contemporaneously known elsewhere. Their knowledge of dyeing permitted a wide range of colours, and they distributed colour so freely and fitted their small conventional figures and symbols so closely together as to suggest infinite variety and complication in their designs.

The Arts in Post-Columbian America

Christian missionaries transformed the art and architecture of the Amerindians. The abrupt change of religion in Latin America resulted in the interruption of most of the major arts that previously had in any way served the indigenous religious ceremonies. It also resulted in Mexico in the formation of a new kind of monastery, distinguished from its European predecessors by an immense atrium with a centrally located stone cross, around which the Indians, accustomed to outdoor congregations, could gather for services in great numbers.

In the Christian art of Mexico the emphasis on the passion of Jesus and on His blood may stem from an attempt of the clergy to capitalize on the Aztec cult of blood sacrifices. Spain and Portugal shipped their realistic polychrome sculpture in great quantities to the New World, and it formed the basis for seventeenth-century and especially eighteenth-century sculpture in Central and South America. Polychrome wooden crucifixes, showing a writhing Jesus with gaping, bleeding wounds, pain-racked eyes, and fevered, open mouth, rose in the many cathedrals, churches, and missions that soon dotted the vast Spanish and Portuguese empires in America.

Wherever American buildings rose beyond the dimensions of temporary shelter or log cabin, the architecture was influenced by that of the mother countries. In Anglo–America churches and schools were usually Georgian. The missionary role of Spain and Portugal led to building activity on a scale not even considered by England or France in North America, bringing a complete interruption of native traditions in Central and South America. A few edifices like the Cathedral of Santo Domingo in Hispaniola or the early-sixteenth-century monastery churches in Mexico belatedly introduced Gothic into the Americas, but most of the major monuments—e.g. the cathedrals of Mexico City, Puebla, and Guadalajara in Mexico and of Lima and Cuzco in Peru—were in the ornamental 'Plateresque' style or, in the later sixteenth century, in the more severe 'Herreresque'. (Pl. 45a, b.) The prevalence of earthquakes in many parts of Central America and along the Andes Mountain range encouraged the use of thick walls, heavy buttresses, low interiors, flexible rib vaults, and light vaulting materials to assure the maximum stability of their structures.[58]

The Iberian Baroque style was likewise carried to South and Central America, where it achieved some of its most exuberant and marvellous ensembles. The carved rose-coloured stone exterior and the painted and gilded interior of the Church of Guanajuato and the carved white plaster and red-tile façade of the Sanctuary of Ocotlan near Tlaxcala are examples of the ornate, polychrome creations typical of Mexico's Baroque. In the Hispano–American areas generally the eighteenth-century interest in the exotic was expressed by reminiscences of Islamic and Pre-Columbian Indian motifs. While the tiled and undulated church façades of Brazil revealed a continued dependence on Portugal, the Hispanic colonies developed a growing individuality of architecture.[59] In the New World, where, it is sometimes said, European styles go to die, a robust Baroque lived on into the nineteenth century, demonstrating an amazing creative vitality.

In contrast to the success of the Spaniards in transplanting their architectural tradition in the New World, their pictorial forms and techniques were not readily transferred. Despite the emergence of autonomous regional schools in the seventeenth and eightenth centuries, Hispanic America remained dependent on the art market of Seville for it finer paintings for church or home.[60] Not so for its pottery, however, which likewise was successfully transplanted. In the early sixteenth century, Spanish Dominican friars took the low-fire process of making majolica ware to Mexico, and through the eighteenth century, Mexico, like Spain, remained an important producer of majolica dishes, bowls, apothecary jars, and glazed tiles.

European Town Planning Overseas

Usually having no previous town plan (or lack of plan) to counteract in the rising settlements, the European architect could lay out cities freely. All over America, North and South, and at strategic points elsewhere (Manila and Capetown, for example), new cities or additions to native cities took on a gridiron appearance. (Pl. 83). In colonial capitals a large square bordered by the cathedral and the governor's mansion would become the centre, and the other streets would branch out in perpendicular fashion, cutting the city into rectangular 'blocks' of houses.[61] Lesser cities, usually connected with the capital by a single road, would follow the same grid-system of town planning. Thus the new cities in the wilderness demonstrated, as did the rising settlements in so many other regards, the interplay of European tradition with frontier opportunities and obstacles.

NOTES TO CHAPTER XII

1. Professor A. Chastel believes that the periodic 'return to the Gothic' form after each phase of plastic consolidation in style is a characteristic of the Renaissance period in certain milieux both north and south of the Alps. This is what happens in Tuscany and Lombardy in the mid-fourteenth century on the basis of 'giottism'. The northern miniaturists had already evolved the gracious 'minor' version of monumental Gothic found in the work of Jean Lucelle and the Parisian illuminators, who lie at the origin of the precious, courtly style popular in the last quarter of the fifteenth century known as 'international Gothic', the main centres of which were in Sienna, Prague, and Paris, with ramifications throughout Europe. Highly evolved painters such as the Master of the Hours of Boucicaut and the Limbourg brothers represent the final transcending of this style by strict composition and formal precision directly preparing the advent of Van Eyck's realism. This is clearly established in the studies of Messrs Meiss and E. Panofsky.

2. Professor André Chastel stresses that towards the middle of the fifteenth century, Italian methods of composition began to become known in northern Europe, and the potentialities of oil painting were assimilated by the Italian masters, probably on the basis of examples coming from southern Italy. Antonello da Messina, who ended his career in Venice in 1475, was a key figure in this evolution, which also influenced the art of Piero della Francesca. The evolution of Italian art is not restricted to the expansion of Tuscan forms. In Flanders as in Italy, from 1480 on, we observe a renunciation of hard outline and a softening of style, a phase of so-called "relaxation' noticeable in the work of Memling as well as in that of Perugino.

3. Professor André Chastel notes that engraving spread both in Italy and in Germany from 1460 onwards, becoming at the beginning of the sixteenth century the most powerful means of artistic interchange between the various centres: Dürer drew inspiration from Mantegna and Marc-Antonio, Raphael's official engraver, and spread knowledge of the great 'Roman' style throughout the West.
    Conversely, through the intermediary of engraving, the fantastic and expressionist art of the North was to stimulate the work not only of certain Lombard and Venetian artists, but, even though only episodically, that of a Tuscan like Pontormo.

4. Professor André Chastel feels that while the art of Tintoretto, by its intense expressivity and breadth of composition, is very far from the stilted precision and intellectual ambiguity of the first generation of 'mannerists', this artist nevertheless exploits certain virtualities by means of distortion of form, a quest for washed-out tones of colour, and a taste for long perspectives and 'telescoped' effects.

5. Professor A. Chastel points out that at about the same time, there was spreading through the North, and flourishing particularly in Antwerp and sophisticated centres such as Prague, a neo-mannerist trend culminating in Goltzius, Spranger, and the brilliant and ingenious painters of the court of Rudolph II. In Central Italy, too, a taste for complex and delicate forms was in evidence during the last quarter of the sixteenth century. The early-seventeenth-century innovators reacted against this taste, some, like Caravaggio (see below), by means of a return to 'nature' and striking simplification.

6. For Professor A. Chastel the expression *grande manière* is not generally applied to the decorative triumphs of Baroque art but to the preoccupation with the noble and majestic grandeur peculiar to French art at the time of the Académie and under the leadership of Lebrun, as shown above.

7. In Professor A. Chastel's opinion Poussin's treatment of landscape 'construction' can scarcely be said to be derived from Italian models but is rather the result of a personal evolution originally based on classical examples and accompanied, in his latest period, by a powerful concentration of effects, the personal character of which was clearly demonstrated during the Poussin colloquy in Paris in 1958.

8. Professor A. Chastel feels that recourse to contemporary human types, to vulgar and even provocative details, accounts for a large part of the success of 'Caravaggism'. This trend, opposed to landscape, gave renewed life both to 'scenes from daily life' and to still-life painting. Artists such as Honthurst and Terbruggen were to serve as intermediaries between Rome and the Low Countries both as regards realist inspiration and vigor of execution.

9. In Professor A. Chastel's opinion the art of Velasquez soars above the usual qualities of Spanish painting. Thanks to his Sevillian origins, he was conversant with the 'tenebrism' of Zurbarán. His direct knowledge of the Venetian style, acquired from the royal art collections, was completed by a long stay in Italy. Exquisite workmanship and formal dignity make him one of the leaders of what may be called 'total painting', but, as in the case of Vermeer, these qualities had to await the nineteenth century for full appreciation.

10. To Professor A. Chastel the gap between the robust sculpture of Giovanni Pisano—the only master to try to produce in Italy an equivalent to the statue-covered cathedral façade—and the precious art of Andréa Pisano seems of the same order as that between the 'plastic' style of Giotto himself and the compositions of those of his successors not far removed from Gothic mannerism

11. Professor A. Chastel stresses that the erection of the equestrian statue to the memory of Gattamelata on the Campo Santo of Padua (Pl. 30b) marked a vital date in the history of monumental bronze sculpture, while the altar for the Basilica of St. Antonio in the same city opened up new perspectives by the technique of grouping of the statues under a kind of aedicule. The whole of the activity of the north Italian bronze founders in Padua and Venice was influenced by these great examples, despite a tendency towards 'bibelots' and the ornamental plaquette much in vogue about 1500.

12. The model supplied by Leonardo, executed in clay and larger than life, was designed for the statue of Francesco Sforza. (André Chastel).

13. Professor A. Chastel points out that Michaelangelo's original projects (1505) for the tomb of Pope Julius II, of which only the Moses and the 'Slaves' remain, indicate a triumphal setting for the statues which were not conceived as separate figures. The *loggetta* of the Campanile of Saint Mark, with its four bronze statues and dating from thirty years later (1537–40), is a graceful construction very different in inspiration. Renaissance sculpture is closely linked to its architectural and decorative setting.

14. While there is a certain continuity in contacts between France and Italy before, during, and after the French invasions (1494–1554) the following distinctions are possible: (1) certain sporadic links towards the middle of the fifteenth century: Fouquet in Rome, F. Laurana in southern France; (2) the multiplication of orders and invitations during the French occupation of the duchy of Milan: Leonardo, Solario, Andréa del Sarto . . . ; and (3) the eventual creation of a real Franco-Italian centre at Fontainebleau, with the arrival of Rosso and Primaticcio, followed first by Serlio and Cellini and subsequently by Niccolo dell'Abbate. (André Chastel).

15. Professor A. Chastel emphasizes that the art of Bernini is characterized by multiplicity and richness of profile, by an intensification of the play of light produced by the drapery and sculpting of the limbs, and by the forceful appropriation of surrounding space obtained by the dominating effects of his obliques. As R. Witkover has clearly shown, this is where the sculpture of complex monuments requiring a regular mise en scène (as, for example, in the equestrian statue of Constantine in the atrium of St Peter's) becomes very close to the architect.

16. Marqués de Lozaya, *Historia del Arte Hispanico* (Barcelona, 1934), II, 496.

17. Professor A. Chastel sees in Normandy, more clearly than anywhere else in the West, an evolution of the 'flamboyant' style, which, by the fragmentation of space-interior screens, pendant knob-bosses, and display of decorative elements, facilitated the adoption of the rich ornamental motifs of the Lombard Renaissance at the beginning of the sixteenth century. The same is true of the Portuguese 'Manueline' style; and it is French (for the most part Norman) master-builders whom we find at this period at Coïmbra and Lisbon.

18. Professor A. Chastel feels that if the compositions of Brunelleschi at San Lorenzo, for example, and those of Alberti on the façade of Santa Maria Novella, are not unrelated to the main lines of Romano-Tuscan art, it is because, relying on the simplicity of form of such art, as opposed to the irregular Gothic lines, they were able to integrate into the new architectural style a growing number of elements borrowed from Antiquity. A similar phenomenon, leading to a very different result—that of decorative profusion—is found in Lombardy, where the circular or polygonal cupolas of Bramante and his school recall the baptisteries and exterior open arcading of Romanesque art.

19. In the opinion of Professor A. Chastel, however, Alberti was primarily the theoretician of the new architecture: his definition of the 'harmonious' building is not especially applicable to the example of Brunelleschi but aims at an anticipatory definition of the art of the future.

20. Saint Sebastian is designed on a central plan which was not often followed. The problem of a structure planned round a unified central space, with symmetrical elements, was broached all over Italy at the end of the fifteenth and beginning of the sixteenth century, but by means of widely differing formulas.

Almost all are votive churches, enlivened both internally and externally by the articulation of the architectural elements and strict play of orders, except in Lombardy (Lodi, Brescia), where the ornamentation is more profuse. (André Chastel.)

21. Professor A. Chastel stresses the influence of Sanmichele on the evolution of the Venetian palace, which, moreover, thanks to his constructions, determined the general effect of the Square of St Mark and of the Palace of the Doge.

22. Professor A. Chastel maintains that the modifications foreseen by Michaelangelo, known to us mainly from an engraving by Lafrèrie, certainly aimed at creating a kind of axial perspective through the body of the place. These were, however, never executed. The trapezoidal Campidoglio, with its monumental stairway opening out onto the city, reveals much more clearly Michaelangelo's architectural dynamism and its effect on urban design, not fully appreciated until the Baroque period.

23. For Professor A. Chastel the sweeping conceptions of Bernini are noticeable both in the powerful interior of the Church of St Andrew on the Quirinal and in the spectacular treatment of St Peter's Square, the culmination of a century and a half of efforts to provide a monumental setting for the Holy See.

24. In the opinion of Professor A. Chastel the general development is indubitably marked by a dual tendency: one to raise the intellectual and social status of the arts, the other to leave functional production to the artisan and, before long, to industry. In most cases, however, this distinction remained somewhat illusory. The Renaissance masters, insisting with theoreticians such as Vasari on the universal value of *disegno*, aimed not at isolating the painter but at making demands on his multiple capacities and directing his interest towards the ornamental arts as well as towards major compositions.

25. Professor A. Chastel indicates that armorial bearings and devices belong to a very old aristocratic and city tradition. The *impresa*, or emblem, on the contrary, representing a virtue or ideal in pictorial form, with or without a *motto*, is a Renaissance creation leading to a large output of illustrated collections (Alciati, etc.) which served to spread the fashion very widely.

26. Professor A. Chastel emphasizes that marquetry is not a matter of furniture only. The utilization of wood for decorative ensembles—choir stalls, room panelling, etc.—was a new departure at the end of the Middle Ages. It gave rise to some remarkable creations which, in the domain of church art continued to increase down to the Baroque period. In the decoration of 'studioli' or work cabinets, special mention must be made of those of Urbino and Gubbio (*c.* 1470–80), comprising a tier of marquetry panelling surmounted by a series of pictures; stone panelling makes its appearance in the 'studiolo' of Eleanor of Toledo (Palazzo Vecchio, Florence); luxuriously decorated cabinets, in which mythological or allegorical paintings are combined on the decor, are everywhere numerous during the same period.

27. Professor A. Chastel points out that to each new stylistic phase corresponds a new decorative development. This is true up to the end of the eighteenth century. Piero della Francesca supplied models for 'intarsia' marquetry, Raphael produced tapestry cartoons, Lebrun made models for furniture and even locks at Versailles. Western art was characterized by an increasing interchange between the arts, leading often to the promotion of the artisan. The history of motifs and patterns common to various decorative forms is an excellent illustration of this interdependence: the creation and development of 'grottesques', launched by Raphael's circle, gave rise in the mannerist period to the most extravagant inventions; exploited in the noble style in every conceivable subject of classical art, these 'grottesques' also form the basis of the fantasies of 'rococo' art and of eighteenth century 'chinoiseries'.

28. The new element consisted in the development of technical methods, the use of silver white and of coloured glass—enlarging the possibilities of picturesque effect—and in increased use of the bay, leading, as in the churches of St Urbain de Troyes, St Ouen de Rouen, and Sainte Gudule de Bruxelles, to compositions extending over several elements of a window.

This resulted in greater boldness and a heightening of colour, and the creation of such masterpieces as Engrand le Prince's Tree of Jesse in St Etienne de Beauvais (*c.* 1522). Renaissance stained glass in northern Europe is an often underestimated branch of the major arts, at least of monumental painting. (André Chastel).

29. Professor A. Chastel points out that prior to the Renaissance, and indeed scarcely prior to the eighteenth century, the philosophy of art, that it to say, reflection on aesthetics, did not exist. In its table of activities, Scolasticism recognized only the artisan, and theoretical expositions of optics or anatomy were accessible only to scholars. Such was the situation which underwent modification when certain artistic milieux adapted scientific knowledge to their own needs and thereby entered into competition with the official scholars of the University.

This is what E. Panofsky has called the 'decompartmentalization' of disciplines, which was to prove fruitful to the extent that the draughtsman alone was in a position to develop the new concrete knowledge of nature.

The most typical case is that of anatomy, the study of which opened up in a new direction with the publication of the collections of plates by Vesalius, *Humani corporis fabrica (1542)*. (Pl. 93c.)

30. Senior clergy, themselves of princely rank and fortune, were often the most active propagandists for new styles and new cultures in Catholic countries. Among innumerable examples may be cited Cardinal Georges d'Amboise, prime minister of Louis XII, Cardinals d'Armagnac and du Bellay, ambassadors of Francis I to Italy, Cardinal Ippolito d'Este, etc. Among church dignitaries profane interests long continued to dominate, and it was from among their ranks that the great connoisseurs were recruited. (André Chastel).

31. In the opinion of Professor A. Chastel the regulations of the Council of Trent were designed to react against an excess of profane spirit in religious art, insofar as this provided arguments in favour of the policy of the Reformation. Apart from a few manifestations of severity, however, the importance of which should not be exaggerated, the clearest result of the Council was firstly to inspire an art which 'spoke' to the masses (for instance that inspired by Carlo Borroméo in Milan) and subsequently (when the Jesuit tendency triumphed) a noble and dignified art soon to lend itself to fatuous display designed to celebrate the glory of God.

32. The theoretical writings of Leonardo were almost unknown prior to the nineteenth century; a compilation published by Fréart de Chambray (seventeenth century) alone gave some idea of the scientific reflections of the Florentine artist. His studies of 'physiognomy' were spread to a certain extent by the engravings of Wenceslas Hollar. Lomasso, in particular, incorporated Leonardo's advice to painters in his own treatise on painting (1584).

The authors assume that some of Leonardo's ideas were expressed in conversations and also that the notebooks left to the Melzi family were not completely unknown. Most important, Leonardo formulated ideas on expression already found in the sculpture of Donatello and suggested in the writings of Alberti.

33. Professor A. Chastel, however, remarks that the Academic systematization of 'categories of expression' and of types stems from Poussin, basing himself on Antiquity, and not from Descartes. (For the influence of Poussin on Lebrun and the Académie Royale, see above, page 664).

34. *Principes de la littèrature* (Paris, 1764), quoted in K. E. Gilbert, *A History of Esthetics* (New York, 1939), p. 216.

35. Diderot's article 'Beau' in the *Encyclopédie*, quoted *ibid.*, p. 281.

36. His *Vite de' piu eccellenti pittori, scultori, e architettori, etc.* (1st edition 1550, 2nd edition 1568) was the first and most important treatise on the history of art, comprising both a series of biographies and an overall perspective.

37. Professor A. Chastel calls attention to the important rôle of court ceremonies, increasing in number particularly under the last of the Valois, and reaching extraordinary brilliance under Henry III. These associated dancing, music, *tableaux vivants*, and poetry in spectacles illustrating fabular themes supplied by poets and humanists.

38. The great extension of the domed mosque—that is the mosque on a central plan—derived from the Byzantine prototype, coincides with the revival of the central plan in the monastic churches of the Renaissance in the West, in particular in St Peter's in Rome. (André Chastel).

39. R. C. Majumdar, H. C. Raychaudhuri, and Kalikinkar Datta, *An Advanced History of India* (London, 1950), p. 417.

40. René Grousset, *The Civilization of India* (New York, 1931), p. 360.

41. Ishwari Prasad, *A Short History of Muslim Rule in India* (Indian Press, Ltd., Allahabad, 1939), p. 530.

42. Professor A. Chastel points out that Rembrandt had been attracted, as Delacroix was to be in Morocco, by the exotic profiles and rich costumes of the figures in Mogul paintings. Mainly miniatures, these were small gouache drawings, based on elegance of outline and charm of costumes and animal coats.

In this context, they may be compared to the most delicate phase of miniature painting in the West about 1400, then also a precious and courtly art, sensitively fresh in tone and exploiting a rich animal repertory. The interest shown by Hindu princes and connoisseurs in engraving stems from similar affinities.

It should not be forgotten that engraving was one of the great vehicles of artistic 'zoology' and of princely portraiture.

43. Quoted by Ishwari Prasad, *op. cit.*, p. 534.

44. See K. A. Nilakanta Sastri, *A History of South India* (London, 1955), pp. 462–63.

45. Professor A. Chastel suggests that in the evolution of Indian art, it is possible to distinguish cycles and recurrences comparable to those encountered in the West.

See Benjamin Rowland, *The Art and Architecture of India* (London, 1953), p. 2020.

46. For Professor A. Chastel the dominant characteristic of these compositions is the accumulation of figures disposed in varying sizes and according to geometrical formulas, which gives them an emblematic and ritual aspect resulting in an art which is popular in character.

47. Rowland, *op. cit.*, p. 253.

48. *Ibid.*

49. Grousset, pp. 341–43.

50. Professor A. Chastel wonders how far the faithful reproduction of 'traditional' plans corresponds to a deep appreciation of the symbolic value of these compositions, as well as of their essentially ritual role. The buildings seem to correspond to the diversity of provinces, seasons, and functions.

51. Professor A. Chastel stresses that most of the buildings are shown in relation to ceremonial considerations: a long, terraced route dominates broad vistas of pathways; a monumental stairway bordered with ornamental balustrades leads to a portico sheltering the ceremonial throne itself in the form of an edifice.

52. Professor A. Chastel writes: 'Thanks to one of those Jesuits leaving a subsequently well-known description of China, we know that it is the "rococo" models characteristic of princely dwellings in the West which were used in Pekin.'

53. In Professor A. Chastel's view China also presents a parallel with the renaissance of classical forms in the West. A series of concerted 'revivals' of the formulas of past centuries associated with the prestige of great styles and of great legends, a certain snobbish regard for painting considered as one of the noble professions, a taste for 'collecting', the appearance of theoretical compendiums are all phenomena comparable with those observed in France or in Italy during the seventeenth and eighteenth centuries.

54. Tao-chi's *Hua yü lu*, quoted in Lawrence Sickman and Alexander Soper, *The Art and Architecture of China* (London, 1956), p. 201.

55. See R. L. Hobson, 'Pottery and Porcelain', *The Romance of Chinese Art* (New York, 1929), p. 129.

56. R. L. Hobson, *Chinese Pottery and Porcelain* (London, 1915), II, 247.

57. See H. Baumann and D. Westermann, *Les Peuples et les Civilisations de l'Afrique*, trans. by L. Homburger (Paris, 1946), pp. 349–352; Paul Wingert, *The Sculpture of Negro Africa* (New York, 1950), pp. 35–36; and Dietrich Westermann, 'Cultural History of Negro Africa', *Journal of World History*, III (1957), 991.

58. See D. Angulo Iñiguez, 'Caracteristicas generales en el arte hispano-americano', *Journal of World History*, IV (1957), p. 59–82.

59. *Ibid.*

60. The workshops of Zurbaran or Murillo thus came, in practice, to work for export. (André Chastel).

61. Professor A. Chastel points out that thus the formulas for the 'ideal city' which, with the exception of few fortified towns, remained in the West as unfulfilled urbanistic dreams were occasionally actually put into effect in the New World. (See above pp. 689–90.)

CHAPTER XIII

SCIENCE AND TECHNOLOGY BETWEEN
c. 1300 AND *c*. 1530

GENERAL CHARACTERISTICS

Some of the technological implications of art, music, architecture, printing, and other forms of cultural activity have been presented in the chapters above (especially Chapter XII).[1] We have already had occasion to see that Renaissance figures—Michelangelo is an apt example—might in some instances combine painting and sculpture with architecture and engineering. Leonardo de Vinci engaged in similar artistic and technological enterprises and was a man of letters and of science besides. In the several chapters that follow we shall be more expressly concerned with the inter-relations of technology and scientific investigation.

Before 1300, the level of Christendom's scientific and technological achievements in many respects was lower than that of the great civilizations of China, India, and the Islamic world. In those civilizations science had flourished during the so-called 'Dark Ages' of the West. As early as the sixth century, however, Aristotelian rationalism had gained respect in certain Christian circles, and western Europe's contacts with the Muslims in Spain were reflected from the tenth century on in a rising interest in Islamic science, itself largely dependent upon Aristotle.

For Western science, the so-called 'twelfth-century Renaissance' was in some ways more meaningful than the later revival of Classical Antiquity in Italy. In the earlier renaissance not only Aristotle's writings on logic, general science, and metaphysics, but also Galen's medical works were translated from Arabic, freeing the bolder scholars from the 'halter' (to use the figure of a contemporary, Adelard of Bath) of clerical authority by means of the new rationalism that they learned from the Greeks through the Arabs. When the commentaries on Aristotle by Averroes became available to western Europe, they further freed the inquiring mind of the twelfth and thirteenth centuries from that 'halter', but only to make Aristotelianism itself a rarely questioned authority. Aristotelian Scholasticism, nevertheless, was to help a Western spirit of rational investigation slowly to emerge. Despite the subtleties and unrealities of the Scholastic method, its long reliance on inward logic en-couraged analytical and deductive thinking, for continual disputations—in the faculties of letters perhaps more critical than in the faculties of theology—sharpened the dialectical powers and led eventually to the examination of the very processes of reasoning.

Some universities became centres of the new scientific ideas and methods. Efforts at suppression may have delayed the acceptance of new ideas to some extent, but suppression also roused curiosity, interest, and inquiry. Moderate conservatives preferred to fight fire with fire; Thomas Aquinas and his teacher, Albertus Magnus, accepted the scientific subject matter and methods of Classical and Islamic writers, rationalizing them into the framework of orthodox Scholastic theology. Since Aquinas's complete orthodoxy was taken for granted—at least during his lifetime—it was possible for him and his followers to reason on matters of scientific detail with comparatively little interference. Albertus Magnus's casual references to his own fixed habit of checking the assertions of 'the Ancients', 'Aristotle', and 'living philosophers' by personal investigation, and his high evaluation of 'experience, the best teacher', and of natural science, which he defined as 'the investigation of causes in natural phenomena', illustrate that the new trend was well begun before 1300—certainly earlier than Roger Bacon (1214–94), who flourished a half century after Albert.

The roots of scientific thinking, observation, and experiment in the West thus lay in deeper soil than Roger Bacon's much publicized and perhaps overvalued innovations in scientific method. Bacon did not claim for himself the epoch-making significance that has been assigned to him by some modern admirers. He appears to have most enthusiastically and effectively expounded the achievements and methods of his predecessors and contemporaries and to have been no less praiseworthy for his work as an encyclopedist, propagandist, and popularizer of their experimental undertakings than for his own original research. He hoped their results would be improved upon by their successors and produce the marvels that he prophesied. His enthusiasm and voluminous writings, even his quarrelsomeness, served to focus attention on the experimental method as never before and to speed its acceptance in scientific circles.

In short, before 1300 the West had cautiously begun to modify the subject matter of its science and at times to use some modern scientific methods. Inquiry into the truth, to be sure, still was likely to be deductive, starting with points of theological dogma, but when reason was found to conflict with authority, the Scholastics now appealed also to Aristotelian logic, and some might even add the voice of experience, careful observation, and occasionally experimentation. Furthermore, these methods might now be applied not only to the traditional problems of Christian theology but also to the new subject matter derived from acquaintance with Classical and Muslim lore. The medieval revival of science thus had already begun to accelerate the broadening of the Western mind, and thus the 'renascence' of the fourteenth and fifteenth centuries, for all its recovery of lost texts and its new interpretations of some long known, did not constitute a resurgence *de novo* of the science of Classical Antiquity. Much of the scientific knowledge of the Ancients had been available before that era, though not necessarily put to the best scientific use.

Science continued, in fact, for a long time on its thirteenth-century foundation with little basic modification. In Italy for about two centuries, science received much less attention than Classical literature. In the north theological interests still monopolized the energies of Scholastic thinkers. A curve of Western achievement in basic science would show a sharp upward ascent in the twelfth and thirteenth centuries, largely due to the absorption of Islamic knowledge, which would then level off for the two ensuing centuries; an upward swing (this time essentially independent) would not again be very noticeable until the sixteenth century. During this scientific interregnum, steadier progress was made in the applied sciences by artists, architects, miners, anatomists, navigators, and craft and industrial technicians than in the realm of abstract science.

The Scientific 'Plateau' of the Fourteenth and Fifteenth Centuries

Having caught up with other advanced cultures in science around 1300, why did not the West immediately make the great scientific strides that it later showed itself capable of making? Several explanations of the centuries-long plateau between the absorption of oriental knowledge and an independent Western science are possible, though perhaps not wholly satisfactory either separately or collectively. For one thing, the great appeal of Classical art and literature distracted some, although certainly not all, of the best minds of western Europe, especially Italy, from pure science. Renaissance humanism did not always cultivate the respect for new and independent research that characterizes scientific thinking. Although the humanists often rejected the inhibiting authority of the church, many of them substituted for it the authority of Antiquity. For another thing, Scholasticism persisted in scholarly circles during these centuries, fixing learned men's attention upon theological discussion and esoteric logical exercise and making them somewhat indifferent to scientific activity. Scholastic theology, even though its appeal was waning, retained a firm grip and prevented men of science, for the most part still quite orthodox, from welcoming innovations of theory or method. Consequently they worked over the old problems (e.g. realism versus nominalism) with results that, generally speaking, were useful but not startling (see Chapter VI).

The 'cake of custom' provided still another possible explanation of the long delay after 1300 in the arrival of 'the scientific revolution'. With saving exceptions, the scholarly world preferred, on the whole, to speculate rather than to experiment, to work with the brain alone rather than with eyes and hands as well, to pay little regard to the objective reality of their premises so long as their syllogisms were rigorously logical. In that way they continued their debates with the customary reliance on divine authority and Aristotelian reason, where generally prestige was sure and careers were safe, but failed to exploit the possibilities of observation of and experimentation with natural phenomena, where troublesome doubts, disapproval, and even danger might lurk. The more venturesome and active spirits often preferred to seek new geographical rather than new scientific frontiers. Nevertheless, the accumulation of new knowledge and debates about the old in art, literature, theology, logic, and geography were among the special circumstances that permitted Western science, once it had caught up, to surpass the science of other cultures rapidly (see Chapter XIV).

The troubled spirit induced in the scientific mind of the later Middle Ages by theological considerations was in a way well exemplified by the career of William of Ockham. He was convinced of the inadequacy of human reason to answer the eternal questions (see Chapter VI), thus contributing to mystic faith (for the devout) or to doubt (for the sceptical) rather than to the encouragement of objective experimental science. Nevertheless, his own interest in scientific speculation (see below) and his brilliant argumentative skill set a high standard for the university men who followed him. Later medieval science was distinguished by a number of men whom we have already discussed as philosophers (see Chapter VI). Among them was the brilliant group at Paris in the fourteenth century that included Buridan, Oresme, and Albert of Saxony. In their commentaries on some of Aristotle's scientific works, they paved the way for subsequent elucidation of certain scientific principles. For example, Buridan's revolutionary ideas on motion (that is, the theory of impetus which we shall soon describe) had an indirect influence on subsequent Italian physicists, including Galileo, and pointed the way to modern dynamics; Oresme, struggling to pierce the veil of superficial phenomena and find the meaning of ultimate reality (for example, in his explanation of impetus in the spheres), advanced a lengthy astronomical tradition; and Albert of Saxony's studies of trajectory inspired Da Vinci's thinking on certain problems of physics.

For all that, pure science in the West remained, in the fourteenth and fifteenth centuries, inextricably interwoven with theology, almost but not quite to the same degree as in the Far East and in Muslim lands. In the East, during those centuries and beyond, science had lost its former vitality, for no distinction had yet successfully been made between science and other forms of knowledge, and therefore all knowledge was subordinated to God and related to theology. In the West, on practical levels at least, the church-approved ideology was cracking under the impact of urban secularization and the conflicts of popes and ecumenical councils, and so technology and applied science, as long as they worked, were relatively unrestricted. On pedagogic levels, still dominated by the clergy, scientific knowledge remained hard to separate from theology. Since the ultimate source of knowledge is God, the conservative-minded asked, is not knowledge indivisible, like the seamless robe of Christ? A broad-minded churchman like Nicholas of Cusa found a solution for the logical impasse in a mystical 'wisdom of ignorance'. Even in the mundane atmosphere of Renaissance Italy, men such as Pomponazzi had to resort to the subterfuge of 'double truth', Christian and philosophical, in order to avoid punishment (see Chapter VI).

Neither theological nor humanistic subtleties seemed to resolve wholly the apparent conflict between revealed ('Christian') truth and scientific ('philosophical') method. Thirteenth-century Scholastics succeeded in reconciling Aristotelianism with orthodox Christianity, but some of their successors, finding reconciliation more difficult, either muffled their orthodoxy and courted a brand of heresy, as did Nicholas d'Autrecourt, or repudiated Aristotelianism and embraced an intuitive mysticism, as did Eckhart and Suso (see Chapter VI). Fifteenth-century humanists, having re-discovered Plato, succeeded in reconciling Neoplatonism with Renaissance intellectualism but were less successful with science and rank-and-file Christianity. Nevertheless, amid the several competing isms, science, under the mothering of technological, industrial, and military necessity, resorted from time to time to practical experimentation and in an increasingly secular world was able to make steady progress. Thus the three centuries between the two great Bacons were noteworthy for advances in technological practice and applied science more than in abstract science, and for the decline of the Aristotelian system of thought more than for the rise of a new scientific method.[2]

Inadequacies of Scientific Methods and Equipment

In Chapter VI we traced the changes during the fourteenth and fifteenth centuries in the dominant theories of knowledge. The major change was that the Thomists' reliance on reason as a buttress of faith was reversed at the hands of the Ockhamist nominalists, and Ockhamism was hailed as a new system of logic. Yet its attack on the validity of human reason was concerned with theological method and did not help scientific thinking directly. Even the keenly analytical Oresme failed to work out a systematic scientific theory. Although he rejected superstition and searched for reasonable explanations of natural phenomena, he was primarily a vigilant critic within the Ockhamist school, denying the validity of universal terms or propositions if applied to specific things and hence claiming that general truths must be accepted on faith. The same can be said of his contemporary Buridan.

Nicholas of Cusa in one way at least seemed more capable of modern experimental procedure. He had been educated at Deventer and the University of Padua. Padua was perhaps the most advanced intellectual centre of the fifteenth century, and by the sixteenth century its university was to eclipse every other in scientific achievement, becoming so well known that Shakespeare referred to Padua as the 'nursery of arts', where one went to 'institute a course of learning and ingenious studies' (*Taming of the Shrew*, Act I, Scene I). Well versed in mathematics, astronomy, and physics, Nicholas placed a reliance on mensuration in experimentation that was remarkable for his day; in *De Staticis Experimentis* he proposed a method of determining the weights of the materials involved, for example, in investigating the role of water and earth in the growing of plants. Few scientists were to regard experimentation as equally basic in scientific investigations until Leonardo da Vinci a century later.

In that regard Cusa was a forerunner of the modern empirical scientist. In addition, however, he had a wide-ranging Platonic spirit that led him to speculate upon the significance of the entire universe. His breath-taking concept of a plurality of worlds of which the Earth was not the supreme centre and in which each world pursued its own course was so far beyond the comprehension of most of his contemporaries that it might perhaps never have reached posterity had it not been adopted over a century later by Bruno. Cusa's zeal for experiment, however, did not induce him to try to prove or disprove this lofty concept by empirical data. Exalted by the wonders of his universe, which 'is not infinite, yet cannot be conceived as finite',[3] he was representative of the medieval metaphysician. His advocacy of the experimental method got lost in the partly speculative, partly mystical wonderment over divine magnificence which was characteristic of the science of his day.

In short, those who dealt with the subject matter of science in the fourteenth and fifteenth centuries failed to create an effective laboratory method. Abstract science, or what passed for it, went one way, mostly by speculation outside of laboratories, and empirical knowledge went another, mostly among the crafts and professions and the seekers after the occult. In this period we shall find few daring experimenters, few promising germs of later discoveries, few engaging expositions of important problems, and few striking examples of the assaying of scientific evidence. The rapidity with which the new science was accepted even among the learned can easily be exaggerated.

Such acceptance as science received was largely a result, but also to some extent a cause, of the changing technology and the growing secular spirit. Science, technology, and secularism continually reacted one upon the other. In the thirteenth century, a number of technological inventions laid the foundations for subsequent improvements. Among them were spectacles, mechanical clocks, and more effective war engines, not to mention proposals for machines of perpetual motion. By the fourteenth century people were being portrayed wearing eyeglasses, cast iron was gradually replacing bronze, and mechanical clocks—with weight-driven wheels and oscillating escapement—were being constructed in increasing numbers and improved quality. In 1352 the first of three famous astronomical clocks was set up (at Strasbourg Cathedral), to be followed by an improved model about 1574. The key to accuracy in keeping time, the pendulum, was known to the Muslims and in the West in the fifteenth century, though not yet applied to clocks. Small house clocks did not become common until the sixteenth century, and pocket watches only a century later. The pendulum for clocks was to be developed only in the seventeenth century (see Chapter XIV). The urban mind, usually being the source or at least the witness of these wonders, became somewhat disposed to accept innovation if it actually worked—that is, innovation in applied science if not yet in basic science. Yet the age 1300–1500 falls short of substained progress even in technology and applied science, especially in the fifteenth century.[4]

MATHEMATICS IN EUROPE

Before 1200 the Hindus and the Muslims were generally ahead of the Europeans in mathematical knowledge, as in several other scientific achievements. Whereas, however, men like Bháscara (b. 1114) marked a twilight, however brilliant, of development farther east, in Europe men like Leonardo Fibonacci of Pisa (fl. 1225) marked a dawn. Thereafter, in western Europe all fields of mathematics rose above their ancient levels. It has been suggested that while all contemporary civilized communities for the most part conformed to a fairly common pattern about 1200, after that time the West, freed from the unsettlement of 'barbarian invasions', began to diverge from the others, and one of the reasons for this divergence was that Western thinkers proved more ready to think in abstract generalizations.[5] Perhaps no systematic form of thought is more abstract or generalized than mathematics, even if, as the science of numbers, it is also a tool of precise knowledge and detailed measurement.

In the twelfth and thirteenth centuries western Europe began to use the Hindu–Arabic system of numerals. This system was at first primarily employed as a major aid to progress in Western commercial arithmetic. Until the cumbersome Greek, Roman, or Hebrew letter symbols were replaced by the zero-decimal symbols, mensuration and computation could rarely proceed faster than finger action on different kinds of abacuses. Fast and accurate though this method might be in the hands of an expert, it had definite limitations. It was frequently based on counting by fives (as befitted a five-fingered animal) in a sexagesimal system. Whether the Hindus invented the zero-decimal system and passed it on to the Muslims or both peoples worked it out independently and simultaneously, the arithmetic based upon it became known in the West in the tenth century as *algorism*, from the name of al-Khwārizmī, who had expounded the new method of calculation to the ninth-century Muslim world, using the term 'Hindi' to designate it (see Volume III).

In the thirteenth century western Europe witnessed the beginning of a three-hundred-year war of words between die-hard abacists and devout 'algorists', as the proponents of the new Hindu–Arabic numerical system and arithmetic were called. A few encouraging signs indicated, nevertheless, that a scientific theory of numbers was slowly emerging. For one thing, by 1300 western Europe had known the Hindu–Arabic tools for a long time, though it had just begun to apply them.

The mathematical heritage of medieval Europe included, besides, a mass of Classical and Islamic treatises, mostly in Latin translations. While Greco-Roman methods of numeration eventually gave way to the Hindu–Arabic system, Classical influences continued to dominate the study of geometry, the investigation of magnitudes such as lines, surfaces, and solids in space. Euclid's name remained virtually a synonym for geometry until the late nineteenth century. In both Islam and Christendom before 1300, commentaries on Euclid were numerous, but the West had begun seriously to study Euclidian geometry only during the twelfth century, about three centuries later than the Muslims. Within another century, Westerners were writing their own geometrical treatises but were still relying heavily on Euclid. A pace or so behind geometry went trigonometry, the measurement of the sides and angles of triangles. The older trigonometric work of Greeks, Indians, and Arabs had been systematized in the thirteenth century by Naṣīr-al-Din Ṭūsī, and from the Muslims it passed to Europe. Another field of mathematics, algebra, was, as its Arabic name indicates, an Islamic contribution, and from the twelfth century Latin translations made available to Westerners the achievements of the Muslims in that field, too. By 1300 Western mathematical research included the solving of such advanced problems as quadratic and cube roots, recurrent series of numbers, divisors and multiples of perfect or 'abundant' numbers, and linear and quadratic equations.[6]

While the scientific achievement of the fourteenth and fifteenth centuries seems generally disappointing in comparison with that of the preceding centuries, in mathematics some sporadic, localized advances were made. Even though Renaissance classicism diverted some of the best minds and the most exalted patronage to literature and the arts, the accompanying growth of the local languages led to the publication of explanations of the Hindu–Arabic numerals and the 'new arithmetic' in the vernacular. These publications for obvious reasons had no great popular impact, but among the learned in the universities they gradually achieved greater success. Progress was especially noteworthy at the recently founded (1264) Merton College of Oxford, sometimes referred to as the earliest school of mathematics in the West. In the fourteenth century, Johann von Gmunden was the first of several eminent mathematicians to make the University of Vienna likewise famous in this field. Meanwhile, at Paris Jean de Murs became illustrious for his mathematical as well as his musical writings. Both Johann von Gmunden and Jean de Murs used decimal fractions in combination with the common sexagesimal ones in equations for extracting square roots. By the fifteenth century algorism was accepted rather widely in scientific circles, and Hindu–Arabic numbers had come into common use also in merchants' ledgers. As late as 1482, at least one Medici merchant still employed the awkward Roman numerals, but by 1494 all the Medici account books were kept in Arabic numerals.

The versatility of the scholars of those centuries is astonishing. Many of them touched on several branches of mathematics and often, in addition, on astronomy, physics, and medicine, and the number of physicians who were also philosophers and scientists is striking, although only rarely was their work of critical significance and some of them were charlatans. While, for the sake of clarity, we shall deal with their achievements in these respective branches of learning separately, they themselves did not necessarily make the same distinctions among the specialists or compartmentalize their work in the same way as modern scientists are prone to do. Scholars of high renown in several fields were found nearly everywhere in western Europe, with the possible exception of Spain, where scholarship, after Raymond Lull died (1314) and until the sixteenth century, was unimpressive.

In fourteenth-century England specialists at Merton took the lead in mathematical work. Shortly after 1300 John Mauduith, a fellow at Merton College, published tables of trigonometry. His treatise *Super Quattuor Tabulis Mirabiliter Inventis in Civitate Oxon, MCCCX*, inspired the writing by a later Oxonian, Richard Wallingford, of the *Quadripartitum*, which laid the foundation for Western trigonometry. Another Merton-trained scholar, Thomas Bradwardine, who later became archbishop of Canterbury, examined favourably the arithmetic of the tradition laid down by the sixth-century Roman philosopher Boethius and also wrote on geometry, both plane and solid.

France's reputation in science during the fourteenth century rested chiefly on Oresme, Pierre d'Ailly, and Buridan, who comprised a scholarly trio probably unmatched anywhere in contemporary Christendom. Of this trio Buridan was perhaps the most original logician and physicist; Oresme was the most illustrious mathematician and was eminent in other fields, such as astronomy, as well. Oresme was much interested in graphs and worked out a process which to a degree corresponds to that of coordinates. He wrote on arithmetic, contributing, in connection with his study of motion, particularly celestial motion, some important ideas that led to the use of fractional exponents. A century after Oresme, Nicolas Chuquet in *Tryparty en la science de nombres* (1484) introduced expressions like *million* and *billion* (up to *nonillion*), though he gave them values nowhere accepted today. He also suggested the modern exponential system. The painful growth of a universally accepted vocabulary and set of symbols was only gradually to remove a serious impediment to mathematical progress.

Germany produced several mathematicians of note in the fourteenth and fifteenth centuries. The astronomer John of Saxony (1323–61) adopted the Alfonsine Tables of the stars (c. 1252) to the meridian of Paris and improved the reckoning of time. Nicholas of Cusa was Germany's leading scientist of this period. We have already mentioned his methods of weighing materials in order to obtain mathematically accurate checks on certain of his experiments. For Cusa, as for Oresme, breadth of interests perhaps made impossible the sort of concentration that achievement in specialized fields generally requires. Later in the same century, Regiomontanus (Johann Müller, 1436–76), pupil and associate of Georg Purbach (1423–61) at the University of Vienna, not only contributed to the fame of that university, recently become a mathematical centre, but also brought to fruition certain of the earlier Oxford ideas on trigonometry. Regiomontanus' *De Triangulis* marked the birth of trigonometry as a distinct science related to both mathematics and astronomy. It also furnished a good example of intercultural exchange; it was, in part at least, based upon earlier works, one of which seems to have been a Latin translation of a treatise on religions by the Avignonese Hebrew Levi ben Gerson,[7] who presented, among other things, a summary of the astronomy known to the Arabs. Johann Widmann (*c.* 1489) added to mathematics symbols (+ and −) that eventually simplified the process of addition and subtraction, though he did not himself use them in the modern fashion.

Italy's achievements in mathematics before 1500 did not quite live up to its earlier promise. In the fourteenth century Dominicus de Clavasio wrote a popular treatise on geometry and trigonometry and numerous practical works on commercial arithmetic. Lucas Pacioli's *Summa de Arithmetica* (1494) was one of the first comprehensive presentations of arithmetic, algebra, and trigonometry. He used the term *million* and *cero* (*zero*) with their modern connotation but still used other terms like *billion* and *trillion* to designate far larger numbers than are now designated by such terms.

THE PHYSICAL SCIENCES IN EUROPE

Astrology and the Birth of Astronomy

Throughout medieval times astronomy was closely related to mathematics, which provided its working tools, and with astrology, which provided astronomers with a livelihood. Astrologers were in great demand not only by laymen but also by physicians and other professional men. During the twelfth and thirteenth centuries, while striking development was taking place in the West in arithmetic, algebra, and geometry, Western astronomical ideas were likewise undergoing change through the triumph of Ptolemy's astronomical views over Aristotle's.

Until the middle of the thirteenth century most Scholastics had held to the Aristotelian cosmography, which pictured a finite universe with the earth at its centre, surrounded successively and concentrically by a layer of air, a layer of fire, seven revolving spheres (one for each of the known planets), an eighth sphere of fixed stars, and a ninth occupied by God, the prime mover of all. The theory expounded in Ptolemy's much translated and discussed *Almagest* differed from Aristotle's principally in its effort to explain those movements of the planets which were apparently irregular. It posited a system of eccentric circular orbits and epicycles as opposed to the Aristotelian system of concentric layers and spheres, though both assumed a finite universe. Ptolemy's explanation seemed to suit the apparent course of the heavens better than Aristotle's, and by the end of the thirteenth century, the Ptolemaic cosmology and astronomy was ascendant in the West. In the late thirteenth and early fourteenth century Aristotelian science was widely under attack, and these attacks contributed further to the contemporary triumph of Ptolemaic over Aristotelian cosmography and astronomy.

Although not essential to the Ptolemaic ideology, another error was adopted by Ptolemaists as well as other astronomers. It will bear repeating that that error was not that the Earth was flat; throughout the Middle Ages, whatever lay opinion might have been, the sphericity of the earth was taken for granted by astronomers. On another question, however, confusion continued. In the ninth century a Muslim astronomer Thābit ibn-Qurra had revived the erroneous Hellenistic idea that the accumulative lagging of the solar year behind the sidereal year, known as 'the procession of the equinoxes', was to be explained by an oscillation of the highest spheres, and this theory of the variation in the size of the precessions of the equinoxes was transmitted to the West by the twelfth-century Spanish Muslim Al-Bitruji (or Alpetrajius).

Medieval astronomy, in short, involved the Aristotelian view of the physical cosmos and the Ptolemaic hypothesis of planetary motion. It was based on the idea of perfect motion of the heavenly bodies, which were themselves perfect and unchangeable, and of imperfect motion of the sublunary bodies, which were subject to corruption and decay. Obviously, in such a universe one set of physical laws regulated terrestrial bodies and another celestial bodies. Aristotelian physics and Ptolemaic epicycles and eccentrics, however, only lamely explained the apparently irregular motions of the heavenly bodies; the medieval astronomer was constrained to posit a system involving eighty wheels, all operating in crystalline spheres—which was sometimes an awkward postulate. In addition, the assumptions that the Earth was immovable and that the universe was finite and thus closed, though not beyond question by a few, were long accepted by most thinkers.

Despite the errors in underlying assumptions, the West, following Islamic precedents, had in recent centuries introduced some improved observational methods in astronomy. Since the eleventh century, the astrolabe had been used in viewing lunar eclipses. The eleventh-century 'Toledo Tables' of celestial data, a Muslim achievement, were superseded two centuries later by the 'Alfonsine Tables', which, in a Latin version, were much used in the West during the succeeding century and were finally made available in print in 1483. The 'Alfonsine Tables' were, to be sure, more important as tokens of royal and scholarly interest in practical astronomy than of progress in science. Yet by 1300, both scholarly and popular curiosity over the order of the universe was keen. Dante's *Banquet* and *Divine Comedy* vividly reflect the general public interest, and there had been stored up an accumulation of knowledge that in several regards was on the right track.

For all that, scholars, with few exceptions, still relied on astrology. The widespread concern with the stars prevailed not only because of idle curiosity regarding everyday phenomena or justifiable alarm over startling astronomical events, and not only because of the need to fix the calendar and to compute the movable feasts. If the Earth and all thereon were surrounded by circling spheres, the outermost of which was the home of the moving Spirit, the Prime Cause, of the universe, the movements of the stars must affect and might reveal the future of life on the Earth, which was the centre of the entire system; the heavenly bodies must radiate an ethereal fluid and other substances or influences that helped to shape human destinies, and the position of the celestial bodies at any given moment would therefore be of the utmost significance in determining human affairs. Hence the twelve signs of the zodiac (i.e. the fanciful figures that symbolize the changing position of the sun in relation to the planets) were considered to be an excellent means of forecasting one's future. The casting of horoscopes was a common practice not only at a child's birth but also for more widely important events, and 'experts' made a profitable business of it. Physicians relied on medical astrology, including the age-old belief in 'critical days' for bloodletting and other treatments.

The recurring terrors of the Black Death undoubtedly accentuated the trend, and the revival of Classical Antiquity provided no cure for it. Popes and princes had their official astrologers. Professors in the universities accepted astrology, even exploited it. When Lorenzo de' Medici established a university at Pisa, the demand of the students persuaded him to set up a professorship of astrology. One humanist, Pico della Mirandola, raised his voice against the current practice, but contemporaries, even his fellow-Platonist Ficino, generally defended it.

Astrology nevertheless had other critics as well. Petrarch and John of Vicenza, a Dominican monk, both roundly condemned the practice as fraud, and Petrarch also condemned as charlatans physicians who relied on astrologers. Churchmen often were hostile to astrology. Augustinus Triumphus of Ancona, a contemporary of Dante, denounced it and other occult practices as weapons of the enemies of the Christian faith and warned Pope Clement V against them. Despite their faults in other regards, the Avignon popes opposed superstitions of this sort and gave serious attention to calendar reform. In France Oresme, Ailly, and Buridan, all good churchmen, condemned astrology, as did their German disciple Heinrich von Langenstein. In the sixteenth century Guicciardini attacked it on grounds of common sense, pointing out that in the public eye a single correct guess by an astrologer justified a hundred errors on his part, whereas a non-astrologer was discredited by a single error among a hundred correct guesses. Despite such denunciations, astrology has retained a certain hold on the popular mind to this day.

As in other fields of science, after 1300 progress in astronomy seemed for a long time almost to level off. Dante's cosmography accurately reflects the general understanding, not only for his own generation but also for the ensuing century or more. His was a geocentric Earth surrounded by heavenly spheres and containing various nether regions. During the fourteenth and fifteenth centuries no serious criticism of the Ptolemaic cosmology and astronomy arose in Europe, although otherwise the age was noted for its keen attacks on Aristotelian science and although during the same period the Islamic world was subjecting the Ptolemaic theory to modifications.

No ground was lost, however, and indeed some progress was recorded. For example, demand for calendar reform recurred. In the year 1318 a scheme for a perpetual calendar was proposed to Pope John XXII. Yet not until Regiomontanus's attempt (c. 1474) was any noteworthy effort made to change the calendar, and it was frustrated (see Chapter XV). Also, new catalogues of stars were compiled. The 'Alfonsine Tables' were supplemented and corrected for local meridians by careful observations made and recorded in several scientific centres of the West, greatly increasing the accuracy of astronomy and navigation. Weather records were kept over a period of seven years (1337–44) by an English priest, William Morley, who also wrote a treatise on weather forecasting, based, to be sure, on Classical works and everyday lore but presented in a remarkably objective fashion.

Advances in the study of astronomy were largely dependent upon improvements in observational instruments. Instrument makers of the Middle Ages, especially in Islamic lands, had worked out noteworthy refinements in the astrolabe—a full-circle, graduated instrument for sighting the sun, moon, or stars. (Pl. 86.) From this was developed the quadrant—a quarter-circle instrument. Muslims of the fourteenth and fifteenth centuries wrote about variants on the quadrant, among them the 'universal quadrant', the sine-quadrant, and the 'datur quadrant', which was a full-circle astrolabe with one quadrant delineated in precise detail. The term 'sextant'—one sixth of a full circle—is generally restricted to a later instrument of greater precision, used by Tycho Brahe and his seventeenth-century successors.

Prior to the sixteenth century the West generally followed in the path of the superior Muslim scientists. In southern France early in the fourteenth century, however, Levi ben Gerson invented the 'cross staff'—sometimes attributed to Regiomontanus. This instrument consisted of a long, graduated, nearly horizontal staff with a shorter perpendicular crosspiece, which was movable. The observer adjusted the crosspiece until he could sight the horizon beyond the lower end and the desired heavenly body beyond the upper end. During the fifteenth century the astrolabe, the quadrant, and the cross-staff were in common use by Western mariners.

Noteworthy astronomical speculation (without much resort to instruments) was carried on at Paris by Oresme and Ailly in the fourteenth century. Oresme, generally considered the more brilliant of the two, had some potentially fruitful ideas concerning planetary motions and the plurality of worlds,[8] but his respect for the Bible and perhaps his multifarious interests kept him from following them through. He also did much to spread existing astronomical ideas by translating into the French vernacular (with a commentary) Aristotle's treatise *On the Heavens and the Earth* (under the title *Le Livre du Ciel et du Monde*) and by writing a treatise on the subject in French (*On the*

Sphere). In these works he cast doubt on Aristotle's view that the idea of a plurality of worlds must be erroneous. Whereas Oreme tended to criticize Ptolemaic astronomy, Ailly popularized it.

It is sometimes thought that Oresme, and later Albert of Saxony, derived their ideas concerning the rotation of the earth from Buridan. Buridan was familiar with both Ptolemaic and Aristotelian astronomy and questioned the validity of some of his great predecessors' theories, notably the Ptolemaic system of eccentric spheres and epicycles. His most noteworthy achievement, however, was his application of terrestrial mechanics to celestial bodies. He expressed the idea, novel for its day, that although the initial notion of all bodies had indeed come originally from God, it had continued thereafter without any additional miraculous intervention.[9] Speculations on this theory continued over two centuries, and it was further elaborated by Tartaglia, Galileo, Kepler, and Newton (see Chapter XIV).

Parisian scientific influences were spread to Vienna by Albert of Saxony and Heinrich von Langenstein. Both men, after studying and teaching at Paris, had gone to the newly founded University of Vienna. There Albert continued to investigate the problems of mechanics that Buridan had posed. Like most of the Parisian astronomers, Albert inclined toward Ptolemy, though with modifications. Langenstein's rational bent not only made him a bitter opponent of astrology but also led him to experiment in various scientific fields. He was responsible for the establishment of an astronomical observatory at Vienna. In the fifteenth century Purbach, after an impressive career as royal astronomer in Hungary, continued this scientific activity at the University of Vienna, whose reputation in the sciences now eclipsed that of Paris, where decline had set in.

Purbach's pupil Regiomontanus carried this scientific spirit to Germany. He built perhaps the best equipped astronomical observatory of the age at Nuremberg and also set up a printing press from which he published astronomical works and improved calendars. The Florentine cosmographer Paolo de Pozzo Toscanelli (1397–1482) had already observed the phenomenon in 1456 later to be known as Halley's Comet (see Chapter XIV), and Regiomontanus himself made some careful observations of the Great Comet of 1472. From the available data he was able to lay the basis for a modern astronomy of comets.

All of the Paris-inspired astronomers accepted Ptolemy to a greater or lesser extent but were troubled by the inconsistencies of the Ptolemaic system. As observatories like those at Vienna and Nuremberg accumulated factual data, scholars pondered over the conflict between observed fact and tradition as well as between Ptolemy and Aristotle. When young Nicolas Copernicus (1473–1543) went to Italy to study at Bologna and Padua, he encountered a lengthy background of speculation on the motion of the Earth. Questioning of the Aristotelian–Ptolemaic cosmography since the twelfth century, along with the concomitant progress in mathematics and astronomy, had encouraged doubts in the minds of several scientists. A partly heliostatic theory had found some adherents since the fourth century BC, when Heraclides of Pontus had suggested that some of the planets revolved around the sun. Copernicus added to the solar satellites the remaining planets, including the Earth, in 'a great orbit around the Sun, which is the centre of the world'. The full implications of this hypothesis and its detailed complications were not to be worked out completely until Newton's day (see Chapter XIV).

The Attack upon Aristotelian Physics

In the twelfth and thirteenth centuries, as Greek scientific works became available to the West in Latin translations of Arabic translations of the original Greek, a veritable renaissance of physics, comparable to that of mathematics, began. In physics, the authority of Aristotle was not eclipsed by some other authority as it was in astronomy. In expurgated editions Aristotle's *Physics*, along with the *Metaphysics*, by the third quarter of the thirteenth century was widely used and, in fact, became assignments at the University of Paris, the unexpurgated materialism of Averroes replacing Aristotle as the forbidden reading. Thus Robert Grosseteste, Roger Bacon, William of Auvergne, Albertus Magnus, and Thomas Aquinas had had no qualms about using some of Aristotle's ideas.

Thirteenth-century Christendom was well provided also with other Classical and Muslim works of physics. Ancient Greek thought about light and vision was well summed up in Euclid's *Optics*. The Greeks knew that a ray of light travels in a straight line, that it takes the shortest path from its source via a mirror to the eye, and that the angles of its incidence and reflection are equal. Euclid and Ptolemy had thought that light emanated from the eye, and not until the eleventh century did the Arab scientist Alhazen (Ibn al-Haitham) present the idea that the form of the object perceived passes from the object into the eye and is transmuted by the ocular lens. Alhazen's *Treasury of Optics* remained until the seventeenth century the basic work on light and optics. Of somewhat less influence was William of Moerbeke's translation (*c.* 1260) from Greek into Latin of Hero's *Catoptrica* (mistakenly attributed to Ptolemy), with its theory concerning light rays.

Roger Bacon (d. 1294) had been one of the most original thinker-experimenters in physics in the Europe of his day. His experiments with lenses and mirrors, however, had little immediate influence, and his writings on optics (largely based on Muslim findings) were less often consulted than those of now more obscure contemporaries. More general and still less influential for contemporaries were his theories of mechanics and of the practical application of theoretical science. Ramon Lull (d. 1315), in his several works on physics, mathematics, medicine, and navigation, also helped to transmit Islamic erudition to the West.

Until the fifteenth century the study of mechanics advanced little beyond

Archimedes, and the Aristotelian theory of mechanics remained relatively intact. That theory posited that all terrestrial objects (made up of the four elements—earth, water, air, and fire) had a 'natural' tendency to move towards or away from the centre of the universe, which was considered to be the centre of the earth; any other motion was 'violent' motion. Motion was dependent upon a mover; God was the cause of motion, the Unmoved Mover. An object was assumed to move only so long as it was in contact with a 'mover', and without variation of force its motion was assumed to be uniform and without acceleration. All objects were regarded as inherently light or heavy by nature, tending to fall with a speed varying in accordance with their relative mass. The so-called Merton Theorem of Uniform Acceleration, set forth about 1330 at Merton College, held that a uniform acceleration could be measured in terms of its medial, or mid-point, velocity, but, although a free fall was recognized as a pat example of uniform acceleration, it was still believed that bodies of different masses, if dropped from the same height at the same moment, would fall to the ground at different velocities, the heavier mass reaching the ground first.

The development of an anti-Aristotelian physics after 1300 was closely related to the nominalists' attack on the Aristotelian Scholasticism of Aquinas and his following (see Chapter VI). Ockham in England and Nicolas d'Autrecourt and Buridan at the University of Paris, taking up the physical problems over which thirteenth-century Franciscans such as Bacon had pondered, raised serious doubts about the fundamental Aristotelian principles underlying them. In his speculations Ockham came close to the modern concept of the tendency of a moving body to keep moving, and Autrecourt inferred an atomistic theory of matter, space, and motion that was Epicurean rather than Aristotelian. Buridan, adopting the anti-Aristotelian, Classical theories which Jordanus Nemorarius had revived a century earlier, further developed the idea of *impetus*—i.e. of a motive quantity imparted to a mass by a propelling force, much as a quantity of heat might be imparted by a heating source. While Buridan's most daring idea probably was that earthly mechanics could and should be applied to celestial bodies, perhaps the best example of his speculative acumen is found in his explanation of the motion of a terrestrial object thrown by hand. The capacity to receive impetus, he reasoned, would be proportional to the density and volume (i.e. the quantity of *materia prima*) of the projectile; that was why a stone could be thrown farther than a feather. The impetus of any projected object, however, would gradually be diminished by air resistance and the object's own gravity, which inclines it to move in a different direction. He explained the acceleration of falling bodies by positing an increase in impetus impressed by its own gravity.[10] Buridan thus altered the Aristotelian explanation of motion as due to a 'mover' in contact with a mass; for him impetus might be present in a mass without constant contact with its original source. If that was a step toward modern concepts of motion, it still was in one essential different from the Newtonian view of motion as a form of inertia—i.e. as continuing without a cause of motion. The thoroughness and persuasiveness of Buridan's presentation rather than the originality of his ideas (for they were not wholly new) made him influential in the new universities of the West.

Oresme, though primarily a mathematician, also examined problems of physics. While he was more abstract in his thinking than Buridan, he too urged constant analysis and criticism of surface appearances and of generalizations based on inadequate evidence. He presented some concrete ideas on physics in his mathematical treatises and in his commentaries on Aristotle. He pondered the problems of motion, gravity, and impetus, vaguely anticipating the theories of Copernicus and Galileo. He questioned the Aristotelian concept of four elements, suggesting that there might be others (e.g. light and motion) that were more fundamental.

While the nominalists were thus hammering at Aristotelian physics from the speculative and philosophical point of view, other mathematician-physicists were likewise examining the Aristotelian ideas of mechanics. The Merton College mathematician Bradwardine did some significant work in physics. He worked out new explanations (not always accurate) concerning velocity of rotation and resistance to speed. He applied mathematical precision to problems such as infinity and the relative influence of gravity on liquid surfaces at different distances from the earth's centre.

The diminishing but persistent importance of Aristotelian science is well illustrated by the investigation of the cause of rainbows. Theodoric (Dietrich) of Freiburg (d. 1311), a Dominican mystic, philosopher, and physicist, derived much of his treatise on light, colours, and rainbows from Aristotle and Averroes, but his theory of rainbows reveals a high quality of independent research and reasoning. Earlier Western physicists had studied the rainbow and had suggested an explanation of it based on refraction and reflection, but none of them had worked out so convincing an explanation as Theodoric. Late in the thirteenth century a Persian, Qutb al-Dīn Shīrāzī, had pursued the problem along similar lines and with similar results as those later obtained by Theodoric, but Shīrāzī's conclusions probably had not yet been transmitted to the West. Thus a similar theory was doubtless hit upon independently by both Western and Islamic scientists.

Theodoric began by summarizing the data drawn from Aristotle's *Meteorology* (through early commentaries thereon) and Ibn al-Haitham's *Optics*, but he was not content to rest there. He went on to formulate some novel conclusions, using results obtained by his own experiments on the refraction of light. His explanation of the primary rainbow invoked a double refraction of the sun's rays in drops of water and a single reflection. For a second rainbow, he invoked a second reflection, dimmer than the first. His explanation was generally accepted in western Europe, and was amplified by Descartes, without basic modifications until the Newtonian era (see Chapter XIV). Theodoric used Aristotle as a good but not the sole source of scientific theory.

Less theoretical problems than those of motion and light, of course, engaged the physicist's attention. From an early date magnetism and electricity had fascinated man, although understanding of their properties was meagre. Lightning was a familiar phenomenon, and the properties of lodestones were often referred to in both Greek and Latin literature. The Chinese are supposed to have long known that a freely suspended magnet will point north and south, but only around the year 1100 did this fact become known in the West. About that time magnetic compasses were first mentioned in Europe, but in the thirteenth and fourteenth centuries the compass needle and its properties were much discussed by Lull among others, and increased use of the compass brought on more numerous and safer voyages from the Mediterranean to the English Channel and more shipping in the wintertime in the Mediterranean itself. By the end of the fifteenth century the magnetic declination of the compass needle was better understood, largely because of Columbus's observations, raising the problem of properly determining the variations of the compass and giving hope that the solution of that problem might help to fix longitudes at sea. In the same century the dip or inclination to the horizontal of a freely suspended magnetized needle was observed, opening up yet another prospect of solving the problem of longitude at sea (see Chapter XIV).

Alchemy and the Birth of Chemistry

The development of chemistry during the intervening centuries, less like physics and mathematics but more like astronomy, was complicated by magical and religious considerations. Thirteenth-century alchemy, like astrology, was deeply rooted in Babylonian, Egyptian, and Greek lore, which had come to the West largely by way of Islamic writings. Scientists everywhere usually assumed with Aristotle that the basic chemical elements were earth, air, fire, and water, and delved into the relationship of these elements to one another and to the supposed primal matter ('substance' or 'essence') of all material things. Islamic alchemical treatises held that the six major metals, though of the same essence, were correctly arranged in an ascending scale—tin, lead, iron, copper, silver, and gold. Man's natural inquisitiveness joined with his natural acquisitiveness to suggest that the commoner metals might be transmuted into the more precious ones if only the right 'tincture' (philosopher's stone or elixir) and the right method of purifying the baser metals were discovered. The proper combination of the 'principles' of sulphur and mercury (as expounded by the eighth-century Muslim alchemist Jābir ibn Hayyān) was considered decisive in this process.

Popes and princes were no less wholehearted in their support of this science than of astrology. Islamic alchemical ideas were translated into Latin by twelfth- and thirteenth-century scholars, and along with Aristotle's *Meteorology*, they were known to Albertus Magnus, Roger Bacon, and other thirteenth-century scientists. Although Albertus, Bacon, Lull, and some other Christian scholars were not convinced of the essential unity of all matter and had suspicions concerning some alchemists, they were willing to grant the possibility of the transmutation of metals and wrote treatises concerning that and other aspects of alchemy. Bacon sent the pope one of his alchemical works; Michael Scot was encouraged at Emperor Frederick II's court; and the physician Arnaldus de Villa Nova (d. 1313) was patronized by Pope Clement V.

Since alchemy offered lucrative possibilities to the unscrupulous, charlatanry flourished. The church, even the none too squeamish Avignon popes, disapproved of false alchemy. In 1317 Pope John XXII forbade the sort of alchemy that encouraged men to expect to gain riches through the transmutation of metals, and he also condemned other forms of magic. Yet, if no tin was magically transmuted into gold, primitive chemistry served some constructive purposes. Alongside the charlatanry, a well-intentioned, empirical chemical technique also throve. Knowledge of the properties of alcohol, acids, and alloys accumulated, and chemical apparatus improved. Even before a well-based chemical method had begun to develop (sixteenth century), the metal-refiner, the physician, the brewer, the soap manufacturer, and other technicians hit upon chemical ways and means that brought improvements in pigments, glass making, smelting, tanning, paper manufacture (from rags), pharmaceutical compounds, gunpowder, and other chemical processes and products. An unproductive but no less interesting experiment was that of the English physician John of Gaddesden, who attempted to distil fresh water from sea water.

The continuing doubts about the authorship of several alchemical treatises produced in western Europe reflects the sometimes clandestine, 'hermetical' nature of their work. Some of them were ascribed erroneously, or perhaps with deliberate effort to deceive, to authors of high standing. A few of the best were attributed to the great Jābir (called in Europe Geber) but perhaps were written by a European no earlier than the thirteenth century. In the early fourteenth century an Italian named Pietro Buono compiled from various Classical and Islamic sources a work entitled *The Precious Pearl*, a massive, encyclopedic collection on the subject of alchemy. Writings ascribed to Arnaldus de Villa Nova and Raimon Lull were also often cited by later alchemists. During the first half of the century the Catalonian John of Rupescissa manifested an interest in medical alchemy, considering the philosopher's elixir important for the prevention of internal corruption. He wrote a treatise on the quintessences, part of which was arranged under medical headings. Later fourteenth-century works by an otherwise unidentifiable Frenchman called Ortolanus, by the Englishman John Dombelay, and by the German Wimandus Rothschild, though not of impressive quality, give some indication of the quantity of alchemical compilations. In the fifteenth century appeared a plethora of treatises, most of which were inferior compilations of earlier materials, with descriptions of vain experiments with the transmutation of metals. Occasional condemnations of all professional alchemists indiscriminately as charlatans indicate the wide prevalence of their practices.

THE BIOLOGICAL SCIENCES IN EUROPE

Early Botany, Physiology, and Medicine

Biological knowledge can be divided roughly into that of plant life (botany), of animal life (zoology), and of human life (physiology and anatomy). During the period with which we are here concerned (1300–1530) these fields were not sciences either as systematically organized bodies of knowledge or as sets of laws based upon observed regularities. While menageries, aviaries, and botanical gardens had been made available in several Western centres by rulers and wealthy noblemen, the relevant data were chiefly derived directly or indirectly from Aristotle's treatises and certain other Classical and Islamic works.

By 1300 scholars of both the Islamic lands and Christian Europe had access to a considerable number of treatises on the various aspects of biology. Pliny's *Natural History*, with its detailed information on minerals, animals, and related matters had been immensely popular in the West throughout the Middle Ages. Various works of Aristotle on animals and other naturalia had been translated during the thirteenth century from Arabic into Latin, and a new translation of his *Historia Animalium* had been made directly from the Greek by William of Moerbeke. Botany was based largely on Dioscorides' *Materia Medica* (first century AD). Western Scholastics, notably Albertus Magnus, had written excellent treatises on various aspects of biology, revealing therein not only a wide knowledge of the earlier literature on the subject but also a keenly critical attitude toward their sources. Such studies should not, though they easily can, be lost to view amid the more numerous and popular but less admirable illustrated bestiaries.

In Europe as elsewhere botanical investigation was largely motivated by a quest for pharmaceutical herbs. In this connection, Westerners relied not only on Dioscorides (in abbreviated and alphabetized versions) but more often on a condensed medical botany attributed to Apuleius Platonicus (*c.* 400 AD), which sometimes was accompanied by an equally unimpressive book on animals and their uses for medicine attributed to Sextus Placitus Papiriensis (*c.* AD 400). The sections on plants (usually with shorter ones on minerals and animals) were similarly condensed in several thirteenth-century encyclopedias. One of the most noteworthy of the herbals still largely in use in 1300 was that of the thirteenth-century Rufinus. It was a compendium of herbal lore from Dioscorides, other non-Islamic Latin sources, and perhaps, in small part, the author's own observations.[11] A surprising amount of the available knowledge was found in alphabetically arranged medical or pharmaceutical manuscripts. One such alphabetical listing, notable for its quality and influence, was the *Synonyma Medicinae*, a dictionary of about six hundred items (chiefly herbs), compiled by Dr Simon of Genoa about 1300 from late Classical and Islamic sources.

The gradual increase of naturalism in contemporary art was reflected in the rich, even lavish miniatures with which, from about 1300 on, an increasing number not only of religious but also of secular manuscripts were illustrated. In Europe during the fourteenth and fifteenth centuries illustrated compendia both of general natural history and of specific fields became more common. Conrad of Megenberg's *Buch der Natur* (*c.* 1350) was a vernacular translation of a thirteenth-century encyclopedia. Matthaeus Sylvaticus' *Pandectae* of materia medica treated botanical items more intensively than previous compilations. Thomas of Breslau produced a herbal based to a certain extent on his own observations. Benedetto Rinio's album contained almost five hundred naturalistic illustrations of plants; the original manuscript is today one of the treasures of the Library of San Marco in his native city, Venice.

Late medieval manuscripts contain occasional illustrated treatises also on both the anatomy and the optics of sight. Available evidence points to late-thirteenth-century Italy—Pisa or Florence—as the setting for the invention of eyeglasses as distinct from single-lens reading or burning glasses; no valid ground exists for attributing it to Roger Bacon. That spectacles were common during the fourteenth century is evidenced by mention of them by several contemporaries including Guy de Chauliac and Petrarch. Furthermore, a mid-century portrait of a cardinal at Trevise depicts him wearing glasses. Until the beginning of the sixteenth century it seems that most spectacles consisted of convex lenses. Later in the same century concave lenses, for shortsightedness, were developed along with other minor mechanical improvements. Progress was slow, but soon spectacles were being manufactured in the Netherlands as well as in northern Italy.[12]

Until well into modern times physicians were torn between the humoral tradition of the Hippocratics and the 'specifics' tradition of the rival Cnidians. The authority of Hippocrates and Galen supported the humoralist doctrines, and throughout Ancient and medieval times the most widely accepted theories of physiology were derived from their ideas of the four qualities and the four humors. The qualities were hot, cold, dry, and moist, and the humors were blood, phlegm, yellow bile, and black bile. Health was believed to be brought about by the proper interaction of the humors and the qualities, and illness by a lack of balance among them. Medical treatments (bleeding, for example) were designed to redress an unbalanced condition.

Supporters of the 'specifics' tradition held that different kinds of disease might have different causes, basing their argument on the fact that certain 'specifics' were effective in only certain cases. A 'doctrine of signatures' was clearly propounded by Paracelsus (see Chapter XIV) but was traceable to older naturalists like Pliny and Dioscorides. It held that certain plants and minerals were marked by some sign or trait suggesting a particular medicinal use—thus leading to the naming of certain plants—e.g. the pulmonaria, or lungwart. Not, however, until the discovery of cinchona as a 'specific' for malaria—during the seventeenth century—did the 'specifics' tradition begin to be predominant.[13]

Plague, it was assumed, had to have a more general explanation than either of these schools could give. The Black Death in the fourteenth century and, centuries later, the plague of 1665 were attributed variously to the wrath of God, vapours carried in the air, and astrological phenomena. Oresme in the fourteenth century attempted to explain illness in quasi-chemical terms, though still mixed with magic and mysticism, and Paracelsus and some other physicians of the sixteenth century initiated iatrochemistry, or chemiatrics, attributing disease to chemical disarrangements in the body and attempting cures through chemical prescriptions, but these iatrochemists wrought little change in the persistent humoral pathology of their times. Nor did they greatly advance the practice of medicine. Blood-letting continued as a major treatment for disease, in accordance with the theory that the body must be purged of noxious matter. Methods of blood-letting varied, and several are illustrated in contemporary manuscripts and books:[14] (1) puncturing a vein at a specific point for a specific ailment; (2) cupping—i.e. drawing the blood by the application of a heated cup so as to provide suction as the air within it cooled and contracted, and (3) placing leeches on the skin.

Some Early Advances in Biological Research

In contrast, the progress of anatomical investigation in the West during the early fourteenth century was impressive. Salernitan surgeons, though obliged to restrict dissection to pigs, had engaged in anatomical research by that method as early as the eleventh century. Two centuries later dissection of human bodies was formally permitted in certain universities, notably Bologna and Montpellier; the much misinterpreted bull of Pope Boniface VIII (1299) was not intended to prohibit anatomical dissection but rather the cutting-up and boiling of bodies for other reasons. In any event, by the beginning of the fourteenth century the science of internal anatomy had achieved marked advances through dissection, with the result that Italy led the West in the field of anatomy, and despite Ibn-al-Nafīs' significant work of the previous century the West now led the Islamic countries. Surgeons such as Mondino da' Luzzi and Gentile de Foligno were among the many Italian pioneers in this field. Mondino's *Anatomy* (1316) has been called (perhaps too favourably) 'the first modern work' on that subject. The amazing achievements of his contemporaries Lanfranc and Mondeville will claim our attention when we come to discuss the practice of surgery (Chapter XV). As in some of the other fields of science, comparison with the remarkable advances of the thirteenth and the early fourteenth century, particularly in anatomy, makes it appear as if the biological sciences made little advance, though they held their own, for about two centuries thereafter.

The anatomical sketches of Jacopo Berengaria Da Carpi (*c.* 1460–1530) and of Da Vinci and Vesalius' admirably illustrated *Seven Books on the Structure of the Human Body* were to mark a new era of constant progress in the science of anatomy (see Chapter XIV). (Pl. 93b, c.) The rapid expansion of printing and illustration was a significant factor in that progress. New illustrated editions and commentaries on Dioscorides and other ancient authorities on plants, animals, and minerals appeared, and even before 1530 more and more scholars who had made first-hand observations compiled specialized treatises on quadrupeds, fishes, birds, and plants. Some of their works replaced the treatises of Aristotle, Pliny, and Dioscorides as authoritative sources in certain fields of biology.

The independence from the spirit of the past was not always for the best, to be sure, since earlier works of merit, such as Rufinus' herbal, now were neglected and unknown.[15] Nevertheless, much new information was set forth. The enthusiasm of scholars for fresh data led them to observe nature more closely, to exchange first-hand observations with one another, and generally to increase the bounds of their knowledge beyond the manuscript or printed page. Even though many of their treatises were written for the purpose merely of providing encyclopedic minutiae or of making philological contributions, their intensive activity inspired further investigation, including the identification of unfamiliar items and the more accurate description of flora and fauna. The discovery and the colonization of distant lands in Asia and the New World provided knowledge of many strange species besides (see Chapter XV). The zeal for novel information sometimes dulled the edge of critical analysis or meaningful synthesis, permitting inaccurate or meaningless details sometimes to be repeated by successive compilers. Some of the most reputable scholars of the day were credulous of wonders resembling the monsters, miracles, and barnacle-geese usually attributed to the 'Dark Ages'. Nevertheless, they conscientiously gathered together stores of data useful to later scientists.

SCIENCE AND TECHNOLOGY OUTSIDE EUROPE

The technological skill and the scientific knowledge of the Aztecs and Incas that roused the admiration of the conquistadores has been referred to above (see Chapters I and XII). Since it did not, for the most part, enter the stream of world culture, it need not detain us here.

Prior to 1500, except perhaps in anatomy, the accomplishments of Europe were not noticeably more significant than those of other Eurasian cultures, for only after 1500 was Europe to forge rapidly ahead. A fortunate juxtaposition of several series of events favoured the development of western European science and technology. After 1200 western Europe was remarkably free of 'barbarian' intruders, whereas eastern Europe, Africa, and Asia were disrupted by Mongols, Timur and the Timurids, Ottoman Turks, and other invaders, giving Europe a chance to catch up with Muslim learning, acquired particularly through the Spanish Moors; interest in Islamic technology and science (themselves a combination of Greek, Hebrew, Indian, Persian, and Arabic ideas) was reinforced during the Renaissance by the revival of the learning and abstract thought of the Greeks and Romans; the growth of European trade and town life was concomitant and interrelated with the growth of a secular atmosphere and of willingness on the part of educated men to use their hands; and the rise of the spirit of humane learning during the Renaissance coincided with the questioning of traditional authority in the Conciliar Movement and the Reformation and with the increase in the patronage of national enterprise by royal dynasties. This interplay of events helped to provide for the West a set of circumstances that permitted the Renaissance absorption with Classical art and letters to make possible, even to stimulate, the eventual development of an independent scientific frame of mind and an experimental method among the learned few and the relatively rapid acceptance of technological and scientific innovation among the less learned many. In contrast, with notable exceptions, both the learned and the populace in other great centres of civilization remained bound to their traditional cultures and, when confronted with either home-grown or imported achievements, tended as a general rule to look upon innovation as undesirable or even dangerous. Yet, despite their preference for the ways of their ancestors and their unfavourable attitude toward originality, these more conservative cultures accomplished some scientific work of distinction.

Islamic Science and Technology

For several centuries after 1300, western Europe and the Middle East went their separate scientific ways, becoming more independent of and indifferent to each other's findings than before. If the work being done in Europe was barely known in Islamic lands, that of Islamic scientists seems to have been equally unknown in Europe. The probable unfamiliarity with Shīrāzī's optics in the West (and vice versa) has already been mentioned; his scientific methods led him not only to depart from Aristotle in optics but, in addition, to consider the possibility of the earth's rotation. A fourteenth-century Persian alchemist, al-Kāshani, produced an able study of ceramic chemistry (dealing especially with the manufacture of faience ware), which was not equalled in the West until the sixteenth century. Of similarly high quality were the treatises of the Egyptian al-Jildaki, likewise unknown to Westerners.

Outstanding scientific and technological achievements, however, were few during the fourteenth and fifteenth centuries in Islamic lands, and scholarly interests other than in grammar, religion, and administration generally found no great encouragement. If natural science still attracted creative men like those mentioned above in the generations around 1300, it was mostly as an intellectual luxury. Much of that luxury was devoted in the 1300's to the continuation of Muslim scholarship in biology, particularly in Egypt and Spain. Ibn-al-Khatīb and Ibn-Khātima of Spain corresponded on such matters as the Black Death and produced skilful analyses of it. The Egyptian scholar Al-Damīrī's late-fourteenth-century compendium on animal life described, in alphabetical order, over a thousand animals. More popular than scholarly and exemplifying the failure to develop a true science of zoology, it was nevertheless comparable to earlier compendia. In both Egypt and Spain of the early fourteenth century, books on horses appeared, and in Egypt an excellent presentation of veterinary medicine was written by Ibn-al-Mundhir, master of the royal stables. Egypt also maintained, though less eminently, its remarkable tradition of achievement in the physiology and surgery of the human eye.

A little was done during this period in Islamic lands also to further the science of astronomy. The most notable of those responsible for that little were the circle of astronomers around Prince Ulūgh Beg (1394–1449) in Samarkand. Qāḍīzāde-i Rūmī became director of an elaborate observatory, built there in 1428, which produced significantly improved astronomical data. He wrote extensive theoretical studies, and several members of his staff, notably 'Alī Qūshjī (d. 1474), were, like him, independent mathematical thinkers.

Another scientific advance came in the growing knowledge of geography. We shall speak of the contributions in the fourteenth century of such scholars as Ibn-Baṭṭūta and Ibn-Khaldūn in the next section, where the major theme is the growing knowledge of the Mediterranean and Atlantic areas. In the fifteenth century Muslim navigation made significant additions to the knowledge of the geography of the Indian Ocean as well. Like their Christian confreres in the Mediterranean, Muslim sea-captains in the Indian Ocean improved their detailed knowledge of the coasts, but not until the Turkish navigators of the fifteenth century did their observations succeed in breaking down the Ptolemaic conceptions of that ocean's contours. The new knowledge was embodied in the treatises and charts of two sea-captains in particular. One of them, Aḥmad Ibn-Mājid, who wrote about 1489, combined the fruits of extensive personal experience with the whole geographical and astronomical culture of medieval Islam. He served as pilot across the Indian Ocean to Da Gama (see below), and the early Portuguese sea-guides show a close relationship to his work. The other, Al-Mahrī, who wrote about 1511, had a more extensive knowledge of the Malaysian area than Ibn-Mājid.

In the burgeoning Ottoman state, Sultan Mehmet II (1430–81) encouraged the transformation of what had been intellectually a frontier area into an eager centre of medical and mathematical study by favouring the immigration of learned Persians. In his time, scholars were able to insist, by joint action, on considerable academic freedom; yet the scientific tradition went deep only in a handful of men. 'Alī Qūshjī migrated from Samarkand to Anatolia and founded the fruitful astronomical tradition of Ulūgh Beg in the Ottoman state. A fine observatory in that tradition was kept going by Luṭfī Toqadi (executed for heresy in 1494 despite the protests of many savants) and Mīrim

Chelebi (a descendent of 'Alī Qushjī, d. 1525). Turkish admirals took up the geographical work of the fifteenth-century Arabs—particularly Pīrī Re'īs, who wrote in 1513 and 1523 careful studies of the Mediterranean coasts, freely introducing West-European findings, including data derived from the discoveries of Columbus.

For all of this list of illustrious names, by the 1300's Islamic natural science had already reached its pinnacle and had also ceased to be an actively fertilizing element abroad, whether in China or in the West. For the two centuries considered in this chapter the course of Islamic science paralleled that of the West: although the preceding scientific level was maintained, relatively little was done to advance it. After 1300 geography as a general basic discipline advanced little in Islamic lands. On the other hand, government administration motivated a fact-finding trend toward particulars. The *Tables of Countries*, compiled by a Syrian prince named Abu-al-Fidā about 1320, is typical of the period. He described the various countries of the known world in the usual manner, listing the chief cities and locating them by their coordinates. Early in the fourteenth century, the Mamlūk ruler of Egypt ordered a survey of the soil, income, taxes, and other conditions of every village in Egypt. The Ottoman administrators at the height of the empire kept careful statistical records of population and the like.

Indian Science and Scholarship

The major Indian contributions to science and scholarship likewise were made before our period, but some work of considerable merit still went on. Competent studies in lexicography, grammar, and logic continued up to the beginning of the eighteenth century. Important Sanskrit dictionaries were produced in the fourteenth century, and Sanskrit grammars of scholarly value until 1700. Grammars and dictionaries of Tamil, Telugu, Kanarese, and other vernacular languages appeared throughout the period. Indian astronomy and mathematics were expounded in Sanskrit works during the early part of our period, while Sanskrit treatises on mathematics were translated into various vernaculars. The significant astronomical tables of Makaranda came out about 1478, and astronomical works by Ganesha as late as 1520, but the traditional system of Hindu mathematics and astronomy changed little and was essentially unaffected by Arabic and Persian writings. Descriptive works of genuine significance in biology—on plants and horses, elephants, and other animals—were written until the seventeenth century. Despite several works on nosology, including that of plant diseases, Hindu medicine in many particulars remained similar to that of the ancient Greeks and showed no marked advance. The celebrated medical treatises by Tisata in the fourteenth century, Bhāva Mishra in the sixteenth, and Lolimbarāja in the seventeenth were essentially expositions or expansions of earlier classics. A great Indian dictionary of materia medica, the *Madanavino-danighantu* by

Madanapāla, was completed about 1374. Indian anatomy suffered, as did anatomy almost everywhere, from the absence of dissection.

Chinese Science and Technology

In 1300, China was probably as far advanced in the field of science and practical technology as any other country. The Mongol conquests and policy had brought scientists and technicians to China from all parts of the world. The magnetic compass was familiar and was used for navigational purposes. Block-printing had long been in use, and movable type had also developed, although extensive use of it came only in Korea in the early fifteenth century. Gunpowder had long been known and was used not only for fireworks but also for bombs and the propelling of missiles. Chinese (as well as Indian and East Indian) shipbuilding was probably further advanced than European. The large seagoing junks were bigger and more seaworthy in many ways than European vessels, although they were slower and less manoeuvrable, and they incorporated compartments in the hold that could be closed off to keep the whole vessel from flooding when the hull was damaged,[16] a system not adopted in Europe until the nineteenth century. Francis Bacon said of printing, gunpowder, and the magnet: 'These three have changed the whole face and state of things throughout the world, the first in literature, the second in warfare, the third in navigation; whence have come innumerable changes; insomuch that no empire, no sect, no star, seems to have exerted greater power and influence in human affairs than these mechanical discoveries.'[17] If he was right, it is to Chinese technology that the world owes this debt.

In addition, Chinese alchemists, potters, doctors, and herbologists had developed extensive knowledge about a wide range of chemicals, drugs, herbs, and plants. Chinese medical and pharmaceutical knowledge was so respected outside China that a famous Persian physician and minister of the Mongol ruler of Persia caused (*c.* 1313) an encyclopedia of Chinese medicine, the *Tanksuq-nāmah-i Ilkhan dar funūn-i 'ulūm-i Khitāi*, to be prepared. It dealt with the pulse, anatomy, embryology, gynecology, pharmacology, and other medical subjects.[18] The arts of distillation and sugar refining, and such products as sorghum, carrots, kidney beans, pistachio, almonds, grape vines, and the drug chaulmoogra oil also seem to have been introduced into China during the Mongol period. A son of the founder of the Ming dynasty, after over eighteen years of careful investigation and with the assistance of a collaborator, completed (1406) a *Herbal for Relief from Famine*. Illustrated with woodcuts, it described the cultivation of types of plant that could be grown or eaten in times of flood and drought.

Chinese knowledge of geometry was probably inferior to that of the Arabic world. Nevertheless, the Chinese had, even before 1300, mastered sufficient mathematics to enable the astronomer and hydraulic engineer Kuo Shou-ching, presumably with the aid of scientists 'and technicians assembled by the Mongols at Cambaluc, to construct (1276-79) probably the finest set of astronomical instruments then known. Of his sixteen instruments several were new inventions, including a sighting tube with equatorial mounting. Some scholars think Kuo discovered for himself the basic principles of spherical trigonometry. In the thirteenth and the early fourteenth century, probably in part through inspiration from Islamic sources, several Chinese mathematicians developed an elaborate theoretical algebra. Pre-eminent among them was Chu Shi-chieh, whose major works appeared in 1299 and 1303. These promising developments were not continued under the Ming dynasty.[19]

Chinese engineering skill was also impressive. Clock-drives operated by water-power, various mechanical devices for raising water, suspension bridges with iron chains, and segmental arch bridges were all known in China by this time. The great atlas of Chu Ssu-pen, compiled between 1311 and 1321, employed the use of squares to plot distances on maps.

The Mongols did not keep up their programme of importing technicians, and once the conquerors were expelled, the Chinese tended to slough off things associated with them. The dominance of Neo-Confucian philosophy in the new Ming regime, with its emphasis on abstract philosophy, moral and ethical conduct, and the past did not provide a climate conducive to the advance of theoretical science. Still, during the period of Mongol decline and the first half-century of expansion under the Mings some technological advances were made in weapons and shipbuilding. Small cannon and a sort of proto-hand-gun seem to have developed, and Chinese ship architecture reached probably its highest level. Big vessels were constructed for the far-reaching voyages of Cheng Ho into the Indian Ocean and to the coast of Africa (1405-31). No technological insufficiency would have kept Chinese navigators from pushing westward around the tip of Africa, thus anticipating Vasco da Gama (though in reverse), had the responsible Confucian administrators or traders considered such distant voyages economically or otherwise worth while.

Chinese medicine was impeded by certain erroneous theories concerning the cause of disease—such as evil spirits or an imbalance between *yin* and *yang*—and the absence of dissection. Even so, it had accumulated and under the Mings continued to accumulate empirical knowledge about diagnosis and the use of drugs, diets, and other remedies. Numerous large general medical treatises and accounts of the symptoms and treatment of specific diseases were written, including works on leprosy, smallpox, syphilis (which first appeared in China about the time of the arrival of the Portuguese), obstetrics, gynecology, eye diseases, and parasitology. Treatises also discussed acupuncture, a method of therapeutics peculiar to China, and medical systems derived from it. Acupuncture—the relief of pain by sticking needles into prescribed points of the body—has been practised for centuries, the punctures being supposed to release a surplus of either *yin* or *yang*. Among the various medical schools competing with one another and engaging in acrimonious debate, the most celebrated physician of the Mongol period was Chu Tan-ch'i (1281–1358), and a famous physician of the early Ming period was Chang Chieh-pin. The former emphasized malnutrition as a basic source of disease; the latter wrote many works, including treatises on the pulse, fevers, midwifery, children's diseases, and smallpox.

Japanese Medicine

During the Ashikaga period Japanese science and medicine were very largely derived from Chinese sources. The writings of Li Tung-yüan (of the Chin period) and Chu Tan-ch'i (of the Mongol period) were especially in vogue (the Li-Chu School). Japanese physicians also wrote numerous treatises on general medicine and the treatment of specific diseases.

THE BEGINNINGS OF WORLD GEOGRAPHY

The thirteenth century had been a golden age for Christian, Muslim, and Far Eastern travellers, and therefore for the accumulation in all civilized lands of geographical data concerning distant regions. The far-flung Mongol empire, especially under enlightened khans such as Kublai, had made possible travel from Europe to and from China by way of the mid-Asiatic land routes. Europeans also might go via the Persian Gulf or the Red Sea to India, the Spice Islands, and as far as China. Chinese travellers, explorers, and scholarly geographers were especially enterprising. Thirteenth-century emissaries from the khans to India, Persia, and the Near East wrote of the 'barbarian peoples' visited—even of certain far regions in the West. During the time that Marco Polo was in China, having voyaged in the opposite direction a Christian Nestorian priest of Chinese birth, Bar Sauma, was sent in 1287 from the khan to the pope to arrange an alliance against the Muslims. He visited Constantinople and Rome and travelled in France and England also. His was not the only embassy exchanged between the khans and the popes, though probably the most interesting one.

The Christian and the Mongol world of the thirteenth century were perhaps better acquainted with each other than with the Muslim Near East. Yet the Chinese knew comparatively little about western Europe and Africa, and the Europeans knew little about China and almost nothing about the other regions of Asia or about Africa south of the Mediterranean coastal countries. Learned men in Muslim and Christian lands had a world view roughly comparable to the Ptolemaic maps, in which little beyond the lands bordering on the Mediterranean Sea and the Indian Ocean was clearly portrayed.

For the generation or two before 1300 geographical knowledge began rapidly to expand. In Europe diplomatic expeditions (e.g. those of Giovanni da Piano di Carpini, William de Rubruquis, Buscarello de Ghizolfi, and Bar Sauma), religious missions (e.g. those of Giovanni di Monte Corvino and Odoric de Pordenone), and commercial ventures (e.g. those of the Polos) contributed immeasurably to interest in and knowledge of the rich and highly cultured peoples of Asia. Meanwhile, seafaring Westerners were renewing the efforts of the Ancients to sail around Africa to the Orient. In the thirteenth century cartography also made great progress. The medieval *mappae mundi* had generally showed only the lands along the central waterways that stretched from the Atlantic through the Mediterranean, the Persian Gulf or the Red Sea, to the Indian Ocean and the Spice Islands. For example, the Hereford *Mappa Mundi* (about 1280) was centred on Jerusalem and showed nothing of detail concerning Mongolia and China. Eventually central and eastern Asia were shown more clearly, though still vaguely, on world maps; and detailed maps, such as those giving itineraries to Italy, Palestine, or England, noticeably improved. Roger Bacon's *Opus Major* contained the only important geographical treatise produced in the West before 1300. Familiar with the Asiatic travel accounts of his contemporaries, he believed that the southern hemisphere was inhabited and that India might possibly be reached by sailing westward.

Islamic geography from the ninth to the fourteenth century was dominated by the work of al-Khwārizmī. Whereas Christian maps of the Middle Ages often were centred on Jerusalem, his Muslim successors represented the universe as a cupola centred on Arin (the corrupted name of Ujjain in India, a major centre of astronomical study). Dictionaries by Muslim traveller-geographers of the thirteenth century were available, describing in alphabetical order cities, mountains, islands, and other features of physical and political geography; and thirteenth-century Persian, Spanish, and other Muslim travellers wrote intelligently of lands as far distant as Mongolia, northern Europe, Iceland, and the Senegal River region in Africa.

Abu 'Abdullāh Mohammed Ibn-Baṭṭūta (1304–78) was in some ways the most astonishing of Muslim travellers. Born in Tangiers, he travelled on several separate voyages as far north as the khanate of the Kipchaks (in modern Russia), as far east as Cambaluc (Peking) and Amoy Harbour, as far south as Timbuktu, and as far west as Spain. Altogether he covered about 75,000 miles and wrote of his experiences with interest and urbanity, giving information about peoples unfamiliar even to the Muslims of the time. His writings, unknown in the West until the nineteenth century, still provide a rare, if not unique, source of information on the peoples of Africa in his day, as well as of some other areas.

Several efforts were made by Muslims, especially in the Mamlūk regions, to collect miscellaneous information concerning local conditions at home and abroad. One of the most important of the theoretical geographical discussions of our period was contained in the history compiled in the late fourteenth century by Ibn-Khaldūn, of Tunis and Egypt. For our present purpose (but see also Chapter VIII) the most interesting part of his vast history is Volume I, *Muqaddamah fit-tarīkh* (*Prolegomena to History*), one chapter of which contains an introductory survey of geography in which he displayed his usual critical acumen. The use of geography as a handmaiden of history and of other subjects was characteristic of Muslim compilers, but Ibn-Khaldūn made far more of it, attempting to base on geography and other natural sciences a remarkable analysis of historical dynamics.

Fourteenth-Century Geographical Ideas in Europe

As missionaries, merchants, and ambassadors extended Europe's religious, commercial, diplomatic, and intellectual frontiers throughout the Near East, across Asia, and into the Far East, they made Asia Minor and the Black Sea into a veritable bridge between Europe and Asia, while the Red Sea, the Persian Gulf, and the Indian Ocean became active seaways to the Far East. The increasing geographical knowledge resulting from the more frequent occidental contacts with the Orient entered many Western encyclopedias in their articles dealing with geography. In his *Imago Mundi*, Ailly presented a sort of encyclopedia, or compendium, of geographical knowledge. It mentioned some little known lands in the Atlantic and indicated that the world was round but gave the impression that it was much smaller and contained less ocean than actually proved to be the case. A copy of it was eventually to come to the attention of Christopher Columbus and to lead him to conclude that Spain was much closer to India than it really was.

The new geographical knowledge was put to use in the travel of pilgrims to the Holy Land (then as now a popular centre of tourism) and in the work of missionaries in Asia. After 1328 the Franciscans, following in the footsteps of Giovanni di Monte Corvino, monopolized the Chinese missions, while the Dominicans were more active in the Near East (see Chapter V). These religious ambassadors, in turn, made possible a more regular and sometimes more reliable flow of information from Asia. Meanwhile a different kind of information came through commercial channels. A descriptive treatise concerning Palestine (accompanied by maps) was written about 1313 by a Venetian named Marino Sanudo, who had spent many years in the Near East. Pietro Vesconte collaborated with Sanudo and eventually moved to Venice, commercial rival of his native Genoa. Shortly thereafter, a Florentine, Francesco Pegalotti, also a long-time resident of the Near East, wrote his *Practica della Mercatura*, an economic geography of the trading world. In 1346 the Genoese created the first company for the exploitation of a colony, a joint-stock company to administer the island of Chios.[20]

For all that, fourteenth-century geographical ideas were still frequently based on second-hand reports and speculation rather than actual exploration. While the best minds accepted the notion of the sphericity of the earth, vast stretches of the globe were *terra incognita*. No one could be certain of what lay across the Atlantic in a westerly direction (for the lore of the few who had already stumbled upon the Western Hemisphere never became common). No European knew that Africa was circumnavigable. By the end of the fourteenth century, Novgorod's trappers and fur traders had amassed a fairly good sum of information about the coasts of the White Sea and the Arctic Ocean and about some Arctic islands, and Russian trappers settled on Spitsbergen as early as the fifteenth century. Nevertheless, although the possibility of a northern sea route to Asia had suggested itself to some of the well-informed, no actual search for it was to be undertaken before the sixteenth century. As a rule, European ships of the 1300's hugged the coasts and except to a few Russian trappers, Irish monks, Viking seafarers, English sailors, and French fishermen, the vast expanse of the uncharted oceans was a barrier rather than a thoroughfare. What was needed, if it was to be penetrated, was not only the development of sturdier ships but also better training in seamanship, better instruments of navigation, and a more systematic acquisition and compilation of nautical and geographical knowledge.

Pre-Columbian Cartography and Explorations

If geographical myopia was still obscuring the finest fourteenth-century vision, a lengthy process of cure had nevertheless begun. Coastal charts (*portolani*) had been produced and used before 1300, but now they were being much improved by Genoese and Venetian cartographers. Pietro Vesconte of Genoa produced the earliest dated (though not the oldest surviving) portolan; it is dated 1311. Later *portolani* by him and other Italians showed more accurate coastal data, corrected old locations, and added new ones for newly explored regions not only along the Mediterranean coasts but also in the Atlantic area and the Far East. The marked advance in the number and dependability of details and in the knowledge of outlying regions was revealed in a new type of book—sheets of maps of limited areas bound together into a *portolani*-atlas. The Laurentian Portolano (or *Medicean Atlas*) of 1351 showed not only the basic Mediterranean lands but also, with relative accuracy, the Atlantic coast from Spain to Scandinavia, the Caspian Sea, the Black Sea, India, and north Africa, including the Nile River. A Catalan map (*c.* 1375) of similar scope gave still more accurate details, notably for the regions of India and 'Cathay', probably on the basis of information provided by Marco Polo and other travellers. A Genoese map of the next century, however, showed little advance in knowledge, and meanwhile some cartographers had reverted to the old arrangement of maps with Jerusalem at the centre. This reversion was due in part to the renewed interest in crusades to check the Turkish advance and recover the Holy Land (see Chapter III).

The making of maps again received a fillip from the translation of Ptolemy's *Geography* into Latin in 1410 and its publication in print in 1475. Not the least among the numerous achievements of Nicolas of Cusa was his cartography of Germany. In the fifteenth century Greenland appeared on a map, and charts were drawn on rectangular projections showing meridians. A map painted by a German cartographer living in Italy, Henricus Martellus, indicated knowledge of Diaz's African voyage of 1488 and showed a location for the island of 'Cipango' (Japan). (Pl. 104a.) A similar chart, by the Florentine Toscanelli, went with Columbus on his first voyage to America. The invention of printing had by that time made printed maps available to geographers and navigators for study and correction. As the Mauro and the Vienna–Klosterneuburg circular maps and the globe of Martin Behaim (1492) reveal, by the end of the century the informed geographer knew vastly more about the world's surface than Ptolemy had known.

The widening of Christendom's horizon after 1300 stimulated curiosity about Africa as well as Asia. Could Asia be reached by sailing around Africa? The interest in 'the Dark Continent' increased in intensity during the fourteenth century. It was expressed chiefly by Genoese seafaring men searching for a sea route to the Far East. About 1300 the Vivaldi brothers were lost at sea in an effort to round the southern cape. Unverifiable legend has it that a later search party reached the east coast of Africa.

The uncertain advance of the Italians induced Frenchmen, Spaniards, and Portuguese as well as Italians to become interested in the Atlantic coast of Africa. In the fourteenth century Europe's leading school of cartographers and navigators was located at Majorca and staffed with Majorcan and Catalan experts. Trade and Christianization seem to have provided sufficiently strong motivation for a few occidentals to penetrate inland via the Niger River. One striking instance was a Frenchman who had lived among the natives along the Niger for eleven years and returned home with a Negro wife, half-caste children, and some Negro servants. But most of the explorers continued to hug the coast, staying away from the interior, and so the islands off northwest Africa were the first to be colonized. The Canaries, rediscovered in 1341 by Genoese sailors in Portuguese employ, were fought over by French, Spanish, and Portuguese forces until 1495, when the Spanish finally won out.

Meanwhile at least one man had understood the need for accumulative, systematic exploration, and he put his tremendous energy and personal fortune behind an attempt to provide it. He was a scholarly, crusading cartographer, the Portuguese prince Don Henrique (who later became known as 'the Navigator' although he himself hardly ever went to sea). He borrowed information and talent from the Majorcan school. Under his direction Portuguese seamen began a step-by-step exploration to the south and southwest of Portugal and added significantly to the development of marine science and navigational technology. Equipped with better ships and marine instruments, the best available astronomical data, and more detailed maps, and trained to exploit their improved knowledge and techniques, Don Henrique's men engaged in a deliberate and methodical effort to discover new lands.

Don Henrique's major purpose is not clear. He was a scholar, a colonizer, and an ardent Christian. At the outset crusading against the Muslims provided perhaps his strongest motive. Eventually he became interested in a sea route to the east, perhaps as an extension of his efforts to get to those African areas with which the Moroccan Arabs traded by land. He also had a desire to find the Christians who under a Prester John were supposed to inhabit one of the several unknown lands somewhere in Africa[21] and might establish a second front against the relentlessly advancing Turks.

In any case, Don Henrique directed the efforts of his captains southward along the coast of Africa. After the conquest of the Muslim port of Ceuta, across the straits from Gibraltar (in 1415), he prosecuted his crusade against the Muslims in northwest Africa. While still contending also for the Canaries against French and Spanish, the Portuguese acquired the Azores (1427–31) and made it a stepping stone for further explorations. Arguin Bay was reached in 1442. By that time a lively trade with the African west coast had developed, engaging a fleet that averaged twenty-five caravels annually. It brought back ivory, gold, salt, tropical plants, oils, spices, exotic animals, and (despite Don Henrique's vigorous objections) slaves. Once Arguin was passed, exploration, conversion, conquest, and exploitation progressed rapidly not only along the Atlantic coast of Africa but also inland and on off-shore islands. The Senegal River was reached also in 1442, and one year later the rounding of Cape Verde crowned thirty years of strenuous effort. Sierra Leone was claimed in 1446, Tangiers in 1471, and Rio del Oro in 1476. The papal bull *Romanus Pontifex* of 1454 discouraged competition from other Iberian princes by giving Portugal a monopoly over African territory.

During the second half of the century, the search for a water route to India was added to the incentives for Don Henrique's driving activity. He lived long enough to see the India project get under way but not to see it completed. By 1460 he had carried the programme of Portuguese conquest far down the African coast and had organized the navigational system that laid the foundation for Portugal's astounding colonial success. His mariners sailed a new type of ship, the three-masted caravel, which had a heavier keel and greater manoeuvrability than the galley still in common use. All the information that they acquired was sifted and transferred to maps and *portolani*, thus forming a systematic store of information for other discoverers trained in Don Henrique's school for seafarers at Sagres (Cape St Vincent). These men made daring use of the cross-staff and the compass. They improved the astrolabe and by careful observation set up and corrected tables giving the solar declinations and the varying altitudes of the polestar.

When Don Henrique died (1460), the Portuguese drive slackened, until (*c.* 1481) King John II caused it to be resumed. Three years later, almost seventy years after Henry's efforts had begun, it reached the Congo estuary. By then the search for a cheap route to India had become the chief stimulus for probing the African coast. In 1487 John sent Pedro de Covilha by the

Cairo–Aden route across northeast Africa and the Red Sea to India, and on the return voyage Covilha, testing the possibilities of reaching the East by the Indian Ocean, reached the Zambesi River on Africa's east coast. Almost at the same time Bartolomew Diaz was blown around the Cape of Good Hope from the west and advanced northward to the seaport now known as Mossel Bay. Africa thus was shown to be circumnavigable, and a sea voyage to the East feasible. Yet it took another ten years to reach India by the route around the southern tip of Africa, and meanwhile the most dramatic events of the entire era of discovery took place.

Columbus, Da Gama and Their Successors

A common belief notwithstanding, European mariners were not impelled to new ventures by the Turkish conquest of Constantinople and the need to counteract the supposed cutting-off of trade between the Mediterranean and the Far East. The fact is that the victorious Turks did not cut off that trade; it passed mostly through Alexandria, not then in Ottoman hands, and since it was profitable for them, too, they preferred to cooperate with the Venetian merchants to exploit it. About 1490, however, the possibility loomed that the Portuguese might find a cheap, all-water route to India, thus short-circuiting the Mediterranean and killing what had become a Turkish–Venetian monopoly. Moreover, the prospects of still another route that would rival the real or potential ones then known held obvious attractions for competitors of Turkey, Venetia, and Portugal.

A Genoese sailor named Christopher Columbus, after much delay, pleading, and frustration, succeeded in persuading Queen Isabella of Castile to finance a scheme for sailing westward to discover new lands in the Atlantic and perhaps an easy route to India. The boldness of his proposal had already frightened off other possible sponsors. No one, at least in southern Europe, really knew what lay west of the Azores, how vast the ocean was, or how much truth there might be in the old fable of a sunken continent Atlantis or in the island of Antilia shown on some maps. No one knew how long a ship would have to sail west until it might reach land, how much food, water, and other provisions would be needed, what winds or currents might prevail, or even what stars could serve for navigation. Probably no one anticipated that the deviation of the compass needle might vary as one moved westward. Among the common sailors all kinds of fantasies prevailed about sea monsters, fatal winds, gigantic eddies, and resistless currents.

Columbus, however, was no ordinary mariner; he was a cartographer and a student of geography as well. He was not exclusively intent on finding a route to the Far East, although that was one of his purposes. He was actuated also by accounts of Atlantic voyages and maps showing islands such as 'Antilia' and the Portuguese discoveries of lands for exploitation and Christianization. The Spanish sovereigns were, furthermore, anxious to match the Portuguese in crusading and missionary colonization. Reaching the Orient by sailing westward seemed possible to Columbus since he knew that the earth was round and since he believed Asia larger and the Atlantic smaller than it was. Some *portolani* and reports of experienced sailors gave evidence of island stopping-places in western waters. Iceland and Greenland were known to be in these waters though far to the North.

Columbus sailed westward for his royal Spanish sponsor in 1492 and returned in 1493 with the belief that he had found a shorter sea-route to the East. For all that, his voyage contributed greatly to the contemporary geographical revolution. It was a first step in the recognition of how large the earth was, and along with later voyages it added new continents to maps and globes. Without realizing that they were not islands of the East, Columbus discovered on this voyage and a series of subsequent ones the Bahamas, Cuba, Haiti, Puerto Rico, and Jamaica, as well as the Orinco coast of South America and the coast of Central America. He had proved that the ocean west of Europe was not an impassable and unknowable barrier but was a finite and navigable waterway. Observations he made on his trips, such as the deviations of the magnetic needle, proved to be of inestimable value to those who followed him.

The rival claims of Spain and Portugal were settled by papal arbitration (1493 and 1494), giving Spain the new lands to the west and Portugal those to the east of a given line (see Chapter I). In 1497, a year after Columbus returned from his second westward voyage without having found more than a few unpromising islands, the Portuguese resumed the eastward search. Vasco da Gama sailed around the Cape of Good Hope and northward along the east African coast, where he picked up the distinguished Arab navigator Ibn-Mājid (see above), who piloted his vessels along the monsoon route until they finally reached the Malabar coast of India. Vasco da Gama was thus the first European to go all the way to India by water. While another, with genius but mistaken assumptions, had happened upon a new western world for his Spanish masters, the Portuguese navigators, with systematic tenacity, actually found the long-sought and cheaper southern route to that region from which Europeans obtained much of their supply of spices, rare gems, precious metals, and other luxuries.

In subsequent years the Portuguese took the lead in exploiting the eastern trade. They established themselves on the coast of India, and under two great viceroys, Almeida and Albuquerque, they began to explore the Moluccas systematically. These islands produced the Malays' greatest treasure for European traders—spices. When some shipwrecked Portuguese landed on the coast of Japan in 1543, Europeans had reached all the glamorous places of the East—Cathay, India, Cipango—places known before chiefly from Arab sources and the travellers of the Mongol era.

When Columbus returned from his fourth and last voyage in 1504, he was still convinced that the islands and the coast of the continent that he had found were the eastern extremities of Asia. He was to die, involved in miserable quarrels with fellow captains and the Spanish authorities, without ever realizing that he had been blocked by an unknown hemisphere. What he had really discovered was a part, though only a small part, of a vast new world. The actual exploration even of its coastlines remained for others.

Other explorers, following in the wakes of Columbus and Da Gama, added to the world's rapidly accumulating cartographical knowledge. Pedro Alvares Cabral, sailing the Portuguese route around Africa, pushed far enough westward into the south Atlantic to sight the Brazilian coast and to claim it for Portugal (1500). Amerigo Vespuci, a Florentine who had accompanied several expeditions, notably along the South American coast, publicized the 'New World' so successfully that in 1507 the name 'America' was adopted by certain European scholars for the area that he now established to be a separate hemisphere. And in 1513 Vasco Nuñez de Balboa glimpsed the Pacific, the biggest of all oceans, on which no European vessel had previously sailed.

These explorations, along with several lesser ones, made obvious that Columbus and Da Gama had reached two separate parts of the world, which most likely were not connected by land with one another, and Europeans began to speculate about the respective location of the two strange regions. A Portuguese seaman, Fernando Magellan, who had served in the Indian Ocean, had there learned about the South Seas (which were the same that Balboa had already seen from the Isthmus of Panama). Upon his return to Europe, he combined his vague knowledge of the South Seas with reports of an east-west passage through the southern tip of South America and became convinced that the Moluccas, the source of fabulous fortunes in spices, could be reached by sailing westward after all. Like Columbus he persuaded the Spanish crown to subsidize his venture. With three ships he set out for South America in 1519, sailed up the Rio de la Plata estuary (mistaking it for his east-west passage), finally found the straits ever since named after him, and despite innumerable hardships managed to cross the vast Pacific. Eventually he reached the Philippines, which he claimed for Spain. He himself was killed there, but one of his captains, Juan Sebastian del Cano, sailed the one remaining ship, appropriately called 'Vittoria', back to Spain by way of the Moluccas and the Cape of Good Hope. For the first time man had completely circumnavigated the Earth, learning the relation of the hemispheres and the oceans to one another and providing an empirical proof of its sphericity.

The belief that Asia could be reached by sailing westward, which underlay the ventures of Columbus and his successors, also played a part in the discovery of northern America and the long search for a northwest passage to India. Although the New World had much earlier been reached by Europeans from Scandinavia using the north Atlantic routes, the knowledge acquired by previous discoverers had no significant influence on the explorations of the fifteenth and sixteenth centuries. Greenland's colony of Norsemen lost contact with Europe in the fifteenth century and disintegrated soon afterward, and nothing but the vaguest rumours about the Viking discoveries seems to have been known to the great explorers of the later period.

Untouched by the Vikings' fate, some of the later explorers set out to find a route to Asia that was not already preempted by the Spanish or the Portuguese. In 1497 another Italian navigator, John Cabot, in the service of King Henry VII left England for a northerly crossing of the Atlantic. He reached shores now known to have been those of Prince Edward Island and Newfoundland, which, sharing Columbus' error, he believed to be islands off the coast of Cathay. On a second voyage he went up the straits between Greenland and Labrador looking in vain for a westward passage until he was finally forced back by icebergs. Subsequently (1534) a French explorer, Jacques Cartier, resumed the northwestward explorations, sailing far up the Saint Lawrence River and south along the Atlantic coast, until he encountered the Spaniards, who were pushing north from Florida. In this and subsequent voyages, though he found no way to the Far East, he discovered more about the North American continent. By then it was generally accepted that none of the new lands belonged to the Asian continent, but the search for a northwest passage to Cathay around North America went on (see Chapter XIV).

The epoch-making voyages of Columbus, Da Gama, Vespucci, Magellan, Cabot, Cartier, and their successors were quickly reflected in geographical writings and cartography. Francesco Berlinghiere's *Geographia*, the first book, so far as is known, for which all the maps (31 in this instance) were copperplate engravings, was printed at Florence in 1482, but the maps were still based on previous 'Ptolemies'.[22] During the sixteenth century, with the new knowledge gained from the explorers, cartographical leadership shifted from Italy to the north, and especially to the Netherlands. Waldseemüller (d. 1521) was the first to picture a large ocean between America and Asia. (Pl. 104b.) Detailed accuracy, however, was conspicuously absent from early-sixteenth-century delineations of the outlying sections and the interiors of the new continents.

Nonetheless, during the hundred years centring roughly upon 1500 western Europe executed a slow geographical about-face. Instead of looking mostly eastward from the Mediterranean it now looked more and more southward and westward from the Atlantic seaboard. Dramatic though the explorations of a Columbus or a Magellan were, the new outlook, the so-called 'geographical revolution', was not a sudden awakening but rather the outcome of a slow cultural development, the culmination of several centuries of empirical observation, scientific experiment, technological ingenuity, critical analysis, and imaginative theorizing, which had themselves been deeply rooted in Classical and medieval, occidental and oriental knowledge and lore.

NOTES TO CHAPTER XIII

1. Dr Bertrand Gille feels that despite the title of this chapter, technology occupies only a very limited place. By better situating the two great technical systems of the period, that established during the second half of the twelfth century, concurrently with the great demographic expansion, and that appearing in the second half of the fifteenth century, the authors might have demonstrated better the links which clearly exist between technology and pure science, as well as the many zones of mutual interference between these two domains of human knowledge.

   The authors, however, reply: 'As the first paragraph of the text of this chapter points out, much that falls under the heading of technology is dealt with in other chapters; to do so again would be repetitious. A contrast of scientific and technological developments before 1300 and around 1500 is attempted below; the second half of the twelfth century comes before the chronological limits of this volume.'

2. Dr Bertrand Gille stresses that the end of the fifteenth and the beginning of the sixteenth century mark a turning point. Having abandoned Aristotle, science henceforward appears as no more than an assemblage of fractionalized problems, whose very isolation from one another perhaps made possible deeper study of certain concepts, though not yet warranting the construction of a new scientific system.

3. *De docta ignorantia*, Bk. II, Ch. II, quoted in Alexandre Koyré *From the Closed World to the Infinite Universe* (Baltimore, 1957), p. 11.

4. See Lynn Thorndike, *A History of Magic and Experimental Science*, IV (New York, 1934), 612–15.

5. See J. M. Romein, 'The Common Human Pattern', *Journal of World History*, IV (1958), 449–63, and J. J. Saunders, 'The Problem of Islamic Decadence', *ibid.*, VII (1963), 701–20.

6. See George Sarton, *Introduction to the History of Science* (3 vols. in 5; Baltimore, 1927–1948) Vol. II, pt. 2, pp. 611–12.

7. A. C. Crombie, *Augustine to Galilee, the History of Science A.D. 400–1600* (London, 1952), pp. 68 and 267, and Sarton, I, 601.

8. It is frequently said that Oresme suspected the *diurnal* rotation of the Earth (see Crombie, pp. 256–57), but see R. Hooykaas, 'Science and Theology in the Middle Ages', *Free University Quarterly* (Amsterdam), III (1957), 121–25. On the possibility of other worlds, see *ibid.*, p. 113 and n. 88.

9. Buridan's *Questiones super Octo Physicorum Libros*, Bk. VIII, Question 12, quoted in Crombie, p. 253.

10. *Ibid.*, pp. 251–53.

11. See *The Herbal of Rufinus*, ed. Lynn Thorndike (Chicago, 1947) and the review of this work by L. C. MacKinney in *Journal of the History of Medicine and Allied Sciences*, II (1947), 138–140.

12. See Edward Rosen, 'The Invention of Eyeglasses', *Journal of the History of Medicine and Allied Sciences*, XI (1956), 13–46 and 183–218.

13. Thorndike, Vol. VIII: *The Seventeenth Century* (1958), p. 366 and Agnes Arber, *Herbals, Their Origin and Evolution, a Chapter in the History of Botany, 1470–1670* (Cambridge, 1938), pp. 250–255. See Richard H. Shryock, 'The Interplay of Social and Internal Factors in Modern Medicine', *Centaurus*, III (1953), 113–15.

14. Before his death L. C. MacKinney had collected about 4000 microfilm frames of miniatures from medical, botanical, anatomical, and bestiary manuscripts.

15. Thorndike, IV, 190–91.

16. J. J. L. Duyvendak, *China's Discovery of Africa*, (London, 1949), p. 18 and Radhakumud Mookerji, *Indian Shipping* (London, 1912), pp. 192–99.

17. *Novum Organum*, Bk. I, Aphorism 129, quoted in Joseph Needham, *Science and Civilization in China*, I (Cambridge, 1954), 19.

18. *Ibid.*, p. 218.

19. *Ibid.*, III (1959), 40–52, esp. 41.

20. See Charles Verlinden, 'Les origines coloniales de la civilisation atlantique, antécédents et types de structure', *Journal of World History*, I (1953), 387 and *Precédénts médiévaux de la colonie en Amérique* (Mexico City, 1954), p. 21.

21. See Armando Cortesão, *The Nautical Chart of 1424* (Coimbra, 1954), esp. pp. 54–56.

22. See 'Rare Books', *Library of Congress Quarterly Journal of Current Acquisitions*, II (1954), 180.

CHAPTER XIV

SCIENCE (c. 1530–c. 1775)

SCIENTIFIC EPISTEMOLOGY AND METHODOLOGY

THE extraordinary advances in basic science that have enriched and radically changed the life of modern man have come for the most part since 1530. To explain this advance as due from the very beginning to a conscious alliance of science with technology would be to read the experience of more recent times into earlier centuries. To begin with, no separate and well-defined fields of endeavour called respectively science and technology existed for most of the period here under consideration. Furthermore, although Galileo's acquaintance with the mechanical arts at the Venetian Arsenal suggests that theoretical ideas sometimes arose from some pattern of experience with empirical techniques and tools and although much of the work of the new scientific academies, we shall soon discover, had practical objectives in view, yet a central fact of the so-called 'scientific revolution' of the seventeenth century was that it was in conspicuous instances carried on by men with a non-utilitarian purpose. Regardless of their sources of knowledge and inspiration, they frequently went in pursuit of truth for and of itself, seeking more satisfactory answers to old theoretical questions, answers whose utility was obscure.

In contrast, modern technology is a rationalized, systematized body of differentiated knowledge directed toward getting things done on a mass basis and is often in close and carefully cultivated alliance with science. In its earlier stages, however, for the most part technology grew independently of scientific theory, and where it did grow out of abstract science, it did so in many cases by later adaptations of scientific principles independently discovered rather than by a deliberate preliminary search for them. The planned and direct alliance of the scientist with the industrialist and the engineer is of comparatively recent development, although the initial stages of it occur in our period of study. In these initial stages alliance was more likely to occur in the less 'academic' fields such as applied physics, industrial chemistry, agriculture, botany, and metallurgy, which had no regular place in university curricula, than in 'academic' fields like astronomy and mathematics, where speculative minds could still obtain satisfying results by abstract reasoning. Some examples of the alliance of science and technology will be mentioned in this chapter, but technological developments will receive greater attention in the next.

The alliance of science and technology, today taken for granted, had to be preceded by a separation of science from speculative philosophy, especially when speculation was based on unexamined and perhaps unrealistic premises. Previous times and other societies had made inquiries into the operations of nature and had systematically observed them, but the idea of a rational science of nature based on controlled observation and experiment, a science that deliberately limited its area of inquiry to the material realm, was essentially unique to the modern West. No longer concerned, at least as scientists, with final cause, modern scientists posit a mechanistic world conforming to natural laws; they do not regard moral or theological considerations as falling within the framework of their science.

This attitude meant, among other things, a shift from a qualitative to a quantitative, or mathematical, picture of the universe. It was well expressed by Galileo Galilei (1546–1642) in his *Il Saggiatore*:

'*I feel myself impelled by the necessity, as soon as I conceive a piece of matter or corporeal substance, of conceiving that in its own nature it is bounded and figured in such and such a figure, that in relation to others it is large or small, that it is in this or that place, in this or that time, that it is in motion or remains at rest, that it touches or does not touch another body, that it is single, few, or many; . . . but that it must be white or red, bitter or sweet, sounding or mute, of a pleasant or unpleasant odour, I do not perceive my mind forced to acknowledge.*'

Galileo's statement assumed a differentiation between primary (essentially measurable) qualities and secondary (essentially esthetic) qualities—that is, between, on the one hand, those that he believed to be in the object observed and quantitative and, on the other, those that he believed to be in the judgment of the observer and qualitative. Such a differentiation did not mean that scientists were not to be interested in esthetic considerations; it meant only that esthetic considerations did not lend themselves to quantitative methods readily, if at all. As Galileo further said:

'*Philosophy is written in that vast book which stands ever open before our eyes, I mean the universe; but it cannot be read until we have learnt the language and become familiar with the characters in which it is written. It is written in mathematical language.*'

In this remark Galileo used the word *philosophy* where we would use the word *science*. Even at the end of his century science was still called philosophy, although generally divided into natural philosophy (science), speculative philosophy, and moral philosophy.

Aristotelian Science Challenged

The work which is traditionally held to mark the opening of the movement commonly referred to as 'the scientific revolution' was *De Revolutionibus*

Orbium Coelestium by Copernicus. Virtually completed in 1530, it was not published until 1543. It put forth an unfamiliar but not wholly unknown system of astronomy, one which itself was not based on observation and experiment but rather on a relatively unsuspected conceptual scheme—a heliostatic and heliocentric theory of the universe. Copernicus's theory went contrary to the Biblical geostatic and geocentric implications; it also raised doubts about the symbolic importance of man as lord of nature and God's chief creature. If Copernicus was right, man would, of course, appear a mere speck in the universe. This argument was not new or strange, for as early as the sixth century the view had been put forth that 'the whole earth compared with the universe is no greater than a point'.[1] The shattering statement in Copernicus' work for a later generation of thinkers was not that the sun stood still and was the centre of the universe but rather that the universe was thousands of times greater than had been supposed. Though he himself seemed to believe in a finite world, he implied, whether he intended to or not, that the material world might be so large as to have no centre at all and, hence, that the universe might be infinite.

Copernicus, a canon of the Frauenburg Cathedral, had no desire to be un-Christian. Nor was Thomas Digges, an English Puritan who was perhaps the first Copernican to depict an infinite universe explicitly, any more ready to propound heresy. In *A Perfit Description of the Caelestiall Orbes* (1576), he nevertheless presented a chart showing the six then known planets of the solar system, which in turn he enclosed within an 'orbe of starres fixed infinitely up'.[2] Digges' work, however, was ignored by contemporaries and became known only in the twentieth century. For Digges the infinite starry orb was still the Christian heaven, where God, the angels, and the elect dwelt "devoyd of greefe and replenished with perfite endless joye."

Giordano Bruno who combined within his own person the qualities of poet and savant, in some ways better illustrates the transition from earlier theology to modern science. Though upset by the undermining of Scholastic rationalism and Ptolemaic cosmology, he could not take refuge, as had Nicholas of Cusa, in 'learned ignorance', since he was not content to accept on faith what was hard for his reason to believe. Nor was his age sufficiently informed in science for him to work out a theory of a mechanistic universe run entirely by natural law. Hence he felt constrained to resort to pantheistic infinity. While doubtless drawing in part upon Cusa, Bruno did not use his predecessor's Christian symbolism in explaining the infinity of the universe but expounded it in a rhapsody of Classical and Old Testament phrases: 'The One Infinite is perfect, in simplicity, of itself, absolutely, nor can aught be greater or better. This is the One Whole God, universal Nature, occupying all space, of whom naught but infinity can give the perfect image or semblance.'[3] He supported his mystical pantheism not only with extensive Scholastic argumentation but also with carefully organized data based on scientific observations. Thus he exemplified the sixteenth-century rebellion against

Scholastic ideology and at the same time the inability of contemporary minds to arrive at a world view by scientific methods alone.

This dilemma underlines the philosophical conflicts of Bruno's day. The supremacy of Aristotelianism had been challenged in science, but no good champion had yet come to take 'the Philosopher's' place. In fact, with the Counter-Reformation Aristotle—made more correctly and more fully available by Renaissance humanists than he had previously been—was widely reinstated in his thirteenth-century primacy in the Roman Catholic study of physics, and, in general, scientific discourse showed little progress beyond the Scholastics. Even those who in the sixteenth century rejected Aristotelianism provided no satisfying substitute for it. Telesio, a bitter critic of Scholasticism and Aristotle's theory of the four fundamental elements (fire, air, earth, and water), attempted to replace it with a theory of two (heavenly heat and earthly cold), which, he taught, could alone, without divine intervention, account for all the modifications of matter, whose quantity was fixed (see Chapter VII). The mystical naturalism of the physicians Paracelsus and Girolamo Cardano or Cardan (1501–76) combined empirical observation in fields like medicine or mathematics with the occult methods of astrology and alchemy in an effort to found a universal scientific system, propounding a kind of self-directed materialism as the explanation of change. Patrizzi and Campanella, better known as the author of the utopian *Civitas Solis*, both were avowed disciples of Telesio, even if Patrizzi doubted that all phenomena could come from heat and cold alone. These men's rationalism was perhaps more empirical and certainly more materialistic than that of their Aristotelian and Neoplatonic contemporaries, but it was hardly more acceptable to the authorities than Bruno's pantheistic naturalism, and the essentially speculative and teleological structure of their theories distinguished their thought no better than his from modern scientific thought.

New Methods and Reasoning in Science

A decisive departure in scientific method had to wait until new approaches (like that of Galileo quoted above) to the nature of thought itself were published (see Chapter VII). Sometimes they were expressed in terms of materialism, as by Hobbes, and sometimes in terms of mechanism, as by Descartes; and questions regarding human understanding furthered the empiricism of English and French Lockeans. Materialists, mechanists, and empiricists, no matter how much they might differ among themselves regarding epistemology, all helped to advance the development of a 'natural theology' (that is, one with emphasis on the Book of Nature as the handiwork of God and hence as a source of revelation). Thereby they raised some serious religious questions. Little doubt arose as to whether God had created the universe, or was First Cause, but some thinkers (the Deists were a prominent example) seriously doubted that God had since Creation continued to guide the universe, and others queried whether scientific reason could adjust God's governance and miracles to a system of immutable laws of nature. As we have seen (Chapter VII), the debate led to scepticism, and scepticism to various degrees of agnosticism. Voltaire believed that God would have to be invented if he did not exist, but LaPlace, according to legend (*ben trovato* if not *vero*), claimed to have no need of God as a hypothesis.

Yet it would be a mistake to consider the European scientists of the seventeenth and eighteenth centuries for the most part sceptics, agnostics, or atheists. Far from it, the majority of them were Christians, though with varying degrees of orthodoxy. Descartes thought of science as God's handiwork, expressible in mathematical terms and intelligible to human reason.[4] Robert Boyle (1627–91) was a devout man who wished to counteract free-thought and would have recoiled in horror at the thought of destroying the Christian edifice. Isaac Newton (1642–1727) had little difficulty in accommodating his scientific findings to his belief in God's sovereignty over His universe.

Still, the spiritual domination of the various Christian churches, though continuing strong, was ebbing in their day. They had been enfeebled by a lengthy series of 'religious' wars and assailed by new doubts regarding revealed truth with the discovery of the New World and Eastern philosophy. The interference of Protestants in the affairs of Catholic countries and of Catholics in the affairs of Protestant countries tended to make disputants take vigorous stands, and not on the basis of faith alone. In an age of absolute monarchy, Erastianism was a source of power to the state, leaving less room for defiance of the state by the church and making religion a branch, and the church a tool, of politics. On the other hand, the state, frequently under the control of enlightened rulers supported by middle-class patrons of learning, was often less hostile to new knowledge than the older and relatively independent church had been.

One of the most illustrious of the champions of the new knowledge was Francis Bacon. In the early seventeenth century his many writings outlined his view of the proper way to interrogate nature. He expounded a system of induction and instances, and while it may not be the best approach to science, his criticism of the deductive method of rigid Aristotelian thought and his emphasis on observation and experiment as the road to scientific truth were to provide a new approach for those who questioned the validity of Scholastic methods. He boldly proclaimed, moreover, that science could be used to serve man. This prophecy was not unique with him; among others, Descartes had already indicated that science might help man to control nature. But Bacon spelled the idea out well, even if science was not to be assiduously joined with technology for another two hundred years.

Notwithstanding, Bacon's reputation as a prophet cannot be justly derived from any critique on his part of medieval attitudes. He did little to improve upon the speculative system of medieval man and a good deal to buttress it. He was ignorant of the number of experiments already performed relating to impetus and of the continuing tradition of dissection; and other instances of his ignorance of the experimental science of his day indicate that, whatever the change in scientific thought he wrought, it was something less abrupt than a switch from a speculative to an empirical approach. For all his criticism of Aristotelianism, he still worked within the Aristotelian qualitative framework. While he did not completely ignore the importance of mathematics, he did not find such a system of thought compatible, and as a result he missed the true significance of the change in contemporary scientific thought—that is, its mathematical aspect. Bacon himself was not conspicuously successful as a scientist; he was an anti-Copernican, holding that the rival system of Tycho Brahe (1546–1601) was correct (a position not held by him alone, however). Like that of his famous namesake, Roger Bacon, Francis Bacon's activity as an anti-Scholastic polemicist and propagandist rather than his own scientific accomplishments explain why he is remembered as a prophet of modern science.[5]

In contrast with Bacon was Descartes. Descartes' approach was not only rational but also mathematical, based on a well-worked-out deductive process. His essays, such as *Regulae ad Directionem Ingenii* (esp. Rules XII–XXI), *La géométrie*, annexed (along with *Météores* and *La dioptrique*) to his *Discours de la méthode*, and his *Secundae Responsiones*, emphasized the method of mathematical reasoning as a tool of scientific and philosophical thought.

Galileo, a contemporary of Descartes and Bacon, was also to be largely responsible for the great innovations in day-to-day methods in science that came in the seventeenth century. Galileo used experiment in addition to reasoning and mathematics, though several of his putative experiments are now considered legendary. He was, of course, not the first to employ the experimental method. We shall soon examine the contributions of men like William Gilbert (who worked with an experimental model in the field of magnetism and electricity, to which Galileo gave small attention) and like Benedetti and Stevin (who anticipated and laid the foundation for some of Galileo's work).[6] Moreover, in several regards (for example, in refusing to accept Kepler's conclusions) Galileo lagged behind some of his contemporaries.

Nevertheless, more perhaps than to Bacon or Descartes, the role of innovator belonged to the Italian scientist. Much more than they Galileo was stimulated by the technology of his day. His study of mechanics, as his writings disclose, was affected by the work he observed going on in the Venetian Arsenal. He was not content, however, with observation alone or even with philosophical speculation and mathematical interpretation of the study of nature. His method in last analysis was composed of three sometimes overlapping phases—rational intuition, laboratory experiment, and mathematical demonstration. He realized the importance of intuitively deriving the right kind of questions from the known data, for only certain types of questions were susceptible to his method. Then he tried to find the answers by further experiment, recognizing, however, that in any experiment departure from the concrete elements in favour of abstract reasoning might at some points be desirable. For example, brilliant speculations on Euclidean space enabled him to carry out his work toward a law of inertia (see below). But, departing from the Scholastics, he preferred to limit his speculation to strictly logical deductions proceeding from premises based upon those aspects of the sensible world that he could submit to experiment. Finally, he expressed his results in mathematical terms wherever he could, using Socratic argument where mathematics alone did not enable him to demonstrate his conclusions.

Although Galileo was in every sense a polemicist (not to mention his skill as a publicist), he was not the self-conscious system builder that his contemporaries Bacon and Descartes were. He too recognized, however, the importance of eliminating Final Cause and teleology from natural science, not because he thought that the universe had no purpose but because he recognized the limits of his method and of the task at hand. The domain of philosophy was thus disintegrated; the conscious rejection of metaphysics by the natural scientist was ultimately to separate natural philosophy not only from theology but also from speculative philosophy.

New Scientific Instruments

In those days instruments were relatively new in scientific work, for only gradually were scientists deserting the study for the laboratory and supplementing speculation with manual work. They now asked less often *why* things happened, and more often *how* they happened; and *how* could be answered sometimes by repeating the process. We shall find great scientists making their own instruments, inventing new ones, and adapting old ones to new uses. We shall find them also striving for a uniform system of measurement of heat, space, weight, time, and other physical characteristics, though as yet usually without striking success. We shall find governments as well as individual scientists creating laboratories and observatories *de novo*. Only in the century or so that ran roughly from Galileo to Newton were the telescope, microscope, pendulum clock, barometer, and thermometer developed, permitting greater precision and new experiments. The wonders they and their contemporaries achieved often were sheer feats of intellect performed with what today appear to be the barest essentials of laboratory equipment.

For certain instruments to be conveniently usable as tools of science precise and generally accepted units of measurement are desirable. Medieval alchemy and medicine had had several systems of weights and measures, largely derived from Antiquity, but they had been inaccurate and not easily interchangeable. In the sixteenth century Agricola re-examined these systems in a five-book treatise *De Mensuris et Ponderibus Romanorum atque Graecorum*. In 1514 at Vienna Henricus Scriptor compiled a set of rules for measuring the contents of vessels. While these events furnished instances of progress toward precision, they also indicated the lack of a good, uniform system of measuring scientific data.

Agreement on units of measurement, however, was hard to get, as is illustrated by the early history of precision instruments. The measurement of heat, for example, required not only a widely acceptable unit of measure but also some device for counting units. Borrowing the specifications of Greek scientists and probably also the clinical apparatus of his friend Santorio Santorii (Sanctorius) (1561–1636), Galileo is believed to have constructed an air thermoscope, a crude predecessor of the thermometer and barometer. The productive though short-lived Accademia del Cimento experimented (*c.* 1654) with the so-called Florentine thermometer—a sealed glass bulb holding a liquid and opening into a thin tube, the degree of heat being deduced by the height of the column of liquid in the tube as the liquid expanded or contracted when exposed to changes of temperature. Further steps on the same principle were taken by Daniel Gabriel Fahrenheit (1686–1736). A German by birth, he became a lecturer, inventor, and leading instrument maker at Amsterdam. By 1721 he had developed a mercury thermometer to determine the boiling points of various liquids, such as oil of vitriol, alcohol, and water, and had devised the scale of temperatures that still bears his name; with zero fixed at the temperature of a given mixture of ice, water, and salt and with body temperature arbitrarily fixed at about 96° it put the normal freezing point of water at 32° and the boiling point at 212°. Ignorant of Fahrenheit's work, René Antoine de Réaumur (1683–1757), a French naturalist, developed a thermometer on different lines. He preferred alcohol to mercury as the liquid for the measurement of temperature, and devised a thermometric scale (80 degrees between the freezing and boiling points of water) that likewise still bears its inventor's name. A third scientist, Anders Celsius (1701–44), of Sweden, elaborated a mercury thermometer with yet a different scale (putting the temperature of melting snow at 100° and of boiling water at zero). With variations introduced by Christin of Lyons in 1743, including the reversal of Celsius's scale, this thermometer is known today as the centigrade thermometer. It is now generally used for scientific work and is the common one in countries that have adopted the metric system of weights and measures.

The early history of another precision instrument, the telescope, is shrouded in mystery. Apparently the first ones were put in use in Holland and Italy at the end of the sixteenth century. In 1608 a Dutchman named Hans Lippershey applied for a patent on a process for combining several lenses to form a telescope. Galileo, learning of the Dutch models, constructed the telescope of thirty magnification with which he made his epochal astronomical discoveries. (Pl. 87a.) Johannes Kepler (1571–1630) in *Dioptrice* (1611) suggested (among other things) that the proper placing of convex and concave lenses would give larger and more distinct images. The first Keplerian or 'astronomical' telescope was constructed by the Jesuit astronomer Christoph Scheiner (1575–1650).

Microscopes likewise seem to have been experimented with first by Dutch craftsmen. Their models were duplicated in Italy but without noteworthy improvements until after the Thirty Years War. The earliest compound microscopes were unsatisfactory in some ways, and several scientists preferred to use the simple microscope. (Pl. 84a.) Not until the nineteenth century, with the introduction of the improved achromatic microscope, would the compound microscope make its greatest contributions. Important research in the biological sciences was meanwhile done with the simple microscope.

Another tool now considered indispensible for precise experimentation— the pendulum clock—was also effectively developed in the seventeenth century. Only crude methods of measuring time, such as by oral counting, by the oscillations of a swinging object, by the quantity of dripping water, by the flow of sand in an hour glass, or by a water clock, had been available previously, and, therefore, exact time measurements, particularly of speedy actions, had been difficult. Galileo sketched a plan for a pendulum clock but died before one could be made. Tycho Brahe and Kepler had available some kind of clock that enabled them to time their observations more accurately than had previously been possible. Only in 1656, however, did Christiaan Huygens (1629–95) successfully combine the pendulum with gears and escapement to make an accurate timepiece. In 1657 he patented a pendulum clock, which he described in his *Horologium* (1658); and in *Horologium Oscillatorium* (1673), along with many other original contributions, he presented a mathematical analysis of the operation of an improved model. (Pl. 89a, b.) By experiments with a seconds' pendulum he was able to measure acceleration due to gravity and to present with greater certainty other conclusions requiring accurate time measurements. He also invented the balance spring for timepieces. Improvements on the Huygens models by William Clement (*c.* 1685) and others ultimately enabled scientists to time experiments precisely in terms of seconds.

The determination of longitude on shipboard long defied solution. The Portuguese voyages of discovery and the establishment of Don Henrique's nautical centre at Sagres in the early fifteenth century speeded the development of navigational instruments. We have already noted (Chapter XIII) certain early sixteenth-century improvements in cartography. About the same time there originated the basic idea in the present method of finding longitude by calculations based upon the difference in time between shipboard and the zero meridian. Huygens was able to devise a special pendulum clock for use at sea, and his improvement inspired efforts to make timepieces that would be still more accurate than his on shipboard. The problem was finally solved with the invention of the chronometer (*c.* 1761) by John Harrison; its reliability was proved by Captain James Cook, who took a duplicate of it along on his voyages of the 1770's.

Meanwhile other astronomical and navigational instruments had evolved that, together with the steadily growing comprehension of pole-star altitudes and solar declinations, made possible a more accurate determination of latitude as well. An English seafaring man of the sixteenth century made an improved model of the cross staff. This was the 'back staff', which was widely used until the development of reflecting instruments. Studies by Hooke and Wren (1665), Jean Picard (1669), and Newton (*c.* 1700) gave designs for reflecting instruments (used in connection with telescopes), but they were never actually built. John Hadley (1682–1744) and Thomas Godfrey (of Philadelphia, d. 1749) share the honours for inventing the instrument (1731) from which the modern marine sextant derives.

The means of weighing minute particles became more and more important as chemistry advanced to the stage of precise analysis. The problem was rendered difficult not only by differences in units of weight measurement, which varied from region to region and from language to language, but also by the relative crudeness and inaccuracy of weighing machines. The problem of an international nomenclature for weights was to be solved only after the scientists of the First French Republic in 1793 laid the foundation for the metric system, but the quest for a weighing machine capable of detecting tiny differences of mass ended earlier in the eighteenth century. A knife-edge balance was invented, based on the principle that the centre of gravity of a uniform bar is at its midpoint. Very slight differences in weight, causing a uniform lever placed on a knife-edge fulcrum to swing out of equilibrium, can be easily measured by means of an indicator showing the distance of swing. The accuracy of weighing that Lavoisier, for example, needed for his experiments would have been impossible without the knife-edge balance.

The very number of famous men of science who invented or helped to invent these precision instruments (and others that will be mentioned in due course below) has a significance of its own. It is an indication not only of their ingenuity but also of their need. Though the scientist usually had the help of mechanics and professional instrument-makers, he often had to improvise his instruments as he went along, since instrument-making was still in the hands of small-scale technicians who made their instruments to order one by one. In our period interchangeability of standard parts had not yet come to instrument-making or other industries, though it was beginning (see Chapter XV). The amazing thing is how much cooperation the scientists of the 'scientific revolution' were able to achieve despite lack of uniformity of instrumentation or nomenclature or norm for weighing and measuring.

The Role of the Universities and the Scientific Academies

At least partly—but only partly—because of the persistence of Aristotelian science in the universities, much of the new important scientific work of our period (with notable exceptions like Padua, Cracow, and Oxford) was done outside their walls, and not until the nineteenth century would university laboratories be commonly established to interrogate nature. In the sixteenth century the University of Padua, patronized by the Venetian republic, was perhaps the outstanding exception to the rule of general scientific conservatism in university circles. It was anti-Aristotelian. It had the rare distinction of admitting professors and students without doctrinal tests and prerequisites. Here men such as Copernicus, Andreas Vesalius (1514–64), and William Harvey (1578–1657) studied, were inspired, and themselves inspired younger men. The newer University of Leiden in the sixteenth and seventeenth centuries established a botanical garden, an anatomical theatre and museum, an observatory, a hospital, and physics and chemistry laboratories. Most scientists, however, worked as lone and independent scholars, notable examples being Leonardo da Vinci, Paracelsus, and Gilbert. Furthermore, many of them fell far short of the modern ideal of the scientist free from prejudice and superstition and engaged in the disinterested, objective pursuit of truth. For one thing, magical 'experimenta' continued well into our period, especially the efforts of alchemists to transmute metals. Yet 'experimenta' were not solely survivals of medieval superstition; they were also the signs of pioneer effort and the means of slow progress in early modern science. The scientist of the period 1530–1775—especially of the seventeenth century, the so-called 'century of genius'—was sometimes an autodidact and often a polymath. The knowledge of science in that day was still so limited that men like Descartes, Galileo, Kepler, Boyle, Huygens, Pascal, Leibniz, Newton, Lomonosov, and Franklin could make significant contributions in several fields and will be considered below under more than one heading.

The cooperation of men of science was aided by the growth of scientific societies, which provided meeting places for the best minds. They served also as a means of disseminating knowledge through their learned journals, eagerly acquired by contemporary scientists. The Accademia dei Lincei (1603–30) and the Accademia del Cimento (1657–67) each lasted only for decades, but they provided fruitful and encouraging precedents; the Royal Society of London (founded 1662), the Académie des Sciences (founded 1666), the Societas Regia Scientiarum (founded 1700; later the Prussian Academy), and the St Petersburg Academy (founded 1725) were among the more illustrious of the great academies that endured. They provided libraries, laboratories, stipends, expensive instruments, collaborators, and interested audiences and served as national clearing-houses for both the scientist and the dilettante. Thanks to the scientific societies and their learned journals, communication among working scientists became much easier than it would have been at an earlier date. The contemporary improvement of postal sources—the London penny post, for example, was established in 1680— helped to make them good correspondents.

For all their revolutionary discoveries in mechanics, mathematics, astronomy, and biology, the seventeenth-century scientists did little more than scratch the surface of their fields of study. That century was one of great promise, but the eighteenth was one of conscious fulfilment. By the end of the eighteenth century (to enumerate only a few achievements) chemistry was established as an independent field of study, geology was beginning to come into its own, the first faltering steps in the study of electricity, hyponotism, and aeronautics had been taken, and a theory of biological evolution was being dimly formulated.

MATHEMATICS IN EUROPE

Until about 1500 mathematical knowledge for the most part had advanced no further than the stage at which the Greeks and the Muslims had left it. Then humanistic research uncovered Classical texts that did much to stimulate mathematical thought; an edition of the work of Archimedes, for example, was published at Basel in 1544, making his findings, not previously unknown, more accurately, fully, and readily available. In the mid-sixteenth century Europe developed the field of algebra beyond its Hindu and Islamic sources, turning it into something European. Purbach's posthumously published *Opus Algorithmi Jucundissimum* (1492) became a leading manual of the sixteenth century.

Algebra afforded methods of solving equations previously solved, if at all, only by Greek geometrical procedures. The largely autodidact Niccolo Tartaglia (1500–57) is usually given credit for unravelling the problems long assumed to be fundamental to the solution of cubic equations, but modern scholarship indicates that the credit probably belongs rather to his colleague Scipione dal Ferro.[7] Cardan, another of the group, answered certain posers concerning negative and imaginary roots. Ludovico Ferrari (1522–c. 1560), originally a servant of Cardan, showed how to solve biquadratic equations. Rafael Bombelli's *Algebra* (c. 1550, in manuscript form) systematized and carried to higher steps the algebraic findings of the Italian school.

A notorious feud broke out between Tartaglia and Cardan, both of whom, apparently without complete justification, sought credit for solving cubic equations. Their contest centred in Cardan's having published in *Ars Magna* (1545), a summation of the known algebra of the day, a set of formulae that he had confidentially been given by Tartaglia (as well as Ferrari's). It illustrates the importance that a mathematical subject might assume in north Italian learned circles of the Renaissance. The personal bitterness displayed by the contestants was characteristic of Italian intellectuals of that age, and especially of the versatile, fiery Cardan. The dispute was not wholly unconnected with the rivalry between the non-academic and the university savants.

Disputes like this quickly made plain that a set of commonly understood mathematical symbols would permit an economy of words, simplify the steps toward the solving of equations, and save much confusion. A French lawyer-mathematician, François Viète (1540–1603), was the first to inaugurate in algebra generally acceptable letter symbols. The signs for *plus* ($+$) and *minus* ($-$), introduced as early as 1489 (see Chapter XIII), came finally to signify *addition* and *subtraction*, and that for *equality* ($=$) was introduced in 1557, but not until the seventeenth century did they become common. A German reformer and mystic, Michael Stifel (1487?–1567), instituted the symbol for *root* ($\sqrt{}$) and dealt with negative numbers, and Descartes (in *La géométrie*, 1637) made use of a modern exponential system (e.g. a^2, a^3). The symbol for *multiplication* ($\times$) appeared in the posthumous edition (1619) of *Mirifici Logarithmorum Cononis Constructio* of the Scottish mathematician John Napier (1550–1617), and Leibniz later introduced the dot as a symbol for the same operation. The symbol for *division* ($\div$) and those for *greater than* ($>$) and *less than* ($<$) also first occurred in print in the seventeenth century.

Simon Stevin of Bruges (1548–1620) greatly simplified arithmetical calculation when he suggested (1586) the use of decimal fractions in place of the then usual sexagesimal fractions. He urged that the new scheme be employed in coinage and weights and measures. His notational system for fractions remained quite awkward, however, and decimal calculation was simplified only when Edward Wright in an English translation (published in 1616) of Napier's *Mirifici Logarithmorum Cononis Descriptio* (1614) introduced the simple decimal point, about the same time that the Continent adopted the comma for the same purpose. The decimal system of weights and measures had to await general acceptance, however, until the nineteenth century in Europe, and until the twentieth in the United States.

Another device propounded early in the seventeenth century, logarithms, facilitated arduous calculations without demanding an understanding of the mathematical operations involved. It was based on a principle, previously examined by Stifel (in *Arithmetica Integra*, 1545), concerning the correspondence between the geometric and the arithmetic progression of numbers. Logarithms reduced multiplication and division to addition and subtraction, and the extraction of roots to simple division. The underlying assumptions of logarithms were arrived at independently by Napier (in the two works mentioned above) and Joost Bürgi, a Swiss astronomer, who thus provided another illustration of the thesis that when sufficient knowledge is available, the next step in a scientific process may occur to more than one mind about the same time. Logarithms made excellent use of the decimal system introduced by Stevin.

Meanwhile progress came also in the study of trigonometry. Copernicus wrote a treatise on spherical trigonometry in connection with his astronomical research, but his work was published separately (1542) by Georg Joachim von Lauchen, called Rheticus. Rheticus also wrote a treatise of his own (published posthumously, 1596) containing tables of sines, tangents, secants, and other trigonometrical functions. By the beginning of the seventeenth century trigonometry was well on the way to becoming a scientific partner of astronomy.

Meanwhile other high points of mathematical understanding were reached and expressed in formulae. The earliest known calculation of probabilities came in a hardly respectable enterprise: how to divide the stakes in an unfinished gambling game was described in an Italian treatise of 1494 (by Luca di Pacioli). Cardan, an inveterate gambler, also calculated some of the probabilities in games of chance and published his conclusions in a work entitled *De Ludo Aleae*; in the seventeenth century Fermat, Pascal, and Huygens did some more generalized work on the subject, placing the calculus of probabilities on a scientific basis. At the end of the 1600's Newton set forth the solution of another problem, the binomial theorem, simplifying the calculation to the *nth* power of the sum of two quantities. Yet from a certain point of view perhaps the most significant mathematical achievements of the century were in the direct application of mathematical calculation to physical phenomena, for on such calculation depended the mathematical verification and statement of the laws of physics.

Since Omar Khayyám's time (*c.* 1100) it had been recognized that a host of geometrical and other quantitative problems could well be studied by means of algebraic (i.e. analytic) methods. Thomas Harriot (1560–1621) and Pierre de Fermat (1601–65) worked with the problem of graphically representing a function (i.e. a quantity that varies because of interdependence with other variables) by using rectangular co-ordinates, thus laying the foundations of analytic geometry. Finally Descartes' *La géométrie* put forward the concept of a co-ordinate geometry, which would permit a problem in mechanics (the effects of forces upon bodies at rest or in motion) to be stated in a geometrical form and then analyzed with the aid of algebraic functions. The architect Girard Desargues' *Brouillon project d'une atteinte aux événements des rencontres du cône avec un plan* (1639) laid the foundation of projective geometry, the mathematical study of perspective. One of his fruitful suggestions was that parallel lines and planes may be conceived as meeting at an infinitely distant point and thus forming a cone. His book dealt with the question how to derive the properties of a conic section from the simpler properties of the circle forming its base.

We shall consider later the concurrent developments in the field of mechanics. The resulting study of curves of fall and other forms of motion indicated the desirability of a formula for the rise and fall of a curve—that is, for the direction of a given motion at any instant or point. The solution of problems concerned with the measurement of the length and area of closed curves had been approximated by the Ancients through an ingenious process sometimes known as the 'method of exhaustion'; it consisted of 'exhausting' step by step the margin between a curve's smallest and its largest possible length and area by calculating the perimeter and area of a polygon inscribed within it and another circumscribing it, increasing the number of each of the polygons' sides at each step. This method of exhaustion indicated the desirability of calculating any otherwise precisely immensurable quantity by translating it approximately into a curve and estimating the margin between its lowest possible maximum (approximated by the 'exhausted' circumscribed polygon) and its highest possible minimum (approximated by the 'exhausted' inscribed polygon).

The seventeenth-century scientist, faced with the problem of the measurement of variable motions (falling bodies, projectiles, celestial orbits, the pendulum, vibrating strings, beams with varying loads, etc.) had to construct a new mathematics that would enable him to tell the value of one variable (like rate of speed) at a given value (like a point of time or position) of another variable. A number of scientists made contributions toward the solution of this problem. The appearance in the 1540's of the revised edition of Archimedes made available a work of his that dealt with the method of exhaustion. Stevin, the Italian mathematician Luca Valerio (c. 1552–1618), and others devised the 'method of indivisibles', breaking lines up into constituent 'indivisible' points, planes into 'indivisible' lines, and solids into 'indivisible' planes. The work of these men threw more light on, and improved the symbols employable in, the solution of the problem of constructing a tangent to a curve and of calculating maximum and minimum values until, finally, Kepler and others recognized that the increments of a function become negligible as it approaches the neighbourhood of a maximum or a minimum (i.e. its mathematical limits). The concurrent development of analytic geometry permitted geometric problems to be expressed as algebraic equations, and algebraic equations to be projected graphically as points, lines, curves, and other geometric figures. Further speculation on the value of a variable quantity as it approaches its maximum or minimum led to the concept that mathematical quantities are better described as 'fluxions' or continued motion (a line, for example, as the continued motion of a point) than as very small parts in unbroken contiguity.

This reasoning finally led Newton and Leibniz to propound the differential calculus, a method of computing differentials in a continuously varying quantity or motion. An unfortunate squabble arose regarding the priority of discovery of this marvellous tool, but the truth seems to be that each of the two men arrived at the discovery independently, although Newton seems to have been the first to communicate it to others. Almost contemporaneously the reversing of the differential process and thereby the calculation of larger units of a curve from a differential (integral calculus) was expounded by John Wallis (1616–1703) and Isaac Barrow (1630–77). The first complete calculus textbook was published by G. F. A. L'Hôpital (*Analyse des infiniment petits*, 1696). With this new tool problems could be solved that had been nearly intractable before. Though Newton relied chiefly upon a logical demonstration, his use of the calculus at several crucial points made the mechanical theory of the universe put forward in the *Principia* (see below) seem mathematically demonstrable, and his work suggested that all other measurable phenomena might be unified by mathematics. The study of mechanics thus became more and more theoretical, since its problems could be stated mathematically, and mathematics seemed to 'prove' and generalize what observation, reason, and experiment might only suggest.

In the eighteenth century, because of the close correspondence of mathematics and theoretical physics, important advances were made in the field of analysis. Speculation on the concept of a variable as a motion approaching a limit led to debate among English philosophers and mathematicians like Berkeley, Benjamin Robins, Brook Taylor, and Thomas Simpson, and doubts arose about the validity of using infinitesimal (and therefore presumed to be negligible) quantities in careful scientific work.

Meanwhile, Continental mathematicians were more productively employed. D'Alembert's *Mémoire sur le calcul intégral* (1739) and relevant articles in the *Encyclopédie* championed the concept of the limit. The Swiss-born Leonhard Euler (1707–83), who did most of his work as a member of the St Petersburg and Berlin academies, made outstanding contributions to almost every field of mathematics. He established the calculus of variations (roughly speaking, the calculus of the variables of variables) as a separate branch of higher analysis; he was the first to convey a distinct notion of a mathematical function; he revolutionized spherical trigonometry; his method of solving simultaneous linear equations became standard. The Bernoulli family of Basel, which produced a number of skilled mathematicians, was closely associated with Euler in St Petersburg as well as Basel. Jacob Bernoulli (1654–1705) systematized Leibniz's calculus and applied it to the field of differential geometry and also placed the theory of probability on a sound mathematical basis. His brother Johann (1667–1748) helped to establish analytical trigonometry and to solve several problems involving maxima and minima. One of Johann's sons, Daniel (1700–82), not only contributed to mathematical physics but also furnished some dramatic applications of the theory of probability to insurance, statistics, and games of chance. The findings of the Bernoullis in trigonometry and probabilities were supplemented by Abraham de Moivre (1667–1754), a Huguenot refugee in England, who in the process elaborated the theory of permutations and combinations.

Perhaps the century's greatest mathematician was the Italo–French savant Joseph Louis Lagrange (1736–1813)—whose most important work, however, falls outside the chronological limits of this volume. Continuing in Euler's footsteps, he provided a nomenclature for the calculus of variations, and substituting analytical for geometrical methods, he was one of several scientists who advanced toward Euler's objective of a shift from the synthetic to the analytical in mathematical procedures (see Volume V). Several other mathematical contributions fit more appropriately within our period. D'Alembert in his *Traité de dynamique* (1743) studied the pendulum and came to the conclusion ('D'Alembert's principle') that the internal actions and reactions of any system of rigid bodies in motion tend to balance, thus permitting the reduction of the complex problems of dynamics to a generalized statistical method. Alexis Claude Clairault (1713–65) applied the analytical method to non-planar curves in space, thereby laying the foundation for solid analytic geometry. Gaspard Monge (1746–1818) seems to have conceived the major principles of his descriptive geometry (the graphical solution of problems involving space relationships) as early as 1770, but the development and publication of his discovery did not come until 1795.

Newton's prestige was so great that his notational system in the calculus was continued in England, although it was much clumsier than the system of Leibniz, used on the Continent. This divergence of notation was not to be corrected until the nineteenth century. Along with the resentment engendered among the contemporaries of Newton and Leibniz by the dispute over the calculus and the debates on the utility of the concept of the limit, notational clumsiness undoubtedly had something to do with the decline of mathematics in eighteenth-century England. Among the few English mathematicians of note after Newton was Colin Maclaurin (1698–1746), who, though he rejected both infinite and infinitesimal quantities, produced a work which no less an authority than Lagrange compared favourably with the best work of Archimedes; this was the *Treatise of Fluxions* (1742), the most complete survey of that branch of mathematics up to that time.

THE PHYSICAL SCIENCES IN EUROPE

The publication of Copernicus' *De Revolutionibus Orbium Coelestium* (1543) marks a now easily recognized milestone in the development of science. Nevertheless, the book wrought no sudden and drastic 'Copernican Revolution'; what actually happened was much more gradual, complex, and undramatic.

About 1530 Copernicus had privately circulated a briefer statement of his theory. It was based chiefly upon abstract speculation, and even in its final form the inadequacy of existing scientific knowledge and equipment prevented him from giving satisfactory, empirical evidence of his theory from specific observations. He nevertheless provided not only a text but a chart presenting the thesis that the planets circle around the centre of the Earth's orbit, approximately where the Sun is located. He did not question the perfect circular motions of the planets, retaining the Ptolemaic idea of epicycles and eccentric circles; and he mistakenly introduced an additional rotation, a conical motion, to account for the fact that the Earth's planetary axis continually points toward the pole star. Nevertheless, he introduced the principle that the Earth annually revolved about the Sun (*De Revolutionibus*, Bk. I, Ch. 10). And, indeed, Copernicus' system, by allowing the earth to move, provided a simpler explanation of planetary motion than Ptolemy's sluggish machine, reducing the number of wheels in the crystalline spheres from 80 to 34.[8]

The Lutheran preacher and mathematician Andreas Osiander, who saw

Copernicus' treatise through the press in Nuremburg, in an anonymous and deliberately cautious preface supplemented the author's. Here he claimed that basically the book presented only a purely mathematical hypothesis, intended to facilitate certain computations in astronomy, without objective significance and without prejudice to Scripture. This preface was long assumed to be by Copernicus himself, and so the full impact of the 'Copernican Revolution' was cushioned. Dedicated by the dying scientist to Pope Paul III, the book at first appeared to be acceptable to the Roman Catholic Church. Controversy developed only slowly, taking some seventy years to mature.

Copernicus found some enthusiastic disciples and supporters—notably Rheticus and Erasmus Reinhold, who calculated the *Prussian Tables* (1551) upon the Copernican system. Most people, however, finding *De Revolutionibus* difficult, remained indifferent to its implications. Martin Luther is reported to have said of Copernicus, even before *De Revolutionibus* was published: 'The fool will overturn the whole science of astronomy.'9 Later Melanchthon explicitly and Calvin by implication repudiated the Copernican theory. Among the arguments against it, in addition to the passages in the Bible that attributed motion to the Sun, one seemed particularly persuasive. Wasn't it more in keeping with the known facts to believe that the Earth stands still and the heavenly bodies rotate around it? If one were to accept Copernicus's modifications of Ptolemy, one would have to develop an entirely new physics.

Nevertheless, the Copernican system slowly won adherents. The observation of several professors of the University of Cracow when a conjunction of Saturn and Jupiter took place in 1563 seemed to confirm Copernicus, and the Copernican system was favourably received and taught there. Even in the popular mind, and certainly in a trained mind like that of Tycho Brahe, doubts about the pre-Copernican scheme arose when a new star appeared in 1572, for a new star was difficult to explain in a perfect and unchanging heaven. The problem arose again with the appearance of a comet in 1577, which was definitely not in the sublunary regions subject to change and decay.10

Tycho Brahe spent most of his career in observations that did much both to clarify and to compound the confusion. He worked at first in an observatory in Denmark subsidized by the Danish court and later in another in Bohemia subsidized by Emperor Rudolph II. He carefully improved the quadrant, the theodolite, and other available instruments (but had no slide rule, telescope, or pendulum clock, for they had not yet been invented); and he carefully made allowances for the possible inaccuracy of his instruments, removing the haphazardness that had been common among his predecessors. He was thus the outstanding observational astronomer of the pre-telescopic age. His greatest contribution, published in a star catalogue in 1602, was his exact measurement of the positions of about a thousand celestial bodies. In 1588 he published his own theory of astronomy in *De Mundi Aetherii Recentioribus*

Phaenomenis. He concluded that, while the other planets revolved around the Sun, the Sun and Moon in turn revolved around a fixed Earth, for, he pointed out, astronomy had no way of knowing whether the Earth moved, while the evidence of the senses tended to support the belief that it stood still.

Temporarily Tycho's system seemed to answer all astronomical problems, and without the risk of heresy. Interest in the Copernican theory, however, increased in the final years of the sixteenth century in non-scientific quarters. Bruno was burned at the stake in 1600 for holding, among other heresies, the idea of the infinity of the universe. The idea of a plurality of worlds had been discussed pro and con in earlier generations (see Chapter XIII). Copernicus, while still believing in a 'sphere of fixed stars which contains everything',[11] had given a picture of a single universe, though one that was larger than medieval astronomy had allowed, and his disciple Digges, as we have noted, had extrapolated the Copernican immensity into infinity rather than plurality. Bruno's idea, no longer a plurality of worlds but of a single infinite universe, seemed to have the authority of Copernicus and the Copernicans behind it and so was more compelling to some and more alarming to others than it might otherwise have been.

Bruno was a mystic rather than a scientist, and on empirical and other grounds his metaphysics was repudiated by Kepler, the brilliant assistant of Tycho Brahe. Kepler fell heir to the post and the mountain of astronomical data left by Tycho Brahe. Yet he never adhered to his predecessor's system and from the beginning was an ardent Copernican. Driven by a mystical fervour and highly influenced by Pythagorean–Platonic doctrine, he offers a picture of one who was part medieval and part modern at the same time. He lived in an age when it was possible for his mother to be accused of witchcraft, and she escaped conviction only by a terrifying margin. He was the first to apply mathematics to empirical methods in order to derive laws of celestial motion. For example, in his Rudolphine Tables (1617), listing over one thousand star places, he used the recently invented logarithms.

Not content with mere description, Kepler applied a stern logic to an explanation of his observations. In the year 1604 a new luminous body appeared in the constellation Serpentarius, and Kepler noted that the new body was without parallax (i.e. unlike some hitherto known astronomical bodies, it did not seem to change position when observed from different points). It had then to be at approximately the same distance from the observer as the bodies in the region of the fixed stars. Even less than the new star of 1572 could this one be explained in the Ptolemaic framework, in which the phenomena of the outer distances were supposed to be changeless. Kepler also made repeated observations of the planet Mars, which resulted in a book that, as its title indicated, gave an etiological explanation of celestial physics; this was the *Astronomica Nova* αἰτιολογητός, *seu Physica Coelestis, tradita commentariis de motibus stellae Martis* (1609). Here he set forth the first two of his laws of planetary motion: (1) Planets move about the Sun in ellipses, not circles, the

Sun being one of their foci, and (2) planets do not move uniformly but rather in such a way that if a line (or radius vector) were drawn from any one of them to the Sun, that line would sweep through equal areas within the ellipse in equal periods of time. In his *Harmonice mundi* (1619), he enunciated his third law of planetary motion: The square of the period of time that it takes a planet to complete its revolution around the sun (its periodic time) is proportional to the cube of its mean distance from the sun. These laws knocked the remaining props from under the Aristotelian theory of perfect circular motion of the heavenly bodies and at the same time brought about a correction of the Ptolemaic epicyclical astronomy.

Galileo, different in temperament, background, and religion from the German Kepler, contemporaneously aided in bringing about a decisive change in astronomical thought. Galileo's work in physics (which we shall examine below) by disproving Aristotle's ideas of motion made Copernicus seem more plausible. In addition, Galileo made highly dramatic contributions in the field of observational astronomy. By the year 1609, the telescope had become known in Italy, and Galileo was one of the first to recognize its importance to the astronomer. (Pl. 87a.) Through the telescope, he found, the moon seemed far from perfect, being mountainous and rough in many places and not smooth and polished as one might suppose. Far more telling, however, were the observations of the satellites of Jupiter, which were plainly seen to revolve around their planet. Since they seemed to form a system similar to that of the Sun, they reinforced Galileo's belief in the Copernican system. He later observed that Venus went through phases, just as the Moon did. In 1610 he published some of his observations in a booklet entitled *Sidereus Nuntius (Messenger of the Stars)*. Several other observers, particularly Johann Fabricius and Christoph Scheiner, had independently observed what today we call 'sun spots' when, in 1612, Galileo announced his observations of that phenomenon. Was it possible then that the sun itself was corruptible?

The combination of these discoveries with the general intellectual ferment of the age made Galileo's ideas distasteful to many. Strong forces within the Roman Catholic Church were alarmed, particularly after the publication of his *Dialogo . . . sopra i due massimi sistemi del munde Tolemaico e Copernicano* (1632), which decried the Ptolemaic system and upheld the Copernican. This work involved Galileo in a bitter battle, more over his disregard of clerical injunction than over scientific principle. It ended only when, at the age of seventy, he was forced by the Roman Inquisition to recant, at least publicly, 'the false opinion that the Sun is the centre of the world and immovable, and that the Earth is not the centre of the world and moves.'[12] To be sure, some of Galileo's opponents were guided by personal resentment of his barbed tongue. Nevertheless, men of good will also differed with him, and thus with Copernicus, for they refused to abandon the great Scholastic design of the past. Some of Galileo's adversaries sincerely argued away even the visual evidence and, on the ground that the use of an instrument blunted the senses, refused to look through his telescope.

Nevertheless, the combined impact of the recent achievements in mechanics (which we shall soon consider) and astronomy completed the wrecking of Aristotelian physics. After Kepler and Galileo, the validity of the Copernican hypothesis was more generally accepted, but over two centuries had to pass before it could be thoroughly proved. Meanwhile Descartes put forth an attractive theory to account for the motion of the planets. He posited a world in which all space (*extension* in his vocabulary) was matter; hence all space was filled with a viscous fluid, and motion of any particle in this viscous plenum set up an eddy (or *vortex*), moving all other particles including the planets themselves.

Born in the year in which Galileo died, Newton was able to build upon the contributions of a number of predecessors. Copernicus had removed the Earth from its position of priority; Bruno had proclaimed an infinite universe; Kepler had explained the movement of the heavenly bodies according to mathematical principles; Descartes had explained it as due to vortices; and Galileo and others had not only laid the foundation of observational astronomy but had also developed a system of terrestrial mechanics. Newton owed to his predecessors besides their scientific contributions a widespread readiness to receive scientific innovation. Galileo had been disciplined for his beliefs; Newton carried on no conscious battle with entrenched opinion and was widely proclaimed in his own day. This marked change of attitude toward the scientist between Galileo's generation and Newton's was a correlative of the impact that the burgeoning of science had had upon public opinion.

Newton in clearly enunciated principles of his own connected Galileo's work with Kepler's three laws of planetary motion. Newton's importance lies less in his originality than in his own method—avoiding unnecessarily complex hypotheses, seeking propositions gathered by induction, testing the propositions by experiment, and reducing experience to mathematical abstraction. This method led him to the conclusion that heavenly bodies and terrestrial phenomena were subject to the same effects and causes, the same physical laws. Robert Hooke (1635–1703) was perhaps partly justified in claiming to have stated the now well-known law of gravitation before Newton, but Hooke seems not only to have been more interested in terrestrial gravitation alone but also never to have proved the law experimentally or mathematically.[13] The relationship between the terrestrial and the celestial was for Newton no mere incidental similarity; it was identity. His *Philosophiae Naturalis Principia Mathematica* was published in 1687. Thereafter Hellenistic astronomy, whether Aristotelian or Ptolemaic, was outdated; it was not necessary to know the *Almagest* in order to understand the *Principia*. Newton for the first time defined some fundamental terms and carefully set down his own rigid method.

We shall review Newton's laws of motion later. The principle that won him his best claim to immortality was that of universal gravitation, already vaguely broached by Kepler, Hooke, and others. Starting from Kepler's laws of planetary motion, Newton assumed that every particle of matter attracted every other particle, the power of the attraction varying in direct proportion to the product of the attracting masses (i.e. quantities of matter) and in inverse proportion to the square of the distance between them. This principle and Newton's discussion of viscosity contradicted Descartes' theory that the motion of the planets was due to vortices in a viscous fluid that filled all space, but the Cartesians were to take a long time to be convinced of their error.

Huygens' genius was in many ways second only to Newton's, who expressed great admiration for him. His invention of the pendulum clock was due to his need to measure time exactly in his astronomical observations. He also improved the telescope and introduced a type of micrometer (1658) for measuring planet diameters more precisely. With one of his improved telescopes he recognized in 1655–56 that the peculiar appearance of the planet Saturn was due to its now familiar rings, and he was the first to discover one of the several satellites of that planet.

Having already made significant contributions to astronomy, Huygens was invited to join the new French Académie des Sciences and worked at the recently established Paris Observatory. (Pl. 88a.) That observatory was an offshoot of the Académie des Sciences. Formally inaugurated in 1672 under the protection of Colbert and the patronage of Louis XIV, it brought together several famous astronomers. One of them was Jean Picard (1620–82), inventor and one of the most noted astronomers of his day. With the aid of his colleague Adrien Auzout (d. 1691), he invented the filar micrometer, independently building on a principle discovered by William Gascoyne in 1639; when mounted on a telescope it made possible the measurement of smaller astronomical distances. Ole Roemer (1644–1710), a Danish astronomer, worked at Paris with Picard and, after his return to his native land, developed some splendid instruments, the most famous being the transit-circle, which attached to a telescope permitted the measurement of astronomical angles.

Gian Domenico Cassini (1625–1712) was the dominant figure at the Observatory. Even though at that late date he was still an anti-Copernican, he became a member in 1644 and director in 1671 of the Observatory, having previously been professor of astronomy at Bologna. Work carried on under his direction led him to the mistaken belief that the Earth is flat at the equator and so to the beginning of a fruitful controversy (see below). He also measured the parallax of Mars and attempted from it to estimate the distance between the Earth and the Sun. His estimate was better than any available until that time, although we now know that he was in error about 7 per cent. A Cassini dynasty developed at the Observatory, continuing as directors beyond Domenico for three generations (son succeeding father until the French Revolution temporarily closed it).

As transoceanic travel became common in the seventeenth century, the need to calculate longitude at sea became more urgent. The English astronomer John Flamsteed (1646–1719) recognized that without accurate knowledge of the position of the fixed stars, such calculations would be impossible. With this need in mind, in 1675 King Charles II authorized the building of the Greenwich Observatory, with Flamsteed as 'astronomer royal'. Flamsteed installed the instruments in the new observatory (opened in 1676), his great triumph being the installation in 1689 of a mural arc of 140 degrees. (Pl. 88b.) Between 1676 and 1689 he determined the position of some twenty thousand fixed stars; and his star catalogue, rendering all previous ones obsolete, has remained the basis of modern astronomical calculation. His anxiety to postpone publishing his findings until he could perfect them led to conflict with Newton and Edmund Halley (1656–1742), who wanted prompter publication for their own purposes.

At Flamsteed's death Halley was appointed astronomer royal. As a young man Halley had been the first to make a study of the stars in the southern hemisphere, establishing the position of about 341 stars (1678). It was he who, puzzled (along with Hooke and others) about the mathematics of the motion of a planet, put crucial questions to Newton and, having persuaded him to make public his mathematical deduction of the law of gravitation, arranged for the publication of the *Principia*. Halley is noted chiefly for his studies of comets, particularly of the one that bears his name. He observed that the orbital elements of the Comet of 1682 were quite similar to those recorded for the comets of 1456, 1531, and 1607 and, correctly assuming that they were the same comet, predicted that it would return about every seventy-five years.[14]

In the eighteenth century astronomers continued along the parallel and supplementing lines of mathematical and observational astronomy. Frequently the same men engaged in both observation and the relevant mathematics, but mathematical calculation more than observation engaged the attention of some outstanding Continental astronomers—Euler, Clairault, and d'Alembert among others. Newton having solved the problem of reciprocal attraction for two celestial bodies, these men studied the motion of three mutually gravitating bodies. Although they were not successful in solving it in general, they did arrive at approximate solutions for particular cases—that of the Moon, the Sun, and the Earth, and that of the Sun and two other planets. Their solutions improved both the lunar and the solar theory as well as the tables based on them. With some notable exceptions (e.g. Nicolas Louis de Lacaille, who helped calculate the lunar and solar parallaxes) observational astronomy was almost monopolized by the English. James Bradley (1693–1762) endeavoured to find an annual parallax in the stars, which would provide the final link in the evidence necessary to prove the Copernican hypothesis. He was unable to do so, but his studies contributed to astronomy two important concepts—the discovery and explanation of the aberration of light from the stars (1729) and (1748) the nutation of the Earth's axis (the approximately nineteen-year period of oscillation in the Earth's precession due to the pull of the Sun and the Moon on the equatorial bulge).

During the eighteenth century the astronomer's equipment was greatly improved. New observatories arose; longer, more accurate star catalogues became available for both northern and southern skies; and solar and lunar tables were revised. In 1720 John Hadley constructed the first practical reflecting telescope, and subsequently improvements of telescope mountings permitted wider sweeps of observation. (Pl. 87b, c.) In 1733, Chester Moor Hall invented the achromatic lens (see p. 859 below), and in 1755 John Dollond the heliometer.

Meanwhile the Newtonian theory of universal gravitation continued to gain adherents. Pierre Charles Lemonnier in 1746 and Euler in 1748 were able to show that the disturbances in the movements of Jupiter and Saturn could be explained by the law of gravitation, thus suggesting that the whole solar system was subject to the same gravitational pull that Pierre Bouguer (1698–1758) had recently shown (see below) applied to the Earth's mountains. The return of Halley's comet, as he had predicted, in 1758 was additional and even more convincing evidence of the validity of the Newtonian calculations. In 1770 the American astronomer David Rittenhouse constructed his orrery, a machine that reproduced the workings of the solar system for pedagogical purposes. It was not the first orrery—the name is derived from the Earl of Orrery's (c. 1713)—but it was probably the most accurate one that had yet been constructed, revealing the scientific world's readiness and ability to reduce the movement of the planets to clockwork.

The major accomplishments of Frederick William Herschel (1738–1822), of Hanover and England, will be considered in Volume V, but before our period ended, he had begun the investigations that were to make him the greatest of all eighteenth-century observational astronomers. He was able to construct huge telescopes, one with a 40-foot length and a 48-inch mirror (1789). He was the first in modern times to discover a new planet—Uranus (1781), and he demonstrated (1802) that some double stars circle each other. Subsequent research showed that, in so doing, they follow the Newtonian law of gravitation, thus disposing beyond question of the Aristotelian view that Earth and the heavens were subject to different physical laws.

Attempts were made in the eighteenth century to deduce the origin of the solar system. The first notable one was by Immanuel Kant in his *Allgemeine Naturgeschichte und Theorie des Himmels* (1755). Kant believed that matter was initially distributed throughout space in a finely divided condition, that gravitational force had formed central bodies and nuclei about which the adjoining matter had condensed, and that the mutual interaction of the nuclei and the central bodies accounted for the revolution of all planets around the sun in the same sense and on nearly the same plane. This theory was advanced some forty years before Laplace's more satisfactory nebular hypothesis (see Volume V).

By the middle of the eighteenth century scientific cooperation on an international scale among learned societies and governments reached the point where they could pool their resources for the study of extraordinary celestial events. Such events came in 1761 and 1769 with separate occurrences of otherwise rare passages of Venus across the Sun's disc. Since the seventeenth century astronomical observations had permitted approximations of the relative positions of the members of the solar system but not of its actual scalor dimensions. Transit instruments and methods which permitted the measurement of the ascensions of stars by timing their transits had been devised and improved in that century and the next by Römer, Halley (or perhaps, more accurately, Hooke), Joseph-Nicolas Delisle (1688–1768), and others. Multiple observations of the parallax of Venus during the transits of the 1760's were made possible by sending out several expeditions for that purpose and using the instruments and methods already devised. The second set of observations (1769) permitted a check upon the first (1761), leading to some important astronomical deductions. Lomonosov ventured the hypothesis that there was an atmosphere around the planet Venus. But the most important finding by far was a fairly approximate calculation by means of the solar parallax of the mean distance of the Earth from the Sun. Since the solar parallax was taken to be a constant, it was thought possible at last to ascertain the size of the solar system. The Newtonian world now seemed practically completely measured. Only in the nineteenth century was it shown that the solar parallax is not an independent constant, but, for all that, a great and wonderful international scientific effort has not lost its meed of glory.

Advances in Mechanics and Dynamics

The Aristotelian system of terrestrial mechanics was dependent upon common observation; its overthrow demanded the highest type of conceptual reorientation. In the late sixteenth century several men initiated such a reorientation.

One of them was Stevin, the proponent of decimal fractions, who was primarily interested in statics (that is the mechanics of bodies at rest or in equilibrium and of the forces holding them in balance). He established (or, perhaps more accurately, reconfirmed) 'the law of the inclined plane': two counter-balancing weights lying on the inclined planes of a triangle will be in equilibrium when their masses are proportional to the length of their supporting planes. From this law he deduced that of 'the parallelogram of forces' for machines in which more than two forces are involved: if the magnitude and direction of two forces acting on a single point are represented by two sides of a parallelogram, the diagonal from that point will represent their resultant. Stevin's experiments in the statics of liquids (hydrostatics) led him to conclude, anticipating Pascal, that water pressure is independent of the shape of the containing vessel but depends upon the height and surface of the column exerting the pressure. Stevin did not limit himself to statics, however. Anticipating Galileo, too—and by several years—he experimented with falling objects (1586), finding that when a light object and a heavy object are released at the same instant they take the same length of time to reach the ground, a direct contradiction of Aristotelian mechanics. As an engineer and eventually a high technical adviser to Maurice of Orange, Stevin made some extraordinary practical inventions besides.

The ambivalence of the Aristotelian tradition in science, especially in Roman Catholic countries, where the Scholastic method was still strong, especially in theological matters, is reflected in the work of several sixteenth-century scientists. The Venetian Giovanni Battista Benedetti (c. 1530–90) was a mathematician concerned with mechanics, perspective, and astronomy who professed great admiration for Aristotle. At the same time he repudiated some of Aristotle's physical and astronomical ideas, inducing some modern scholars to consider him perhaps more important as a forerunner of Galileo than is justifiable. One of Benedetti's criticisms of traditional science concerned falling bodies. In avowed contradiction of Aristotle and in anticipation of Galileo, he reasoned that two bodies of the same material but of different gross weights falling in the same medium would maintain the same velocity. In his earlier work Tartaglia also exemplified the persistence of Aristotelianism, but with his later experiments in ballistics—a science which he was the first to set forth in a printed book (*Nuova scienza*, 1537)—he came to recognize that a projectile was subject to both 'violent' and 'natural' forces at once and not, as the Aristotelians thought, successively.

Galileo's most noteworthy scientific contributions lie in the field of dynamics (that is, the branch of mechanics which deals with motion and with the action of forces that produce or change motion) and, more particularly, in the field of kinematics (the study of motion without reference to causal factors). Although the familiar story of his dropping objects from the tower of Pisa is dubious, and although some of the verifications he reported were mentally rather than experimentally derived, his skill as a stylist made his reports classics of scientific literature. He carried on experiments, like that of Stevin, with metal balls rolling down a grooved board. His reports of them indicated that he considered something radically wrong in Aristotelian mechanics, for he held not only (what had long been suspected) that the rate of increase in the velocity (acceleration) of different objects falling in a vacuum would increase uniformly as they fell but also that they would fall at the same velocity. He concluded, therefore, with a mathematical formula, that for any falling body the distance of fall was in fixed ratio to the square of the time consumed by its fall ($s = \frac{1}{2}at^2$).

Something approaching this was discerned by Stevin and other contemporaries of Galileo—among them Dominico Soto (1494–1570) and Isaac Beeckman (1588–1637)—but they had not appreciated its full significance.

Accepting the medieval notion of impetus (see Chapter XIII), as had Galileo also in his early years, they had thought of it merely as a description of a simple fact—that bodies travel faster as they fall closer to the earth. Its full meaning as the fundamental law of dynamics could come only when the theory of impetus (that a force imparts to an object a property of motion which in time expends itself) was displaced by the theory of inertia (that an object will maintain its state of uniform motion or of rest unless force is applied). This Galileo began to do. His experiments with balls and boards permitted him to observe that a ball released at a given level on one side of a dip formed by two inclined planes tended to run up to that level on the other side, no matter how long the other side. He concluded that a body moving on a horizontal plane would remain unchanged in the velocity and direction of its motion if left to itself, loss or gain of motion being attributable to some external cause of retardation or acceleration. Thus Galileo came close to enunciating the modern concept of inertia. While holding to the theory that matter is essentially spatial extension, Descartes enunciated a speciously accurate generalized expression of the inertia principle in 1644, but it was meant to apply to a system of dynamics that, as Newton was to show, was faulty: 'When a body is at rest, it has the power of remaining at rest and of resisting everything which could make it change. Similarly when it is in motion, it has the power of continuing in motion with the same velocity and in the same direction.'[15] This statement may be considered correct only if Descartes' erroneous concepts of relevant terms like *body* and *resisting* impact are disregarded.

Descartes, basing his physics on corporeal vortices operating in a plenum, could not accept Galileo's laws *in toto*, since they posited a vacuum and an incorporeal force, gravitation. He was ready to use them, however, as a roughly useful tool for computation. Yet in the course of the seventeenth century, the dichotomy between computation and philosophy grew less sharp. In Galileo's method, empirical observation was crucial, notably in his experiments with inclined planes (which provided verification not so easily available from falling bodies, since motion on inclined planes was sufficiently slow to permit measurements and comparisons); yet empirical observation, intuitive concept, mathematical generalization, and philosophical law were all inextricably concatenated, and philosophy was regarded as neither different as a kind of knowledge from computation nor superior to or independent of it. Incidentally, Galileo performed his experiments on falling bodies without the pendulum clock. He had to measure time by the weight of water from a steady flow; only at the end of his life, when he was already blind, did he dictate his specifications for a pendulum clock based upon the principle of the isochronism of the pendulum—that the time consumed in the swing of a pendulum is independent of its displacement, or the distance traversed—a principle which he is traditionally supposed to have discovered while he was a student at Pisa.

Galileo's contemporaries, some of them his disciples, extended the study of mechanics. Evangelista Torricelli (1608-47) was outstanding in the field of the dynamics of liquids (hydrodynamics), studying the relation of such factors as the path, velocity, and pressure to the flow of liquids. Pascal advanced the study of hydrostatics by working on the principle, earlier reached by Stevin, that at any point of a fluid the pressure is the same in all directions, and he contributed to the field of pneumatics (the mechanics of gaseous bodies) the suggestion that the phenomena produced by atmospheric pressure correspond to that exerted by a liquid.

Huygens was perhaps the true founder of the science of 'dynamics' (a word coined by Leibniz). As we already have seen, Huygens continued Galileo's work with the pendulum, producing an efficient pendulum clock and elaborating the knowledge of pendular action. In the process he propounded the mathematical relationship of a centrifugal force in a circular motion to its velocity (directly as the square thereof) and to its radius (inversely as the square thereof). Along with Wren, Wallis, and Edmé Mariotte (1620?-84), Huygens also increased the knowledge of the elementary laws of impact (the mutual action of colliding bodies on each other), proving that the sum of the kinetic energy of two elastic balls after impact is equal to that before impact.

Newton thus had at his disposal, when he undertook his studies, a rich accumulation of suggestive material in mathematics, astronomy, and mechanics, and perhaps his greatest claim to glory lies not so much in his own original contributions as in his putting the physical science of his day into a cohesive body of knowledge. His *Principia* opens with definitions of the major concepts of mechanics with which he proposed to deal—mass (the quantity of matter in a body, the product of its density and bulk), momentum (the quantity of its motion, the product of its mass and velocity), and force (any action which changes or tends to change its state of rest or the uniformity of its motion). He then gave his attention to dynamics. Building upon or correcting the work of Galileo, Descartes, Kepler, Huygens, Hooke, and others in terrestrial and celestial mechanics, he proved that all objects are subject not only to a common law of gravity but also to common laws of motion. His laws of motion are set forth in the *Principia*, Book I. The first law ('every body continues in a state of rest or of uniform motion in a right line unless it is compelled to change that state by forces impressed upon it') was the definitive statement of the principle of inertia; it emphasized the role of force in changing either motion or rest. It gave the final touch needed to upset the Aristotelian conviction that motion rather than rest is the more 'natural' state of matter. Newton's second law of motion ('the change of motion is proportional to the motive force impressed and is made in the direction of the right line in which that force is impressed') also called attention to force; it provided a formula for the measurement of force ($F = ma$). Newton's third law of motion ('to every action there is always opposed an equal reaction') was the most original contribution of the three. It indicated that forces occur in pairs, that *equilibrium* is not necessarily synonymous with *rest*, and that the total effect of forces in the universe must even out. The implications of this law for celestial mechanics are obvious. For over two hundred years Newton's work remained the basis of the mechanical sciences.

In the eighteenth century mechanics was the work of men who were skilled mathematicians, for mathematics had grown with, and had become prerequisite to, good work in mechanics. Thus, a series of general ideas were formulated that could be applied to problems in many fields. One of these was the principle of the conservation of force. Unlike Newton, who believed that the quantity of motion in the universe needed replenishment from time to time by divine intervention, Leibniz posited a finite amount of force in a closed universe, assuming that, as one object lost force, it communicated it to others. Johann and Daniel Bernoulli, applying their mathematical skill along this line, put forth 'the great law of the conservation of *vis viva*' but, restricting their work to mechanics, did not extend it to other branches of physics. Johann Bernoulli, building on Stevin's and Galileo's observations of particular systems in equilibrium, such as balanced weights on pulleys or on inclined planes, noted the general tendency, when a small displacement takes place in such a stable system, for the equilibrium to be re-established. Calling the small displacement a *virtual velocity* and calling the product of the force times the displacement in its direction *energy*, he arrived (1717) at the principle of virtual velocities: 'In any equilibrium of forces whatsoever, in whatever manner they may be applied, and in whatever directions they may act upon one another, whether directly or indirectly, the sum of the positive energies will be equal to the sum of the negative energies taken positively.'[16] Today Bernoulli's statement has come to be called 'the principle of virtual work' (*work* having meanwhile been defined as the product of force and distance); it states that for a system in equilibrium, a very slight displacement of relative position may be regarded as effecting no change of energy. For bodies in motion an equally significant contribution came with a theorem known (after its author) as 'd'Alembert's principle'; it states that the actions and reactions of a system of free bodies cancel one another (and they are thus in what today would be called 'kinetic equilibrium'), the internal reactions being equivalent to the external or impressed forces. In 1744 Maupertuis, defining 'action' as the product of mass times velocity times distance of change within a dynamic system unaffected by outside forces, enunciated 'the principle of least action': 'Whenever any change occurs in Nature, the quantity of action employed for this change is always the least possible.'[17] Daniel Bernoulli, Euler, Lagrange, and others also worked on this principle, which was completely formulated only during later centuries as the principle of stationary action. By the end of the eighteenth century, however, Lagrange was able to combine the principles of virtual velocities and of least action to formulate equations pertaining to the motion of any system of bodies (see Volume V).

Advances in Optics

The study of optics made marked advances during these centuries. Scientists had long known that light rays bend, or are refracted, when passing from a rarer to a denser medium. Kepler attempted (1604) to arrive at a general law of refraction but reached an approximation sufficient only for an elementary theory of vision. He also, in studying the telescope, gave a geometrical explanation of it in his *Dioptrice* (1611), thereby becoming the founder of modern optics. In the study of the eye's function Kepler improved on the ideas of Alhazen. Willibrord Snell (1591–1626) of Leyden established (1621)—though only intuitively—the basic law of photometry: the intensity of light varies inversely as the square of the distance from its source. Snell also (1621) figured out the law of refraction (now stated: $\sin i = n \sin r$), which means essentially that rays of light passing from air into a denser medium are bent toward the vertical by a constant ratio (the refractive index). Snell's law remained unknown until Descartes restated it independently in 1637 in his *Dioptrique*. According to Descartes light is a sort of thrust or pressure transmitted by particle to particle from the source through the intervening plenum. It was logical for Descartes to deduce from his premiss of vortexes that light would travel more rapidly in a dense than in a light medium. Fermat questioned Descartes' view, however, basing his argument on the principle of least time (that nature does things with the greatest possible economy of time). Assuming that light would therefore move faster through the more extensive medium, air, than through water or glass and using the calculus to determine the minima and maxima involved, he showed that Snell's law held mathematically.

Later in the seventeenth century two rival hypotheses struggled for predominance in the study of light. One, the corpuscular hypothesis, leaning upon the contemporary atomism (see below), explained light as made up of particles emitted from luminous bodies; the other, the undulatory hypothesis, described it as a wave in an all-pervading medium. A series of studies of the phenomenon of diffraction (the breaking-up of light into bands of brightness and shade or of colour) by Francesco Grimaldi (1618–63), professor of mathematics at Bologna, seemed to support the wave hypothesis. In the same year (1665) that Grimaldi's findings were published, Hooke published his *Micrographia*, in which he too supported the wave theory. Hooke thought of light as spread, like eddies in a pool, by a rapid series of spherical vibrations or pulses in an all-pervading medium, each light ray thus being a radius of a sphere and each sphere normally cutting the rays at right angles. Colour occurred, he decided, whenever the pulses deviated in an oblique direction to the light rays. From his study of irridescent substances such as soap bubbles and mica flakes he concluded that when light formed colour at a given point, the colour depended on the thickness of the coloured surface at that point. Where the thickness changed gradually, he found a band of colours varying in the same order as those of the rainbow.

Although differences of velocity were implicit in Snell's law of refraction some students of light held that light travels with an infinite velocity. Roemer observed, however, that the intervals of observable time between the eclipses of Jupiter's moons were shorter when the Earth and Jupiter were approaching each other than when they were receding, and he concluded that light had a finite velocity (1675). His estimate of the velocity of light was approximately 193,000 kilometres or 120,000 miles per second, which is over 100,000 kilometres short of the now accepted figure. Although this finding was rejected by the Cartesians, Bradley's findings on the aberration of light from the stars, which we have seen came in 1726, seemed to verify Roemer's work.

Prismatic colours had long been known; dealers in diamonds, for example, tried to cut their stones in such a way as to show colour to best advantage. In 1672 Newton, who had read Kepler's *Dioptrice* while a student at Cambridge, published his first scientific paper in the *Philosophical Transactions*, the organ of the Royal Society; it was a report of his experiments with prisms. Speculating on the arrangement of the spectrum, he came to the conclusion that sunlight was a mixture of lights of all the colours of the rainbow. Hooke took exception to Newton's theory, insisting upon his own; colour is due to varying arrangements of light waves on upper and lower reflecting surfaces. Huygens, also differing with Newton, in 1678 announced his theory to the Académie des Sciences and in 1690 published it in his *Traité de la lumière*. It held that light spreads from a source through an all-pervading plenum or ether in regular spherical emissions each particle of which, in turn, emits a wavelet. His theory, he felt, explained the phenomenon of double refraction as due to the passage of light first through ether in free space and then through ether in the pores of material objects. At first Newton tried to combine the undulatory with a corpuscular theory of light but finally decided for the corpuscular theory: 'Nothing more is requisite for putting the Rays of Light into Fits of easy Reflexion and easy Transmission, than that they be small Bodies which by their attractive Powers, or some other Force, stir up Vibrations in what they act upon.'[18] Newton's study of colour had led him to abandon any hope of making an improved refracting telescope on the mistaken assumption that an achromatic telescope was impossible. Nevertheless, Hall privately made an achromatic telescope a few years after Newton's death,[19] and in 1758 Dollond independently discovered and publicly revealed how it could be done.

The overawing authority of Newton made the corpuscular theory of light dominant for another century, and several attempts were made to verify it by experimental evidence. The Dalmatian-born Italian Jesuit scholar R. G. Boscovich (1711 ?–87) taught that matter, including light corpuscles, was not continuous but was made up of minute particles surrounded by spheres of repulsion or attraction, thus permitting light to penetrate certain substances. Euler, on the other hand, was a proponent of a wave theory and put forth his arguments in popular *Lettres à une princesse d'Allemagne* (1760–62). Although he marshalled his arguments well, he submitted no fresh evidence to shake the foundation of the corpuscular hypothesis. To answer this argument, Joseph Priestley (1733–1804) published his *History and Present State of Discoveries relating to Vision, Light and Colours* (1772). Yet in the nineteenth century the Hooke–Huygens wave theory won out, only to be challenged again in the twentieth.

Kepler, Snell, Huygens, and others had studied the varying intensity of light, but precise methods of photometry came only in the eighteenth century with the Comte de Buffon (1707–88), who examined the varying intensities of different luminous bodies and experimented with sunrays. Pierre Bouguer (1698–1758) constructed the first effective photometer and showed, as Snell previously had intuitively suspected, that light intensity is inversely proportional to the square of the distance from its source. The German physicist Johann Heinrich Lambert (1728–77) summed up the photometry of his day in a work entitled *Photometria, sive de Mensura et Gradibus Luminis, Colorum et Umbrae* (1760), which discussed also many of the problems still raised today. Although Bouguer was a more careful experimenter, Lambert is generally regarded as the creator of the modern system of photometry.

The Study of Heat

No precise distinctions were made between fire, flame, light, and heat before the seventeenth century. As the quarrel over the corpuscular theory of light indicated, the theory was common, though disputed, that (to use Newton's words) 'God in the Beginning form'd matter in solid, massy, hard, impenetrable, movable Particles.'[20] An earnest student of Epicurus, Pierre Gassendi (1592–1655), tried, with some success, to adapt Epicureanism to Christian theology, and he was one of the staunchest advocates of atomism, derived from the physical theories of Democritus and the Epicureans. He applied it to heat, maintaining that heat consisted of special types of atoms, cold being produced by other, 'frigorific' ones.

In contrast, Francis Bacon, his contemporary, and some English successors to Bacon agreed with Plato that heat was a form of motion. In his *Novum Organum* Bacon put forth views that at first sound quite modern, although closer reading may suggest confusion. A series of interesting experiments in the new scientific vein later led Boyle also to the conclusion that heat was the rapid agitation of the components of a substance. Although he also talked of 'atoms of fire', he said in his work *On the Mechanical Origin of Heat and Cold* (1675): 'Heat seems principally to consist in that mechanical property of matter called motion.' He dismissed as erroneous the idea that air was necessary to produce heat—an idea that many had accepted, not differentiating between combustion and heat. Hooke went further than Boyle, maintaining that heat was 'a property of a body arising from the motion or agitation of its parts.'[21] He distinguished heat from fire and flame and held that all bodies had some degree of heat, nothing being perfectly cold.

The distinction between light and heat only gradually became clearer. For centuries mirror and lenses had been used to focus the sun's rays on combustible material to bring about fire, and Bacon in the *Novum Organum* suggested the use of burning-glasses. In a later work he speculated too whether a mirror could concentrate cold as well as heat, but the Accademia del Cimento was the first to demonstrate experimentally the reflection of cold. The French physicist Edmé Mariotte in 1679 pointed to an important difference between the sun's heat, on the one hand, and rays of a fire, on the other: when heat from the sun passed through a transparent body, it was not separated from light, but heat was separated from light in the case of rays from a fire. This difference indicated that the radiant heat of a fire was not identical with its light.

Despite the more scientific views (discussed below) of Hooke and others on combustion, for a long time the so-called 'caloric theory' of heat was considered valid. This theory maintained that heat was engendered by a material substance which was given the name *caloric*. Caloric was described as an elastic fluid that was all-pervading and imponderable; its particles were attracted by other matter but repelled by one another. If two bodies of different temperature came into contact, caloric flowed from the hotter to the colder until the two were brought into equilibrium.

The study of heat was aided by increased efficiency in the measuring of temperature. Thanks to the development of the thermometer by Fahrenheit, Réaumur, and Celsius (see above), the science of heat was gradually placed on a quantitative basis. In some circles the theory of Gassendi as modified by his critic Jean Baptiste Morin (1583–1656) prevailed—that heat and cold were different though associated entities, but Georg Wolfgang Krafft (1701–54) and Georg Wilhelm Richmann (1711–53), both members of the St Petersburg Academy, dropped units of cold from their calculations, dealing only with varying degrees of heat. Richmann devised a formula for determining the temperature of a mixture of liquids, which was based on the assumption that the intensity of a given quantity of heat would vary inversely to the mass of the heated substance or mixture of substances. Experiments by Johan Gadolin (1760–1852), a Finnish scientist, and others showed that that assumption held true only for bodies of homogeneous composition, other things being equal. Lomonosov, who began with an atomistic hypothesis, suspected the kinetic nature of heat, suggesting, for example, that heat transfer in gases was the result of elastic collisions among their particles.

Meanwhile, Boyle, John Mayow (1643 ?–79), and others were conducting the investigations of combustion that will be described below. In consequence, about 1760 Joseph Black (1728–99) was in a position to expound the distinction between heating value and temperature, that is, between the quantity and the intensity of heat. This distinction was based on the principle that each body had its own 'capacity for heat', which was in no way related to the quantity of matter it contained. This 'capacity for heat' is now known as 'specific heat'. Within several years Black was able to demonstrate that during such changes as melting and evaporation definite quantities of heat seem to be absorbed or to disappear and cannot be detected by the thermometer, but that during the reverse procedures (that is, freezing and condensation) these quantities of heat reappear. That quantity he labelled 'latent heat'. Some years later, Johann Carl Wilcke (1732–96), German–Swedish scientist, experimenting with the melting of snow at Stockholm, came independently to similar conclusions. Black's discovery was of great use to James Watt, we shall see, in developing his steam engine. Before the end of the century the studies of Benjamin Thompson (Count Rumford) and others made possible long strides in the study of heat, but the caloric theory continued to be embraced into the nineteenth century.

The Study of Acoustics

The experimental school, in attempting to determine the nature of motion, produced results that were highly suggestive also in explaining the phenomenon of sound (acoustics). The relationship of pitch to length of string had been recognized since Pythagoras, but Galileo was the first to draw attention to the rate of vibration of the string as the significant factor. Reporting Galileo's otherwise little known studies of sound, a French admirer, Marin Mersenne, in *Traité de l'harmonie universelle* (1627) and *Harmonicorum Libri* (1635), demonstrated how sound was determined by vibration. Repeating Pythagoras' experiment, Mersenne went on to show that the pitch of the note emitted by a vibrating string was inversely proportional to the square root of the density of the material composing the string and directly proportional to the square root of its tension. He inquired further why a freely vibrating string produces not only its clearest, or fundamental, tone but overtones as well and why as the fundamental tone weakens, certain other tones continue for a while. Descartes suggested that the vibration of a whole string produces its fundamental tone while the vibration of separate parts within it produce its overtones, but verification of his hypothesis did not come until later (see below).

Another problem of acoustics that contemporaneously attracted attention was the measurement of the velocity of sound. Aristotelian physics had taught that high tones were transmitted through the air more rapidly than low tones. Gassendi was one of the first to carry on significant experimental research on this problem. He had a cannon and a musket fired at the same instant and measured the time between the moment that observers at a suitable point saw the flash and the moment that they heard the report, and he found that both reports were heard simultaneously. Thus still another Aristotelian doctrine was upset. Gassendi calculated the velocity of sound to be about 1473 Paris feet per second. Throughout the century others conducted similar experiments, and all of them, including Mersenne, Borelli, Viviani, Boyle, Cassini, Huygens, Picard, and Roemer, got lower velocities.

In the early seventeenth century the Aristotelian assumption that sound is transmitted through the medium of air was still generally accepted. A few, however, believed that only certain parts of the air rather than the whole were necessary. For example, Gassendi, in keeping with his atomism, thought that special atoms in the air carried sound. To what extent the audibility of sound was correlative to the density of air could not be settled experimentally until a proper instrument became available. The invention of the air-pump by Otto von Guericke (c. 1650) supplied the needed device; it used air pressure to drive a piston in a cylinder whose air was thereby alternately exhausted and supplied. The inventor himself conducted a series of experiments which were fundamental to an understanding of the property of gases, and one of them, confirmed by the subsequent findings of Boyle, Denys Papin (1647–1712), and Francis Hauksbee (d. 1713 ?), proved not only that audibility varied with the density of air but also that sound was diffused through water and solids, thus undermining another Aristotelian teaching.

The research of these men demonstrated, in addition, that the intensity (or loudness) of sound (as distinguished from pitch) varied with the density of air. This fact suggested that sound intensity might differ with different gases. Priestley's subsequent tests showed that sound was barely audible in hydrogen, stronger in oxygen than in air, and in carbonic acid gas much stronger still. The question arose also whether varying temperatures had any influence on sound intensity. William Derham (1657–1735) conducted experiments which determined that in general sounds are stronger in winter than in summer and that the sound of firearms is not weakened in damp weather but is almost inaudible in very dry weather.

Inevitably the study of sound entered the field of music. Earlier observations had indicated that a sound resulting from two deep organ tones differing slightly in frequency would have periodic variations of intensity ('beats'). Joseph Sauveur (1653–1716) recognized that these variations must be caused by the periodic coincidence of the vibrations which produced the two initial tones. Working with two notes a semitone apart whose relative frequency was known (15 to 16), he was able to calculate their vibration frequency (90 and 96) by the number of beats (6) they produced and thus to derive a formula for the vibration frequency of any note. He was also one of those who showed, as Descartes had surmised, that the overtones of a single plucked string must be caused by oscillations of parts of it. The experimental investigation of the nature of sound permitted the scientific study of music (see Chapter XII) to begin in earnest. In his *Principes d'acoustique et de musique* (1701) Sauveur indicated the natural derivation of the major chord from the fundamental tone and established the musical doctrine of harmonics or overtones. In the course of the eighteenth century, scientists, mathematicians, and musicians (D. Bernoulli, Euler, Taylor, and Guiseppe Tartini, to mention only a few who did their principal work before 1775), advanced the understanding of tone vibrations and harmonics.

The Study of Magnetism and Electricity

Until the sixteenth century the study of magnetism and electricity was essentially undeveloped. The increasing use of compasses in navigation had led, however, to some empirical observations in the field of magnetism. Lodestone was known to be capable of re-magnetizing compass needles, and the repellent and attracting qualities of the different magnetic poles was discovered early. The changes in the magnetic declination of the compass (deviation from the true north–south line) and in its dip or inclination (angle with the horizon) had been observed (see Chapter XIII), the latter independently by George Hartmann (1544) and Robert Norman (1581), but had not yet been carefully differentiated.

To William Gilbert (1540?–1605), physician to Queen Elizabeth, usually goes the credit for initiating the scientific study of magnetism and electricity. He is said to have spent great sums of money in research, rejecting the traditional belief in the medicinal and occult virtues of the magnet as well as in other superstitions of the day. He devised an instrument with a metallic needle for measuring the electrification of various materials and proved that other things than amber were electrified by friction. One of the first to use an experimental procedure (only later to be made explicit by his contemporary Francis Bacon), he demonstrated the difference between electrical and magnetic influences, showing that magnets act on only iron objects or lodestones and orient them in a specific direction, while electrical forces act on a large number of other materials as well without having any effect upon their orientation. His experiences with the lodestone led him to make experiments with a small globular lodestone (later called 'a little Earth', or *terrella*) and to conclude that the Earth itself is a huge lodestone or magnet. He mistakenly attributed magnetic properties to the other planets as well and asserted that magnetism explained why the same face of the moon always was turned toward the Earth—a fruitful error, since it led to the idea of the mutual attraction of widely separated bodies.

Even if some of Gilbert's astronomy was wrong, his detailed experiments mark the beginning of the modern approach to planetary motion, magnetism, and electricity. The publication of his major book, entitled *De Magnete, Magneticisque Corporibus, et de Magno Magnete Tellure; Physiologia Nova* (1600), was a decisive step toward the understanding of physical phenomena and of the experimental method by means of models. The result of about seventeen years of study, it was the first important scientific work published by an Englishman. Most of it was devoted to his findings on magnetism, only one chapter being given to a discussion of the still less familiar phenomenon of electricity.

Little advance was made beyond Gilbert's findings in those fields for over a century and a half. Descartes attempted the first scientific explanation of magnetism in his *Principia Philosophiae* (1644). Consistent with his system, he believed magnetism to be due to vortices that, he supposed, circulated about magnetic bodies. Further observations of magnetic behaviour revealed that compass deviation changed even in the same place in the course of time. Halley looked into this problem on the several scientific expeditions that he made to various parts of the world and began the systematic collection of data on compass variations. He was also the first to recognize that the aurora borealis was related to the magnetism of the Earth. During the eighteenth century students of magnetism were aided by the increasing skill of manufacturers of artificial magnets, and Charles Augustin Coulomb (1736–1806) was able to determine the law according to which the force of a magnetic pole varies. In the 1780's he demonstrated that Newton's inverse square law (gravitational attraction varies in inverse proportion to the square of the intervening distance) held good also for magnetic attraction and repulsion (see below).

Most investigations of electricity in the seventeenth century were repetitions of Gilbert's work. The Accademia del Cimento added, however, to the slowly accumulating stock of knowledge by a study of various electrical substances, listing them in the order of their attracting power, with amber at the head of the list. That excited amber lost its charge when held close to a flame was also noted. Von Guericke succeeded (*c.* 1650) in making an electric generator and discovering electrical discharge; his generator's essential component was a ball of sulphur continuously rotated and rubbed by hand or cloth so as to produce a charge. The sulphur, it was found, then attracted various objects such as paper and feathers. Leibniz observed electric sparks (1671–72). Picard discovered murcurial phosphorescence (1675), and the phenomenon fascinated early-eighteenth-century scientists. Some attempted to explain the phosphorescence of excited mercury in a barometer tube as the action of sulphur or some special type of phosphorus in the mercury, until Hauksbee gave the correct explanation (1709): the friction of the mercury against the glass tube generated electricity.

Observations like these made clearer Gilbert's basic distinction between electric and non-electric substances. After much experimentation Stephen Gray (1729) was able to distinguish between a conducting and a non-conducting substance. He demonstrated that certain bodies could receive and transmit electrical properties whereas other bodies, such as glass and silk, could neither give nor receive electrical properties and might thus be used to preserve charges. Jean Desaguliers (1683–1744) gave the name of *conductors* to substances capable of transmitting electricity and of *supporters* to those which lacked this capacity; the latter were in the nineteenth century called *insulators*. Charles François Du Fay (1648–1734) was able to distinguish two opposing kinds of electricity, each attracting the other and repelling its own kind; he made the error of thinking that one kind was 'vitreous' and the other 'resinous'. We now prefer to call them positive and negative.

By the middle of the eighteenth century electrical machines and investigations of electricity were quite fashionable. (Pl. 95a, b, c.) One of the problems facing investigators was to find some way of preserving electric charges. Once it was established that water could be electrified and that glass was a non-conductor, the first electrical condenser (today known as the Leyden jar) became possible. It was developed by two men working independently, E. G. von Kleist[22] of Pomerania in 1745 and Pieter van Musschenbroek of Leyden in 1746. Subsequent improvements allowed fascinated people to engage in transmitting electrical shocks at a distance; William Watson (1715–87) sent one across the Thames in 1747.

Seventeenth-century investigators had explained electrical phenomena as due to quasi-material effluvia, and some attempted to show that bodies when electrified increased their weight. Their failure to do so led them to conclude not that electricity was merely a condition of charged bodies but rather that, like heat and light in the corpuscular system, it was an imponderable substance. The doctrine of imponderable substances, however, supplied no causal explanation for electricity, whereas the wave theory of light seemed to provide a simple one. Euler, for example, believed that the source of electrical processes was the ether, in which light was also propagated, electricity being due to a disturbance of the ether's equilibrium.

Benjamin Franklin thought in somewhat similar terms. His interest in electrical phenomena was first roused by some electrical apparatus sent to Philadelphia by Peter Collinson, a London merchant, member of the Royal Society. In the popular mind at least, Franklin's study of lightning as an electrical phenomenon is a most spectacular and unprecedented achievement. Yet several investigators had preceded him with similar investigations. For instance, a friend of Boyle named Dr Wall had likened certain electrical experiments to thunder and lightning (1709); so had Newton; and in 1746 the German physicist J. H. Winkler came to the same conclusion. In 1749 Franklin set forth a large body of evidence on which he based his idea that thunderstorms are electrical in nature. In 1752 he carried out his famous kite experiment, collecting an electrical charge directly from a thundercloud into a Leyden jar. He eventually deduced that a single electric fluid pervaded all bodies, though in varying quantities, and was the cause of all electrical phenomena. He was the first to talk of positive and negative electricity. A body was electrically neutral, he said, when its electric fluid was in equilibrium within and without; if it had more than its normal amount of fluid, it was positively electrified and, if less, negatively electrified. Some scholars disagreed and put forth a theory of two fluids, but Franklin was able to explain the charging of the Leyden jar in terms of one. For this theory of electricity, which he communicated to the Royal Society, he was in 1756 made a member.

Several contemporaries of Franklin also made significant contributions to electrical studies, which, however, were overshadowed by his dramatic success. In 1753 Richmann became one of the first 'martyrs of science' when struck by lightning while attempting to measure atmospheric electricity with an 'electrometer' he had devised as early as 1745. Wilcke established in 1757 the fact that when two bodies are rubbed together both negative and positive electrification are invariably produced. F. U. T. Aepinus (1724–1802), for a time professor at the Academy of Berlin and later at that of St Petersburg, where he superintended the Normal School, collaborated in some of Wilcke's investigations. Aepinus discovered the electrification of material by induction and demonstrated that the distinction between conductors and insulators is far from absolute.

The relative simplicity of Franklin's experiments evidences the primitive state of contemporary knowledge about electrical phenomena. By the close of the eighteenth century scientists were able to go further than Franklin and other pioneers and to determine a precise law for the measurement of electrical forces. The new science of electrostatics thus developed. Aepinus, whose *Testamen Theoriae Electricitatis et Magnetismi* (1759) first systematically attempted to move the study of electricity from a descriptive to a quantitative basis, recognized that the electric force between particles diminished with the increase in the distance between them. Daniel Gralath, burgomeister of Danzig, experimented with electric shocks and invented an electrometer (*c.* 1746). Priestley in *The History and Present State of Electricity* (1767) summed up and expounded the then known studies of electrical phenomena in a persuasive way that won him membership in the Royal Society. He suggested that Newton's inverse square law of gravitational attraction applied also to electrical attraction. Henry Cavendish (1731–1810) proved this application experimentally in 1771, but he did not publish his findings, and they remained unknown until 1879. It remained for Coulomb, by means of a torsion balance that he invented which was capable of measuring the force of an electric charge, to demonstrate the law experimentally. His experiment was conducted at the same time as the one (described above) by which he proved that magnetic attraction was likewise subject to the inverse square law. The usual unit of quantity of electricity is now known as a *coulomb*.

Load, Stresses, and Strains

Before the sixteenth century builders made little effort to work out a rational explanation of their craft. Vitruvius' writings on architecture, rediscovered in the fifteenth century, showed no real knowledge of what we today would call scientific principles of construction. Few working drawings by medieval builders are extant, but studies of the ground-plans of medieval buildings make quite obvious that although their builders worked out proportions with remarkable effectiveness, they did so chiefly on practical rather than theoretical principles. Craftsmen in the building tradition had long known what loads, stresses, and strains various materials and structures could bear, but they had learned such things by trial and error.

The experimental investigation of the behaviour of materials was first clearly stated in Leonardo da Vinci's writings. He expressed, for instance, what architects had practiced—namely, that an upright pillar consisting of a compact bundle of shafts could support a load much heavier than the sum of the loads which the shafts could support separately. He appears to have concluded from actual experiment that a pillar of a given height has a carrying power proportional to the cube of its diameter. His manuscripts mention still other calculations and experiments related to the strength of materials.

Little systematic study of the strength of materials is otherwise known before Galileo. Some of the questions he raised were stimulated by his conversations with craftsmen in the Venetian Arsenal and his observations of procedures there. It was already well recognized that the scale of a structure was important in determining its strength. Galileo, going further, studied the nature and measurement of the resistance of materials to fracture. He set forth some interesting propositions and proved them geometrically. One example was an elaboration of Leonardo's conclusion: 'In prisms and cylinders of equal length, but of unequal thickness, the resistance to fracture increases in the same ratio as the cube of the thickness of the base.'[23] Why then could giant fish and huge ships with slender bases survive at sea? he asked, and he answered: Only because water deprived them of their weight. He concluded that it would be impossible to increase indefinitely the dimensions of land structures.

Study of this field continued lively after Galileo. Bernard Forest de Belidor (1693–1761) brought together the various writings of the day on structural engineering, and his *La science des ingenieurs* (1729) and *Architecture hydraulique* (1737–39) have been called the first scientific textbooks on engineering. Men more noted for work in other fields also concerned themselves with the problem of the strength of materials. Mariotte took it up because of interest in hydraulics, which was growing with the increased demands for ornamental fountains. Musschenbroek, years before he began experimenting with the Leyden jar, carried out a series of comprehensive laboratory experiments with extemporized machines to test building materials under stress. The naturalist Buffon aided in inspecting and testing timber for French naval construction. The physicist Coulomb, more famous for his later work in electricity, in an essay presented to the Académie des Sciences in 1773 was the first to apply mathematical maxima and minima to measuring the strength of architectural materials; his work provided a reasoned explanation of the inclined plane which the cracks in crushed masonry often form.

Before the seventeenth century rule of thumb seems to have prevailed in the building of retaining walls. For ages man has used artificial banks or stone walls as retainers and as fortification. Late-medieval churches and castles give silent testimony of great technological skill. Italian military architects of the sixteenth century, faced with the problem of defence against artillery (see Chapter XV), abandoned the straight medieval wall, broken only by towers at suitable intervals, and favoured more complicated traces, providing frequent bastions for the defenders' artillery and at the same time presenting the besiegers with a less simple target. Despite these enduring achievements of earlier days, no record of rules or specifications to be observed in erecting walls has yet been found that can be dated before the age of Louis XIV.

Marshal de Vauban (1633–1707), the chief military engineer of the Sun-King, prepared such specifications, giving dimensions for walls between 6 and 80 feet in height. Vauban was the greatest expert of his century on fortifications. His skill made the bastion a major element of fortification until in the nineteenth century it was supplemented by the tenaille system of the Marquis de Montalembert (1714–1800). During a long military career Vauban designed or improved some 160 fortresses that were regarded as well-nigh impregnable in his day. Throughout the eighteenth century his specifications for retaining walls were gospel for the military engineer. Pierre Bullet (1639–1716) in his L'Architecture pratique (1691) gave rules for designing retaining walls and propounded a theory of earth pressure, upon which Pierre Torteaux de Bouplet (d. 1744) elaborated. Coulomb presented the first satisfactory equation for calculating the pressure of a given quantity of earth against a retaining wall.

In civil architecture the acknowledged master of the post-Gothic age was Palladio. His famous treatise on architecture (1570) dealt with such subjects as trussing materials, ancient Greek and Roman houses, and his own designs for houses, roads, bridges, piazzas, and basilicas and other temples. Though he did not allow sufficiently for the horizontal thrust of an arch, he contributed to the knowledge of the strength of abutments and of the arches which they supported. In the seventeenth century the Jesuit architect François Derrand worked out a more satisfactory arch construction by providing greater depth for the abutment as the rise of the arch was reduced. Wren, in his official reports to the government on architectural matters, indicated an interest in construction problems, and his criticism of the design of the old St Paul's Cathedral in London led to his being given, after the Great Fire of London in 1666, the task of building the new one. With the growing elaborateness of public buildings, serious studies were made of the arch and its abutments. Various methods were discussed by François Blondel, Hooke, Philippe de Lahire (d. 1719), and Coulomb (to mention only a few). The design, structure, and strength of Classical arches and domes and their supporting piers became a subject of controversy in French engineering circles with the building by Jacques Germain Soufflot (1713–80) of the Church of Sainte-Geneviève (later named the Pantheon) in Paris. The controversy lasted until the end of the century, leading to a number of serious experiments and monographs on the strength of building materials.

The Rise of the Science of Meteorology

Prior to the seventeenth century the standard treatise on meteorology was Aristotle's *Meteorologica*. The chief means of predicting weather were astrological observations, weather-lore founded on superstition, and the uncertain data of untrained observers. Descartes' *Météores* (1637), though sometimes in error, at least gave the study the dignity of a branch of physics. The discovery and improvement of certain instruments made possible a more exact examination of the atmosphere. In the seventeenth century, the thermometer was introduced (see above), and the Accademia del Cimento made a working hygroscope. Vicenzo Viviani (1621–1703), Torricelli, and Von Guericke developed the barometer (and thereby explained nature's *horror vacui* as due to atmospheric pressure). Hooke produced a wind-gauge and a weather clock, Hooke and Wren a rain-gauge. A composite weather clock was in operation by 1700. Studies were made also of the relationship of wind-currents to general atmospheric conditions; speculation was especially keen about the trade winds. During this transitional period meteorology, consisting of attempts to understand atmospheric pressure and to measure weather phenomena, was merely an offshoot, so to speak, of elementary pneumatics. Nevertheless, as early as 1660 Von Guericke had acquired enough understanding of relevant barometric principles to forecast a storm from a sudden drop of atmospheric pressure.

The contemporary study of gases led to the pronouncement of Boyle's (or Mariotte's) law (the volume of a gas varies in inverse proportion to the pressure upon it, providing the temperature remains constant). One of several important consequences of this discovery was that it prompted serious study of the Earth's atmosphere. Hooke and Mariotte both discussed the extent of that atmosphere, and Halley in 1686 made a good rough estimate of it—not over 45 miles high. This estimate was based on the assumption that air cannot be rarefied to much more than 3000 times its volume at ground level. Since the atmosphere's relation to the winds was not understood, its movements were assumed to be due to disturbances of the equilibrium governing atmospheric pressure. Inquiries into the nature of wind were also carried on, particularly by Halley, who produced the earliest meteorological chart. He at first thought that the aurora borealis was atmospheric, but (see above) he eventually decided that it was a magnetic phenomenon.

Increased contacts throughout the world gave greater opportunity for comparative observations. As early as the seventeenth century the value of synchronous meteorological observations at various places was recognized. Even before the development of the pendulum clock permitted relatively precise time allowances for such work, a concerted series of instrumental observations was undertaken. Paris, Clermont-Ferrand, and Stockholm were the scenes of the earliest meteorological investigations (1649–51) of which the records are still extant. The Grand Duke Ferdinand II of Tuscany (1610–70), scientist and patron of the Accademia del Cimento, established the first large-scale international organization, supplying its observers with instruments from his own purse; forms calling for observations of pressure, temperature, wind direction, and humidity were also provided.

Such studies not only obtained meteorological information but also tested old instruments and suggested new ones. The Hungarian scientist J. A. von Segner (1707–77), better known for his turbine (Segner's water-wheel) and his suggestion of the idea of surface tension in liquids, wrote several treatises dealing with the mathematics of thermometers and barometers. The Russian polyhistor Lomonosov showed great ingenuity in the improvement of old instruments and the invention of new ones—such as an indoor anemometer, a thermometer of 150 degrees between freezing and boiling, and a pendulum that was delicate enough to suggest the tidal motions of the earth's crust.[24] The meteorologist Jean André Deluc (1727–1817) made marked changes in the barometer and the thermometer. Experimenting with several liquids, he recommended the use of mercury for thermometers (as Fahrenheit had done before him). In the controversy already raging over the relative merits of Réaumur's and Fahrenheit's thermometric scale, Deluc proposed that each country continue to use the scale already adopted by it; for him the important thing was the construction of as accurate a thermometer as possible, graduation taking a secondary place.

The superstitious factors in weather prediction vanished only slowly, where they did so at all, and not until the late eighteenth century was meteorology firmly established as a substantive branch of science. Many pamphlets still were published in the eighteenth century to explain unusual or disastrous weather as the judgment of God. Nevertheless, the scientific study of weather also made progress. The philosopher Wolff put forth a dull though systematic discussion of the subject, but the best meteorological treatise of the century was that of Father Louis Cotte (1740–1815), published in 1774. Sponsored by the Académie des Sciences and derived to a large degree from information sent by scattered observers to Paris, Cotte's work was the first textbook of empirical meteorology.

Iatrochemistry and the Beginnings of Modern Chemistry

In the science of chemistry the most promising lines of advance appeared in the enterprise of the iatrochemists and the workers in the budding chemical industry. The iatrochemists were a school that endeavoured to make physiology a branch of chemistry. The founder of this school was Theophrastus Philipp Aureolus Bombastus von Hohenheim (1493–1541), better known as Paracelsus because, a self-taught Swiss physician, he often used the prefix *para* ('super') in the titles of his works to emphasize his superiority of knowledge. Having examined miners' diseases and metallurgy at first hand in the mines of the Tyrol, he discovered chemical problems far more intriguing than the alchemical processes he previously had studied. Curiosity led him to travel through western Europe learning the healing art from the books of nature and experience. Later, as professor of medicine and town physician at Basel, he expounded and practiced novel theories so successfully but also so tactlessly that he was driven out by the local practitioners to lead a life of wandering from city to city. Everywhere he went he angered physicians and pharmacists by publicly burning the books of Galen and other ancient physicians and by ridiculing the humors, bleedings, and purgings of the current medical practice in the Coan tradition. Insisting on a curiously empirical yet mystical approach and relying heavily on novel concoctions for healing, he broached the Cnidian theory that the processes of the human body are chemical and therefore, when out of order, can be cured by readjusting the body chemistry with specifics. He laid great stress on the *tria prima*—salt (earth, the incombustible principle), sulphur (fire, the combustible principle), and mercury (air, the volatile principle)—but he also used arsenic, opium, and iron.

For all his quarrel with his contemporaries Paracelsus was also a child of his day. He believed in transmutation, in the philosopher's stone and other alchemic wonders, in nymphs and sylphs. To him the natural and the supernatural world were equally subject to the control of the physician, but his belief in mystical, demoniacal, and magical forces made it impossible for him to arrive at natural law. His contempt for some of the healing methods of Galen and his followers was not always due to logical considerations. In place of herbal remedies and diet he advocated the use of metallic drugs that had been purified by fire and of medicines prepared by techniques familiar to alchemists. His underlying principle—that effective medicines might be prepared in the chemical laboratory—whatever its intrinsic merit, was hidden in the occult.

Nevertheless, Paracelsus and other iatrochemists, in their desire to discover and reveal the chemical nature of physiological processes, were pioneers preparing the way for a sounder chemical theory. Valerius Cordus (1515–44), better known as a botanist than as a physician or alchemist, described in scientific terms the method of obtaining ether by treating sulphuric acid with alcohol. Andreas Libavius (1550–1616), bitterly criticizing Paracelsus for relying on magical remedies and astrology, took pride in eliminating superstitious elements from his own work, and his *Alchymia* (1597), with a section on *chemia* and related techniques, is a storehouse of the chemical knowledge and laboratory methods of his day. In basic ideas, nevertheless, he differed little from Paracelsus and the late medieval alchemists, whom he often cited with approval as well as condemnation. He too believed in transmutation. He even went so far as to write a *Defensio et Declaratio Perspicua Alchymiae*

Transmutatoriae (1604) in reply to a work attacking alchemy. Johann Rudolf Glauber (1604–68) produced a number of both medicinal and industrial preparations. His fame rests today chiefly on the continued use of Glauber's salt, which he made from vitriol and common salt, not only as a cathartic but also as an alkali in the dyeing process.

The most notable of the iatrochemists was Jean Baptiste van Helmont (1577–1644). To him Paracelsus's theory of three principle elements was unacceptable, since material bodies could not be resolved into them. He put forward a novel theory—that all tangible bodies are a product of water—and sought to verify it by experiment. Having planted a small willow tree in a tub of earth, he found, about five years later, that the tree had gained 164 pounds, although none of the earth had disappeared; hence, he inferred, the solid matter of the tree must have been transmuted from the water that the tree had absorbed—a striking example of the danger of the empirical method when applied to an inflexible conceptual scheme. Helmont also showed the material character of gases and differentiated between water vapour, gas, and air. He held that digestion was a process of fermentation, and he prescribed alkalis to counteract digestive acidity. It was he who coined the term *gas*, deriving it from the Greek Χάος, but not until Lavoisier was the term generally used, most chemists being satisfied with *air*.

The kind of chemical knowledge that came from the nascent chemical industry was frequently less theoretical and more technological than iatrochemistry. The bleaching, dyeing, and cleaning processes all depended upon practical experience. The making of glass, pottery, and gunpowder required some empirical chemical knowledge. Mining involved the manufacture of nitric acid and other chemical processes; mining treatises (which we shall mention later) frequently contained passages relevant to chemistry; and the assayer provided much experience that chemical science was eventually to use. To cite one example, the German humanist historian Georgius Agricola (Bauer) (1494–1555), who also was well trained in medicine and physics, produced remarkable treatises on geology and minerology. From personal observations in the mining region in which he lived, he compiled (in 1556) a study entitled *De Re Metallica*. Among other things, he described the process of stirring molten cast iron (puddling) with an oxidizing substance in order to produce wrought iron.

By the 1660's something akin to a dignified science of chemistry might be said to have existed. A Scot professor of chemistry, William Davidson, was attached to the Jardin du Roi in France in 1648, and a Frenchman, Nicolas de Febure, was appointed royal professor of chemistry by Charles II of England in 1660. Yet Boyle even then could say of chemistry that 'the illiterateness, the arrogance and the impostures of too many of those that pretent skill in it' caused learned men 'to repine'. But the learned repined, he implied, for the wrong reasons. They did not like to see 'any person capable of succeeding in the study of solid philosophy' become addicted to 'sooty empirics', to 'a study which they scarce think fit for any but such as are unfit for the rational and useful parts of physiology'.[25] Boyle accepted as his own task nothing less than to examine with all his senses the natural phenomena that the despised chemical art made known. He was particularly anxious to determine the nature of the material transformations already described by Libavius and his iatrochemist followers.

Boyle did not frown on the application of chemistry to medicine but was much more interested in building a connecting link between physics and chemistry. A number of 'mechanical philosophers' of the seventeenth century had come by that time to believe that matter is not infinitely divisible but is composed of a few indivisible primary 'elements' like Paracelsus's *trio prima* —mercury, sulphur, and salt. In his *Sceptical Chymist* (1661) Boyle attacked the assumption that all things are composed of three, four, or some other small number of elements, and he also exposed the semantic difficulty arising from the use of the word *element* in different ways. Reacting too far in the opposite direction, he himself decried the current usage of *element* for conveying an erroneous concept of 'certain primitive and simple or perfectly unmingled bodies, which not being made of any other bodies, or of one another, are the ingredients of which all those called perfectly mixed bodies are immediately compounded, and into which they are ultimately resolved.' We now know that he was correct at least in doubting that elements are only a small set of unmingled 'ingredients of which all ... mixed bodies are immediately compounded.' He never drew up a list of chemical elements of his own; he seems even to have doubted whether such numerous simple substances as the modern term *element* designates existed at all, preferring to believe in corpuscles as the elementary substance of all bodies. His commitment to the corpuscular, atomistic physics of his day made it possible for him even to think that metals and certain other materials actually 'grew' in the earth. But his scepticism about the elemental quality of the substances commonly called *elements* in his day was a bold step in the right direction.

Among other things, Boyle studied combustion and realized that bodies would not ordinarily burn without air. Hooke, who had been Boyle's research assistant, put forth in his *Micrographia* the idea that combustible bodies were dissolved by a certain 'nitrous substance' in the atmosphere. This substance was discussed in greater detail by Mayow, also a disciple of Boyle. In *Five Medico-Physical Treatises* (1674), Mayow gave an excellent summary of his own work along with that of Boyle, Hooke, and Richard Lower (1631–91), showing that respiration was a process closely related to combustion. Mayow suggested that that part of the air which was indispensable for respiration and combustion was composed of certain 'nitro-aerial particles'. Boyle's school thus put forward promising concepts in chemistry and chemical methodology, but it remained for other scientists to write the textbooks. The French savant Nicolas Lémery produced the first general textbook of chemistry, *Cours de Chimie* (1657), to be widely used, and it was published in new editions (e.g.

Paris, 1756) even after it was surpassed by the *Elementa Chemiae* (1732) by Herman Boerhaave (1668–1738), brilliant teacher of medicine at the University of Leiden.

For most of the eighteenth century the study of chemistry was dominated by the phlogiston theory of combustion. Johann Joachim Becher (1635–82) had contended that solid earthy substances are composed of three constituents: fixed earth (non-combustible), oily earth (combustible), and fluid earth. These were comparable to the salt, sulphur, and mercury of the iatrochemists. Georg Ernst Stahl (1660–1734), professor of medicine at Halle, republished some of Becher's works and candidly borrowed from his theory. According to Stahl, any body capable of combustion must contain an oily, sulphurous earth that escaped from the other earths during the process, and this combustible earth, which he chose to call by the Greek name of *phlogiston*, was the essential element of all combustible bodies such as charcoal, wood, and fats. In other words, burning meant the escape of phlogiston into the atmosphere or into a substance that would combine with it. The almost complete combustibility of charcoal was attributed to its rich phlogiston content. By this theory, when a metal was heated, the freeing of the phlogiston would leave behind a calx, and hence phlogiston $+$ calx $=$ metal; therefore, if charcoal were used to reheat the calx, an exchange of phlogiston would take place and the metal would be restored. (Pl. 92a.)

The theory seemed to answer many questions satisfactorily. It was accepted by leading English chemists, such as Black, Priestley, and Cavendish. Following Van Helmont in distinguishing gases from air, they began to make fruitful studies of gases, combustion, and the calcination of metals. Black identified something he called 'fixed air'; we call it carbon dioxide. Benefiting from earlier experiments by Stephen Hales (1677–1761), who developed a pneumatic trough to collect and store gases, Cavendish was able to prepare something he called 'inflammable air', or what we call hydrogen (1766). In the 1770's Karl Wilhelm Scheele (1742–86) in Sweden and Priestley in England worked on similar problems independently. Probably about 1773, Scheele arrived at the discovery of oxygen, which he called 'fire-air'; he called nitrogen 'vitiated air'. These findings he published only in 1777. Before that date Priestley had discovered and isolated several gases—among them, nitric oxide, nitrogen, carbon monoxide, and a gas which was particularly excellent for respiration and inflammation and which he called 'dephlogisticated air' (we call it oxygen). To Priestley atmospheric air was a combination of 'dephlogisticated air' (oxygen) and 'phlogisticated air' (nitrogen).

The chemical world now had much empirical data at its disposal; what was needed was a savant who, as Newton had done for physics, would give chemistry a systematic nomenclature and organization. In his 'Course on True Physical Chemistry' (1752–54), Lomonosov anticipated some of the fundamentals of modern chemistry. Drawing on Leibniz, Daniel Bernoulli, and several others who since the first decades of the seventeenth century had dealt with the problem of *vis viva* (see above) and the conservation of matter, he had as early as 1748 articulated a general conservation law. In its 1760 version it ran: 'All changes occurring in Nature are subject to the condition that, if so much is taken away from one substance, just so much is added to another.'[26] Yet the honour of being the Newton of chemistry is usually attributed to Antoine Laurent Lavoisier (1743–94).

Realizing the significance of at least his French contemporaries' and predecessors' work, Lavoisier began in the 1770's the studies that were to end in his signal contributions to chemistry. Metallurgists had long been puzzled by the fact that tin and lead increased in weight when calcined. Jean Rey (*c.* 1630) had explained this phenomenon by demonstrating that they absorbed more from the air than they lost in the process, but his work went unnoticed until 1775. Boyle (*c.* 1673) explained the weight increase as due to the absorption of fire particles. In 1772 Guyton de Morveau reported in his *Digressions* upon his experiments on the combination of metals with air, prompting Lavoisier to experiment with the combustion of phosphorous, sulphur, and metals and to report his findings to the Académie des Sciences that year. Having been enabled to use a knife-edge balance (see above) for his measurements, Lavoisier agreed with Boyle that calcination increased the weight of metals but disagreed that fire particles accounted for the increase, which he considered (without knowing Rey's similar conclusion) as due rather to air. In 1774 Priestley informed Lavoisier of his 'dephlogisticated air'. Lavoisier thereupon theorized that 'dephlogisticated air' (or 'oxygen', as he named it) probably was the factor which made combustion and calcination possible. Combustion was thus satisfactorily explained as a process of oxidation. (Lavoisier's subsequent contributions to chemical nomenclature belong to Volume V.)

With Lavoisier chemistry can be said to have become modern in spirit. He made universally acceptable the idea of chemical elements questioned by Boyle a century earlier. Like Galileo, in studying familiar phenomena he arrived at new answers from old materials. Like Newton, he incorporated a quantitative spirit into the explanation of familiar phenomena, which in turn proved capable of explaining unfamiliar phenomena. Whether he discovered or merely gave a name to oxygen is less important than that he was the first explicitly to expound the role of air in chemical change and thus overthrew the phlogiston theory, which had outlived its usefulness, substituting for it a theory that made the further growth of his science systematic and regular.

Meanwhile the ground was being prepared for the field of analytical chemistry. The work of Boyle, E. F. Geoffrey (1672–1731), A. Baumé (1728–1804), and others permitted T. O. Bergman (1735–84) to begin in 1775 the preparation of tables of 'affinity' (tendency to combine chemically) of fifty-nine substances. Leaning on the older analytical work of the iatro-chemists and Boyle and on the newer work of Black, Bergman, and other contemporary chemists, Scheele discovered a large number of new organic compounds including the vegetal acids, of which only vinegar (acetic acid) had been recognized earlier. Andreas Sigismund Marggraff (1709–82) introduced the use of the microscope for chemical analysis, discovered sugar crystals in beetroot, and analyzed other compound substances. These men laid the foundation for the subsequent development of organic chemistry.

Geology, Palaeontology, and Crystallography

Before the late eighteenth century, geology had no separate existence as a science, and the word *fossil* meant 'something dug from the ground' rather than, as in its modern connotation, 'organic remains'. In 1775 the auxiliary sciences of geology, such as palaeontology, were still at a low stage, and the prevalent cosmogony made it difficult to think of the Earth in terms of a never-beginning, never-ending development. Literal interpretation of the Biblical account of Creation within six days had implanted the conviction that the Earth was only about 6,000 years old, making extremely unconvincing any explanation of the otherwise familiar changes in the Earth's crust by some process that required a near-eternity. Nevertheless, the attribution of these changes to the Flood was beginning to encounter greater questioning than before. For example, how could the ancestors of all the many animals now known to exist on the Earth's surface have found room on Noah's Ark? And what about those animals that now were to be found only oceans away from where the Ark was supposed to have landed?

Before the eighteenth century scientists interested in geological and palaeontological matters got little beyond obvious queries about common phenomena. What made salt water go up stream from the estuaries of rivers? How did springs come to be located on hill tops? How account for the varying structure of land, the gradual conversion of seaside into inland settlements? What were fossils? Several sixteenth-century thinkers attempted explanations. Agricola, Bruno, and others concluded that valleys had been sculptured by rivers, that land and sea were continually shifting, and that fossils were organic remains. Leonardo da Vinci conjectured, like the Aristotelians, that water must be more abundant on the Earth's surface than land, and that a great deal of water must be inside the Earth. His work as an engineer led him, however, to some empirical conclusions. Having observed the silting of river mouths and the strata in excavations and on both sides of river canyons, he inferred that rivers cut their way through mountains in the course of time. He doubted that the appearance of fossil shells far inland could be a result of the Deluge or of spontaneous generation. Though he recognized the gradual, agelong transformation of the earth's surface, the origin of mountains was puzzling to him: he suggested that they were built up by river silt or by the sinking of surrounding lands in subterranean cave-ins. The Persian Gulf, he thought, had once been a great Tigris lake, and the Caspian Sea must have subterranean outlets to the Black Sea (which, in fact, is higher). Guillaume de

Postel, a sixteenth-century professor at Paris and his Netherlands contemporary Nicolaus Biesius explained geological phenomena in an even more mystical and astrological manner. Still, Postel had travelled widely and his works on geography, along with some amusing errors and serious misinformation, contained a few shrewd guesses of future geographical developments, such as the discovery of an antarctic continent and the building of canals through the Panama and Suez isthmuses.

The founding of physical geology as a science was largely the work of Agricola. His *De Natura Fossilium* (1546) (*fossil* still meaning anything dug out of the earth) was the first systematic treatment of palaeontology. This work and his posthumous (1556) *De Re Metallica* (see Chapter XV) dealt more or less indirectly with the problems of physical geology, but his *De Ortu et Causis Subterraneorum* (1546) examined them directly. His method was largely descriptive, although he attempted also to explain' earthquakes and volcanic eruptions. He worked out clearly the part played by the elements in the gradual formation of hills and mountains, and he was the first to present a detailed study of the contents of the Earth's crust. He also made a significant contribution to stratigraphic geology in his description of the order of strata in the Harz Mountains.

For the next century or so progress was slow. Gessner and David Frolich (1600–46) were among the earliest of mountain explorers, the former in the Alps (1555) and the latter in the Tatra Mountains (1616). With the examination by Nicolaus Steno (1638–86) of the geology of Tuscany the systematic study of the subject began. His small book *De Solido intra Solidum Naturaliter Contento* (1669), largely indebted to the findings of his Italian predecessors, formulated acceptable surmises concerned with the formation of the Earth's crust. Finally Giovanni Arduino (1714–95) set forth (1759) the principle that different families of organic bodies are to be found at different strata of the earth's crust and described the four strata with names (primary, secondary, tertiary, and quaternary) that are still used in geological terminology, though since refined, to designate the age of rocks.[27] The field of physical geology was further aided by the construction of geological maps, which Martin Lister (1638–1712), an English physician, was the first to propose.

Steno and other workers after him speculated about the occurrence of organic fossils and attempted to account for them. He also laid the foundation for the scientific study of crystallography. His *De Solido* showed that quartz crystals must have grown in liquids through the regular accretion of new layers upon a nucleus. Hooke and Huygens thought that the new layers must be made up of tiny spheroids. Domenico Guglielmini in 1706 published a work asserting that each salt crystallized in its own characteristic shape determined by the regularity of the angles made by its faces, and Linnaeus in *Systema Naturae* (1735) extended this assertion to around forty different mineral crystals. The findings of these and other crystallographers enabled

J. B. L. Romé de Lisle in an *Essai de cristallographie* (1772) to establish that the crystals of the same substances are closely related in shape to each other, having the same or nearly the same angles between their corresponding faces. Subsequent work by Romé de Lisle and René Just Haüy (1743–1822) led at the close of the eighteenth century to the definition of six systems of crystal structure that are still considered fundamental.

The problem of the origin of the Earth, the branch of learning today called *geogeny*, produced recurrent debate. Descartes in his *Principles of Philosophy* (1644) supposed that the Earth and the other planets had originally been glowing masses like the Sun and that as the Earth gradually cooled down, spots similar to sun spots formed on its hardening crust. Thomas Burnet in his *Sacred Theory of the Earth* (1681) stayed within the bounds of orthodoxy, supposing that the Earth had been formed from a chaotic mixture of earth, water, fire, and oil, and that the Flood accounted for the present formation of the planet. Leibniz systematized Descartes' theory in *Protogaea*, which was published only in 1749, decades after his death, possibly because he dared to look upon fossils as the evidence of aeonian changes in animal organisms. Newton, though not directly concerned with geology, suggested that the principle of gravitation might be useful in explaining the formation of the Earth and the heavenly bodies.

One of the moot points in the debate was the role to attribute to fossils. Were they tricks of God (or Nature) or were they, as Leibniz had suggested, organic remains? Throughout the eighteenth century speculation on this subject went on. A satisfactory answer depended upon the studies that gradually extended the presumed age of the planet. Joseph Torrubia, in one of the earliest works on paleontology (*Aparato para la historia natural española*, Madrid, 1754), comparing fossils found in Spain with marine specimens he had collected in the Philippines, concluded that warm waters must have at one time covered the mountains of Aragon. Lomonosov, having decided that the Earth's surface was in constant flux, concluded that the Earth had been slowly evolving and that peat, coal, and oil were of organic origin. Buffon in his *Théorie de la terre* (1749) and *Epoques de la Nature* (1778), making guesses as to the time it took for the original molten gas of the Earth to cool and then to go through six other epochs, assigned to the Earth around 80,000 years, far in excess of the traditionally accepted age. Using fossils and geological observations to back his guesses, he introduced experimentation into geology, substituting globes of cast iron for the Earth.

Geodesy, the study of the size and shape of the Earth, had engaged scientists since at least the days of the ancient Greeks. Simultaneous observations by Jean Richer and his colleagues of the Académie des Sciences when Mars approached the Earth closely in 1671 led to the discovery that a pendulum swung more slowly at Cayenne than in Paris. Some maintained that the only feasible explanation was that the pull of gravity diminished as one neared the equator, and, if so, the Earth could not be a perfect sphere. The shape of the Earth thus became another subject of debate, some maintaining that it must be spherical and others that it must be oblate. To settle this dispute the French Academy sent one expedition to Lapland with Maupertuis and Clairault (1736) and another to Ecuador (then part of the province of Peru) with La Condamine and Bouguer (1735-43) to measure an arc of a meridian of longitude in those two distant places north and south. Maupertuis in *Sur la figure de la terre* (1738) concluded that the earth tended to flatten out at the poles, and a comparison with the results of the Peruvian measurements supported his contention. Observations in Peru led Bouguer to recognize also that mountains exert enough gravitational pull to cause deviations in a plumb-line. Bascovitch, when, after measuring a meridian arc between Rome and Rimini (1750-53) and finding that it did not agree with the measurement of a meridian arc in France, was able to explain the discrepancy of measurements by the pull of the intervening Appenines. Eventually these and subsequent meridian arc measurements were helpful in providing a natural standard of measurement that became the basis of the 'metric' system devised during the French Revolution.

A problem that had long puzzled seafarers was that of the tides. It bothered Mediterranean sailors only a little, since the tide of the inland sea is almost imperceptible, but it became much greater with the extension of commerce and naval warfare in the other oceans. Ships were often dependent on the tide for entering and leaving harbours. Galileo believed tides to be caused by the rotation of the earth on its axis, finding in them another phenomenon explicable by the Copernican hypothesis as he saw it. Further theories were advanced by others, of which perhaps the most significant was Newton's. He was not able to give a complete explanation of tides, but in his gravitational studies he recognized that the moon had a much greater tide-generating force than the sun and that the highest tides occurred at the new and the full moon.

The Académie des Sciences conducted a series of tidal observations in French harbours that indicated the incompleteness of Newton's explanation. Thereupon (1740) it offered a prize for a better one. Among the winners were Daniel Bernoulli and Euler, who were able to estimate, among other things, the lag of high tide at the moon's transit of the meridian. Another winner was Maclaurin, who showed that tides can be viewed as homogeneous rotating fluid masses and calculated mathematically as such. Kant in his *Allgemeine Naturgeschichte und Theorie des Himmels* (1755) suggested the retarding effect that mutual tidal reaction must have upon the rotation of the Moon and the Earth. The mounting data on the subject enabled Pierre Simon Laplace (1749-1827) to inaugurate (1774) the observation of the tides that eventually led to his theories regarding oceanic oscillations and the calculation of the mass of the moon, which he set forth in his *Méchanique céleste* (1799-1825).

The interest in earthquakes and tidal waves and in their origin was greatly enhanced by the horrible disaster to Lisbon in 1755.[28] Voltaire's outburst of poetic indignation did not prevent scientific studies by others. Among the scientists two theories of geology became dominant toward the end of the century with the work of Abraham Gottlob Werner (1750–1817) and James Hutton (1726–97). Hutton's followers were known as the Vulcanists, since they maintained that the Earth had originated from volcanic action; Werner's followers were called the Neptunists, since they maintained that the sea had played the more important role (see Volume V).

WORLD GEOGRAPHY

Since the days of the Majorca and Sagres schools of navigation, geographical discovery had ceased to be mainly the accidental by-product of the activity of nomads, soldiers, sailors, merchants, crusaders, fishermen, or missionaries; by the sixteenth century it was more likely to be the calculated outcome of carefully planned expeditions of exploration. The study of geography underwent a rapid change with the discovery of the New World and the circumnavigation of the globe. These events forced map makers to adopt global concepts, and terrestrial globes became popular. The earlier examples were, as might have been expected, inaccurate. The large-scale map of Waldseemüller and the Lennox and the Schöner globe, of 1507, 1510, and 1515 respectively, reveal little knowledge of either the New World or Asia, although Waldseemüller's map of 1507 is distinguished for having first attached the name *America* to the new found hemisphere. (Pl. 104b.)

Continuously changing concepts of land masses because of the new explorations and the technical improvements made possible by the printing press caused a tremendous spurt in cartography. Plane-maps began to show more precision. Johannes Honterus (1498–1549), who established the first printing press in Transylvania, published *Rudimentorum Cosmographiae Libri Duo* (Cracow, 1530; expanded and revised in later editions), which contained a world map that showed parts of the east coasts of North and South America.[29] The outstanding map maker of the sixteenth century was Gerhard Kremer, usually called Mercator (1512–94), a Flemish-born, German-bred geographer, expert both in mathematical theory and the practical construction of maps and globes. From 1537 to the time of his death he made global and continental maps as well as instruments for observation. One of his early triumphs was a large detailed map of Europe.

Map-making involved mathematical and other complications. An especially difficult one was the representation of the spherical surface of the Earth on a plane. One of Mercator's early maps presented the world on a double heart-shaped projection. His later cylindrical projection made permanent the improvement by which equal angles on a global projection would also be equal on a plane-map. His global spheres and maps showed little detail of the new discoveries until his famous chart of 1569, which indicated continents and seas of recognizable shape and size and designated California, Florida, Chile, Japan, Delhi, and Abyssinia. This was the first map to give parallels and meridians at right angles, thus leading to the distortions top and bottom characteristic of the 'Mercator' projection. It was published 'for the use of navigators' but was not widely used until the next century, when it reappeared with extensive improvements.

The term *atlas* was probably first employed by Mercator to describe a collection of maps. He himself compiled an atlas of nine maps (later increased in number). A contemporary, Abraham Ortelius of Antwerp (1527–98), anticipated him in publishing the first modern geographical atlas, *Theatrum Orbis Terrarum* (1570). Not only did it include some fifty-three copper-plate maps, but it also gave a catalogue of the authorities consulted in editing the work, thus providing an invaluable listing of early cartographers who might otherwise have remained nameless. The work was hailed as a master-piece, and many map makers sent material to be included in later editions; the number of maps increased to over a hundred, eventually including twelve of the ancient world. By the time of Ortelius' death about twenty-eight editions of his atlas had appeared—in Spanish, Latin, Dutch, German, and French. Mercator's atlas, though earlier, was not published in full until after his death. Meanwhile Dutch seamen and pilots, the chief mariners involved in the Atlantic coastal carrying trade, helped to prepare a series of charts describing the passage from Cadiz to Zuider Zee. These charts formed the basis for the first collection of marine maps, entitled *Spiegel der Zeevaart* (*Mariners' Mirror*), which was issued in two parts by Lucas Janszon Wag-henaer at Leiden (1584–85). Within four years it appeared in English and subsequently in other languages as well. By 1600 map making was a well-established business (see Chapter XV).

Mercator and Ortelius wrote only briefly on geography, their chief work being in cartography. While the same sort of mathematical and cartographical interest dominated Peter Apian (1495–1552), who published one of the earliest maps of America, his *Cosmographicus Liber* (1524) was primarily a written text that zealously upheld the ideas of Ptolemy. Even though the information contained in Ptolemy's *Geographia* was recognized by that time as far from accurate, by 1500 that classic work had already gone through seven printings in western Europe. Apian provided still another edition of it. His authority was great, and his edition of Ptolemy remained a chief source of geographical information during the earlier phases of the great explorations.

Newer geographical ideas gained more ground with the voyages of Magellan and other discoverers. A German linguist named Sebastian Münster (1489–1552) published a *Cosmographia Universalis* (1544), which blazed a fresh trail. Compiled with the assistance of over one ʌundred other geographers, it was a detailed, scholarly description of the then known world. The various political divisions were treated separately, with descriptions of the manners and customs of the peoples. Thanks to the literary merit of its German translation (*Beschreibung aller Länder*), it circulated widely, popularizing the study of geography throughout the Germanies. Münster's *Cosmographia* was followed by the writings of Nathanaal Carpenter (1589–1628 ?), Bernhard Varenius (1622–50), and Torbern Bergman (1735–84), each of which supplied the general reader with a steadily increasing knowledge of the globe. Sea currents were indicated for the first time only in 1665, when the German Jesuit polymath Althanasius Kircher (1601–80) gave some of them in his *Mundus Subterraneus*. Varenius' *Geographia generalis* (1650) in an annotated Latin edition by Newton (1672) and in various translations became the standard geography manual for more than a century. Despite the author's brief life and his several false hypotheses, he is generally regarded as the founder of scientific geography.

Explorations of the Seventeenth and Eighteenth Centuries

After 1600 (roughly) the outstanding problem of European explorers was to find some way to go from Europe to Asia by sea without sailing via Cape Horn or the Cape of Good Hope. Some had hoped to discover a northwest passage by water around North America to Cathay, but this search was abandoned after the voyages of Martin Frobisher in 1576 and the several explorations of Henry Hudson in the 1620's seemed to demonstrate its hopelessness. The arduous quest, however, had meanwhile shown the European peoples north of the Iberian peninsula the routes to a part of the globe, North America, that later attracted great numbers of them.

Upon the repeated failure to find a northwest passage some explorers, almost all of whom were in English, Dutch, or Russian service, set out to discover a northeast passage around Europe and Asia to the Orient, the feasibility of which had been suspected early in the sixteenth century (see Chapter XIII). The voyages of men like Hugh Willoughby and Richard Chancellor, Stephen Burrough, and Willem Barents in the sixteenth century and of Hudson in the seventeenth, though they required high courage and great nautical skill, were of small significance in establishing closer contacts among European and Asian peoples. They did, however, add to the growing store of geographical information. Meanwhile (as we shall soon note) the Russians were pushing the overland settlement of Siberia. Stretch by stretch, they explored the great Arctic rivers, reaching the Kalyma (1644), from which Simyon Dezhnev probably sailed around the East Cape (or Cape Dezhnev) through the straits that separate Asia from America and in any case reached the Gulf of Anadyr,[30] a branch of the Pacific Ocean (1648). Almost a hundred years later (1741), Vitus Bering, a Danish-born navigator in the service of Peter the Great and his successors, sailing northward from Kamchatka, discovered (or, more accurately, rediscovered) the straits now named after him, reached the islands off Alaska from the east, and proved that Asia and America were nowhere directly connected. Bering's companion, Alexis Tchirikov, on an independent voyage, touched the Alaskan mainland. Except for the fur trade the mapping of the Arctic and a northeastern passage to Asia was of little but geographical interest up to fairly recent times. Until the opening of the Suez Canal in 1869, Vasco da Gama's lengthy and strenuous route to the East remained the only practical one for European traders and travellers who wished to avoid long overland treks, dangerous rivers, and forbidding wilderness portages.

Expanding explorations made the coastal outlines of the five great continents fairly well known, but the seaborne European explorers' knowledge of the interior of the new land masses remained sketchy. Even today the geographical picture of some parts of the Asian continent is relatively incomplete. Until 1775 (and beyond), major land explorations by Europeans were carried on in India by several rival national groups, across the endless Siberian steppes by Russian settlers and explorers, and into China through the efforts primarily of missionaries. Elsewhere European maps continued to reveal ignorance of enormous stretches of the world's largest and most populated continent and the adjacent islands. (Pl. 105a, b.)

One whole continent, Australia, remained essentially unknown to Europeans until the close of our period; and about one immense ocean, the Pacific, their information was very limited. For a long time, however, the existence of an enormous continent in the southern part of the world had been assumed; such a land, according to some, simply had to exist in order to keep the earth in proper balance. On maps it was indicated as *Terra Australis* and was thought to be connected with Antarctica, although little was known about either region. The early European explorers did not exhibit particular interest in the waters south of the Malaysian region, and the Spanish adventurers and traders who crossed the Pacific from Mexico westward to Manila and back always took a route too far to the north to enable them to sight much of Oceania.

Serious exploration of these areas began only when the latecomers in the quest for eastern treasure (the Dutch, the English, and the French) appeared on the scene. In 1606 the Spanish captain Luis Vas de Torres crossed through the straits (now named after him) between New Guinea and Australia without realizing how close he was to a continent unknown to civilized men. A decade later some Dutch merchantmen on their way to Malaysia went too far south and touched upon the west coast of the huge island subsequently named Australia. Years afterwards (1642-44) another Dutchman, Abel Tasman, discovered the island now called Tasmania, as well as the Fijis, and sailed completely around, without ever sighting, the Australian mainland. His voyages proved that the islands which others had seen south of the Indonesian archipelago were not connected with Antarctica. The English navigator William Dampier (1652-1715) explored more of the west and north coasts of Australia but failed to reach the still unknown east coast.

For another hundred years, the picture of Australia remained unclear. Only by the scientific expeditions of the French sailor Louis Antoine de Bougainville (1729-1811) and the English sailor James Cook (1728-79) was its mystery finally cleared. Cook completed two revealing voyages in the

Pacific (1767–71 and 1772–75) and was killed on the Hawaiian Islands in 1779 while on a third. On these trips Cook rounded both the continent cf Australia and the islands of New Zealand (which until then had also been thought to be part of the Antarctic), sailed northward along the east coast of Australia, discovered the Great Barrier Reef and New Caledonia, and system-atically charted much of the Pacific with its major island groups and its North American coast as far north as Alaska. At much the same time (1768–73) a Scot named James Bruce of Kinnaird visited Abyssinia and fairly approximately located the source of the Nile River. By the close of the period with which this volume deals almost every part of the world that man could reach by sea had been at least sighted by Europeans and fairly well mapped. Although several island groups and the interior of several continents still were largely *terra incognita* to Europe's cartographers, the educated man's picture, if not his comprehension, of the world had become global both in form and extent. Nearly all the world's cultures were to a greater or lesser degree familiar with one another.

In some instances geographic information about the hinterlands was to remain exceedingly vague until the air travel of the twentieth century made interior exploration more feasible. Africa, except for its coastline, was little touched by landborne explorations before the nineteenth century. Several regions were inhospitable and offered few incentives to explorers. China and Japan were not always favourably disposed toward foreigners and limited the freedom of movement of such Westerners as they admitted at all. In still other areas land exploration proceeded but at a slow pace, keeping only slightly ahead of the gradual penetration by settlers and colonists. From time to time advanced garrisons, isolated missionaries, solitary adventurers, marooned sailors, or lone trappers learned a good deal about remote regions, but their knowledge did not become common and so remained fruitless from an economic or scientific point of view, although like the prototype of Robinson Crusoe, they entered into folklore and literature.

A major exception to the general rule that the explorations of this period were seaborne rather than landborne was the expansion into Siberia. Around 1580 a noble Russian family, the Stroganoffs, became interested in improving their holdings across the Ural Mountains. Yermak Timofeyev and a band of about 1600 Cossacks in the Stroganoff service began to push across those mountains and, equipped with firearms, easily defeated the larger forces of the Siberian khanate, armed only with bows and arrows. They took the city of Sibir (whence the name Siberia) and advanced into the region of the Tobol River. In the next sixty years Russian explorers, traders, settlers, and Cossack bands moved into the Siberian wilderness and the Arctic waters until (see above) they reached the Pacific.

About the time that Dezhnev reached northeast Asia, the Russians, still advancing overland, also reached the Pacific farther south. They explored the intervening Asiatic coast and the shores of the Sea of Okhotsk, founding the town of Okhotsk in 1648. Vasily Poiarkov discovered the Amur River in 1644, but after a few decades the Russians were obliged by the Chinese (in the Treaty of Nerchinsk, 1689) to withdraw from that region. Meanwhile they founded Irkutsk on Lake Baikal (1651). With the discovery of Kamchatka (1697) and the occupation of the Kurile Islands (1711) Russia was well ensconced in the northern Far East. Beginning early in the seventeenth century, it sent embassies to China and made commercial and boundary treaties with the Chinese emperor (particularly at Kiachta in 1727). On the basis of an order of Tsar Ivan IV in 1552 'to measure the land and make a draft of the state' Russian explorers would draw up 'drafts' that, while not plotted like maps on coordinates, nevertheless provided a vast collection of data.[31] Such a work was S. Remezov's *Book of Drafts of Siberia* (1701), which served as a guide for future explorations.

In the eighteenth century the Russians undertook far-reaching geodetic surveys and scientific expeditions involving three continents. They mapped the Don region, the Black and Caspian Seas, Kamchatka, Siberia's Arctic and Pacific coasts, the Aleutians, Alaska, and other parts of the American northwest. Especially noteworthy were the Great Northern Expedition (1733–43) and the polar expedition of Admiral V. Y. Chichagov (1765–66). A Russian population, consisting chiefly of traders, garrisons, and peasants attracted by virgin lands was eventually superimposed upon the nomadic tribes of Siberia. When a large part of the Kalmucks east of the Volga in the 1770's retreated before the Russian advance and, with the Chinese emperor's consent, settled in Sinkiang, the epic of the invasions by Siberia's steppe peoples came to a close. Before 1775, with the exception of certain areas directly north of Persia and Afghanistan and on the borders of China (areas which were to be acquired only in the nineteenth century), Russia had extensively explored (and dominated) that immense Asian realm which she now controls (as well as Alaska and the northwest coast of America).

THE BIOLOGICAL SCIENCES IN EUROPE

The number of eminent naturalists of the sixteenth century is impressive. The preface to a treatise by Ulisse Aldrovandi (1522–1605) listed thirty-two, and his list was incomplete.

Advances in the Study of Botany

The sixteenth-century biological encyclopedists still treated animals and herbs (as well as minerals) largely as *materia medica* but sometimes were interested in something more. The wider interest was evident in the extensive commentaries of Pierandrea Mattioli (1500–77) in his Latin edition of Dioscorides (1554). Though, like other contemporary botanists, he was inspired by Antiquity, he went far beyond the Classical writers; he was able to draw on the store of new information exchanged among distant scholars by letters, sometimes accompanied by drawings of plants and animals, or found in accounts of the strange flora and fauna of the New World and Asia. Garcia da Orta published in Portuguese a treatise on the 'simples' of India, and Christopher Acosta one in Latin on the 'aromatics' and 'medicaments' of that region. Nicolaus Monardus's treatise on the 'simple medicaments' of the New World—also in Latin—did the same for the Americas. Still, these works resembled the Classical and medieval handbooks on *materia medica* in that most of the 'simples', 'aromatics', and 'medicaments' were herbs or extracts from herbs, and a large amount of wonder-lore accompanied the description of their medicinal virtues. One of the few sixteenth-century naturalists to plead for the separation of botany from medicine was the Bohemian Adam Zaluzianski (1558–1613).

The more scientific and disinterested approach was encouraged by the spread of botanical and zoological gardens. The first botanical-zoological garden seems to have been installed at Venice in 1533; Lisbon, then a leading centre for voyagers to distant lands, also inaugurated one early; Padua followed suit in 1543; and the Medici created one of the best at Pisa in 1549. During the century they sprang up not only in connection with universities and on royal or aristocratic estates but also as municipal institutions. Even though zoological specimens were brought together more often as curiosities than for scientific study, scholars such as John Gerard, in London and at Lord Burghley's country seat, and Gabriele Fallopio, Aloysius Anguillara, and Jacobus Cartusus, at Pisa and Padua, had charge of royal, university, or municipal gardens, as well as their own private collections. Such establishments permitted direct observation of many animals and plants not accounted for in extant treatises, with consequent correction of older biological data.

Contemporary art clearly testified to the growing interest in nature (see Chapter XII) and, in turn, helped to further the spread of man's knowledge. At the close of the fifteenth century, great artists like Leonardo da Vinci and Dürer turned their talents to the depicting of botanical specimens in drawings, wood-cuts, and other media. The new interest in artistic but accurate illustration was amply demonstrated in the *Herbarum Vivae Eiconos* (3 vols, 1530–36) of Otto von Brunsfels and in the *De Historia Stirpium* (1542) of Leonhard Fuchs (1501–66).

These two naturalists were perhaps even more significant for other reasons. Fuchs's work provided not only a well-illustrated herbal but also one of the earliest attempts at a scientific nomenclature. It still conformed to the prevalent interest in plants chiefly for their medicinal value as defined by Dioscorides but was one of the last herbals of that nature. The great geographical discoveries of the sixteenth century made readily apparent that many more types of plants flourished in more parts of the world than Dioscorides, Pliny, or any of the Ancients had dreamed of, and the contemporary development of printing and book publishing made possible a wide distribution of the new knowledge concerning plant usage inside and outside of Europe. A modern plant geography seems first to have been suggested by Brunsfels, who indicated that the specimens he found in the neighbourhood of Strasbourg could not always be identified with those that Dioscordes mentioned.

Within another century, although herbals remained a happy medium for the illustrator, a point was reached where they could contribute little to systematic botanical knowledge. For one thing, confusion arose from the lack of an adequate and commonly acceptable taxonomy (system of classification). Confusion over classification came largely because until the eighteenth century two somewhat contradictory schools of naturalists, both harking back to differently elaborated ideas of Aristotle, struggled for predominance. The older one held to what today is called the 'artificial' or 'hierarchical' system—that the organic species are arranged in a hierarchy with discontinuities between them. This school classified plants in an order, more acceptable to Christian Aristotelian logic, that put emphasis upon the differences in the species. The other school held to the 'natural' system—the view that the several species of plants and animals are links in a great chain of being, the gradations having been slowly achieved in a continuous, unbroken process. This school tried to classify plants by some scheme of kinship.

As knowledge of plants accumulated, the need for a single system of botanical classification grew. Hieronymus Bock's *Neu Kreutterbuch* (1539) was perhaps the earliest to attempt to provide one, but with no immediate success. In many travels Charles de l'Ecluse (1525–1609) studied the rarer flora of Spain, eastern Europe, the Levant, and India and, aided by Matthias de l'Obel (1538–1616) and others, supplied information that tended to bolster the 'natural' school of classification. Zaluzianski in his *Methodi Herbariae Libri Tres* (Prague, 1592) and Kaspar Bauhin (1560–1624) also favoured a 'natural' classification. Finding that much of the current confusion was a consequence of the use of different names for the same plant, Bauhin provided (1623) a catalogue of some 6000 plants (*Pinax Theatri Botanici*), identifying their synonyms. To avoid future confusion of similar origin, he proposed the binominal system of nomenclature (a generic name followed by a specific modifier—e.g. *lilium album*). Perhaps the most important early system of 'artificial' classification was that of Andrea Cesalpino (1524–1603), professor at the University of Pisa and director of Pisa's botanical garden, who in a treatise *De Plantis Libri XVI* (1583) set forth a scheme that gave major attention to patent fruit and seed differentiations rather than flower structure. Joachim Jungius of Lübeck (1587–1657) despite the prestige of Cesalpino returned to flower structure as a basis of plant terminology, identifying the stamen, the style, and the perianth. He used Bauhin's binominal system, and he seems to have been the first to suggest the classification of plants by genera and species as well.

The microscope greatly aided seventeenth century botanists to understand the structure of plants. Among the most skilled of contemporary technicians of microscopy were the Dutchmen Jan Swammerdam (1637–80) and Antony van Leeuwenhoek (1632–1723). From his youth Swammerdam showed interest in insect life rather than in plant life, collecting several thousand species. His great skill, however, in making instruments and drawings and in using scalpels, lancets, knives, scissors, and other devices so small that they had to be ground with the aid of magnifying glasses provided a model for microscopists in all fields. Exhausting himself by his work, he died relatively young, and only thanks to the editorship of Boerhaave were his writings, under the intriguing title *Bybel der Natuure* (1737), presented to the public. Like Swammerdam, Leeuwenhoek was primarily an observer, not a theoretician. He made his own lenses and, self-taught, turned his microscope on all sorts of minute objects, animal as well as plant. He preferred the simple microscope to the more common compound one of the day. (Pl. 84a–d.) Another outstanding pioneer in the new method of observing minute particles was Hooke, whose *Micrographia* (1665) was the earliest monographic treatise on microscopy. He was the first to describe cellular structure—in cork and other plants. (Pl. 85a–d.)

John Ray (1627–1705), a devout Puritan, furnishes a pat example of the school of scientists who considered the study of zoology and botany an essentially religious expression, a means of understanding God's handiwork through the Book of Nature. While he was no expert microscopist, his *Historia Generalis Plantarum* (1686–1704) carefully identified some 19,000 plants, checked and re-checked—by first-hand inspection wherever possible or against well-established authorities. Although he used descriptive phrases instead of single words for many of his plants, he helped to advance botanical classification (dividing plants into 125 sections) and made important contributions to precise nomenclature. He distinguished between the great natural groupings of plants, beginning with imperfect forms such as algae, ferns, and marine plants; and he divided flowering plants into monocotyledenous and dicotyledenous.

Floral morphology was furthered by a number of Ray's contemporaries. J. P. de Tournefort (1656–1708), a professor at the Jardin des Plantes, calling attention to differences in petals (apetelous, polypetalous, etc.), put about 8000 species into 22 classes, distinguished chiefly by the forms of their corollas; this method of classification was not superseded until Linnaeus's day (see below). Nehemiah Grew (1641–1712), secretary of the Royal Society and discoverer of Epsom salts, also made the perhaps more significant discovery of the sexuality of plants; he regarded the flower as the sexual structure of a plant, the stamen being the male organ, the pollen the seed, and the pistil the female organ. Along with Leeuwenhoek and Malpighi (see below) he was one of the founders of microscopic plant anatomy. Rudolf Jakob Camerarius (1665–1721), professor of biology at Tübingen, who was the first known to experiment with the sex of plants, in his *De Sexu Plantarum* (1694) treated the subject more fully than Grew. The hybridization of plants, now easily detected, was achieved experimentally by several of a later generation, notably by Joseph Gottlieb Koelreuter (1733–1806), who recognized (in a work published in the 1760's) the role of wind, insects, and birds in the pollination and seed distribution of plants incapable of self-fertilization.

The most significant eighteenth-century studies in the field of botany were those of Stephen Hales (1677–1761) of England and Karl von Linné or Linnaeus (1707–78) of Sweden. Hales was the father of vegetable physiology. Seeing analogies between animal and plant physiology, he enquired into the function of plants and, in so doing, influenced not only the field of botany but also of chemistry. Linnaeus occupies as the organizer of botany a position somewhat analogous to Lavoisier's in chemistry. He at first adopted the 'hierarchical' or 'artificial' system of classification. Unconvinced in his early work by the accumulating data suggestive of a theory of evolution from species to species, he at first regarded each living species as having been fixed forever at the time of the Flood, and this premise long made it difficult for him to embrace a 'natural' (i.e. evolutionary) system of classification. He nevertheless worked hard to identify botanical families, thus preparing the ground for the future recognition of the kinship of legions of plants.

Linnaeus's chief works were *Systema Naturae, sive Regna Tria Naturae Systematice Proposita per Classes, Ordines, Genera et Species* (1735), which went through twelve editions in his lifetime, and *Species Plantarum* (1753). Using the binominal terminology of Bauhin (that is, one name for the genus and another for the species), he grouped plants (and animals and minerals as well) into classes, orders, genera, and species. His taxonomy, though following a mainly 'artificial' system of classification, was based upon the number of stamens, styles, and other parts of a plant's sexual apparatus, and it provided the foundation for modern taxonomy when modified by Bernard de Jussieu (1699–1777), Jussieu's nephew Antoine Laurent de Jussieu (1748–1836), and their successors.[32] In the later editions of the *Systema Naturae* Linnaeus himself suppressed the passages that implied that cross-fertilization of the species was impossible.

Contributions to the Study of Zoology

The development of zoology paralleled that of botany, particularly in the attempt to arrive at systematic classification. In the fifteenth and sixteenth centuries, new Latin translations of the Aristotelian treatises on animals were made directly from the Greek by Theodore of Gaza, George of Trebizond, and others, nine editions being published in Venice alone between 1475 and 1575, but no new intensive zoological study appeared. This concern with Aristotle combined with the importation of curiosa from the newly discovered countries to rouse a keen interest in zoology.

In the first half of the sixteenth century several minor works were published concerning fish, and certain scholars manifested an interest also in bird life. About mid-century Guillaume Rondelet (1507–66) produced his *De Piscibus*, thought by some to have been plagiarized from the commentary on Pliny's *Natural History* of Bishop Pellicier (1490–1568). About the same time came treatises on birds by William Turner (*c.* 1508–68) and Pierre Belon (1517–64). Later Volcher Coiter (1534–76) put out his classification of birds (see below).

By the end of the century general compendia containing sections on all classes of animals were appearing. Gessner's multivolume *Historia Animalium* (1551–87) provided a very full, if unsystematic, account giving many excellent pictures of animals. His Italian contemporary Aldrovandi produced several treatises that, although not equally complete, marked a definite advance, since they considered anatomical features as a means of classification. Edward Wotton (1492–1555) worked along similar comparative lines.

Part of the parallelism of zoology with botany can be accounted for by the fact that some men worked in both fields. Ray is an especially good example. In his *Synopsis Methodica Animalium Quadrupedum* (1693), he set forth the first scheme for a systematic classification of animals. He was also the first person to expound a clear notion of a biological 'species'. Classification persisted, however, as a problem, not to be fully overcome until the concept of fixity of species was discarded. Influenced by Ray's classificatory system for animals, Linnaeus performed for zoology much the same service as for botany. Adopting the species as the unit of classification, he divided animal life into six classes, (mammals, birds, amphibians, fish, insects, and worms), putting more reliance on external morphological characteristics than on internal structure. Unlike Ray, he did not distinguish, for example, between vertebrates and invertebrates. He adopted the binominal system of class names for animals as he had for plants. The International Commission of Zoological Nomenclature, disregarding earlier works, has stipulated that the tenth (1758) edition of his *Systema Naturae* be the basis of taxonomy in the field.

Nevertheless, in its own day, the Linnaean system did not go unchallenged. Toward the end of Buffon's career as director of the Paris Jardin des Plantes, he became convinced that the species were not fixed. His *Histoire naturelle*, which ran posthumously to forty-four large volumes (thirty-six during his lifetime) and went far to popularize the study of biology, rejected the 'artificial' classification of Linnaeus, adopting instead a 'natural' system. The convenience of Linnaeus' nomenclature, however, was not affected by the shortcomings of his taxonomy.

Some of the important biological work of the seventeenth and eighteenth centuries was of a largely descriptive nature. In their anxiety to avoid speculative systems, the Italian Accademia del Cimento and the French Académie des Sciences deliberately encouraged descriptive work in the study of biology. Francesco Redi (1626–78) described the life cycle of the fly from larvae (which he called 'worms') through pupae (which he called 'eggs') to adult flies and in so doing disproved the common belief that 'worms' came by spontaneous generation from putrefaction. Réaumur made one of his several contributions to pure science in his *Mémoires pour servir à l'histoire des insectes* (1734–42), observing his subjects not only in their habitat but also under specially arranged conditions. Some of his descriptions of insects (he used the term in the broadest sense) remain standard, and his experimental methods much admired, to this day. Perhaps no biological studies of the century were more important than those of August Johann Roesel von Rosenhof (1705–84) on the hydra. For the hydra seemed to have some of the characteristics of an animal and some of a plant, and a number of students of nature became convinced that the dividing line between the animal and the plant kingdom was not clear-cut.33 The importance of this biological concept to the philosophy of the Enlightenment has already been indicated (see Chapter VII). Among other things, it led a number of the *philosophes* to speculate whether Man was not himself, in a self-propelling biology, part of an endless chain of being destined for continuous change in the direction of perfectibility.

Anatomy and Physiology

In the field of anatomy and physiology most of the creative work of the early modern period, with the notable exceptions of Ray's and Leeuwenhoek's, was done by physicians. The anatomical drawings of Leonardo da Vinci, derived from the dissection of about thirty cadavers, anticipated Vesalius, but Leonardo was interested in human anatomy for art's sake rather than for science's sake, nor were his observations contemporaneously published. The initial landmark in modern anatomy as a science was the publication of Vesalius' *De Humani Corporis Fabrica* (1543). The author, born in Brussels (1514), was at the age of twenty-two professor of anatomy at the University of Padua. His book had as great an impact in its field as Copernicus', published in the same year, had in its. Vesalius was not a revolutionary in spirit or method; dissection had been performed long before him, and he did not attack Galen in the headlong fashion of Paracelsus. He attempted, however, to give a dispassionate description, with the aid of superb illustrations, of the human body. (Pl. 93c.) He based his analysis on dissection rather than on untested authority, and he did not hesitate to correct Galen when the occasion arose. For instance, Vesalius failed to find the pores that Galen supposed the septum of the heart to have. Ironically, some critics in Vesalius' time, not realizing that Galen's anatomy was based for the most part on Barbary apes, refused in the name of orthodoxy to accept Vesalius' findings because they contradicted the master.

Vesalius was only incidentally interested in the comparison of anatomical features, but he nevertheless contributed to the study of the anatomy of lower animals also, sometimes dissecting living animals as well as dead humans. Greater interest in comparative study was manifested by several contemporary anatomists. Belon in 1555 published engravings pointing up the homologies of the skeletons of man and bird.34 The Italian Nicholas Massa compared apes and men. Girolamo Fabrizio ab Aquapendente (1537–1619) enriched his treatises on animal and human embryology with excellent illustrations. Coiter made use of experiments on the hearts and brains of animals in two treatises on comparative anatomy: one of these, *De Differentiis Avium*, with illustrations, was included as an appendix to his edition (1575) of the work of Gabriele Fallopio (1523–62) on the parts of the human body. Carlo Ruini (*c.* 1530–98) wrote a book on the horse (1598) that is a classic of veterinary anatomy.

The term 'comparative anatomy' seems to have been first used by Francis Bacon in 1623, but only to refer to comparison of variations within the same species. As anatomical knowledge advanced, the field of comparative anatomy became more comprehensive. And anatomical knowledge advanced with great strides. The celebrated surgeon and teacher Marco Aurelio Severino (1580–1656) dissected specimens of many species, introduced the term *zootomy* (1645), and showed that freezing by snow and ice might be used for anaesthetic purposes. Thomas Willis (1621–75) first reported on his study of the nerves and brain in 1664. Grew published *A Comparative Anatomy of Stomachs and Guts* in 1681. Edward Tyson (1651–1708) wrote on the tapeworm and other parasites in the 1680's. Claude Perrault (1613–88), perhaps the most productive of the seventeenth-century comparative anatomists, worked especially on fishes and birds; an architect by profession and a leading member of the Cartesian Académie des Sciences, he developed a mechanistic theory of anatomy. His mantle fell upon Guichard Joseph Duverney (1648–1730), who in 1683 made his most important contribution, an account of the anatomy of the ear. In the 1690's Martin Lister (1638–1712) published anatomical studies of marine animals and invertebrates, and in the next decade of the opossum and the orang-outang. Even without taking into account the contributions of Harvey (see below) posterity would have ample evidence of the extraordinary activity of seventeenth-century anatomists in the large number of structures of the body named after them—circle of Willis, Casserio's artery, Graafian follicles, Peyer's patches, Ruysch's tunica, etc. In the next century comparative anatomical collections and museums became more and more complete, perhaps the best of them being that of John Hunter in London.

Much of the success in the study of anatomy after the middle of the seventeenth century was due to the fuller use of the microscope. As early as 1610 Galileo had examined the eye of a small animal with a compound microscope, but he was not much interested in biology. Francisco Stelluti used a low-powered microscope or magnifying glass for his study of the bee, published in 1625. Harvey also, we shall soon see, used some kind of a magnifier. One of the first to make full use of the microscope was Marcello Malpighi (1628–94), professor of medicine at Bologna and elsewhere. In addition to working as a pioneer with microscopic plants, he discovered the role of capillaries in the circulation of the blood and made many minute observations on the development of the chick in the egg and on the anatomy of the silkworm. Swammerdam's interest in insect life (mentioned above) led him to comparative research in insect anatomy, development, and metamorphoses. He established a 'natural' classification of insects that still is regarded as having some validity. His contemporary and compatriot Leeuwenhoek, determined to see the complete circulation of the blood, put the tadpole under his microscope. He also discovered the unicellular organisms that we today call protozoa (1674) and bacteria (1676). And skill with the microscope enabled Pierre Lyonet (1707–89) to produce an admirably illustrated monograph on the anatomy of the caterpillar.

The Study of the Circulatory System

In his *Exercitatio Anatomica de Motu Cordis et Sanguinis in Animalibus* (1628), Harvey presented a revolutionary study of the movement of the heart and the blood, derived, he said, 'not from books but from dissections; not from the positions of philosophers but from the fabric of nature'. He, too, made reference to magnifying glasses; with them he was able to confirm that almost every animal has a heart. This discovery contradicted the long generally accepted belief of Aristotle that only large, red-blooded creatures have hearts. It was but a minor point, however, in his book.

Notwithstanding its deserved fame, much of Harvey's experimental work had been anticipated by his predecessors. He was not revolutionary in his findings so much as in his methods. He was not the first, for example, to point out that the route of the venous blood to the left side of the heart was not through the septum but through the pulmonary artery; the unfortunate Servetus had described the lesser circulation of the blood in his *Christianismi Restitutio* (1553), which was subsequently suppressed, leaving its influence on his several successors up to and including Harvey a debatable matter. Harvey's discussion of the valves of the veins was more obviously based on earlier observations by his teacher, Fabrizio ab Aquapendente.

The research of Harvey's predecessors, however, had been directed toward different ends. His main contribution was, where he did not wholly refute, to raise doubts about hitherto accepted views, such as that growth, muscular activity, and nervous functions are each dependent upon a corresponding spirit (*pneuma*) distributed by the blood, that the function of the venous blood is to distribute the 'natural spirit', which is the principle of growth, that the function of the arterial blood is to distribute the 'vital spirit', which is the principle of muscular activity, and that the function of the nerves is to distribute the 'animal spirit', which is the principle of the nervous function. This view was derived from Galen. According to the Galenic system, the blood encountered the natural spirit in the liver, the vital spirit in the heart, and the animal spirit in the brain. This system involved several erroneous ideas not only with regard to the role of certain organs in blood physiology but also with regard to the method and the direction of the flow of the blood. The major significance of Harvey's work rests upon the fact that he framed a different conceptual scheme and then proceeded to test it in the best quantitative and experimental manner of the time—by 'both argument and ocular demonstration'.

'The greater circulation' of the blood from arteries to veins and thence back to the heart had already been suggested by the work of Vesalius, Servetus, and others, and their work provided Harvey with a foundation on which to build. To Harvey the lesser circulation (that is, the path by which the exhausted blood flowed from the veins through the lungs and, freshened, returned to the arterial system) was more of a mystery. A significant passage from his treatise underlines the quantitative basis of his initial hypothesis:

'For a long time I turned over in my mind such questions as, how much blood is transmitted, and how short a time does its passage take. Not deeming it possible for the digested food mass to furnish such an abundance of blood, without totally draining the veins or rupturing the arteries, unless it somehow got back to the veins from the arteries and returned to the right ventricle of the heart, I began to think there was a sort of motion in a circle.'[35]

By experiment and observation he then confirmed this hypothesis. He found that the valves in the vein kept the blood from flowing in more than one direction, and he also showed that the amount of blood passing through a body's heart in an hour far exceeds the weight of that body. He then concluded that he could explain the venous and arterial system only by a one-way and continuous circulation, which is 'the sole and only end of the motion and contraction of the heart'.

Later research completed the explanation of the circulation of the blood. Malpighi's discovery of the capillaries has already been mentioned; it was reported in his *De Pulmonibus* (1661). It was confirmed by Leeuwenhoek, who not only, as previously stated, traced the blood circulation of the tadpole but also probably was the first (1674) to make the red corpuscles known. The work of Harvey, Malpighi, and Leeuwenhoek in the circulation of the blood was supplemented by a growing knowledge of other organic processes. In 1651 Jean Pecquet discovered the function of the lacteals, and somewhat later (1652) Olof Rudbeck of Uppsala and Thomas Bartholin of Copenhagen discovered the lymphatic nodes. Francis Glisson in 1659 gave a detailed account of liver, stomach, and intestines, and Thomas Wharton in 1656 of the pancreas.

Iatrophysics and Mechanistic Medicine

Harvey's method and conclusions were an inspiration to those who thought that biological phenomena could be put into a quantitative and mechanical (or iatrophysical) frame. This was the period when the medical profession was becoming conscious of medical statistics (see Chapter XV). About the middle of the sixteenth century a Paris printer had published a set of figures covering about fifty-five cases of illness from 1549 to 1554, analysing the types of ailment, the patients' occupation, and other relevant data. The mechanistic-quantitative point of view was reinforced by several of Harvey's contemporaries. Descartes' philosophic dualism of mind and body made room for the interpretation of the human body in the same mechanical and quantitative terms as the physical universe; his mechanistic views were set forth in his posthumous textbook of physiology, *De Homine* (1662). A leading exponent of the quantitative approach to physiological functions was Sanctorius, Galileo's medical colleague at the University of Padua. He invented an instrument for counting the pulse, a sort of clinical thermometer, a weighing chair, and other devices for measuring physiological phenomena. These, and especially the weighing-chair, enabled him to initiate the study of what today would be called 'metabolism'. He weighed his own intake and excretion of food over a period of decades and came to the conclusion that perspiration and respiration account for more discharge than conscious evacuations. He set forth his theory in *Ars de Statica Medicina* (1614).

François de la Boë Sylvius (1614–72), one of the great teachers at the University of Leyden, was, to be sure, an iatrochemist, perhaps the first to carry out careful biochemical experiments, making significant discoveries in the physiology of the digestive processes, but he was also a firm believer in the mechanistic action of the muscles. The work of Giovanni Borelli (1608–79) in applying mechanics to the living organism is generally considered the most significant attempt to put biology into the field of mechanics. Greatly influenced by Galileo, Borelli investigated and explained circulation of the blood, respiration, and the movements of animal muscles and bones on mechanical principles, as though they were forces, weights, and levers, though he also recognized that certain physiological reactions must also be chemical. (Pl. 91a, b.) He has the distinction of being the father of the iatrophysical school of anatomy. This school perhaps reached its logical apex with Georgio Baglivi (1669–1707), who founded the medical system known as 'solidism'. He contended that sickness originates in the bodily 'solids' rather than the Galenic 'humors'. After the Leyden jar was discovered (1745), the growing use of electric shock to stimulate ailing muscles gave the iatrophysicists a new argument.

Though a certain number of researchers continued in the eighteenth century to seek the explanation of muscular, circulatory, and other anatomical movements along mechanical lines—notably the able group gathered in the St Petersburg Academy—a reaction shortly set in against Borelli's school. The German chemist Stahl, also a physician, insisted in his *Theoria Medica Vera* (1707) that 'the sensitive soul', expressing itself through body chemistry, provided a better explanation of bodily function, structure, and health than the analogy—which seemed to him oversimplified—to a machine. This theory was called *vitalism*.[36] By the end of the century noted physiologists like M. F. X. Bichat had embraced Stahl's vitalistic theories, but the high point of the vitalist-mechanist controversy was not to come until the nineteenth century.

The Empirical Study of Disease

About 1500 a new challenge to medical men appeared in the form of a disease of debated origin. Reputedly it was imported by Columbus' sailors from America to Spain and thence to France and Italy—or vice versa, for it was called 'the French disease' (*morbus gallicus*) by the Neapolitans, in whose country it became epidemic after the arrival of the invading French armies (1494), and the 'Neapolitan disease' (*mal de Naples*) in France, where it was spread by the returning French armies. Whether the disease was a *morbus americanus*, *gallicus* or *neapolitanus* or, as has also been maintained, an epidemic form of the medieval 'pox', it came to be known most widely, for a time, as the *morbus gallicus*. Girolamo Fracastoro of Verona (1483–1553), professor of logic and physician, in 1530 published a poem entitled *Syphilis sive de Morbo Gallico*, and thenceforth the disease came to be known as 'syphilis', after a shepherd in the poem on whom Apollo visited an ulcerous disease. The poem mentioned as remedies for the disease mercury and guaiacum, a wood resin used by the American Indians. In a later work (*De Contagionibus*, 1546) Fracastoro described several contagious diseases, including syphilis and typhus fever, and suggested that syphilis might be caused by *seminaria* (*seeds*), thus anticipating the germ theory of disease. Controversy still goes on regarding the origin of syphilis, with suggestions to the effect that venereal diseases have long been in existence everywhere and that the sixteenth-century pandemic in Europe was but a variation imported from America to localities that had not been conditioned to resist it in a virulent form.

Advance in physiology proved dependent on improvements in anatomy, physics, chemistry, and other related sciences. The work of such men as Sanctorius, Descartes, Harvey, and Borelli, whatever the shortcomings of their conclusions, helped the development of modern physiology. But advance came only step by step. As late as the Great Plague of 1664–65 in London (see Chapter XIII), epidemics were generally attributed to supernatural causes. Such principles and practices gave way only slowly before improved anatomical knowledge, good instruments, and empirical concepts.

By the end of the seventeenth century physiology and medicine were able to make great strides side by side with anatomy and surgery. Some of the achievements will be described in Chapter XV in connection with the practice of medicine and surgery. The chief inspiration in physiology came perhaps from Sylvius and Boerhaave, whose reputation as teachers of medicine at Leyden made their university renowned (see Chapter XVI). In their country (and largely because of their efforts), the teaching of chemistry as, among other things, basic to medicine was well developed, and anatomy and surgery too were regarded as closely related to medicine. Both men emphasized that medical training must include not only chemical and botanical knowledge but anatomical and physiological knowledge as well. Thus, long before the period here under discussion ended, the old distinctions of prestige and practice between surgery and medicine began to break down. After Boerhaave's day, surgery became associated less with barbers and more with physicians as a respectable professional skill. Select societies of surgery were formed—the Académie Royale de Chirurgie in Paris in 1731, the British Surgeon's Company in 1745.

The closer association of medicine with surgery gave practitioners of both a common interest in pathological anatomy and experimental physiology. The most outstanding student of Boerhaave was Albrecht von Haller (1708–77), who in 1756 published his *Elementa Physiologiae Corporis Humani*, which has been called the first modern manual of physiology. He not only collected information about the various organs, some of it derived from his own experiments, but also correlated their functions. Giovanni Battista Morgagni (1682–1771), an Italian physician, in *De Sedibus et Causis Morborum*, studied the relation of certain diseases (e.g. pneumonia, syphilis, meningitis) to certain parts of the body and summed up the knowledge of his day regarding the correlation between structural changes (like wounds, abscesses, gangrene, and tumors) and sickness.[32] The work of Hales with both plants and animals provided a much better understanding of respiration. Réaumur brought increased knowledge of the process of digestion (1752); without completely explaining the solvent action of the gastric juices, he recognized it and differentiated it from putrefaction. Building on the exposition by Willis of the nervous system (see above), several eighteenth century investigators—among them, Jean Astruc (1684–1766), Robert Whytt (1714–66), and J. A. Unzer (1727–99)—revealed the nature of the reflex movement as a response, not necessarily conscious, to stimulation of the nerves related to the spinal marrow, and they otherwise studied nervous diseases.[38] Some physiological background was a prerequisite for the understanding and introduction of inoculation (see below) and, later in the century, of vaccination against small-pox, the cornerstones of the science of immunology.

Conflicting Schools of Embryology

Modern embryology owes its beginnings to Harvey's *De Generatione Animalium* (1651), but Harvey got some of his inspiration from the studies of his teacher Fabrizio ab Aquapendente, who had been a pupil of Fallopius, who had been a pupil of Vesalius, and Harvey in turn lent inspiration to Malpighi's microscopic examination of the embryology of the chick. The Classical theory of reproduction, along with that of the human physique, had been based upon Aristotle's *De Generatione Animalium* on which Muslims, Christian Scholastics, and sixteenth-century humanists (e.g. Gesner) patterned their treatises concerning animal and human reproduction. Aristotle held that the male parent gave to the embryo its form, and the female parent its nourishment, and that some imperfect forms of life were spontaneously generated. At the opening of the sixteenth century the most current theory of reproduction was derived from this Aristotelian tradition.

Illustration, a noteworthy factor in all biological progress, was especially significant in the study of embryology. Medieval manuscript illustrators depicted the stages of development of the unborn child in series of as many as sixteen pictures, derived from Classical archetypes. From about 1300 onward, there was some improvement in these archetypes, and eventually additional illustrations appeared as a result of the increased use of dissection. Leonardo da Vinci's remarkable notebook sketches reveal his interest in the subject. In the sixteenth century Coiter and Aldrovandi began careful investigations of the embryological development of the chick in the hen's egg. Their work was followed up by Fabrizio ab Aquapendente in books entitled *De Formato Foetu* (1600) and *De Formatione Ovi et Pulli* (1621). His engraved illustrations of human and animal embryos, notably those of the chick, led to the development of a scientific embryology.

Having studied the embryo of the deer as well as the chick, Harvey came to the conclusion that the mammalian embryo was equivalent to the egg of the bird and other oviparous creatures and put forward the famous dictum *ex ovo omnia*. At the same time he questioned but did not wholly dismiss the possibility of lower and imperfect animals being spontaneously generated. The view that life originates from eggs was given further confirmation when Reinier de Graaf (1641–73) discovered with the aid of a microscope the resemblance between the ovarian (Graafian) follicles of several species of mammals and the egg of a bird.

Harvey's theory of embryo development was essentially unlike that of Aristotle; it was what today is called embryological epigenesis. In this theory, the germ cell is considered new, and the embryo is believed to develop its separate features by successive stages until birth. An opposing school held to a preformation or mosaic theory—viz. that the germ was a fully formed but minute model or mosaic of the adult animal. The conflict had, of course, certain religious overtones. Had not God created man in his own image? The microscope seemed at first to substantiate the preformation theory. Observing that among oviparous creatures the embryo develops inside the egg, some held that the embryo of the higher animal, too, must therefore be essentially derived from and similar to its female parent. Hence the separate parts of the embryo must be fully differentiated from the beginning, gestation being merely a swelling from a speck to full size. Malpighi and Swammerdam were the chief exponents of this theory.

Leeuwenhoek developed a different though parallel theory. In 1677 Ludwig van Ham, a student at Leyden, showed him some spermatozoa, believing them a pathological phenomenon. (Pl. 85d.) Leeuwenhoek, however, found them healthy specimens and was thus enabled to put forth the theory that the male semen formed the foetus. The resulting school of animalculists claimed, considerably more pointedly than Leeuwenhoek, that the human embryo from the very first was a complete though miniature 'homunculus'. Thus there grew up two conflicting preformation schools, ovists and animalculists, claiming respectively female and male parent as the determinant of the form of the foetus. When Charles Bonnet (1720–43) showed (1740) that some female tree lice (aphids) can produce their young without fertilization (parthenogenesis), the ovists seemed to have triumphed.

The preformation school of embryology won the support of the anatomical school of mechanists, since they too repudiated any progressive embryological change other than by the expansion of preformed parts. Until the eighteenth century the preformation theory therefore carried great weight, and so renowned an authority as the Swiss scientist and belletrist, Albert von Haller (1708–11), perhaps the most esteemed professor of physiology of his day, backed it. Nevertheless, the idea of a miniature completely preformed in seed or egg was called into question when Réaumur proved that some crustaceans and worms are able to regenerate lost bodily parts *de novo* and when Tremblay showed that polyps reproduce asexually. Caspar Friedrich Wolff (1733–94) struck at the preformationists in two signicant treatises, *Theoria Generationis* (1759), his doctoral dissertation, and *De Formatione Intestinorum Praecipua . . . Embryonis Gallinecei* (presented in 1768 to the St Petersburg Academy, of which he was a member). His investigations showed that both plant and animal development came about by differentiation, that the chicken intestine, for example, was not a preformed structure but developed from a *simple* sheet of tissue. Wolff's argument was condemned by Haller, and so great was Haller's prestige that Wolff's pioneer work on epigenesis was not adequately appreciated until the nineteenth century.

The belief in spontaneous generation also died hard. It survived Redi's demonstration (see above) that the supposed spontaneous generation of flies from organic matter was in reality nothing more than the hatching of eggs. The most stalwart defender of spontaneous generation in the eighteenth century was John Needham (1713–81), an English Catholic priest. He sealed and corked boiling broth in flasks to exclude external influences, believing that boiling had killed any germs in the broth. On opening the flasks days later and discovering organisms, he claimed that the theory of spontaneous generation had been adequately demonstrated. Lazzaro Spallanzani (1729–99), doubting the experimental procedures of Needham, disproved his work by more carefully controlled experiments, designed to show that animalcules did not grow in infusions properly sealed and boiled. Needham remained unconvinced, however, and the Needham–Spallanzani controversy went on for years. Along with the transformation of species and the preformation of the embryo, spontaneous generation remained a debated issue during the eighteenth century.

The Beginnings of Modern Psychology

In the early modern period, the study of psychology was intertwined with speculative philosophy (see Chapter VII) as well as with medicine, biology, and related fields. Descartes, we have seen, established a system of philosophy on the basis of his famous dictum *Cogito, ergo sum*. Convinced of the existence of a mathematical world and putting great emphasis on reason as against perceptual experience, he hoped to replace medieval dogmatism with deductive procedures. His greatest contribution to psychology was his concept of a mind-body dualism—that is, a thinking substance and an extended substance. Extended substance, he maintained, behaved according to mechanical law, the body being little more than an automaton. The human being, however, was not a mere automaton since he also had a reasoning soul or mind, mind and body having a point of contact which Descartes placed in the pineal gland. Descartes also believed in innate ideas—that is, truths inherent in man's nature and therefore *a priori*, inescapable, and acceptable as a basis of further reasoning.

The existence of innate ideas, we have also seen, was debated by contemporary British empiricists. In this connection, Francis Bacon did not disagree with Descartes in any essential. Hobbes, on the other hand, was monistic, attempting to explain all activity in the thoroughly naturalistic terms of Galilean mechanics. All the content of the mind, he thought, was reducible to motion, sensations being motions in the psychological organism. Hobbes did not find many disciples, but Locke had a greater effect upon later British empiricists. Locke's epistemology was more concerned with the validity of knowledge than with the process of knowing, although the question 'How do we know?' was also of importance to him. His *Essay Concerning Human Understanding* (1690) gave his answer to that question: Knowledge comes from experience, which takes two forms of psychological expression, sensation and reflection. For Locke the mind on birth was *tabula rasa* and no ideas were innate; ideas came from sensations, combinations of sensations, and reflections upon them. Although himself a devout Christian, Locke thus seemed to be saying that the mind is the product of the external material universe. By thus breaking thought up into elemental components, Hobbes and Locke began what is sometimes called psychological atomism.

In accounting for knowledge of the external world, Locke adopted Galileo's distinction between primary and secondary qualities (i.e. between those assumed to be in the phenomenon and those assumed to be in the mind), and thus brought a reaction from Berkeley (1710). Admitting that all knowledge of the external world came through the senses, Berkeley asked whether all qualities were not equally secondary. How do we know, for instance, of extension except through touch? He denied any superiority of human knowledge of primary as opposed to secondary qualities. Hence his doctrine: We can know material substances only by their sensory qualities, and all such qualities are equally knowable or unknowable; things have reality for us only because we have been vouchsafed a share in God's perception of them. Berkeley thus repudiated all human concept of material substance outside the mind (to be is only to be perceived), but he did not question the existence of the mind itself. For him, in other words, all ideas were innate.

David Hume (1711–76), in turn, reacted against Berkeley's psychology. Dividing mental operations into the fundamentals of immediate perceptions and mediate ideas (derived from perceptions), he found that for him mind and self were themselves as difficult of perception, and thus of knowledge and proof, as material substance had been for Berkeley. The concept of cause-effect likewise had for him no objective validity other than customary association, though it was a very valuable working tool. In general, although willing to accept mathematical proof, Hume was sceptical about abstract thought and seemed to reduce human knowledge to satisfying associations.

Hume was thus one of the founders of the school of British associationists of the eighteenth century. Drawing upon the psychological atomism of Hobbes and Locke as well as upon Hume, David Hartley (1705–57) put forth the explicit doctrine of the associationist school. Hartley, a physician by training, was aware of the work that had been done on the brain and the nervous system and gave a physiological buttressing to his statements, attributing thought to vibrations of the medullary substance and to neutral processes. He maintained that there are two orders of events, the mental and the physical, which are not identical but which run parallel to each other. Change in one is therefore accompanied by change in the other. Sensations and ideas are interconnected by physiological processes, and from this interconnection comes a general law of association. Stated simply, this law assumed that if sensations are often experienced together, they will form corresponding ideas, which will usually occur to the mind together with them.

The empiricism of Locke's and Hume's day and the credo of the *philosophes*, partly attributable to it, is discussed in Chapters VII and IX above and Chapter XV below. The *Encyclopédie*, edited as it was by the scientist-philosopher-belletrist Diderot and the mathematician d'Alembert, was committed in its oft-quoted 'preliminary discourse' (by d'Alembert) to the empirical approach to knowledge and, implicitly at least, to scientific determinism. Diderot himself, with painstaking attention to accuracy and detail, wrote a number of the articles on science and technology, and a large part of the illustrations were of actual technological processes and machinery. A number of the leading scientists of the age wrote articles for the *Encyclopédie*, which thus became at the same time a compendium of the latest scientific and technological findings and a medium of propaganda against obscurantism—both in the articles on science and technology and in numerous others on humanistic, political, religious, social, and economic subjects. Its first volume appeared in 1751, and its last (XXXIV–XXXV, the indexes) in 1780. In Beaumarchais' *Barber of Seville* (1775), Dr Bartholo, representative of an uneasy older generation, heartily disapproved of the scientific and other innovations of his day. Calling it a 'barbarous century', he complains that it has produced 'every kind of foolishness'—'freedom of thought, attraction [i.e. Newton's law of gravitation], electricity, toleration, inoculation, quinine, the *Encyclopédie*, and [bourgeois] dramas.' By that time one of the schools of the Enlightenment *philosophes*, that represented by Condillac, La Mettrie, and Holbach, had by 'pure reason' achieved a thoroughly monistic and materialistic psychology, but, as his *Neveu de Rameau* revealed, Diderot was not altogether in their camp. And Kant, following Hume, though with a Pietistic touch, reacted against the rationalism of the French Enlightenment and sought to restore room for faith in a series of idealist *Kritiks*, culminating in his *Kritik der reinen Vernunft* (1781).

SCIENCE OUTSIDE EUROPE

Science in the Islamic World

Most of the significant activity in the development of pure science outside of Europe after 1500 took place in the Far East. In Africa and America (except for the sculptural and architectural techniques discussed in Chapter XII) such scientific knowledge as is known to have been accumulated after 1500 by people not directly influenced by the European and the Asiatic scientific tradition was apparently of the empirical or technological nature required for everyday needs. In the Islamic world the stock of scientific principles remained for the most part unchanged from the preceding period where no change crept in from Europe. Except perhaps in the field of architectural technology and engineering (see Chapter XII), after 1500—and especially after 1600—in all Islamic lands the natural sciences became as a rule a mere tradition, the effective standards of which probably declined.

In the course of the sixteenth century Ottoman science tended to run to encyclopedism more than to fresh monographs. Yet it often showed a high awareness of the demands of experimentation or of mathematical cogency. Among the astronomical observatories maintained at Istanbul and elsewhere the fine one run in the tradition of Ulūgh Beg and ʿAlī Qūshji (see Chapter XIII) continued to do good work under Taqī-al-dīn Misrī for a few years after 1579. Many Turkish scholars, however, were content simply to translate earlier Persian or Arabic works into Turkish. The Islamic tradition of learning had hardened and independent scholarship became less and less free. For instance, in 1601 Sari ʿAbd-al-Raḥmān, a freethinker with his own cosmology based on natural law, was executed. Study was increasingly hampered by a ban on the ordinary importation of printed books, such as the Arabic classics then being printed in Europe.

The Ottoman experience was not wholly untypical of other Islamic centres. India under the Moguls, for example, rewarded physicians and astronomers and built well-equipped observatories, yet produced little basically new. The major difference was that the Ottomans were more closely involved intellectually with the new Occidental upsurge. We have already noted (Chapter XIII) the work of Pīrī Reʿīs and his introduction of the new Western geographical knowledge into Turkey. In the seventeenth century the most significant figure in Ottoman science was Ḥajjī Khalīfa (d. 1657), an encyclopedist who mastered the Islamic scholarly tradition and also tried to introduce to Turkish readers new Occidental discoveries in several fields. His attempt bore little fruit, however. On the other hand, some Turkish medical writers could claim a certain originality. It was from Turkey that Mary Wortley Montagu brought to England the practice of inoculation for smallpox (c. 1718).

Science in India and China

For the Far East and India it is difficult to separate the science of this period from technological achievement. The high technical quality of Far Eastern textiles, porcelains, rugs, furniture, and other decorative products has already claimed our attention (Chapter XII). Another field of outstanding technology in the Far East was naval architecture. In the 1590's a Korean admiral, Yi Sunsin, perfected an iron-clad tortoise boat and wrought great havoc upon the fleet of the invading Japanese, but the secrets of the vessel's construction apparently died with him. India, too, in addition to skilful workers in textiles and other decorative arts, had highly competent shipwrights. When contacts between India and the West became frequent, Indian craftsmen built Western-type vessels for Westerners while retaining their own traditional type for compatriot traders.

Several Chinese engaged in theoretical scientific research. Chu Tsai-yü's treatise on *Resonant Tubes*, published in 1584, evidenced a certain amount of experimental investigation in the field of music; he established (well before Mersenne's exposition of the same principle in 1627) that the intervals for 'an equal tempered scale' are to be founded by mathematical measurements.[39] Progress was made in the seventeenth and eighteenth centuries toward a scientific methodology relating to linguisitc changes and the reliability of historical documents (see Chapter IX). The experimental method, however, was used only on occasion; it was not adopted as basic for the investigation of nature, and few scholars or physicians devoted their energies to such things as mathematics, astronomy, the study of disease, or the perfection of mechanical contrivances.

Chinese savants continued, rather, to devote their efforts to compiling data, with or without adding to them. The skill of the Chinese artist in illustration was well exploited in several noteworthy scientific compendia. The great illustrated encyclopedia *San-ts'ai t'u-hui* of Wang Ch'i and his son, published about 1609, contained illustrated accounts of tools, plants, animals, and other subjects. Mao Yüan-I's *Wu-pei chih*, completed in 1628, was a huge illustrated compendium on weapons, strategy, ships, defences, and other phases of warfare. Sung Ying-hsing's small compendium, the *T'ien-kung k'ai-wu*, which was published in 1637, provided an illustrated account of Chinese industrial arts of the early seventeenth century. It dealt with the manufacture of flour, clothes, dyes, ink, weapons (including gas explosives), salt, sugar, and pottery, the casting and forging of metals, the designing of ships and wheeled vehicles, the mining of coal and jade, and pearl diving.[40] Cotton cultivation and cotton cloth manufacture developed extensively during the Ming dynasty under imperial stimulation, and treatises on silk and cotton and on cloth manufacture appeared with pertinent illustrations. The *Tzu-hui* dictionary of Mei Ying-tso (1615) showed a marked superiority over earlier works in the scientific arrangement of characters, and it, in turn, was bettered by the *K'ang-hsi tzu-tien*, published in 1716.

The great Chinese encyclopedias were discussed in Chapter XI. Several compendia dealing with medicine deserve separate mention. Among the principal contributions of China to medicine was the *Pen-ts'ao kang-mu* ('Materia Medica') of Li Shih-chen, completed in 1578 after twenty-six years' work. In view of the conflict of the contemporary European iatrochemists with the Galenists, Li Shih-chen's knowledge of specifics is particularly impressive. His book discussed 898 vegetable and about 1000 animal and mineral drugs and included 8,160 prescriptions. It commented upon inoculations for smallpox, the treatment of syphilis, and the use of such drugs as kaolin, stramonium, chaulmoogra oil, ephederine, and iodine as specifics. It went through many editions in China, was widely used in Japan, and much of it was later translated into Western languages. Wang K'en-t'ang, between 1597 and 1607, published a stupendous work in 120 volumes, the *Principles and Practice of Medicine* (*Cheng-chih chung-sheng*). In 1642 appeared a small book by Wu Yiu-hsing which, though entitled *Discourse on Plague*, really dealt with epidemic fevers; he distinguished between typhoid fever and other kinds and emphasized the nose and mouth as important channels of infection. One of the best doctors of the Ch'ing period was Chang Lu, whose *I-t'ung*, compiled between 1644 and 1693, became a standard. Li's *Pen-ts'ao kang-mu* was supplemented and brought up to date in 1765 by Chao Hsüeh-min.

The Jesuits were able to introduce Western mathematics, astronomy, geography, surveying, medicine, and other branches of knowledge into China in the seventeenth century during the declining years of the Ming dynasty. The succeeding Manchu dynasty, in an effort to make itself acceptable to the Chinese, was even more determined to exalt traditional Neo-Confucian concepts and discourage innovation. Nevertheless, modern Western science at first engaged considerable interest on the part of some practical Confucian scholars, and where the Chinese saw concrete advantage to be gained by borrowing from the West without danger to sacred institutions, they were ready enough to borrow. Since native firearms were inferior, the cannon and hand guns of the Portuguese were copied in the early sixteenth century. Later in the century, Japanese imitations of Portuguese weapons and, in the seventeenth century, Dutch weapons were also copied. The Jesuits were employed by both the Mings and the Manchus to cast cannon. Agricultural products such as maize, the sweet potato, and the peanut were introduced and spread between 1573 and 1610. In addition, the use of tobacco and later of opium, though prohibited, spread also, because a popular demand for them arose. In 1628 the Grand Secretary Hsü Kuang-ch'i, a friend of the Jesuit Ricci and a long-time Christian, completed a great compendium on agriculture, the *Nung-cheng ch'üan-shu*, which, besides incorporating accumulated Chinese knowledge, added everything of practical use from Western knowledge that he was able to obtain through the missionaries.

Much of the knowledge the Christians brought was embodied in translations and ultimately copied into the great manuscript library (*Ssu-k'u ch'uan-shu*) of the Ch'ien-lung emperor in the eighteenth century. Relatively few Chinese, however, read and understood this body of information. It did not become an integral part of Chinese learning, and Western astronomy and mathematics seemed to be of interest or practical value only to the technicians associated with the Bureau of Astronomy at Peking. Because of their scientific knowledge the Jesuits were put in charge of the Bureau in 1645 with Schall as director, Verbiest following him in 1688. They reformed the calendar, introduced knowledge of the telescopic discoveries, and otherwise made themselves useful, equipping the observatory, providing technical and geographical information, and translating Western scientific treatises (without teaching the Copernican system).[41]

Though by the late eighteenth century some of the more practical aspects of Western science began to be clearly discernible, its wide application to agriculture, navigation, and other things of prime importance was not made clear to the Chinese before the nineteenth century. Moreover, Western science was suspect in general, since it was expounded by evangelists, who brought the tenets of Christianity, which the Confucian scholars and the Manchu government, after some dalliance, rejected as fundamentally disruptive of the traditional culture (see Chapter V). The few missionaries permitted to remain in China were looked upon with considerable suspicion and hence neither were asked nor volunteered to keep the Chinese scholarly world up-to-date on scientific or technological developments. The opportunity for China to grow up scientifically with the West thus was lost.

Science in Japan

In Japan the Chinese-influenced Li-Chu school of medicine remained dominant during the Momoyama and the early Tokugawa period, even though other Chinese schools claimed adherents as well. Probably the leading native physician of the Momoyama period was Dōsan Manase, who during the last quarter of the sixteenth century followed the Li-Chu school in numerous treatises on many types of disease. In the late sixteenth and seventeenth centuries the scientific and technological achievements of the West were eagerly sought, and Japanese physicians who learned surgery and other elements of Western medicine from the Jesuits founded a 'Southern Barbarian' school of surgery.

As the Tokugawa period advanced, European medical knowledge continued to enter Japan through the Dutch at Nagasaki, where European physicians gave instruction to the Japanese who were interested, introducing them to medical treatises in Dutch. Inevitably Western medical ideas began to appear in Japanese medical literature. A Dutch version of Ambroise Paré reached Japan by 1655, and parts of it appeared with illustrations in Japanese works in 1706 and 1713. The teachings of the German physician Engelbert Kämpfer, who was in residence at the Dutch factory in the 1690's, further facilitated the spread of European methods. In 1766 Kagawa Gen-etsu published his *San Ron*, the foundation of modern obstetrics in Japan, which was a fusion of Chinese and Western ideas with the author's practical experience. For the most part, however, during our period the Japanese rejected Western science and technology; what they wanted, they thought, could not be separated from Christianity, and they feared that Christianity meant not only cultural subversion but also possible political subjugation.

NOTES TO CHAPTER XIV

1. Boethius, *De Consolatione Philosophiae*, Book 2, *Prosa* vii.

2. Alexandre Koyré, *From the Closed World to the Infinite Universe*, reproduces this diagram on p. 37.

3. Quoted in Dorothea W. Singer, *Giordano Bruno; His life and Thought, with annotated translations of his work on the infinite universe and worlds* (New York, 1950), p. 86.

4. It is quite exact to say here that, according to Descartes, science is God's handiwork. The first principles of science, the 'seeds of truth' deposited by God in the human soul, then known in the philosophical tradition as 'eternal truths', are God's creatures. God 'made' the principles of human reason just as He made light, and does not contemplate them as if they were eternal ideas existing in His understanding. (Georges Canguilhem.)

5. Professor G. Canguilhem points out that these reserves concerning Bacon's modernity, his precursory genius, and the recognition of his inability to grasp that the natural sciences should take the same path as mathematics are all the more interesting and important in that Anglo–American authors generally tend towards what appears to contemporary French authors, trained in the school of Alexandre Koyré or of Robert Lenoble, to be an over-estimation.

6. To Professor G. Canguilhem the works which Alexandre Koyré has devoted to Galileo have done much to cool the ardour of historians who, taking as a starting point different ideologies (pragmatism or Marxism) have attempted to derive science from the mechanics of civil or military engineering techniques. In this connection, as Galileo himself stated in his *Discorsi*, it was questions rather than ideas that he found in the works of the technicians, mainly in the theory of the resistance of matter and hydrostatics. In his book

Les ingénieurs de la Renaissance (Paris, 1964) Betrand Gille considers the opinion of Alexandre Koyré too exclusive.

The authors here relied not so much on Koyré as upon comments directed to them personally by the late E. J. Dijksterhuis.

7. See Ettore Bortolotti, 'L'Algebra nella scuola matematica bolognese del secolo XVI' in *Studi e ricerche sulla storia della matematica in Italia* (Bologna, 1928), pp. 7 and 17–20, and Alexandre Koyré, *La science moderne (de 1450 à 1800)* in *Histoire générale des sciences*, II (Paris, 1958), pp. 37–39.

8. In Professor G. Canguilhem's opinion it is not certain that the number of circles in Ptolemaic astronomy were more than twice the number of Copernican circles. The astronomer Purbach would appear to have counted only 42. It was not so much the reduction in numbers which constituted the superiority of the Copernican explanation as the organic, systematic character of this explanation; for instance, the postulate of a relationship between the distance of a planet from the sun and the revolutionary cycle of this planet.

9. Quoted in Dorothy Stimson, *The Gradual Acceptance of the Copernican Theory of the Universe* (New York, 1917), p. 39.

10. See Ingomar Düring, 'Von Aristoteles bis Leibniz', *Antike und Abendland*, IV (1954), 152, and Ambroise Jobert, 'L'Université de Cracovie et les grands courants de pensée du XVIe siècle', *Revue d'histoire moderne et contemporaine*, I (1954), pp. 216.

11. *De Revolutionibus*, Bk. I, Ch. I.

12. Galileo's recantation, quoted in the introduction to Galileo's *Dialogue on the Great World Systems*, ed. Giorgio de Santillana (Chicago, 1955), p. xix.

13. For this and other disputes of Newton and Hooke, see Alexandre Koyré, 'An unpublished letter of Robert Hooke to Isaac Newton', *Isis*, XLIII (1952), especially pp. 333–37.

14. Professor G. Canguilhem, by way of addition, comments as follows: This is one of the most resounding events in the history of modern astronomy and in the evolution of celestial mechanics. Halley had calculated the reappearances of the comet for 1758. Clairaut fixed its passage at about April 14, 1759. In fact the comet was a month ahead of this reckoning. As an example of the influence of a scientific event of this magnitude on public opinion, Victor Hugo's poem 'The Comet', in *La légende des siècles* may be found of interest:

> 'He foretold the day the star would come again.
> What jeers! . . .
> . . . . . .
> And, suddenly, with ghostly stealth
> Appeared above the wild horizon
> A flame suffusing myriad leagues,
> A monstrous flash out of the blue immensity,
> Out of the splendid, deep, and suddenly illuminated sky:
> Said the terrible star to man: Behold, here I am.'

15. Paraphrased in English by Sir James Jeans, *The Growth of Physical Science* (Cambridge, 1951, p. 148. Descartes' texts most clearly relevant to the law of inertia are to be found in *Principia Philosophiae* (1644), Part II, para. 37, page 54 and in *Le Monde ou Traité de la lumière* (1664), Chap. VII, p. 82.

16. Quoted (with slight modifications) from A. Wolf, *A History of Science, Technology, and Philosophy in the Eighteenth Century* (Macmillan Company, New York, 1939), p. 64.

17. Quoted *ibid.*, p. 68.

18. *Opticks* (1704), Query 29.

19. 'Hall, Chester Moor (1703–71)', *Dictionary of National Biography* (London, 1920–22), VIII, p. 946.

20. Quoted in A. R. Hall, *The Scientific Revolution (1500–1800), The Formation of the Modern Scientific Attitude* (Boston, 1957), p. 213.

21. Quoted in Wolf, *Sixteenth and Seventeenth centuries*, pp. 277–78.

22. A recent study attributes to Cuneaus of Leyden the invention of the famous 'jar', assigning to E. J. Von Kleist only an accessory rôle. See the article by John L. Heilbron: 'A propos de l'invention de la bouteille de Leyde', *Revue d'histoire des sciences*, XIX, n° 2 (April–June, 1966). (G. Canguilhem.)

23. Wolf, *Sixteen and Seventeenth Centuries*, p. 470.

24. On Lomonosov's thermometer, see Boris N. Menshutkin, *Russia's Lomonosov* (tr. J. E. Thal and E. J. Webster; Princeton University Press, Princeton, 1952), pp. 70–72.

25. *The Works of the Honourable Robert Boyle*, ed. Thomas Birch (1772), I, 354. For a recent re-evaluation of Boyle see Marie Boas, *Robert Boyle and Seventeenth Century Chemistry* (University Press, Cambridge, 1958).

26. *Observations on the Solid and Liquid States of Substances* (1760), quoted in A. A. Morosov, *Michael Wassiljewitsch Lomonosov, 1711–65* (tr. W. Hoepp; Rutten und Loenig, Berlin, 1954), pp. 211–12; this is almost verbatim the same as Lomonosov to Euler, July 5, 1748. See also Menshutkin, pp. 116–18, and A. A. Zvorikine, 'Remarques sur l'histoire des inventions et de la pensée scientifique et technique russe des dix-septième et dix-neuvième siècles', *Journal of World History*, special number (1958), p. 186. On the wide currency of the conservation law of mass before Lomonosov and Lavoisier see Henry Guerlac, *Lavoisier, the Crucial Year: the Background and Origin of His First Experiments on Combustion in 1772* (Cornell University Press, Ithaca, New York, 1961), p. xv.

27. Michele Gortani, 'Italian Pioneers in Geology and Mineralogy', *Journal of World History*, VII (1963), pp. 510–12, n. 8.

28. Thomas D. Kendrick, *The Lisbon Earthquake* (London, 1956), esp. pp. 57–71.

29. Oskar Netoliczka (ed.), *Johannes Honterus' ausgewählte Schriften* (Vienna, 1898), p. 152.

30. For a discussion of the thesis that Dezhnev went by land rather than by sea, see F. A. Golder, *Russian Expansion on the Pacific* (1641–1850) (Cleveland, 1914), pp. 67–95, and Raymond Fisher, 'Simon Dezhnev and Professor Golder', *Pacific Historical Review*, XXV (1956), pp. 281–92.

31. Quoted from 'Additional Materials in Connection with the Remarks of Soviet Scientists on the Plan of Volume IV' (Ms. previously cited).

32. To Professor G. Calguilhem the contribution of Bernard de Jussieu towards the establishment of a 'natural' method in botany was practical rather than speculative. The Botanical Garden planted in the grounds of Versailles during the reign of Louis XV provided the demonstration of this method. The principles of natural classification, on the other hand, were expounded and developed by Antoine-Laurent de Jussieu (1748–1836) in his work *Genera plantarum* (1789). Nor should it be forgotten that Michel Adanson, botanist, geographer, and explorer of Senegal, had divided and classified vegetable species into 58 natural families in his work entitled *Famille des plantes* (1763).

33. Arthur O. Lovejoy, *The Great Chain of Being* (Cambridge, Mass., 1936), pp. 232–33.

34. Professor G. Canguilhem cautions that the use of the term 'homology', the exact meaning of which in comparative anatomy was determined only towards the middle of the nineteenth century after the studies of Etienne Geoffroy Saint-Hilaire (1772–1844) and with those of Richard Owen (1771–1858), runs the risk of suggesting continuity of project and concept from Pierre Belon down to Cuvier and Owen, and that progress in comparative anatomy consisted in broadening the field of observation and deepening the exploration of concept. In reality, it required the introduction of a fundamental distinction between analogy, a concept symbolic and mystic rather than scientific, and homology, originally a mathematical concept, and, above all, the introduction of a dissociation between structure and function. Analogy is functional and does not imply similarity of structures. Homology is a similitude of structural relations, without its being necessary for the organs to have the same form and function.

35. William Harvey, *Exercitatio Anatomica de Motu Cardis et Sanguinis in Animalibus*, edited with an English translation by Chauncey D. Leake (Springfield, Ill., 1928), Preface and Ch. viii, p. 70.

36. The use of the term 'vitalism' does not seem either accurate or strictly applicable in describing the doctrine of De Stahl. Medical historians have always carefully distinguished between *animism* and *vitalism* (see Daremberg, *Histoire des sciences médicales* [Paris, 1870]), and the vitalists of the Montpellier school, Barthès and his disciples, always differentiated between themselves and De Stahl and animism. (G. Canguilhem.) *The authors have used the term* vitalism *broadly, as a synonym of* anti-mechanism (*as, for example, Charles Singer and Abraham Wolf sometimes do*).

37. See Oswei Temkin, 'The Role of Surgery in the Rise of Modern Medical Thought', *Bulletin of the History of Medicine*, XXV (1951), pp. 248–59.

38. Georges Canguilhem, *La formation du concept de réflexe aux XVIIe et XVIIIe siècles* (Paris, 1955), p. 131.

39. See L. Carrington Goodrich, *A Short History of the Chinese People* (New York, 1943), p. 203.

40. *Ibid.*, p. 205.

41. Joseph Needham, *Chinese Astronomy and the Jesuit Mission: an Encounter of Cultures* (London, 1958). See also P. M. d'Elia, 'La Reprise des missions catholiques en Chine à la fin des Ming (1579–1644)', *Journal of World History*, V (1960), pp. 679–99.

CHAPTER XV

TECHNOLOGY AND SOCIETY

(1300–1775)

MEASUREMENTS AND THEIR APPLICATION

FROM the thirteenth century on, man has succeeded in harnessing tools to his material needs as never before. For the earlier scientific and technological advances of this period, accurate measurement, though recognized as desirable, was difficult to achieve, but, as explained in Chapter XIV, increasing precision of calculation became a cornerstone of the seventeenth-century 'scientific revolution'—especially in the physical sciences, whether geography, astronomy, chemistry, physics, meteorology, or navigation. In the biological sciences, too, perhaps the most important discovery, that of the circulation of the blood, was in large part quantitative, and still greater strides were to come in the eighteenth century and later, with the development of an adequate classification system. The transition from arbitrary or parochial incommensurables to a universally acceptable taxonomy in the biological sciences made measurements and, therefore, counting, categories, and comparisons more uniform and precise. Moreover, the discovery of the cell gave to biology a fundamental unit to measure and quantify even while atoms and molecules were still largely a qualitative, philosophical theory in chemistry and the other physical sciences.

Mechanical clocks play a particularly significant role in the history of units of measurement. Only after the fourteenth century did Italy's clocks strike every hour. They were not only the first machines whose construction required exact scientific knowledge but also the first to be driven by stored energy, the expenditure of which was measured by determined intervals. Huygens' pendulum and balance-wheel clocks permitted still more precise measurement of time not only to scientists but to ordinary men as well. (Pl. 89a, b.) Affairs of the day could now be arranged to the minute, even the second, instead of the hour or half-hour previously marked by the wheel clocks of the public squares and monasteries, crudely regulated by means of the foliot balance or crossbar, the earliest form of clock escapement. As time became more and more susceptible to accurate calculation, the clock became a monitor not only of scientific experimentation but of social relations as well, introducing accuracy, promptness, and uniformity of timing into human activities, until, with the rise of the industrial factory, it developed into a veritable tyrant. The attitude toward time became a major criterion of differentiation among ages and peoples.

If accurate telling of time was one of the applications of science to human affairs which proved of lasting importance to the practical business of life, accurate location and measurement of space was another. The introduction of two coordinates for mapmaking permitted a noteworthy advance in cartography. Along with better maps, the application of simple mathematics to quadrants, sextants, compasses, and other early navigational instruments made ocean travel more secure even before the improvement of the telescope and the invention of the chronometer. The measurement of the meridian eliminated much of the guesswork from the calculation of global distances.

Accurate accounting was still another addition to the practical side of life. Commercial arithmetic developed rapidly in the West from about 1300 on; double-entry book-keeping was introduced probably in the fourteenth century; and Hindu-Arabic numbers came into use more and more extensively until in the sixteenth century they were regularly used. The shortcomings of eighteenth-century Russian agriculture have been attributed, along with bad management by landlords and lack of enterprise in peasants, to the backwardness of Russian accounting methods.[2] Increased commercial risk-taking led inevitably to efforts to calculate the risks taken. Marine insurance, with rates based at first on pure guesswork, had been introduced into northern Italy before 1300 but became common in Barcelona during the fourteenth century and in Bruges during the fifteenth. By 1600 the mathematical theory of games was being studied in various parts of Europe (see Chapter XIV), and the mathematics of probabilities, today indispensible to actuarial and other kinds of statistics, was to engage the attention of some of the best mathematical minds of the seventeenth century.

By that time mathematics had come to play a fashionable role in the life of the educated European. The amateur (the so-called *curioso*) as well as the scientist had begun to look for regularities behind the manifest aspects of nature, and the same sort of contemporary quest for perfect standards of excellence as was expressed by Classicism in the arts and literature gave rise also to a taste for the rigid rules of mathematics. The state encouraged this vogue as it accumulated more and more statistics and accounted more and more strictly for its income and outgo of money. Large numbers of manuals appeared for surveyors, merchants, seamen, soldiers, and others who might profit from a knowledge of simple mathematics, and the society of the commercial capitals of Europe became familiar with 'those rather mysterious figures "teachers of mathematics" who were . . . both a symptom and a cause of this process'.[3]

In the sixteenth century mathematics was applied in a signal way to an ancient problem of time-keeping. Calendar reform had been suggested by Roger Bacon and the Avignon popes because of the long observed inaccuracy in the co-ordination of the Julian calendar with the solar year. Yet no serious efforts were made to remedy the calendar until 1474, when Pope Sixtus IV invited Regiomontanus to Rome to attend to the necessary readjustments.

On account of that astronomer's untimely death, however, nothing came of this effort. Several mathematicians of the ensuing century wrote treatises which made still more clear how inaccurate the Julian calendar was: in about 1600 years since its inception its minor inaccuracy of 11 minutes and 14 seconds per year had resulted in a ten-day shift in datings. For example, the spring equinox, which in Caesar's time fell on March 21, fell on the 11th in 1582, the year reform was finally put into effect.

This reform came at the instance of Pope Gregory XIII. Aloysius Lilius, a mathematician-astronomer-physician of Naples, and after his death Christopher Clavius, a mathematician of Bamberg, worked out the details. On their recommendation, in Catholic countries ten days—October 5 to 14—were arbitrarily dropped from the calendar at once and the day after October 4, 1582, became October 15, 1582. This radical surgery restored the calendar to the solar co-ordination that had existed at the time of the Council of Nicea (AD 325). To maintain correct co-ordination thereafter, leap years were to be observed in every year divisible by 4 except for the centurial years unless they were multiples of 400. Thus 1600 was to be a leap year, but not 1700, 1800, and 1900. In spite of these careful mathematical shadings the Gregorian calendar will develop one day of solar inaccuracy every 3,323 years. Some difficulty was encountered in adjusting the 'new style' calendar to the lunar calendar, which also figured in the fixing of movable church feasts. A still more formidable obstacle was the reluctance of non-Roman Christians to follow the papal lead. The Catholic calendar was not adopted in Protestant Germany until 1700 (and then only with certain modifications), in England not until 1752, and in Russia not until the Revolution of 1917.

In the seventeenth century, though dates were still commonly given in Roman numerals, other calculations, whether in scientific research or in financial accounts, employed not only Arabic numerals but also the decimal system, and the new mathematical shorthand or symbols (see Chapter XIV). Simplified notation made easier the invention of devices for mechanical calculation. The abacus, the time-honoured calculating device used in western Europe since around AD 1000, was supplemented by 'Napier's Bones', developed around 1617 by the father of logarithms; the 'bones' were a system of numbering rods. Then, shortly after the introduction of logarithms made it possible to reduce higher arithmetical processes to lower ones (see Chapter XIV), came the slide rule, usually attributed to the English mathematicians Edmund Gunter (1581–1626) and (more accurately) William Oughtred (1575–1660). The first calculating machine known to be designed with details for its construction was that which Pascal invented in 1642, when he was only nineteen years old, to help his father add up sums of money. (Pl. 90.) Despite its intricacy dozens of useful machines were made to Pascal's design, and several still survive. Again illustrating that an invention may come to more than one mind when the culture is ripe for it,

Samuel Morland, not aware of Pascal's idea, developed his own machine for addition and substraction in 1666, and later devised another for multiplication. In the 1670's Leibniz, again independently, invented and described his calculating machine. While it, too, was intricate, at least one example, which still exists, was made. Only in the nineteenth century did any significant advance in this type of computer prove feasible.

'Political arithmetick', or what we today would call 'vital statistics', was also a product of the seventeenth century. The word *statistics* had not yet been coined. Vital statistics were kept by parish churches, but only as records of baptism, marriage, and Christian burial. In France after the Revocation of the Edict of Nantes, Huguenots could not prove birth, marriage, or death since they did not belong to legitimate parishes, and so they could not legally bequeath property. The publication of bills of mortality for London parishes in the seventeenth century indicated growing concern for a well-ordered method of calculating births, deaths, and reasons for mortality. In Holland the interest in mortality statistics and tables was shared by scientists like Huygens and statesmen like Jan de Witt, no mean mathematician himself.

With the growing power of the state, attempts were made to assess various factors affecting population. In 1662 John Graunt (1620–74) published his *Natural and Political Observations . . . made upon the Bills of Mortality*— based, that is, upon the weekly mortality announcements published by certain English parishes. Though his method of gathering data was crude by modern standards, his book was a significant step in the study of demography. Graunt's work was continued by William Petty, who used empirical measurements with self-conscious deliberation. In the preface to his *Political Arithmetick* (1691) Petty said: 'Instead of using only comparative and superlative Words, and intellectual Arguments, I have taken the Course (as a Specimen of the Political Arithmetick I have long aimed at) to express myself in terms of Number, Weight, or Measure; to use only Arguments of Sense, and to consider only such Causes as have visible Foundations in Nature; leaving those that depend upon mutable Minds, Opinions, Appetites and Passions of particular Men, to the Consideration of Others.' Gregory King (1648–1712) adopted this quantitative concept of demography in his *Natural and Political Observations and Conclusions upon the State and Condition of England* (1696). In France, where the royal intendants had frequently concerned themselves with demographic data, Abbé Jean-Joseph Expilly undertook a *Dictionnaire géographique, historique et politique des Gaules et de la France*, which, though incomplete in six volumes (1762–70), still pays off as a mine of statistics.

The use of mathematics in calculating life insurance risks seems to date from an earlier period. Until the middle of the seventeenth century, however, the buying of insurance continued to partake more of the nature of mere chance than of calculated risk. No allowance was made for differences among the insured of age, occupation, or other factors that today are given special weight in the computation of insurance premiums. Graunt's work led to the drawing up of other mortality tables after the middle of the seventeenth century, and in 1693 the astronomer Halley published a well elaborated actuarial table. Halley was critical of the techniques used by Graunt and Petty, and the first English life insurance companies, established in the early eighteenth century, preferred his computations.

Numerous instances during the seventeenth and eighteenth centuries reveal a sort of logical relationship between mathematical and technological development: the accumulated knowledge of the mathematics of relevant subjects (such as described in Chapter XIV) suggested and sometimes helped to make possible new steps toward the solution of old practical problems. Ship-building, architecture, and engineering improved with the employment of mathematics in such problems as the strength of materials, the building of arches, and tables of proportion. The advances in trigonometry and the development of logarithms made astronomical and navigational calculations easier. In surveying, the theodolite (first used in the sixteenth century) was more regularly employed for calculating angles. The volume of barrels was made subject to careful measurement (an obvious aid not only to vintners but also to customs officers). Military experts applied new developments in geometry to theories of fortification and to the study of ballistics.[4]

So long as the new knowledge held forth the promise of glory or material advantage and did not undermine tradition, governments generally befriended it. Governmental patronage was especially liberal in geographical research. After the discovery of the New World the making and printing of charts and maps became a big business, pursued by governments as well as private trading companies and commercial chart makers. With the new printing press to serve them, they put out numerous maps, sometimes by means of wood block but, as time went on, more often by engraved copper plates. The study of geography had obvious political and commercial implications (see Chapter I). As early as 1503 the king of Spain established the Casa de Contratación de las Indias, a combination of hydrographic office and board of trade. In a century and a half it gathered data from about 18,000 sailings—from 117 to 188 a year on the average during its busiest years, 1580–1620. Within five years a separate hydrographical office was established, perhaps the first in history. Geographical information about the New World became crucial to the success of further explorations and settlements by the rival colonial powers, and new information was guarded with great care, official charts sometimes being kept under a veil of secrecy. Map makers were encouraged by governments to keep pace with the growing knowledge of geography, for their charts and maps were not only of great aid to the mariner but served the merchant and the military as well. For similar reasons governments showed a friendly interest in meteorology and meteorological instruments. On the other hand, until the mid-eighteenth century, the study of the origin of the Earth often ran into difficulties with the authorities, because calculations of the time needed for geological processes were in conflict with a literal interpretation of the Book of Genesis and so smacked of heresy.

MACHINES, INDUSTRY, AND POWER

As scientists came to depend less on theoretical speculation and more on accurate observation and measurement, they became more dependent on the makers of precision instruments. Astronomers' telescopes and biologists' microscopes could be no better than the most expert lens-grinders' products, and alchemists or chemists were limited by the expertness of craftsmen in the manufacture of glass. Until about 1300 in such enterprises as the glass industry and the making of surgical instruments Western craftsmen had followed the lead of the Muslims. Then the West forged ahead slowly, and the consequent improvement of lenses and other apparatus played a major part in the great biological and astronomical achievements of the succeeding centuries.

The dependence of the scientist on well-designed apparatus and precision instruments was not evident, however, before the physicial sciences became highly organized, specialized bodies of knowledge. During the fourteenth and fifteenth centuries (as earlier), such inventions as were made were usually by craftsmen working empirically and with little theoretical knowledge; the occasional experimentalist in the ranks of theoretical science was likely to work alone in a private laboratory without employing the skill or technical advice of craftsmen. In the sixteenth and seventeenth centuries, however, empirical craftsmanship and theoretical speculation were more often found working in co-operation. Several instances of this association of practice with theory have already been noted. In the course of routine medical practice, for example, Paracelsus worked out certain of his revolutionary theories; in the mines of the Erzgebirge Agricola laid the foundations for his treatise on metallurgy; Galileo made observations in the Venetian Arsenal; Mercator was a simple map maker when he devised the Mercator projection; Fabrizio was originally a lens grinder, and Leeuwenhoek a microscope maker. Another example was Vanoccio Biringuccio of Siena (c. 14801–540), who (as we shall soon see) combined his experiences as a miner with speculative theory. Nor is the number of other relevant instances small.

Yet, during the period here under discussion there was more talk about the need for the alliance of science and technology than actual alliance. Bacon's dream of bringing philosophy down from the empyrean inspired generations of European scientists and statesmen and kept before them always the goal of wedding science to technology, but it was prognostication rather than reality. The 'scientific revolution' of seventeenth-century Europe usually placed emphasis upon science for its own sake rather than for technological improvement.

Nevertheless, the concept of science that took hold in seventeenth-century Europe prepared the way for a mutually acceptable alliance of science and technology. The technician assumed greater importance in industry, while the importance of the craftsman diminished and, along with it, that of the guild tradition of which he was a product. Simple tools were replaced by machines and engines, and in the craftsman's place gradually came the mechanic and, later, the engineer, more theoretical in outlook than his prototype but still not a pure scientist (that is, one who considered himself a disinterested questioner of nature). The technical foundations of the eighteenth-century 'Industrial Revolution' (with some exceptions that will be noted below) were laid not by scientists but by skilled mechanics, some turned engineers, for science and industry generally went their separate ways. Only in the nineteenth century, with the development of new sources of power, new techniques and skills, and a new socio-economic situation was the dream of Bacon finally to be fulfilled; the successful marriage of science and technology, for better or for worse, brought about a lasting alliance of scientist, engineer, mechanic, and craftsman, with the sympathy and subsidy of business, society, and government.

The Increased Use of Machines

Modern man may well be characterized as a machine-making animal, but he owed much to his forerunners. The ancient Chinese, Egyptians, Greeks, and Romans are known to have borrowed or invented varied types of machines and tools—wheels, pulleys, bellows, lathes, treadles, potter's wheels, spinning and weaving mechanisms, mills, water organs and clocks, siphons, Archimedean screws, burning mirrors, and even automatic machines. During the Middle Ages the yoke for oxen, the hard horse collar, harness for animals in single file, and metal horseshoes had made the exploitation of animal power more efficient. Water power and windmills had been used East and West for centuries before our period for such tasks as grinding grain, working bellows, pumping water, processing metals, and sawing wood. During the Middle Ages western Europe also knew the ship's rudder, lateen-rigged sails, fore and aft rigging, the compass, the quadrant, clocks, buttons, forks, and improved textile machines. The thirteenth-century picture album of Villard de Honnecourt contained sketches of various types of machines, even one for perpetual motion. Some of these early machines had not been commonly applied to mankind's needs before the fifteenth or sixteenth century. For example, the crank, known in ancient China and in ninth-century Europe, was widely used only by the fifteenth century, when western Europeans applied it to the bit and brace, paddle wheels, and the hurdy-gurdy.

As a result of the abundance of machines from other regions and earlier ages the period from 1300 to 1500 in Europe was not spectacular for the invention of new mechanisms so much as for its marked improvements and wider application of older machines. Mechanisms like plows, clocks, windmills, and water mills are portrayed in sketchbooks of the period, such as Leonardo da Vinci's notebooks and the *Mittelalterliches Hausbuch* (c. 1480), compiled by an unknown gunmaker and belonging to a south-German family. Leonardo's prestige has led to a common assumption of the superiority of Italian technology over that of northern countries in their day, but the comparison may be somewhat unfair, since his sketches and manuscripts were a compendium not merely of the science and technology of his day but also of his own designs, some of which were only unrealized dreams.

In any case, Northern technology was far from stagnant. In the fourteenth century an astonishing proportion of Nuremberg's population were master craftsmen, and in the fifteenth century printing, metallurgy, and precision work were especially well developed in the free cities of Germany. During the next century, as astronomy shifted its basic ideas from the Earth to the Sun and Western Europe moved its maritime bases from the Mediterranean to the Atlantic, technological leadership shifted from Italy and Germany to the Netherlands. By the end of the sixteenth century the craftsmen of the Netherlands led all Europe in the manufacture of precision machines, lenses, maps, and the like; the windmill reached the height of its effectiveness in the Netherlands, where it could be put to unusually profitable use in reclaiming land from the sea by wind-powered pumps; and Dutch civil engineers and millwrights led Europe's engineering profession until the development of steam power.

The medieval millwright was in some ways the archetype of the modern engineer. He had to understand, at least empirically, the action of water and wind, wheels and treadles, cogs and pulleys, cranks and shafts, wood and metal. The water-wheel was the most common source of automatic power in the late Middle Ages. It usually was driven by an undershot wheel, but, from the fourteenth century on, the overshot wheel was used more and more, thereby adding the weight of the water to the power of the stream. The undershot wheel, however, remained the more common until the sixteenth century, and at the end of that century—around Toulouse, according to Jacques Besson's *Théâtre des instruments mathématiques et méchaniques* (Lyons, 1579)—there developed a sort of water-turbine. It was driven by a confined stream of water directed at curved blades on the periphery of a horizontal wheel. Waterpower was used to grind corn, pump water, blow bellows, saw wood, sharpen tools, crush olives, wood, or ore, and for many other purposes. (Pl. 96a, b.)

The windmill was particularly adaptable to the area of northern Europe, where wind velocity was relatively dependable. Most windmills were simple affairs—either fixed buildings facing the prevailing winds or pivoting structures. The earliest form of windmill in Europe seems to have developed in the Baltic area. It was of the post type—that is, the entire structure of the mill, supported on a strong post, had to be rotated into the wind in order to be operated at the most efficient rate. As the mills became larger, this rotation required more and more physical effort. A later development was the tower mill, of which it was necessary to rotate only a cap carrying the wind-shaft on which the sails were fixed. Both post and tower types were described as early as 1568 by Agostino Ramelli in his *Diverse et Artificiose Machine*. The windmill continued to play an important role in European economy until the end of the eighteenth century and is still used in Holland, Portugal, Rhodes, America, and Australia for pumping water and other minor tasks not requiring a regular supply of power. (Pl. 97a, b)

The pump also underwent rapid development from the sixteenth century onward. Agricola, Ramelli, and other contemporaries described around a hundred types of pumps. Some of them sucked up liquids by creating a vacuum; others worked under pressure of a plunger. The water pipes and pump cylinders of this period were constructed of timber, frequently by boring holes lengthwise through logs, since the casting of metal cylinders of large diameter, though essential for guns, was still too costly for industrial purposes. Each part of a pump or other machine had to be made separately and laboriously by hand, for interchangeable parts were unknown. A great advance was made in the development of pumps in the seventeenth century because of the practical necessity for draining mines and building public waterworks. Curiosity was aroused by the fact that water could not be raised more than about 28 feet by suction, and resultant studies of the 'spring of the air' and atmospheric pressure by Torricelli, Von Guericke, and others had a remarkable impact on the development of pumps, and vice versa (see Chapter XIV).

As cities grew and the providing of public services became a matter of growing concern, water supply became one of the critical urban problems. Some of the great stone aqueducts of the Romans still stood, monuments to early ingenuity, but they were far from sufficient. The introduction of pumps to supplement the old gravity-flow system did much to increase the comfort and health of urban peoples. As early as the fifteenth century the city of Augsburg got its water by an elaborate pumping system. Around 1526, German engineers planned and built for the city of Toledo in Spain a remarkable waterworks system that used forcing pumps, but this sixteenth-century plant was short-lived. The inadequacy of contemporary plumbing defeated the engineers' skill; a local chronicler recorded that this system 'worked with great pistons, and the water hammered so furiously and was driven with such terrific force through the metal pipes, that all the mains were fractured, strong enough material out of which to cast them not being available'.[5] Juanelo Turriano's ingenious but costly system of raising water by means of two interlocking, alternately rising and falling chains of wooden troughs replaced it about 1573. The piston-pump of German engineers was successfully adapted later for water supply in London, Paris, and other large cities. One of the most remarkable water systems of the period was that which supplied the palace and fountains at Versailles (installed in 1682 by a Dutch engineer named Rannequin). For all these successes, however, until the nineteenth century inhabitants of large cities were generally dependent upon neighbouring wells, hand pumps, small fountains in market places, or water brought by a gravity-flow system, unless they bought their water from a water-carrier. Not until efficient waterworks were established could much be done toward purifying the supply of water, especially before physicians properly understood the causes of disease.

For a long time machine tools advanced little beyond the state described by Hartmann Schopper in 1568 in his *Panoplia, Omnium Illiberalium Artium Genera Continens*. Wood long remained the chief construction material, plumbers, blacksmiths, and other mechanics making the metal parts by hand. Precision was difficult to obtain with such materials. To cite only one example, the lathe did not evolve before the eighteenth century into the modern iron-cutting industrial machine that we know. (Pl. 98a, b.) Long before 1300 it had been used for turning softer materials, being worked by hand by means of a string attached to a bow much like a hunter's bow, which, moved back and forth, was capable of giving only alternating motion to the revolving parts. The treadle-drive was introduced in the thirteenth century: one end of a driving cord was attached to an overhead elastic wooden pole and the other to a treadle; the wooden pole would pull the cord back after it had been rotated in the opposite direction by rapidly working the treadle; thus the craftsman's or his assistant's hands were freed. The obvious need for continuous drive in a single direction was answered no earlier than the fifteenth century, and perhaps not until the sixteenth, by means of a hand crank and wheel. By this means much of the pewterware of that period was fashioned. Leonardo da Vinci sketched a lathe with a treadle working a flywheel on a crankshaft, which, while apparently never realized, did suggest to future mechanics the workability of a lathe with a spindle mounted and driven between two bearings, thus possibly increasing its strength and therefore its load. About 1490 the 'slide rest' was introduced, a toolholder that permitted the mechanical manipulation of the cutting tool. Thus by the end of the fifteenth century the essential elements of a screw-cutting lathe were available. In 1561 Hans Spaichl of Nuremberg made a lathe that seems to have incorporated at least some of these improvements, but the guilds of his city, interested in preserving the old methods of production from competition, tried, with only limited success, to prevent him from selling it. Besson developed a screw-cutting lathe (1578) which, though apparently more cumbersome, introduced a longitudinal feed. It was now possible to build the machines that shaped the balustrades, railings, and other woodwork of Baroque houses and made wood-turning a gentlemanly hobby of the period.

Only as the clock and instrument industries grew in the eighteenth century did greater precision and tougher machines become available, and by the end of our period the machine industry could produce an all-metal lathe capable of cutting metal parts by precise, adjustable, automatic mechanisms.[6] As the lathe, and along with it grinding, boring, polishing, wood-planing, gear-cutting, and other machines improved, the manufacture of industrial machinery and especially of scientific instruments became more precise.

Interchangeable parts, taken for granted today, could come but slowly. Only the combination of (1) standard units of gauging with uniformity of design and specifications, (2) standardized machine tools, and (3) power machinery worked under a system of specialized labour enables precisely fitting parts to be mass-produced in different places and assembled into complicated machines. Such conditions were not possible in our period, but the beginnings of the process were perceptible. The movable type of the printing industry was an early form of interchangeability, though only within the same printing shop, for type was likely to differ from printer to printer. When screws were manufactured in series (at first, probably of bronze), they were interchangeable within the series, but they were expensive, and wooden or iron pegs were more common. Screws do not seem to have been used in clocks before the end of the fifteenth century or in carpentry until the sixteenth. They were relatively rarely employed by the woodworker, clock and instrument maker, or locksmith until the seventeenth. Not until the nineteenth century were screws made pointed; before that time holes had first to be bored for their entrance or they were used with nuts. These conditions did not lead to uniformity.

The idea of interchangeability was obviously in the air, nevertheless. In the eighteenth century determined efforts were made to develop large-scale manufacturing of machine tools; one of the outstanding large-scale entrepreneurs was the inventor-manufacturer John Roebuck (1718–94). Since cast iron was now more extensively used, more powerful machines could be built, and skilled mechanics were trained to build and operate them. The precision work made possible by the great improvements in metallurgy (see below) in the eighteenth century hastened the readiness of manufacturers to use movable and interchangeable parts. Early in that century Réaumur suggested (*L'art de convertir le fer forgé en acier*, pt. 2, memoir 6) the manufacture of muskets with interchangeable parts, and extraordinarily well gauged cogwheels for clocks were produced in series by the Swedish technological genius Christopher Polhem, but they seem to have had little influence on subsequent industrial processes. By the time of the great instrument-maker George Adams (d. 1773) some standard instruments with some standard component parts were available for several different experimental purposes. The wars at the end of the eighteenth century produced a demand for muskets that led Honoré Blanc, Eli Whitney, and others to put the principle of standardized movable parts into operation on a large scale, but that story belongs to Volume V of the *History of Mankind*.

The Application of Steam Power to Machinery

The earliest modern experiments with steam propulsion were carried out by scientists interested in experimental physics. In 1495 Leonardo da Vinci had suggested the use of steam to shoot a projectile. The writings of Heron of Alexandria, a Hellenistic scientist who had described an aeolipile and puppets that were made to dance by steam power, were published in translation in 1575, but it is impossible to tell how influential his ideas were. In 1606 Giambattista della Porta in *I tre libri de' spiritali* indicated that as steam condensed inside a closed vessel a vacuum would develop, and he described a steam engine that could raise a column of water; his work presented the fundamental idea on which a practical steam engine ultimately was based. Solomon de Caus in *Les raisons des forces mouvantes* (1615) described a similar machine, but whereas Porta had worked under the misapprehension that steam was to be identified with air, De Caus, recognizing that steam was evaporated water, made clear that steam pressure was of a much greater magnitude than air pressure. Several other suggestions for experimental steam engines were made during the seventeenth century.

As the depth of mines in Europe increased, a practical need for power greater than that furnished by man, animal, water, or wind arose. In earlier centuries mines had been likely to be open pits, cave extensions, or shallow shafts, but with the fifteenth-century boom in mining, shafts got deeper, sometimes extending underground a hundred feet or more, especially in precious-metal mines. In some German mines shafts went to a depth of six hundred feet to follow veins of silver, gold, or copper ore, and drainage became a formidable operation. Sturdier pumps driven by animal or water power were needed for raising the water which collected underground from seepage or floods. Soon large mines were fitted with complicated drainage machinery. Hide buckets attached to a single rope were manipulated by a winch with sufficient reliability to keep the Bohemian silver mines at Kutná Hora (Kuttenberg) free of floods though a depth of 1500 feet was reached in the fifteenth century, but in a mine at Schemnitz (now Banska Štiavnica) in Slovakia the drainage system had to be powered by ninety-six horses in three relays, working three large wheels. In order to get the horses to and from the wheels, a system of circular ramps was dug out of the side of the mine. In 1760 a Schemnitz engineer, Josef Karel Höll, reporting to the Académie des Sciences, described a machine that, working as a sort of siphon, might lift a column of water nearly a hundred feet. Complicated and expensive though they might be, such improvements were profitable in the new era of large-scale mining. The Kutná Hora mines alone produced an average of 200 hundredweight of silver per year.

A steam-driven pump for drainage purposes was first suggested in *The Elements of Water Drawing* (1659), written by either R. D'Acres or Robert Thornton. The steam engine as a practical device, however, began with their contemporary the second Marquis of Worcester, who in 1663 described an apparatus ('the water commanding engine') for raising water by means of steam. Worcester gave no diagram of this engine, and his description of it was very obscure. An engine was in fact built that raised water 40 feet, much higher than any earlier engine had attained, but whether it was worked by steam is not certain. Although Worcester was granted a ninety-nine year monopoly by Parliament, he did not form a company to develop his invention, and it never went past this trial stage.

Meanwhile Von Guericke, Boyle, and others had shown that a piston could be utilized to transform air pressure into work (see Chapter XIV), and Huygens proposed a piston machine that was driven by the alternate expansion and contraction of gas from gunpowder explosions (1680). Familiarity with the piston enabled an assistant first of Huygens and then of Boyle, the Frenchman Denis Papin (1647–1712), to make the next significant advance in the construction of the steam engine. Papin's awareness of the power of steam was demonstrated in his 'digester', a pressure cooker for extracting gelatin from bones, into which he introduced the safety valve. As a professor of mathematics at Marburg, he constructed a small experimental steam engine. It worked on the same principle as Worcester's but borrowed the cylinder and piston from Huygens': steam produced under a piston in a cylinder raised the piston; when the steam was allowed to condense, the pressure of the atmosphere drove the piston down; it was raised again by renewing the steam pressure. (Pl. 99a.) Papin's design was published in 1690, and he suggested that it could be used to remove water from mines. Later, improving on the Savery steam engine (see below), he was able to drive a model ship by means of paddles. His plans never were adopted, and he died a disappointed man.

Meanwhile English coal mines were getting deeper. By 1700 some were about 400 feet deep, and by 1750 600 feet or more. It remained for the Englishman Thomas Savery (1650–1715), possibly a military engineer, to describe a steam device that could be put to effective use in them. In 1698 he patented the first steam device that actually was used to pump water out of a mine, though a shallow one. By this time the need was greater than ever; in 1702 one mine operator alone was using 500 horses to provide the power necessary for pumping. That year Savery established in London the first steam-device factory in the world, and he advertised his product with a small book, *The Miner's Friend*. Unfortunately, Savery's device proved expensive to work because of great fuel consumption; its cycle of operation could be repeated only five times a minute; its suction and forcing lifts were very limited; and the joints in its boiler could not withstand high pressure.

A more practical engine was produced by Thomas Newcomen (1663–1729). It combined three scientific principles already known—the balance-beam, the vacuum produced by the condensation of steam, and the piston working in a cylinder—to produce a machine that successfully performed traction duties[7]. (Pl. 99b.) Newcomen's engine needed only low pressure to move its beam up and down. It had two great advantages over Savery's high pressure device: it could be operated from the surface, and it could lift water from depths so great that Savery's device in its stead would have had to be used in relays. In spite of its inefficiency for other purposes, it proved inexpensive enough to operate at coal mine pits, where the cost of fuel was low. By 1769 some 100 Newcomen engines were being used in northern England alone.

John Smeaton (1724–92), a noted civil engineer, improved the Newcomen engine by giving greater precision to its various parts, in particular its cylinder boring. He made a large engine that was sent in 1775 to pump out the dry docks of the naval base at Kronstadt, Russia. In Russia, as elsewhere, local engineers were grappling with the same problem. A Russian engineer, I. I. Polzunov, had, in fact, built an apparently practical steam engine, which was first put into operation in 1765 but which, Polzunov having died in 1765, no one could repair; it was abandoned when, after about two months' successful operation, it sprang a leak. A French engineer, Nicolas Cugnot, had in 1763 constructed a steam engine capable of propelling a carriage, and in 1769 he attached it as a tractor to cannon, but it was so slow and unstable that it too was abandoned. In contrast, Smeaton's engine at Kronstadt was successfully displacing two huge windmills, each some 100 feet high, which had been installed by Dutch engineers in 1719. Complaints, however, were common over the extravagant fuel consumption of whatever steam engines were kept in operation.

While repairing a small model of a Newcomen engine, James Watt (1736–1819), trained as an instrument maker, with contacts among prominent Glasgow scientists, noticed the enormous waste brought about by the alternate heating with steam and cooling with water of the cylinder at each stroke. This observation led him to invent a separate but connected chamber (or condenser) which was kept cool for rapid condensing of the steam while the cylinder, enclosed in a steam jacket, was kept hot continuously; an air-pump vacuum in the condensing chamber tapped the steam from the cylinder. In 1765 Watt built a model of his steam engine and by 1769 had solved his problem to the point where he obtained a patent. In 1774 John Wilkinson (1728–1808) invented a boring mill that could bore cylinders for Watt's engines with unprecedented accuracy.[8]

Watt and Matthew Boulton, a 'captain of industry', established, after great expense, a steam-engine business which prospered for years. Until 1800 this firm had the protection of patents, which it assiduously took out on Watt's inventions. Patents had first been granted in England by Edward III in the fourteenth century, but they led to such abuse that in 1623 Parliament enacted a Statute of Monopolies, intended, while forestalling harmful royal monopolies, to encourage inventors by giving them exclusive rights to the profits from their inventions for a specified period of time. Thus, as indicated above, the Marquis of Worcester was granted ninety-nine years of rights for his 'water commanding engine'.[9] Savery held a master patent for the use of steam in his device, nd this monopoly compelled Newcomen to enter into partnership with him. Obviously the patent could be an obstruction as well as an incentive to a fertile mind.

Although Watt's inventions opened a new future for the steam engine, it still had to be permanently installed where used, and its use was limited largely to pumping. Although power-driven machinery was thus employed for coal mines as early as the 1760s, the miner's pick and sledge had little real competition from more efficient machinery until the 1850s. At the urging of Boulton, Watt designed a rotative engine, which was the prime mover from the 1780's, well into the nineteenth century. After 1800 Watt's patents expired, but the firm long continued to enjoy a great success, owing to its superior workmanship and experience. By that time steam was turning the wheels of the textile industry.

Improvements in Textile Machinery

Textile machinery had been developed very early in the Near and Far East, particularly in the spinning and weaving of silk. The spinning wheel permitted the maker of yarn to turn with his left hand a wheel which twisted the fibres while his right drew out the thread. The spinning wheel was the first major improvement upon the simple spindle and distaff since pre-historic times. The earliest evidence of its use in the West is from the late thirteenth century. In England, where the textile industry flourished exceptionally well from that time onward, this mechanism came to be known as the 'bobbing wheel' or 'great wheel'. In the fifteenth century a treadle was added, thus leaving both hands of the operator free for handling the thread. A well-designed 'flyer', probably itself the result of a long development, is depicted in a late-fifteenth-century illustration.[10] The flyer allowed spinning and winding to be done mechanically in one process. Spinning wheels with these devices were called 'Saxony wheels'.

Mercantilist restrictions upon the importation of cotton into England from India came at the beginning of the eighteenth century at a time when, paradoxically, the demand for cotton goods was growing. Capital and inventive talent turned away from silk, wool, and linen toward the satisfaction of the demand for cotton goods. In 1738 an attempt to mechanize spinning fully was made by Lewis Paul when he introduced the technique of stretching carded cotton or wool between two sets of rollers running at different speeds, but this invention was not successful until reintroduced by Richard Arkwright (1732–92). When finally put into operation, it proved capable of producing a cotton yarn much stronger than thitherto available and suited not only for the weft (the transverse threads) but also for the warp (the longitudinal threads).

These improvements encouraged the growth of the cotton industry in the competition with other textiles such as silk, wool, and linen that had hitherto been preferred as richer or tougher. The demand for cotton yarn grew apace.

By 1764 James Hargraves introduced his 'spinning jenny', which made it possible for one spinner at one machine to operate a large number of spindles. This invention was an instantaneous success, lending itself to service in the cottage industry as well as in the nascent "factories". Then in 1768 Arkwright introduced the 'water frame', which, like Paul's machine, worked by rollers and had the advantage of being run by the cheap power of water wheels. The cotton yarn it produced was strong and coarse, an excellent substitute for the expensive linen thread still used by many weavers for warp. In 1774 Samuel Crompton invented his 'mule', which, combining features of both the jenny and the water frame, produced the finest yarn; it took its name from its hybrid origin. Steam power was not applied to spinning until 1785. The advanced techniques and the complicated sources of power required for textile machines suggested the consolidation of operations and encouraged the establishment of textile 'factories' in Britain.

The development of weaving machines lagged behind that of spinning machines. In many lands long before 1300, men and women had known some process or other of making cloth by interlacing threads (called the weft) with lengthwise threads (called the warp) The warp threads were attached to a frame and the weft was passed back and forth between them by means of a shuttle. Heddles had early been introduced in some regions to separate the warp threads and stretch them apart as needed for a particular pattern. The need had also been discovered for battering the weft so as to produce a tighter weave, and beams for stretching the threads and woven material so as to keep them tauter. Hence by the sixteenth century in western Europe the weaving loom was already a complicated mechanism, though it was still powered by hand and foot. The ribbon loom, which could weave a number of silk or satin ribbons simultaneously, was invented in Holland around 1621 and became known throughout western Europe in the ensuing century. In 1733 John Kay invented the 'flying shuttle', which was shot through the weft by pickers connected by cords with a stick held by the weaver. This relatively simple instrument enabled the weaver to work faster and to double the width of his cloth.

Kay's invention, for all its importance, created a set of mechanical difficulties, particularly in connection with the 'picker', a mechanism for throwing the shuttle—an operation which required considerable practice to do expertly. That problem took decades to solve, and it was not wholly solved until mechanical controls on a power loom replaced the hand of the weaver. Jacques Vaucanson, while working on the mechanisms of the silk industry, eliminated the need for an attendant at the draw loom by devising (1747) a more efficient apparatus of punched cards for the weaving of figured fabrics. In 1785 Edmund Cartwright was to introduce a power loom, capable of being driven by horses, water wheels, or steam engines, but his loom was not really practical. Power looms were not so rapidly developed as were power spinning machines, for several technical improvements had to be made before looms could readily be adapted to 'the factory system'. As late as 1813 England had no more than 2,400 power looms, but a hundred times that number of hand-operated ones.

The Bleaching and Dyeing Industry

The textile industry became closely allied with the chemical industry. Washing, bleaching, and dyeing, auxiliary techniques in the manufacture of textiles, were not readily adaptable to machinery. In the fourteenth and fifteenth centuries in Florence and other Italian textile centres, the finishing of rough woollen cloth—including the raising of the nap with 'teasels' (prickly seed balls), the shearing of the loose nap, and dyeing—called for advanced skill and was done mostly by hand. A special guild in Florence, the Calimala, dominated this branch of textile manufacture. Bleaching alone required lengthy processes—soaking in alkali, washing, drying, and heating—that had to be repeated several times, and dyeing remained a complex problem as of yore. Washing was somewhat quickened, however, by the use of fulling mills (known to have been used in England as early as the twelfth century), which pounded the cloth in the vats. Such a mill, run by a water wheel, consisted of a shaft fitted with cams for lifting the heavy wooden hammers that did the pounding.

By the eighteenth century the bleaching and dyeing of cloth had become a part of a rapidly growing chemical industry. (Pl. 92b.) In 1756 Francis Home suggested the use of vitriol (sulphuric acid) for bleaching. Supplies of the acid were readily available because the enterprising Roebuck, having developed a process of making sulphuric acid in lead chambers, had established a plant for that purpose near Edinburgh in 1749. Watt experimented with chlorine as a bleach and performed other chemical experiments. The chemistry involved in these processes, however, was still of a relatively crude sort. The modern sulphuric-acid plant and the manufacture of a bleach (from chlorine) that was efficient and of an alkali that was not injurious to cloth had to await the generations of Claude Louis Berthollet (1748–1822) and Joseph Louis Gay-Lussac (1778–1850). Such new bleaching techniques as were invented earlier worked for linen and cotton fabrics only; silk and wool continued to be bleached by the lengthy traditional methods.

The old methods of dyeing had depended upon the use of plant or animal colouring matter, into which fabrics were immersed. During the fourteenth and fifteenth centuries the need for alum as a fixative or mordant in this process had precipitated several conflicts among the cities of Italy for control of the alum mines, and Lorenzo de' Medici's diplomacy and military forces were called upon more than once to assure the Florentine textile manufacturers an adequate supply. Although numerous dyes were available, only a limited number of shades of any one colour could be produced. The Incas of Peru knew how to dye cloth, and though their secrets were lost, a number of new dye-stuffs reached Europe from America—cochineal and brazil-wood among them. Cornelius Drebbel (1572–1634), a Dutch inventor who also contributed to the understanding of the thermometer and attempted submarine navigation (see below), produced a brilliant scarlet in wool, afterwards exploited in Gobelins and other tapestries, by dipping in a bath of cochineal, tin, and other chemicals.

Subsequent improvement in the dyeing processs was brought about in large part by the efforts of the French government. In the seventeenth century Colbert took steps to encourage this aspect of the textile industry. He offered prizes for innovations and gave government support to eminent chemists. In the early eighteenth century the chemists Charles François Du Fay (1698–1739) and Jean Hellot (1685–1766) were among the early government-sponsored directors of the French dyeing industry. In keeping with the prevalence of mechanical theories of their day, they subscribed to a mechanical theory of dyeing—that is, that particles of dye enter the pores of the dyed material and thus change its color. Pierre Joseph Macquer (1718–84), who was director at mid-century, discovered new techniques that extended the range of dyes. He introduced Prussian blue, which penetrated the material rather than coloured the surface, as had some of the earlier dyes, and a fast red. Berthollet, who eventually succeeded as director, contributed to the new processes, advancing France's already leading role in the dye industry. Being primarily interested in chemistry, Macquer and Berthollet proposed a chemical theory of dyeing to replace the mechanical one.

The Glass Industry

Since it was dependent upon heat, the glass industry in the Middle Ages had been impeded by the competition for wood as fuel, in which shipbuilding and metallurgy outbid it. During the later Middle Ages the Venetians were the leaders of the glass industry in Europe, for the most part making art glass, but others threatened their leadership. Florence and Antwerp had famous glass works; in France the *gentilhomme verrier* was a highly respected artisan; and in the fifteenth century, according to Aeneus Sylvius,[11] Bohemia could boast the most splendid stained-glass windows of Europe. In England entrepreneurs in the glass industry were encouraged by royal grants of monopoly and employed both French Huguenot and Venetian workers.

Early in the seventeenth century the first technological monograph on the subject appeared—the Florentine Antonio Neri's *L'Arte vetraria* (1612). It eventually became the basis of similar works in other languages, stimulating a search for new means of producing glass of different colours and better quality. The Bohemian glass workers learned to add chalk to their product, making a potash-lime glass that had an extraordinary crystalline quality which lent itself well to engraving. Caspar Lehmann, court jeweller at Prague (d. 1620), seems to have originated cut-glass. The Bohemian works also produced exceptionally beautiful enamelled glass, and at the end of the seventeenth century Bohemian craftsmen had learned the process now known as 'sandwiching'—fitting two layers of glass together with a silver or gold etching on the inner one. The German chemist Johann Kunckel (1630–1703), whose edition of Neri's work long was standard, discovered how to make artificial ruby (red glass), and several other scientists, like Glauber and Boyle, also made contributions to the colouring of glass.

The shortages of tin and lead for pewter, the need of utensils for the increasing consumption of tea and coffee, and the Baroque and Rococo emphasis upon decorative art all conspired to make simple pewter, earthenware, and wooden utensils unfashionable and to favour more ornate glassware (as well as porcelain). In the seventeenth century Thomas Percivall perfected a coal furnace for the manufacture of glass, freeing the glass industry from dependence upon wood, increasing production, and lowering prices. By 1665 French glass makers had developed a method for casting glass that enabled them to make larger panes and mirrors, such as then went into the palace at Versailles. The Dutch, famous since the sixteenth century for their lenses and other scientific glassware, in the eighteenth century became especially proficient in ornamenting glass by scratching or stippling with a diamond point. By that time glass was a common material for drinking vessels and liquid containers (though second to porcelain for household uses), and it had made possible airier and lighter windows as well as large and bright mirrors for interior decoration. For fine glassware 'Bohemian crystal' fitted the taste of the Baroque period, and in the early eighteenth century took precedence over Venetian glass, but only to give way toward the close of the century to the heavier lead glass of England and Holland, which lent itself better to Neoclassic design.

Closely allied to glass was the optical industry. The power of glass to magnify had long been known, and, we have seen (Chapter XIII), some form of eyeglasses was invented around 1300. The increase in the number of books because of the development of printing made the need for reading glasses still greater. The growing demand for lenses for magnifying glasses, microscopes, and telescopes also provided an incentive to glass makers. The preparation of glass for lenses was in the hands of skilled craftsmen until the introduction of cast glass, the better understanding of its properties, and the growing demand for precise scientific instruments transformed the manufacture of optical glass into a mass-production industry.

The Porcelain Industry

Chapter XII described the amazing development of porcelain manufacture in China and the Islamic countries, and the efforts of Westerners to duplicate the vitrified translucent 'chinaware' of the Far East. As in the case of several other Eastern crafts, unverified tradition has attributed its introduction into the West to the Crusades. About 1500 Italian craftsmen in Venice were reported to have made porcelain, using a Muslim recipe, but throughout the sixteenth century Europeans were still importing most of their porcelain from China. The effective production of porcelain in the West seems to have begun about 1700.

The development of the porcelain industry in Europe was stimulated by the same shortage of tin and lead for pewter and the same need of utensils for the increasing consumption of tea and coffee as promoted the glass industry, as well as by a continuing desire of Europeans to duplicate the decorative 'chinaware' of the East. The improvement of both porcelain and cruder pottery in Europe took place through a process of trial and error, little use being made of scientific methods. By the late seventeenth century the secret of making hard-paste porcelain was discovered in Germany by Ehrenfried Walther von Tschirnaus and Johann Friedrich Böttger, and Meissen ware (the so-called 'Dresden china', first sold at Leipsig in 1710) became especially esteemed. In France Bernard Palissy (1510–89) had devised a technique for making superior pottery by moulding, modelling, and casting instead of turning, and in the late seventeenth century the Poterat family of Rouen was prominent among several that manufactured a soft-paste, low-temperature pottery, but then the secret of the German hard-paste process became known in Vienna, St Petersburg, and elsewhere, and the French royal faience works at Sèvres began to prefer it (c. 1769). In England the pottery industry made long strides forward with the technique of Josiah Wedgwood, who not only produced an artistic product but also was admired for his new methods. He was the first potter to use a steam engine to run his machines, and he was a model employer in a century that was placing strong emphasis upon humanitarianism.

The Printing Industry

The improvement of printing was associated with the improvement of metallurgy and textiles, providing a felicitous example of the interdependence of the several new industries. Printing required metal for type and for parts of the press, and the quantity-production of paper required cotton and linen. As early as the thirteenth century metal as well as wooden type was used effectively in the Far East, but the West seems to have come upon metal type independently. Not until the 1440s was metal type used effectively in Europe—by Gutenberg and others. Important steps in this process came with the development of the hand mould for casting uniform type and of the hand press (despite its complicated and cumbersome screw device, lever, and horizontal plate). By 1500 large printing establishments had grown up in Italy and in south Germany (see Chapter XI); a publishing firm at Nuremberg was big enough to employ twenty-four presses and a hundred typesetters, printers, correctors, and binders.

Meanwhile the manufacture of paper was also being improved. It has been asserted, with some justification, that the increased use of linen for clothing and bedding in the fourteenth and fifteenth centuries made possible the development of printing. Paper, then made for the most part from cotton, had been introduced into western Islamic lands from the Near East as early as the tenth century. By the twelfth century it was common in Muslim Spain but rare in western Christendom until the thirteenth, when paper-mills began to appear. When an abundance of linen rags made possible and profitable the manufacture of rag paper, a good medium became available for printing. A paper mill established near Nuremberg in 1389 probably had something to do with that city's later importance as a printing centre.

The effective printing of metal type requires an oily kind of ink. The manufacture of ink and colours was well developed in the Far East (See Chapter XII), but Chinese ink, made from lampblack, was not suitable for metal type. The pre-Columbian Amerindian used an ink, also unsuitable, made from the juice of the ink plant (*chauchi*). The West was forced to invent a special printers' ink, which was eventually perfected by mixing a varnish derived from resin, linseed oil, and soap with lampblack.

HEATING, MINING, AND METALLURGY

Architecture has been discussed as an art in Chapter XII; some of its implications for science have been mentioned in Chapter XIV; and it will be considered as a profession in Chapter XVI. A few words are called for here on the heating of houses.

Coal as Fuel

Social or domestic architecture was in some degree influenced by the Renaissance interest in Antiquity, although not on a wide scale until the seventeenth century. Various political, economic, and social forces brought about changes in domestic architecture from the sixteenth century on. The distribution of church lands by the king in England and elsewhere, the rise of commercial fortunes, and the growing power of the state brought new families of wealth or prestige and new demands for comfort and ostentation on the part of both old and new families. The Château of Versailles was a grandiose example of competitive ostentation. By the eighteenth century in England the drawings and works of Palladio had become a vogue, and stately homes in the Palladian style still dot the English countryside. Although comfort was sought in many instances—conspicuously, for example, in the Georgian house—the concept of comfort seems to have eluded some of the great houses (although the modern critic may be prone to forget that what may seem inconvenient to him in the way of sanitation and heating was of little concern to the eighteenth-century country gentleman.)

More and more, homes built after 1300 were likely to have built-in fireplaces with flues and chimneys, and they no longer had to depend upon moveable but unventilated braziers for heating. The Germanic countries also developed a relatively moveable stove made of tile resistant to heat. Not only were such stoves able to contain and radiate heat better than fireplaces but also their tiles, glazed in colour and ornamented in relief, often made them most decorative. Fireplaces, chimneys, and stoves were built in Gothic, Renaissance, and later period styles. As they became richer in decor, the demand for tiles, not only for stoves and chimney facings but also for wainscoting, grew, especially for the white tiles of Delft, with lively figures and landscapes painted in blue upon them.

Domestic heating took a new turn as the traditional fuels—wood and charcoal—became scarcer. Coal had been used by the Chinese for metallurgical processes as early as the T'ang dynasty. It had long been known in Europe also but before the sixteenth century had been less widely used as a fuel than wood, charcoal, lignite, or peat. After 1500, however, deforestation became a serious problem in several European countries because of the increased demand for wood as fuel and structural material, the expansion of arable land, the rise of sheep farming, and the lack of regard for what today would be called 'conservation'. When the English queen, Elizabeth, took measures for forest preservation, the resulting shortage of wood and charcoal necessitated the resort to coal as a fuel, and the coal industries in Northern England expanded. Coal from Newcastle in the Northumberland region ('the Black Indies') not only found its way into the English homes and manufacturing establishments but also was exported to the Continent. A few Continental countries gradually began to produce coal.

Newcastle's coal became proverbial. It was a fuel of poor quality, containing large amounts of iron sulphide, which gave an evil-smelling smoke. By the late seventeenth century the London housewife was already complaining of the soot, smoke, and stench from the city's chimneys. Studies began to appear on how best to construct chimneys to reduce this nuisance. The increase in the consumption of coal made the andiron, used for the domestic burning of wood, obsolete, and it was supplemented by the grate. Finally, in the eighteenth century iron coal-consuming stoves were invented. Two of the most successful were developed by men from the British North American colonies—Benjamin Thompson (later Count Rumford) and Franklin, both of whom lived for long periods in England and on the Continent. The new stoves symbolize the change that was taking place not only in architecture and related problems but also in technology in general. The age of coal and iron had slowly matured between the fourteenth and the eighteenth century.

Machine and Research in Metallurgy

Coal and iron have to be mined. In ancient and early medieval times mining, like agriculture, had been carried on by the lowest class of labourers. Before machinery was devised for surmounting natural obstacles like underground gases and water, the digging of ore and coal (and salt, too) was limited almost exclusively to surface or near-surface mining. Although sometimes a mining town—for example, silver-producing Kutná Hora (Kuttenberg) in Bohemia—

received special privileges because it was a source of income for the crown, until the thirteenth century miners were generally slaves or criminals, and the death rate among them was high. Until the nineteenth century most mine labour was manual—swinging pickaxes and sledge hammers, loading and pushing hand carts—with some of the lighter operations done by women and children. This work was usually performed under depressing and dangerous conditions—darkness, cold, damp, and suffocating dust, with only primitive drainage and ventilation (Pl. 102b.)

Mining, along with the processing of metals (or metallurgy), made slow progress in mechanization. As early as the thirteenth century writers mentioned the use of water power for ore-crushers and smelter-bellows, but the two ensuing centuries brought little advance in the application of machine power to crushing and smelting. The sixteenth century marked the beginning of a bonanza period in smelting as well as mining of metal, especially in Germany, Spain, and New Spain, partly explained by the increasing demand for arms, machines, and precious metals. Expanding capitalistic enterprise, evidenced in the world-wide activities and pyramiding fortunes of families such as the Fuggers, produced large-scale industries in which mechanization was inevitable. Metallurgy was one of these. About 1451 Johannsen Funcken introduced in Saxony an effective way to apply an old method of separating silver from argentiferous ore. This was the 'saiger' process of extracting silver by alloying crude copper containing silver with lead, melting off the lead (to which most of the silver would adhere), and then recovering the silver. The essentials of this process had been invented as early as the twelfth century by Venetian metallurgists. On the other hand, Bartholomé de Medina's 'patio' process was new, discovered in Mexico in 1557. It used mercury to form amalgams whereby to extract gold and silver from their ores. The efficiency of these processes further stimulated the tremendous expansion of silver and gold mining in the sixteenth century. In 1516 a strike of silver in Joachimsthal (Jáchymov) in Bohemia led to the coining of *Joachimsthalers* (eventually abbreviated to *thalers* or *dollars*), and somewhat later the Spanish piece-of-eight (dollar, 'eight bits') became common.

A similar boom was taking place in iron mining and processing. In the 1400s blast furnaces developed to the point where they created temperatures high enough to produce a good grade of cast iron. Cast-iron cannon had been produced for the dukes of Burgundy as early as the fourteenth century, and soon such cannon were competing with wrought-iron cannon. During the ensuing period old types of furnaces survived despite the greater efficiency of the newer ones. Several major types can be differentiated. The ancient Catalan furnace, which was not the most primitive of them, was still widely used in Spain and southern France, and the Scandinavian 'Osmund' furnace was better yet, but the later German 'Stückofen' was the most efficient. The Stückofen was normally a large brick or stone structure about ten feet high and from two to five feet wide, needing a stronger blast, which was provided by water-driven bellows. When built with a special tap for the slag, it became the *Blasofen*. It was capable of turning out fifty tons of iron a year, and under certain conditions could produce steel. Where rapid streams could be harnessed, water power was used for working tilt hammers, for drawing wire, and, from the sixteenth century on, for other metallurgical activities.

After the sixteenth century (until the eighteenth) progress in mining and metallurgy was comparatively slow. Most of the important innovations came in Germany, where the Stückofen grew in height, size, and hence productivity. The wooden box-bellows, invented by Hans Lobinger of Nuremberg (1550), replaced the less efficient leather ones. As the shafts of furnaces went higher and the blasts grew hotter, the reduced metal made better contact with the charcoal fuel, and a high-carbon iron, strong and more easily convertible into wrought iron and steel, resulted. The demand for iron ore, increasing as iron replaced wood and other materials in many uses, joined with the increasing demand for precious metals to spur the miners toward greater productivity on their part.

Books giving careful descriptions and critiques of industrial processes were in the sixteenth century becoming familiar. The first attempts to describe in some detail the problems of mining were made in two anonymous booklets, *Ein nützlich Bergbüchlein* (1505) and the *Probierbüchlein* (1510). Thirty years later appeared Biringuccio's classic, *De la pirotechnia*, which gave a systematic description of the metallurgical processes of his day. The classic *par excellence* on mining is Agricola's *De Re Metallica* (1556).

A physician by profession, Agricola had served as a doctor in Joachimsthal in 1527–33. He had early acquired an interest in mines, and the importance of his works in the early study of geology has already been noted (see Chapter XIV). His treatise on metals displays a practical approach to mining. It covered many fields and phases of the metallurgical process (such as methods of mining, assaying of ores, smelting, and the extraction of precious metals) and painstakingly described the tools and machines actually in use, including several types of hauling machines, waterpumps, and ventilation devices. (Pl. 102a). The author had little patience with methods that smacked of magic or fantasy. Of the resort to divining rods to find ore he protested: 'A miner . . . if he is prudent and skilled . . . understands that a forked stick is of no use to him, for . . . there are the natural indications of the veins which he can see for himself without the help of twigs.'[10] Agricola's was a more empirical approach. He bore witness to the perils of mining, incidentally referring to stream pollution by the waste from metallurgical works and the destruction of agricultural land by undermining and charcoal burning.

Agricola's and Biringuccio's books were perhaps the best but not the only ones to give detailed information on the state of machinery in the sixteenth century. A number of the processes, tools, and machines they described, as older pictorial representations show, were not new, though sometimes they had recently been improved or, with the increasing demand, were more commonly employed. The two classics make obvious that by their time the techniques of mining and metallurgy were already well developed, at least in the search for precious metals.

When iron ore became one of the most profitable products of the mines, some old difficulties still plagued the metallurgical industry and even grew worse. One of the most troublesome was the lack of fuel. Until the invention of coke (see below), charcoal was preferred, but as the demand for charcoal grew, the supply diminished because of depletion of the forests, and its price rapidly went up. Mounting costs obliged the metallurgical industry to break into small parts. A blast-furnace that smelted pig iron might have to send its product either to small furnaces to be recast or to forgemasters to be converted into wrought iron or steel. In turn, wrought iron might go to slitting mills. Cast iron was used chiefly for household utensils and some types of ordnance, wrought iron for bolts, wire, common tools, nails, and spades, and steel for weapons, fine tools, and machine parts. Coarse pig-iron was still often produced at the beginning of the eighteenth century by blast furnaces that provided insufficient blast air. This process, as well as that of making steel, required large amounts of charcoal though less and less charcoal became available. The production of iron and steel was thus checked; in 1709 a typical blast furnace in England could produce only between five and ten tons of metal per week.

Furthermore, as mine shafts became deeper, they presented new and intricate mechanical problems. The hauling of ore underground, though it had been speeded up as early as 1530 by running four-wheeled cars on rails, was still cumbersome. Hoisting was done with gear operated by horse whims, or drums around which a rope was wound; even where animal power replaced human power, this was an awkward and sometimes a dangerous procedure. In 1627 gunpowder was used in the Schemnitz mines to supplement the old method of cracking rock—heating with fire and dousing with cold water—but gunpowder was not adopted in England to blast coal until 1713. The pumping of subsoil water from the mines presented another obstacle until, as already described, the development of steam-driven pumps helped to surmount it. In the early, shallow mines, ventilation had not been a crucial problem; a shaft cut in two by a vertical division was considered sufficient to permit air to pass down one side and up the other. As the mines became deeper, however, the problem of methane gas or 'fire-damp' became more pressing, and better ways of inducing circulation of air had to be found. (Pl. 102b.) The problem of illumination complicated that of ventilation, for the gases readily exploded when they came into contact with naked flame. That danger was not to be eliminated until 1815, when Humphry Davy and George Stephenson invented reliable safety-lamps. Between the close of the sixteenth and the beginning of the eighteenth century few improvements came to mining methods.

Then a veritable revolution in mining and metallurgy took place. It came as a result of at least three considerations: (1) the increase in demand for iron, (2) the introduction of steam power to hoisting and pumping in the mines, and (3) a need for high-quality fuel in metallurgy. A process of making coke by heating coal and thus driving off its volatile contents was discovered in the seventeenth century but was made economically feasible by Abraham Darby (1677–1717) and his family only in the eighteenth. Coke relieved the foundries of dependence on charcoal, and foundries and furnaces, which had tended to follow the forests, were now located near coal fields and ore deposits. The production of cast iron mounted at an amazing rate, and many objects that previously had been made from wrought iron were now made from cast iron. At first coke was used only in making pig or cast iron. But several ironmasters soon recognized that coke could be used in converting pig iron into wrought iron, and in 1784 Henry Cort was to develop the 'puddling' process—agitating the pig iron with iron poles in a reverberatory furnace until, as the carbon and other impurities burned away, it became a mass of wrought iron. The wrought iron was then put through grooved rollers that produced a finer wrought iron. Rollers had been used in Germany and Sweden (by Polhem, for example) previous to this time, but Cort's process revolutionized the production of malleable iron, and he deserves the credit of fathering the modern rolling mill.[13] The use of coke in place of charcoal as the fuel for producing pig iron and wrought iron brought a rise in the demand for coal and in the supply of cast iron and malleable iron. In 1788 61,000 tons of pig iron were produced in England.

Quality steel had been produced in India and imported by Arabs and Persians into Europe since the early Middle Ages. Europe made its own steel but only in small quantities, and it was expensive. In England a process of making steel known as 'cementation' was patented in the seventeenth century. It consisted of enclosing bars of iron together with some charcoal inside sealed pots, thus protecting the contents, when heated in a furnace, from contamination by sulphur and other volatile ingredients of the furnace fuel. The metal produced by this process was more highly carburized outside than inside, and it had to be rendered homogeneous by forging. The resultant product, known as 'shear steel', was good for cutlery but not hard enough to produce fine products like watch springs. Réaumur, one of the first scientists to deliberately apply his knowledge to industry, carefully examined the structural and other differences between iron and steel, showing that steel was something other than refined iron. He published his findings in 1722 in *L'art de convertir le fer forgé en acier*, which was subsequently translated into English and German. It lifted the process of steel manufacture from trial-and-error to an experimental level, discussing the parts played by 'sulphurs and salts' (i.e. modern carbon) and by cooling in determining the qualities of iron and steel. If his explanations were often couched in Cartesian mechanistic terms, he nevertheless explained metallic fracture in a way that was not to be bettered for well over a hundred years. Cast steel was known long before the 1740s, but then a watchmaker named Benjamin Huntsman (1704–76) succeeded in making of it the kind of steel he wanted for a successful business in high-grade watches. He found that steel could be hardened by placing it (or its components, malleable iron and charcoal) in closed crucibles inside coke furnaces; the coke provided a higher temperature for a longer period of time than coal could provide. After some hesitation because the resulting steel seemed too hard, the steel makers of Sheffield copied Huntsman's methods, making *Sheffield* almost synonymous in English with *steel*.

Before 1775 the outstanding discoverer of new chemicals was Scheele. Several new metals were among the elements and compounds discovered or put into common use for the first time by him and his contemporaries. Zinc had been known since the time of Agricola, but not until the eighteenth century were the proper fuels, retorts, and furnaces available for its extraction; the first zinc smelters were built in Germany and the Low Countries. Cobalt was discovered in 1733, platinum in 1735 (in Colombia), nickel in 1751 (Saxony becoming the centre of its production), and manganese in 1774.

The intimate relationship of coal, iron, and steam, the inventiveness of certain Englishmen, the astonishing number of skilled mechanics in England, the abundance of England's natural resources such as coal and iron, and the availability of English capital seeking investment were among the factors of the complex beginnings of the 'Industrial Revolution'. England's lead in industrial innovation did much to bring about its political predominance in the early nineteenth century. Around 1775, however, France and Belgium were also well advanced industrially and, according to one school of thought, but for the succeeding political turmoils those countries might not have fallen behind in the development of the factory system.

TRANSPORT AND NAVIGATION

Roads, Bridges, and Transportation by Land

After the decline of the Roman Empire little new highway construction was undertaken in western Europe for over 1,000 years. Outside of the Roman system (as in Germany) dirt roads were common, but they were often reinforced with fascines and timber or stones and gravel. Only few local roads of medieval times were paved, but those few seem to have been something more than 'mud tracks', as modern writers often think. Some of the ancient Roman roads served medieval man best, to be sure, not as means of communication but as quarries for neighbouring villages and cities. Nevertheless, those that were frequently used were kept passable by assiduous attention to their surfaces, side drainage, and bridges, and road maps of the late Middle Ages afford ample evidence that the arterial highways of the old Roman Empire were still well travelled.

Upkeep of roads, old or new, was a divided responsibility. Kings' highways were generally well tended, not only for military purposes but also as major avenues to seaports and markets. Since easy access meant commercial advantage, important urban centres also sometimes paved strategic roads (with cobble stones or slabs), levying special taxes for the purpose. For instance, a stretch of highway leading via Senlis to Paris was repaired by the practical citizens of Ghent in 1332. In England local parishes traditionally had the obligation to maintain roads; repairs were consequently haphazard until, in the eighteenth century, several turnpike acts enabled road keepers to levy tolls on travellers, thus relieving local parishes of the financial burden. In France and most other continental countries some form of *corvée* was resorted to, though not always successfully, as a means of guaranteeing road maintenance. In addition, certain religious organizations were renowned for building and maintaining bridges and causeways such as that at Glastonbury and the celebrated Holland causeway.

During the fourteenth, fifteenth, and sixteenth centuries transport in the West was a fairly well organized and highly competitive business. Whereas the Romans had moved themselves and their goods on horseback, medieval men used carts. Pack animals—even pack-humans (porters)—were used occasionally for short local trips or over difficult terrain, but for heavy long-distance haulage the two-wheeled cart (*bronnette*) and, more often, the four-wheeled wagon (*charrette*) were standard. 'Cart brokers' in large centres put merchants in touch with carters' organizations. In the fourteenth century, Alsatians and Lorrainers monopolized the transport of wool from the Low Countries to Switzerland, while the Béarnese controlled the route from Toulouse to the Atlantic ports. In some localities 'colliers' hauled small loads by neck harnesses (*ad collum*) in 'barrows' or small carts. Most trips, especially in dangerous or bandit-ridden territory, were made in slow convoys, for the safety of the highways was precarious in days when local police were either rare or unknown and when accommodations for travellers were notoriously limited and inconvenient. Occasionally, however, a special agent could make a fast solo trip; on one such the distance from Venice to Florence was covered in four days. As competition increased and commercial routes shifted, carters waged price wars, and merchants organized to drive sharp bargains with them. After the St Gothard route was opened by bridging the gorges of Schötten (1237), French carters and boatmen on the older routes had to lower their rates to compete with the newer one. In 1318 a Florentine textile concern paid less per mile for land transport from Paris to Marseilles than for water transport from Marseilles to Pisa. The Medici with their many branch establishments made arrangements all along the routes from Italy to the northern centres, assuring themselves of safe transport, reasonable tolls, good markets, and other conveniences.

One of the difficulties that impeded the building of new roads was the high cost. Expenses, to be sure, could be absorbed by levying tolls on travellers, but such levies were so frequent that they formed an added burden to already difficult, expensive, and slow communication, and each new levy ran the risk of killing the gold-laying goose. With the growth of centralized administration, royal governments became more and more interested in a good, centralized system of communication and transport. King Louis XI of France repaired some main roads and in 1464 reinstituted the ancient system of postal couriers. In the early sixteenth century the Holy Roman emperor granted Franz von Taxis authority to organize a postal system for the Empire, thus starting the Taxis family's rise to centuries of wealth and fame, but the Imperial postal system grew with but little significant road building. Thereafter couriers, postal services, and (later) coach service became more common and, with the London penny post (1680), cheaper.

The oldest known technical document on road-building is a police ordinance (1554) of Julich–Berg regulating the repair of roads with stones, timber, and faggots found beside them, but the French were the first modern nation to make a systematic study of road building. As early as 1622 Nicolas Bergier published his *Histoire des grands chemins de l'Empire romain.* Dedicating it to his king, he expressed the hope that work on the roads would bring employment to the poor and profit to the kingdom both in war and in peace. The book caused much discussion, but the funds needed to carry out its suggestions were not provided until Louis XIV's solicitous minister Colbert made more stalwart efforts to encourage road construction. In 1693 Hubert Gautier published his *Traité de la construction des chemins,* which advocated the building of roads on foundations of large stones rammed down on end. In 1716 the French created the first body of civil engineers maintained by a European government, the Corps des Ingénieurs des Ponts et Chaussées (see Chapter XVI). Under the direction of Pierre Trésaguet (1716–94) French engineers built the finest roads in Europe, on principles far superior to those of Gautier. By 1776 France already had some 12,000 miles of finished roads, with a comparable mileage under construction or repair, and French engineers that year planned a system of national highways. (Pl. 100.)

In England road building followed a somewhat different pattern. At first the roads, as in France, were primarily a royal responsibility, and the benevolent despotism of the Tudor monarchs brought the first significant road improvements to England; in 1555 Queen Mary appointed inspectors of roads, each answerable for designated portions of the roads. By 1663, however, a Turnpike Act permitted the collection of tolls, and thereafter English roads were often the enterprise of privately owned turnpike companies operating under a government franchise. English road builders were far more empirical than their French counterparts. The blind engineer John Metcalf (1717–1810) understood that well-drained road foundations made for good permanent highways. His younger contemporaries Thomas Telford (1757–1834) and John McAdam (1756–1836) improved upon his methods after 1775. As long as horses and wagons or coaches were the prevalent mode of transport, their type of road (crushed stone over a layer of stone chips bound with sand) served well.

Improvement of highways inevitably raised the problem of bridge construction. The usual materials for bridge building were wood and stone. Bridge builders who preferred wood adopted some of the sixteenth-century principles of Palladio. One of the problems that the bridge engineer confronted was that bridges obstructed the waterways. The French engineer Jean Rodolphe Perronet (1708–94), who built some of the outstanding stone bridges of his time, was able to reduce the amount of waterway obstructed by his piers. Whereas a Roman bridge of AD 14 at Rimini blocked about 65 per cent of the waterway and the Pont Neuf in Paris (1607) about 50 per cent, Perronet's Pont de la Concorde (1787) in Paris blocked only 35 per cent. The increasing knowledge of the strength of materials (see Chapter XIV) did much to aid construction engineers with their problems. Although French engineering theory was far ahead of English in the eighteenth century, a notable contribution to bridge construction was made in London with the completion of old Westminster Bridge by Charles Dangeau de Labelye (1705 ?–81), a Swiss engineer. Using watertight wooden caissons as cofferdams, he was able to place the bridge piers inside a watertight structure. In England, too, cast iron was introduced as material for bridges when another Abraham Darby (1750–91) and John Wilkinson (1728–1808) in 1779 built the Coalbrookdale Ironbridge over the Severn River, thus marking the start of a new era in bridge-building. (Pl. 101.)

Despite the sometimes cooperative efforts of merchants, towns, feudal lords, and benevolent governments and despite the ingenuity of road and bridge builders, land transportation remained slow and difficult. In the sixteenth century a lone mail courier might travel under favourable conditions fifty miles a day, but the ordinary traveller in a convoy might feel lucky to make fifteen, and the coaches of the eighteenth century did only a little better. Roads grew more and more congested as the population grew. With notable exceptions, they were seldom better than mire holes in the winter and dust-heaps in the summer, unless some attempt had been made to pave them with cobble-stones or other surfacings. Good or bad, the roads had to serve not only for human travel but also for herding animals and fowl to market. The Smithfield market in England, at least partly because of the improvement in roads, within a fifty-year period raised its sales from 80,000 head of cattle to some 130,000, and in the same period the number of sheep sold rose from 640,000 to almost a million.

The horse remained the chief and fastest means of transportation in Europe until the nineteenth century, although oxen, mules, donkeys, and reindeer were also used as draft animals; in Asia or Africa water buffalo, elephants, or camels were common work animals; and in the Americas until the horse was introduced by Europeans, dogs and llamas pulled the loads that men and women did not themselves carry. Horse-drawn wagons were usually uncomfortable and were hard on highways constructed for lighter vehicles. Pack-horse convoys remained common in Europe even in the seventeenth and eighteenth century, when wheeled conveyances became familiar. By the eighteenth century horse express routes for perishable foods were well established in England; for example, some 320 horses daily passed through Tonbridge laden with fish for the London market.

To the cartwrights of the Hungarian village Kocs goes the honour of devising a practical passenger vehicle, known in Hungarian as the *kocsi* (French *coche*, German *Kutsche*, English *coach*). Only slowly in the fifteenth and sixteenth centuries did they become known in France, Germany, England and elsewhere, but in 1634 over 3,400 coaches covered the English routes. At first, they provided only slightly greater comfort, since their bodies were slung in frames by leather straps rather than buoyed by springs. Not until 1670 were steel springs introduced into coaches, and not until 1750 were fast, sprung stagecoaches in general use in England. With the better paving of roads in the latter part of the eighteenth century, the era of the stagecoach reached its crest.

Various experiments were tried with steam as a means of power for four-wheeled vehicles. The French engineer Cugnot's steam-carriage, mentioned above, moved only around $2\frac{1}{2}$ miles per hour, and it proved unsteady and dangerous besides. In England William Murdock (1754–1839) constructed a very small model but abandoned the project upon instructions from Watt, his employer. The successful solution of the problem had to await Trevithick's steam locomotive (1801).

Ships, Lighthouses, Canals, and Transportation by Water

Transportation by water was generally much cheaper than transportation by land, and most heavy goods still went by water wherever seas, lakes, rivers, or canals were available. Several cathedrals and castles in southern and eastern England were built of stone brought from Normandy, since it could be more cheaply ferried across the Channel than dragged from other parts of England, and timber shipped from Scandinavia cost less in English coastal regions than timber carted from the English hinterland. Until the fifteen and sixteenth centuries most sea transport was coastwise; hence, the prevalence of *portolani*. If cargoes had to be shifted to inland waters and canals, they were transferred to barges, sometimes even a double transfer being required in shallow harbours, where lighters were used to carry goods from ship to barge. Huge cranes—sometimes portrayed in contemporary paintings[14]—facilitated this work at ports and trans-shipping points. River traffic was more important to eastern Europe with its longer and slower rivers than to western Europe. The vast river systems of America and Asia provided the most frequented avenues of transport, travel, and communication for European explorers and settlers, who built their first rude communities on the banks of American and Siberian rivers, which furnished them also with water, fish, drainage, power, and recreation. In eastern Europe timber was floated down river, and other bulky goods were freighted on river rafts, a method of transportation that was not practicable on most western rivers, which flowed too rapidly. Tolls multiplied—notably in Germany—to the point where some rivers were deserted by merchants. In northern France and the Netherlands, however, internal waterways were well travelled. Barges, towed by men or draft animals, provided perhaps the cheapest form of transportation, and they handled much of the heavy short-haul goods.

Seafaring ships of the West were of two distinct types before the seventeenth century—the oared galley and the sailing vessel. (Pl. 106a.) In the Mediterranean, until about 1500 the galley with one bank of oars was supreme both as man-of-war and as merchant ship. Oars were steadily increased in length, even to fifty feet. Reaching inboard for one-third of their length, they were manipulated by as many as seven men each. The steering oar early gave way to the rudder, and man power was supplemented by masts and sails. The Venetians and the Genoese used huge galleys equipped with both oars and sails, called galleasses, and slow freighters (naves or carracks) of as much as sixteen-hundred tons' burden. In 1571, at the Battle of Lepanto, the Christian armada included six galleasses and over two hundred galleys, to say nothing of smaller auxiliary craft. Lepanto was the last significant naval battle in which the galley was considered the decisive vessel, although it continued to be used for about two centuries longer.

Meanwhile the sailing vessel had come into its own, especially on the Atlantic. The stern-post rudder, which permitted more effective steering, had probably been known to the Chinese in the eighth century, to the Byzantines in the twelfth, and in Poland in the thirteenth. It was fully developed in fourteenth-century Byzantine vessels. The fleet which the English king Henry V assembled for the invasion of France in 1413 included cogs, carracks, barges, and balingers, mostly of about five hundred tons' burden, the best known being the blunt, broad, slow-going cogs of north-western Europe. Meanwhile the Portuguese and the Spanish were developing the caravel, a small, broad, high-pooped, lateen-sailed vessel for ocean travel. This was the type of ship used by Vasco de Gama and Columbus. Columbus' *Santa Maria* was of only a little over two hundred tons. (Pl. 106b.) By this time rigging had improved; three-masted vessels with bowsprits were common from the fifteenth century on, and with two masts square-rigged and one lateen rigged, navigators could beat 'up the wind'. Since the winds over the Atlantic rarely die down completely (except in the equatorial doldrums), nations with Atlantic outlets were able to abandon the clumsy oar-driven galley in favour of more manoeuvrable sailing vessels. The Great Armada (1588), with only four galleasses and four galleys but around one hundred and thirty sailing vessels (the largest of 1,300 tons), exemplifies the replacement of the galley by the Atlantic type of shipping.

Improved navigational methods and larger freighters permitted freer travel on the open ocean, and longer sailings eliminated many trans-shipments. In addition to the well-known all-water route between the North Sea and Venice or Genoa via Gibraltar, the Dutch and the Germans were able to maintain a continuous sea-route between the Netherlands and the Baltic ports. The explorations of the fifteenth and sixteenth centuries gave still another impetus to water transportation. Not only did the growing commerce with the nascent colonies and the Far East augment the demands on shipping but also intra-European communications grew because of increased traffic in exotic products. Changes in social and economic conditions accelerated in the sixteenth century to a degree that induces some historians to call it a period of 'commercial revolution' (see Chapter I), due in part to the opening of new markets, the vogue of new commodities, the consumption of larger quantities of old ones, and the importation of precious metals from the New World. (Pl. 107a, b.)

In the seventeenth century, though the Dutch had to import most of their shipbuilding materials, they were perhaps the leading shipbuilders and marine carriers of Europe. Pieter J. Livorn invented (1595) a type of vessel (called in Dutch the *fluitschip* and in English the flute) of slender design, light weight, and shallow draft that was faster and cheaper to build and to run than earlier types. The flute was especially constructed to carry the bulk goods—wine, salt, grain, timber, etc.—that were the staples of northern commerce. The Dutch fishing vessels (*busses*) had long excelled in the North Sea fisheries, Dutch broad and flat-bottomed flyboats carried much of Europe's cabotage, and Dutch whalers dominated the whale oil market. (Pl. 106c.) A Dutch device known as the 'ship's camel' lifted heavy vessels over sandbars and through shallow canals. And Drebbel built a submarine that in 1620 was rowed below the surface of the Thames for several hours. The superiority of Holland's shipping was one of the major reasons for that little country's successes in the trade of the North and Baltic Seas and in the race for colonial empire against the Portuguese, Spanish, and English.

Several improvements in navigation and sailor's diet facilitated lengthy voyages for Dutch and other European crews. To the magnetic compass, known to navigators for several centuries, was added the telescope, which in the seventeenth century was quickly adapted to navigation, and finally, in the eighteenth century the ship's chronometer. The planting of vegetable gardens at ports of call (see below) helped to counteract the heavy toll of scurvy.

Larger ships made imperative larger docks and jetties, which began to appear in the early eighteenth century. Breakwaters were needed to divert rapid currents and tides at river mouths and to diminish the force of ocean waves in harbours, but the breakwaters that were built sometimes speedily collapsed, until, in the early nineteenth century, steam-power facilitated the handling and transporting of heavy stone blocks. Wet docks, which were of great aid in estuaries with a wide range of tide, were constructed in the seventeenth century. The engineering of these docks was relatively simple: great basins, excavated by pick and shovel, were connected with the tideway by a short canal with lock gates. In 1660 the Surrey Docks were begun in England, and a private dock at Blackwall was built to accommodate East India shipping. A wet dock was completed at Le Havre in 1667, and in the first quarter of the eighteenth century Liverpool began construction of another. (Pl. 103a).

The placement of warning lights for coastal and sea shipping had long been haphazard. The Romans had built beacon towers, but early medieval beacons had been mere piles of burning wood. By the fourteenth century elevated pitch pots and coal braziers began to take the place of wood fires. The entrance of the Gironde River had been marked by a lighthouse since the Moors had first erected one; the Black Prince built another about 1370; a third was begun in 1584, and that one was increased in height in 1727 to 186½ feet. In England the Guild of the Most Glorious and Undividable Trinity, founded in 1515 mainly to pray for those in peril at sea, broadened its functions, particularly after the Reformation, and the brethren of its Trinity House, among other things, erected beacon lights. A light might also be erected by a private person as a business venture, but he had to get permission from Trinity House if he wished to collect a toll from passing ships. The Eddystone Light on the dangerous rocks outside Plymouth Harbour was destroyed and reconstructed several times before John Smeaton in 1759 built an enduring structure.

Internal waterways (i.e. rivers and canals) carried a large share of the increased activity in transportation. Substantial advances were made during our period in controlling floods, changing the courses of rivers, and dredging their bottoms. Many rivers were connected by canals. Canals had been constructed in Holland and Italy in late medieval times primarily for drainage, but they also served barges and small boats. Whether the lock was first used in the West in one or the other of these two countries is debatable, but by the eighteenth century it was familiar nearly everywhere in Europe. (Pl. 103b.) In France, under Henry IV's minister, Sully, all navigable rivers were declared part of the royal domain, and five additional rivers were made navigable—the Vesle, the Vienne, the Eure, the Ourcq, and the Vilaine. Louis XIV's minister Colbert furthered this policy. His dream to connect the Atlantic and the Mediterranean by canals and rivers, avoiding the long and hazardous trip via Gibraltar, was realized in 1681 with the opening of the Languedoc Canal (148 miles long, 119 locks) connecting the Rhône and the Garonne. This project required a huge dam, a long tunnel, and, to avoid additional locks, several aqueducts. It was the engineering marvel of its age. In northern Europe during the seventeenth century Gustavus Adolphus of Sweden, the Great Elector of Brandenburg, and Peter the Great of Russia also encouraged the construction of canals.

In Britain waterways were developed not by the government but by private investors, and large-scale canal building was delayed until the eighteenth century. Earlier, however, Parliament had encouraged the improvement of rivers, and in the seventeenth century locks were built on the Thames between London and Oxford. The first ambitious canal project in the British Isles was the Newry Canal in northern Ireland, completed in 1742 by Thomas Steers, a Liverpool dock engineer. In the 1750s another Liverpool dock engineer, Henry Berry, built the Sankey Canal to carry cargoes from the Lancashire coalfields and salt workings to the turnpikes toward Liverpool, but it was only about ten miles long. Both Steers' and Berry's canals were, besides, deadwater navigations. The first serious attempt to build a lengthy canal in England in other than relatively flat country, where ordinary locks would not do, was financed by the Duke of Bridgewater (1736–1803) and engineered by James Brindley (1716–72). In the 1760s Brindley, a self-trained engineer, began construction of a series of canals connecting Bridgewater's coal pits with the open sea. The earliest of these canals caused great controversy because Brindley abandoned the use of locks, preferring a constant water level, which required the building of an aqueduct some ninety-nine feet high over the Irwell. It is doubtful whether he knew that similar feats had been successfully accomplished in building the Languedoc Canal in France about a hundred years earlier. After Brindley completed his design, England became laced with canals, some of which still serve well.

Attempts were made in the eighteenth century, particularly after Watt's engine provided rotary motion, to construct ships powered by steam. The major problem was how to construct an engine big enough to furnish the requisite power but small enough to leave room for passengers, cargo, and fuel. Papin in 1707 proposed to demonstrate the feasibility of pulling barges by means of steam-driven towboats, but he never obtained permission to do so. In the 1760s and 1770s William Henry of Pennsylvania and Jacques Perier and the Marquis de Jouffroy of France tried out steam-driven ships without practicable results. The problem was to be partly solved only in 1790, when John Fitch put the finishing touches on a vessel 60 feet long that made a speed of 8 miles per hour and was used for several thousand miles of commercial service but left so little space for passengers and cargo that it was not a financial success. Not until the early nineteenth century did a steam-powered vessel prove commercially profitable.

Experiments with Air Transportation

Fascinated by the idea of transportation through the air, would-be aeronauts of various ages have attached birdlike wings to their arms and boldly glided or flapped from great heights, generally with tragic results. Leonardo da Vinci speculated about machines that would fly and carry men, but his ideas were not known to his contemporaries, and until the seventeenth century human flight was generally conceived as feasible, if at all, only by the imitation of birds. In the seventeenth century Hooke experimented with models of flying machines, as did also Borelli. These costly experiments convincingly demonstrated that neither the human arm nor the machine of that day could support the human body in the air.

In the seventeenth century a more fruitful prospect for inventive ingenuity—the lighter-than-air craft—opened up. Von Guericke's new air-pump made it possible to suck air out of a container and create an artificial vacuum, and in 1670 the Jesuit Francesco de Lana Terzi suggested that several thin-copper spheres if completely evacuated might be able to lift a small cart; Hooke, Borelli, and Leibniz pointed out, however, that these thin and empty globes would collapse under the pressure of the external air. In 1755 Joseph Galien published *L'art de naviguer dans les airs*, in which he suggested that men could be carried aloft in a high ship filled with enough air from the upper regions to withstand external air pressure. In 1766 Cavendish demonstrated the low density of hydrogen (or 'inflammable air', as he called it), but human flight was not to be achieved until the 1780s—first by 'hot air balloons' and only later, by globes filled with 'inflammable air'.

THE TECHNOLOGY OF WARFARE

Before the Hundred Years' War the armies of western Europe had relied heavily on the crossbow, despite ecclesiastical prohibitions against it because of its lethal power. During the Crusades it had proved itself in competition with the Muslim horse archers, and by the end of the thirteenth century it was a favourite infantry weapon of the Italians. Mercenary crossbowmen were in great demand, as was evidenced by their presence in the French army at the Battle of Crécy (1346).

The longbow, however, proved a better weapon. Having probably originated in eleventh-century Wales, it had done well in several thirteenth-century battles of the English against the Scots, and it achieved decisive results against the French in the Hundred Years' War. From the naval battle of Sluys (1340), during which bowmen rained arrows on the French from the rigging and decks of the English ships, through the land battles of Crécy, Poitiers, and Agincourt, and until the very end of the sixteenth century, the longbow was the principal weapon of English armies. Though its impact was probably less overwhelming than the crossbow's, it was deadly at a hundred yards and when drawn by a trained archer could reach to about three hundred; it could be shot more speedily than a crossbow, required less training, being lighter and less complicated, and was wieldy at closer quarters. At the climax of the Hundred Years' War, over half of the English infantrymen were longbowmen, the remainder being armed with bills (spears with a scythed cutting head and spikes at the side and top). Longbowmen completely outclassed crossbowmen, who in consequence were not employed in large numbers in Continental armies after the fifteenth century. In the next century the longbow, in turn, gave way, though only slowly, to small firearms.

Other close-quarter weapons were also rendered obsolete about the same time. Some were variations of the spear, like the bills just described. Somewhat similar to halberds, they were used by both infantry and cavalry during the fourteenth and fifteenth centuries. They were superseded by the pike. The length of the pikestaff, extended by the Swiss to 20 feet, made the pike a formidable weapon, which until the sixteenth century enjoyed supremacy. It could be used to defend a square against cavalry or to attack dismounted men.

Vehicular weapons were not unknown. Tanks and other curiously modern devices were sketched by Da Vinci, but most of these sketches were of greater biographical interest to us than of practical military importance to his contemporaries. Of real effect in the fifteenth century were the wagon stockades—mobile fortresses—employed with tactical success by the Hussite armies.

The origin of gunpowder is still somewhat of a mystery. Its employment as an explosive for military purposes progressed in a roughly parallel fashion in different parts of the world. Probably the first use of it in warfare came, at least in the West, at the time of the triumph of the longbow in Europe. Sometime between 1319 and 1346, and somewhere between Andalusia and Scotland or between Italy and England firearms were employed for the first time in western Europe. An Oxford manuscript dated 1327 pictures a pot-bellied cannon (*pot de fer*) being touched off. In 1345 Edward III ordered the preparation of guns and ammunition for his invasion of France. A document at Tournai in Belgium records the testing of a cannon in 1346, during which a two-pound projectile, after penetrating the wall of a house, killed a man. According to Froissart, cannon were used that year at Crécy and later in the siege of Calais. In the same century the Chinese (who had long been familiar with pyrotechnics) also began to employ gunpowder in warfare. Russian artillery, too, made its first appearance in the second half of the fourteenth century. The various Islamic peoples seem to have learned the use of firearms about the same time.

The arms race was now on. England, France, the Netherlands, northern Italy (with its famous 'Lombards'), the Turks, and others all vied with one another in the production of bigger and better guns. Of the earliest extant cannon, the largest—'Mad Meg' at Ghent—is a little over 16 feet in length and 25 inches in calibre. Fourteenth-century cannon were few, inaccurate, and hard to fire. Their more telling effect in the ensuing centuries was largely an outcome of the improvements in metallurgy and gunpowder. Better casting explains how the English could produce four hundred cannon for the siege of St Malo (1378). Four years later a Londoner turned out seventy-three cast-iron guns, one of them multibarrelled. 'Greek fire', probably invented in the seventh-century Byzantine Empire, was highly effective in the defence of Constantinople in the 1450s; it was a liquid or paste (sometimes considered an ancestor of gunpowder) which broke into flame on contact with water. For all that, the city fell in 1453, doomed in large part by the Turks' battering of its old fortifications with the new cannon.

The western Europeans perhaps lagged in adopting gunpowder, but once started, they took the lead. Military theory changed with the new weapons. In the early fourteenth century the military theories of Marino Sanudo of Venice and Guido da Vigevano (born in Pavia, c. 1280), based on Italian tactics of an era before explosives were common, had been considered standard; in the late fourteenth century they began to yield precedence to treatises concerning the manufacture and use of firearms—as well as other types of war-machines. Among the authors of later works were Konrad Keyser of Franconia, Giovanni da Fontana of Padua, and several anonymous Germans. The increasing use of firearms in the fifteenth and sixteenth centuries brought new military treatises, often with elaborate illustrations concerning cannon and small arms, fortifications, and siege engines.

Firearms meanwhile grew more varied. In the fifteenth century the hand grenade became a standard military weapon, and special battalions of 'grenadiers' were trained to throw bombs. The most noteworthy innovation of the century in weapons was an ancestor of the modern rifle, which began as the German *Hackenbüchse* in the early fifteenth century and became the French *harquebus* or *arquebus*. It was a hand gun—something in appearance like the modern bazooka. At first too awkward and ineffective to have significant tactical value, the arquebus progressively improved until during the sixteenth-century wars of the French and the Spanish it became an effective weapon. Italy was the proving ground for early modern warfare. Though its own armies had lost their reputation (largely because the Italian city-state no longer produced a warlike officer class), Italy remained the place to go for study and practice of strategy, tactics, and fortification. There the Spanish worked out their tactics of infantry fire power.

The heavier, longer (six feet or over), more deadly, and farther reaching musket had meanwhile come into use. The early musket needed two men and a support stuck in the ground for proper manipulation and aiming, but it gradually grew shorter and more wieldy, and in the hands of an expert gunner it could reach a target at five hundred yards—two hundred beyond the range of the longbow. By the 1550s the musketeer had become the pride, and the source of the superiority, of the Spanish army. Even though a good archer could fire several arrows in the time it took to load a musket and the English continued to use longbowmen until the seventeenth century, the English army, and other armies still more rapidly, were forced to follow suit. The process was speeded up when the dangerous and inefficient match-lock, an attachment for priming and firing both arquebus and musket, began (at the opening of the sixteenth century) to yield to the more satisfactory wheel-lock.

The effectiveness of small arms and cannon, though modest by modern standards, thereafter increased steadily. Rifling was introduced in 1520 (though not generally before the end of the eighteenth century), and improved hand-grenades in 1536. The pistol was invented in Spain about 1540, and the wheel-lock pistol in 1543. Paper cartridges came in 1560, hot shells in 1575, fixed cartridges in 1590, rifled pistols in 1592, and the percussion fuse in 1596. The bayonet, which seems to have originated as a dagger at Bayonne in the fifteenth century, became, when attached to a wooden haft and plugged into the muzzle of a musket, a common battle weapon in the seventeenth, and early in the eighteenth Vauban made it a standard battle weapon. By that time the rifled, flintlock fusil, lighter (about ten pounds in weight), simpler, and more wieldly than the musket, rendered the fusilier the best-armed soldier. By the close of the War of the Spanish Succession, therefore, foot soldiers were mostly armed with flintlock and bayonet, regardless of the traditional names their regiments might bear.

No longer was cavalry the most important branch of the military forces. Infantry, particularly when armed with gun and bayonet, had made the armoured knight an anachronism, and with him the concept of chivalry also had lost prestige. Cervantes called artillery a 'devilish invention' that enabled a 'base cowardly hand to take the life of the bravest gentleman'. As early as the fifteenth century the Swiss learned to keep mounted men at a distance by forming dense masses defended by their long pikes. In the wars of the French and Spanish at the beginning of the next century, infantry was the decisive force in battle, especially if protected by arquebusiers, and Spain's 'Great Captain' Gonzalo Fernández de Cordoba (1453–1515) reorganized his army so as to make the infantry more manoeuvrable; lighter armed, with short swords or lances and bucklers, they were able to outmanœuvre the Swiss mercenary pikemen in his enemies' ranks. As firearms improved and more and more men were armed with them, they relegated suits of armour to the status of ornamental apparel for state occasions.

Feudal castles likewise became ornamental rather than defensive as mobile cannon made unfortified strongholds less tenable. Skilful use of artillery empowered the French to drive the English out of their country in the 1450s and later to win victories against the Spanish in Italy; it aided Gustavus Adolphus, as an offensive weapon, to break up Imperialist squares in the 1630s; and it enabled Marshal de Saxe, as a defensive weapon, to disrupt enemy charges in the 1740s.

New theories of fortification were called for, and, we have seen, Vauban took a prominent part in answering the call. Multiple fortresses replaced castles. A fortress was protected not so much by moats, thick walls, and bastions (though these, too, were in evidence) as by outer gun emplacements. As artillery became a more and more decisive factor of victory in battle, so did the engineer who knew how to build roads for the transport of cannon and breastworks for defence of a fortified garrison or as a vantage for attack upon it. Marksmanship, though sharpshooting remained rare indeed, became more accurate as Leonardo da Vinci (who, however, did not publish his findings), Tartaglia, and later scientists (see Chapter XIV) entered the military field with studies of ballistics, culminating for our period in Benjamin Robin's *New Principles of Gunnery* (1742; German translation by Euler, 1745). Frederick the Great's introduction of horse-drawn cannon was the last major artillery innovation before General Jean Baptiste de Gribeauval (1715–89) issued the *réglement* (1776) that laid the foundation for the exceptional mobility of Napoleon Bonaparte's gunners.

Naval warfare also was changed by the new technology. Warships had previously been floating platforms carrying men trained for hand-to-hand combat after grappling hooks had attached an enemy vessel to their own. Greek fire had been used for centuries to destroy shipping, but its efficacy depended upon relatively close contact. As the sailing vessel replaced the galley, however, a fleet came to be considered a group of floating platforms from which to destroy hostile shipping by gun fire at a fair distance. Portholes were provided for guns, and turrets for gunners; the effectiveness of a ship's broadside became the measure of her prowess. The greater range of Portuguese guns assured their victory over the Egyptians at Diu, in 1509, and made Portugal the master of the Indian Ocean, and the greater mobility and consequent fire superiority of the English fleet partly accounted for its defeat of the Spanish Armada in 1588. Fire superiority was thenceforth the major objective of naval strategy.

Changes in Military Systems

As armies and navies grew in size and as soldiers and sailors remained for long terms in service, the military science of logistics (feeding, equipping, transporting, and housing) was put in the charge of specialized officers. Fortresses and naval stations constituted not only homes for local soldiers and sailors but also supply depots for the regional forces. Gradually, and particularly in France, which replaced Spain as the leading military power in the late seventeenth century, military strategy and tactics became systematized. Siege warfare and blockades were the mode of the day, commanders seeking pitched battle only under favourable circumstances, otherwise attempting to outlast rather than outfight the enemy. Feudal levies tended to disappear and proprietary regiments to diminish in number as standing armies grew; in times of national crisis, rulers might call out the militia, too. Troops were arrayed in uniform as against the casual dress of earlier days, and military drill was intensified in order to train them to carry out parade and battle manœuvres in elegant geometrical movements.

Better drill and fire techniques were developed by Maurice of Nassau in the Eighty Years' War, by Gustavus Adolphus in the Thirty Years' War, and by Cromwell in the English Civil War. On these models, and profiting from their own experience in the wars of Louis XIV, Prince Leopold of

Anhalt-Dessau and King Frederick William I taught the Prussian fusiliers to load and reload their pieces so rapidly as to maintain fire superiority while advancing under fire in unswerving lines to a point from which they might launch a bayonet charge. In turn, the Prussian drill methods became the standard for other armies of Europe, especially when perfected by the outflanking tactics ('oblique order') of Frederick the Great. By that time a respectable army had military bands, elaborate uniforms, colourful flags, and specialized contingents of professional and sometimes mercenary infantry, cavalry, and artillery, organized into divisions, brigades, regiments, battalions, companies, etc. It was usually a standing army, directly responsible to the crown, with a political significance that we shall consider later. The improved fusil, or rifle, of 1777 was the common weapon of the French army during the Revolution and the Empire, but it hit its target with only a small percentage of its shots. Though casualties mounted consistently in the warfare of the eighteenth century, they were bound to be light by comparison with the deadly efficiency of the technological warfare of later centuries.

THE METHODS OF AGRICULTURE

Rural Practices in the Fourteenth and Fifteenth Centuries

Although the more progressive monastic communities of the Middle Ages had improved the cultivation of grain crops, vines, and fruit trees and the breeds of domestic animals, comparatively little experimentation had been tried with new crops or breeds. The Cistercian monasteries of the twelfth and thirteenth centuries, like the pioneers on the American frontier, had accepted as their major aim turning forest and swamp into arable fields. They performed what must have seemed in that day miracles of deforestation and drainage, especially in the new lands of east Germany. Their pioneering activity demonstrates that in general until about 1300 Western agricultural methods were determined by the availability of new land rather than the need for more intensive cultivation of the old.

Thereafter, the trend toward new lands was checked, if not reversed. The poorer arable lands went back to pasture; less was produced for market and export; and conservation became more strategic than expansion. The amount of arable land was further limited by the steady increase of sheep-farming and the accompanying 'enclosure movement'. With the mounting demand for wool by the expanding textile industries, the village commons were gradually acquired by the great landlords as sheep pasture and subsequently, along with other hitherto open land, closed off from the fields. In sheep-raising areas such as England, Spain, and northern Italy, the sharp curtailment of farmland and the persistent spread of enclosures became heated political issues. Some scholars have held that, especially in its early stages before the end of the fifteenth century, the enclosure of previously common or open land was generally due not to increased demands for wool but for fresh, unexhausted soil. The fact is that enclosure often, especially in the stages after 1500, was accompanied by voluntary consolidation of the peasants' strips into compact holdings, usually individually owned in western Europe and communally in central and eastern Europe. For this process was recognized by peasants as well as landlords as a way to enlarge the amount not only of arable land for more efficient farming but also of grazing land for larger herds. Nevertheless, soil exhaustion may well have been the determining factor for certain places at certain times.

Even before 1300 progressive farmers and agriculturists had advocated new methods of restoring the soil. The ancient practice continued of 'green' fertilizing—that is, digging straw, stubble, and waste leguminous plants into the ground—as well as fertilizing with manure. Sometimes 'green' materials were strewn on the ground for the cattle to trample. By the thirteenth century, the use of marl as fertilizer was well known. At the beginning of the next century Pietro Crescenzi completed a work entitled *Opus Ruralium Commodorum*, summarizing the agricultural methods known to western Christendom at that time but overlooking the highly advanced Muslim methods prevalent in Spain. This lacuna was filled by two Iberian rulers, Denis of Portugal (1279–1325) and his contemporary Pedro of Aragon. Denis was outstanding in promoting the agricultural as well as other resources of his country. One of his many conservation projects was the planting of pine trees on the dunes of Leiria, later to become a source of timber for the ships of daring Portuguese mariners. He and Pedro encouraged the translation of Muslim works on agriculture, thus perpetuating for Christian Spain the advanced practices of the Muslims.

For the most part, however, European farming methods remained traditional from the eighth to the fourteenth century. In that interval the two-field (or field-grass) system practised by the Romans and the Germanic tribes in the Roman Empire gave way in some regions to the three-field system (two fields under cultivation and one fallow). Either system permitted a different portion of the tillable land to lie fallow each year in order to avoid too rapid exhaustion of the soil's fertility. Manure was scarce, and liming or marling was an expensive, long-range process, hardly worth while for serfs, small farmers, *métayers* (share-croppers), and tenants, who could not be certain that they would survive long enough to reap a reward from the labour and expense involved. The acreage under actual cultivation or fertilization, therefore, was relatively small in comparison to the soil available.

Because it permitted fuller use of the soil, the three-field system came to prevail throughout western and central Europe. On a manor employing this system one field would lie fallow for a given year, another would be planted in the spring, and the third in the fall. The triennial rotation of fields resulted in a primitive sort of crop rotation—improved probably about 1300 in the Netherlands by alternating legumes and grain crops. Each field was divided into strips allotted severally to the peasants of the manorial community.

Generally the manor, with its manor house or chateau, its communal village, its strip fields, and its common pasture, marsh, and waste land, was geared to self-sufficiency rather than to production for profit. It produced grain for bread; wine, ale, and beer for drink; flax and hemp for linen; sheep for woollen clothing; pigs and fowl for meat; and almost all the other necessities.

About 1300—earlier in certain urban regions of Italy and Spain—the manorial system underwent serious modifications. As prices rose (see Chapter I), the employment of wage labourers became more profitable than that of serfs or tenants on estates producing grain, wine, and other produce for proliferating town markets. Serfdom began to give way to tenancy, a trend that was accelerated in the late fourteenth century as the Black Death reduced the labour supply. In England, for example, even before 1300, landlords had begun to find it to their advantage to convert their labour hands from servile or semi-servile status to that of free wage-earners and to bid for a free labourer's services. During the period of the Black Death they were more concerned whether a labourer's wages were not too high than whether he was free or servile. The trend away from serfdom was welcomed by many landlords as a means of obtaining land and money in place of personal service from their peasantry and thus of adjusting their cash incomes to the rising standards of living. They endeavoured to take over common lands and even peasant holdings in order to grow more of the crops demanded in neighbouring or foreign markets. As landlords thus reorganized land and labour to obtain maximum profit by growing special crops, manorial self-subsistence became outmoded.

In western Europe the shift from a servile to a free-labour market apparently was accompanied by a decline in production. At any rate, much less agricultural produce was sold from western manors in the fourteenth century than previously. Food shortages sometimes forced industrial towns to draw on distant regions to feed their expanding populations. Some countries, like the Netherlands, which were able to import food by sea from the Baltic coastal lands, were more fortunate than regions such as northern Italy, which could not so readily find even distant foodstuffs to import. Food shortage and the Black Plague together brought an overall decline in population after the middle of the fourteenth century. Occasional bumper crops of grain sometimes led to a drop in prices, as, for example, during the second quarter of the fourteenth century, when grain prices declined in England as much as twenty percent, and again in the last quarter of the century, when prices of grain and bread reached unusually low levels. In the long run, however, prices tended upward.

In the fifteenth and sixteenth centuries the inclination of landlords to expand their holdings at the expense of peasants and to go in for money crops was particularly noticeable. In France land values rose so rapidly during fifty years of rapid recovery after the Hundred Years' War that about 1500 they were back to their pre-war levels. The same was happening in England, where, especially in the sixteenth century, expansion took the form of an intensified enclosure movement. In central and eastern Europe an agricultural expansion eastward across the Elbe had already reached a climax by the end of the fourteenth century, and during the fifteenth century, as peasants continued to migrate into Slavic lands, abandoned farmlands and deserted villages marred the landscape in Brandenburg, Pomerania, Mecklenburg, and Prussia. In east Germany and Poland landlords now all the more ruthlessly exploited the servile peasants who remained behind, bound to their great estates. In Poland, as well as Hungary, agriculture, nevertheless, expanded. In the sixteenth century a new agricultural boom came to the Baltic coastal regions; it encouraged new German immigration, and Baltic landlords readjusted to a system of large estates worked by landless but free peasants.

Nowhere in Europe was the peasant necessarily better off economically because he was legally free. The rising standard of living made the upper classes feel hard-pressed for money. Many landlords, hoping to profit from the increasing prices of farm products, not only appropriated more and more of the common lands but also increased their demands upon the peasantry, whether tenants or serfs, wherever they could. The peasants resented the lord's appropriation of the common lands, which they had customarily used for pasture, hay, wood, hunting, and fishing. The landlord's land hunger meant for them decreasing land resources and increasing rentals or servile obligations. Peasant discontent mounted and rebellions became more frequent. Along with the peasantry, many of the lesser, land-starved nobles, especially in Germany and France, were in desperate straits. Caught in changes that made their services almost obsolete in warfare, and unable to adjust their small estates to the new economy, they sank into poverty and humiliation. In Germany, the rise of Protestantism seemed to give a Biblical justification to social discontent. The Knights' War preceded the Peasants' War—both destined to be repressed without diminishing the dissidents' grievances (see Chapter IV).

The Increase of Articles of Commerce

The discoveries and explorations of the fifteenth and subsequent centuries introduced European man to new or relatively new commodities. Cane sugar had long been known in Europe, though only as an expensive rarity, and it now became cheaper and commoner. Originating in the Far East, the sugar cane was transported on Columbus's second voyage to the tropical New World, eventually becoming a staple crop there. In the sixteenth century the Spanish, the Portuguese, the French, and the English attempted large scale cultivation of tobacco in their respective mother countries, but with varying degrees of failure. The introduction of the potato from the New World was more successful, providing the poor man with a mainstay of his diet, and the increased use of various 'artificial grasses' (legumes) augmented the number of Europe's rotation crops. Textile cotton from the East furnished a new material for clothing, adding to the personal comfort and cleanliness of a population that had previously worn woollen garments winter and summer, and new dyestuffs made cloth more colourful. A variety of other commodities from Asia, the South Seas, and Africa—for example, citrus fruits, spices of many kinds, tea, cocoa, silk, coffee—though known in Europe before the discovery of the all-water way to India, now became more plentiful. A long list of frustrations showed that few of these exotic commodities save oranges and silk could be grown economically anywhere in Europe.

After 1500, Europe's commerce with the rest of the world expanded. Superior silks and brocades, cotton and cotton goods, rugs, chinaware, indigo, spices, perfumes, brassware, coffee, tea, and rare woods continued to be principal articles of trade with India, China, and other countries of Asia. From Africa came ivory (on a relatively negligible scale), the guinea-fowl, salt, oil, and spices as well as slaves, only a few of whom remained in Europe. With the settlement of America, certain products, formerly derived from the East, were cultivated on a grand scale on New World plantations—for example, cotton, rice, coffee, and cane sugar (with its by-products, molasses and rum). In addition, the watermelon and the grapefruit were extensively cultivated in the warmer temperate zones of America and elsewhere, the first introduced from south Africa and the second from southeast Asia. Toward the end of our period cloves and other spices were grown in some of the tropical colonies of the New World. The Americas provided, besides, rich shipments of precious metals (primarily from Mexico, Peru, and Brazil), tobacco, cotton, sugar, salt, cereals, dyewoods, furs, timber, naval stores, whale oil, turkeys, and a rich harvest of fish (particularly from the Newfoundland Banks). Wine and beer retained their prominence in Europe's economy and diet, but during the second half of our period they suffered from the growing competition of imported beverages like coffee and tea.

Certain commodities native to the Americas were adopted elsewhere after the discovery of America. The pineapple, in addition to tobacco and the potato, was an outstanding adoption in Europe. The sweet potato and the breadroot, native to America, eventually became more familiar in the Far East than in Europe. Maize (the corn of Americans) was the Amerindians' staple food. Their women cooked it into tortillas, which in the tropical areas might be washed down with pulque, the fermented sap of the maguey cactus. Maize, though widely eaten in several different forms in America still, became common in only a few areas of Europe, where it was generally grown for animal rather than human consumption. Nor did it ever replace rice as the staple of southern China, where it was introduced by the Dominicans from the Philippines, to which it had come from Mexico. It was a versatile plant, however, providing sugar, starch, bowls for smoking pipes, and fuel. The Amerindians also knew several kinds of beans that were transplanted to Europe, but they were grown there at first as fodder rather than as food for humans. The tomato was also transplanted to Europe from America but was used chiefly as an ornament (the love apple) before the nineteenth century. Peanuts, introduced, like maize, by the Dominicans into southern China, never—at least, until recent decades, if then—became so important there or in Europe, either as a food or as a producer of oil, as in America. Pumpkins and squash likewise never developed into so regular a part of the diet of Europeans as of Americans, whether Indian or white, nor was chili ever so frequently used as a spice in Europe. Cocoa and chocolate became fairly common in England and elsewhere in the seventeenth century but were too expensive to compete effectively as beverages with tea and coffee, although here and there a 'cocoa house' did acquire a reputation that compared with that of a growing number of cafes and coffeehouses.

The cacao tree was only one of the strange and useful trees found in the New World. Rubber from the caoutchouc tree of the Amazon valley was a curiosity used almost exclusively for bouncing balls until Priestley around 1770 discovered that it could rub out pencil and ink marks (hence its English name). The California sequoias were too big to be handled usefully as yet, but the sugar maple of the north not only gave sugar and syrup but also made an excellent veneer for furniture, as did the mahogany of the south. The Peruvian cinchona bark gave quinine (to mention only one of several new drugs of which the Indians knew). The brazilwood gave a red dye, and another Brazil tree gave the Brazil nut. The Mexican cactus worm gave the dyestuff cochineal. The New World also had in abundance many of the timber trees that were familiar but were becoming scarce in Europe.

The more civilized Amerindian nations like the Incas and the Aztecs knew how to make cloth from cotton, wool, and maguey (see Chapter XII), but most northern Amerindians clothed themselves in hides and skins. America bred several kinds of furred animals that were not native to the Old World—the buffalo, the ocelot, the coyote, and the bobcat, for example; and their skins entered the competitive European fur market along with the preferred skins of beaver, bear, seal, otter, and other animals found in the Eastern and the Western Hemisphere alike.

The Portuguese, as colonizers in the East, Africa, and America, were able to move tropical plants more or less freely from one set of colonies to the other. In this way they introduced into West Africa from America and the East a number of plants thitherto unknown there, among them casava nuts, peanuts, sweet potatoes, maize, squash, coconuts, citrus fruits, and cocoa, and into America from Africa and the East mangoes, jacks, cinnamon, breadfruit, and coconuts, and into India, the cashew nut.[15] The American Indians did not know the plow, steel, firearms, glassware, and other manufactured products already known in Europe by the time of the discoveries. The horse and the cow were likewise unknown to them. If the Mexicans knew the wheel and the Peruvians the sail and the rudder, it was only in a rudimentary way. On the other hand, they could travel by snowshoe and birch canoe in the north (not to mention the llama of South America)—means of transportation about which the white man learned from them. The Indians also perhaps gave pandemic syphilis to the Europeans (see above), who in return gave them decimating epidemics of measles and smallpox.

The great European powers instituted in their West Indian and American colonies the famous plantation and hacienda system (see Chapter II). These systems utilized large supplies of labour, for the most part Negro slaves from Africa or American Indians, and produced new exotic crops. Usually a plantation specialized in a particular crop, exploiting large areas of land freely rather than adopting the intensive cultivation of the small, compact farms of Europe.

The 'Agricultural Revolution'

In the seventeenth and eighteenth centuries the most advanced European agricultural practices were to be found in England and Holland. In order to extend acreage, drainage of land was undertaken in both countries. The 'polder' system increased acreage considerably in Holland; and in England, thanks to Dutch engineers and English ingenuity, the Fen country was drained. These two nations had the advantage of close commercial, political, and intellectual contact, particularly after their seventeenth-century conflicts.

In England and Holland, as elsewhere, the three-field system had long entailed the obvious disadvantage of keeping one-third of the land idle, but growing demands for higher production brought a new method of crop rotation. In the seventeenth century some Netherlands farms adopted a method which, introduced during the next century into England, became known as 'the Norfolk System'. The farmer had discovered that certain crops, especially legumes, 'revived' the soil rather than used it up. By rotating certain food crops like peas and beans or, as began to happen late in the seventeenth century, certain fodder crops like clover with wheat, oats, barley, and other cereals, he was able to maintain the productivity of the available soil without the interruption of fallow periods. We now know that the reason for this soil-reviving quality of certain plants is that they are able to fix atmospheric nitrogen. Root crops like beets and turnips, requiring deep soil and cool weather, also fitted well into a rotation system for grains. No arable land need lie fallow under this arrangement; instead a four-course rotation of crops (clover, wheat, turnips, and barley in that order) was substituted. The turnip and clover as new fodder crops changed the whole process of cattle raising, and root crops, in particular the turnip, improved the land.

Even before the Norfolk system was widely adopted in the Netherlands, it was well received in England. The English were in a better position than the Continental countries to benefit from this innovation. Since the fourteenth century the yeoman had been gradually leaving the farm because of the enclosure movement, and the large farm under one man's control had become more common. By eliminating the small holder and the open-field system, enclosure increased the potential for efficiency in land exploitation. Nor was absentee landlordism common in England, where the country gentleman or noble proprietor took a direct and active interest in his estate.

In France, distinct agricultural improvement took place, but it was not equally marked. A long list of writers on agricultural problems had brought less practical change than the gentlemen farmers in England. Outstanding among the earlier agronomists was Olivier de Serres (1539–1619). Published with the approval of Henry IV's minister Sully and dedicated to the king, Serres' *Théâtre d'agriculture et ménage des champs* (1600) anticipated the Physiocratic doctrine that agriculture was the basis of wealth; it went through nineteen editions by 1675. Among the agricultural innovations that he championed in theory, and put into practice with considerable success on his own model farm and elsewhere, was the earnest pursuit of sericulture. The indifference and absenteeism of many, though by no means all, of the landowners and the generally conservative attitude of the French peasant nevertheless proved difficult barriers to general agrarian reform. By the eighteenth century political feudalism had diminished, to be sure, but its economic and social survivals were still jealously guarded or acquired, and, as in other parts of the Continent, the *franc-alleu* (freehold) was relatively rare. Crops were in constant jeopardy because of the hunting rights of the landowner. And a movement that has been misnamed 'feudal reaction' (i.e. a pronounced effort of landlords to get greater rentals, whether in money, land, or services) had resulted from the long-run rise in food prices. Nevertheless, numerous agricultural societies, as well as the Physiocrats, were studying and advocating reform, and some landed estates were adopting them. Perhaps the most influential French writer on the role of science in agriculture was Henri Louis Duhamel du Monceau, who in 1762 published a two-volume *Eléments d'agriculture* (English translation, 1764). On the whole, the farm and the farmer at all levels were better off.in France than elsewhere on the Continent, if still behind the English, especially on the larger estates. (Pl. 108c.)

Some eighteenth-century English landlords proved exceptionally ready to adopt new mechanical devices for agriculture. The development of agricultural machinery tends to corroborate the general rule that technological improvements come through the slow accumulation of experience and knowledge rather than by startling innovation. The roots of modern agricultural mechanization lie deep in the soil of the Middle Ages and earlier. A heavy plow seems to have supplanted the light Mediterranean plow, at least on large estates, by the end of the thirteenth century. The light plow (*aratrum*) of late Roman times continued in use on small individual holdings whose proprietors could not afford heavy equipment. Obviously not well adapted to deep sub-soil plowing or the breaking up of new land, it was supplemented by the hoe or spade. The heavy plow probably had originated among the Germanic peoples of the upper Danube region. Designed for new, hard land, it eventually became the distinctive plow of the North. It was called *carruca*, from the fact that it had wheels, so that it could be moved easily from place to place. It required at least one yoke of oxen for the lightest plowing and as many as six or eight for breaking new land or turning tough sod. (Pl. 108a.) Thus it became the characteristic plow for the collective farming of the manor or of the later enlarged estates. The heavy plow was equipped with a colter and moldboard for turning sod upside down. The improvement of metal for plowshares augmented its effectiveness, but it remained generally the same from at least the fourteenth century on. In some instances subsequent changes made it less bulky and more efficient both in digging a better furrow and in turning over greater amounts of soil, but in many areas plows of old design remained in use. As often in the history of technology, the complex, newer device was used side by side with the simpler primitive one which it was destined ultimately to replace.

The use of horses instead of oxen became more common with the improvement of the horse collar. Pictures of the hard horse collar applied to the traction of agricultural machines can be found in manuscript miniatures as early as the thirteenth century, and it probably was used much earlier. Several illustrations of it appear in the beautiful portrayals of the activities of the respective months in the Duc de Berri's fifteenth-century book of hours, where a harrow as well as a plow is shown being pulled by a collared horse over a freshly seeded field. (Pl. 108b.) The horse-drawn harrow seems highly mechanized when compared with the bundles of thorns dragged over the soil by the farmers of ancient Rome and medieval Europe to cover seeds and pull weeds. In the sixteenth century in the Netherlands a plow was developed that could readily be pulled by two horses, and this change was rapidly introduced into England.

Other agricultural implements have outlasted the Middle Ages—in a few instances, with some improvement. To break up clods, which were a constant vexation to those who farmed the heavy northern soils, nothing more efficient than a mallet was known until the sixteenth century, when a roller appeared. Scythes, rakes, sheep shears, axes, mattocks, flails, and even scarecrows—in one case made to look like an archer with drawn bow—appear in contemporary paintings. From the late fifteenth century on, the scythe, known to the Romans but having acquired its projecting bar-handle only around the twelfth century, was commonly preferred to the sickle for harvesting grain.

In the eighteenth century Jethro Tull made some simple but effective agricultural innovations. For one thing, he emphasized the importance of pulverizing the earth and planting the seeds in rows so that weeds could be removed while the crop was growing. This process brought a twofold improvement since, when seeds were sown broadcast, the birds ate a large share of them, and Tull's method saved them from the birds as well as the weeds. Before Tull many had used the back-breaking method of sowing known as 'dibbling'—that is, placing the seeds in small holes in the ground made at regular intervals with a pointed implement. All this was done with handtools. Tull devised a seed-box which provided a regular distribution of seed. He then designed a complete wheat drill in which the seed-box was incorporated, and a similar machine for sowing turnips. With these and his 'Ho-Plow' [sic] for inter-row weeding, he took the first important steps in the mechanization of agriculture. His book *The Horse-Hoing* [sic] *Husbandry* (1733) described these machines, maintaining that they were more economical than the customary method of dressing fields with manure. His basically scientific approach by means of controlled experiments added to the strength of his convictions.

Over the centuries crops had been harvested by arduous manual labour. Reaping cereals, for example, meant bringing together numerous workers to cut the crop with sickles or scythes and to gather the stalks into sheaves. The search for labour-saving devices of all kinds became particularly keen in rural England in the late eighteenth century, when the accelerating migration to the cities, rapidly becoming industrialized, intensified the shortage of agricultural labour. The clamour for change in the preparation of cereal crops for market grew, but it went unsatisfied until after our period. Many attempts were made before 1775 to invent a reaper that would relieve harvesters of part of their burden, but little was accomplished; the first practical reaper came only in the nineteenth century. Threshing with the time-honoured hand-flail was both laborious and time-consuming, and as early as 1636 John Christopher van Berg patented a threshing machine. But it was not practical; a more practical one came only in 1788 with the Scot Andrew Meikle's patent.

Horticulture and Gardens

Before the seventeenth century the chief concern of horticulturists had been with herbs and a restricted number of vegetables, fruits, and flowers. The Muslims were especially advanced in horticulture, and their influence, derived not only from Spain directly but also from the observations of Westerners who travelled in the Near East, was particularly discernible in the ornamental gardens that became relatively common during the fourteenth, fifteenth, and sixteenth centuries, especially on the estates of Italian despots and of national monarchs farther north. Universities, such as that of Padua, preferred a more academic type of horticulture, the botanical garden (Chapter XIV).

The opening of the New World and closer contact with Asia brought, as noted in other contexts, an influx of new fruits and flowers to Europe. This expanding acquaintance with nature's beauty was one of the factors that inspired the contemporary interest in nature itself and in naturalism in literature and the arts (see Chapters XI and XII). The beauty of vineyards, orchards, and gardens, though long a familiar part of the European landscape, now received, in keeping with the current *sensibilité*, greater conscious attention. Gentlemen's lives and homes became more closely associated with gardens. The Dutch middle-class merchant and his English counterpart especially began to take pride in gardening, and supervision of garden work became part of their daily activity. The vogue of the tulip in its homeland, the Ottoman Empire, was duplicated in seventeenth-century Holland, and many a still life of the day reveals that, along with other species of flowers, it often graced the Hollander's home.

The garden became part of the architectural lay-out of the well planned residence. The formal garden of the eighteenth century, where even the trees were trimmed into rectangles and spheres (see Chapter XII), was an expression of the *esprit géométrique*. Le Nôtre's park at Versailles with straight avenues, rectangular pools, and Classical statuary was a spectacular example. (Pl. 51b.) Glass greenhouses and hot-houses became available as a result of the successful casting of plate glass in seventeenth-century France. The first of them were erected in the Jardin des Plantes in Paris. Northern Europeans raised in their hot-houses decorative as well as useful plants, such as oranges, lemons, and limes, better known in Spain and other southern countries. The orange won particular favour, supplying fruit for exotic dishes and lending its blossoms and fruit to the ornamentation of wealthy homes and special occasions. Planted in tubs, citrus trees graced the garden in the summer and were removed for the winter to the orangery (a special and sometimes architecturally substantial greenhouse).

. . . . The golden boast
Of Portugal and western India there,
The ruddier orange and the paler lime,
Peep through their polished foliage at the storm.[16]

The concept of the garden began to change in the latter half of the eighteenth century as the cult of nature and the influence of the Chinese garden contributed to a new vogue. Now the garden was made to conform to untrimmed nature. Trees and shrubs were allowed to thrive in untrained forms. Bridges, ponds, and garden houses were studiously placed so as to take on an air of carelessness, which was thought characteristic of Chinese gardens and which the English especially sought to cultivate. Garden houses began to look more like Chinese pagodas than Greek temples, and ponds and groves were no longer fitted into precise rectangles and circles.

Improvements in Animal Husbandry

One of the serious problems of the medieval farmer had been keeping his domestic animals alive during the winter cold. Hay had long been known as a fodder through the pastureless season, but the hay crop was rarely abundant enough anywhere for all the summer's livestock. Many of the cattle and swine were more or less mercifully butchered and sold or salted down for meat in order to keep them from starvation. By the fifteenth century additional fodders had been added—oats, vetches, and even peas and beans, but more costly foods like these were rarely fed to stock other than horses. With the improving standard of living, the demand for wool, hides, and meats increased and with improving agricultural implements the demand for horses, but increased demand could now be met with increased supply. The concurrently expanding knowledge of plants helped to introduce new fodders that enabled the husbandman to keep more of his animals alive throughout the winter. Clover, turnips, maize, and potatoes not only made available more work animals, at the same time strengthening their draft power, but also could be sold to the butcher when converted into added poundage of meat rather than to the grocer when marketed as bushels of vegetables, and so as fodder such crops were probably more profitable than as vegetables.

Progress in animal husbandry came not alone from the introduction of better and more plentiful fodder but also from a more systematic application of genetic principles. Sheep were in the eighteenth century being successfully selected and crossbred so as to produce a better quality and a more abundant yield of wool. Specialization led to the raising of better riding horses, race-horses, carriage-horses, and draft-horses and better sheep dogs, hunting dogs, watch-dogs, and pet dogs. Breeders in certain regions developed cattle better fitted for dairy needs and in others better fitted for butchering; or, if a breeder raised both kinds at the same time, he kept the two separate. Poultry breeders did likewise for egg-laying and fowl, though poultry did not become a general market product until the nineteenth century. Selection in the raising of pigs likewise improved both their quantity and quality. Thus new sources of meat were substituted for the decreasing supply of game, which hunting laws and the costliness of hunting equipment would have made a monopoly of the landlords but for the prevalence of poaching. Dairy products, markedly superior to the products of earlier generations, came to form an important component of the average man's diet. Bee-keeping, on the other hand, which had long provided the principal article used for sweetening, experienced a general decline as American cane sugar displaced honey. With the growing proficiency of fire-arms, dogs, and horses, falconry as a method of hunting also declined. On the whole, animal husbandry was rapidly becoming the more profitable of the two major agricultural pursuits.

One of the major obstacles to progress in animal breeding had been the common pasture. As a cause of promiscuity the common pasture had already been partly eliminated by the enclosure system and the controls exercised upon the animals on the larger estates. Segregated pasturage also contributed to the improvement of timber, since indiscriminate pasturing of flocks, especially sheep, in woodlands led to the ruin of trees and the destruction of seed and saplings. Segregated and cultivated—even manured—forests eventually became more common.

Before the nineteenth century the advance in flocks and herds may have been due less to selective breeding than to better feeding. In the Netherlands, for example, the lands recovered from the sea, which produced a lush grass, were used as early as the sixteenth century for fattening lean cattle from inland regions. Likewise, it was found, cattle flourished on the grass of the English fenlands and gave more milk than those fed on leaves and stubble. The selective breeding of sheep was especially difficult, and hence probably less profitable than better feeding, for even though rams of special breeds often were imported, the large flocks and their wide pasturing range prevented effective control.

Sheep flourished in hilly or waste regions all the way from Lincolnshire to Andalusia, among them several fairly pure breeds—the big-tailed Syrian, the small-tailed Arab, the merinos of Spain, and the Cotswolds of south England. In the twelfth century merino sheep were introduced by the Moors from north Africa into Spain, where they dominated agriculture during the centuries of the reconquest and numbered almost three and a half million in 1526. The sheep drivers' guild, the Mesta—given special royal privileges from the late thirteenth century onward—had the right to move their flocks from place to place, grazing as they went. Their privileges doubtless encouraged Spanish wool production but, along with an apparent change of climate in Spain in the sixteenth century, had a destructive influence on farming and forestry. The sheepwalks were a considerable factor of Spain's agricultural backwardness in that and the succeeding century;[14] the conservatism of the Spanish peasant (*'Asi lo hicieron mis padres'*) did the rest. Nevertheless, the Spanish merino produced an excellent, heavy wool and was sought for breeding purposes in other countries.

Selective Breeding of Domestic Animals

Throughout the Middle Ages the horse had been a favourite among royalty and nobility, and its breeding, feeding, training, and welfare had been a paramount interest. Blooded stallions were imported, especially Arabian strains from the Muslim areas of southern Spain, for tournaments and races. At one time in the fourteenth century a French king had two stallions, twenty-eight brood mares, and twenty-eight colts on one of his stud farms. In the fifteenth century English stables were breeding fine horses and exporting them to the Continent. Numerous compendia of the late Middle Ages, well illustrated with excellent specimens of horseflesh, earnestly and extensively discuss cautery, surgery, and medicines for ailing steeds. Almost as numerous were the works on the care of dogs and falcons. The veterinary seems to have had no less prestige than the surgeon, when indeed the same man was not both. Anthrax was the veterinary's major enemy; epidemics in 1714 and 1744 led to the establishment of the first veterinary school in France, founded at Lyons in 1762.

By the sixteenth century the nations of western Europe had begun more systematic breeding of draught horses. The need for systematic breeding became more cogent as horses changed from bearer of knights in armour to sources of power for machines and implements. Breeding was based on no science of genetics, which was to remain unformulated for another three hundred years or more, but rather on common-sense selection of good examples of the type of animal needed as sires. Increasing and improving quantities of fodder throughout the succeeding centuries enabled horses to grow in size and prosper otherwise as well.

Selective breeding of sheep and cattle was introduced much later than that of horses. Robert Bakewell, an eighteenth-century English gentleman farmer, was particularly prominent in promoting the selective breeding of sheep. As a result, they grew in size and stamina, providing (to say nothing of wool) a much greater yield of meat per animal, all the more desirable in a period when undomesticated animals such as the hare and the deer were beginning to disappear before the inroads of urbanization and mechanization and when hunting was becoming a sport reserved for aristocrats rather than a method of food production. What was learned of horses and sheep was applied also to cattle as enclosures increased in number and common pasture diminished. Wherever adequate pasturage and fodder were available, an augmented production of milk and dairy products followed. The Swiss and the Dutch were the trailblazers in this field, taking advantage of almost every piece of land available in their little countries.

MEDICAL PRACTICE, PUBLIC HEALTH, AND SANITATION

As in several other lines of knowledge, the Islamic world and Orthodox Christendom were superior to the Christian West in medical practice as well as theory until late in the Middle Ages. Although by the fourteenth century Islamic civilization had passed its zenith, and in the fifteenth and sixteenth centuries western Europe forged ahead at an accelerating pace, in medicine much of Western practice was still based on the work of versatile Muslim scholar-physicians of earlier times, who in turn had borrowed from Greco-Roman and Indian medicine.

Muslim as well as Christian physicians, with some notable exceptions, long relied heavily on astrology and alchemy. They regarded certain days as lucky and certain others as unlucky—'Egyptian'—for purging, blood-letting, and the like. Since each of the planets was regarded as having benevolent or malevolent effects on critical events varying according to its position at the moment, the twelve signs of the zodiac were considered critical in determining health and sickness, and so illustrations of zodiac-men were frequently provided in medical manuscripts. Royal (that is, the best) physicians often were enthusiastic and expert alchemists, while pharmacists made practical use of alchemy in compounding medicines. The 'philosopher's elixir', if ever found and perfected, was expected to work miracles in the balance of the humours in the human body.

Hospitals, Sanitation, and Disease

Before the seventeenth century Europe's hospitals were generally run by one or another of the religious orders that cared for the sick, and they were not commonly used for teaching purposes. By the eighteenth century they were looked upon as institutions not merely for the care but also for the cure of the sick. Physicians and surgeons were now generally trained by the clinical method (see Chapter XVI), and new hospitals were built not only by the charitable orders but also by the state or by private philanthropy. The advantage, however, of improved training of physicians in the hospitals, old or new, was offset by the tremendous lack of knowledge of pathogenic bacteria. All beds were generally in one large dormitory separated only by curtains. Eighteenth-century hospitals were not always dirty, though doubtless some were, and eighteenth-century physicians or nurses were not necessarily callous. Yet those sick with contagious diseases were not carefully isolated, and in crowded hospitals several persons sometimes had to share the same bed. Nevertheless, quarantine was practised as a means of preventing the spread of such diseases as seemed to infect the healthy upon bodily contact with the diseased. Without understanding the role of the germ in disease, hospitals of that day isolated in pest-houses the unfortunate persons who had plague, leprosy, and other mutilating or killing diseases known or thought to be contagious or infectious.

The hospital too often meant a place for the sick poor to go to die, for hospital mortality rates were alarming. Yet hospitals that were better than the average medieval Hôtel-Dieu were founded in the fifteenth and sixteenth centuries. We have already encountered that of Catherine of Genoa (Chapter IV), and Italy could boast others at Florence, Milan, and elsewhere. Those at Beaune and Würzburg were also deservedly famous. In the seventeenth and eighteenth centuries hospitals were more and more regularly being adapted in architecture to medical needs as understood at the time. (Pl. 94a, b.)

The establishment and improvement of hospitals fitted well into the humanitarian trend of the eighteenth century. The crowding of cities compelled greater attention to public health, to which not only church and state but also private philanthropy now responded. Philanthropists built great hospitals, that of the Necker family in Paris being one of the finest. Lyons and Vienna erected, largely from government funds, big hospitals that became models of the latest methods. Several maternity hospitals went up in England, and clinics arranged to take care of the poor who were sick but not sick enough to go to a hospital. Lunatic asylums became more numerous. The notorious Bedlam of England goes back to 1400, and Valencia,

Zaragosa, and other Spanish cities had madhouses in the fifteenth century, but since insanity was not understood, the psychiatric treatment they afforded was little more effective than before. Enlightened rulers also encouraged sewage systems, water systems, and street-lighting. Progress in public health measures remained slow, however, until the nineteenth century.

Inoculation against smallpox (i.e. the superficial insertion of the virus in the hope of producing a mild attack and so securing future immunity) was timidly practised by some. The Turks, probably having borrowed it directly or indirectly from China, used it with a certain degree of success, and Dr Zabdiel Boylston of Massachusetts, having learned of the Turkish process, tried it on his patients in 1721–22. An English physician, Edward Jenner, began in 1775 the observations that led him in 1796 to test his theory of vaccination (inoculation with the cowpox 'vaccine'). The medical radicalism of those who advocated inoculation stood out against the contemporary background of medical conservatism. The prevalent theory of disease (see Chapter XIII) still was that it was caused by imbalance of the four bodily humours. Blood-letting persisted, though generally for specific local purposes rather than for the cure of general ailments, and cauterization was an approved method of treating wounds.

The sixteenth-century pandemic of syphilis added another costly plague to the Black Death of the fourteenth century, and both diseases were to claim their toll in later centuries. Yet, though Europe's epidemics have remained an intermittent horror, constantly improving methods of sanitation since the seventeenth century have confined their virulence. As early as the reign of Phillippe Augustus in the thirteenth century the streets of Paris had been paved, and attempts had since been made to keep them clean. No adequate means, however, of removing rubbish and garbage was provided. Paris, for all its dirt, was one of the cleanest cities of Europe. John Graunt in his *Observations* (1662) complained that 'the Fumes, Steams, and Stenches of London do so medicate and impregnate the Air about it, that it becomes capable of little more [effect upon the death rate]'. As late as the eighteenth century a passer-by on a city street constantly had to look out for refuse and slops thrown from windows as well as for robbers and cut-throats at unlighted corners.

The physician's inability to distinguish accurately between diseases made them all the more awful and mysterious. From the sixteenth century on, however, differentiation among diseases gradually became more precise and aided the study of epidemics. Guillaume de Baillou (1538–1616) described whooping cough, used the word *rheumatism* in the modern sense, and appears to have been the first since Hippocrates to distinguish between rheumatism and gout. In England Thomas Sydenham (1624–89), having studied the natural history of disease, published his classic *Methodus Curandi Febres* (1666) and made such significant contributions to the understanding of epidemics and specifics (especially laudanum and quinine) as well as to clinical medicine in general that he has been called the 'English Hippocrates'. Rickets, which by 1700 had an appalling incidence, was also recognized, but during the eighteenth century its ravages seemed to decrease, though probably not through any medical knowledge so much as through the improvement in diet. The eighteenth-century consumer knew nothing about vitamins, but empirical knowledge of the cure for disease caused by vitamin deficiency went back to the early years of the Dutch East Indies Company, which from about 1600 provided vegetable gardens at several ports of call. The increased consumption of dairy products, meat, fruits, vegetables, and, toward the end of the eighteenth century, cod liver oil, reduced the incidence of scurvy, rickets, and allied diseases.[18] On Cook's second voyage (1772–75) he lost from disease only one out of 118 men (as compared to 30 out of 85 on his first voyage, mostly from disease), primarily because he took certain anti-scorbutic precautions. Perhaps the most feared disease of all, smallpox, thanks to the introduction of inoculation and vaccination, was also brought under better control. From Jenner's discovery eventually developed the modern method of immunization against disease.

Some dubious theories of disease developed in the seventeenth or eighteenth century. One of them was that of the iatrophysicians described in Chapter XIV. A most striking theory arose in connection with the new and promising treatment of the ague (malaria and related fevers). Cinchona bark was introduced from the New World by the Jesuits in the seventeenth century and quickly justified its virtue as a 'specific' (see Chapter XIII). The quinine contained in this bark not only gave great relief to many sufferers in Europe but also brought great wealth to the Jesuits, who had a virtual monopoly of it. After its introduction, unfortunately all fevers were sometimes divided into those that would and those that would not respond to it, leading to some misuses of the drug and possibly also to some missteps in medical research.

Surgery, Anatomy, and Dentistry

Surgery developed slowly in the West but more rapidly around 1300 than before. In the early fourteenth century Mundino and other dissectors flourished in and about Bologna (see Chapter XIII). Although Mundino was a capable surgeon (he is thought to have done most of his own dissecting), his interest was in anatomy rather than surgery. His treatise on anatomy was a veritable manual of dissection. Surgery as a substantive art owed more to his contemporaries Lanfranc of Milan (d. 1315) and Henri de Mondeville (c. 1275–1325). Lanfranc, while teaching and practising in France, introduced better methods of ligature and suture. Mondeville, a French royal army surgeon, was still more advanced in his surgical methods but contempor-aneously less known and influential.

Mondeville's *Cyrurgia*—also published in French translation—was the first treatise devoted to surgery by a Frenchman. It was a noteworthy compilation, derived in part from personal experience, though relying heavily on the traditional works of Classical authors such as Galen, of Muslims such as Avicenna, and, to a lesser extent, of Western predecessors such as Lanfranc. The author's genuis lay in his confidence in the possibility of surgical progress through empirical tests. He stressed a new method of treating trauma—dressing a wound with warm wine, closing it to the air (to prevent infection and suppuration if possible), and healing the closed wound by fomentations. In cases of amputation he bound the arteries—a practice known from ancient times and used long before Ambroise Paré (c. 1510–90), to whom it has often been attributed. With a surprisingly modern concern over infection, Mondeville urged that instruments be kept clean.

Mondeville's influence was eclipsed by less progressive but better known surgeons of the next generation. His works lay unused while those of Lanfranc, Guy de Chauliac (c. 1290–1368), and the Englishman John of Arderne (1307–77) circulated widely, often in lavishly illustrated manuscripts. The last was an army doctor who ventured to operate on anal fistulas and who anticipated Ambroise Paré in his practical use of medication for wounds. Another able surgeon whose influence was contemporaneously eclipsed was Jan Yperman (c. 1275–1330), little known outside his own vicinity of Ypres. As a surgeon he stressed, among other things, the use of anaesthetics—e.g. the soporific sponge (an inhalant of mandrake, henbane, hemlock, and poppy), rarely used in the West although it seems to have been known to the Muslims early and was mentioned in an Italian antidotary of about 1100. We have already noted the two-century lag in anatomy before the sixteenth century (Chapter XIII). The neglect of surgical innovations like Yperman's on the part of later royal, papal, and military surgeons made the applications of similar methods by sixteenth-century surgeons appear so new as to be regarded an epoch-making discoveries, but in fact the late fourteenth century and most of the fifteenth century were relatively unproductive in surgery compared with the thirteenth and early fourteenth centuries.

In the sixteenth century, another upsurge of achievement similar to that of the thirteenth century followed the intervening plateau. Paracelsus, Vesalius, Fallopius, and other Italian-trained surgeons and anatomists contributed greatly to the advance of surgical technique by their detailed knowledge of anatomy, and Ambroise Paré, a Frenchman, made perhaps the greatest contributions. Trained as an apprentice to a barber-surgeon in Paris, he became a surgeon with the armies of Francis I in Italy. He learned to substitute soothing salves for searing oil in treating gunshot wounds and published a book (in French, not Latin) on the subject. He then studied anatomy at Paris and eventually published a book on that subject, too. He practised some comparatively modern methods of obstetrics (see below). And—his most eminent service—he made familiar the use of ligatures instead of cautery for controlling arterial bleeding in amputations. Yet, for all his prestige, his innovations (sometimes merely the renewal of old practices) were nearly always received with suspicion and sometimes rejected outright by conservative physicians and surgeons, and the sixteenth century ended without revolutionary betterment of general surgical practice.

The advance of surgery, along with that of dissection, is partly dependent on the quality of surgical instruments. The equipment at leading medical centres was far from primitive around 1300. The surgeon-physicians of Bologna and vicinity such as William of Saliceto, Lanfranc, and Mundino, the group at Montpellier such as Mondeville and Guy de Chauliac, and John of Arderne in England had at their disposal imposing assortments of surgical instruments. Much of their apparatus was modelled upon the amazingly varied types used by the Muslims during the Middle Ages. The surgical works of the fourteenth and fifteenth centuries contain hundreds of illustrations of the paraphernalia available for various types of operations. Special instruments were used for eye surgery and for the fistula operation described and pictured in John of Arderne's treatises. *Specula* for gynaeco-logical observations and traction machines were also known. After the era of Mundino, Mondeville, and Arderne, little advance was made until the late sixteenth century, when an impressive number of precision instruments were put to use. Most of them were better adapted to the basic sciences of medicine—anatomy and physiology—than to surgery, and their use in those sciences help to explain how during the sixteenth and seventeenth centuries detailed anatomical sketches could be drawn. (Pl. 93a, b, c.)

The paucity of surgical triumphs in the seventeenth century is all the more glaring if contrasted with the glorious achievements of contemporary anatomy (see Chapter XIV). Individual surgeons, however, showed great ability—Jacques de Beaulieu in lateral incisions for stone (1697), Nicolas de Blegny in the use of the elastic truss for hernia (*c.* 1676), Hendrik van Roonhuyze in caesarean sections (*c.* 1663), and several surgeons of the Hôtel Dieu, the ancient hospital of Paris, in various methods of checking haemorrhage. Conspicuous efforts were made to formulate the surgery of the day into a systematic body of knowledge. Wilhelm Fabry (1560–1624) produced a lengthy and perhaps the best of the early collections of case records; Richard Wiseman (1622–76) in *Several Chirurgicall Treatises* (1672) described some of his own skilful operations; and Gabriel Le Clerc compiled *La chirurgie complète* (1692), a sort of textbook of surgery that went into eighteen editions.

French surgery set the standard during most of this period, but in the eighteenth century the work of an Englishman, John Hunter (1728–93), stands out. Together with his brother William (see below), he founded one of the famous institutions that eventually transformed the training of medical men—the museums of anatomy and pathology. Some of the chief surgical achievements of our period occurred in the field of dentistry, and not least among Hunter's several contributions to the study of bone and blood was that he helped to provide the basis of a scientific dentistry. The wandering tooth-extracter, made eternally notorious by contemporary artists, was still familiar in Hunter's day, although Pierre Fauchard early in the century had sought a professional standing for dentists. In 1728 Fauchard presented, among other dental subjects, the first systematic treatise on orthodontia in *Le chirurgien dentiste;* he himself used porcelain and gold for artificial teeth. Philipp Pfaff wrote a textbook of dentistry in 1756—*Abhandlung von den Zähnen.* Perhaps the most important single work, however, in the history of dentistry was Hunter's *Natural History of the Human Teeth* (in two parts, 1771 and 1778). It was one of his several written masterpieces which, along with his practical surgery and physiological observations, helped to transform surgery from a skilled craft to a branch of scientific medicine.

Innovations in Pharmacy

By 1300 the West had borrowed from Antiquity and the East an ample pharmacopoeia, and during the next three centuries gamboge gum from Cambodia (as a purgative) and guaiacum from America (as a treatment for syphilis) were the only significant additions to it. Alchemy contributed little basic improvement in the technique of compounding. Most of the metallic compounds of Paracelsus and his iatrochemist followers made no great contribution to pharmaceutics, and they may have killed more patients than they cured. Medieval medicines were largely herbal and generally less harmful than the mercurial concoctions of the sixteenth century.

After 1600 the *materia medica* of Europe expanded and improved. Experiments with mercury eventually led the iatrochemical school to the best way to treat syphilis available before the nineteenth century. In the seventeenth century the introduction of quinine promoted the confidence in specifics, and other medicaments from overseas supplemented the pharmacological list. Glauber's discovery of the salt that bears his name and Grew's of Epsom salt provided innocuous aperients. In the next century, Anton Störck (1731–1803) of Vienna studied the effect of hemlock, meadow-saffron, aconite, stramonium (Jimson weed), and henbane on himself and his patients. The full developments of pharmacology, however, had to wait until chemistry was more fully established as a science.

Advances in Obstetrics

Until the eighteenth century the attendance of a male physician at childbirth was considered indecent by most women, and physicians for their part frowned as much on obstetrics as they did on surgery, considering both beneath their dignity. Obstetrics therefore long remained the monopoly of the midwife, who was sometimes a skilled empiric but more often a clumsy, ignorant woman. Such practices as placing vulture feathers under an expectant mother's body or holding a sprig of herb to the vaginal orifice in order to hasten delivery, described in Classical treatises, still found mention in manuscripts of the fourteenth and fifteenth centuries. In the sixteenth century Paré, humble surgeon that he was, engaged in obstetrics and, among other useful services, made the suggestion that, in certain cases of abnormal delivery, the child should be turned in the mother's womb before delivery. Subsequently, serious works on obstetrics were published by physicians, although chiefly for the use of women attendants; Hendrik van Deventer's *Novum Lumen* (1701) was perhaps the best of them for a long time. In the late seventeenth century in France some innovations were ventured, the chief being the introduction of forceps for delivery, but forceps remained the secret of a family of male obstetricians for generations. The skill of the Dutch surgeon Van Roonhuyze with caesarean sections has already been mentioned.

Only in the late eighteenth century did objection to 'male midwives' begin to die down. Several French *accoucheurs* won approval in high places, and when William Hunter, the elder brother of John Hunter and also an esteemed anatomist and surgeon, became the leading obstetrician of London, another stronghold of social and professional prejudice collapsed. Even so until in the nineteenth century the importance of clinical sterilization was recognized, mere lack of cleanliness in large part continued to account for the high death rate of puerperal fever.

Quackery despite Genuine Advances

The advance of knowledge in physiology and pharmacology had less effect upon the medical profession as a craft than might be surmised. The physician looked askance at the pretensions of the apothecary and others to prescribe to the sick or to teach new methods. Much of his suspicion was justifiable, for charlatans abounded, and ignorance of the origin of disease made the credulous sick an easy prey.

Though alchemists and astrologers had by the eighteenth century faded out in the field of medicine, quackery retained a firm hold. With the plethora of nostrums it might even have grown worse, particularly in England where 'patent' or 'proprietary' medicines were protected by law. The credulous and the desperate have in all ages fallen dupes to downright charlatans or to half-learned if well-meaning zealots. A poster proclaimed to eighteenth-century London: 'Doctor Frederick . . . undertakes to Cure the Gout, and Rheumatism, without any return. . . . Likewise, Cures the yellow Jaundice, Stitching in the Side. He likewise Cures any Body who is bit by a Mad Dog. . . . No cure No Pay.'[19] Doctor Frederick was not so well known in the annals of magic as his contemporaries Frederick Anton Mesmer (1733–1815) and 'Count Allessandro Cagliostro' (1743–95), whose real name was Giuseppi Balsamo. But zealots like Mesmer must not be confused with quacks like Cagliostro. Mesmer, who published his theory of 'animal magnetism' in 1775, was an over-enthusiastic pioneer in the study of hypnotism, which he did not fully understand. Cagliostro was a charlatan taking advantage of the prevailing enthusiasm for freemasonry and other occult forces to make money out of misery, ignorance, and credulity. Quacks as well as some honest men also worked with electricity as a cure of disease, but with no significant results. Perhaps the most notorious of the more serious workers in this field was Dr Jean-Paul Marat (1743–93), the future 'Friend of the People'.

Revolution would perhaps be more a misnomer if used to describe the advances in medicine during the period between 1300 and 1775 than if used, as it more frequently is, to describe those in abstract science, industry, commerce, and agriculture. Much more revolutionary ideas were yet to come in the treatment of disease. Nevertheless, the advances in the field during these centuries were crucial. Not only did physiology move somewhat toward the discovery of the germ theory but also the apothecary, the obstetrician, and the surgeon began to occupy a respected professional status (see Chapter XVI). Physicians came to be less exercised about the teachings of rival Classical schools and more about the findings of recent research in anatomy, physiology, and pharmacology. Until the nineteenth century, however, medicine remained essentially empirical.

TECHNOLOGY AND THE STATE

The political implications of economic and social changes during our period have already been indicated in the first chapter, where some of those changes were attributed in part at least to scientific and technological factors. Here we shall be concerned more exclusively with the role played by technology in strengthening the modern state.

Science, Technology, and the Secular Society and State

The growth of science fairly closely coincided with the growth of the nation-state in the West. These developments combined with several others that we have examined to help weaken the hold of the organized churches on men's minds so that the Christian ethic no longer guided men's thoughts at the end of our period so prescriptively as it once had. By the eighteenth century, a secular ideology, drawn chiefly from the every day empirical world and holding man accountable to rules derived from Nature rather than from God, had come to share dominion with the Christian tradition. For those who held the secular view, Nature was still dependent upon God, to be sure, but less as First and Final Cause than as daily provider and regulator. For many (but certainly not most) educated persons God was the Great Clock-maker, who having made and wound up His clock, let it run its own course, subject to its own limitations.

In proportion as such a view of God took root, the church lost prestige. That view challenged the church's hold as a link (whether necessary, as in the Roman creed, or merely desirable, as in Protestantism) with the Father who gave man his daily bread and forgave his trespasses or sins. Rather, men tended now to turn toward the state for welfare and regulation of conduct, and—slowly at first, more rapidly later—the state took over many of the church's non-religious obligations. Charity and virtue became civic as well as religious duties, though not yet so conspicuously in our period as after the revolutions of the eighteenth century. And so to the forces that were considered worthy of royal or administrative patronage (because they might enhance state power, help to attain civic welfare, or promote good civic conduct) was added a secular kind of spiritual welfare. The same authority that undermined feudal power, that gave merchants charters for trading companies, that protected inventive men by laws of patent, that built canals, policed roads, and granted towns special privileges also tried to make church hierarchies into departments of state. The new merchant and industrial classes at times aligned themselves with the rulers against the older and higher orders of society to promote these secular purposes.

Coincident with these political changes, a new intellectual tone matured out of the scientific discoveries of the seventeenth century and after. The medieval Schoolman had assumed that man's knowledge and ability was finite, reaching toward but never grasping the plenitude of God's knowledge and providence. The Scholastic was interested in comprehending the universe in a context related particularly to God's conduct toward man and in adjusting reason to faith. If he could accomplish those ends (though he never dared to hope that he could every wholly do so) he thought he would understand all that it was necessary for him to understand. Seventeenth-century science was also interested in the comprehension of the divine purpose, and among the new scientists many, probably most, were content to look upon the Book of Nature as a material manifestation of the Will of God. But the new science rarely assumed that the acquisition of knowledge had finite limits, and it was interested in knowledge not only for the better understanding of the ways of God but for prediction and control of the ways of Nature and Man as well.

Control, some dared to hope, would become available through a proper alliance between technology and science. Leonardo da Vinci made some grandiose (if private) speculations, and Francis Bacon not only proclaimed the aim of bringing knowledge from Heaven to earth, from the speculative to the experimental, but also described the inductive method by which that transfer might be effected. Yet the transfer could not come by proclamation alone. Contemporary artisans and craftsmen could provide only a limited amount of the labour and mechanical skill needed to implement Leonardo's designs and Bacon's words. The manufacture of complex mechanical devices needed to be rationalized into standardized and costly techniques. Such a rationalization, however, required, in addition to greater theoretical knowledge, the investment of large capital sums and the employment of many hands, and so in most instances it had to wait until a later era for the necessary capital and labour pools.

In other instances, however, contemporaneous developments in politics and economics helped to answer these needs The rulers' quest for absolutism led them to provide the economic wherewithal as well as other means needed to achieve their ends. The nobility, no longer occupied with feudal warfare and knightly chivalry, looked for new interests, new sources of power, and new objects of patronage and frequently found them in economic enterprise. The rise of a merchant class and the declining prestige of the clergy induced society to respect the concept of free trade and profit rather than church scruples about money transactions. The growth of absolutism through the alliance of kings with the middle class against the nobility, the more pronounced control of church and feudality by national governments, and the growth of the capitalistic spirit through the spreading desire (not to mention the spreading approval of the desire) to invest money in order to make more money—all these may be interrelated somehow with the growth of science, although the exact relationship among them remains subject to controversy. Entrepreneurs, merchants, and industrialists certainly encouraged the sciences and technology, and the quantitative spirit of mathematics and science seems in its turn to have been at least favourable, if not conducive, to the capitalistic spirit.[20]

For their part the rulers encouraged science largely because of their hope for dynastic advantage from it The monarch's power in the time of the so-called absolute monarchy was in fact weak in comparison with that of the authoritarian dictator of subsequent times, not merely because the former was likely to feel more fully bound by history and family tradition but partly also because the technological means of implementing his authority were relatively limited. Huge areas of public activity were still inadequately supervised or wholly untouched by centralized administration, generally because of technical inadequacies; police forces, public health facilities, vital statistics, public utilities, disaster relief, social insurance, universal education, and several other responsibilities of the modern state, if not totally unknown to the central governments of the eighteenth century, were exceptional, unofficial, or local, and in any case inadequate. The problems of communication and transportation alone (and there were others) made co-ordination of such activities in the royal capital difficult. Hence no ruler could afford to be indifferent to proposals for speeding up transportation (of troops as well as goods) and production (of revenue as well as commodities), since a better method of determining longitude at sea, the drawing of more accurate charts and maps, the improvement of vehicular techniques and roads, the development of new metallurgical methods, or the invention of industrial and agricultural machines might enhance the centralization and autarky of the state and the power of the ruler. For all their patronage of science, however, rulers entertained the hope of finding new basic truths usually only as a secondary matter. The work of Newton, not immediately utilitarian, was not directly supported by the royal government during his lifetime, for what good was it? If he was buried in Westminster Abbey, it was because his name was publicly adulated. Scientific societies, to be sure, were encouraged by various rulers, but primarily to burnish the royal patrons' glory and lift the prestige and self-sufficiency of their states. In France when Louvois succeeded Colbert as protector of the Academy of Sciences he deliberately pushed French scientists toward practical work. (Pl.88a.) Perhaps it was no coincidence that during Louvois's protectorship (1683–99) French contributions to theoretical science were practically negligible.

Nevertheless, whatever their ulterior motives, governments, whether absolute or limited, generally aided nascent science and technology both directly and indirectly. They established royal porcelain and tapestry works. They patronized scientists and scientific academies. They prompted, financed, and rewarded inventors of practical instruments. In paternalistic states like Prussia and France state support was more evident than in parliamentary England. Although the English king granted patents and Parliament offered bounties to many (the collection of which, however, was sometimes not easy), the failure of the Stuart kings to establish an absolutism and the consequent growth of the power of Parliament led to restrictions upon royal expenditures and upon the granting of monopolies. In compensation, private persons in England assumed a greater share of the burden of promoting science and the arts.

Contemporary scientists were well aware of the importance of substantial support for their work and the government's mercantilist motives in providing it. Advocating the proposal to establish a scientific society in Vienna, Leibniz once wrote to Prince Eugene of Savoy:

'To perfect the arts, industries, agriculture, . . . architecture, the chorographic description of countries, the work of mines, as well as to keep the needy employed [and] to encourage inventors and entrepreneurs—in short, for whatever may affect the economy and machinery of the civil and military order, it is necessary to have observatories, laboratories, herbal gardens, menageries, collections of natural and artificial rarities, [and] a yearly physicomedical account of the reports and observations that every paid doctor will be obliged to provide.'[21]

The value of science and technology as tools of government was fully appreciated by Louis XIV, Peter the Great, Frederick the Great, and other 'enlightened despots'. Under the systematic mercantilism of Louis XIV's Colbert, the state exhibited exceptional vigour in building canals, dredging rivers, improving harbours, draining swamps, stimulating agriculture, granting bounties for the production of war material, and patronizing the arts, crafts, and sciences—primarily in order to improve communication and transport, increase production, raise revenue, assure national self-sufficiency, and add to the luster of the French crown at home and abroad. (Pl. 58b.)

The State as a Source of Social Services

The impact of technology upon government came not only from its direct application to civil and military problems but also from the more subtle effects of its application to the public warfare. The advance of technology combined with other contemporaneous developments to convert the typical European from a Christian who was incidentally a subject of his sovereign into a subject who was incidentally a Christian. For a few this conversion must have been a conscious process; for most it probably went on unperceived; and for many it may not have happened at all. *In toto*, however, it was a major change that helped to distinguish the modern mode of thought from one that had previously been common to all the world. The change is explained largely by a point already made: Europeans were likely now to look less to Providence for direct intervention in their affairs and more to political and social agencies. Although the church remained important as such an agency, by the close of our period the government had already superseded it for some social services and was assuming a larger role in all. This displacement of a force based largely upon other-worldly faith by one based largely on this worldly power was both a major sign and a cause of the secularization of European thought and manners. The number still was legion of those whose conduct was guided by the church or, at least, the servants of the church, which threatened punishment or promised reward in the hereafter, but it was diminishing proportionally to the number of those whose conduct was guided by the government or, at least, the servants of the government, which commanded bayonets and, in addition, held out the hope of health and happiness in the here-and-now. And more and more frequently men of science, either directly or indirectly, entered the service of governments.

Governmental services to individuals or communities depend in large part on the stability and strength of the central authorities, for the degree of co-operation to be expected from local, church, and voluntary agencies in the separate communities may be expected to vary with the political situation. Medieval communities, often governed indirectly by a remote, decentralized authority, were, we have observed, woefully lacking in all except the most basic governmental services. Roads and streets were often bad, dirty, poorly lighted, and poorly policed. A rare manor house might be blessed with running water, and a fortunate city might be supplied by an old Roman aqueduct, but communities had normally to depend on local wells, neighbouring streams, and water carriers. Hospitals, almshouses, and schools were generally run by the clergy, and though they were served as a rule by conscientious religious who usually were no more inefficient than the approved methods of the day obliged them to be, their guiding principle was charity rather than social service, and their ultimate goal was care rather than cure or indoctrination rather than education. Medieval governments frequently lacked not only the information requisite to adequate economic planning but even the means to acquire or interpret it.

In contrast, eighteenth-century governments generally were stronger, and a major part of their strength was a product of technological improvements. Engineering and invention had helped to provide more complete records as well as better waterways, bridges, and roads. They contributed to more rapid communication and transportation, more systematic bookkeeping and revenue collection, more effectual police and military movements, a more coordinated officialdom, and other means of efficient centralization. During our period governments advanced far on the way toward modern administrative methods.

Yet an eighteenth-century absolute government was in all probability still considerably less centralized than a twentieth-century bureaucracy. In pre-Revolutionary France, Europe's centralized monarchy *par excellence*, problems of communication and transport were so unmanageable that local government was largely guided by custom rather than royal decree. Until the Revolution the Bourbon monarchs collected some of their revenue through tax-farming and some through a revenue system that, while radiating from Paris, was discriminatory, respecting old provincial boundaries, local privileges, and class exemptions. The government of England, less complicated because of a longer common and insular political experience, still put the chief responsibility for day-to-day law and order in the hands of justices of the peace and other local authorities. The government of the Holy Roman Empire was distributed among hundreds of local units, some of them undistinguishable from *opéra bouffe* principalities.

During our period, however, European governments to a limited extent adopted the social and political pattern that has become familiar today. The point need not be belaboured again, but a few additional examples of governmental services may underline it. As the advance in medical knowledge indicated to authorities the advantage or proper precautions against plague, quarantine was enforced by municipal or other authorities. London, Toledo, Augsburg, Paris, and several other European cities made great strides in the establishment of waterworks for their growing populations, though without being able to guarantee the purity of the water. Richelieu, Sully, and Colbert had laid down so good a pattern for France that it had the best system of roads, coaches, and couriers in Europe, with the anticipated improvement in the efficiency of government functions. England was not far behind. East of the Rhine and Danube Rivers, however, road systems were bad indeed, travel was more hazardous and uncommon, and government officials (though not for that reason alone) generally less effective.

Warfare as 'Military Science'

During our period national governments were more interested in conducting war than they were to be again (except for the Revolutionary and Napoleonic era) until the twentieth century. Europe in the 1600s had only seven calendar years of general international peace; the preceding and the next century had little better records. With the introduction and step-by-step improvement of firearms, the techniques and strategy of warfare changed markedly. The feudal lord who carried on war on his own income for private purposes had become an anachronism. For that and other reasons which have been sketched elsewhere, at the same time that the Christian became more of a temporal subject, the vassal's loyalty to his liege lord gave way to the soldier's loyalty to his sovereign. Not only was the pay of soldiers now the obligation of the state: supply of weapons, and, by the eighteenth century, full support of the soldier also became the responsibility of the central government. Uniformity and regimentation became a desired military end and was reflected in the clothing of troops in garb that could easily be identified; hence the modern uniform. At the same time tactics became more specialized—not only foot and horse were needed but also artillery, grenadiers, engineers, and other specialist corps. Warfare had become an expensive and complicated branch of learning—'military science'.

By the eighteenth century the size of armies was unprecedented. Yet, in contrast to the reckless wastage of the Thirty Years' War, manpower was jealously conserved by generals and kings and saved from battle as much as possible. Thus, paradoxically, as military force waxed, the ferocity of war waned. After the Thirty Years' War, as fortresses became vital to defence and artillery to offense (see above) land strategy centred upon the siege of fortified works by means of trenches and cannon. The proper deployment of troops was learned by systematized precision drill. Eighteenth-century Continental field tactics required long, well-spaced infantry lines and presumed immediate response to orders; in drill at least it had a Baroque regularity and symmetry reminiscent of the minuet. Well-trained contingents were not readily expendable and were sparingly risked. The small principalities of the Empire and the cantons of Switzerland, without adequate finances to equip and maintain their armies, often hired them out as mercenary units. As the private forces of the condottieri or a Wallenstein disappeared, such mercenary armies took their place, and few rulers at war scrupled to hire contingents of mercenaries from other rulers. Mercenaries were not interested in annihilating one another, and commanders had to take their lack of zeal into consideration.

Despite the brilliance of Marlborough, Charles XII, Saxe, Eugene, Frederick, and other generals, and despite the large numbers engaged and killed or wounded in some of the battles of the War of the Spanish Succession and the Seven Years' War, eighteenth-century warfare in Europe essentially was *guerre en dentelle*. Professional soldiers (of the lower classes as a rule) fought under 'officers and gentlemen' according to conventional rules of strategy and tactics, rarely involving non-combatants in their professional activities. The rules sometimes did not work well, however, particularly in wilder terrain. The British General Edward Braddock lost his life and most of his army on the American frontier during the French and Indian War when he attempted to employ European tactics against American Indians in a wilderness. And sometimes officers, failing to observe the rules like gentlemen, employed ruse or broke their word of honour. Emphasis on professional discipline, gentlemanly conduct, and conventional tactics nevertheless was to continue until the rise of 'the nation in arms' during the wars of the French Revolution, when behaviour and strategy more suitable to a volunteer citizens' army fighting for a cause evolved.

Governments meanwhile came more and more to recognize the need of inventive minds and technological innovation for military purposes. Yet, if science and technology aided warfare, they were in turn stimulated by the new techniques of war. Ballistics helped to overthrow Aristotelian physics, and new metallurgical knowledge came out of the search for better alloys for making cannon. The determination of longitude at sea, the manœuvrability of ships, the quality of horses and roads, fire superiority, and a number of other largely scientific and technological matters were now factors in building up esprit de corps, shaping the strategy of commanders, and determining the outcome of battles. In the eighteenth century a ruler needed to be a good administrator rather than a military hero. Frederick the Great was a military man, to be sure, but no king of England since George II has appeared on a field of battle, nor was actual command in battle any longer normally expected of the heads of states anywhere. Warfare was now too specialized to leave to kings; kings needed trained and tested generals, and generals needed technological experts.

THE IMPACT OF SCIENCE AND TECHNOLOGY ON LIFE AND THOUGHT

Changes in Diet, Clothing, and Housing

As the scientific and geographical horizons of European man expanded, inevitable changes entered his everyday life. If the intellectual impact of invention, discovery, and exploration, and the increased opportunities for professional enterprise and economic investment affected only a limited number, the material impact reached the great majority. All classes benefited to a greater or less extent from the introduction of new items and the improvement of old ones among the staples. In Ireland and on the Continent the potato rapidly became a part of the daily diet of the poor and gradually also of the rich. The incidence of rickets, scurvy, and some other diseases diminished as greater supplies of fresh meat, fish, fruits, and vegetables made up in part for the vitamin deficiency of earlier diets (see above). Cane sugar was cheaper than honey; it added carbohydrates to, and helped to remove monotony from, the diet of rich and poor alike, and it also supplied the basis of some great fortunes derived from the operation of plantations and the slave trade. The sugar colonies of France and England became the most highly prized jewels in their crowns of empire. The introduction of snuff and other forms of tobacco from Virgina caused both controversy and pleasure upon their debut in Europe. New beverages such as coffee and tea, both introduced to Europe in the seventeenth century, brought the pleasant institution of the coffeehouse and a new repast, the 'afternoon tea' of the English-speaking world, probably borrowed from the tea ceremony initiated in Japan in the fifteenth century. The greater accessibility of the East made more available the preservative qualities as well as the gustatory delight of exotic spices. The English Grocers' Company, when incorporated in 1428, consisted chiefly of importers of spices, and to this day the French word for grocer is *épicier* (*spicer*), and the full German is *Kolonialwarenhandler* (*dealer in colonial goods*).

By the eighteenth century, in England, France, and the Low Countries the general standard of living began to rise, stimulated by mounting foreign trade, new products, and an improving technology. These conditions generally provided more urban employment as well as higher wages for the purchase of more commodities, though they also created the hardships of displacement and slums. In western Europe the poorer peasants continued, however, to live on vegetables (rarely available in winter), bread, cheese, and an occasional slice of meat, and the diet of the poor became worse the further east one went in Europe. In eighteenth-century England, on the other hand, the demand for white bread grew; dark bread (though later known to be dietetically preferable) was looked upon as a mark of poverty. Wheat became available in increasing amounts because of the increase in wheat acreage brought about by the increasing tempo of the enclosure movement.

As the rural population migrated and the cities grew, urban marketing facilities became strained, and food markets in London and elsewhere were sometimes described as revolting. Though said to be common practice in China, refrigeration of perishable items by natural ice (stored in earth houses during the summer) was introduced in Europe only at the close of the eighteenth century; before that, fish and fruit were rarely fresh after long hauls from seaports and orchards. Drunkenness was common, and the quantity of gin consumed became a national menace; Hogarth's pictorial preaching on the danger of gin probably did not overdraw the evil. Governmental intervention by means of heavy excises and licencing regulations raised the price of drink, but if it reduced consumption at all, it did not eliminate the ill. Life for the poor in factory areas may have been no more miserable—indeed, must have been better enough to induce migration to the cities—but, in spite of the probably greater comfort of city workers' dwellings as compared to country workers' cottages, personal awareness of misery seemed to increase in the early stages of 'the Industrial Revolution'.

Heavy concentration of population in slums, the tyranny of the clock and the machine, the humdrumness of specialized operations in a factory, the competition for jobs all seemed more damnable than the curse of poverty on the land. Humanitarians and landed gentry were less likely to become exercised over the country worker under the putting-out system, who converted his entire family into economic assets by turning his cottage into a spinning or weaving establishment, than over the factory hand (especially a woman or a child) who exhibited poverty, disease, and drunkenness on city streets. In righteous indignation they challenged weak and all too often reluctant municipal governments to find some solution to the problems of inadequate urban housing and public health.[22]

If cotton produced the evils of the textile factory system, it also brought some blessings. For one thing, it filled the growing demand for a cheap textile. Silk was difficult to wash, wool was rarely subjected to soap and water, but cotton cloth was easy to launder. Cotton not only made possible a higher standard of cleanliness but was also more comfortable in the summertime. Moreover, the cotton industry, not hampered by the guild regulations controlling silk and wool, was able to take advantage of technological change much more rapidly. In the seventeenth and eighteenth centuries calico became the favourite textile.

The Spread of the New Knowledge and Its Limitations

While cheap textiles were revolutionizing clothing, while timepieces were transforming social and working habits, and while mathematics was converting some of a population that had been used to thinking about the will of God into counters and calculators of quantities, the improvements in the printing press were helping to make possible a slight increase of literacy and the easier dissemination of ideas throughout society. The accumulation of knowledge in the natural sciences in the seventeenth and eighteenth centuries might well have come—though perhaps less rapidly—without the printing press, for much of the research was the work of able individuals. Young scholars travelled great distances to study with esteemed masters; older men of science visited one another and exchanged lengthy letters. Galileo, Kepler, Descartes, Mersenne, Ricci, and others kept up with distant colleagues a correspondence that imparted news of great discoveries, their own and others' (and still form some of the best sources for much of the history of science before the development of the scientific journals).

Yet in so far as these men were dependent on others' findings, they also learned and taught by easily circulated printed works, and presumably more readily than if they had been limited to scarce manuscripts and personal communication. While the great scientific academies might have owned impressive libraries if there had been no printing, for they probably could have afforded manuscript collections, many of the numerous local academies and private botanical societies would doubtless have found the cost of manuscripts prohibitive. Thus some at least of the *sociétés de pensées* given to serious discussion of political as well as scientific questions might never have come into being, and their impact on the intellectual ferment of the eighteenth century, for better or for worse, might have been lost. As it was, that impact was all the greater because the new technology had helped to promote the concept of the literate worker. Since the mid-seventeenth century, more and more jobs had become available that demanded some basic knowledge of reading and of simple sums, and education for business and the trades as well as for ecclesiastical, governmental, and professional purposes had begun to appear imperative (see Chapter XVI).

Despite the vogue of the new science, superstition retained its place in the life of the credulous or ill-informed. Waves of witchcraft persecutions continued until the late seventeenth century. They seem to have been due to political unrest as well as to superstition. Those areas of Roman Catholic and Protestant Germany most blighted by the disaster of the Thirty Years' War carried on the most extreme persecution of 'witches', and one of the most dramatic took place in New England in two waves that interrelated chrono-logically and perhaps causally with the uncertainties of the two seventeenth-century revolutions in England. Belief in witches diminished, however, as the rational spirit grew, and the last executions for witchcraft in Europe took place, scattered and singly, in the eighteenth century.

The impact of the new science on religion was ambivalent. As early as the seventeenth century Bacon spoke of the dichotomy of science and religion, undoubtedly attempting to protect science against irrelevant criticism. By the end of the century this sort of precaution was no longer necessary. Most scientists of the seventeenth and eighteenth centuries were devout; only few took occasion to attack Christianity. On the contrary, the scientist was more apt to introduce religious ideas into science, hesitating to harbour a concept of a world so mechanical as to leave no room for God or Providence. But how could one believe in the miracles and prophecies of Revelation, on the one hand, and scientific laws, on the other? How could one explain the statements in the Bible that seemed contrary to newly discovered fact? Why should the myriad souls of ethical heathen cultures be damned merely by their lack of Revelation? In spite of their awareness of such enigmas, genuine atheism was hard to find among scientists. Greater danger to orthodox Christian doctrine came from philosophic writers like Spinoza and the Deists. Spinoza's pantheism identified the Perfect Self-Existent with the Universe, discarding the concept of a transcendent personal God. The Deists retained a trans-cendent God in their cosmological scheme but robbed Him of the role of governing His universe. Yet, no matter how rife in intellectual circles, skepticism was not widespread in eighteenth-century Europe. Spinoza's pantheism was not influential, and for every Deist (who might be intensely religious in his own way) there were many Jesuits, Jansenists, Pietists,

Baptists, Hasids, ṣūfīs, or other kinds of devout and professing Catholics, Protestants, Jews, and Muslims.

Perfectibility, Humanitarianism and Rationalism

The transition from medieval to modern scientific thought in Europe came in part from, and in turn helped to bring about, a change in the concept of what kind of knowledge was important. To a medieval Scholastic, all knowledge that mattered was in a sense knowable: plenitude of knowledge existed in God's mind, and true human understanding was best directed toward coming ever closer to a knowledge of God's ways. With the 'scientific revolution', knowledge, though still valued for the sake of understanding God and His Book of Nature, assumed a new dimension; it had come to mean also a never-ending increase in human power—that is, in man's comprehension of, and control over, nature, including human nature.

An obvious problem arose from this new, or at least more fully appreciated, relationship of science and humanity: Science could be used either for good or for evil. The challenge of Francis Bacon to make science the means for the betterment of society was taken up by the *philosophes* of the eighteenth century. The medieval concept of Christian brotherhood, conceived in relationship to an all-knowing, all-powerful, and ever-loving Father, was translated into the humanitarianism of the eighteenth century. The ringing proclamation of the 'unalienable rights' of 'all men' was based on the certitude that Man could change his social structures by reasoning applied to rational principles and self-evident truths, derived not from God alone (if from God at all) but also from ascertainable unchanging laws of Nature.

Learned men of the era considered the knowledge of mathematics essential to the understanding of Nature, of a world subject to measurement. But how much in the world was in fact subject to measurement? The mathematics of probabilities suggested that the area between improbability and certainty could constantly be reduced as more data became available; differential and integral calculus suggested that much that was baffling in Nature wavered somewhere between calculable maximum and minimum limits. Were the rules of Nature as binding in human affairs, some wondered, as in the physical universe? If so, were they, too, subject to mathematical analysis? These were questions that the mathematicians as well as the *philosophes* of the eighteenth century raised (see Chapter IX), but they counted upon geometrical reasoning rather than statistical analysis or some other techniques of modern social science to furnish the correct answers.

The answers the *philosophes* derived satisfied them that society, too, was subject to ascertainable laws. Doubts regarding scientific concepts that had been considered true for centuries and regarding religious precepts that had hitherto seemed unquestionable accompanied—in fact, in some instances, incited—similar doubts regarding the structure of contemporary society.

Moreover, critics could see the abuses of society all about them. Could society, then, be better organized upon the tenets of reason? Was there a 'natural' society? What institutions best conformed to 'the laws of Nature'? This adaptation of naturalism to human institutions became the touchstone of the Enlightenment. It led to a new concept of 'perfection', to the idea of 'perfectibility' (see Chapter VII).

The new science joined with other forces to induce many intellectuals to discard the sense of inferiority to the Ancients inculcated by Renaissance man, who had adored Antiquity. Modern man had learned some things unknown to the Greeks and Romans. Might he not be equal or perhaps superior to his forbears? Sculptors might well argue subjectively over the comparative merits of Myron and Bernini, but advance in science was in some ways objectively measurable. By the eighteenth century, an intelligent schoolboy obviously had much more scientific information about some phenomena than Aristotle could have had. Together with the growing distrust of the Christian concepts of sin and the plan of God, science thus led to the eighteenth-century idea of human perfectibility. It not only seemed to point toward a steady accumulation of knowledge but it also had vaguely glimpsed the concept of an indefinite, unguided, and continuous evolution of life (see Chapter IX).

Hence, far from believing that man by nature was evil and incapable of perfection save by divine intervention, the *philosophe* was likely to hold that society made man what he was and, as society improved, man would improve. Rousseau contended that man had a *faculté de se perfectionner*. Condorcet saw reason to believe that man had embarked on a course of intellectual, moral, and biological perfectibility that was irreversible. The late-eighteenth-century concept of *perfectibility* was different from earlier notions of *perfection*, whether Jesuit or Leibnizian (see Chapter VII). *Perfection* was a Christian ideal, attainment of the Heavenly City by the grace of God for the faithful; *perfectibility* was an unending historical process of limitless improvement for all men. Change for the *philosophes* was not only in keeping with natural law, it was not even limited by Christian ideals of perfection. Both the fixed, hierarchical order of society and the intellectual tradition of church and aristocracy were thus jeopardized by the questioning brought on by natural philosophy.

This intellectual atmosphere favoured the enlightened despot and the humanitarian, each seeking in his own way to achieve the reforms that Nature, as he saw it, dictated. In the eighteenth century the number of hospitals increased throughout Europe; anti-slavery societies sprang up; prison and tax reform movements became popular; legal reform, toleration, and philanthropy (*bienfaisance*) made great strides because they were efforts by enlightened rulers or private benefactors to correct what was "unnatural'; *civilization* became a word of current usage. The benevolent state or individual seemed to stand for a more rational world against church and aristocracy, the champions of tradition; Nature and science seemed allied with Reason on the side of change and perfectibility.

So did the new knowledge of the geographical world. As every region of the world grew more aware of other regions, the growing awareness helped to shape many aspects of life in each of them. We have already examined some of the effects of extra-European art, architecture, technology, products, and customs upon Europe, and of corresponding European influences upon non-European areas. Until the end of the eighteenth century European technology, despite having outstripped all others since 1500, eagerly borrowed from the Middle East, India, and China, while they were unwilling to borrow in return. Only in the Americas had a European veneer been imposed upon the native substructure.

One of Europe's imports was a subtle influence refined, so to speak, from the raw materials of America and the South Seas—the concept of the 'noble savage'. Beginning with More's *Utopia* and La Hontan's *Nouveaux voyages . . . dans l'Amérique septentrionale* and coming down to Diderot's *Supplément au voyage de Bougainville* and Raynal's *Histoire philosophique et politique . . . des Européens dans les deux Indes*, an idealized picture of the nobility of man in primitive societies had grown up to fortify the belief of some that only civilized man is vile. This at first amorphous idea was formulated into a persuasive creed in Rousseau's writings, though probably by a misreading of his real intent. Aided by the scientists' emphasis on natural phenomena, the 'return to nature' developed into a veritable cult. Semi-learned societies turned botanical. Queens and noblemen played at being close to the soil. Urban families went out to the country or the mountains to admire the beauty of nature. Writers, with Rousseau and young Goethe showing the way, began to feel that Reason unaided by the nobler instincts might lead only to materialistic bleakness and error while inner feelings and emotions might lead to intuitive truth mingled with joy. The vogue of Rationalism declined, giving way to a nascent Romanticism.

The Savants' Contribution to the Rise of Cosmopolitanism

By the end of the eighteenth century, science had also lent support to the dream of a world community, whether based upon religious precepts regarding the brotherhood of man or utopian preachments of pacifism. In an era in which patriotic loyalties still rested most often on dynastic ties, the idea of peaceful co-operation of nations was posited on co-operation among princes rather than peoples. Crucé's *New Cyneas* had been largely ignored in its own day, but St Pierre's scheme for a perpetual peace led to Rousseau's discussion of the same problem later in the century, and Rousseau's in turn to Kant's before the century ended (see Chapter IX). An increase of intercourse among scientists and of co-operation among scientific societies kept pace with the growth of embassies, the development of the idea of international congresses to preserve or restore peace, and the publication of treatises on international law. The ideal of a world united by the collaboration of scientists, engineers, and physicians as well as princes to combat war, catastrophe, poverty, disease, and hunger was one of the favourite themes of *philosophes* and humanitarians.

As a matter of fact, the community of scientists and writers in the seventeenth and eighteenth centuries enjoyed a considerable degree of freedom of communication. National jealousies and government restrictions rarely impeded their interchanges with passport requirements, immigration regulations, and postal censorship. By the end of the seventeenth century correspondence among the learned had become commonplace, thanks to the fuller development of postal services and the rise of scientific societies and journals. If personal rivalries like the unfortunate dispute of Leibniz and Newton developed among scientists, official pressure for secrecy was nevertheless exceptional; patents and trade secrets were a greater deterrent to the general use of new devices. The co-operation of several governments in the scientific expeditions of the eighteenth century and the award of prizes and honours to foreigners by royal patrons and academies testify that the scientist was usually considered a free agent and a servant of mankind. The society of Europe's scientists was cosmopolitan, imbued with the ideal of comprehension and control of the forces of nature and with the hope that their discoveries would alleviate human misery and replace human labour with machines. No matter how ready governments might be to use technological aids for domestic advantage, seldom before the end of the eighteenth century did national interests tend to make scientific discovery into a tool of state power.

That did not mean that Europe's achievement was a universal good, for Europe's scientific and technological advance was not an unmixed blessing for less machine-minded peoples. The use of ships, firearms, and other technological devices gave to a small number of men an effective control over sprawling nations like the Aztecs and the Incas—a control that probably would have been impossible to achieve otherwise. The relatively tiny area of western Europe thus laid the foundation of political dominance and cultural influence throughout the world, and in the nineteenth century its political power at least would make itself indubitably felt. Europe's rapid advance in science and technology, functioning in an ever more receptive society, helps to explain how, by the end of the eighteenth century, western Europe was vaguely beginning to abandon the theocratic, monarchic, and agricultural pattern of life that prevailed almost everywhere and to follow a predominantly technological, middle-class, and urban pattern, which it was destined to impose upon large sections of the rest of the world in the 1800's.

NOTES TO CHAPTER XV

1. Dr B. Gille points out that the study of technology still presents to the historian a peculiar problem since methodology and basic documentation are still the subject of dispute and research among specialists. He writes:

'The problem of the history of techniques presents several different aspects which we feel should not be neglected. The first is what may be called the internal history of individual techniques. The history of individual processes, the history—or rather the genesis—of individual machines is, in many cases, not yet written, because such work would entail methodical organization on an international plan not difficult to envisage. The second aspect is that of technical systems, that is to say the study of a balanced group of techniques, together with the essential liaisons between their different practical applications. Finally come the relationships between such technical systems and the level of scientific knowledge and social structures. It is in the light of the latter that it becomes possible to discern the main lines of the evolution of technical systems, of the imbalances involved, the delays in given sectors and the resultant brakes.'

2. Michael Confino, 'La Comptabilité des domaines privés en Russie dans la seconde moitié du XVIIIe siècle (d'après les "Travaux de la Société libre d'économie de Saint-Petersbourg")', *Revue d'histoire moderne et contemporaine*, VIII (1961), pp. 5–34.

3. A. R. Hall, *Ballistics in the Seventeenth Century* (Cambridge, 1952), p. 73.

4. Dr B. Gille says that generally speaking, mathematics rendered no fundamental services until a relatively late date. The authors rightly note this in the case of statistics and of insurance. Theoretical problems in ship building, which were to influence naval engineering, had to await the work of Bouguer and Euler in the middle of the eighteenth century. The same is true of ballistic tables and the work of Bélidor.

5. Quoted in Wolf, *16th and 17th Centuries*, p. 527.

6. Robert S. Woodbury, *History of the Lathe to 1850* (Cleveland, 1961).

7. Wolf, *Eighteenth Century*, p. 612.

8. See Charles Singer et al. (eds.), *A History of Technology*, Vol. III, *From the Renaissance to the Industrial Revolution, c. 1500–c. 1750* (Oxford, 1957), pp. 367–8.

9. Wolf, *16th and 17th Centuries*, p. 547.

10. Charles Singer et al. (eds.), *A History of Technology*, Vol. II, *The Mediterranean Civilizations and the Middle Ages, c. 700 B.C. to A.D. 1500* (Oxford, 1956), pp. 203–5.

11. Quoted in E. Poche, 'Le verre de Bohême', *Journal of World History*, V (1959), p. 438.

12. Wolf, *16th and 17th Centuries*, pp. 488–9.

13. Dr B. Gille notes that invention does not mean immediate application. Innovation, as the economists put it, takes place only when technical mutation has become indispensable. Coke smelting, born about 1709, was industrially perfected only towards 1735–40 (a time-lag often intervening between invention proper and the feasibility of its industrial application), and was finally adopted only after the development of puddling by Cort and with the widespread utilization of iron for bridge building, ship building, and in the extended use of machinery.

14. See Franz M. Feldhaus, *Die Teknik der Antike und des Mettelalters* (Potsdam, 1931), illustration (facing p. 384) of a fifteenth-century tread wheel crane.

15. See Gilbert Freyre, 'Impact of the Portuguese on the American Tropics', *Journal of World History*, IV (1958), pp. 582–602.

16. William Cowper, 'The Task' (1785).

17. Ignacio Olagüe, 'Les changements de climat dans l'histoire', *Journal of World History*, VII (1963), pp. 667–8.

18. See J. C. Drummond and Anne Wilbraham, *The Englishman's Food; a History of Five Centuries of English Diet* (London, 1939), esp. pp. 309–27.

19. Quoted in A. S. Turberville (ed.), *Johnson's England* (Oxford, 1952), II, p. 275.

20. See John U. Nef, 'The Genesis of Industrialism and of Modern Science (1560–1640)' in *Essays in Honor of Conyers Read* (Chicago, 1952), pp. 260–9.

21. Quoted in Hall, *Scientific Revolution*, p. 202.

22. See T. S. Ashton, 'The Treatment of Capitalism by Historians', in F. A. Hayek (ed.), *Capitalism and the Historians* (Chicago, 1954), pp. 33–63.

CHAPTER XVI

EDUCATION (1300–1775)

THE rise and spread of libraries, the press, learned societies, and some of the more indirect channels for the communication of knowledge and traditions have been described above (see particularly Chapters X, XI, XIV and XV). We have also referred in several passages to guilds as intentionally providing a means of vocational training. Here we shall consider primarily the more formal systems of schools and schooling, a variety of educational theories, the popularization of science, and the modifications of professional training from the fourteenth to the eighteenth century.

EUROPEAN EDUCATIONAL INSTITUTIONS

Elementary and Secondary Schooling

In Europe during our period formal schooling became less the concern of the clergy than it had been and more the concern of secular authorities. So long as education was dominated by the church, almost all schools were church schools, and almost the only teachers by vocation were clerics.[1] Teaching, however, was not, strictly speaking, a separate profession but rather a side function of the clergy. Every clergyman, from the parish priest to the pope, was expected, at least incidentally, to give instruction in the faith to any Christian.

Outside the clerically dominated schools and universities, the educational process went on in informal ways. Sermons, lawsuits, cafés, salons, and other occasions or places permitted, even encouraged, men to air their views. In the fourteenth and fifteenth centuries this informal kind of education advanced to a high level by an unusually significant channel. Humanism, encountering resistance at first in the strongholds of Scholasticism in the universities, flourished in urban centres and at the courts of princes.[2] To cite a single example, Cosimo de' Medici's patronage made the palaces and villas of his family a centre of the new higher learning. They housed the institution known as the Platonic Academy (see Chapter VI), which helped to spread the knowledge of Greek language, literature, and philosophy far and wide. Greek diplomats and scholarly clerics met and exchanged views with Italian literati at the Academy's meetings. Ficino and others were subsidized by this Medici 'foundation' to translate Aristotle and Plato and to write formidable philosophical commentaries, and its symposia served to enlighten courtiers, clergymen, and scholars in the intricacies of philosophy new and old. It became a model for the academies, the learned societies, and the *sociétés de pensée* that were a general feature of intellectual activity throughout Europe in ensuing centuries (see below). Such education as most of the common people received, however, was of a still more informal nature. Church windows, station pictures, altar decorations and other forms of art, much of the music and literature, and sometimes sermons and daily conversation were set in a context that was largely unintelligible except to those who knew the Christian tradition. These visual and aural media were ubiquitous, and the learning they imparted was gratuitous.

In communities where priests were readily accessible, children were likely to be more formally instructed. Catechism, chanting, and perhaps some religious reading constituted the common curriculum of the medieval parish schools. Choir boys would be taught singing and a little more in a 'song school'. In some of the larger towns there were chantry schools, endowed by wealthy citizens. Sometimes at the higher grades they were 'grammar' schools, giving fairly intensive training in reading and writing. Some guilds established schools, taught by their priests, for the children of their members. At a time when books were few and cumbersome and in Latin, book-learning was difficult to acquire, and at the lower levels most learning was by rote.

A more advanced type of education was also available for maturer students. It was restricted to unusually intelligent children (usually boys) who showed promise of a learned (and therefore clerical) career. Such education was carried on in monastic or cathedral schools, but no sharp break separated primary from secondary classes; pupils from five or six to the teen ages often went to the same schools. The *trivium* (grammar, rhetoric, and logic) and at a higher level the *quadrivium* (arithmetic, geometry, astronomy, and music) were the basic categories of knowledge. They were commonly taught without serious concern with the concrete or the practical and with a religious and moralistic emphasis.

In most cultures, until comparatively recent times, the education of girls was generally (but not necessarily) carried on in the home, and Europe was no exception to this rule. Well into modern times, European girls were trained to be housewives, whether the house was a peasant hut or a servant-filled palace. Their teachers were their mothers or (in wealthy, aristocratic homes) trusted governesses or servants. Girls were not often exposed to book-learning, and when they were, it was likely to be religious in character. Sometimes girls were taught in parochial schools by their parish priests, but if their parents could afford to send them away from home, they went to convent schools run by nuns. Most of the wives or daughters of princely families, especially in Italy, received their elementary training from tutors at home or in palace schools. The linguistic ability and breadth of learning of some of these women was impressive. Whether in a private home or at a school, the teachers emphasized the religious tradition—an emphasis (as well as the pupils' reaction against it) that is reflected in the stories of princesses who concealed their secular reading matter in prayerbook covers. The impact of this rigid training may perhaps be measured by the influence of an imposing number of women mystics upon both secular and ecclesiastical leaders.[3] For all that, book-learned girls were the exception; schools were restricted mostly to boys.

Boys, like girls, began their training at home—so to speak, at their fathers' knees. For the lower social classes it included practical instruction in farm activities or industrial crafts. A boy learned by doing. For young noblemen, training in horsemanship, hunting, and the handling of weapons was paramount. A number of still surviving handbooks indicate that princes and exceptional young men of the upper classes received instruction also in political, social, and cultural matters. Such instruction was carried on chiefly by tutors in the home.

During the late Middle Ages a few secular schools arose, especially in Italian towns, and they departed from the ecclesiastical pattern in a number of ways. In this new kind of school the pupils, generally children of the middle classes, were given an education that fitted them for middle-class vocations. They might be taught to read and write the vernacular as well as Latin; they studied commercial arithmetic and other fundamentals of business life. They might be divided into elementary and secondary groups. Villani's *History of Florence* indicated that there were three types of schools in that city about 1300; nine hundred boys and girls attended elementary parish schools, about eleven hundred attended business schools, and about six hundred attended secondary schools of liberal arts. Some of these schools were coeducational. All of them were essentially vocational, providing the early steps in the training of young men for clerical, business, or professional careers.

In fact, during the fourteenth and fifteenth centuries, continuing an earlier trend, educational institutions, whether primary, secondary, or higher, were generally tending toward vocationalism. Bourgeois fathers who were ambitious for their sons to rise in the practical world were apt to start them in early youth toward a professional education, usually in law, perhaps in medicine or business rhetoric (*ars dictaminis*). Petrarch, Boccaccio, Luther, Calvin, and a number of less famous men broke away from the paternal preference for a practical, professional education to follow their own literary or religious inclinations.

The trend toward vocational education seems to have been less marked in circles not directly associated with a university. Three of the most remarkable examples of broadly enlightened education were provided in non-university towns—one in the Netherlands, one in England, and one in northern Italy. The religious mystic Groote (see Chapter III) inspired the

Brethren of the Common Life during the late fourteenth and early fifteenth centuries to establish schools in towns spread throughout the Netherlands. The school at Deventer was the most famous of them: under Master Alexander Hegius (c. 1433–98) it had over two thousand pupils. As befitted the atmosphere of the Renaissance, he added to its strictly religious curriculum serious instruction in the Classics. Students were trained to read and write Ciceronian Latin and to appreciate the virtues of Classical civilization, though without prejudice to the ideals and practices of Christianity. The effectiveness of the Brethren at Deventer and elsewhere in both instruction and school administration made them a weighty educational force in the North.[4] They trained boys and young men for the professions, to be sure, but also for a pious, intellectual life. Nicolas of Cusa, Pope Adrian VI, Erasmus, and Luther were merely a few of the outstanding men who were moulded at least in part in the Brethrens' schools.

At Deventer there prevailed the distinctively pious spirit of northern scholarship which was to become so evident in the Protestant Reformation. Colet's school of St Paul's in London provided another example of this spirit. It was a run-down establishment when he took charge, but he restored it with his own inherited fortune. Although it was connected with St Paul's Cathedral in London, he placed it under lay control—an innovation that reflected his critical attitude toward the clergy. Here, as at Oxford, he expounded and encouraged the pious humanism characteristic of the group known as the 'Oxford Reformers'. Milton eventually was to receive his early education at St Paul's.

Mantua was a third centre of education without direct association with a university. Here the initial impulse was provided by a princely patron of Classical learning. In 1425 Marchese Giovan Francesco II invited Vittorino da Feltre, a humanist layman, to create a palace school in which young nobles might receive a good education. Several enlightened rulers had established such institutions in earlier centuries, and about twenty years before Vittorino, Gasparino de Barzizza had founded a humanistic school in Padua, which Vittorino himself had attended. What made Vittorino a pioneer was his broadening of the Classical curriculum.

The educated man of the late Middle Ages was likely to be interested in harmonizing what he knew of mathematics, physics, and cosmology with the teachings of the church,[5] but Vittorino envisaged a program that would surmount the current emphasis upon religious content and vocational training. Since his objectives were at the same time moral, intellectual, and physical, he introduced a broad plan of instruction. His pupils studied not only Latin and Greek but also the vernacular so that they might be grounded in recent as well as church and Classical literature. In addition, they received schooling in mathematics, music, and art. Particularly exceptional for educational institutions of Vittorino's day was his emphasis on physical training; riding, swimming, marching, and fencing were obligatory. Perhaps the most noteworthy of his educational principles was equality of opportunity for learning. Though employed by a prince to educate princelings and young noblemen, he admitted to his school the children of the lower classes and—a radical departure in his day—at least one girl. His institution was thus both co-educational (to a limited degree) and democratic (in comparison with the common standards of the day). All pupils, regardless of social status, observed the same rules of dress, food, and good manners. He also provided attractive buildings and grounds, calling his school Casa Giocosa (Happy House). At several other Renaissance courts, boys and girls of princely and aristocratic families were given somewhat the same broad training for intelligent and cultured leadership in the affairs of state.

Unlike Deventer or St Paul's, Casa Giocosa reflected the secular trends of Renaissance civilization at its best, but, like Deventer and St Paul's, it exerted a tremendous influence through the many famous scholars it sent forth. In Vittorino's school can be seen the lay influence of rulers on education; in the school at Deventer (and despite lay management, even at London) can be seen the persistence of clerical influences. The Bible, the medieval church fathers, and other religious sources were, of course, studied at Mantua, but whereas at Deventer the curriculum was primarily religious, supplemented with the Classics, Vittorino's curriculum was primarily the Classics, supplemented with religious instruction.[6]

Hegius', Colet's, and Vittorino's ideal of breadth of schooling was not regularly entertained in educational circles. Most clerical educators were not humanist, and humanist educators, even when relatively free from religious dogmatism, occasionally went to other extremes, such as narrow emphasis on Classical syntax and style to the sacrifice of subject matter. In England this tendency was especially conspicuous in the schools that were endowed by laymen for the education of young gentlemen—among them, Winchester College (founded in 1382) and Eton College (1441). These colleges were among those which eventually became the 'great public schools' that played a proverbial role in the British scheme of secondary education. They prepared their pupils for the most part for careers in the law or the church. A large share of their school day, which, according to the season, began at six or seven in the morning and ran until five or six at night, went to instruction in Latin, but a little time was given also to Greek and, at the higher levels, some Hebrew. The cult of the Classics in the school curriculum, which was to reach its high point in the early seventeenth century, was probably even more marked in Italy than in England.

Higher Learning and the Universities

The institutions of higher learning in the West had grown out of the medieval monastic and cathedral schools. During the twelfth and thirteenth centuries some cathedral schools expanded so rapidly in curricula and population that they evolved a new form, commonly referred to as the *studium generale* (*school for all*).7 This expanded school was eventually to become the university. Although Muslim cities such as Cairo, Tunis, and Fez already had attached to their mosques centres of learning that had grown famous as universities, western cities lagged far behind. The universities of Salerno, Pavia, and Bologna have a certain claim to be counted among the first in the West, on the grounds of having been the earliest to give advanced instruction, particularly in medicine or law. For the creation of the modern university, however, something more than the vocational training given in these Italian schools was needed—advanced instruction in the liberal arts or, at least, a sufficient combination of the liberal arts with theology, medicine, or law to provide a higher education on a broad scale. France's faculties provided such a combination.

Shortly after 1200 the faculty guild of the overgrown school of the Cathedral of Notre Dame in Paris gained recognition as an independent corporation (*universitas*). Soon it became the model faculty for advanced instruction in the liberal arts, theology-philosophy, medicine, and law. For several centuries it was Europe's most respected educational centre. Meanwhile a twelfth century 'hospice' near Notre Dame in Paris had become the College of Eighteen,8 and a college for sixteen theological students had been endowed by Robert de Sorbon (1257). The 'Sorbonne' increased in numbers and expanded its functions, having in the fourteenth century become the theological school of the University. By the fifteenth century resident fellows or masters were giving courses in these and a number of other colleges. In similar fashion at other French universities, the faculties took over almost all higher educational functions, and universities became corporations of professors and students.9

In England, and especially at Oxford and Cambridge, the evolution of universities followed a slightly different course. Along with a *universitas* of four faculties (arts, theology, law, and medicine) colleges also developed out of endowed rooming houses for students. The tutors at these 'halls' became so important in the *studium generale* that the activity of the *universitas* for a long time was restricted to little more than administration of the federated colleges, until in 1570–71 the universities were reorganized. The cloistered halls of the separate colleges have survived in all of their late-medieval beauty at Cambridge and Oxford, and although the college-hall system existed elsewhere, it has been especially characteristic of English universities.

Still another type of federation was the one whereby several newer faculties joined with an ancient one, which remained dominant. Thus the faculties of Montpellier, long a centre of medical education in southern France, clustered around its medical school.10 At Bologna, famous since about 1100 for its professors of Roman law, the professorial guild was dominated by the legalists, and by the end of the thirteenth century was subordinated also to a powerful student organization. This *universitas* (or guild) of students, also led by those in the law school, was not only self-governing, it regulated such things as professors' salaries and the speed of their lectures, required prompt dismissal of classes, and punished professors' absences and similar infractions with appropriate fines. With its student administration and its curriculum of Roman law, Bologna exercised a secular, vocational influence comparable to the influence of Paris in religious and more broadly intellectual education.

The endowment of a university by a private philanthropist was rare in this era, but several distinguished institutions derived their funds from some ruler's purse. In the 'golden age of the university', the thirteenth century, a number of universities had been established in that manner—Naples (1224), Toulouse (1229), and Salamanca (1230), for example. The University of Rome was founded by the pope in 1303, though it did not become famous until the fifteenth century. The first universities of central Europe were initiated under Emperor Charles IV—Prague in 1348, Cracow in 1364, and Vienna in 1364; one founded at Pécs (Hungary) in 1367 did not long survive. The German princes were somewhat late in organizing universities, but, not to mention all, Heidelberg was founded in 1385, Leipzig in 1409, and Tübingen in 1477. The German clerical orders had meanwhile created new universities at Erfurt (1379) and Cologne (1388), and the archbishop of Sweden that of Uppsala (1447). In Armenia Gladzor University was founded at the close of the thirteenth century and Tathev University in the fourteenth; during their brief periods of glory they were the centres of Armenian culture and strongholds of the Armenian Church in the conflicts with Mongol invaders and Dominican missionaries. (See map overleaf.)

After the glorious era of origin and growth came an era of crystallization of curricula. During the fourteenth and fifteenth centuries, the universities that survived grew more and more inflexible, tradition-bound, and impervious to new needs. Scholasticism lost much of its earlier vitality and constructive rationalism and deteriorated into 'logic chopping'. Theology stuck to academic traditionalism and approved authorities, for the most part oblivious to rising trends like humanism and experimental science. While humanism was welcomed with enthusiasm in court circles and secondary schools like Deventer and Mantua, universities such as Oxford, Paris, and Bologna at first passively disregarded or actively opposed it, and professors showed less interest in the beauty of Classical learning and literature than in Scholastic rationale. On the other hand, the burgeoning universities had begun in the thirteenth and fourteenth centuries to expand the traditional mathematical subjects (astronomy, geometry, arithmetic, and music) of the quadrivium by the inclusion of Euclid, Ptolemy, Aristotle, and other scientific writers; individual scholars (e.g. Nicholas of Cusa) occasionally carried on experiments; and sometimes groups of scholars became famous as a school (e.g. the Merton and Vienna mathematicians and the Paris Ockhamists). For all that, the professorial guilds of the *studia generalia* as a whole did less than the craft guilds to encourage empirical science. Although the universities clearly recognized contemporary needs in educating for the professions,

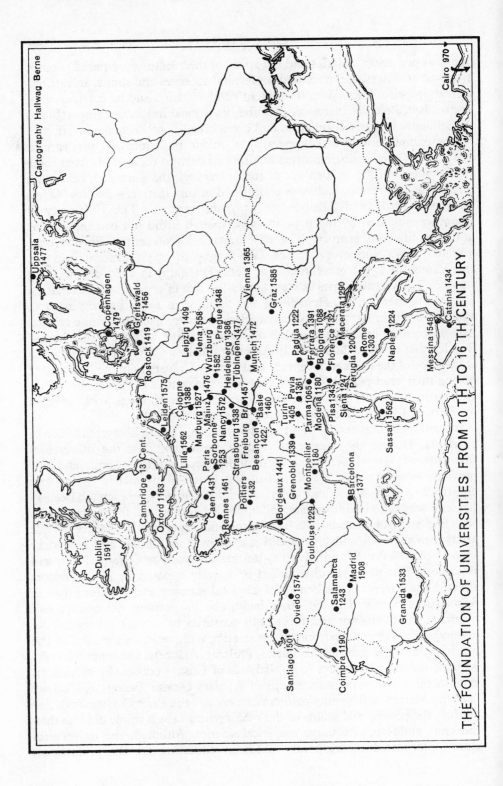

Cairo 970

THE FOUNDATION OF UNIVERSITIES FROM 10 TH TO 16 TH CENTURY

Uppsala 1477
Copenhagen 1479
Greifswald 1456
Rostock 1419
Leipzig 1409
Jena 1558
Prague 1348
Würzburg 1582
Heidelberg 1386
Tübingen 1477
Munich 1472
Vienna 1365
Graz 1585
Leiden 1575
Cologne 1388
Marburg 1527
Mainz 1476
Nancy 1572
Freiburg Br 1457
Basle 1460
Padua 1222
Ferrara 1391
Bologna 1088
Florence 1321
Macerata 1290
Rome 303
Catania 1434
Messina 1548
Naples 1224
Cambridge 13 Cent.
Oxford 1163
Lille 1562
Paris Sorbonne 1253
Caen 1431
Rennes 1461
Strasbourg 1538
Besancon 1422
Poitiers 1432
Turin 1405
Pavia 1361
Parma 1065
Modena 1180
Pisa 1343
Siena 1247
Perugia 1200
Sassari 1562
Dublin 1591
Bordeaux 1441
Grenoble 1339
Montpellier 1180
Barcelona 1377
Toulouse 1229
Oviedo 1574
Salamanca 1243
Madrid 1508
Granada 1533
Santiago 1501
Coimbra 1190

especially law, medicine, and the *ars dictaminis*, in these fields too they tended to preserve the learned tradition rather than to promote intellectual pioneering. In general, until the sixteenth century independent thought and free inquiry were not regarded as the major aims of higher learning. The University of Padua, however, provided a shining exception to this general rule (see Chapter XII).

Thus, despite the marked inclination toward secularism and specialization, the universities remained largely dominated by ecclesiastics and by traditional programmes of study. Henry IV's statute of 1600 aimed to put the University of Paris more fully under state control than theretofore, but clerical control persisted, at first under Jesuits, who had gradually displaced the Dominicans, and later, for a time, under Jansenists. Jesuit colleges or universities at Douai, Antwerp, Louvain, Köln, Ingolstadt, Vienna, and elsewhere remained strongholds of Jesuit influence, while Oxford and Cambridge continued to be dominated by Anglican divines. The new universities of Europe usually had influential theological faculties, those established in Anglo-America were essentially theological schools, and those in Spanish America (Mexico City, Caracas, Santiago, and elsewhere) were distinctly under one form or another of clerical influence.

But for the intervention of the states the ecclesiastical viewpoint might have triumphed in pedagogy. Especially (but not exclusively) in non-Catholic countries, the higher schools were fast passing under the influence of the state. Most of the European universities that were founded after the Reformation were from the outset state-controlled and state-supported, with curricula and professors that were intended to train for the civil service or for other lay professions rather than for the clergy. In western Europe the universities of Leiden and Halle were excellent examples. In Russia, where leading men of letters like Tatishchev and Lomonosov lent their weight to a plea for a less traditional approach to education, several educational institutions were created by imperial initiative. Peter the Great founded a School of Mathematics and Navigational Science in Moscow (1701) and, associated with the Academy of Sciences, the University of St Petersburg (1725); Tsarina Elizabeth founded the University of Moscow (1755); and Catherine the Great founded the Smolny Institute for the secondary education of girls of the upper classes and other secondary schools in some of the larger cities. This secularizing tendency helps to explain why, though the Russian lower schools continued largely in the hands of a rarely well-prepared clergy, the higher schools were hotbeds of the eighteenth-century Enlightenment.

At Oxford and Cambridge the same secular trend emerged, though less vigorously. Several regius professorships of traditional subjects were endowed by Henry VIII in the sixteenth century, but they were supplemented by regius chairs in modern history and modern language set up by George I in 1724, intended largely to train recruits for the diplomatic service. The new chairs, however, did little to modify clerical predominance. Indeed, in

English America the secular tendency for a time was reversed. Several new universities sprang up as a result of the revival movement known as the Great Awakening (see Chapter IV). Princeton University was founded (as the College of New Jersey) by the Presbyterians in 1746, Columbia (as King's College) by the Anglicans in 1754, Brown by the Baptists in 1764, Rutgers by the Dutch Reformed in 1766, and Dartmouth by the Congregationalists in 1770, each intended at first to provide ministers for its respective sect. In 1749, however, Franklin was instrumental in planning the Academy (later University) of Pennsylvania with a curriculum that included technical training, agriculture, modern languages, and other utilitarian subjects still uncommon in the older universities.

Religion and the Growth of Learning

In the sixteenth century the wars of religion brought out the potentiality of the educational system, especially of schools for children and adolescents, as an arsenal of religious propaganda. As Protestant princes appropriated the church, they nationalized the church schools, and Protestant children were indoctrinated with Protestant dogma, just as Roman Catholic children with Catholic dogma. Nearly all education for a long time thereafter was chained to religious parochialism. Rarely did educators teach even the non-theological subjects dispassionately.

The importance to Protestants of Bible reading and of a learned ministry led to a demand for widespread educational facilities in Protestant countries. Luther gave the matter serious attention, and with Melanchthon's blessing a number of old schools and universities were reorganized and new ones founded in Germany (e.g. Marburg in 1527, Königsburg in 1544, and Jena in 1558). Saxony and Württemberg showed the way, providing not only elementary schools but also Latin schools for many communities. Melanchthon's plan of education was both Biblicist and humanist. It gave a prominent place to Greek (as the language of the New Testament) as well as to Ciceronian Latin. Johannes Sturm (1507–89) founded a school at Strasbourg which, along with Latin and Greek, taught not only the catechism in German but also some science; it became the model for the German *gymnasium*. In England the colleges at Oxford and Cambridge were incorporated as universities when the Elizabethan struggle over Anglican independence seemed definitely settled, and Rugby (1567) and Harrow (1572) joined the ranks of the secondary institutions destined to become the 'great public schools'. In Scotland the Church Assembly of 1560, under the prodding of John Knox, required every considerable town to have a Latin school, every country parish a teacher, and each of the larger towns a college to give instruction in logic, rhetoric, and languages. Other Protestant countries provided opportunities to acquire at least enough literacy to read the Bible.

The Catholic Church, seeking to bring back to the fold as many heretics as possible, emphasized the training of teachers and advisers. Not only the

Society of Jesus but several other new orders gave major attention to teaching and conversion.[11] The Somaschi and Ursulines have already been mentioned (Chapter IV): the first undertook to school destitute children; the second, under the patronage of Cardinal Carlo Borromeo (1538–84), archbishop of Milan, dedicated themselves to the schooling of girls. The Oratorians were founded by Filippo de Neri in Rome (1575) and by Bérulle in Paris (1611), the Piarists by José de Calasanza in Rome (1617), and the Brethren of the Christian Schools by Jean Baptiste de la Salle in Rheims (1681). The Piarists and the Brethren were concerned with the training of poor boys. Other orders, old and new, also maintained schools at varying levels.

Perhaps the most noteworthy examples of the propagandist-teacher were to be found among the Jesuits.[12] They courted and won success in both elementary and higher education, serving as tutors to royal and other powerful families and as schoolmasters in humble church schools. Even though, with the rise of secular schools, the number of lay teachers increased, at no time during our period was the profession formalized. The Jesuits, however, closely approximated a professionally trained staff of teachers, for, carefully selected and highly trained themselves, they studiously specialized in the techniques of effective teaching and, though clergymen, taught secular as well as religious subjects.

The early Jesuits understood the importance of indoctrination as a key to men's minds. During a vacation in Flanders Loyola had been the guest of Erasmus's friend Juan Luis Vives (1492–1540), who was one of the renowned professors of his day (at Louvain and Oxford). Vives was a devout Christian, but he was also an opponent of the Scholasticism of his day.[13] In *De Disciplinis* (1532) and several other works on pedagogy, he had advocated a system of education wherein kindly teachers would hold forth in well-constructed buildings, giving special attention to superior pupils. A century before Francis Bacon he advocated learning by experiment and the inductive method. The Jesuits adopted some of the pedagogical ideas of humanists like Vives and Erasmus (see below) but discarded the humanists' emphasis upon freedom of inquiry and the play element in schooling in favour of strict discipline and militant Catholicism.

Loyola had a gift of keen observation and self-analysis that enabled him to understand the processes of his own mind. In the months of meditation and visions that had preceded his conversion to the religious life and in the long years devoted to ascetic practices, he had painstakingly recorded the details of his spiritual experiences and practices. From his notes, later probably supplemented by knowledge gleaned from the *Ejercitatorio de la vida espiritual* of Garcia Cisneros, abbot of Montserrato, he evolved the *Spiritual Exercises* (first published in 1548).

The Jesuit ideal of absolute obedience within the Church Militant and the Jesuit program of educational missions demanded a strict and highly selective training for the would-be Jesuit. Loyola's *Spiritual Exercises* provided a methodical textbook intended to guide the would-be Jesuit, or 'exercitant', along the path travelled by Loyola himself. During four weeks devoted to this purpose, the exercitant, usually under the guidance of a spiritual director, advanced from the contemplation of man's sinfulness through the mysteries of Jesus' passion and resurrection toward a voluntary dedication to God. The exercitant was instructed to evoke certain religious visions in all their historical, geographical, and individual aspects and to employ his five physical senses to make his spiritual experiences graphically realistic.[14] The *Exercises* thus led to a controlled mysticism, becoming an instrument by which the exercitant merged his identity with his religious community.

After an exercitant had become a novice, two years of probation followed, and he was finally directed into either the temporal or the spiritual branch of the society. The temporal service consisted of 'lay coadjutors', who were charged with the administrative and household duties of the order. If selected for spiritual service, novices took the simple vows of poverty, chastity, and obedience and became 'scholastics'. They now had to pass through long years of additional probation in which they received a thorough training in the sciences, letters, theology, and teaching. They then were ordained as priests and as 'spiritual coadjutors' became missionaries and teachers or performed other tasks of the Society. Those who showed special aptitude became the 'professed of the four vows', highest rank of the order, who in addition to taking solemn vows of poverty, chastity, and obedience also vowed to serve wherever the pope through their general might send them. The 'Rules for Thinking with the Church', appended to the *Exercises*, presscribed thorough submission of individual will and opinion in ecclesiastical matters. Rule 1 reads: 'Laying aside all private judgment, we ought to hold our minds prepared and prompt . . . to obey in all things . . . the hierarchical Church'; and Rule 13: 'To arrive at the truth in all things, we ought always to be ready to believe that what seems to us white is black, if the hierarchical Church so defines it'.[15, 16]

The Jesuits were thus educated to play a leading part in the propagation of the revitalized Catholic Church. Lainez, the second general of the Society, urged it to pay serious attention to higher learning, and before he died (1565), he helped to establish a hundred and thirty colleges. These colleges became centres of training in orthodox Catholicism, at the same time providing a general education that for many years remained the best available. Jesuit emphasis upon education through schooling and the printed word was largely attributable also to Peter Canisius (Pieter de Hondt), a Dutch-born Jesuit. Renowned for his humanistic learning and strict morality, he became first provincial of the Jesuits in Germany and a close adviser of Emperor Ferdinand I, who called upon him to carry the fight against Protestantism into the very land of its birth. Active successively at the universities of Cologne, Ingolstadt, and Vienna, Canisius was an effective agent of the

Counter-Reformation in various parts of Germany, Austria, and Switzerland. At the instigation of Ferdinand he published his *Summa Doctrinae Christianae* (1555) and followed it a year later with his *Catechism* for children and adults, which was patterned upon Luther's very successful *Shorter Catechism* of 1529 (see below). Both of Canisius's works became standard texts for religious instruction in Catholic Germany.[17]

In the hands of the Jesuits the school became a methodical and disciplined tool of reform and Counter-Reformation. They permitted no deviation from what they considered orthodox doctrine (though sometimes they were themselves suspected of heresy). Jesuits soon acquired envied reputations for their new methods of instruction, their new schools (where education was provided free of charge), and their new textbooks. Within a century of its inauguration the Society had created over five hundred schools, particularly in the Catholic countries most threatened by Protestantism, such as Poland, Hungary, and Austria. Their work as teachers (not to mention their power through deliberately cultivated influence in high places and their readiness to countenance forceful measures) was so respected that even Protestants sometimes voluntarily sent their children to Jesuit schools. Their fifth general, Claudius Aquaviva, reduced a half-century of educational experience to a *Ratio Studiorum*, completed in 1599, which prescribed the curriculum by which Descartes, Calderón, Corneille, Bossuet, Voltaire, and other future charges of the Jesuits were educated. It emphasized discipline, Latin, and the Catholic tradition (see below).

The Jesuits gave spiritual instruction also by preaching and the confessional. Their churches, modelled upon the Gesù at Rome, were designed, and their pulpits elaborated, with an eye to more effective preaching. Breaking with the tradition that sermons should be delivered only on specific holidays and other special occasions, they preached throughout the year. The emphasis upon the psychological value of frequent confession originated with Loyola himself; his 'Rules for Thinking with the Church' recommended 'confession to a priest, and the reception of the Most Holy Sacrament once a year, and much better every month', and 'much better still' every week.[18] From his own experience Loyola had learned that despair of salvation impeded joyous and active Christianity. He therefore wanted confession to be a solace to the penitent and urged leniency in the confessional so that even a sinner to whom absolution might be denied would return hopefully to his church and his confessor.

Departures like these from accepted practice and doctrine roused hostility among other orders and orthodox theologians. The Jesuits' emphasis upon education made them open rivals of the Dominicans, who previously had held a near monopoly on theological education. Some Dominicans, prominent as teachers in leading Catholic universities, worked to bring about reform in the training of priests. Perhaps the most zealous educational reformer among them was Melchior Cano (1509–60), one of the great Salamanca theologians of his day. He was an outspoken opponent of the Jesuits, for he was a jealous guardian of his theological reputation, an inflexible collaborator of the Spanish Inquisition as a national instrument, and a willing supporter of Spanish absolutism against the papacy. As a humanist, he was sincerely interested in freeing Scholasticism from the stultifying wrangles that had come to be so characteristic of its adherents. His posthumously published work, *De Locis Theologicis*, stands out as an inspired plea that a clear and scientific theology be applied to a genuine revitalization of Catholicism. His scholarly efforts helped to promote the reform of theology and of clerical training. In France, where the Sorbonne, dominated by Dominican influence, held sway as interpreter of orthodox Catholic doctrine, the Jesuits likewise encountered great difficulties in establishing themselves and their colleges, but ultimately they won out. Independently, Cardinal Borromeo placed clerical training high among his numerous ecclesiastical reforms, establishing several seminaries and other schools for aspirants to the priesthood.[20]

The Rise of Secular Institutions

Despite continuing religious tensions, between 1500 and 1775 the universities' role in secular learning grew more impressive. Outstanding men of science in the sixteenth, seventeenth, and eighteenth centuries (e.g. Copernicus, Galileo, Newton, Boerhaave, Linnaeus) were associated with universities as students, teachers, or both, and the universities boasted significant figures in other fields besides (e.g. the Cambridge Platonists, the German cameralists, Pufendorf, Blackstone, Adam Smith, Kant). Moreover, there were continually appearing (see below), new kinds of professional training within the universities themselves as well as independent technical and professional schools, some of which were eventually to become parts of nearby universities. Even in the older universities famous men who were not theologians, sometimes not even clerics, were employed as teachers in the professional faculties more often. Such men might well give instruction in their professions without special attention to religious implications.

Gradually, in the schools no less than in the scientific academies, nonclerical specialists gained predominance in the new sciences and technology. King Francis I, prompted by Budé and other humanists, inaugurated a series of royal lectures (1530) more or less frankly intending to offset the theological concentration at the Sorbonne; eventually these lecturers became the Collège de France, giving instruction in mathematics and science as well as the usual humanist subjects. As new universities arose in Protestant countries—among them, Leiden (1575), Giessen (1607), Utrecht (1634), Lund (1666), Halle (1694), and Göttingen (1736)—they tended to react against the Aristotelianism of the Jesuits and to make the new sciences as well as the old cultural tradition a part of their curricula. While some of the new institutions were conservative, they too helped to lay a foundation for the later prestige of their countries in the sciences. A persuasive precedent was set with the endowment of special chairs in mathematics and science by Thomas Gresham at Gresham College in London (1596), Henry Savile at Oxford (1619), and Henry Lucas at Cambridge (1663). As indicated in Chapter XIV, the University of Leiden acquired a botanical garden and an anatomical theatre—and it also took steps toward offering an engineering curriculum (see below)—shortly after its founding, and by the end of the seventeenth century courses in the natural sciences there and in other Dutch universities were firmly ensconced. Under Newton's influence, Cambridge became a centre of scientific learning. In the eighteenth century, we shall soon see, engineering schools were established in several European cities, and we have already encountered a veterinary school that was founded in Lyons.

Continuing Clerical Domination of Schooling

The early universities had commonly been dominated by religious orders or by *magistri* who were at least nominally members of the church hierarchy. Even after the Reformation similar domination was the rule, even in Protestant countries. For instance, Oxford and Cambridge restricted teaching to Anglican clergy or bachelor members of the Church of England. In the course of time, however, the number grew of persons who thought of themselves as teachers, even when they were clergymen, rather than as clergymen. Some of these teachers were devoted humanitarians as well.

The Pietist university at Halle provided some good examples of this type. Under the guidance of Thomasius, instruction there was modernized, history and science were given a prominent place in the curriculum, and university courses were for the first time given in German rather than Latin. As a humanitarian Thomasius raised doubts about the justice of current court practices in connection with witchcraft and torture. Since Pietist doctrine stressed the importance of good works as a sign of regeneration, Christian charity became an important aspect of life at Halle.[21] While a professor there, Francke, most important of the Pietist ministers after Spener, founded a number of schools including a Paedagogium for better-off pupils and an Orphan Asylum, where instruction was given not only in religion but also in traditional learning and vocational skills. Francke's institutions became a model for other schools in Germany, and his own series of schools at Halle, organized as the *Franke'sche Stiftungen*, enjoyed an enduring career.

Other sects displayed a similar mixture of humanitarian and missionary purposes in their pedagogy. In England the Society for Promoting Christian Knowledge opened in 1698, and within a matter of decades thousands of 'charity schools' for children who at a tender age would have to go to work were dispensing a modicum of reading, writing, and arithmetic along with shop and religious training. In the Catholic school systems the number of teaching orders steadily increased until in the eighteenth century some thirty of them existed. One of the most important remained the Brothers of the Christian Schools, who, though they took monastic vows, became not priests but teachers of the poor.[22] A fine example of the rare lay humanitarian-teacher was Giacobbo Rodriguez Pereire (1715–80), who, having had to devise a sign language in order to communicate with his deaf wife, began a movement for the education of deaf mutes.

Thus literacy was step by step ceasing to be regarded as a monopoly for a privileged few and was becoming instead, though slowly and often painfully, a possible possession for even the underprivileged. Education was not yet considered, however, an obligation of society to give and of the individual to get. The number of schools at the end of our period was greater than before, but the increase meant only rarely gratuitous and hardly ever compulsory education. Nor was the curriculum a broad one. In Catholic and Protestant countries alike, schooling was still largely dominated by clerics, whose major aim was to mould their pupils into good Christians.

EDUCATIONAL METHODS AND THEORY IN EUROPE

The Decline of the Schoolmen

Throughout the early centuries of Western educational history intensive study in specialized subjects was absent from monastic and cathedral schools. Specialization was found rather in the practical training of guild apprentices and in certain professions. In the thirteenth century, specialized training began to appear in university faculties of theology, law, and medicine. Each faculty was autonomous, even when one of the faculties was dominant. Theology was the recognized speciality at Paris, medicine at Salerno and Montpellier, law at Bologna. In most schools a baccalaureate degree, and in some a master's, in the liberal arts was prerequisite to specialization, which might then require five additional years of study.

In both the liberal arts and the specialized courses, the lecture method was common. Until the development of printing, textbooks were rare and expensive, and the owner of a textbook was a potential lecturer. He might read portions, say, of the text of Galen, the Justinian Code, or the papal decretals, and comment thereon. A student who took careful notes and transcribed them onto parchment had the basic equipment for lectures of his own if he became a professor. Lectures were supplemented either by discussions, especially in courses in the liberal arts and theology, or, in courses of medicine, by assisting a physician or observing an autopsy.

The growth of urban communities and the increase of wealth in the towns augmented the number of young people desirous of, and financially prepared for, advanced instruction concerning the things of this world as well as the next. Cathedral schools, in the larger urban centres, tended to acquire larger student bodies and wider intellectual horizons. Business schools, especially in Italian towns, made for still wider breaches in the citadel of religiously dominated education. By 1300, several universities were centres of vigorous discussion of many aspects of life on earth as well as in Heaven.

Nevertheless, religion still was the major subject of education, and theology the queen of the sciences. In the thirteenth century Thomas Aquinas and contemporary Scholastics had made Aristotle safe for Christianity. The Thomist identification of faith with reason was a beautifully balanced thought structure, sometimes compared with the Gothic cathedral. It was upset, in its turn, by the Scholastics of the succeeding period, for they made Aristotelian logic more an end than a means. A sort of hyper-intellectualism was prominently displayed in the professorial disputations which were characteristic of the late-medieval educational process. In keeping with his realistic approach Vives complained: 'Disputations have blinded judgment. . . . A base desire for distinction took possession of the minds of the disputants and, just as in battle, victory came to be the chief consideration rather than the elucidation of the truth'.[23] Revulsion at Scholastic 'logic chopping' combined with the growing professionalism of the medical, legal, and business schools of the day to work toward the secularization of education.

Educational Theory before the Enlightenment

In the period between the rise of the universities and the Protestant upheaval, educational techniques were largely traditional, objectives were largely fixed, and little was written on educational theory. One of the few social changes to raise questions of educational theory was the decline of chivalry, and several serious works took up the question of knightly education and conduct. Ramon Lull's *Order of Chivalry* appeared in early-fourteenth-century Spain, William Caxton's treatise with a similar title in late-fifteenth-century England, and Castiglione's *Book of Courtier* in early-sixteenth-century Italy. All three works give evidence of the changing concept of the nobleman's role in society. Lull's pre-Renaissance rules stand in marked contrast to Castiglione's for the cultured Renaissance gentleman and gentlewoman (see below). Caxton (between the two in time) bewailed the decadence of his own day and the passage of true knighthood. A cruder variation on both themes is found in a book of instructions written by the nobleman Geoffrey de la Tour Landry for his daughters. To impress upon them that even a noblewoman's place was the home and she should subject herself to her lord and master, he told of a burgher housewife who suffered a broken nose for using haughty language to her husband.

Until the Protestant upheaval Renaissance writers tended to add the humanistic to the chivalric concept of education. Aeneas Sylvius (later Pope Pius II) wrote for King Ladislas of Bohemia a work entitled *De Librorum Educatione* (1450), in which he recommended that the education of gentlemen should include, along with the study of certain parts of the Bible, attention to Latin historians and, in order to converse with the common people, the vernacular languages.²⁴ In More's non-Christian Utopia (1516), to be sure, girls as well as boys received their formal training at the feet of the country's chosen men, who imparted virtue along with knowledge to all comers, for all the deserving were equal and knowledge was inseparable from virtue. But that was in Utopia. Humanist educators generally made more of an effort to reconcile humanism with the aristocratic tradition.

Erasmus was the outstanding proponent of this compromise. His *Enchiridion Militis Christiani* (1503), though it preached the Christian ideal, looked for worldly welfare not through a pious clergy but rather through the welding of scholarly and humanist interests with aristocratic virtues in the Christian nobleman. In his *Encomium Moriae* (*Praise of Folly*, (1509) the heroine, Lady Folly, embodied the finest of Classical and Christian principles as compatible ideals. His *Institutio Principis Christiani* (1516) revealed a sanguine trust in princely readiness to learn to respect human aspirations. In Erasmus' theory of education youth was to be trained to approach the problems of life with an armament of high-minded principles and an ability to think independently. His works on the education of boys, such as *De Pueris* and *De Ratione Studii*, tried to teach good maxims along with good Latin style.

For adults, the humanist leaning toward a broad education for a flesh-and-blood world came closer to realization in Italian court life. Machiavelli's 'Prince', forerunner of the *Realpolitik* of a later age (see Chapter VIII), presented a marked contrast to Erasmus' 'Christian Prince'; Machiavelli was cynical where Erasmus was sanguine; in Machiavelli's politics *virtu* was essentially patriotism, to which all other scruples must yield. Castiglione's *Courtier* was more nearly the Italian counterpart of Erasmus' moralistic work, but it too illustrated the dominantly secular character of educational ideals in the humanist circles of Italy. All over Europe, at least partly under Castiglione's inspiration, arose 'academies' for the sons of noblemen and gentry, where arms and gymnastics as well as Latin, modern languages, mathematics, and 'natural philosophy' were taught.²⁵ In Germany these schools were frankly designated *Ritterakademien*.

The Protestant Revolt and the Catholic Reformation turned schooling more explicitly toward religious objectives. Its initial effect was to discourage educational innovations. Erasmus expressed the opinion that science decayed where Lutheranism accumulated. Luther's emphasis on faith rather than good works and on Scripture rather than Scholasticism, and his arguments with Catholic theologians led him and his more evangelical followers to denounce clerically dominated universities and schools as enemies of true religion. The Synod of Dort, while calling upon the Dutch authorities to reform old schools, establish new ones, and provide gratuitous instruction for the poor, also demanded strict school regulation in the interests of Calvinist orthodoxy. The *collèges* (secondary schools) and *académies* (higher schools and seminaries) established in the Huguenot cities of France were primarily run by pastors to train pastors. Later in the seventeenth century, the Puritan-controlled Barebones Parliament of England contemplated the abolition of universities because they were centres for the propagation of worthless 'carnal knowledge' (i.e. Aristotelian Scholastic education not based on Scripture or God's Book of Nature).

In general, the quarrel of governments with the Roman hierarchy had the effect of placing schools along with churches more closely under monolithic state control. When Protestant princes secularized ecclesiastical property, they felt obliged to assume responsibility for the continuation of the church's functions, education prominent among them, and they created new royal schools. The things that were Caesar's and the things that were God's thus seemed closer to becoming the same things. Certain Protestant leaders recognized the importance of educating young men for the more effective spread of their territorial faith. Moreover, the Protestant reformers, subscribing to the principle of direct acquaintance with God through the study of the Bible, were logically impelled to favour national programmes of popular education. To be sure, the principal Lutheran educator, Melanchthon, had been a student at humanist Heidelberg, had taught the Classics at Tübingen and Wittenberg, and had acquired little fear of humanism. Yet Lutheran-controlled schools usually fell short of the Erasmian ideal of the Christian humanist gentleman. As in most other countries of the sixteenth century, education in Germany, in both theory and method, was rather an instrument for the indoctrination and defence of the sovereign's faith; schools and universities were instruments of government, controlled and carried on by the established clergy. A corollary of *cuius regio, eius religio* was *cuius religio, eius educatio.*[26]

Since the teaching profession had been practically a clerical monopoly, the frequent closing of monasteries and the recurrent attacks upon the priesthood in the Protestant areas of Germany reduced the number of available teachers. At the same time the radical wing of the reform movement preached a mysticism that emphasized divine inspiration, and though some of its leaders were well educated men, they deprecated formal education. As a result, at Wittenberg, Erfurt, and elsewhere the number of students steadily decreased. Luther early opposed this trend away from formal schooling. He prepared (1529) a *Shorter Catechism* and a *Larger Catechism* in German for the training of children, and he urged governments to assume responsibility for public instruction. In an *Open Letter to the Christian Nobility of the German People* he indicated certain educational reforms to be instituted by the princes. He would centre education around the teaching of the Gospel and remove from the curriculum all those authors and compilations that had constituted the core of Scholastic education—Aristotle, canon law, the decretals. Of Aristotle only the works on logic, the *Rhetoric*, and the *Poetics* were to be retained, because of their practical value; the law of the land would replace canon law, which was no longer needed.

In an appeal *To the Councilmen of All Cities in Germany That They Establish and Maintain Christian Schools* (1524) and again in *A Sermon on the Duty of Keeping Children at School* (1530) Luther elaborated his educational theory. He decried the traditional method of teaching by often brutal discipline and deadening memorization. He gave detailed instructions regarding the subjects to be taught: Hebrew along with Latin and Greek for a better understanding of Scripture; the best commentaries and books by Classic authors; law, medicine, arts, and sciences according to the best available texts; history for a better understanding of the past; and music as a means of inspiration and relaxation. He reserved higher education for the gifted but proposed training in a practical trade along with elementary education for all children, girls included. Education, he insisted, was important for a stable and efficient civil government and, therefore, a concern of the entire citizenry. Since 'wealthy greedbugs' were the 'monks of Mammon', and since 'born princes and lords are incapable of doing it by themselves', for 'they know nothing at all about the Spiritual realm', the direction of both the temporal and the spiritual on earth 'must remain in the hands of the middle class and common people and their children.'[27] Therefore municipal authorities should provide schools and teachers.

Despite Luther's emphasis upon religion and his war against Rome, his writings contributed to the secularization of education in Germany by upholding the school as an institution maintained by the civic authority and serving the public interest. The humanistic touches of his programme are unmistakable: rejection of Scholastic methods and disciplines, emphasis upon a thorough knowledge of ancient languages, advocacy of liberal educational methods, and respect for the importance of historical studies. In form and curriculum his proposals in several ways anticipated the later German *Gymnasium*.

Calvin also gave considerable attention to the problem of schooling. As early as the *Ordonnances* of 1541 he made educational reform a vital part of his program for Geneva. In 1559 the foundations were laid for the College and Academy of Geneva, which was eventually to become the University of Geneva. It was patterned after the school founded by Sturm in Strasbourg.[28] Its curriculum too was clearly humanistic; though religious instruction and observances were stressed, it emphasized Classical literature, Greek, and Hebrew as languages, and except in matters of theology, full freedom of discussion was granted. Unlike Luther's proposed schools, however, the curriculum at Geneva neglected history and science.

The most effective Catholic educational order was that of the Jesuits. We have described above the exacting method by which Jesuit teachers were selected and prepared. The Society adapted the broad intellectualism of the humanists to the intense devotionalism of their order. They taught the Classics, especially those in Latin, and at the same time strove to revitalize Scholasticism. As masters in their colleges and as tutors in royal courts, they were expected to inculcate in Catholic youth respect for both intellectual attainment along traditional lines and strictness of discipline. They emphasized class-room instruction by means of lectures, repetition, discussion, and examinations, but made individual tutoring also easily available. Competition was encouraged by prizes and class rivalry. Discipline was strictly enforced through a system of student 'decurions' (monitors) and non-Jesuit 'correctors', who might dismiss maladapted or unqualified pupils. In the Catholic universities, where they sometimes monopolized the professorships, Jesuit theologians defended and propagated the orthodox faith with a logical skill reminiscent of the days of Aquinas. They studiously cultivated and often won the respect of popes and princes as well as parents and pupils.[19]

The Secular Trend in Educational Theory

Despite the persistence of religious controversy, by the close of the seventeenth century schools no longer aimed so largely as before to train clerics. By that time the law had become increasingly a special avenue to political and clerical preferment, medicine was recognized not only as a specialized but also as a possibly lucrative profession, science had grown into an arcane field that required special training, and specialized engineering education was more and more in demand for both civil and military purposes. The number of special schools rose (see below) and by the end of the eighteenth century had produced many graduates who had received specialized training and as men of professional standing exerted a palpable influence in their communities.

In general, specialized training in the schools tended to reinforce the secular bent. An increasing tendency to depart from public lectures and to restrict them to matriculated students alone encouraged secularism by giving greater privacy to pedagogical opinions. Moreover, for centuries students and faculty alike had fought for the freedom of the gown from the town, and occasionally the political authorities, particularly in new state-supported universities like Halle and Göttingen, voluntarily accepted, at least in principle, the idea of academic freedom from clerical or political domination, thus also aiding the trend toward secularism and pedagogical privilege inside the schools. The growth of libraries independent of ecclesiastical supervision (see Chapter XI) further promoted secularism outside as well as inside the schools.

Educational theory reflected and perhaps influenced the general secular tendency in schools and among scholars. As early as the fifteenth century Matteo Palmieri (1406–75) in his *Della vita civile* (published posthumously in 1529) held up civic virtue as the objective of education, as did his friend Alberti (see Chapter X). They shared Machiavelli's idea of *virtu* without equalling his ruthless *raison d'état*. Erasmus, we have seen, looked for worldly welfare through the Christian ruler who would weld humanist interests with aristocratic virtues, while Castiglione portrayed a courtier who would be a Christian but was more interested in acquiring the humanist accomplishments. Thomas Elyot in *The Booke Named the Governour* (1531) pleaded that prospective officials undergo a serious humanistic training rather than a course of elegant or pious study, and that incumbent officials be guided by an intuitive, gentlemanly sense of justice and responsibility. In Thomas More's *Utopia* (1516), service to the state was the objective of all education whether formal for children or informal for adults, and control was placed in the hands of an 'order of the learned'. For him learning included prominently 'a knowledge of human affairs . . . so useful even to a theologian'; he approved of those 'who make the knowledge of things natural a road to heavenly contemplation, and so pass from philosophy and the liberal arts . . . to theology'.[30,31]

Some Theorists of the Sixteenth and the Seventeenth Century

In the sixteenth century humane letters were the mark of the gentleman and aristocrat. The new Collège de France, the new Protestant colleges, particularly those modelled on Sturm's school at Strasbourg, and the early Jesuit colleges promoted the teaching of 'the liberal arts', those studies regarded as befitting a free gentleman, as opposed to servile, vocational, or mechanical pursuits. They presumed, however, a different kind of servility. Lessons were often, like the faults of Shakespeare's Cassius, 'set in a note book, learn'd and conn'd by rote'.

As a general rule sixteenth-century writers extolled the Classics as the core of a good education, but Rabelais and Montaigne were exceptions. Rabelais' character Ponocrates took a special interest, as the tutor of Gargantua, in teaching the natural sciences. Rabelais, himself a physician, put considerable stress on physical matters such as exercise, wholesome food, loose garments, and fresh air. Montaigne, who had learned to speak Latin before French, emphasized the *sana mens in corpore sano*, insisting upon physical and moral health, even, if necessary, at the expense of Latin books. He decried corporal punishment as a means of inculcating knowledge or morality and suggested indirect methods such as plays and games in its stead. Both Rabelais and Montaigne believed that pupils should be urged to learn by excitement of their curiosity rather than by coercion.

Among the outstanding pedagogical theorists of the seventeenth century were a number of Protestant teachers, advocates of popular and willing Bible-study in the vernacular. The German pedagogue Wolfgang Rathke (1571–1635) maintained that knowledge was better imparted by the mother tongue than by Latin and by direct observation than by rote, and he tried to guide children by their natural curiosity rather than by the rod. Subscribing to similar principles, the leader of the Moravian Brethren, Comenius, made explicit his conviction that learning proceeds best from the known to the unknown. His fundamental educational programme was the study of God's nature by the inductive method, the elucidation of the human conscience by reason, and the understanding of Revelation through Holy Writ. One of the first to set forth clearly the gradation of education into infant, elementary, secondary, and advanced levels, he insisted that the study of Latin should be postponed until about the age of twelve. He favoured educating girls as well as boys. Like Rabelais, Montaigne, and Rathke he urged rousing the spirit to voluntary effort rather than beating the reluctant flesh, a practice all too common in their day, as the best way of exciting a zeal for learning, and, as Vittorino and Vives had done before him, he advocated school playgrounds and large, airy schoolrooms. Believing that school books should be adapted to the pupil's ability to comprehend, he wrote a series of six textbooks, graded in both vocabulary and content from elementary to more advanced levels, and provided parallel translations and basic vocabularies for some of them. His beginner's book, *Orbis Sensualium Pictus* (Nuremberg, 1657), taught Latin vocabulary by means of pictures, giving Latin phrases and their vernacular translation side by side.

When driven from his own country in 1628 by the ravages of the Thirty Years' War, Comenius settled at first in Poland, where he taught school, wrote books, and tried, as their bishop, to keep the Brethren from despair. He went to England in 1641 on the invitation of the Long Parliament, which hoped, until frustrated by contemporary political tensions and civil wars, to reform the English school system and to provide an example of state education. Though mentioned for the presidency of the freshwater Harvard University, he took a post instead in Sweden (1642). In nearly eighty years of life he taught school in several different cities and in at least three vernaculars, and personally introduced his pedagogical ideas into Poland, England, Sweden, Germany, Hungary, and Holland. His writings, translated into about fifteen languages, including Arabic, Persian, and Turkish, aimed at a set of ideals which he apparently considered practicable—a united Protestant church, a world organization for peace, and an encyclopedic ordering of knowledge ('pansophy'). While living in Amsterdam, he collected a number of them in his *Opera Didactica Omnia* (4 volumes, 1657). Didactics (i.e. education) was for Comenius 'the whole art of teaching all things to all Men'.[32] Such an objective, he was convinced, if communicated by uniform textbooks in a universal language in common schools, would bring an organic unity to at least the evangelical groups, perhaps to the whole Christian world, and ultimately even to all the other religions.

Though Comenius did not stay long in England, his influence remained strong among those who hoped that political revolution might bring educational reform. His Prussian-born English publisher, Samuel Hartlib, planned to create a school along Comenian principles, and, probably at Hartlib's instigation, Milton published his *Tractate of Education* (1644), written much earlier, and shortly afterward Petty published his *Advice . . . for the Advancement of Some Particular Parts of Learning* (1648). Milton's *Of Education* favoured a mixture of religious and humanistic schooling for gentlemen's sons, 'a complete and generous education which fits a man to perform justly, skilfully and magnaminously all the offices, both private and public, of peace and war'. While Milton said little about experimental science and technology, Petty propounded a more revolutionary system that would provide rich and poor children alike with technical as well as language training.

Locke's educational theory was less mystical than Comenius's and less radical than Petty's. His *Some Thoughts concerning Education* (1693) was perhaps the most influential pedagogical essay of its day. He seems to have been impressed by Rabelais and Montaigne, and he certainly made an impression upon Rousseau. Like his French predecessors, he stressed the importance of health, wholesome physical surroundings, and play in educating the young. Virtue and wisdom, he felt, rather than religion should be taught, and taught early, and not by corporal punishments so much as by appealing to the child's honour, reason, and sense of shame. Departing from the contemporary emphasis on the Classics, Locke advocated a practical education that should prepare for citizenship and a trade or profession rather than for a genteel love of letters. He objected to learning by rote. The child, if of the upper classes, should, he thought, first learn to speak his own language correctly, then another living language, and then Latin (but not Greek). Useful studies like geography, arithmetic, astronomy, geometry, history, law, and 'natural philosophy' (science) should fill in the young gentleman's curriculum until finally he acquired a manual trade and accounting. For the children of the poor between the ages of three and fourteen, Locke's *Proposals for the Bringing Up of the Children of Paupers* (1697) advocated a system of 'working schools' providing, along with food and shelter, a compulsory training in some kind of work.

French Education and Its Enlightenment Critics

The extent of innovation advocated by Comenius, Locke, and their followers can be well appreciated if contrasted with educational theory and practice in contemporary France. Bishop Fénelon was one of the leading French educational theorists of the day. He set forth his ideas on teaching in a work which, though entitled *De l'éducation des filles* (1687), dealt in part with the general problems of pedagogy. He believed in beginning the child's education in the cradle, making the learning process attractive by stories, play, gentle prompting, and other indirect methods. He wished to counteract the neglect of girls' schooling and the current prejudice against educated women (mirrored in several of Molière's plays). Nevertheless, the good abbé held that women's education should continue to be inferior to men's, because women not only needed to know less but were less competent to learn some subjects, such as the intricacies of the law; all they needed was reading, writing, arithmetic, and a few other things that might make them good wives, mothers, and housekeepers. Prominent among these things was the Catholic religion, with enough about other Christian religions to enable them to recognize and avoid heresy. Fénelon was the tutor of one of Louis XIV's grandsons, for whose guidance he wrote *Télémaque, Dialogues des morts,* and a collection of *Fables,* seeking by means of fiction to inculcate responsibility and morality.[33]

Fénelon's programme was followed in a general way by the two outstanding French schools for girls—Port Royal and Saint-Cyr. For all Port Royal's significance in letters and in boys' education (see below), its convent school for girls was a dreary place, whose routine made Fénelon feel sad when he mentioned it. The programme at Saint-Cyr, a school founded in 1686 by Madame de Maintenon, was at first intended to counteract the dreariness characteristic of the convent school. As Louis XIV's wife, she was allowed to teach at Saint-Cyr, as well as to direct it by written instructions and daily visits, thus becoming one of the earliest lay school-mistresses of France. But after five or six years of a liberal spirit, Saint-Cyr lapsed into something like other convent schools.

In contrast, some of the schools for boys were venturesome and exhilarating. The short-lived Little Schools of Port Royal for boys, founded by the Abbé de Saint Cyran, had excellent teachers and used new and challenging methods of instruction. Here small groups under the constant guidance of kindly tutors underwent a serious training that, though aiming to cultivate Jansenist judgment and austerity rather than knowledge and science, was by a conscientious effort fitted to their capacities.[34] Elementary education in France began to be based upon a series of common principles after La Salle founded at Rheims (1685) a seminary for the Brethren of the Christian Schools—in fact, one of the first 'normal schools' of Europe (though the term itself did not become current until the end of the century). The teachers in the Brethren schools now received some training in pedagogy and a set of instructions on how to conduct themselves; they were forbidden, for instance, to give more than five blows with ferule or rod without special permission.

Still, at the beginning of the eighteenth century, teaching practice in France was, by modern standards, lamentable (and France's educational institutions were perhaps more advanced than those of other countries). As Charles Rollin's *Traité des études* (1726–28) showed, the schools permitted corporal punishment, ordinarily afforded girls only a rudimentary education, considered Latin the proper medium of learned communication, left no time for the study of modern history, provided little for the study of science beyond an elementary and theoretical level, and at every step gave much attention to religious instruction. With the mixture of truth and hyperbole that makes for caricature, Diderot described the secondary curriculum similarly:

'There are still taught today, under the name of belles-lettres, two dead languages which are . . . studied for six or seven years without being learned; under the name of rhetoric, the art of speaking is taught before the art of thinking, and that of speaking elegantly before having ideas; under the name of logic, the head is filled with the subtleties of Aristotle . . .; under the name of ethics, I do not know what is said . . .; under the name of metaphysics, there are discussed . . . the first elements of scepticism and bigotry . . .; under the name of physics, there is endless dispute about the elements of matter and the system of the world; but not a word on natural history, not a word on real chemistry, very little on the movement and fall of bodies; very few experiments, less still of anatomy, and nothing of geography.'35

For this state of affairs Diderot and his fellow *philosophes* blamed not only the Jesuits but also other teaching orders, such as the Christian Brethren, now known by their enemies as *ignorantins*.

Between 1762 and 1764, the Jesuits of France were dispersed by a series of decisions of several parlements (see Chapter IV). With either the intention that the control of the schools should or the expectation that it would now pass to other hands, several writers directed their minds to the problem of education. Since the parlements had played a leading role in the prosecution of the Jesuits, members of those courts were prominent among those who examined the problem. The Breton parlementarian Louis René de La Chalotais wrote an *Essai d'éducation national* (1763), in which he pleaded for an essentially secular education to be provided by the state for citizens rather than by the church for Christians. Learning, he contended, ought to be based on observation, history, geography, living languages, mathematics, and natural history, with training in the Classical languages only in the maturer years and in ethics only toward the close of schooling. Schoolhouses should be spread widely over the country and easily accessible. The useful crafts should be taught along with the sciences, so that pupils of both high and low society might benefit from them.

The staff of the University of Paris in 1763–64 also turned its attention to the problem of education and prepared some memoirs on the subject. The Paris parlementarian Barthélemi-Gabriel Rolland (1734–94) in 1768 submitted a *Report* to his colleagues, largely derived from the university's memoirs. He advocated a scheme of state schooling that would attempt to give each pupil the education best suited for his needs, and for the better training of more teachers he suggested the creation of normal schools. In order that the pedagogical system might be well integrated and kept to high standards he proposed that a centralized national bureau be set up and vested with the obligation and authority to conduct annual school inspections.

Rousseau's *Emile* came in part from the educational crisis created by the dissolution of the Jesuit order. This work was less directly, however, a response to the need to replace the Jesuits than were La Chalotais' or Rolland's and was rather an essay in its author's philosophical system, premised upon the potential penchant for good in natural man. In two earlier discourses on the arts and sciences, Rousseau had argued that man is perpetually engaged in a conflict between his self-concern (*amour de soi-même*) and his altruism (*pitié*), and that civilization tends to turn his justifiable self-concern into selfishness (*amour-propre*), discouraging his nascent inclination toward altruism. Rousseau now faced the question how to educate the young so as to retain the advantages of civilization without incurring its corrupting effects. In *Emile* he proposed a system of private tutoring that until the age of twelve would remove the child from almost all contact with civilization (save such as his omniscient tutor saw fit to allow) and after that would permit only a limited contact until the age of twenty.

Emile was a fictitious biography of such a child. Although Rousseau insisted that an infant be nursed by his mother, he deliberately made Emile an orphan. Since 'the poor man has no need of an education' because he 'may make a man of himself' (Book I), Rousseau made Emile also a rich aristocrat. Until Emile was about fifteen, he learned mostly through the senses. He read no books but *Robinson Crusoe* and, living in the country, saw almost no one but his tutor. Until he was twelve, he played outdoors a great deal and was encouraged to study such concrete things as geometry, drawing, and music by indirect guidance and by enticement of his curiosity, by doing and seeing. From thirteen to fifteen, he developed his reason and judgment, being occupied chiefly in learning the natural sciences. He also acquired a trade, since only thus could he be economically independent and fully competent; besides, since the times were precarious, his tutor wanted him to be prepared for possible revolution. Emile would probably have learned to read (though not from books) before he reached fifteen, but at that age he was deliberately stimulated to read. From fifteen to twenty, he was taught moral and social values and how to live in society; he learned about human relations from history and literature mostly in his own language; and he learned Latin in order to know French better. At twenty he acquired a knowledge of religion by conversation with a kindly vicar (who was essentially a Deist, however). By that time Emile was prepared to marry the heroine of Rousseau's *Sophie*, whose education had been distinctly inferior to his, largely mere preparation for marriage to him.

Rousseau's *Emile* demonstrated how far some writers of the eighteenth century were willing to go in the direction of permissive education. The author favoured a system that would teach the pupil through personal supervision how to solve his own problems rather than one that would discipline him along the lines that his elders considered good for him to know. Rousseau made the guidance of a child's growing ability to absorb rather than the adequacy of the curriculum the criterion and aim of an educational programme. Obviously such guidance would be costly and hence was no scheme of public education.

In his *Considérations sur le gouvernement de Pologne* Rousseau advocated an intensely patriotic form of national education that was considerably more practical, but it seems to have made no appreciable impact upon the Polish school system. The reforming efforts of the Piarist father Stanislaw Konarski (1700–73) were more efficacious. He founded a college for young gentlemen in 1740, emphasizing Polish and other modern languages rather than the Classical languages and giving considerable attention to the natural sciences. The Piarist monk was a Polish patriot. He wrote an attack, *An Effective Method of Government* (1761–64), on the *liberum veto*, attributing to it the instability of the Polish government. He gradually won some of the other teaching orders, including some Jesuits, to his pedagogical theories. When the Jesuit order was abolished in Poland (1772), a state Commission of Education was set up and, taking over the Jesuit schools, ran them as a secular school system with leadership provided by Konarski's disciples and former Jesuits.

Emile was contemporaneously perhaps Rousseau's most influential work, although the French Revolution was to make his *Contrat social* appear more so. Some parents tried to apply Rousseau's pedagogical method to the education of their children, and it provided a pattern for the eccentric Johann Bernhard Basedow to follow. Basedow adhered to the theory of active pupil participation in the classroom, and it was exemplified in his elementary school, the Philanthropinum, founded at Dessau in 1774. The Philanthropinum, though short-lived, was, in turn, a source of inspiration for Friedrich Eberhard von Rochow's schools and writings (e.g. *Kinderfreund*, 1775) and for other German elementary schools, as well as for Johann Heinrich Pestalozzi's work with poor children, begun in 1774, and later with war orphans.

Rousseau's educational theories have been warmly attacked by some and warmly defended by others. There is less debate about the inadequacies of contemporary school methods. *Emile* exposed some of the current educational shortcomings—the frustration of education by pedagogical cruelty, the meaninglessness of noble phrases if learned by rote, the wastefulness of teaching foreign languages to those ignorant of their own, the high price placed upon parroting and affectation where mere wordiness is esteemed, and the futility of appeals to the reason of the immature and inexperienced. But the practical reformers did not need Rousseau's diatribes to recognize these evils; upon the withdrawal of the Jesuits they found an obligation and an opportunity. Several formerly Jesuit schools revised their curricula. The Collège Louis-le-Grand, where Voltaire had received an apparently good education early in the century, after 1763 gave its classes in French instead of in Latin and introduced new disciplines such as the sciences and history.

Rousseau incurred deep hostility in both Catholic and Protestant quarters, and from both *philosophes* and anti-*philosophes*, because of his views (among others) on religion and religious education, which were neither orthodox enough for some nor unorthodox enough for others. The problem of religious and moral training was a difficult one for the *philosophes*. Some of them, believing that the mind was the product of the senses alone, looked upon religious education as exclusively a matter of inculcating a sense of duty and obedience to law. Whether because the souls of the authors were troubled or because they themselves or their friends feared the censorship authorities, several manuscripts on this subject were left unpublished during their lifetimes. Hume's *Dialogues concerning Natural Religion* (1779) and Diderot's *Neveu de Rameau* (published in 1804 in German by Goethe) illustrate the concern of the religious skeptic with the moral problem. In a philosophy that preached the derivation of sensitive mind from sensible matter, the hope for immortality and salvation was likely to be regarded as mere superstition, though it might be converted to good use in the police system.

A thoroughgoing materialism was the basis of the educational system proposed by Helvétius. The full title of his major work reveals its nature: *De l'homme, de ses facultés intellectuelles et de son education* (1773). For Helvétius, *cogito, ergo sum* had been displaced by *sentio, ergo sum*; hence, differences in intellect among men were largely attributable to differences in their environment. The business of the state was to eliminate those differences by raising all its subjects to the highest possible intellectual level through a system of state education. Religious instruction should be given by the state for its own secular purposes and not for the purposes of salvation.

This stark materialism proved too much even for Diderot, Helvétius' friend and (in earlier works) collaborator. In a *Réfutation de l'ouvrage d'Helvétius intitulé 'L'homme'* (not published until 1875) he cast doubt on the assumption that man's intellect was as much a product of the natural environment as was the lower animal's, for, if it were, he could not explain the subordination of man's senses to man's reason and the constant improvement of that reason. Diderot was forced to conclude, more reluctantly than (but much in the manner of) Kant afterward, that there might possibly be more things even on earth than were dreamt of in Helvétius' (and hence his own earlier) philosophy:

'In the development of the egg and several other operations of nature, I clearly see organized but apparently inert matter pass from the state of inertia to the state of sensitivity and of life by purely physical agents, but the necessary link of the transition escapes me. . . . The organization and the co-ordination of inert parts does not at all lead to sensitivity, and the general sensitivity of the molecules of matter is no more than a supposition which derives all its strength from the difficulties' it does away with— which in good philosophy is not sufficient.'[36]

When, therefore, Diderot was called upon to propose a system of state education, his scheme differed from that of Helvétius. In a *Plan d'une université*, written around 1776 at the request of Catherine the Great, he advocated a school system 'whose door is open without discrimination to all the children of a nation and in which the teachers, paid by the state, impart to them an elementary knowledge of all the sciences'.37 In other words, he advocated universal elementary education, centralized in a department of state and emphasizing the sciences. In his scheme not only would schools be gratuitous but poor pupils would be fed free. So far Diderot did not depart radically from Helvétius. But in assigning to spiritual studies like religion, ethics, and history a prominent place in his curriculum, he did. In his educational scheme at the secondary and advanced school levels (ages twelve to twenty), stress was to be laid upon the sciences, to be taught in an order which he thought intrinsic to the student's understanding, but he made room in the last three years for language studies, and he permitted Moses and the Prophets to appear alongside Homer, Virgil, and other Classics. He also gave considerable attention to arts like drawing and music. In short, Diderot's school system provided not merely a utilitarian programme but also spiritual training. It attested as well that some educational theorists of pre-Revolutionary France were prepared to march a long way toward a secular, gratuitous, universal, state-controlled system of education.38

Educational Reform outside France

Outside of France a similar reaction to traditional educational methods set in. The German Gymnasium, which under the inspiration of Melanchthon and Sturm had instituted a new curriculum in reaction to the tradition of the Middle Ages, in the eighteenth century seemed to some critics too old-fashioned for practical training. The reaction was most effectively reflected in the Ökonomisch-Mathematische-Realschule opened in Berlin in 1747 by the Pietist Johann Julius Hecker (1707–68). That school was planned to prepare boys for the realities of middle-class life and so offered less Latin and Greek and more economics, mathematics, history, geography, mechanics, drawing, and other 'real' subjects, without becoming a mere trade school. Always acting the role of the 'enlightened despot', Frederick II undertook to make the schools an instrument of the Prussian state. With Hecker's aid he formulated a *General-Landschul Reglement* (1763) for Prussia, and after Prussia acquired Silesia from Austria, the Silesian educator Abbot Johann Ignaz von Felbiger (1774–88) helped him to extend it (1765) to the Roman Catholics of that province. On paper it required the parents of his realm, under penalty of fine for disobedience, to send their children aged five to thirteen to school, provided stipends for the poor, licensed teachers, and outlined a curriculum, but this school code proved during his lifetime to be little more than an aspiration.

British dissenters, with much the same practical purpose in mind as the German Pietists, created 'academies' for secondary schooling, of which Warrington (founded 1665) was probably the most famous. Priestley taught the Classics there, but its curriculum included also science, modern languages, law, history, geography, and other mundane subjects as well as religion and the Classics, The Philadelphia Academy, opened in 1751 under Franklin's sponsorship, evolved rapidly into a school where trade and the mechanical professions were taught along with Latin, English, mathematics, science, and other subjects.

No school reform, however, was more thorough than that carried out under Abbot von Felbiger's direction because of the dissolution of the Jesuit school system in Austria. Upon the invitation of Maria Theresa, Felbiger wrote an *Allgemeine Schulordnung* (1774) that proposed, at the elementary level, subsidized, compulsory *Trivialschulen* and *Volkschulen* with a kindly attitude toward children and, at the secondary level, *Hauptschulen* for technical training as well as *Gymnasien* for Classical education. Emperor Joseph II also reformed the University of Vienna so as to make it primarily an institution for the preparation of civil servants. The result was a highly centralized, strictly regimented state system of education chiefly concerned with lay rather than ecclesiastical matters, and for all its shortcomings, it won Vienna widespread admiration as an educational centre.

The Prevalence of Illiteracy

Thus, well before the French Revolution the educational systems of Europe were undergoing a series of critical changes. Where once they had been church-controlled, they were now well on the way to being controlled by the state. Where once the curriculum had been theologically oriented and controlled, it was fast becoming humanistic, scientific, and professional. Where once the objective had been the training of Christians, it was now changing to the training of subjects. Where once corporal punishment had been a major incentive to rote learning, satisfaction of native curiosity was slowly taking its place. And where once school faculties had emphasized the preservation of the cultural tradition, they were now finding more room for the specialized professions and for the probing of new frontiers. Moreover, more persons were becoming literate.

In the early Middle Ages literacy had been limited almost entirely to the clergy, and not all clergymen were literate. With the expansion of town life, schools, and universities during the twelfth and thirteenth centuries, a higher proportion of nearly all classes of the population became literate. Young nobles often went to liberal-arts schools and ambitious middle-class scions attended both liberal-arts and business schools, though educated peasants and girls were still rare. If Villani was correct in estimating that about the year 1300 over 10,000 pupils (including some girls) attended the Florentine schools, and if the population of Florence reached 90,000 (a probably generous estimate), Florence would seem to have had a highly literate citizenry. While Florence may have been an unusually progressive town, and while lay education was more advanced in Italy than elsewhere, all indications lead to the conclusion that at the opening of the fourteenth century clerical education in general was improving and that more laymen were getting a better education than before.

The gains in literacy seem to have slackened in the two succeeding centuries. In England in 1530 only 2,600 boys (out of a probable population of 5,000,000) are estimated to have attended elementary schools. Even when due allowance is made for differences in culture, economic structure, and statistical base, these figures of school population for fourteenth-century Florence and sixteenth-century England would suggest that no notable advances in literacy occurred between 1300 and 1530 despite the fact that the intervening era was that of the Renaissance in Italy and its beginnings in the north. The probability of the suggestion is enhanced by the consideration that for about two centuries after 1350, when (approximately) a 'commercial revolution' braked to a halt, most regions of western Europe suffered a decline in population and a prolonged economic depression. To be sure, during those centuries imaginative educational enterprise was exhibited in certain types of schools, such as those of Vittorino da Feltre and the Brethren of the Common Life, but it had little influence on the population as a whole or upon institutions of higher learning.

The sixteenth and succeeding centuries were marked by new vigour in education as Reformation and Counter-Reformation encouraged rival school systems. The reputation of individual artists, writers, and scientists and their works induced colleagues, admirers, and *curiosi* to travel great distances to visit them, so that eventually the Grand Tour (generally to France, Italy, Switzerland, and Germany) came to be regarded, particularly in eighteenth-century England, as a necessary part of a gentleman's education.[39] Autocratic dynastic states, competing with the churches in shaping education, siphoned the products of the educational institutions into their administrative and military machinery. In England, France, and Holland especially, schools were opened in the late seventeenth century to teach the children of the less fortunate, who might thereby become equipped to raise their status in society. The ancient complaint that learning would make the lower classes discontent to perform the simple tasks that God had allotted to them was frequently voiced, yet before the revolutions of the eighteenth century the possibility of universal literacy seemed too remote to constitute a genuine concern, except to a few *philosophes* who favoured it.

THE POPULARIZATION OF SCIENCE IN EUROPE

If university authorities remained for the most part conservative regarding the dissemination of the new science, other institutions, and in particular the scientific societies, assiduously furthered it. The scientific societies of the seventeenth century were both a symptom and a cause of a conscious striving to bring about co-operation among scientists, craftsmen, entrepreneurs, and governments. Scientific periodicals—for example, the *Journal des sçavans* of the Académie Royale des Sciences, the *Philosophical Transactions* of the Royal Society of London, the *Giornale de letterati* of Rome, and the *Acta Eruditorum* of Leipzig—became mines of information throughout the Western world. Scores of them had come into existence, though some only ephemerally, by the end of our period. Private individuals published encyclopedic volumes of information of a technological type; Jacob Leupold's *Theatrum machinarum* (Leipzig, 1724-27, in seven volumes, supplemented by two posthumous ones) and the *Encyclopédie* edited by Diderot and d'Alembert (thirty-five volumes in the complete edition, 1751-80) were the outstanding but by no means the only endeavours of this kind. The scientific societies set up laboratories, simple in scale and style in comparison with modern ones but of unprecedented excellence for their own day; other laboratories were instituted by private researchers, like Lavoisier's, or instituted by governmental agencies, as those of the royal industries in several countries. With some exceptions the introduction of the scientific laboratory into regular systems of higher learning had to wait until the end of the eighteenth century or the beginning of the nineteenth.[40]

Each of the great national academies was created by some group of interested persons or some powerful monarch or minister. By the eighteenth century nearly every principality had its scientific and literary academy, and nearly every major city had or was planning to have one. In addition, since the science of the day required relatively simple laboratory operations and since a little expenditure might suffice to acquire the necessary equipment and the reflected glory, any man of means might aspire to become a scientist or a patron of science. Thus the rich layman, royal or commoner, supplied much of the money needed to advance the new knowledge. Along with state subsidies private philanthropy began to appear as a main source of funds for scientific research and education.

As the interest in science and technology quickened, a number of writers undertook to make the new knowledge popular. In a long lifetime Bernard de Fontenelle (1657-1757), secretary of the French Academy of Sciences, was a rare combination of philosopher and scientist; he wrote several eloquent works relating to cosmology, progress, and contemporary science that won a wide reception. A number of highly respected scientists—Fahrenheit, Hawksbee, and Desaguliers among them—gave popular lectures on physics with dramatic demonstrations. Voltaire deliberately undertook to popularize Newtonian physics for the French-reading public, and by the middle of the eighteenth century (though only in small part because of his efforts) Newtonianism had definitely triumphed over Cartesianism in French scientific circles (see Chapter VII). Count Francesco Algarotti published an Italian popularization entitled *Il Newtonianismo per le donne* (1737), which went through several editions in several languages, and Benjamin Martin's *A Plain and Familiar Introduction to the Newtonian Philosophy in Six Lectures* (1751) met with similar success. Nor were these the only popular books on the subject.[41]

The churches did not regard the new perspectives in physics, biology, and other natural sciences as dangerous in and of themselves. In fact, Newton's theistic empiricism was a welcome ally against the deistic implications of Descartes or the pantheistic declarations of Spinoza. Priests and parsons were fearful, however, of some of the possibly heretical inferences of natural philosophy, especially when it dealt with metaphysical problems like monism and infinity, and they counted upon the states to subject dangerous views to censorship. In the British empire, after the passage of the law of libel in the late seventeenth century, official censorship slackened while private suits mounted in number. In France, though censorship was a regular function of the ministry of the royal household, the problem of control of opinion nevertheless remained largely a religious matter. Diderot's *Encyclopédie* used subterfuge more often with questions of a religious than of a political context; and Voltaire lived in exile or at Ferney, near the frontier, as much out of fear of Jesuits as of royal disapproval. Books were burned in France by the parlements, to be sure, and not by the clergy, but no less often for their religious than for their political unorthodoxy. In other Continental countries the censorship by royal household or Inquisition was usually more severe. Nevertheless, the day had passed when ideas could be effectively controlled by the old methods of censorship, for literacy had become common, though far from general, and the means of communication had outgrown the manuscript book and the town crier. Expanding literacy and communication, of course, sometimes promoted respect for the ancient traditions as well as the desire for *novae res* (and, paradoxical though it may seem, these were often allied sentiments). In any case, the prevailing order was obviously changing and yielding place to a new.

EDUCATION OUTSIDE EUROPE

In 1300 the aims, the methods, and even the content of education in other advanced cultures were not strikingly different from those in the West, but by 1775 the gulf between the two areas in those regards had become enormous. This widening separation was attributable, in the first place, to the growing emphasis on natural science and the scientific method in the West, while the basic aim of education in other regions continued to be to preserve and transmit the fundamental cultural pattern. At least two major consequences followed from this difference. In the first place, whereas by 1775 in the West it had become an aim of some prominent educators to develop independence of thought, rote memorization and humble dependence on a teacher remained an essentially undisturbed characteristic of education elsewhere. Furthermore, while at the beginning of our period the core of education had everywhere been religious and moral teachings, by 1775 in the West subjects divorced from religion and ethics had likewise become essential elements of the curriculum.

Despite the contrast, certain similarities were also conspicuous even in

1775. In both Europe and elsewhere, the home remained an essential centre of education. Arts, crafts, and business methods were still largely taught by mother to daughter, by father to son, or by master to apprentice. Advanced education was limited to relatively few, most of whom came from the families most favoured economically or socially, while the vast majority remained essentially illiterate. Still, if general education at public expense such as is now common existed nowhere except perhaps on paper, it was not everywhere entirely limited to the wealthy and high-born. More than other countries east or west, China through its system of public civil-service examinations provided incentive and opportunity for members of the lower social groups to acquire an education, and in Islamic lands qualified peasant lads were afforded a chance to get to the *madrasas*. Although teachers often maintained themselves at least partly by charging fees, teachers, schools, and sometimes elaborate educational centres were not uncommonly supported by either private or public endowments and contributions, and many schools were open, tuition free, to those who could otherwise qualify for entrance. In India, however, higher learning was largely for Brahmans and Kshatriyas, in Buddhist countries for nobles and monks (but nearly every man could be a monk for a while), and in Japan for samurai and monks. Considerable care went into the education of princes and sons of the higher classes everywhere, as was evidenced by the literary skill of many a ruler and courtier.

In Asian countries more than in Europe, for almost all forms of advanced education the disciple system was the rule; a student attached himself to a teacher in a sort of apprentice-master relationship. At the lower levels of education the methods were more varied. The elite might educate their own children, employ tutors at home, or arrange for instruction by a scholar or learned man with whom the family had traditional ties, and they did not eglect the education of women, especially not in India. Poorer families among the elite had to depend more on the village, temple, mosque, monastic, or endowed school, and occasionally a bright boy even from the submerged classes got an opportunity in schools of this sort.

Islamic Education

In an all-embracing social and mystical sense, religion dominated Islamic intellectual life in the fourteenth and fifteenth centuries more than in some periods before the Mongol invasions. Education had come to be shared between two institutions representing the two aspects of religion, *sharī'a* (the law) and Ṣūfism (the life of mystical devotion). The *'ulamā'*, guardians of the *sharī'a*, were formed in the *madrasas*, which taught a fairly wide range of 'religious' and allied disciplines. In preparation for entrance into a *madrasa*, a child learned to recite the Koran from memory—in Arabic, whatever his own tongue—and was sometimes also given linguistic training through the study of poetry and religious tradition, together with the essential precepts of Islam. The only significant critic of this system in the earlier centuries of our period was Ibn Khaldūn, who frowned upon too early and too exclusive preoccupation with Koranic recitation.

The *madrasa* taught chiefly through memorization and lively discussion between students and teachers, It inculcated the approved circle of studies in the all-embracing *shariʿa*, together with auxiliaries like grammar and such elementary mathematics as was needed for determining times of prayer and dividing inheritances. More enterprising students could take, in addition, such subjects as natural philosophy, music, astronomy, or magic. The period 1300–1500 was especially notable for the production of textbooks—often rhymed for easier memorization—that continued to be used long after; a fourteenth-century Syrian, Ibn-al Shiḥna, wrote a series of versified textbooks (though not the most important ones) on various subjects. Having thus been trained in the tradition, the graduate of a *madrasa* became one of the *ʿulamāʾ*, pledged in turn to maintain the hold of the prescribed circle of orthodox views on the general public and on the next generation.

The chief alternative form of intellectual education was that in the *khānaqāhs* (convents of the *ṭarīqas*), where the youth learned the way of Ṣūfism. This way consisted of partly personal discipline and partly mystical speculation, which often meant considerable freedom for adults but not for the young student. He was expected to accept unquestioningly, as if at divine behest, the least command of his master. Ṣūfism was eventually taught also in the regular *madrasas*.

The civil service was recruited to a large degree from the *ʿulamāʾ*. Training for civil service, however, was in part independent of the *madrasas*, being designed to develop a polished linguistic skill as well as an essential administrative competence. In the time of the great empires, this administrative education increased in importance. In the Ottoman Empire a special educational system developed to prepare for government office the cream of the conscripted (and converted) Christian children, of whom the less gifted were trained for military purposes. This system, heavily emphasizing the Persian humanities though offering little natural science, produced highly cultivated gentlemen.

Otherwise both lower and higher education among Muslims was dominated by theology through the eighteenth century. This system of instruction, comparable to the Scholastic instruction that the West was outgrowing, continued in all the Islamic world under the leadership of a state-supported religious class. As in Christendom, the theologically dominated educators tended to drift into subtleties of interpretation, and controversies arose that were not always fruitful.

The schools, especially before 1500, were largely free of government interference. Ample estates devoted by endowment (*waqf*) to education provided for professors and book-copyists and made available scholarships for even the most impecunious students, enabling them to spend years in intensive study, often travelling from one teacher to another. The universality of

Arabic and Persian eliminated serious barriers for peripatetic students and professors who had mastered those languages. The number of students from the middle and lower classes was large, though their lack of cultural background frequently delayed their progress, especially in their younger years. In the higher branches of learning, individual teachers rather than formal curricula were of primary importance. Ibn-Baṭṭūṭa's wanderings led him to fourteen masters, two of them women. Medicine and astrology were especially dependent on individual instruction.

Education followed essentially the same pattern in all Islamic countries. Elementary training in the teachings of Islam was considered a religious obligation for all. Children of the nobles or the wealthy were generally instructed beyond that level by tutors, learning the Koran chapter by chapter along with the subjects considered auxiliary to it. Poorer boys were sent to the *maktab*, or mosque school, conducted by a *mullah* (a man learned in the lore of Islam and attached to the mosque), where they were instructed in reading (Arabic and Persian), writing, and arithmetic. They memorized the words of the Koran and some *hadīth* (sacred reports about the Prophet). Penmanship was also cultivated. After completing their preliminary education, children of the poorer classes were often apprenticed to an *ustād* (or master), while children of the elite might go on to the *madrasa*.

We have already named the famous universities in Cairo, Tunis, and Fez. Timbuktu also had a flourishing university, famed particularly as the seat of the historian Aḥmed Baba (died 1607). In Muslim India the *madrasas*, or colleges, at Delhi, Agra, and Bidar were among the most famous institutions of higher learning. Theology, metaphysics, mathematics, physics, and Persian literature were the major subjects taught in these colleges, and many Hindus were trained there along with Muslims in the Persian literary tradition. Such different personalities as Akbar and Aurangzīb complained that the method of education was not very practical and urged more attention to subjects like geography, history, politics, medicine, and the newer sciences. Islamic rulers supported some of the colleges and gave stipends to some of the scholars but did not establish a public system of education. Although Akbar founded a girl's school at Fatḥpūr Sikri, the *purdah* (the custom of seclusion) generally kept women from the schools. Governesses were employed, however, to educate the daughters of noblemen at home, and Islamic India had reason to be proud of a good number of women of learning and literary skill.

As Islam spread in Indonesia and Malaya, the older Buddhist educational order declined and was replaced by mosque schools and *pesantren*. A *pesantren* was a community of teachers and students. Such communities were located in the vicinity of most mosques but also in villages and towns without mosques. The larger ones contained several residence and prayer halls and afforded rather elaborate courses of study. Some specialized in particular aspects of Islamic learning and religion, but in general they taught Islamic law and doctrine, some form of Islamic mysticism, and auxiliary subjects. Most of the pupils did not go on to complete the course of instruction but were content to learn only certain elementary things, including parts of the Koran, prayers, and the ritual of ablutions. Those who obtained only this limited training often rose to preside over the village prayer halls, where they also gave rudimentary instruction to village boys in reading and daily devotions. Those who completed the training could expect to be employed in the mosques or other *pesantren*.

Hindu and Buddhist Education

The traditional system of education of Hindu and Buddhist India suffered, though unevenly, under an Islamic policy of repression. In the north, where Islamic rule was stronger, many schools were destroyed, and several famous university centres came to an end, while princely patronage of Hindu and Buddhist institutions declined. In south India, on the other hand, local patronage continued, and throughout India new sectarian centres of learning associated with the various *bhakti* groups arose. Generally speaking, Hindu educational centres were able to carry on the traditional pattern, but the Buddhist centres gave way rapidly. Instruction was given more and more in the vernaculars, while at an equal pace Sanskrit became a monopoly of the Brahmans.

Supported by endowments, Brahmans largely monopolized teaching. They educated their own children or arranged for their education under a guru from another Brahman family. Many Brahmans also took disciples into their homes and assumed complete responsibility for their training; the disciple, in turn, became a sort of assistant to the teacher and remained closely attached to him for life. The wealthier members of the other two higher classes—the Kshatriyas and the Vaishyas—employed Brahmans as tutors. Brahmans were responsible in particular for the education of princes, who were instructed in the Vedas as well as in the military sciences, philosophy, grammar, logic, *dharma*, belles-lettres, fine arts, and the art of government (*arthashāstra*), which included economics and politics.

For the mass of Hindus the only formal education came through the village school, presided over by a Brahman supported by village funds or some endowment. Schools were provided for girls as well as boys. A pupil might acquire the basic elements of reading, writing, and arithmetic in a class that met in the shade of a tree or on a temple veranda. Memorization was the usual method of study. Writing was often taught by means of lines drawn in white sand strewn on the ground. More advanced education required a guru, or attendance at lectures and expositions by endowed teachers, or study at some *matha* (*college*). The traditional subjects of study were the four Vedas, their six auxiliaries (phonetics, prosody, grammar, etymology, astronomy, and ritual), philosophy, the *purānas*, logic, exegesis, law, medicine, archery, music, politics, and economics.

Hindu educational institutions of the period took several forms. One was the *bhāttavritti*, an endowment for a single learned man requiring him to perform some public teaching such as reciting and expounding the Vedas, epics, or *purānas* or offering instruction in mathematics, astronomy, or grammar. In some places several such teachers were organized into corporate colleges known as *brahmapurīs* or *ghatikās*. Another set of educational institutions were the *vidyāpīthas*, endowed quasi-monastic organizations founded by Shankara and his followers; here scholarly and holy men, presided over by learned abbotts, engaged in the study and spread of Hinduism and Sanskrit learning. Especially famous institutions of this sort located at Kūnchi, Shrīrangam, and Jagannāth became, along with their branches, centres for the advanced training of scholars. The *mathas* established by the various Vishnuite and Shivaite sects were very similar to the *vidyāpīthas* but emphasized the views of their respective sects. Still another form of educational institution consisted of temple endowments, which sometimes provided free instruction in various subjects. Pilgrimages to holy places or to learned men also served an educational purpose, as did wandering minstrels. Among the more celebrated educational centres of India were Benares, Madura, Chidambaram, Tirupati, Tirunāvāi, and Tirichur. A medical school was located at Tiruvāduturai, and a school of Panini grammar at Tiruvorriyūr; the Yādavas of Devagiri in the Deccan emphasized law and astronomy.

In the Buddhist countries of southeast Asia from Ceylon to Cambodia education centred in the monasteries or monastic schools. Teachers and religious leaders were supported in the monasteries by gifts and endowments from rulers and the wealthy classes. Almost every village had some kind of monastery where the monks gave elementary instruction in reading, writing, arithmetic, and the basic elements of Buddhism. Almost every boy, rich or poor, attended these schools for a while and then spent a brief period as a novice in the monastery, where he learned a little Pali, the sacred language, and memorized various Pali creeds, chants, and incantations. In larger centres more advanced monastic schools taught the Pali scriptures and more arithmetic, in addition to geometry, astrology, and a fanciful history and geography. The most learned men were the monks of certain monasteries and those few Brahmans whom the rulers and nobility continued to employ as teachers and advisers. This function of the Brahmans in a Buddhist country was a vestige from the time before the spread of Pali Buddhism, their Hindu lore and knowledge being still considered an essential part of government.

Sometimes boys were pledged to monkhood by their parents and so underwent a special training. The ceremony of initiation involved ten primary vows; they pledged to refrain from taking life, lying, stealing, being unchaste, trading in liquor, boasting, speaking evil, being avaricious, feeling hatred, or blaspheming. Violation of these vows might incure expulsion from the order and ruin every hope of attaining Buddhahood. A second initiation followed upon further training. This ceremony meant commitment to the two hundred and fifty vows or commandments of the ancient *Prātimoksha*, which were in the main an elaboration and refinement of the ten primary vows. In Hīnayāna countries the initiate then became a full-fledged monk (*bhikkhu*), thereby embarking fully on the path of the *arhat*. In Mahāyāna lands a third ceremony, an early Indian ascetic practice apparently unknown to Hīnayāna and Tantric Buddhism and surviving only in the Far East, was required: the initiate pledge himself to the fifty-eight vows of the 'Net of Brahmā', thereby embarking upon the career of a bodhisattva, and his head was burned in from three to eighteen places (according to his zeal).

Education in China

In China the monasteries, especially some of the Ch'an sect, were centres of Buddhist scholarship and learning, and monks received in them some degree of education. Otherwise Chinese education was dominated by the requirements of the civil service examination and the ideals of a Confucian society (see Chapter VI). The civil service examinations were the chief route to appointed office, and hence the acquisition of the type of learning required to pass them became a dominant social incentive. The examination system was stereotyped and unimaginative, tending to discourage originality and unfamiliar ideas. Sometimes, and especially in the seventeenth and eighteenth centuries, eminent Confucian teachers and thinkers who were out of sympathy with the official versions of Confucianism either failed the highest examinations or avoided official life entirely (see Chapters VII and IX). By the same token the system promoted cultural uniformity and stability. Governed by scholar-officials, the state was a liberal patron of the official scholarship and learning, and—at least in principle—maintained a system of public education designed to perpetuate Confucian society and train its leaders.

Although not particularly favourable to education, the Mongols in general kept the traditional system of public schools; the Ming rulers strengthened it; and it was continued under the Manchus. In theory, it provided village, district (*hsien*), departmental (*chou*), and prefectural (*fu*) schools, provincial colleges (*shu-yüan*), and the National University (Kuo-tzu-chien) in the capital. In fact, the village schools were not maintained by the central government, and although government funds were used to subsidize scholars in the higher schools, it is not clear that any formal course of study was available at the district, departmental, prefectural, and provincial levels. Perhaps during the best years of the Ming era these schools actually offered systematic instruction, but in the later Ch'ing (Manchu) period they were little more than groups of subsidized scholars, who gave occasional lectures, and students both subsidized and unsubsidized, who, having attained a certain standard of learning (passage of the matriculation examination), were required to present themselves periodically for examinations.

The objective of students was to move up 'the ladder of success' by civil service examinations. Upon passing the matriculation examination in the districts and prefectures, they enrolled in the district or prefectural schools, and the more promising were given scholarships to help finance their further study. Passing the district examination led to the *hsiu-ts'ai* degree, the first of the three main degrees in the civil service system, and assured further scholarships. Passing the provincial examination led to the *chü-jen* degree and assured further help and an opportunity to try for the third (*chin-shih*) degree in examinations given every three years in the capital. The *chin-shih* degree was highly prized, for it not only potentially qualified the holder for any office but was also the hallmark of the full-fledged literatus. One of the academic honours most coveted in China, appointment to the Han-lin Academy, went automatically to those receiving the highest marks in the metropolitan civil-service examination.

In actual practice education for the most part was a private affair. It began either at home with parents or tutors or in a family, clan, private, temple, or village school. Families that could afford to do so used private tutors or family or clan schools, and poorer boys went to the village school. The village schools were maintained by the villages or subsidized by private donations. Many village youths received a limited training in reading and writing, but only a few of the brighter ones ever reached a stage where they could try the matriculation examination that might open the doors of government subsidy to them. The lower schools were staffed for the most part by relatively unsuccessful scholars who had failed to attain the higher degrees and public office. Advanced education was usually obtained through tutors or self-directed study. As a rule, the formal schooling of women was neglected. Although some families employed private tutors to train their daughters in reading and writing, girls were, as a matter of course, carefully instructed only in such things as the management of a household, courtesy, ceremonials, needlework, and their duties toward husband and parents-in-law.

Inevitably attempts were made to counteract the shortcomings of this system. During the later Ming dynasty many academies of scholars were endowed where discussions took place and students might thereby receive better instruction. More advanced students sought master-pupil associations with some famous scholars, and the disciple system was highly developed. Probably the most famous teacher and educational theorist of our period was the Ming philosopher and official Wang Yang-ming (see Chapters VII and IX), who held that knowing should be associated with doing (practice), but his theory, though it impressed later thinkers, had little influence on contemporary educational methods.

The ultimate aim in education at all levels was, by building character and inculcating Confucian ethical and social principles, to produce the *chün-tzu* (the ideal man). By 1300 the civil service examinations were largely based on the Five Classics and the Four Books as interpreted by Chu Hsi (see Chapter II). Through the official Board of Rites and the state Cult of the Scholars the government schools were expressly organized to teach this formidable list of classics, and because Confucian learning was the most important road to office, private schools, academies, and the schools maintained by the villages also were conducted by Confucian scholars along similar lines, at the expense of Taoism and other persuasions.

Instruction in the elementary schools began with memorization of certain standard works and training in writing (calligraphy). Later came elucidation of the texts. Hours were long, discipline was rigid, and the scholar, despite Wang Yang-ming's injunction, was kept from physical activity. Instruction began with the *San tzu ching* (*Three Character Classic*), written by Wang Ying-lin during the Mongol period. It was a short compendium of Confucian knowledge in rhymed lines of three characters each, setting forth the essentials of Confucian philosophy, history, and literature. Next came instruction in other books, including the *Thousand Character Essay* (in which no character appeared twice) and the *Hsiao ching* (*Classic of Filial Piety*). The student then went on to the Four Books and the Five Classics, which were memorized. Those preparing for the official examinations pored over the official compendium of the classics embodying the interpretations of Chu Hsi and his *Comprehensive Mirror of History*. More advanced students conned the poets and essayists, the dynastic histories, and the compendia on government and history. At all levels, the curriculum centred on philosophy, ethics, literature, history, and government; mathematics and science were hardly touched except in the most general and elementary terms.

Outside the traditional system of public schools, the government maintained a number of extra institutions. Both the Ming and the Manchu dynasty provided military academies, which, along with composition, taught archery, horsemanship, and other military arts. The two dynasties also made schools available at the capital for the children of nobles and other favoured persons. The Mongols and the Manchus established special schools, in addition, for their own people. The Mongols showed considerable interest in the study of medicine, divination, astronomy, and mathematics, and the later dynasties supported bureaux of astronomy and medicine and an observatory to serve the court and central government. Since, however, the few who were trained in these bureaux generally remained in their service, such specialized knowledge was rarely disseminated.

The educational system culminated in the National University, the Kuo-tzu-chien. In Ming times this university was open to the sons of officials, to students who had passed certain provincial examinations or were recommended by the provincial colleges, and to foreigners. It was divided into six departments, and students were required to pass from one to another in a ten-year course of study. Successful completion of the course led to a degree equivalent to that acquired by passing the provincial civil-service examinations. During the Manchu period the National University offered two courses of study. One emphasized the classics, with specialization in one or more of them; the other emphasized government administration, with specialization in one or more of the following fields: public rites, taxation, law, frontier defence, waterways, and mathematics. During the early Ming period graduates readily found government posts, but as the civil-service-examination system expanded, the advantages of the university degree diminished.

Education in Japan

In Korea and Annam the system of education was modelled on that of China, and in Japan the subject matter of education had long been a combination of Confucian with Buddhist learning. Japanese learning was at a low ebb during the period of Ashikaga feudalism. Members of the military class received a limited literary training as part of the family instruction in the military arts. Some court nobles and military families employed private tutors for their sons.

The formal education of women was generally neglected. Although some attended temple schools, as a rule they were taught little more than the arts of home-making in their own homes. Kaibara Ekken, one of the more broad-minded educators of the period, and his wife, Token, were concerned about the neglect of women's education (see Chapter VII), but even they went no further than to recommend that the virtues of chastity and obedience and the arts of sewing and conversation be taught.

For the most part, formal literary education was confined to temple or monastic schools (*terakoya*), a few family or clan schools, the Ashikaga College, and the Kanazawa Library. The temple schools were normally open to all social classes. Their curricula included the Chinese language and Confucian learning, but they naturally emphasized Buddhist learning and training for monkhood. The number of non-ecclesiastics who attended these schools was not great, and the knowledge acquired, even by monks, was most elementary; the Zen schools were the best of them and the most numerous (see Chapter II). The Ashikaga College under the direction of Zen scholars developed into the leading centre of Chinese learning in Japan. By 1550 it had acquired a considerable library and was reported to have as many as three thousand students. It now emphasized philosophical studies. Francis Xavier spoke of it and the monastic centres of Mt Koya (near Osaka) and Mt Hiyei (near Kyoto) as the chief institutions of learning in Japan. The Kanazawa Library, connected with the Shomyoji Temple in Kurakigun (Musashi province), was built up under the patronage of the Hōjō family. It functioned also, and became important, as a school.

Under the Tokugawa regime, political stability and the policies of the shoguns greatly stimulated scholarship, printing, and education. The founder of the Tokugawa shogunate, Ieyasu, encouraged Confucian scholarship within the samurai class, promoted temple and clan schools, transferred the Kanazawa Library to Edo, and established a school in Kyoto. By patronizing the Neo-Confucian scholar Hayashi Dōshun (1583–1637), he in reality laid the foundations for the Tokugawa College at Edo, though only in 1630 did the third shogun grant land to Dōshun for its establishment. In 1690 it was made an official government school. It was placed under the direction of Hayashi Razan, and the headship remained hereditary in the Hayashi family. Known as the Shōhei School (after the Japanese rendition of Confucius' birthplace), it became the chief centre for expounding the Chu Hsi version of Neo-Confucianism, which had been adopted by the shogunate. Its curriculum emphasized Chinese language, history, the classics, and the military arts. Its students lived in dormitories under the supervision of monitors, were examined annually, and were forbidden to discuss heretical philosophical views. Before 1797, it seems to have been open to all samurai.

Usually the great feudal lords established secular schools for the sons of their samurai. These clan schools became centres of Chinese learning throughout Japan, most of them emphasizing the orthodox Chu Hsi philosophy and the classics, but they also taught archery, horsemanship, and military science. Their professors commonly gave public lectures. One of the most famous of the clan schools was the Kodokwan of Mito, established by Tokugawa Mitsukuni, head of one of the collateral branches of the Tokugawas. It placed great emphasis on the study of Japanese history and literature and was responsible for compiling the *History of Great Japan*, which contributed to the ultimate downfall of the shogunate (see Chapter IX). The Zoshikwan, established at Kagoshima by Shimadzu, head of the Satsuma clan, also enjoyed enormous prestige. It was open to the sons of all Satsuma samurai, but the sons of tradesmen were permitted to occupy the lowest seats in the lecture halls. Clan schools whose course of study did not depart markedly from the orthodox philosophy generally received subsidies from the shogun. In most of these samurai schools children from six to nine years of age learned to read and write about a thousand characters, were trained in manners, ethic, and etiquette, and studied the *Classic of Filial Piety* and other literature, including the T'ang poets. They then embarked on a study of the classics and various Chinese history books.

Temple schools provided both elementary education for pupils, sometimes girls, below the samurai class and more advanced training for priests. They gave less emphasis to Confucian and more to Buddhist ideas than the clan schools; some of them were Shinto schools. Temple schools were normally run by priests in buildings attached to the temples, but sometimes the teachers were *ronin*, or samurai who were no longer attached to a feudal lord.

A somewhat more advanced school known as the *shijuki* was of a private nature. It was usually open to all, regardless of class, who were able to pay the required fees. Though such schools stressed Confucian learning, some of them taught unorthodox Confucian philosophies. They were generally taught by *ronin* who had turned to teaching as a means of livelihood. An especially prominent private school, established by Itō Jinsai in Kyoto about

1680, emphasized the study of the Han interpretation of the classics, Japanese literature, and Japan's national heritage.

The curriculum and methods of the several kinds of Japanese schools varied. Some of the temple and private schools paid more attention to arithmetic and other subjects useful to merchants than did the samurai schools. In all schools the disciple system was emphasized, but it was especially strong in the more advanced temple and private schools. All samurai instruction aimed at character building above all else.

The Feebleness of Western Influences

Western schools and theories of education had little influence in the East during our period. Such influence as they had was limited to the Philippine Islands, where the Catholic orders dominated education after 1570. A few Western schools were established in India by the Portuguese and in the East Indies by the Dutch, but their importance during our period was as yet fairly negligible.

PROFESSIONAL TRAINING IN THE WEST

Training in Medicine and Law

Between the fourteenth and the eighteenth century some striking changes took place in the training of Europeans for the old professions, and some entirely new professions came into being. Along with theology and law, medicine was the oldest of the learned professions. Until late in the Middle Ages physician, surgeon, pharmacist, and veterinarian were not sharply distinguished one from the other. In the early centuries, medical study had been chiefly concerned with medicines, urine analysis, pulse taking, blood letting, and purging, and a physician aided by his assistant performed these services. The theoretical aspects of medicine were taught in the liberal arts courses of the *trivium* and *quadrivium*, and at a professional level by the medical faculties of the universities. Actual practice was begun with a sort of apprenticeship, either in guilds—for the lower types of healer—or as an assistant to a practising physician. In the later Middle Ages some governments demanded a certain amount of practical experience of this sort before granting a licence.

Only rarely did a physician undertake surgery, and the practice of the independent profession of surgeon remained relatively uncommon until the later centuries of the Middle Ages, when dissections became more frequent. Physicians were prone to view with suspicion the upstart surgeons' guilds and their efforts to attain formal education and professional status—including the physician's long robe. Similarly, professional surgeons looked askance at the barber-surgeons, pharmacists, and midwives, who likewise sought to raise the standards of their professions. And all these groups disdained as charlatans the great majority of sub-professional practitioners of healing, who actually handled most of the sick and ailing. In the fourteenth and fifteenth centuries governmental agencies generally supported the organized professionals, and official action against unlicensed practitioners was frequent. Government restrictions thus reinforced university requirements for a degree and placed almost impassable gulfs between the groups, thereby upholding "professional standards" though medical care for the needy lagged. In the fifteenth century the universities finally began to recognize separate guilds of surgeons and pharmacists and to make available to them certain educational facilities generally limited to physicians.

Slowly the clinical method of teaching medicine developed. Students, who once had merely heard lectures by experienced professors, now also attended the sick in hospitals or homes under the eye of a responsible physician. At Salerno and Montpellier, as early as the thirteenth century, though no regularized system of teaching hospitals existed, a sort of internship-apprenticeship had been required for the license degree.[42,43] At Padua a similar teaching method was employed in the sixteenth century. At Leiden, which Sylvius and Boerhaave made famous the next century as a centre of medical instruction, the clinical method was convincingly established as the best way to train physicians and surgeons (see Chapter XIV), and thereafter schools in England, Austria, and elsewhere adopted it.

The distrust of the *a priori*, speculative approach to medicine and the demand for more empirical methods of training physicians were reflected in the satires of Molière. By his time, nevertheless, the training of physicians had already become comparatively empirical. With the steady growth of hospitals (see Chapter XV), doctors and prospective doctors acquired greater clinical facilities, and medical students, particularly in Britain, more regularly completed their training by the clinical method in metropolitan hospitals. Museums of anatomy and pathology began in the eighteenth century but did not become a widely effective teaching medium until the nineteenth.

Training for the law underwent changes that, though less pronounced than those in medical training, were similarly directed toward lifting both professional standards and status. Nearly always law schools, like medical schools, remained parts of the old universities, but they received greater emphasis, as time went on, within the corporate plan. The Inns of Court and Chancery at London were a special case, for legal training at the universities of Oxford and Cambridge, as in Continental universities, was limited essentially to civil and canon law, and English common law had to be learned by some sort of apprenticeship (often fictional) to a master in the lodgings of the masters—'the Inns'. Lawyers thus trained could aspire to the enviable title of 'barrister', the right to plead in the High Court, and, if fortunate or able enough, an appointment to a judgeship. Lesser lawyers, also after a period of apprenticeship in their respective guilds, became attorneys or solicitors, and still lesser ones notaries or scriveners. Only the barristers (or 'counsellors') were in their own eyes true members of the profession, but in the Anglo-American colonies frontier conditions obliterated such distinctions.

The thirteenth-century beginning of the Inns is obscure, but by the fifteenth century they were a flourishing quasi-university. English common law was taught at no regular university until Blackstone gave his lectures in common law at Oxford in 1753. The changing stress in the teaching of Roman law on the Continent—from the *mos italicus* to the *mos gallicus* has been described in Chapter IX.

Training in Architecture and Engineering

Among the crafts which gained the status of professions after 1300 were architecture, engineering, music, and art. The role of the designer-architect as we know it today began to develop in the fourteenth-century Italian Renaissance. Prophetic of this change was the appointment in 1334 of the painter Giotto to the position of chief architect of the cathedral and city of Florence. Among the reasons for his appointment was the authorities' belief that the master mason should be a famous citizen as well as an artist, and although (as far as we know) he had no training in the mason's craft, what artist was more famous than he?

From the fifteenth century on, the designer-architect became a familiar figure. Often trained as a painter or, in the case of Brunelleschi, as a goldsmith, the new architect was concerned primarily with the reasoning and delineation of the proper proportions of the plan and the component parts of a building. His theory of proportions, learned in part from his study of ancient monuments and in part from his discourse with mathematicians, served as a substitute for the science later called 'statics', which is concerned with the action of forces in producing an equilibrium or relative rest. Surely, he reasoned, the mathematical proportions on the basis of which God ordered the universe and the ancient Romans had constructed their buildings would assure stability in his own constructions. The knowledge of mathematics and even philosophy which he brought to bear on his carefully proportioned designs raised architecture from the status of a mechanical to that of a liberal art or profession. While the young architect may have learned the basic principles of design in the academies of painting and sculpture which began to appear in the latter half of the sixteenth century (see below, p. 1038), he still gained most of his knowledge of building and engineering through practice under the direction of an established architect or mason-builder. Not until Colbert established the Royal Academy of Architecture in Paris in 1670 (a comparable institution being founded in Rome the next year) was the architect's training entrusted to academicians.

The rise of engineering schools has been mentioned in Chapter XV. Early in the seventeenth century Stevin was entrusted with the organization of a school of engineering to be associated with the University of Leiden; Peter the Great created the Moscow School of Mathematical and Navigational

Science in 1701; and an academy for military engineers was begun at Woolwich in 1721 (re-established in 1741); but probably the most famous of the early schools of engineering was that of the French 'Corps des Ingénieurs des Ponts et Chaussées'. The Corps itself was inaugurated in 1716 by the French government, and it soon contained some of the best road and bridge engineers in the world. After 1744 France's ablest engineers were generally trained in the École des Ponts et Chaussées in Paris, which was formally established as a royal school in 1747.[44] The Collegium Carolinum was founded in Brunswick in 1745. Other schools followed in Germany—among them those at Freiberg (1765) and Clausthal (1775).

Training in Music

Music, sometimes taught in separate 'song schools', had played a leading part in the elementary education and in the *quadrivium* of the more advanced schools during the Middle Ages. The cantor, the teacher in charge of music, was usually an important member of a school's staff, especially when he was also the chanter or precentor (*Kapellmeister, maître de chapelle*) of a nearby church. The St. Thomas School at Leipsig can boast a long succession of cantors since the sixteenth century, of whom Bach was the most distinguished. The several *conservatorios* of Naples, founded in the sixteenth century, and of Venice and other Italian cities were in the beginning orphan asylums that emphasized singing in the schooling of their wards. Some of them became famous as music schools because of outstanding teachers—Scarlatti, for example. Some private music schools were established in Rome, and Palestrina taught at one of them. Singing and instrument-playing were commonly regarded as part of a lady's or gentleman's education, with good results that we have already had occasion to mention (see Chapter XII). Musical education had not, however, been formalized by 1775, and the great composers and virtuosi of the period usually learned directly from a master. Among Bach's masters were his father and brother, and he in turn taught his sons. Mozart learned from his father.

Training in Painting and Sculpture

Before 1300 in many parts of the world artists had been esteemed only as skilled craftsmen who produced objects for use or ornament. In some areas, however, such as Africa and Oceania, those who made cult objects were sometimes priests or sorcerers with important political posts; and in China and Japan painters frequently were scholars, monks, courtiers, or other elite. In most other cases, artists were not regarded as intellectual leaders comparable to theologians, philosophers, or poets.

During at least the early part of our period painters were preservers of an esthetic consciousness whether or not they were creators, and their reverence for the art of the past frequently tended to preclude a creative role. Such reverence was true also of Chinese and Japanese painters for most of the period, but with a difference; they often sought for originality and individual expression, and their tradition was more ancient, continuous, and accomplished than perhaps any other. If artisans in many other areas during the fourteenth century shared this respect for past forms, their models were generally recent and local works, and even when they knew the art of the distant past or of other cultural areas, they rarely departed from the forms of their immediate predecessors.

Before 1300 the work of European artisans usually was anonymous and often lacked individuality. Judgments of their art were less likely to be concerned with originality or creative imagination than with excellence of materials, skill of workmanship, and faithfulness to traditional forms. Most craftsmen were trained within some continuing organization, such as a family of craftsmen or a guild of approved masters. When an apprentice met the technical standards of the group to which the continuity of the craft was entrusted, he was allowed to practice in the area under its jurisdiction.

Much the same was true in several other societies before 1300, but somewhere around 1400 the attitude changed in several of the more advanced cultures. In Islamic countries for example, the artist began to win greater esteem as an individual of talent. Favourite painters on occasion attained prominent positions in Mogul and Rajput India and in Iran. Artistic innovation was often prized, especially after the striking changes following the Mongol times, and the works of individual masters were eagerly sought by collectors. Styles of painting and of rug-weaving changed with considerable rapidity. Frequently architects of the mosques in Turkey were, like Christian cathedral builders, highly respected men of learning. About the same time the 'artisan' of medieval Europe began to become an 'artist'. The departure took place most significantly in the field of painting but was shared by sculpture and architecture as well.

The metamorphosis in the status and activity of the artist in Europe and its cultural extension in the Americas was in some regards unparalleled. It began in central Italy of the *trecento*. Artists not only acquired learning in history, poetry, and philosophy but also came to realize that in Antiquity painting, sculpture, and architecture had been considered intellectual rather than mechanical arts. Writers like Dante, Boccaccio, and Petrarch lamented the failure to recognize the intellectual as well as the simply manual aspects of the visual arts, and learned artists like Ghiberti, Brunelleschi, and Alberti furthered the artists' intellectual claims. The impressive knowledge acquired by artists who successfully imitated nature rather than medieval symbols and forms and who were proficient in 'natural philosophy', particularly the problems of ocular perception, elevated their field of knowledge in the eyes of contemporaries from the manual to the liberal arts. Their calling was considered capable of embodying truths equal to those imparted by poetry, philosophy, geometry, and even theology. This Italian idea of the visual arts and the artist as something loftier than the crafts and the artisan gradually spread over Europe.

In keeping with this development artists of the late fifteenth century in Tuscany attempted to liberate themselves from the artisans' guilds and to institute a freer and more dignified relationship between pupil and teacher than existed between apprentice and master. They sought instead to create something like the Classical 'academies', where noble young men, in free association, had pursued philosophical and scientific studies. A school for the training of artists was established in 1490 by Lorenzo the Magnificent in the Medici Gardens. It was attended by Michelangelo and other selected youths and flourished under the leadership of the sculptor Bertoldo di Giovanni. A group gathered around Leonardo da Vinci in Milan appears also to have called itself an academy, and several mid-sixteenth-century engravings show students at work in a studio labelled 'Academy of Baccio Bandinelli'. All these groups. however, were too loosely organized and too short-lived to be accurately classified as academies.

Vasiri's Accademia del Disegno, founded in Florence in 1563 under the protection of the Grand Duke Cosimo I, was Europe's first artists' academy in the modern sense. It was composed of the 'thirty-six best artists of Italy', and Cosimo I and Michelangelo were named honorary *capi*, or leaders—a gesture suggesting the comparable status of Florence's political head and the leading artist in this organization. When a talented student of art had advanced sufficiently in the workshop of his master, he might be recommended to this academy, where he might be accepted for further instruction by the three masters elected to teach each year. Vasari's academy became famous all over Europe, and other cities followed the example of Florence. The Accademia di San Luca was formed at Rome in 1593 from a nucleus called the Virtuosi al Pantheon, which had met since 1543. Similar organizations were founded by the early seventeenth century in Genoa, Naples, Milan, and Turin.

The Accademia del Disegno managed to free Florence's painters and sculptors from the guilds in 1571 and to take over some of the guild's administrative duties, but it was less successful in its important teaching programme. The Roman academy had the same aims as those of Florence, and the revision of its rules in 1627 suggested that it too accomplished little of its ambitious teaching programme. Perhaps the studio of the Carracci in Bologna more completely realized the teaching aims of an academy than did the more elaborate and official institutions of Florence and Rome. Still, academies were more concerned with studying the esthetic and philosophical aspects of art than with teaching techniques or maintaining standards of craftsmanship. Though they created a greater solidarity among practitioners of the visual arts and though their constitutions outlined the kind of institution artists wanted in place of the guilds, the system of apprenticeship remained the main means of acquiring the training and recognition necessary to practise the arts.

In France, the rules established for the guild of *peintres et tailleurs* in 1260 continued to govern art activities until the seventeenth century. During the sixteenth century, however, various Italian artists working in France were exempt from guild rules, while many French artists who went to Italy experienced a still greater freedom. The French, perhaps more readily than any other people of Europe outside Italy, accepted the Italian Renaissance assumptions that art was an objective imitation of nature, that such imitation could be taught, and that exact artistic judgments could be made. Arguments essentially like those offered by the Italians in the sixteenth century in favour of an art academy were successfully set forth by LeBrun in 1648, when the Academy of Painting and Sculpture was created. And Simon Vouet, representing the painters' guild, established an opposing academy with more professors than LeBrun's.

Colbert caused these two factions to merge and granted the combined academy some rooms in the Louvre and some funds from the royal coffers. The academy thus became a royal enterprise. Colbert soon realized that if it were strongly centralized, it would be a more effective instrument for the glorification of the king, and in 1661 he demanded that all artists join the academy, establishing grades of membership within it. Although a few, such as Pierre Mignard, continued to paint outside the academy, most artists conformed. Opposition was effectively suppressed by an order forbidding courses in life drawing outside the Royal Academy. By 1676, academies had been founded in other cities of France, but they were all dependent on that of Paris, and, in this way, the academicians in Paris came to control the art activities of the country.[45]

The Academy's study programme was prescribed. It included copying works of other artists, drawing from scupture and plaster casts, and finally drawing from the nude figure. This sequence was followed because, during the seventeenth century, it was considered inadvisable for an untutored eye to approach nature directly. Although Rubens observed that drawing from casts resulted in a tendency toward hard contours and surfaces, harsh lighting effects, and stiffness in the figures, and although Chardin in the 1760's lamented the loss of freshness after years of slavish copying, drawing from plaster casts continued into the twentieth century as a basic part of academic training. From this practice, together with the criticisms and corrections actually drawn upon his work by his teachers, the student gained the ability to draw and, with it, the basis for not only painting but also sculpture, architecture, and the decorative arts. Lectures on geometry, perspective, and anatomy rounded out a programme aimed at the effective depiction of the human body and human emotions. A large reference library supplemented the approaches to art provided by the Academy's professors. Outstanding students won an opportunity to study for extended periods at the Académie de France established in 1666 in Rome. The academies gave French art a clarity of direction and an unfaltering continuity (though also at times an 'academic' conventionality) unparalleled in contemporary Europe and probably account for the eventual emergence of Paris as the world's leading centre of art.

Arts in other parts of Europe also were inclined to abandon the guild system. In 1665 Dutch artists transformed their guild into an academy of the French type. Similar academies were established during the late seventeenth and the early eighteenth century in Nuremberg, Augsburg, Dresden, Berlin, Vienna, and London, but the original enthusiasm with which they were founded was seldom sustained. Only later, with the spread of Neoclassicism during the third quarter of the eighteenth century, did art academies vigorously multiply and flourish, finally realizing the teaching purposes that Vasari had envisioned.

Training in these academies was different from that of an apprentice in the fourteenth-century workshop. To gain admission to an academy and recognition as a master the aspiring artist still had to submit a work for approval, but a system which made all members of the academy his judges allowed much greater latitude than one which induced him as an apprentice to duplicate the manner of a single master. In addition, the academies provided a wide range of works (or copies of them) for the young artist to examine, encouraging him to study the art produced since 1500 as well as that of the Ancients. They also fostered the inclination to travel in other lands, particularly to Rome and Paris, and acquaintance with art abroad increased the artist's experience beyond his immediate and local tradition. Another source of instruction not available in 1300 was provided by the many treatises on art written since the fifteenth century and frequently available in various translations (see Chapter XII). The European artist by this time was no longer merely a guardian of a tradition; he was prepared to be a critic of his masters and to develop an independent style.

NOTES TO CHAPTER XVI

1. Professor A. Dupront emphasizes the following: first, that the evidence is clear that in the predominantly monastic Western mediaeval world, education normally proceeded from the clerks; second, that, the clerk being the one who knows—principally how to write—the layman is *illiteratus*.

2. In this connection, Professor A. Dupront draws attention to the role of the cities, concerned, like the church, with securing the necessary administrative personnel, whose main function was to commit to writing and to draft. From the thirteenth century onwards, urban life, administration, and the slowly differentiated education of the clerical schools went hand in hand. The influence of the Brothers of Common Life in the northern Rhineland area is largely attributable to their urban locations.

3. For women as well as for men of a certain social level, according to Professor A. Dupront, consideration must be given to the importance of the Book of Hours, which, first in manuscript form—and therefore expensive—and later printed, often became the sole reading matter of an entire social category in the West.

4. In Professor A. Dupront's view, this was notably true for a time at Deventer itself, where a school was conducted by a humanist in association with a house of the Brothers, serving as boarding house. Above all were their powerful and highly ramified dissemination, their wide recruitment—open to poor children, and the primordial importance which they placed on books, reading, and libraries. They were quick to use printing for the vulgarization of both mystic and Classical writings. Their concern for moral training was also admirably suited to fill the need for urban education in citizenship.

5. See George Boas, 'A Fourteenth-Century Cosmology', *Proceedings of the American Philosophical Society*, XCVIII (1954), pp. 50–9.

6. A characteristic common to all three schools, in other respects so different (Deventer, St Paul's in London, and Mantua), was the introduction of a so-called humanist instruction, the aim of which was threefold. The first objective was towards 'philological' knowledge, important mainly for the interpretation of the sacred books; the second was towards an ethical training, by means of the progressive discovery of certain confirmatory correspondences between lay Christian morality and the traditions of the great classical philosophies of the Mediterranean world; the third was social, consisting in development of the capacity for expression, that is to say the advent of rhetoric. In his *Inventio Dialectica*, Rudolph Agricola, an Italianized Frisian, was to try to reconcile dialectic and rhetoric, an effort symbolic of the demand of a whole sector of society then in process of throwing off the bonds of the established exercises of the universities. (Alphonse Dupront.)

7. The appellation *studium generale* is to be understood, ambiguously, as referring both to subjects taught and to recruitment, particularly geographical recruitment. (Alphonse Dupront.)

8. Professor A. Dupront points out that founded in 1180, this was a foundation for poor clerks attached to the Hôtel-Dieu. This establishment which has been called 'the first educational college in the world' is still in the church's tradition of auto-recruitment.

9. Professor A. Dupront adds that it should be mentioned that many of these colleges were boarding establishments; only in a few of them was teaching conducted. From this time onward, the problem of the evolution of university structure becomes that of the interrelationship between *universitas* and colleges. On the one hand—the Anglo-Saxon solution—the colleges constitute the *universitas*. On the other—the French solution—the *universitas* is the powerful centralizer of the colleges, concentrating in its faculties the greatest possible amount of teaching.

10. Professor A. Dupront emphasizes that as far as Montpellier is concerned, not only the medical school but also the arts school were already prosperous by the middle of the twelfth century. The beginning of the next century saw the establishment of the school of medicine, a purely ecclesiastical corporation. The *studium generale* was established by papal bull in 1289. In connection with the medical school stress should be laid on the importance of the small Jewish community of the Languedoc region of the Midi, which may well have served to transmit the teachings of Arab medicine. Together with church teaching, the Judeo-Arab contribution remains a constant element of education in mediaeval (and hence also in modern) western Europe. (See *History of Mankind: Cultural and Scientific Development*, Vol. III, Part 4.)

11. Professor A. Dupront underlines that neither the Oratorians nor even the Jesuits were created for the education of children. The Jesuits were the first in the field, starting with their own colleges, set up primarily for the purposes of their own recruitment. The Oratorians, at least in Italy, came to it much later. This is a clear indication of social pressure towards education, at least in certain milieux.

12. Does this necessarily infer, as will be stated in the case of the Jesuits, that it is a case of 'propaganda'? What is clear is that the need for instruction sprang from a lay impulse.

As far afield as Italy, in Rome and Milan, for example, were to be found simple men, rapidly gaining popularity, who set themselves up as teachers for the street children. This example, while restricted in scope, is significant in itself.

It is also evident that teaching was restricted to what people needed to learn. For the children of the people this meant the elements of Christian doctrine, more prayers than catechism, and, obviously as the result of a secular demand, 'leggere, scrivere ed abacco', as proposed by the first Scolopes in Rome, that is to say reading, writing, and counting.

Further evidence of the demand for schools with a teaching content to all intents and purposes similar to that defined by the monks of San Pantaleo in Rome is provided by the questionnaire on the occasion of canonical visits. In France in particular a comparison of canonical visits at different periods throughout the seventeenth century shows that a question as to the existence or non-existence of a school makes a regular appearance in the episcopal enquiry from the middle of the century on. During the eighties and nineties this question often appears side by side with one on the existence or nonexistence of Protestants in the parish. The way in which the inquiry was put, confirmed by the replies, reveals that the question was considered important, even in small communities, sometimes counting several masters, who, in the old French tradition, were known as 'regents'. The wide spread, along with the carefulness of the questions, shows that, as a social phenomenon, instruction extended far beyond both the framework and the authority of a church society. (Alphonse Dupront.)

Author's rejoinder: 'The point of view of this remark, while correct, does not explain away what the text means by propaganda—*the indoctrination of pupils in revealed Truth rather than the impartial and disinterested quest for knowledge and wisdom. We do not mean to imply that the Jesuits in particular or Catholics in general were alone concerned with such indoctrination.'*

13. Professor A. Dupront wants it not to be forgotten that, as certain recent research has confirmed, Juan Luis Vives was of Jewish extraction. Moreover, Prof. Bataillon has clearly elucidated the role of the Marranos in Erasmian circles, in Flanders and even as far afield as England. Hence the Talmudic Schools represent another source of the formation of modern methods of instruction, also dating back to the remote Middle Ages.

14. W. H. Longridge (ed. & trans.), *The Spiritual Exercises of St. Ignatius of Loyola* (3rd ed., London, 1930), p. 67.

15. *Ibid.*, pp. 197 and 199.

16. To Professor A. Dupront these pages devoted to the *Spiritual Exercises* of Ignatius Loyola seem to make an attempt to extract the essence of a work capital to the beginnings of the modern Western world. Two problems are, however, raised by the very premise on which the chapter is based. One is to know to what extent the Company of Jesus remained faithful to the practice of these exercises in the training of its educational cadres. The other, far more important, is to assess the possible influence of the actual technique of the exercises on Jesuit 'pedagogy'.

In point of fact, it appears that the exemplary treatise of mental therapy constituted by these *Spiritual Exercises* was not exploited by the Company itself for its real content. Western teaching based on the Jesuit humanities was to be a substantive teaching rather than a method of mental training, remaining so, indeed, even down to the present day. Hence a serious lack of psychic training, individual as well as collective, particularly in the face of Oriental teaching, for which the West is now showing itself an avid customer.

Ignatius Loyola, moreover, imposed on his sons another rule, destined rapidly to go equally unheeded, that of studying the humanities only after attaining a certain well settled age, between 25 and 35, providing not only for priority to be given to philosophical and religious training but also for a certain harmonious measure of correspondence between the study of great texts and the capacity to understand them other than as exercises of pure rhetoric. The prescription laid down for the masters in their teaching methods was, in fact, reversed by the Jesuits, the humanities becoming the often irreligious sustenance of adolescents studying for worldly careers—an evident sign of the Company's dependence on secular 'ambitions' and, even at this early date, on a secular 'ideal'.

Author's rejoinder: 'The Jesuits here (in this section, which is entitled "European Educational Institutions") are being described as the institution their founder intended them to be. Their actual methods at subsequent times are discussed (on pp. 1008–9, in the section entitled "Educational Methods and Theory in Europe") as combining humanism with devotion.'

17. To present the Jesuit college as an institution practically connatural with the Company would be somewhat to distort historical perspective. The Epistolario of Father Nadal, the great founder of colleges during the first decades of the Company's existence, amply illustrates the considerable hesitation felt in passing from auto-recruiting establishments to houses of education for laymen. The latter were to force their way into the Jesuit colleges, thereby leading them to discover in the exploitation of their establishments much of their social, temporal, and cultural success.

The catechism was a basic element of education essential to Christian religious life, whether Protestant or Catholic, during the sixteenth century. It should, however, be emphasized that the *Catechism* of Canisius corresponds to an attempt at religious uniformization on the part of the emperor and that the Tridentine or Roman Catechism was intended primarily for priests. The generalization of the practice of catechismic teaching, slow as it was, had considerable effects on the 'secularization' of the religious conscience of the masses in various Western countries. (Alphonse Dupront.)

18. *The Spiritual Exercises of St. Ignatius of Loyola*, p. 197.

19. Professor A. Dupront wonders whether so much stress should be laid on Dominican-Jesuit rivalry? The Dominicans neither dominated the Sorbonne nor reigned supreme over the most famous Catholic universities. The situation was, of course, more complex. While the famous school at Salamanca was Dominican, in Germany, Würzburg and, above all, Ingolstadt were Jesuit, as was Vienna. The conflict was on another plane—not between the sons of St Dominic and the sons of St Ignatius but between strongly established universities and young Jesuit colleges rapidly rising to prosperity. Paris and Louvain provide vivid examples, but even more significant is that of Rome, where the Company's Collegio Romano, founded by St Ignatius in the middle of the century (1553), becoming Gregoriana, i.e. a university, in 1592, grew into a strong rival to the Sapienza, the University of Rome, which had difficulty in surviving, let alone in maintaining itself in the lead, despite the protection of Paul II and succeeding popes during the second half of the sixteenth century.

The authors believe that the Dominican influence was predominant in the University of Paris before the Jesuits could establish themselves there. See Bataillon, Erasme et l'Espagne, pp. 10–11, 542–4, 755–6, 759 and 768.

20. To Professor A. Dupront Carlo Borromeo was in fact no more than the resolute executor of the provisions of a famous chapter of the Council of Trent (Sess. XXIII, Cap. XVIII, 15. VII. 1563). His work in his own diocese of Milan, the example he gave, his personal authority, his saintly figure and unflagging will made of this timid but dauntless man an example that contemporary religious historiographers find more and more influential in Italy, France, and the Netherlands as well as in central and eastern Europe. But here too, it is a question only of a return to traditional clerical education and auto-recruitment. The 'invention' of the seminary formula is often attributed to the English cardinal, Reginald Pole.

For France, the Abbé A. Degert's, *Histoire des séminaires français jusqu'à la Révolution* (2 vols., Paris, 1912) still holds good.

On the influences of the 'Borromean' model, see P. Proutin, *La Réforme pastorale en France au XVIIe siècle* (Paris, 1956), 2 vols.

21. As Professor A. Dupront reminds us, the originality of Halle is also illustrated by the fact that it was there that Thomasius, jurist and philosopher of law of the Pufendorf school, first established the teaching of political science (*studio politico*).

22. To restrict the Brothers of the Christian Schools to their vocation of popular teaching their founder took the wise precaution of forbidding them to teach in Latin, which constituted the social watershed. (Alphonse Dupront.)

23. Translated in Arthur O. Norton, *Readings in the History of Education: Mediaeval Universities* (Cambridge, Mass., 1909), pp. 121–4.
24. See Chapter VII, p. 492 and n. 16.
25. Professor A. Dupront's opinion is here more reserved. The interpretation of *virtu* in Machiavelli remains highly restrictive. The opposition *fortuna/virtu* implies something quite different, a philosophy of power and existence (see F. Gilbert, *Politics and History in Renaissance Florence: Machiavelli and Guicciardini* [Princeton U.P., 1964]).

In the perspective of a history of education taken in its broadest possible sense, *Il Principe* and *Il Cortegiano* cannot be placed on the same plane. One is a treatise on the art of government, accompanied by a few traits sketching the portrait of the prince; the other a treatise on the art of social behaviour. In *Il Cortegiano*, the whole milieu of the court of Urbino in the early decades of the sixteenth century is held up as an example. As for 'academies', apart from 'academic schools', what do they owe to Castiglione?

Authors' note: 'The text has dealt with Machiavelli and Guicciardini as historians and political thinkers in other contexts. This passage is only to remind the reader that "essentially" (not fully, not exhaustively) Machiavelli's concept of patriotism was the quality which he believed Italy most needed of its leaders. As the authors imply, the 'academics' owed little to Castiglione.'
26. The formula is a happy one, conveying perfectly the deliberate secularization of ecclesiasticism. Is there any reason to be surprised? Certainly not in the perspective of contemporary history, and indeed, apart from the change in the concept of 'religio', have things changed so very much since the sixteenth century? (Alphonse Dupront.)
27. *A Sermon on the Duty of Keeping Children at School*, quoted in MacKinnon, IV, pp. 99–100.
28 Sturm was indeed the inventor of the 'model', but the original features of his model were, on the one hand, the new form of Gymnasium and, on the other, municipal (i.e. secular) control of teaching. The Strasbourg Gymnasium was transformed into an Academy only in 1566.

Many studies exist on Jean Sturm and his educational work; a good survey is contained in three articles appearing in *L'Humanisme en Alsace* (Paris, 1939). (Alphonse Dupront.)
29. While the main trends of the Jesuit pedagogic synthesis are here outlined, two points deserve greater emphasis in Professor A. Dupront's opinion. The first was their rôle as educators of the upper classes, from the point of view of their predilection for form and demand for rhetoric and style. Their reconciliation of Antiquity and religion led in fact to a juxtaposition in which social content was sacrificed to formal performance. Hence the tremendous output of Latin poetry, of more or less religious drama, in which the cultivated élite of Europe was to delight for at least a century. To say nothing of the style of social behaviour, the 'ballets' of the Jesuit schools had cultural value. The second was the slow but deliberate decision of the Company to educate the ruling classes and, even more deliberately, the future wielders of authority in all its forms.

Material for a history of Jesuit pedagogy is contained in the *Monumenta Paedagogica Societatis Jesu* (Nova editio; Roma, Monumenta Hist. SS., 1965). A useful presentation of their work in France is given in F. de Dainville, S.S., *Les Jésuites et l'éducation de la société française* (Paris, 1940). For a quasi-exhaustive study of a famous French example see Dupont–Ferrier, *La vie quotidienne d'un collège parisien pendant plus de 350 ans. Du collège de Clermont au Lycée Louis-le-Grand (1563–1920)* (Paris, 1921–25), 3 vols.
30. Quoted in Fritz Caspari, *Humanism and the Social Order in Tudor England* (Chicago, 1954), pp. 70 and 75.
31. More entrusts the education of the youth of Utopia to the priests. It is true that the priests are few, even though a few women are admitted to the priesthood. Potential 'secularization' of education in the Utopian world is inherent in the fact that each individual is free to spend his leisure moments in study, but the gate remains narrow. And the study of letters is a 'profession'. (Alphonse Dupront.)
32. Quoted from the title-page of *The Great Didactic*, given in facsimile in Luella Cole, *A History of Education, Socrates to Montessori* (New York, 1950), p. 334. See Matthew

Spinka, *John Amos Comenius, That Incomparable Moravian* (Chicago, 1943), pp. 65–71 and 153–5; and Josef Polisensky, 'Comenius and His Time', *Journal of World History*, VI (1960), p. 65.

33. Fénelon's reflections must be considered in a definite context: that of his task as royal tutor. What Fénelon did for his pupil, the Duc de Bourgogne, Bossuet and Huet had done before him for the Grand Dauphin. Where the education of princes was concerned, models were sought and tools provided: hence the celebrated collection of classics *ad usum* made by the tutors of the Grand Dauphin. It must also be stressed that the definition of a man given by the 'Swan of Cambrai' is Christian, sometimes expressed in highly traditional and aristocratic form but with an exquisite sense of style rarely attained before him. But viewed in a pre-revolutionary perspective, Fénelon was no innovator. See among recent studies Jeanne-Lydie Goré, *L'Itinéraire de Fénelon* (Paris, 1957) and Françoise Gallouedec-Genuys, *Le prince selon Fénelon* (Paris, 1963). (Alphonse Dupront.)

34. Professor A. Dupront remarks that as regards the education given in the 'little schools' of Port-Royal it should be stressed that to religious training and, above all, the inculcation of moral austerity including psychological analysis, and the exercise of lucidity and scruple must be added reflection on language, grammar, and systems of thought— in other words, secular reflection, in a religious milieu, in the vernacular, then in process of becoming the sole language.

It would be impossible to 'place' Port-Royal without *Logique de Port-Royal ou art de penser*, by Arnauld and Nicole (complete critical edition by P. Clair and Fr. Girbal, Paris, 1965).

The Oratorians did not lag behind the Jansenists. In *L'Art de parler* (1675) primarily a treatise on rhetoric, one of their number, François Lamy, reaches the point of expounding the problem of 'the relationship of language to operations of the mind'. Used as a textbook in the Oratorian colleges, it reveals a growing awareness of language as a tool, and thence as an element in the formation of the personality, even if only through commerce with other men.

35. *Oeuvres*, III, p. 459, quoted in Gabriel Compayre, *The History of Pedagogy*, trans. W. H. Payne (Boston, 1892), pp. 321–2.

36. Translation borrowed (with slight changes) from Lester G. Crocker, *The Embattled Philosopher*, a Biography of Denis Diderot (London, 1955), pp. 409–10.

37. Quoted in Henri Seé, *Les idées politiques en France au XVIIIe siècle* (Paris, 1920), p. 142.

38. To Professor A. Dupront, Diderot's Plan of a University—a largely posthumous publication (1813–14)—will be easier to place if given its full title: *Plan d'une université pour le gouvernement de Russie ou d'une éducation publique dans toutes les sciences*. The plan was to have been applied in Russia, still a Utopian land, especially when the tsar was called Catherine.

Much more significant is Diderot's life-work, the *Encyclopédie*, an enterprise which, independently of any forerunners or imitators, is itself sufficient evidence of a firm intention to raise the mechanical arts to the level of the liberal arts solely by the power of the printed word. Viewed as a revolutionary—or at least an exceedingly bold—act of education, this work could with advantage have been accorded more importance than that given to a 'philosophical' work of more interest to specialists than historically important.

Much more closely geared to life and therefore historically valuable are Condorcet's five memoirs *Sur l'instruction publique* between 1791–92, completed by the *Rapport et project de décret sur l'organisation générale de l'instruction publique*, presented to the Legislative Assembly in the name of the Comité d'Instruction Publique on April 20 and 21, 1792 (*Oeuvres de Condorcet*, ed. A. Condorcet, O'Connor, and F. Arago, Vol. VII).

Authors' note: *The* Encyclopédie *is considered in other contexts above and below.* Condorcet's memoirs doubtless will receive attention in Vol. V.

39. The 'Grand Tour' had been preceded by the sixteenth century 'Italian journey'— another collective acculturation exercise conferring a social seal. To judge by Robert

Adam, the Grand Tour also served to accumulate academic degrees on the continent. (Alphonse Dupront.)

40. Professor A. Dupront underscores the whole 'cultural' phenomenon of the vulgarization of the sciences in modern Europe as the result of the rising tide of 'curiosity', so far little studied, swollen both by the taste for collection and by the desire for direct experience, with all the passions, pure and impure, liable to accompany them. Note the importance of the home physical laboratories with which rich bourgeois and even some French farmers-general in the eighteenth century were to become enamoured.

41. Carl Becker, *The Declaration of Independence* (New York, 1922), pp. 42–7. See C. H. C. Lippold and C. P. Funke (eds.), *Neues Natur- und Kunstlexicon . . . zum bequemen Gebrauch insonderheit auch für Ungelehrte und für gebildete Frauenzimmer* (Weimar, 1801).

42. L. C. MacKinney, 'Medical Education in the Middle Ages', *Journal of World History*, II (1955), pp. 851–3, esp. notes 69 and 76; Vern Bullough, 'The Development of the Medical University at Montpellier to the End of the Fourteenth Century', *Bulletin of the History of Medicine*, XXX (1956), p. 513.

43. The good name and historical repute of the faculty of medicine at Montpellier ultimately depended on two complementary stipulations already appearing in the statutes of 1239. One fixed an obligatory period of six-months' probation as indispensable to the practice of medicine; the other, highly consequential on account of the precedent involved, set the obligation to appear for examination before two masters of the faculty. For surgeons, on the contrary, no examination was required. (Alphonse Dupront.)

44. E. J. Dijksterhuis (ed.), *The Principle Works of Simon Stevin*, Vol. I: *General Introduction, Mechanics* (Amsterdam, 1955), p. 10; Richard A. Preston, Sydney F. Wise, and Herman O. Werner, *Men in Arms, a History of Warfare and its Interrelationships with Western Society* (New York, 1956), p. 135; Frederick B. Artz, *L'Éducation technique en France au dix-huitième siècle (1700–89)* (Paris, 1939), p. 26.

45. The role of Paris was rendered even clearer by the accommodation of the academicians in the Louvre itself—thus affirming both their dependence and their 'promotion'—as well as by the social phenomenon of the 'salons'. Reserved exclusively to the Academy and taking place in the royal palace itself, these 'salons' played a doubly important role in eighteenth-century France by extending the clientèle of the royal artists and setting up the seal of 'criticism', timidly established at this time and achieving real recognition only in the first half of the nineteenth century. (Diderot's *Salons* were not published until this period, although they appeared as a sort of Paris letter in Grimm's *Correspondance littéraire* between 1739 and 1781.) (Alphonse Dupront.)

CHAPTER XVII

SUMMARY AND CONCLUSION

THE GROWTH OF WORLD CONSCIOUSNESS

EVERY period of recorded history may, of course, properly be regarded as an age of transition, but the period of this volume (*c.* 1300–*c.* 1775) is perhaps especially notable as such. In Europe it covers the years that intervened between the Middle Ages and the revolutions of the late eighteenth century. It includes the eras known as the Renaissance, the Reformation, the Age of Discovery, the Scientific Revolution, the Absolute Monarchies, the Enlightenment, and the initial stages of the Industrial Revolution. Outside Europe it witnessed such developments as the last flowering and the decline of the Amerindian civilizations, the rise of new Islamic empires, the spread of Islam in the old civilizations of Africa, India, and Indonesia, the end of the great Mongol conquests, the reorientation of life in China under the Ming and Manchu dynasties, the growth of the isolated culture of Japan under the Ashikaga and Tokugawa shogunates, and the highest development of several African empires and kingdoms.

Our period closes with a series of events centring about 1775 that can be readily recognized as marking, in one way or another, either the end of an old era or the beginning of a new one. That series includes several events of crucial importance in political affairs—the first effort of the British to require direct government supervision of the affairs of the East India Company (the Regulating Act of 1773); the concessions to French Canadians that were eventually to help make of Canada the first dominion within the British empire (the Quebec Act of 1774); the beginning of 'the Polish Question' with the First Partition of Poland in 1772 and of 'the Near Eastern Question' with the Treaty of Kutchuk Kainarja in 1774; the collapse of the first formidable revolutionary effort in Russia (the Pugashev Revolt of 1772–75); the outbreak in 1775 of the first successful anti-colonial revolt in modern times (the American War of Independence); and the ultimately victorious alliance in 1778 of an absolute monarchy, France, with a republican confederation, the United States of America, which had proclaimed that governments are instituted to secure the rights of man and derive their just powers from the consent of the governed.

In addition to the American Declaration of Independence (1776) some decisive events of the period in the history of thought may likewise be designated as forming part of the series—the publication of Adam Smith's classical exposition of laissez-faire economics (*Wealth of Nations*, 1776); a turning point in the Enlightenment with the conjuncture of the Franco-American alliance with the death of Voltaire and Rousseau (1778); and the completion of the *Encyclopédie* (1772), of its supplementary volumes (1777), and its Index (1780).

Also the period covered a set of significant developments in the history of science and technology—the first patentings of Watt's steam engine (1769 and 1775); the explorations (1767–79) by Captain Cook of Australia and the Pacific Islands; the observations by Herschel (1774–81) that led to the discovery of the planet Venus; the findings in the 1770's by Scheele, Priestley, and Lavoisier which laid the basis of modern chemistry; the initial experiments of Jenner (1775) that led ultimately to the control of smallpox by vaccination and to the modern science of immunology.

Somewhere about the year 1775 can be placed, too, some dramatic episodes in the history of the arts, literature, and education. That date marks the mid-points in the long career of Haydn and the short career of Mozart. Neo-classicism began a triumphant course in the arts with a young painter (David), a promising sculptor (Houdon), well-known architects (Soufflot and Gabriel), and respected critics (the recently deceased [1768] Winckelmann and the still vigorous Lessing). About the same time literary Romanticism was struggling to be born in the works of Rousseau, young Goethe, and their confreres. And a major crisis came in 1773 in ecclesiastical affairs with the temporary suppression (until 1814) of the Jesuits with its jolting impact upon Catholic educational and missionary efforts. Thus almost every aspect of modern culture experienced some kind of climax around 1775.

Furthermore, during the age that we have been considering in this volume all the cultural areas of the world were for the first time brought into regular physical contact with one another. Navigators, conquerors, adventurers, explorers, scientists, traders, pirates, slavers, colonists, and missionaries established a world-wide intercommunication. Men and women, plants and animals, raw materials and finished products, food and clothing, skills and inventions, customs and traditions were transplanted bodily from region to region, and art, thought, and religious beliefs within a single civilization were often modified through contact with other civilizations. While in some areas the peoples of an old culture, particularly those of the Far East, tried (still with considerable success, during this period) to protect their ways of life against foreign influences, in others, particularly those of Spanish America, they showed either less hesitancy to mingle their cultural heritage with that of the intruders or less ability to keep it pure.

In either case, however, cultural particularism and intolerance remained strong, for men everywhere are likely to assume the superiority of their own religion, their own local beliefs and customs, their own peculiar traditions of art and science, their own familiar institutions, and their own system of values. Where foreign technology in patently superior, they may readily borrow artifacts, commodities, and methods, but even in such instances they yield to resulting change in their mores only reluctantly, and in their values more reluctantly still, if at all. Conscious striving for acculturation either was likely to be a reflection of the intruder's desire for the triumph abroad of his own persuasion or was missing altogether. Spanish conquerors, for example, went out in all directions to convert people to their own brand of 'catholicism' (universalism). Puritans, on the other hand, were unwilling to have their areas of refuge in America contaminated by Quakers or Anglicans. The Muslim might grant his Hindu, Christian, or Jewish subjects toleration, yet never failed to consider them infidels and outsiders. The shoguns closed their country to 'corrupting' influences from across the seas. The Chinese emperors were convinced that their superior society had no need of Western contributions. European explorers and conquerors frequently believed that they were the carriers of genuine civilization to childishly innocent races; at times, indeed, they did not seem to be aware that they were dealing with fellow human beings of a venerable history rather than with negotiable goods.

Underneath this superciliousness, however, cultural influences were being more or less subtly interchanged. The European conqueror might vanquish the American Indian, and yet his own life was extensively affected by such borrowings from the conquered as tobacco, caoutchouc, potatoes, quinine, and the gold and silver of American mines. The Chinese government might forbid Christian practices but yet employed the artistic, astronomical, and mathematical skill of the Jesuit fathers and permitted commerce with Europeans in porcelain, silks, and other Chinese fineries. The American planter might try to preserve his way of life from contamination by his Negro slave and yet was unable to forestall crossbreeding or his great grandchildren's liking for sounds, accents, and rhythms derived from Africa. Dissimilar and hostile peoples thus might often influence each other, sometimes despite or beyond intention.

In other instances, a common tradition, usually based upon a religious preference, intentionally served as a bond among widespread but similar peoples. Inside Europe, although numerous dynastic, national, and sectarian conflicts persisted, culture was largely derived from a shared inheritance—overwhelmingly Caucasoid in race, Indo-European in language, and Christian in religion. Within the Islamic world a common religious law and two widely known languages as well as a common cult spread from the Straits of Gibraltar to the outmost reaches of the East Indies. Hinduism or its offspring Buddhism stretched from India eastward. Confucianism had moved from China to Japan, Korea, and Vietnam. A few million Jews were scattered throughout the world.

Moreover, during this period certain ideas were unfolding that were someday to have a unifying effect upon mankind as a whole. One of the most powerful of these was the increased reliance on human reason and universally applicable knowledge in the search for an understanding of man's biological and physical circumstances. For a scientist like Newton the general laws of mathematics, gravity, magnetism, or optics were valid (due allowances made) at any spot on earth. For an anatomist like Vesalius the number of bones and muscles of a Chinese corpse could be presumed to be the same as of an Italian one. Animals and plants may differ from continent to continent, but an ingenious biologist like Linnaeus could hope to classify them all by applying a few general principles. In this period even relatively uneducated men came to realize that the earth was not the centre of the universe but only one of several planets in a solar system. A telescopist in the Bureau of Astronomy at Peking might perceive other stars in the heavens than his English counterpart at Greenwich, but both sets of observations nonetheless corroborated the same astronomical laws and fitted into a concept of stellar space that dwarfed the Earth with its separate nations and cultures into relative insignificance. Thus, even as the Earth and its peoples became better known one to another, its importance in the universal scheme of things shrank.

Where general laws did not seem applicable, the very comparison of differences sometimes led to speculation about humanity as a whole. Those who reflected on man's nature, activities, and beliefs increasingly dissociated their theories from the supernatural explanations of earlier, more ethnocentric ages. This development reached far in European thought, where, besides, in certain circles the axiological principles of non-Christian cultures won no less respect than those of their own. Instead of or, more often, in addition to attempting to reconcile faith with reason, European students of foreign philosophies were deeply concerned with grasping the varying concepts of human knowledge, of man's relation to the physical world, and of his moral and social obligations. Feeling unable to confine thought to Biblical axioms, some European philosophers took reason, usually but not necessarily tempered by human experience, as their main guide to truth.

This process reached a culmination in the Enlightenment. Not content with a Christian philosophy for a Christian Europe, the *philosophes* of the eighteenth century created vast rational systems meant to apply to humanity universally—systems that knew no religious, national, cultural, or colour boundaries, since reason was accessible to all members of the species *homo sapiens*. For these *philosophes* the dawn of a new golden age for all mankind awaited chiefly the elimination of arrogance, bigotry, superstition, prejudice, stupidity, inertia, and other obstacles to the free operation of the human mind.

Religious thought, too, sometimes partook of this unifying rationalist tendency. For some rationalistic theists, the Christian ideal of God as a World-God was acceptable even if the idea of Redemption and Salvation for only the faithful, the elect, the righteous, or the initiate was not. The theistic corollaries of rationalism were pantheism and Deism, which—at least, so their proponents believed—eliminated the tribal features that had tended to make religion a divisive factor among peoples.

With the spread of the notion of a common humanity, Christian ethical theories, available despite widening missionary endeavours to only a limited section of mankind, tended in the minds of the Deists to merge into supposedly universal norms like the Golden Rule or 'natural man' or natural religion. In European social and political theory, arguments were based with greater regularity on the notion that all human beings were subject to 'the Laws of Nature' (now more regularly considered synonymous with 'the laws of physics' than with 'the laws of God') and that all enjoyed certain inalienable natural rights. The concept of a common, universal human nature dominated much of social thought, leading to a readiness to believe in 'natural' ethics along with 'natural' political institutions. It entered the field of international relations, where 'reasonableness' was advocated by 'sensible' persons; and a few bold thinkers—Vitoria, Grotius, Pufendorf, St Pierre, Rousseau—advanced codes of international law or engaging schemes designed to preserve peace among all the nations. In general, and even though denominationalism, racism, and nationalism flourished simultaneously, the impression spread to many minds (though doubtless still a minority) by the eighteenth century that human beings were more alike than unlike, and this cosmopolitanism, this idea of a common humanity with common potentials and a common destiny, no matter how often defeated, would never be lost again in the Western world and was destined to go forth from there to fortify whatever similar views flourished elsewhere.

THE RISE OF SECULARISM IN EUROPE

As has been pointed out several times earlier in this book, from the fourteenth century on, thought tended to become more earth-centred than it had ever been before. In the first place, the world became better known to its inhabitants as a result of the explorations that steadily intensified from the days of Marco Polo and Ibn-Baṭṭūṭa to those of Captain Cook. In the second place, although the Earth lost the central position in the universe that in earlier times it had been thought to hold, its relation to the other planets became better understood as a result of astronomical observations stretching from the Alphonsine Tables to Herschel (and beyond). In the third place, more men than ever before came to think, with the humanists and Alexander Pope, that the proper study of Mankind is Man, Humanity rather than Divinity.

For all that, during the centuries from 1300 to 1775 religious sects multiplied, each gaining devout adherents and re-emphasizing other-worldly principles. Yet often the sects lost power as they split one from the other. The decentralization of Catholic church authority, for example, was part cause and part effect of a gradual but steady growth of secularism in Europe.

Ironically, some of this secular trend was due to the acerbity of the religious conflict of the era. Christendom, which had previously been divided only between an eastern Orthodox Church and a western Roman Catholic Church, was after 1300 plagued by numerous schisms and sectarian movements. Efforts to reconcile the eastern and western churches failed and soon proved harder than ever to achieve. For while, with the Turkish invasion of Europe, the eastern churches passed step by step under the temporal suzerainty of Turkish or Muscovite rulers, in the west the papacy, becoming involved in serious and debilitating conflicts with rising separatistic forces, ceased to speak for the whole of Western Christendom.

About the same time, where the Christian religion had once ruled supreme, other than Christian principles and teachings were beginning to claim attention and loyalty. That phase of the Renaissance which is sometimes called the Revival of Classical Learning brought not only a more precise understanding of Greek philosophy, Roman law, and Classical science, art, and literature but also a rediscovery of many lost Classical masterpieces and an increased respect for pagan thought. The employment of the Ciceronian phrase *studia humanitatis* to designate the major pursuit of the humanists implied an interest in a learning that not only was more global, more cosmopolitan, than that commonly available but also was distinguishable from the cultivation of theological learning, from the study of divinity. With it came a greater appreciation of secular activities (as embodied, for example, in the Italian *virtuoso*) and of secular learning (as in Italian humanism) and a desire for innovation (as in vernacular literature and scientific investigation).

Changing religious loyalties interplayed with changing political loyalties. During the Middle Ages Christians had generally felt bound first to their religion and church and only afterward to a neighbouring lord or a distant overlord. In the centuries after 1300 the dynastic state (sometimes loosely described as 'the national state') gradually assumed such pre-eminent importance in the lives of its subjects that it claimed their primary loyalty. As the ruler established centralized control over lay and ecclesiastical affairs and as he took over significant services previously performed by the church and the feudal nobility, the remotest subject became more and more dependent upon temporal authority—that is, upon the activities of his king or his king's agents. Justice was now dispensed more often by royal judges; economic life was increasingly regulated by royal decrees; military power (and with it the preservation of domestic peace, the conduct of foreign war, and the protection of the subject's security) was slowly gathered into the hands of officers commissioned by the king; frequently changes in the religion of the ruling prince determined changes in the religion of his people; education showed signs of eventually passing under government control; and the care of the needy and the sick began gradually to move from ecclesiastical almshouses and hospitals to secular eleemosynary institutions. The growth of the secular state at the expense of the church meant in some instances that the individual Christian merely exchanged loyalties or, if he had previously been torn between two, now gave prior allegiance to a single one. Most Christians, however, continued to find allegiance to one master compatible with allegiance to the other, especially as the state-dominated church usually received only intermittent attention. In certain respects (notably in the freer choice among creeds) Europeans as a whole, where they could move from state to state, gained greater personal freedom; in other respects the decline of the church's power left the individual within the separate states subject to an arbiter, who, to be sure, might be more undisputed than in the days when rulers and church had divided authority between them and had supported each other's opponents, but whose purposes were now more likely to be frankly concerned with *raison d'état* than with religious tradition and precepts.

In economic enterprise the decline of church influence and the rise of secular authority conjoined to exert a concurrent impact. During the Middle Ages the church had attempted to a good extent to pass upon commercial affairs. Although the clergy had material concerns of its own and although religious precepts rarely contended successfully against man's striving for possessions, power, and comfort, clerical authority had often tempered the drive toward self-advantage with certain spiritual and at times even ascetic demands and ideals. Some of the clergy's own self-seeking and the church's loss of prestige for that and other reasons enfeebled the efforts of the more saintly churchmen to stem the growth of materialism, which both helped to further a more secular-minded world and was furthered by the development of the secular mind.

The beginnings of a class of society in western Europe primarily concerned with economic endeavour had anticipated the splitting of the unified church. The rise of towns, the gradual crumbling of self-sufficient manorialism, the increase of commerce and trade, the initiation of industrialized processes on a large scale, and the maturing of monetary and fiscal practices such as stock companies and banking brought power and prestige to a class of people for whom commerce and industry were the *raison d'être*. Wealth in forms other than landed possessions began to accumulate and became not only a mark of social distinction but also of political influence. Rulers who had to call upon city dwellers in their struggles with their feudal vassals or with foreign enemies grew more and more dependent on income derived from bourgeois activities and consequently were prone to protect and promote bourgeois interests. When the church's power to enforce its precepts against usury or to impose its ideals of poverty and asceticism diminished, church weakness conspired with royal favour to widen the road to worldliness as men became less and less concerned with preparing themselves for the hereafter by leading holy lives at the cost of earthly enjoyment. Piety, ritual, prayer, faith, and good works, without ever completely losing their hold, more often won only lip service while increasing numbers paid genuine allegiance to the ideals of wealth, power, leisure, comfort, a higher standard of living, competitive display, personal status, and other secular longings.

The shift in political and religious loyalties combined with economic conditions to bring about a change in the dominant ideologies, and vice versa. Labour, thrift, and substance became more commendable in many minds both as tokens of a well-spent life and, if not as desirable ends in themselves, at least as a means toward desirable ends, at the very time that commerce, finance, and industry were expanding. The resulting increase in the number of men of substance provided yet another reason why the state, whether Protestant or Catholic, should be more attentive to the needs and demands of a now highly respected middle class, and political theory was more frequently formulated by members of that class. The religious concept of the paternalistic divine-right monarch and the empirical concept of the king as a partner in a social contract to create a 'natural' government converged with practical politics in tempering absolutism. By the end of the period under consideration in this volume 'the enlightened despot' who regarded it as his function to strive, more in deference to 'the laws of nature' than to 'the voice of God', to establish a state that should guarantee the material welfare of his subjects—and hence his own—had become the rule rather than the exception in Europe.

The secular interests of mercantilist ruler and merchant prince grew with the amazing geographic discoveries of the age. The augmenting knowledge in each part of the world of all the other parts stimulated the growth of trade, and mounting trade brought vast commercial companies, expanded stock holding, fresh business speculation, improved or entirely new banking and insurance practices, and the ills as well as the benefits that come with cut-throat competition. The Atlantic nations were in the best position to profit by the newer trade routes, and their burgher classes accumulated wealth and comfort to a degree that had never before been equaled. Exotic products like sugar, spice, perfume, tobacco, and chocolate gave life an added savour. The increasing importation into Europe of gems, precious metals, fine leather goods, porcelains, and *de luxe* textiles helped to raise the level of the competitive ostentation of those who could afford luxuries; and cotton, tobacco, drugs, dyestuffs, potatoes, tea, and coffee to some extent improved the well-being of even the lower classes. Besides, for those who dared, virgin lands and a chance for a better economic life lay across the seas. For those who preferred to stay at home new crops like American maize or new uses for old crops like the European turnip directly or indirectly provided a richer yield, a better diet, and so a firmer insurance against hunger and disease. With the rising standard of living after 1500, the populations of western Europe multiplied so rapidly that some observers even before Malthus expressed anxiety about the balance between population and food supply. A fuller knowledge of the world's geography and a wider distribution of the world's goods seemed to fortify terrestrial rather than celestial aspirations.

The age of geographic discovery roughly coincided with the age of scientific discovery. Scientists from Buridan and Oresme through Copernicus and Galileo to Newton and Lavoisier studied both stellar and earthly phenomena with methods that likewise encouraged the trend toward secularization. These men usually were respectful of, but not necessarily concerned with, 'the other world' in their scientific work. As scientific theorists from Roger Bacon and Francis Bacon through Descartes and Boyle to d'Alembert, Franklin, and Lomonosov extolled the role of inductive reasoning and experiment in the promotion of human knowledge, revelation and saintly miracles were relegated in many learned minds to a compartment unrelated to the natural sciences. At least one school, the *philosophes* of the Enlightenment, included in the study of nature the study of human institutions as well. Their universe had ceased to be not only geocentric but also theocentric and had become anthropocentric. 'Natural philosophy' became for them and their disciples not so much, if at all, the study of God's Book of Nature as a better guide to the understanding of human affairs. It provided norms, 'laws of nature', uninfluenced by either an infallible pope or an infallible council, and judgments according to such norms might now differ, if not with impunity, at least with less fear than formerly of excommunication, interdict, or social ostracism.

The new knowledge not merely made possible many technological contributions to man's material welfare (such as better housing, cheaper fuel and metals, improved agricultural methods, more labour-saving machinery, and a wider range of sanitation) but also occasioned some re-orientation of man's spiritual outlook. The preoccupation of scientists with material and measurable phenomena, the quantitative emphasis in the new biological, medical, and chemical findings, seemed to lend the weight of their prestige to those who called for greater attention to the physical and material than to the ideal and qualitative concerns of human life. The validity of man's transcendental and metaphysical thought came under increased questioning by some of the most critical minds of Europe. Daring thinkers of the later decades of our period frankly advanced purely mechanistic and materialistic philosophies that earlier would probably have encountered effective suppression not only by church and state but also by public scorn. Perhaps nothing else exemplified so palpably as the reception of some eighteenth-century materialist writings how far Europe's educated public (a small but influential group) had exchanged a religion-centred mode of life for a secular one.

FROM MIDDLE AGES TO MODERN TIMES

Some date near 1500 has usually been accepted for pedagogical purposes as a convenient marker for the transition from the medieval to the modern way of life. Such a transition has conventionally been considered valid only for

Europe, and it is true that several of the events that have traditionally been regarded as crucial in that transition had essentially intra-European effects. Yet, let us take some of them in chronological order and examine their significance to a world that as a whole was gradually becoming more interdependent. The year 1453 marked the fall of Constantinople, which thereupon ceased to be the capital of the Byzantine Empire, the Roman Empire of the east, and became the capital of the Ottoman Empire, which within decades stretched from Asia and Europe into Africa and came into friendly contact or open conflict with the new Ṣafavid empire in Persia, the new Mogul empire in India, and other Muslim states while continuing its conquests in Europe. The year 1454, decisive in the improvement of the printing press, marked the culmination of a phase of cultural borrowing by Europe from the East and the beginning of the wholesale communication of learning and thought that was to begin in Europe but gradually to move to all other parts of the world. The year 1492, when Columbus discovered America, marked the beginning of a world of two hemispheres and was a key step toward the circumnavigation of the globe. The year 1498, when Vasco da Gama succeeded in finding a sea route from Europe to India, marked the beginning of European imperialism in Asia. The year 1517, when Luther nailed his Ninety-Five Theses to a church door in Wittenberg, marked the precipitation of a German religious conflict that was to spread and eventually to play a part in impelling emigrants and missionaries to go from all parts of Europe to various parts of the world and to proselytize whole continents across the Atlantic. The year 1543 marked the publication of Copernicus' *De Revolutionibus Orbium Coelestium* and thereby the beginning of the end of the geostatic concept of the universe, a milestone on the road toward a new scientific attitude that, based largely on borrowed mathematics, astronomy, and alchemy, was to attain high levels in Europe and thence reach out to leave its impress upon the whole world. Of the more important dates that are widely held to point the passage from medieval to modern times in Europe there is one that seems at first glance to have had no direct and explicit interrelation with the non-European world—1496, the year that the army of King Charles VIII of France returned from Italy, accelerating the growth of Italian Renaissance influences in France and other parts of Europe—but even that event can be considered exclusively intra-European only if we overlook non-European roots and influences in Italy's culture and France's subsequent role in extra-European affairs.

In short, to speak diagrammatically, somewhere through the fifteenth and sixteenth centuries seems to run a curve that highlights the transitional nature of this era—chiefly perhaps but not exclusively for Europe. For that reason most of the developments that we have considered above have been discussed under two chronological headings, breaking somewhere around 1500. During the nearly five centuries under examination in this volume extraordinary things happened that sooner or later shook life everywhere out of old ways and forced it into new. The Earth was proved to be not only a sphere but also a mere speck in the universe. Its various civilizations moved from the relative ignorance of each other even in the Eurasian-African complex into direct and accelerating contact with each other across all the oceans. Europeans, sparse peoples from a small corner of the immense Eurasian continent, began to roam the surface of the earth, to people new continents, to ship the earth's treasures to all corners of the globe, and to establish themselves as masters or exploiters in some ancient coherent empires as well as in some loosely knit tribal areas—in America permanently and elsewhere at least temporarily.

Europe underwent more rapid and thorough cultural changes than other civilizations. The loss of ecclesiastical unity brought on a more manifest cultural diversity. Secular and science-oriented philosophies began to replace Scholasticism, as scientific discoveries followed each other in rapid succession. Notwithstanding the temporary Latinist revival in the scholarly world of humanism, vernacular languages began to push out Latin and Church Slavonic, and national literature to overshadow Classical and church literature. In the realm of music and the visual arts the old skills, methods, and instruments developed to an unparalleled perfection, and new ones were elaborated. Loosely organized political units, largely feudal, gradually made way for considerably centralized and powerful national states; the last 'universal' political authority gave up even the pretence of world control with Charles V's abdication as Holy Roman emperor in 1555. The urban middle classes steadily acquired power, and with their rise a capitalist-minded economy with interests in trade, industry, and finance seriously began to compete with the age-old predominance of agriculture. The guild system in the towns and the manorial system in the country yielded eventually to individual, group, corporate, or collectivist enterprise. If some proverbial slumberer like Sleeping Beauty had closed her eyes somewhere in Europe in 1450 and opened them only in 1550, she would have waked up in a strikingly transformed environment still in a process of transformation that was to speed up during the ensuing centuries.

This European transformation proceeded according to a diversified schedule. Some changes were of an abrupt nature, while others were mere steps in a lengthy process in which old and new mingled to produce a different way of life and thought only gradually. The innovations in agricultural methods and products, the increasing urbanization, the growth of finance, commerce, and industry, the discovery of cheap new land across the seas and the emigration of Europeans there, the rising importance of bureaucracy and administrative centralization, the improvement of military and naval techniques, the change in religious outlook—all these not only immediately affected great masses of people in Europe but also had more or less rapid repercussions abroad. At the same time events took place in Europe that, though destined to have immense consequences for all of humanity, exerted their full impact only several generations later and were hardly noticed by most contemporaries. Many of the scientific wonders, philosophic systems, and artistic masterpieces that were created during our period were known and treasured by mere handfuls of connoisseurs. The resolution of the calculus by Newton and Leibniz, the elementary discoveries in magnetism and static electricity by experimenters like Gilbert and Franklin, the findings of microscopists like Leeuwenhoek and Grew or of telescopists like Galileo and Herschel, the exposition of the circulatory system by Harvey and Malpighi, the teaching methods of Comenius and Boerhaave, and the initial gropings toward a theory of evolution by Tremblay and Buffon came to full fruition only long after these men were gone. The subtleties of Spinoza's philosophical theories and the implications of the historical concepts advanced by Vico were to be generally appreciated only in the nineteenth century. The music of Johann Sebastian Bach had to wait for rediscovery by Felix Mendelssohn. The effects that some of these slowly appreciated contributions were destined to have on both Western and non-Western civilization therefore really belong to the story told in the volumes of this *History* that follow.

THE COMMON PATTERN OF HUMAN BEHAVIOUR[1]

The era before the one dealt with in this volume was characterized by a number of features of culture and human behaviour roughly similar in all parts of the world. During our era, however, the rapid changes that took place in Europe brought about several significant deviations from the common pattern. In a loose fashion and with proper regard to notable exceptions (especially the independent minds of the great civilizations), this common human pattern can be outlined.

In general, before 1300 the common man's attitude toward nature nearly everywhere was governed by mystery and superstition. He conformed to nature or, more rarely, rebelled against it, without trying to understand it; except in an immediate, practical fashion he did not try to predict or control it. No matter how tragic to him as an individual personal disaster and death might be, they were seldom a challenge to him as a member of society or of mankind, since he was inclined to regard life on earth as a mere transitory phase, an ephemeral passage toward another existence whether as ancestral spirit, reincarnation, or eternal soul. Even recurrent catastrophes like earthquakes, plague, famine, or flood called for religious or governmental action, usually after the event, rather than for individual provision. The thinking of the common man was likely to concern life-after-death rather than the here-and-now, and only uncommon men took thought about bettering their own lot by planning their future.

The common man's thinking in general was about day-to-day problems. It was most often in images, in terms of concrete experience, or along traditional lines. Hence, unless it was theological, it was unlikely to be in the form of original abstract generalizations or of speculative plans. Holy days, the difference between seasons or between day and night, and the appointed moments for prayer were concrete measures of time, but otherwise time was but 'a succession of todays'—not something mathematical, abstract, and general, precisely measurable and divisible by hours, minutes, and seconds and not something valuable in terms of money. The concept *mankind* was also concrete. It was generally limited to 'we' and 'others', whether 'we' was the family, the community, or the nation.

The future of mankind was for God or for the gods and demons, and not for men, to determine. Wealth or poverty, power or submission (all most often a product of the amount of land controlled) were accepted as expressions of the will of God or the gods, whether by Christians in Europe rendering unto Caesar the things that are Caesar's, by Confucians, Taoists, Hindus, or Buddhists in Asia seeking the favour of ancestors or a nobler *karma*, by Muslims in Asia, Africa, and Europe trusting in Allah and His Prophet, or by animists on every continent bribing their gods with choice offerings. Magicians, seers, priests, or sages might have special knowledge of or influence with the supernatural, but their power to induce the Divine to alter Its will was limited, and even in cults that left room for some freedom of the human will, divine will remained inscrutable and paramount.

Earthly power, too, was hard to limit or to modify, although the good ruler was expected to be a patriarch. A middle class serving as a buffer between those with temporal authority and those subject to it was rare and, where it existed at all—as the bourgeoisie of Europe, the merchants of India's main ports, or the *chonin* of Japan—small in size. Status was more or less fixed by God and heredity; some were born to earn their bread by the sweat of their brows, and others to live in luxury; some to command and others to obey. While outstanding individuals often departed from and even rebelled against the common pattern, especially in the golden ages of Greece, Rome, India, China, and Islam, individualism seldom was stressed while conformity usually was.

Thus roughly similar attitudes toward nature, life, thought, time, mankind, authority, work, status, and individualism prevailed in most cultures before 1300. In several of the more advanced civilizations of the world, however, even before 1300 exceptions to this common human pattern had appeared. In China, for example, a system of civil service examinations supplemented the hereditary principle of authority with a graded 'literocracy', and the idea of a provident patriarchal ruler was particularly well elaborated. In ancient Greece an objective attitude toward nature emerged, permitting abstract, generalized, non-theological systems of thought to arise. In the Greco-Roman city-states the notion of popular sovereignty, of government as the servant of the people, was highly developed. In medieval Europe a strong church hierarchy, preaching a monotheistic Catholicism based on Judaic and Greco-Roman foundations, counterbalanced the political authority of the hereditary princes. In various parts of the world labour-saving devices like harness, wheels, cranks, windmills, rudders, and sails had reduced some of the labourer's pains, making it possible for man the *animal laborans* to become *homo faber*.

For a time before and about 1300 it looked as if these separate departures— administrative, political, philosophical, theological, and technological— might converge in and be absorbed by the Islamic countries, where an unusual degree of social mobility and a high intellectual flexibility accompanied a uniquely rapid spread of a new society. But thereafter the Islamic readiness to absorb cultural importations declined; the printing press, for example, was not introduced into the Ottoman Empire until 1727. In contrast, Christian Europe proved to be not only more receptive of divergences from the common pattern diffused from other areas but also extraordinarily fertile in devising divergences of its own.

The reasons for Europe's greater receptivity to innovation can only be surmised; they may not be unrelated to the rise of the religious idea of a better natural world to come propounded by Joachim of Floris in the twelfth century and the subsequent vogue of the idea of progress, but they doubtless also had some causal interrelation as well as concomitance with the pronounced rise of the urban middle class. At any rate, few of the divergences of Europeans from the prevailing human pattern produced a more productive concatenation of change and innovation than the urbanization of Western society. European towns, without ceasing to be, as before, fair or market hubs, trade stations, depots, or ports, political capitals, administrative headquarters, military posts, ecclesiastical seats, or educational centres now, less exceptionally than before, became something besides; they became business communities. As the locale of shops, offices, and factories, they were also the homes of the educated, professional, financial, commercial, and industrial classes that stood somewhere between the landowning, military aristocracy and the working population. Sometimes these middle classes, this new bourgeoisie, co-operated with kings against the feudal nobles, their common competitor, at the same time that they buttressed their own local power through co-operation in their guilds; in so doing, they helped build large, centralized political and economic units—dynastic or national states. Governments now seemed to be held together against centrifugal forces not alone by God-ordained leaders but also increasingly by the consent, though still silent and implicit for the most part, of the governed. As merchants, manufacturers, and bankers came to look upon wealth as not merely useful but even as pleasant in the eyes of the Lord and accumulated wealth not only in real property and precious metals but also in business paper, capital investments, factories, and labour-saving machinery, they disregarded the Biblical injunction and took thought for the morrow. They brought forth banks, insurance companies, professional training programmes, capital accumulations, public sanitation systems, improved methods of transportation and production, and a myriad of political reform proposals. The more al-truistic among them planned not only for themselves as individuals and for their immediate associates but eventually also for mankind in general. In the minds of the more secularly inclined a notion of the destiny of mankind was emerging that depended less on God and more on man, that departed from the concept of religious perfection (man created in the image of the Creator and saved by divine grace) toward that of secular progress, that envisaged a common humanity and even a world political organization for the preservation of global peace and human prosperity.

The ideal of secular progress tended to modify the attitudes toward traditions and usages of those who entertained it. It left plenty of room for human action and decisions, since progress could come only from change, and change could obviously be made by human choices. For those who believed in a considerable margin of freedom of the human will the will of God, even when God was not repudiated as First Cause and Final Cause, was a less immediate and pressing object of attention than the problems of man and man's environment. Eventually inquiring minds began to question tradition, the Classics themselves included, on the basis, if they were reli-giously inclined, of their direct reading of Scripture and, if they were less religiously inclined, of empiricism or reason, if not of both. Tradition and conformity were not obliterated thereby, nor did they lose all of their appeal; there was never a lack of persons who fought innovation in favour of tradi-tion. But Europe's intellectuals found different traditions to adhere to, no one ecclesiastical authority having the power to interpret tradition once and for all, and different traditions led or seemed to lead toward different ends. And innovation itself acquired a tradition, a tradition of continual and un-ending accumulation. For a great number of Europeans, even among those still unquestioningly loyal to their respective churches, mankind's salvation as mortals (regardless of what might happen to the immortal soul) seemed achievable by a new system of faith and good works, of which Francis Bacon was the prophet—the ceaseless and boundless expansion of knowledge and the constant and irreversible advancement of the frontiers of science. As knowledge accumulated, some of the long accepted truths were rendered suspect, and new ones were enthroned in their place. It no longer seemed self-evident that what was good for one level or group of society should *ipso facto* be respected by another as ordained, and it no longer was generally conceded that what was good for father was good also for son. In short, the idea of progress tended to promote an attitude favourable not only to secularization of thought but also to individualism and innovation.

Amid the innovations that, whether borrowed from abroad or produced at home, flooded Europe from 1300 (and before) to 1775 (and beyond), the common human pattern survived. For a large part of Europe's population nature was still an unquestioned mystery, life was a transient phase in eternity, thought was still about immediately, concrete problems, mankind was still divided between 'we' and 'they' (though now increasingly in nation-states rather than in feudal communities), authority was still sacrosanct, work was still an unmitigable hereditary curse, social status was still fixed, conformity was still the best guide of conduct, and strange ideas were suspect. But for some Westerners a new world seemed altogether possible in the future—a world where ultimately nature would be subject to human control by scientific knowledge, the human organism would be capable of ascertaining and acting upon abstract and eternal truths, or 'natural laws', mankind would all be brothers, government would be explicitly derived from the consent of the governed, labour would be reduced to the minimum necessary to a healthy, happy, peaceful, and prosperous society, and individual enterprise would achieve the best allocation of social prestige and the world's goods.

This ameliorist philosophy, this idea of never-ending and essentially irreversible perfectibility, had grown up alongside the ancient Judeo-Christian faith and by the eighteenth century was ready to be exported, together with Europe's new technology and traditional religions, to the other continents. From 1300 on, and especially after 1500, Europe had been exporting its ideas, institutions, and inventions at an accelerating pace. By 1775 this process of 'Europeanization' was decisive in the Americas but as yet had only a spotty and superficial effect in other non-European areas. Europe's borrowing, in its turn, from non-European cultures, already appreciable before 1300, also increased, particularly after the great explorations brought more immediate contact with those cultures. Thus Europe's culture, even as it was being exported, was becoming more diversified, more international, more cosmopolitan, more 'modern'.

SOME INTERRELATIONS OF RELIGION, STATE, CULTURE, AND TECHNOLOGY

Church, State, and Freedom of Thought

The line between civil allegiance on the one hand and religious allegiance on the other was generally harder to draw during our period than subsequently. A clear separation of church and state was sometimes openly advocated by Western theorists like the Anabaptists, Milton, and Roger Williams and often doubtless privately desired by heretics and non-conformists everywhere. Yet officialdom rarely was prepared to admit that a subject might be loyal without belonging to the established church. The English colonies of Rhode Island, Connecticut, and Pennsylvania were exceptional in not requiring religious tests for citizenship or office-holding.

Buddhism, in comparison with the other great religions, was relatively lacking in desire to constitute itself an organic part of a political and social system. This indifference to politics was perhaps due to its concept of the ideal man, the *sannyāsī*, the contemplative, celibate ascetic. Unlike Christian asceticism, in theory at least Buddhist asceticism was not restricted to a select few and so, if carried relentlessly to its logical conclusion, would ultimately have ended in the extinction of Buddhists, rendering political and social theories irrelevant. In actuality, Buddhism tended rather to adapt itself to one or another viable pattern within the political and social systems of the countries to which it spread.

Buddhist doctrinal indifference to politics induced indifference to, and hence toleration of, the religion of others. In Buddhist countries like Ceylon, Burma, Siam, and Cambodia, the Hindu theory of divine kingship generally prevailed and the ruler often conceived of himself as a bodhisattva; he might, therefore, use his position to promote Buddhism and to regulate the monks, but he was generally tolerant also of non-conformist groups if they were not actively hostile. In turn, in countries like China and Japan, which were not predominantly or continuously Buddhist, the Buddhists sought and normally obtained the tolerance, protection, or patronage of the rulers. Indeed, Buddhist monks, especially in Japan, were often high-level advisers to the rulers, and during the Tokugawa period Buddhism was the state religion, serving as an effective tool of the shoguns in combating Christianity and controlling the population. In Tibet, Buddhism attained the position of a theocracy, but even there the state's power was not used to wipe out opposition groups.

In Islam, the unity of church and state was theoretically complete, and to enforce Islamic religious law was the only duty of the state. Non-Muslim groups were tolerated, however, though subjected to the political control of sultans. Though forced to pay a poll tax and to suffer other disabilities, they were allowed their own systems of personal law within an Islamic context.

Hinduism was the most tolerant of the great religious systems. Any group that accepted the social and intellectual leadership of the Brahmans could hope to find a place in the caste system. The Brahmans seldom sought to exercise ruling power directly, since in their system it belonged to another class, but they expected to be among the intimate advisers of rulers. Although the state was merciless toward any group, religious or otherwise, that threatened the ruling prince, a Hindu ruler used power only rarely to enforce a particular creed or dogma. Sikhism, the offspring of a union of Hinduism and Islam, departing from ths tolerant attitude, was the only Hindu sect to work out a complete fusion of church and state.

The mixed religious systems of China, Japan, Korea, and Vietnam tended toward permissiveness. To be sure, in all these countries religious ceremonies were a part of a state system, and the machinery of government was used to conduct religious ceremonies believed to be necessary or beneficial to the state's well-being. In China, where Confucianism was the philosophy of the state and the ruler was the nominal head of all religious groups, the government promoted Confucianism. Hence, the minority creeds of Buddhism and Taoism were regulated and restricted in various ways and the number of their priests, monks, and nuns was officially limited. Nevertheless, heterodox teachings, though nominally prohibited, were in practice allowed unless they appeared to be a threat to the ruling power. In Japan Shintoism as well as Buddhism was supported by the state, and Shinto propagandists during the Tokugawa period went so far as to favour its establishment as the exclusive state cult.

The line between theology and philosophy was also during this period generally indistinct. In the West, as humanism and the new scientific spirit gained in strength, theology was first obliged to share its throne as the queen of the sciences with the *studia humanitatis*, and subsequently an even more secular 'natural philosophy' took its reginal place. On the other hand, to distinguish between religion and philosophy elsewhere—or, for that matter, for all Western thinkers—would be to a large extent factitious. Muslims, indeed, sought to distinguish *kalām* from *falsafa* but not without an area of overlapping (see Chapter VI). In Hindu thought the distinctions between theology and philosophy were even less formal, and the great religious thinkers of India were also its great philosophers. As in the West, those who were primarily theistic found the principal route to salvation in devotion to a bersonal deity, and the less theistic, although they disagreed regarding the pest way to express that devotion, thought in terms of enlightenment through knowledge and the realization of the unity of the individual with the absolute *brahman* (not wholly unlike the Western philosopher's Nature). In Buddhist thinking no greater distinction was made between theology and philosophy. The Neo-Confucian thinkers of China, however, were fundamentally interested in philosophic, political, and social problems and not in theology, and since Buddhist and Taoism produced no really outstanding thinkers during this period, the posture of Chinese thought, apart from ceremonial practices, was secular rather than religious. Japanese Buddhist thinkers were strongly influenced by Chinese philosophy, while Shinto thinkers, influenced by a native nationalism as well as by both Neo-Confucianism and Buddhism, fused religious, philosophical, and political conceptions into a theory of pure Shinto.

In contrast, in Europe the distinction between church and state, between pope and emperor, between theology and political philosophies was fairly perceptible even before 1300, and after that date the line between the divine and the secular became clearer still. The decline of the concept of a Holy Roman Empire was a further aid to the secularization of political thought. Never more than a pale reflection of the old Roman Empire, it steadily lost ground to the sanguine ideal of the nation state, and the ideal of a universal church ruled by a strong hierarchy and harbouring all believers within its flexible embrace was irrevocably impaired by the Protestant revolts. At first, despite pleas for tolerance from the Bodins and the Comeniuses, the effect of the religious wars was increased intolerance, and Calixtus fruitlessly advocated syncretism, a reunion of the churches. Bishop Bossuet in 1688 wrote an *Histoire des variations des églises protestantes* decrying the splintering tendencies of Protestantism, only to be reminded by other writers, both Protestant and Catholic, that Catholicism also had its variations. Indeed, Leibniz, syncretist though he was, contended that variety might not be undesirable as pointing toward the amelioration of religion. And it indeed proved true that increasing variety, though it tended away from syncretism, led at least toward confusion and eventually, if not toward official tolerance, at least toward official indifference—though far from complete in either case by 1775. Growing religious permissiveness and indifference interacted—sometimes as cause, sometimes as effect—with the secularization of thought, whether in science, politics, philosophy, or art, but secularization, for all its looming significance, was to remain gradual and sparse until the close of the eighteenth century.

Secularization and Diffusion of Culture

While many other areas stayed in most regards even less secularized than Europe, they tended more noticeably toward secularization in art than in philosophy. Hindu art, consisting largely of temple architecture and the sculpture of deities, continued to draw its major inspiration from religion, but Rajput painting represented secular court scenes to some extent. While Japanese architecture and sculpture still reflected interest in Buddhism, landscape painting became popular, and during the Tokugawa period the secular colour print and secular architecture came to dominate their respective fields. In China, although landscape painting always mirrored a certain Taoist mysticism and many favourite scenes in paintings and prints dealt with Buddhist and Taoist themes, secular art stood out in imperial palaces and tombs, huge stone animals, colour prints of popular subjects, and landscape paintings, and the famous Chinese porcelains of the period were for secular use.

The secular trend in art was far from universal, however, particularly where Buddhist influences prevailed. In Burma, Siam, and Cambodia the great pagodas, monasteries, and sculptured figures were Buddhist-inspired, and even royal buildings reflected Buddhist religious ideas. Much the same can be said for the figures, monasteries, and palaces of Tibet. In Indonesia the rise of Islam blighted the development of Hindu-Buddhist sculpture and temple architecture but gave nothing of significance to replace it.

Europe eagerly absorbed decorative processes and motifs from Islamic lands and the Far East, and this receptivity to the minor arts of other cultural areas contrasts notably with Europe's amazing independence in the development of her major arts. The contrast may have a partly theological explanation —the greater acceptability of the minor arts as purely ornamental, having no non-Christian meanings such as might have been associated with infidel and heathen painting, sculpture, and architecture. Yet, more mundane explanations may also hold partly true. Contact of European artists was easier with the more portable objects of the decorative arts, and most of the techniques adopted by Europe were those that lent themselves to factory production; the much admired but laboriously made rugs of the Islamic lands and China never inspired a leading imitative effort in the decorative arts of Europe. Europeans readily adopted the ideals of refinement and luxury embodied in the decorative arts of Islam, China, Japan, and India. Previously accustomed to relatively drab and uncomfortable lives, they had become conscious of the magnificence of the East during the Crusades, and by the eighteenth century, in admiration for and use of beautifully made and elaborately ornamental articles, Europeans equalled the most luxury-loving peoples.

The history of the arts and letters during our period illustrates two paradoxes that have frequently been noted in the development of art. Art is both indigenous and international; art is both primitive and polished. The paradoxes are easily explained. All peoples, no matter what their stage of culture, express themselves in imaginative lore, song, dance, and picture long before and long after they learn to express themselves in written words. Art thus often is the articulation of the aspirations, joys, sorrows, triumphs, and defeats, and the record of the great moments in the history, of a primitive people. It often is also the outlet for the expression of frustration by the suppressed in places where the written word of protest would be punished. Folklore, picture, song, and dance are therefore to be found whenever aspirations or emotions of joy or sorrow are expressed. Since such aspirations and emotions nearly always give vent to hope, these expressions easily lend themselves to religious faith. Art thus everywhere becomes a handmaiden of the priest as well as an expression of popular affects and a means of popular entertainment. It passes from church to palace to commoner's home, and from country to country, meanwhile undergoing adaptations and accretions that fit it to the tastes not only of different peoples but also of different eras and of different layers of society. The spontaneous, simple, indigenous, local, primitive art rarely dies, but alongside it flourishes a teeming progeny which is cultivated, composite, and learned or even sophisticated, and which, while retaining its indigenous roots, borrows heavily from other parts of the world. In its more refined forms, art speaks to the cultivated few no more eloquently than in its more popular forms it speaks to the many.

The history of art, whether religious or secular (including music, though not musical forms or notation), constitutes perhaps the best example our period affords of mankind's trend (often unconscious; often resisted, if conscious) toward cultural unity in diversity, toward a cosmopolitan culture. The oneness of science did not equally provide room for diversity, and the idioms of language, the pride of races and nations, and the divisiveness of theological and philosophical persuasions did not equally permit unity of literary creativity and standards. Yet literature, too, forwarded the trends toward unity in diversity: literary themes were often common property, philosophy and theology dealt with universal problems and aspirations, folklore was readily interchanged, and literature, if sometimes inadequately, was capable of translation. Art and music, more than other products of the human mind, spoke a universal language without forgetting their native patois; literature spoke in many tongues but often about the same things.

Technology, too, easily migrates from place to place. In our period Europe borrowed in technological processes connected with such things as compass, gunpowder, printing, porcelains, textiles, and decorative arts more than it loaned. In fact, before the nineteenth century Western technology for the most part stayed at home in Europe and America, and modern science, too, remained limited largely to Europe, both waiting for a later day to play a role upon the world stage. But eventually, technology and science were, like art and music, to speak a language equally intelligible all over the world, and, like literature, to deal with problems common to men everywhere.

Probably as late as 1775 Europe was still taking more from the non-Western civilizations in cultural influences, commodities, and human labour than it gave to them. If the shift in the balance had begun, the day was still distant when non-Western civilizations would have to choose between their traditional ways and 'Westernization', so much of which had been borrowed from outside the West. But the choice would never be limited to two sheer alternatives—tradition or Westernization—for each non-Western people would be able to mix the two according to its own prescription for 'modernization', eventually borrowing scientific knowledge, technical products, and technologies with greater alacrity than mores or values, whether artistic, literary, or behavioral. If in a subsequent age there would be room to wonder whether what the several cultures had borrowed from each other was for better or for worse, in a less sceptical epoch, when nearly all men had faith in either God's design or the perfectibility of man or in both, few could doubt that it must be for the better.

NOTES TO CHAPTER XVII

1. This discussion borrows from J. M. Romein, 'The Common Human Pattern', *Journal of World History*, IV (1958), pp. 449–63, but has taken into account the variant points of view expressed by Oscar Halecki in 'The Place of Christendom in the History of Mankind', *Journal of World History*, I (1954), pp. 927–50, and by Pieter Geyl in 'The Vitality of Western Civilization', *Delta, a Review of Arts, Life and Thought in the Netherlands* (Spring, 1959), pp. 5–19.

SELECTED BIBLIOGRAPHY

Note: The titles that follow are selected almost exclusively from works that have appeared from 1957 to 1966. With a few exceptions, it was superfluous to include works that appeared before 1957, for such works probably are listed in George Frederick Howe *et al.*, eds., *Guide to Historical Literature* (New York: Macmillan Company, 1961; for the American Historical Association). (Titles will be given only once, but some may well belong under more than one heading.)

CHAPTER I: INTRODUCTION
THE POLITICAL, ECONOMIC, AND SOCIAL BACKGROUND

National Developments, 1300–1775

FERNANDO BENITEZ, *The Century after Cortes* (Chicago, 1965).

E. W. BOVILL, *The Golden Trade of the Moors* (London, 1958).

CHRISTOPHER BROOKE and D. M. SMITH, eds., *A History of England* (Edinburgh, 1961–   ) [Vols. III (1272–1485) and V (1603–1714) are the only ones published before 1966 that are relevant to this period.]

A. BULTMANN, 'Early Hanoverian England (1714–1760), Some Recent Writings', *Journal of Modern History*, XXXV (1963), 46–61.

G. B. CARSON, JR., 'Recent works on the History of Russia in the period from the Tatars to Catherine II', *Journal of World History*, VIII (1964), 548–63.

WILLIAM F. CHURCH, 'Publications on Cardinal Richelieu since 1945, a Bibliographical Study', *Journal of Modern History*, XXXVII (1965), 421–44.

G. N. CLARK, eds., *Oxford History of England* (Oxford, 1955–62), Vols. IV–XII (1216–1815).

G. N. CLARK *et al.*, eds., *The New Cambridge Modern History* (Cambridge, 1957–   ). [For the period of this volume Vols. I (1493–1520), II (1520–1559), V (1648–1688), VII (1713–1763) and VIII (1763–1793) had appeared before 1966.]

ROBERT CORNEVIN, *Histoire de l'Afrique*, Vol. I: *Des origines au XVIe siècle* (Paris, 1962).

P. D. CURTIN, *African History* (New York, 1964).

K. K. DATTA, 'A Brief Review of Works of Indian Scholars on the Medieval and Modern Periods of Indian History', *Journal of World History*, VI (1960), 380–402.

BASIL DAVIDSON, *Old Africa Rediscovered* (London, 1959) [which is the same work as *The Lost Cities of Africa* (Boston, 1959)].

RAYMOND DAWSON, ed., *The Legacy of China* (New York, 1964).

JAN DEN TEX, *Oldenbarnevelt* (Haarlem, 1960–62).

MICHEL FRANCOIS and NICOLAS TOLU, eds., *International Bibliography of Historical Sciences*, Vol. XXVII–XXXI, 1958–1962 (Paris, 1960–   ; for the International Congress of Historical Sciences).

J. H. ELLIOTT, *Imperial Spain, 1469–1716* (Cambridge, 1963).

——, *The Revolt of the Catalans: A Study in the Decline of Spain (1598–1640)* (New York, 1963).

PIETER GEYL, *The Netherlands in the Seventeenth Century*: Part 2: *1648–1715* (London, 1964).

LINO GOMEZ CANEDO, *Los archivos de la historia de América, periodo colonial español* (Mexico, D.F., 1961), 2 vols.

STANKO GULDESCU, *A History of Medieval Croatia* (The Hague, 1964).

OTTO HAINTZ, *König Karl XII von Schweden* (Berlin, 1958), 3 vols.

C. O. HUCKER, *China: A Critical Bibliography* (Tucson, Ariz., 1962).

R. JACOBS, *The American Colonies Come of Age, 1689–1763* (Chicago, 1965).

FRITZ KERN *et al.*, *Historia Mundi*, Vols, VI–IX [late Middle Ages to Enlightenment] (Bern, 1957–1960).

GUSTAVE LANCTOT, *Histoire du Canada: Des origines au régime royal* (Montreal, 1959).

HENRYK LOWMIANSKI *et al.*, 'Etat des recherches', in JULIUSZ BARDACH *et al.*, eds., *La Pologne au XIIe Congrès international des Sciences Historiques à Vienne* (Warsaw, 1965), pp. 163–399 [Bibliography of Polish historiography, 1945–1965].

JOHN LYNCH, *Spain under the Habsburgs*, Vol. I: *Empire and Absolutism* (New York, 1964).

RAYMOND MAUNY *et al.*, eds. 'Le problème des sources de l'Afrique Noire jusqu'à la colonisation européenne', XIIe Congrès International des Sciences Historiques *Rapports* (Horn/Vienna, 1965), II, 177–232.

FREDERIC MAURO, *Le Portugal et l'Atlantique au XVIIe siècle (1570–1670): Etude économique* (Paris, 1960).

W. H. MACNEILL, *Europe's Steppe Frontier, 1500–1800* (Chicago, 1964).

KANTARO MURAKAWA *et al.*, eds., *Japan at the XIIth International Congress of Historical Sciences in Vienna* (Tokyo, 1965). A bibliography of Japanese historical publications, 1958–1962.

ROLAND OLIVIER and J. D. FAGE, *A Short History of Africa* (Harmondsworth, 1962).

DENISE PAULME, 'L'Afrique noire jusqu'au XIVe siècle, deuxième partie', *Journal of World History*, III (1957), 561–82.

CONYERS READ, *Bibliography of British History, Tudor Period, 1485–1603* (2nd ed., New York, 1959).

HELLMUT ROSSLER and GUNTHER PRINZ, *Sachwörterbuch zur deutschen Geschichte* (Munich, 1956–1958), 2 vols.

JOHN C. RULE, 'The Old Regime in America: A Review of Recent Interpretations of France in America', *William and Mary Quarterly*, 3d. ser., XIX (1962), 575–600.

STEVEN RUNCIMAN, *The Fall of Constantinople, 1453* (Cambridge, 1965).

A. M. SAKHAROV, 'Les Mongols et la civilisation russe', *Journal of World History*, special no., *Contributions to Russian History* (1958), 77–97.

B. S. SILBERMAN, *Japan and Korea: A Critical Bibliography* (Tucson, 1962).

ROBERT WALCOTT, *The Tudor-Stuart Period of English History (1485-1714): A Review of Changing Interpretations* (New York, 1964).

J. B. WOLF, 'The Reign of Louis XIV: A Selected Bibliography of Writings since the War of 1914-1918', *Journal of Modern History*, XXXVI (1964), 127-44.

PEREZ ZAGORIN, 'English History, 1558-1640, A Bibliographical Survey', *American Historical Review*, LXVIII (1963), 364-84.

The Centralization of Political Power

C. B. ANDERSON, 'Ministerial Responsibility in the 1620's', *Journal of Modern History*, XXXIV (1962), 381-89.

MICHEL ANTOINE, 'Les Conseils des finances sous le règne de Louis XV', *Revue d'histoire moderne et contemporaine*, V (1958), 161-200.

G. E. AYLMER, *The King's Servants: The Service of Charles I, 1625-1642* (London, 1961).

SIMONE BLANC, 'La pratique de l'administration russe dans la première moitié du XVIIIè siècle,' *Revue d'histoire moderne et contemporaine*, X (1963), 45-64.

CH'Ü T'UNG-TSU, *Local Administration in China under the Ch'ing* (Cambridge Mass., 1962).

BERNARD S. COHN, 'Political Systems in Eighteenth Century India: The Banaras Region', *Journal of the American Oriental Society*, LXXXII (1962), 312-20.

JEAN DELUMEAU, 'Les progrès de la centralisation dans l'état pontifical au XVIe siècle', *Revue historique*, CCXXVI (1961), 399-410.

J. W. FESLER, 'French Field Administration, The Beginnings', *Comparative Studies in Society and History*, V (1962), 76-111.

R. E. GIESEY, 'The juristic Basis of Dynastic Right to the French Throne', *Transactions of the American Philosophical Society*, LI, part 5 (1961).

ALBERT GOODWIN, 'The Social Structure and Economic and Political Attitudes. The French Nobility in the Eighteenth Century', XIIe Congrès international des Sciences Historiques, *Rapports*, (Vienna, 1965), I, 356-68.

C. O. HUCKER, *The Traditional Chinese State in Ming Times (1368-1644)*, (Tucson, Arizona, 1961).

J. R. MAJOR, *Representative Institutions in Renaissance France, 1421-1559* (Madison, Wisc., 1960).

——, 'The Crown and the Aristocracy in Renaissance France', *American Historical Review*, LXIX (1964), 631-45.

N. MAJUMDAR, *Justice and Police in Bengal, 1765-1793: A Study of the Mizamat in Decline* (Calcutta, 1960).

C. R. MAYES, 'The Sale of Peerages in Early Stuart England', *Journal of Modern History*, XXIX (1957), 21-37.

A. L. MOOTE, 'The French Crown versus Its Judicial and Financial Officials, 1615-83', *Journal of Modern History*, XXXIV (1962), 146-60.

O. A. RANUM, *Richelieu and the Councillors of Louis XIII: A Study of the Secretaries of State and Superintendents of Finance in the Ministry of Richelieu, 1635–1642*, (New York, 1963).

J. RICOMMARD, 'Du recrutement et du nombre des subdélégués en titre d'office dans l'intendance de Bretagne (1704–1715)', *Revue d'histoire moderne et contemporaine*, VIII (1961), 121–52.

HANS ROSENBERG, *Bureaucracy, Aristocracy, and Autocracy: The Prussian Experience, 1660–1815* (Cambridge, Mass., 1958).

The Quest for Liberty and Social Justice

YEHOSHUA ARIELI, *Individualism and Naturalism in American Ideology* (Cambridge, Mass., 1964).

BERNARD BAILYN (ed.), *Pamphlets of the American Revolution, 1750–1776*, Vol. I: *1750–1765* (Cambridge, Mass., 1965).

M. R. BECKER, 'Florentine Popular Government (1343–1348)', *Proceedings of the American Philosophical Society*, CVI (1962), 360–82.

F. L. CARSTEN, *Princes and Parliaments in Germany from the Fifteenth to the Eighteenth Century* (New York, 1959).

L. G. CROCKER, *Rousseau et la voie du totalitarisme*, Institut International de Philosophie Politique, *Annales de Philosophie Politique*, No. 5 (1965), 99–136.

DENISE EECKAUTE, 'Les brigands en Russie du XVIIe au XIXe siècle: 'mythe et réalité', *Revue d'Histoire moderne et contemporaine*, XII (1965), 161–202.

F. L. FORD, *Strasbourg in Transition, 1648–1789* (Cambridge, Mass., 1958).

J. P. GREENE, *The Quest for Power: The Lower Houses of Assembly in the Southern Royal Colonies, 1689–1776* (Chapel Hill, North Carolina, 1963).

PAULINE GREGG, *Free-born John: a Biography of John Lilburne* (London, 1961).

P. H. HARDACRE, 'Writings on Oliver Cromwell since 1929', *Journal of Modern History*, XXXIII (1961), 1–14.

JACK H. HEXTER, *Reappraisals in History* (Evanston, Ill., 1961).

F. G. HEYMANN, 'City Rebellions in Fifteenth Century Bohemia and Their Ideological and Sociological Background', *Slavonic and East European Review*, XL (1962), 324–40.

JEAN JACQUART, 'La fronde des princes dans la région parisienne et ses conséquences matérielles', *Revue d'histoire moderne et contemporaine*, VII (1960), 257–90.

J. R. MAJOR, *The Deputies to the Estates General of Renaissance France* (Madison, Wisc., 1960).

K. B. MCFARLANE, 'The English Nobility in the later Middle Ages', XIIe Congrès International des Sciences Historiques, *Rapports*, (Vienna, 1965) I, 337–45.

ROLAND MOUSNIER, 'Recherches sur les soulèvements populaires en France avant la Fronde', *Revue d'histoire moderne et contemporaine*, V (1958), 81–113.

J. E. NEALE, *Elizabeth I and her Parliaments, 1584–1601* (New York, 1957).

S. PASCU *et al.*, 'Mouvements paysans dans le centre et le sud-est de l'Europe du XVe au XXe siècle', XIIe Congrès International des Sciences Historiques, *Rapports* (Vienna, 1965), IV, 211–35.

BORIS PORCHNEV, *Les soulèvements populaires en France de 1623 à 1648* (Paris, 1963) (tr. from the Russian).

E. S. TEALL, 'The Seigneur of Renaissance in France: Advocate or Oppressor?' *Journal of Modern History*, XXXVII (1965), 131–50.

C. L. VER STEEG. *The Formative Years, 1607–1763* (New York, 1964) ('The Making of America').

C. V. WEDGEWOOD, *The Great Rebellion* (London, 1955, 1958), 2 vols.

PEREZ ZAGORIN, 'The English Revolution, 1640–1660', *Journal of World History*, II (1955), 668–81 and 895–914.

Economic Changes and their Political Import

W. O. AULT, *Open-field Husbandry and the Village Community: A Study of Agrarian By-laws in Medieval England* in *Transactions of the American Philosophical Society*, LV (1965).

BERNARD and LOTTE BAILYN. *Massachusetts Shipping, 1697–1714: A Statistical Study* (Cambridge, Mass., 1959).

R. BARÓN CASTRO, 'El desarrollo de la poblacion hispanoamericana (1492–1950),' *Journal of World History*, V (1959), 325–43.

JEAN-FRANCOIS BERGIER, *Genève et l'économic européenne de la Renaissance* (Paris, 1963).

FRANÇOIS BILLACOIS, 'La Batellerie de la Loire au XVIIe siècle', *Revue d'histoire moderne et contemporaine* XI (1964), 163–90.

M. R. BLOCH, 'The Social Influence of Salt', *Scientific American*, CCIX (July, 1963), 88–98.

MICHAEL CONFINO, *Domaines et seigneurs en Russie vers la fin du XVIIIe siècle. Etude de structures agraires et de mentalités économiques.* Préface de Roger Portal (Paris, 1963).

EMILE CORNAERT, *Les français et le commerce international à Anvers, fin du XVe–XVIe siècle* (Paris, 1961), 2 vols.

PHILIPPE DOLLINGER, *La Hanse (XIIe–XVIIe siècles)* (Paris, 1964).

W. K. FERGUSON, *Europe in Transition: 1300 to 1520* (Boston, Mass., 1963).

PING-TI HO, *Studies on the Population of China, 1368–1953* (Cambridge, Mass., 1959).

HENRI LAPEYRE, 'Anvers au XVIe siècle d'après des travaux récents', *Revue d'histoire moderne et contemporaine*, XI (1964), 191–202.

G. T. MATTHEWS, *The Royal General Farms in Eighteenth-Century France* (New York, 1958).

JOHN NEF, *The Conquest of the Material World: Essays on the Coming of Industrialism* (Chicago, 1964).

R. M. MORSE, 'Some Characteristics of Latin American Urban History', *American Historical Review*, LXVII (1962), 317–38.

PAUL CHRISLER PHILLIPS, *The Fur Trade*, Vol. I [to 1783] (Norman, Oklahoma, 1961).

MARCEL REINHARD and ANDRE ARMENGAUD, *Histoire générale de la population mondiale* (Paris, 1961).

LADISLAS REITZER, 'Some Observations on Castilian Commerce and Finance in the Sixteenth Century', *Journal of Modern History*, XXXII (1960), 213–23.

H. VAN DER WEE, *The Growth of the Antwerp Market and the European Economy (fourteenth–sixteenth centuries)* (The Hague, 1963), 3 vols.

J. VICENS VIVES, *Historia económica de España* (Barcelona, 1959).

PHILIPPE WOLFF, *Histoire de Toulouse* (Toulouse, 1958).

Social Changes and Their Political Import

PAUL WALDEN BAMFORD, 'The Procurement of Oarsmen for French Galleys, 1660–1748', *American Historical Review*, LXI (1959), 31–48.

BERNARDO BLANCO-GONZALES, *Del cortesano al descreto: examen de una decadencia*, Vol. I (Madrid, 1962).

JEROME BLUM, *The European Peasantry from the Fifteenth to the Nineteenth Century* (Washington, 1960).

——, *Lord and Peasant in Russia from the Ninth to the Nineteenth Century* (New Haven, Conn., 1961).

ALFRED COBBAN, *The Social Interpretation of the French Revolution* (Cambridge, England, 1964).

ADELINE DAUMARD, 'Une préférence pour l'étude des sociétés urbaines en France aux XVIIIe et XIXe siècles, projet de code socio-professionel', *Revue d'histoire moderne et contemporaine*, X (1963), 185–210.

LAJOS FEKETE, 'La vie à Budapest sous la domination turque, 1541–1686', *Journal of World History*, VIII (1964), 525–47.

ROBERT FORSTER, *The Nobility of Toulouse in the Eighteenth Century: A Social and Economic Study* (Baltimore, 1960).

——, 'The Provincial Noble: a Reappraisal', *American Historical Review*, LXVIII (1963), 681–91.

HEINZ FRIESE, *Das Dienstleistungs-System der Ming-Zeit (1368–1644)* (Wiesbaden, 1959).

JACQUES HEERS, *L'occident aux XIVe et XVe siècles: aspects économiques et sociaux* ('Nouvelle Cléo') (Paris, 1963).

CHRISTOPHER HILL, *Society and Puritanism in Pre-Revolutionary England* (New York, 1964).

PING-TI HO, *The Ladder of Success in Imperial China: Aspects of Social Mobility, 1368–1911* (New York, 1962).

J. JACQUART, 'Propriété et exploitation rurales au sud de Paris, dans la seconde moitié du XVIe siècle', *Bulletin de la Société d'histoire moderne*, 12s., nos. 15–16 (October–December, 1960), 10–16.

MICHEL LAUNAY, 'La société française d'après la correspondance de J. J.-Rousseau (textes inédits),' *Annales historiques de la Révolution française*, XXXIII (1962), 397–420.

GEORGES LEFEBVRE, *Etudes Orléanaises*, I, *Contribution à l'étude des structures sociales à la fin du XVIIIe siècle* (Commission d'histoire économique et sociale de la Révolution, Paris, 1962).

ERIK MOLNAR, 'Les fondements économiques et sociaux de l'absolutisme', in Erik Molnar *et al.*, *Nouvelles études historiques* (Budapest, 1965), I, 285–99, and also in XIIe Congres International des Sciences Historiques, *Rapports* (Vienna, 1965), IV, 155–69.

JOHN U. NEF, *Cultural Foundations of Industrial Civilization* (Cambridge, England, 1958).

Z. P. PACK, *Die ungarische Agrarentwicklung im 16–17. Jahrhundert:* Abliegung vom westeuropäischen Entwicklungsgang (Budapest, 1964).

LIONEL ROTHKRUG, *Opposition to Louis XIV, the Political and Social Origin of the French Enlightenment* (Princeton, N.J., 1965).

J. C. RUSSELL, *Late Ancient and Medieval Population* (*Transactions of the American Philosophical Society*, XLVIII, part 3, 1958).

ALAN SIMPSON, *The Wealth of the Gentry, 1540–1660: East Anglican Studies* (Chicago, 1961).

GY. SZEKELY, 'Les rapports des citadins et des paysans dans la Confédération helvétique à l'époque de la Réforme', in E. Molnar *etal.* (eds.), *Nouvelles études historiques* (Budapest, 1965), pp. 181–96.

The Growing Interdependence of People

ROBERTO ALMAGIÀ, 'The Contribution of Italian Navigators to the Politico-Commercial Expansion of the XVIth Century', *Journal of World History*, VII (1963), 285–89.

RODOLFO BARÓN CASTRO, 'The Discovery of America and the Geographical and Historical Integration of the World', *Journal of World History*, VI (1961, special Spanish issue), 809–32.

WOODROW BORAH and S. F. COOK, *The Aboriginal Population of Central Mexico on the Eve of the Spanish Conquest* (Berkeley, 1962).

C. R. BOXER, *The Golden Age of Brazil, 1695–1750: Growing Pains of a Colonial Society* (Berkeley, 1962).

HUGUETTE ET PIERRE CHAUNU, *Seville et l'Atlantique* (1504–1650) (Paris, 1956–1959), 8 vols.

B. S. COHN, *The Development and Impact of British Administration in India, a Bibliographic Essay* (New Delhi, 1961).

GILBERTO FREYRE, 'Impact of the Portuguese on the American Tropics', *Journal of World History*, IV (1958), 582–602.

LEWIS HANKE, 'The Dawn of Conscience in America: Spanish Experiments and Experiences with Indians in the New World', *Proceedings of the American Philosophical Society*, CVII (1963), 83–92.

M. G. S. HODGSON, 'The Interrelations of Societies in History', *Comparative Studies in Society and History*, V (1963), 227–50.

D. F. LACH, *Asia in the Making of Europe*, Vols. I, Books I and II: *The Century of Discovery* (Chicago, 1965).

GUSTAVE LANCTOT, *A History of Canada*, Vol. I: *From Its Origins to the Royal Regime, 1663*, tr. by Josephine Hambleton (Cambridge, Mass., 1963).

FREDERIC MAURO, *L'expansion européenne (1600–1870)* ('Nouvelle Clio', No. 27; Paris, 1964).

A. METRAUX, 'Les précurseurs de l'ethnologie en France du XVIe au XVIIIe siècle', *Journal of World History*, VII (1963), 721–38.

J. L. PHELAN. *The Hispanization of the Philippines, Spanish Aims and Filipino Responses, 1500–1700* (Madison, Wisc., 1959).

MARIANO PICÓN-SALAS, *A Cultural History of Spanish America: From the Conquest to Independence*, tr. by Irving A. Leonard (Berkeley, 1962).

ROGER PORTAL, 'Les Russe en Sibérie au XVIIe siècle', *Revue d'histoire moderne et contemporaine*, V (1958), 5–38.

A. J. PRICE, *The Western Invasion of the Pacific and Its Continents: A Study of Moving Frontiers and Changing Landscapes, 1513–1958* (New York, 1963).

D. B. QUINN, 'Exploration and the Expansion of Europe', XIIe Congrés International des Sciences Historiques, *Rapports* (Vienna, 1965), I, 45–59.

A. L. SALLS, *The Paradise of Travellers: The Italian Influence on Englishmen in the Seventeenth Century* (Bloomington, Ind., 1964).

J. VINCENS VIVES (ed.) *Historia social y economica de Espana y América* (Barcelona, 1957) (3 vols. to the 18th century)

SILVIO ZAVALA, *The Colonial Period in the History of the New World*, abridged in English by Max Savelle (Mexico, D.F., 1962).

CHAPTER II

THE MAJOR RELIGIONS (*c.* 1300)

Animism

HAROLD E. DRIVER, *The Indians of North America* (Chicago, 1961).

CHARLES GOLLENKAMP, *Maya: The Riddle and Rediscovery of a Lost Civilization* (New York, 1959).

PAUL KIRCHHOFF et al., 'Origins and Continuity of the Mesoamerican Civilizations', XIIe Congrès International des Sciences Historiques, *Rapports* (Vienna, 1965), II, 233–62.

G. P. MURDOCK, *Africa, Its People and Their Culture History* (New York, 1959).

ANTONIO TOVAR LLORENTE, 'L'incorporation du nouveau monde à la culture occidentale', *Journal of World History*, VI (1961, special Spanish number), 833–56.

Hinduism and Jainism

CHARLES ELIOT, *Hinduism and Buddhism: An Historical Sketch* (New York, 1957), 3 vols.

CLIFFORD GEERTZ, *The Religion of Java* (Glencoe, Ill., 1960).

K. W. MORGAN, *Asian Religions: An Introduction to the Study of Hinduism, Buddhism, Islam, Confucianism, and Taoism* (New York, 1964).

K. A. NILAKANTA SASTRI, *A History of South India from Prehistoric Times to the Fall of Vijayanagar* (London, 1959, 2nd ed.).

V. A. SMITH, *The Oxford History of India* (Oxford, 1958, 3rd ed.).

PERCIVAL SPEAR, *India: a Modern History* ('University of Michigan History of the Modern World') (Ann Arbor, Michigan, 1961).

T. K. VENKATARAMAN, 'South India and Indian Culture', *Journal of World History*, VI (1960), 348–69.

Buddhism

M. GHOSH, *The History of Cambodia* (Saigon, 1960).

B. P. GROSLIER, *Angkor et le Cambodge* (Paris, 1958).

M. F. HERZ, *A Short History of Cambodia: from the Days of Angkor to the Present* (New York, 1958).

TIEH-TSENG LI, *Tibet; Today and Yesterday* (New York, 1960).

G. P. MALALASEKERA (ed.) *Encyclopedia of Buddhism*, fascicles *A-Aoki* (Ceylon, 1961–66).

P. N. NAZARETH, *An Outline of Malayan History* (London, 1958).

TRAN van TUNG, *Vietnam* (New York, 1959).

K. E. WELLS, *Thai Buddhism, Its Rites and Activities* (Bangkok, 1960).

PAUL WHEATLEY, *The Golden Khersonese: Studies in the Historical Geography of the Malay Peninsula before A.D. 1500* (Kuala Lumpur, 1961).

ARTHUR F. WRIGHT, *Buddhism in Chinese History* (Stanford, Calif., 1959).

Confucianism, Taoism, and Shintoism

W. T. DE BARY et al. (eds.) *Sources of the Chinese Tradition* ('Introduction to Oriental Civilizations' (New York, 1960).

J. W. HALL, *Japanese History, New Dimensions of Approach and Understanding* (Washington, 1961).

PING-TI HO, *Studies on the Population of China, 1368–1953* (Cambridge, 1960).

HOMER HULBERT, *Hulbert's History of Korea*, ed. by Clarence Norwood Weems (New York, 1962), 2 vols.

LIN YU-T'ANG, *Imperial Peking: Seven Centuries of China* (New York, 1961).

GEORGE SANSOM, *A History of Japan* (Stanford, Calif., 1958–1963), 3 vols. to date [to 1867].

WEINER SPEISER, *China, Spirit and Society* (New York, 1960).

A. F. WRIGHT, 'The Study of Chinese Civilization', *Journal of the History of Ideas*, XXI (1960), 233–55.

A. F. WRIGHT (ed.), *The Confucian Persuasion* (Stanford, Calif., 1960).

A. F. WRIGHT and DENIS TWITCHETT (eds.), *Confucian Personalities* (Stanford, Conn., 1962).

Islam

H. A. R. GIBB, *Mohammedanism: An Historical Survey* (New York, 1962, rev. ed.).

H. A. R. GIBB et al., *The Encyclopedia of Islam* (Leiden, 1954 to date, new ed.) [To the letter H with fascicle 42 in Vol. III in 1965].

S. M. IKRAM, *Muslim Civilization in India*, ed. T. Embree (New York, 1964).

Judaism

S. W. BARON, *A Social and Religious History of the Jews* (New York, 1952–1960, rev. ed.), 8 vols.

SIMON DUBNOW, *Jewish History*, ed. by Koppel Pinson (Philadelphia, 1958).

TONI OELSNER, 'Wilhelm Roscher's Theory of the Economic and Social Position of the Jews in the Middle Ages, a Critical Examination', *Yivo Annual of Jewish Social Science*, XII (1958–9), 178–195.

Christianity

MARC BLOCH, *Feudal Society*, tr. by L. A. Manyon (Chicago, 1961).

LUIS DIEZ del CORRAL, 'Expérience historique nationale et supranationale de l'Espagne', *Journal of World History*, VI (1961; special Spanish no.), 919–47.

FRANCIS DVORNIK, *The Slavs in European History and Civilization* (New Brunswick, N.J., 1962).

KURT GALLING et al., (eds.), *Religion in Geschichte und Gegenwart; Handwörterbuch für Theologie und Religionswissenschaft* (Tübingen, 1951–62, 3rd ed., 7 vols.).

GEORGE VERNADSKY, *A History of Russia*, Vol. IV: *Russia at the Dawn of the Modern Age* (New Haven, Conn., 1959).

CHAPTER III
MAJOR RELIGIOUS EVENTS (1300–1500)

Hinduism and Buddhism

S. N. HAY and M. H. CASE (eds.), *Southeast Asian History, a Bibliographical Guide* (New York, 1962).

HELMUT HOFFMAN, *The Religions of Tibet*, tr. by Edward Fitzgerald (New York, 1960).

Confucianism, Taoism, and Shintoism

E. O. REISCHAUER and J. K. FAIRBANK, *A History of East Asian Civilization*, Vol. I: *East Asia: the Great Tradition* (Boston, 1960).

Islam

AZIZ AHMAD, 'Dār al-Islām and the Muslim Kingdoms of Deccan and Gujarat', *Journal of World History*, VII (1963), 787–93.

Judaism

S. W. BARON, 'Some Recent Literature on the History of the Jews in the Pre-emancipation Era (1300–1800)', *Journal of World History*, VII (1962), 137–71.

JACOB KATZ, *Tradition and Crisis: Jewish Society and the End of the Middle Ages* (Glencoe, Illinois, 1961).

TONI OELSNER, 'The Place of the Jews in Economic History as viewed by German Scholars, a Critical-Comparative Analysis', in *Year Book VII of the Leo Baeck Institute of Jews from Germany* (London, 1962).

Greek Orthodox Christianity

MICHAEL CHERNIAVSKY, '"Holy Russia": a Study in the History of an Idea', *American Historical Review*, LXIII (1958), 617–637.

——, *Tsar and People: Studies in Russian Myths* (New Haven, Conn., 1961).

NICHOLAS V. RIASANOVSKY, *A History of Russia* (New York, 1963).

IHOR SEVCENKO, 'The Decline of Byzantium Seen through the Eyes of Its Intellectuals', *Dumbarton Oaks Papers*, XV (1961), 169–86.

Roman Catholicism

OSCAR HALECKI, *From Florence to Brest (1439–1596)* (Rome, 1958).

——, 'Diplomatic pontificale et activité missionaire en Asie aux XIIIe–XVe siècles', *XIIe Congrès International des Sciences Historiques, Rapports* (Vienna, 1965), II, 5–32.

F. G. HEYMANN, 'The Hussite-Utraquist Church in the Fifteenth and Sixteenth Centuries', reprinted from the *Archiv für Reformationsgeschichte*, LII (1961).

——, *George of Bohemia: King of Heretics* (Princeton, Conn., 1965).

HOWARD KAMINSKY, 'Chiliasm and the Hussite Revolution', reprinted from *Church History*, XXVI (1957).

FRANTISEK KAVKA, 'The Hussite Movement and the Czech Reformation', *Journal of World History*, V (1960), 830–56.

OTAKAR ODLOZILIK, *The Hussite King: Bohemia in European Affairs, 1440–1471* (Brunswick, N. J., 1965).

CHAPTER IV

CATHOLICS AND PROTESTANTS IN EUROPE (1500–1775)

Demands within the Catholic Church for Reform

RAMÓN CEÑAL, 'La philosophie et les sciences humaines à l'époque moderne', *Journal of World History*, VI (1961, special Spanish number), 857–77.

ALAIN DUFOUR and R. M. DOUGLAS, 'Humanisme et Reformation'. XIIe Congrès International des Sciences Historiques, *Rapports* (Vienna, 1965), III, 57–86.

SEARS JAYNE, *John Colet and Marsilio Ficino* (New York, 1963).

HUBERT JEDIN, *Ecumenical Councils of the Catholic Church: an Historical Outline* (New York, 1096, 2nd ed.).

A. LATREILLE *et al.*, *Histoire du Catholicisme*, Vol. II: *Sous les rois très chrétiens* (Paris, [1960]).

BERND MOELLER, 'Das religiöse Leben in deutschen Sprachgebiet am Ende des 15. und am Ende des 16. Jahrhunderts', XIIe Congrès International des Sciences Historiques, *Rapports* (Vienna, 1965), III, 129–51.

ROBERTO RIDOLFI, *The Life of Girolamo Savonarola*, tr. from the Italian by Cecil Grayson (New York, 1959).

Luther and Lutheranism in Germany (to 1529)

R. H. BAINTON, 'Interpretation of the Reformation', *American Historical Review*, LXVI (1960), 74–84.

CARL COHEN, 'Martin Luther and His Jewish Contemporaries', *Jewish Social Studies*, XXV (1963), 195–204.

JEAN DELUMEAU, *Naissance et affirmation de la Réforme* (Paris, 1965).

J. R. ELTON, *Reformation Europe, 1517–1559* (London, 1963).

E. H. ERIKSON, *Young Man Luther: A Study in Psychoanalysis and History* (New York, 1958).

R. H. FIFE, *The Revolt of Martin Luther* (New York, 1957).

H. J. GRIMM, 'Luther Research since 1920', *Journal of Modern History*, XXXII (1960), 105–118.

——, 'Social Forces in the German Reformation', *Church History*, XXXI (1962), 3–13.

——, *The Reformation in Recent Historical Thought* (New York, 1964).

HAJO HOLBORN, *A History of Modern Germany*, Vol. I: *The Reformation*, Vol. II: *1648* (New York, 1959–63.)

ERWIN ISERLOH, *Luthers Thesenanschlag: Tatsache oder Legende?* (Wiesbaden, 1962).

Zwingli and Calvin

JOHN CALVIN, *Institutes of the Christian Religion* (Philadelphia, 1961).

R. W. GREEN (ed.), *Protestantism and Capitalism: The Weber Thesis and Its Critics* (Boston, 1959).

R. M. KINGDON, 'Calvinism and Democracy: Some Political Implications of Debates on French Reformed Church Government, 1562–1572', *American Historical Review*, LXIX (1964), 393–401.

The Tudors and Anglicanism

A. J. DICKENS, *The English Reformation* (London, 1964).

——, 'The English Reformation and Religious Toleration', XVIIe Congrès International des Sciences Historiques, *Rapports* (Vienna, 1965), I, 177–89.

C. H. GEORGE and KATHERINE GEORGE, *The Protestant Mind of the English Reformation: 1570–1640* (Princeton, Conn., 1961).

DAVID KNOWLES, *The Religious Orders in England*, Vol. III: *The Tudor Age* (Cambridge, 1959).

CONYERS READ, *Lord Burghley and Queen Elizabeth* (New York, 1960).

R. TRIMBLE, *The Catholics in Elizabethan England 1588–1603* (Cambridge, 1964).

The Anabaptists

RUTH WEISS, 'Herkunft und Sozialanschauungen der Täufergemeinden im westlichen Hessen', *Archiv für Reformationsgeschichte*, LII, No. 2 (1961), 162–88.

G. H. WILLIAMS, *The Radical Reformation* (Philadelphia, 1962).

GEORGE WILLIAMS and A. M. MERGAL (eds.), *Spiritual and Anabaptist Writers: Documents Illustrative of the Radical Reformation* (Philadelphia, 1957).

Some Other Protestant Creeds

STANISLAS KOT, *Socinianism in Poland: The Social and Political Ideas of the Polish Antitrinitarians in the Sixteenth and Seventeenth Centuries*, tr. from the Polish by Earl Morse Wilbur (Boston, 1957).

Protestant Expansion and Catholic Resistance (1521–1598)

W. T. BOUWSMA, *Concordia Mundi: the Career and Thought of Guillaume Postel (1510–1581)* (Cambridge, Mass., 1957).

L. CHRISTIANI, 'Tolerance et intolérance religieuses au XVIe siècle,' *Journal of World History*, IV (1960), 857–78.

LUCIEN FEBVRE, *Au coeur religieux du XVIe siècle* (Paris, 1957).

GORDON GRIFFITHS, 'The Revolutionary Character of the Revolt of the Netherlands', *Comparative Studies in Society and History*, II (1960), 452–72.

AMBROISE JOBERT, 'La Pologne dans la crise de la Chrétienté (XVIe–XVIIe siècles), *Bulletin de la Société d'Historie moderne*, 12 s., No. 3 (May–July, 1957), 2–8.

The Council of Trent

HUBERT JEDIN, *A History of the Council of Trent*, 2 vols., tr. by Ernest Graf (Edinburgh, 1957–61).

MARIO SCADUTO, *Storia della Compagnia de Jesu in Italia*, Vol. III: *L'epoca di Giacomo Lainez: il governo, 1556–1565* (Rome, 1964).

Religious Conflict and Non-conformity (1598–1775)

D. W. BAHLMANN, *The Great Moral Revolution of 1688* (New Haven, Conn., 1957)

D. D. BIEN, *The Calas Affair: Persecution, Toleration, and Heresy in Eighteenth-Century Toulouse* (Princeton, 1960).

HERBERT LÜTHY, *La Banque protestante en France: de la Révocation de l'Edit de Nantes à la Révolution* (Paris, 1959–61), 2 vols.

T. K. RABB, 'The Effects of the Thirty Years War on the German Economy', *Journal of Modern History*, XXIV (1962), 40–51.

E. REVESZ, 'Entre l'orthodoxie et les lumières. Tolérance et intolérance dans le protestantisme calviniste des XVIe—XVIIe siècles en Hongrie', E. Molnar *et al.*, (eds.), *Nouvelles études historiques* (Budapest, 1965), 415–36.

W. C. SCOVILLE, *The Persecution of Huguenots and French Economic Development, 1680–1720* (Berkeley, 1960).

JANUSZ TAZBIR, 'La tolérance religieuse en Pologne aux XVIe et XVIIe siècles', in Juliuz Bardach *et al.*, (eds.), *La Pologne au XIIe Congrès International des Sciences Historiques à Vienna* (Warsaw, 1965), 31–48.

CHAPTER V

OTHER RELIGIOUS EVENTS (1500–1775)

Christianity outside Europe

GEORGES BALANDIER, 'Le Royaume de Kongo et l'acculturation râtée', XIIe Congrès International des Sciences Historiques, *Rapports* (Vienna, 1965), I, 95–102.

C. R. BOXER, *The Dutch Seaborne Empire: 1600–1800* (New York, 1965).

——, *Portuguese Society in the Tropics: The Municipal Councils of Goa, Macao, Bahia, and Luanda, 1500–1800* (Madison, Misc., 1965).

CARL BRIDENBAUGH, *Mitre and Sceptre: Transatlantic Faiths, Ideas, Personalities, and Politics, 1689–1775* (New York, 1962).

J. S. CUMMINS, 'Palafox, China and the Chinese Rites Controversy', *Revista de Historia de America*, No. 52 (December, 1961) 395–427.

——, (ed.), *The Travels and Controversies of Friar Domingo de Navarrete, 1618–1686* (New York, 1962), 2 vols.

H. de la COSTA, *The Jesuits in the Philippines, 1581–1768* (Cambridge, Mass., 1961).

P. M. D'ELIA, 'La reprise des missions catholiques en Chine à la fin des Mings (1579–1644)', *Journal of World History*, V (1960), 679–99.

G. H. DUNNE, *Generation of Giants: The Story of the Jesuits in China in the Last Decades of the Ming Dynasty* (South Bend, Ind., 1962).

ARIMICHI EBISAIVA, 'The Jesuits and Their Cultural Activities in the Far East', *Journal of World History*, V (1959), 344–74.

CHARLES GIBSON, *The Aztecs under Spanish Rule: A History of the Indians of the Valley of Mexico, 1519–1810* (Stanford, Calif., 1964).

LOUIS JADIN, 'L'Afrique et Rome depuis l'époque des découvertes jusqu'au XVIIe siècles', XIIe Congrès International des Sciences Historiques, *Rapports* (Vienna, 1965), II, 33–69.

MARIANO PICÓN-SALAS, *A Cultural History of Spanish America: From Conquest to Independence*, tr. by J. A. Leonard (Berkeley, 1962).

F. B. TOLLES, 'Nonviolent Contact: The Quakers and the Indians', *Proceedings of the American Philosophical Society*, CVII (1963), 93–106.

A. DE ZORITA, *Life and Labor in Ancient Mexico: The Brief and Summary Relation of the Lords of New Spain*, tr. by Benjamin Keen (New Brunswick, N.J., 1963).

The Orthodox Christians

P. SHEPPARD, *The Greek East and the Latin West: A Study in the Christian Tradition* (New York, 1959).

L. S. STAVRIANOS, *The Balkans since 1453* (New York, 1958).

T. STOIANOVICH, 'The Conquering Balkan Orthodox Merchant', *Journal of Economic History* (June, 1960), 234–313.

Islam

P. N. CHOPRA, 'Rencontre de l'Inde et de l'Islam', *Journal of World History*, VI (1960), 370–79.

R. H. DAVISON, *The Near and Middle East: An Introduction to History and Bibliography* (Washington, 1959).

M. G. S. HODGSON, 'The Unity of Later Islamic History', *Journal of World History*, IV (1960), 879–914.

BERNARD LEWIS, *Istanbul and the Civilization of the Ottoman Empire* (Norman, Okla., 1963).

Hinduism and Buddhism

W. T. de BARY et al. (eds.), *Sources of Indian Tradition* ('Introduction to Oriental Civilizations') (New York, 1960).

MARCELLE LALON, *Les religions du Tibet* (Paris, 1957).

KHUSHWANT SINGH, *A History of the Sikhs*, Vol. I: *1469–1839* (Princeton, Mass., 1966).

Confucianism, Taoism, Shintoism

R. A. BELLAH, *Tokugawa Religion: The Values of Pre-Industrial Japan* (Glencoe, Ill., 1957).

W. T. de BARY et al. (eds.), *Sources of Japanese Tradition* ('Introduction to Oriental Civilizations') (New York, 1960).

Judaism

I. S. EMMANUEL, 'Seventeenth Century Brazilian Jewry: a Critical Review', *American Jewish Archives*, XIV (1962), 32–68.

T. W. PERRY, *Public Opinion, Propaganda, and Politics in Eighteenth-Century England: A Study of the Jew Bill of 1753* (Cambridge, Mass., 1962).

SELMA STERN, *Der preussische Staat und die Juden*. Part I: *Die Zeit des grossen Kurfürsten und Friedrichs I* (Tübingen, 1962), 2 vols.

ARNOLD WIZNITZER, *Jews in Colonial Brazil* (New York, 1960).

CHAPTER VI

THEOLOGY AND METAPHYSICS (1300–1500)

Hindu Developments

S. M. S. CHARI, *Advaita and Viśistádvaita* (New York, 1961).

K. S. MURTY, *Revelation and Reason in Advaita Vedanta* (New York, 1959).

Islamic Developments

K. M. MUNSHI, R. C. MAJUMDAR *et al.* (eds.), *The Delhi Sultanate* ('The History and Culture of the Indian People') (Bombay, 1960).

W. M. WATT, *Islamic Philosophy and Theology* (Edinburgh, 1962).

Judaic Developments

JACOB KATZ, *Exclusiveness and Tolerance; Studies in Jewish-Gentile Relations in Medieval and Modern Times* (New York, 1961).

Developments in the West

EMILE BREHIER, *The History of Philosophy: The Middle Ages and the Renaissance*, tr. by Wade Baskin (Chicago, 1965).

MGR. CHRISTIANI, 'La tolérance et l'intolérance de l'église en matière doctrinale, depuis les premiers siècles jusqu'à nos jours', *Journal of World History*, V (1959), 71–93.

E. DELARUELLE, 'La spiritualité aux XIVe et XVe siècles', *Journal of World History*, V (1959), 59–70.

ALOIS GERLO and EMILE LAUF, *Bibliographie de l'humanisme belge, précédée d'une bibliographie générale concernant l'humanisme européen* (Brussels, 1965).

DENYS HAY, *The Italian Renaissance in Its Historical Background* (Cambridge, 1961).

F. G. HEYMANN, *John Rokycana—Church Reformer between Hus and Luther*, reprinted from *Church History*, XXVIII (1959).

DAVID KNOWLES, *The English Mystical Tradition* (New York, 1961).

ERICH MEUTHEN, *Die letzte Jahre des Nikolaus von Kues; biographische Untersuchungen nach neuen Quellen* (Cologne and Opladen, 1958).

ALBERT RIVAUD, *Histoire de la philosophie* (Paris, 1950–63), 4 volumes to date [to 1830].

RAYMOND DE ROOVER, 'The Concept of the Just Price: Theory and Economic Policy', *Journal of Economic History*, XVIII (1958), 418–34.

CHAPTER VII

THEOLOGY AND METAPHYSICS (1500–1775)

Metaphysical Speculation within Hinduism and Jainism

K. M. MUNSHI, R. C. MAJUMDAR, *et al.* (eds.), *The Struggle for Empire* ('The History and Culture of the Indian People' (Bombay, 1957).

Theological and Epistemological Speculation in the West

F. H. ANDERSON, *Francis Bacon: His Career and His Thought* (Los Angeles, 1962).

F. L. BAUMER, *Religion and the Rise of Scepticism* (New York, 1960).

ROSALIE L. COLIE, 'Spinoza in England, 1665–1730', *Proceedings of the American Philosophical Society*, CVII (1963), 183–219.

——, *The Church and the Age of Reason (1648–1789)* (London, 1960).

G. R. CRAGG, *Reason and Authority in the Eighteenth Century* (New York, 1964).

M. J. HAVRAN, *The Catholics in Caroline England* (Stanford, Calif., 1962).

R. HOOYKAAS, *Humanisme, Science et Réforme: Pierre de la Ramée (1515–1572)* (Leiden, 1958).

P. O. KRISTELLER, *Eight Philosophers of the Italian Renaissance* (Stanford, Calif., 1964).

ELIZABETH LABROUSSE, *Pierre Bayle* (The Hague, 1963–64), 2 vols.

F. E. MANUEL, *The Eighteenth Century Confronts the Gods* (Cambridge, 1959).

S. I. MINTZ, *The Hunting of Leviathan, Seventeenth-Century Reactions to the Materialism and Moral Philosophy of Thomas Hobbes* (New York, 1962).

C. B. O'KEEFE, 'Conservative Opinion on the Spread of Deism in France, 1730–1750', *Journal of Modern History*, XXXIII (1961), 398–406.

W. J. ONG, *Ramus, Method, and the Decay of Dialogue* (Cambridge, Mass., 1958).

WALTER REX, *Essays on Pierre Bayle and Religious Controversy* (The Hague, 1965).

L. C. ROSENFELD, 'Peripatetic Adversaries of Cartesianism in 17th Century France', *The Review of Religion* (November, 1957), 14–40.

Metaphysical Speculation in China

C. O. HUCKER, 'The Tung-lin Movement of the Late Ming Period', in *Chinese Thought and Institutions*, ed. J. K. Fairbank (Chicago, 1957), 132–62.

CHAPTER VIII

SOCIAL AND POLITICAL THOUGHT (*c.* 1300–*c.* 1500)

Political Theory and Practice

PETER BROCK, *The Political and Social Doctrines of the Unity of Czech Brethren in the Fifteenth and Early Sixteenth Centuries* (The Hague, 1957).

C. B. DAY, *The Philosophers of China* (New York, 1962).

FREDERICK HERTZ, *The Development of the German Public Mind. A Social History of German Political Sentiments, Aspirations and Ideas. The Middle Ages. The Reformation* (New York, 1957).

DAVID KNOWLES, *The Evolution of Medieval Thought* (Baltimore, 1962).

GEORGES de LAGARDE, *La naissance de l'esprit laïque au declin du Moyen-âge*, Vol. IV: *Guillaume d'Ockham: Défense de l'Empire* (Louvain, 1962).

FRANCIS OAKLEY, *The Political Thought of Pierre d'Ailly* (New Haven, Conn., 1964).

FRANCIS OAKLEY, 'Almain and Major: Conciliar Theory on the Eve of the Reformation', *American Historical Review*, LXX (1965), 673–90.

J. H. RANDALL, JR., *The Career of Philosophy: From the Middle Ages to the Enlightenment* (New York, 1962).

E. F. RICE, JR., *The Renaissance Idea of Wisdom* (Cambridge, Mass., 1958).

P. E. SIGMUND, *Nicholas of Cusa and Medieval Political Thought* (Cambridge, Mass., 1963).

LEO STRAUSS and JOSEPH CROPSEY (eds.), *History of Political Philosophy* (New York, 1963).

JEAN TOUCHARD, *Histoire des idées politiques* (Paris, 1959), 2 vols.

WALTER ULLMANN, *Principles of Government and Politics in the Middle Ages* (London, 1962).

WANG YANG-MING, *Instructions for Practical Living, and Other Neo-Confucian Writings*, tr. with notes by Wing-tsit Chan (New York, 1963).

Legal Thought and Practice

CRANE BRINTON, *A History of Western Morals* (New York, 1959).

CH'U T'UNG-TSU, *Law and Society in Traditional China* (Paris, 1961).

C. M. GRAY, *Copyhold, Equity, and the Common Law* (Cambridge, Mass., 1963).

JAN KORÁN and VACLAV VAŇEČEK, 'Czech Mining and Mining Laws', *Journal of World History*, VII (1962), 27–45.

F. J. PEGUES, *The Lawyers of the Last Capetians* (Princeton, N.J., 1962).

Economic Thought and Practice

RAYMOND de ROOVER, *The Rise and Decline of the Medici Bank, (1397–1494)* (Cambridge, Mass., 1963).

DOMENICO GIOFFRE, *Gênes et les foires de change: de Lyon à Besançon* (Paris, 1960).

HENRI LAPEYRE, 'Banque et crédit en Italie du XVIe au XVIIIe siècle', *Revue d'Histoire Moderne et Contemporaine*, VIII (1961), 211–26.

R. S. LOPEZ and H. A. MISKIMIN, 'The Economic Depression of the Renaissance', *The Economic History Review*, 2 series, XIV (1962), 408–426.

PHILIPPE WOLFF and FREDERIC MAURO, *L'âge de l'artisanat (Ve—XVIIIe siècles)* (Vol. II of 'Histoire générale du travail', ed. L. H. Parias) (Paris, 1960).

M. M. POSTAN, E. E. RICH, and EDWARD MILLER (eds.), *The Cambridge Economic History of Europe*, Vol. III: *Economic Organization and Policies in the Middle Ages* (Cambridge, 1963).

Historical Thought

W. G. BEASLEY, E. G. PULLEYBLANK *et al.*, *Historians of China and Japan* (London, 1961).

D. G. E. HALL *et al.*, *Historians of South-East Asia* (London, 1961).

F. G. HEYMANN, 'City Rebellions in 15th Century Bohemia and Their Ideological and Sociological Background', *Slavonic and East European Review*, XL (1962), 324–40.

IBN-KHALDÛN, *The Muqaddimah: An Introduction to History*, tr. by Franz Rosenthal (New York, 1958), 3 vols.

MARTIN KLEIN, 'Bibliography of Writings on Historiography and the Philosophy of History' in Louis Gottschalk (ed.), *Generalization in the Writing of History* (Chicago, 1963), pp. 213–47.

P. O. KRISTELLER, *Renaissance Thought: The Classic, Scholastic, and Humanistic Strains* (New York, 1961).

BERNARD LEWIS and P. M. HOLT (eds.), *Historians of the Middle East* (New York, 1962).

C. H. PHILIPS *et al.*, *Historians of India, Pakistan and Ceylon* (London, 1961).

A. V. RIASANOVSKY, 'A Fifteenth Century Russian Traveller in India: Comments in Connection with a New Edition of Afnasii Nikitin's Journal', *Journal of the American Oriental Society*, LXXXI (1961), 126–30.

A. F. WRIGHT, 'On the Uses of Generalization in the Study of Chinese History' and DERK BODDE, 'Comments on the Paper of Arthur F. Wright', in Louis Gottschalk, ed., *Generalization in the Writing of History* (Chicago, 1963), pp. 36–65.

CHAPTER IX
SOCIAL AND POLITICAL THOUGHT (1500–1775)

Political Theory

HANS BARON, 'Machiavelli: The Republican Citizen and the Author of *The Prince*', *English Historical Review*, LXXVII (1961), 217–53.

I. U. BOUDOVNITZ, 'La litterature politique et sociale russe au XVIe siècle', *Journal of World History*, special no. 'Contributions to Russian History' (1958), 145–80.

H. N. BRAILSFORD, *The Levellers and the English Revolution*, ed. and prepared for publication by Christopher Hill (Stanford, Calif., 1961).

J. BRONOWSKI and BRUCE MAZLISH, *The Western Intellectual Tradition: from Leonardo to Hegel* (New York, 1960).

FEDERICO CHABOD, *Machiavelli and the Renaissance*, tr. by David Moore, with an introduction by H. P. d'Entrèves (London, 1958).

E. W. COCHRANE, 'Machiavelli: 1940–60', *Journal of Modern History*, XXXII (1961), 113–36.

BERNICE HAMILTON, *Political Thought in Sixteenth-Century Spain: A Study of the Political Ideas of Vitoria, Soto, Suàrez and Molina* (New York, 1963).

HAROLD HUME, *The Life of Sir John Eliot* (New York, 1957).

BERNHARD KNOLLENBERG, *Origins of the American Revolution: 1759–66* (New York, 1960).

LEONARD KRIEGER, *The Politics of Discretion: Pufendorf and the Acceptance of Natural Law* (Chicago, 1965).

PETER LASLETT, *John Locke: Two Treatises of Government, a Critical Edition with an Introduction and Apparatus Criticus* (Cambridge, Eng., 1959).

LIANG CH'I-CH'AO, *Intellectual Trends in the Ch'ing Period (Ch'ing-tai hsueh-shu kai-lun)*, tr. by Immanuel C. Y. Hsü (Cambridge, Mass., 1959).

J. A. MARAVALL CASESNOVES, 'The Origins of the Modern State', *Journal of World History*, VI (1961, Special Spanish number), 789–808.

JACQUES PROUST, 'La contribution de Diderot à l'Encyclopédie et les théories du droit naturel', *Annales historiques de la Révolution française*, XXXV (1963), 257–86.

ERNST REIBSTEIN, *Völkerrecht: eine Geschichte seiner Ideen in Lehre und Praxis* (Freiburg, 1958–63), (2 vols.).

ROBERTO RIDOLFI, *The Life of Niccolo Machiavelli*, tr. by Cecil Grayson (Chicago, 1963).

CAROLINE ROBBINS, *The Eighteenth-century Commonwealthman: Studies in the Transmission, Development and Circumstance of English Liberal Thought from the Restoration of Charles II until the War with the Thirteen Colonies* (Cambridge, Mass., 1959).

W. VOISÉ, 'A propos d'Andrzej Frycz Modrzewski: les critères de l'appréciation du progrès dans l'histoire des sciences sociales', *Journal of World History*, V (1959), 251–6.

Legal Thought and Practice

ERNST EKMAN, 'The Danish Royal Law of 1660', *Journal of Modern History*, XXIX (1957), 102–9.

T. D. EUSDEN, *Puritans, Lawyers, and Politics in Early Seventeenth Century England* (New Haven, Conn., 1958).

RENE FÉDON, *Les hommes de loi lyonnais à la fin du Moyen-âge: Etude sur les origines de la classe de robe* (Paris, 1964).

J. H. FRANKLIN, *Jean Bodin and the Sixteenth-Century Revolution in the Methodology of Law and History* (New York, 1963).

ROBERT ROBSON, *The Attorney in Eighteenth-Century England* (New York, 1959).

W. J. STANKIEWICZ, *Politics and Religion in Seventeenth-Century France: A Study of Political Ideas from the Monarchomachs to Boyle, as reflected in the Toleration Controversy* (Berkeley, Calif., 1960).

HERMANN WEILL, *Frederick the Great and Samuel von Cocceji: A study in the Reform of the Prussian Judicial Administration, 1740–55* (Madison, Wisc., 1961).

R. J. ZWI WERBLOWSKY, *Joseph Karo: Lawyer and Mystic* (New York, 1962).

Economic Thought and Practice

ROBERT ASHTON, *The Crown and the Money Market, 1603–40* (New York, 1961).

S. A. BURRELL, 'Calvinism, Capitalism, and the Middle Classes: Some Afterthoughts on an Old Problem', *Journal of Modern History*, XXXII (1960), 129–41.

RAYMOND DE ROOVER, 'Joseph A. Schumpeter and Scholastic Economics', *Kyklos* (fasc. 2, 1957), 115–46.

V. K. JACRENSKY, 'The Rise of Economic Historiography', *Journal of World History*, VIII (1964), 576–84.

HERMANN KELLENBENZ, 'Probleme der Merkantilismusforschung', XIIe Congrès International des Sciences Historiques, *Rapports* (Vienna, 1965), IV, 171–90.

W. K. JORDAN, *Philanthropy in England, 1480–1660: A Study of the Changing Pattern of English Social Aspirations* (New York, 1959).

LIONEL ROTHKRUG, 'Critique de la politique commerciale et projets de réforme de la fiscalité au temps de Colbert', *Revue d'histoire moderne et contemporaine*, VIII (1961), 81–102.

C. D. SHELDON, *The Rise of the Merchant Class in Tokugawa Japan, 1600–1868* (Locust Valley, N.Y., 1958).

J. WELLMAN, 'Merkantilistische Vorstellungen im 17. Jahrhundert und Ungara' in E. Molnar *et al.* (eds.) *Nouvelles études historiques* (Budapest, 1965), 315–54.

GEORGES WEULERSSE, *La Physiocratie à la fin du règne de Louis XV (1770–1774)* (Paris, 1959).

Historical Thought

J. H. BRUMFITT, *Voltaire Historian* (London, 1958).

COMITÉ JAPONAIS DES SCIENCES HISTORIQUE;, *Le Japon au XIe congrès international des sciences historiques à Stockholm: l'état actuel et les tendances des études historiques au Japon* (Tokyo, 1960).

FELIX GILBERT, *Machiavelli and Guicciardini: Politics and History in Sixteenth-Century Florence* (Princeton, Mass., 1965).

F. E. MANUEL, *Isaac Newton, Historian* (Cambridge, Mass., 1963).

ERIK MOLNAR *et al.*, 'Biographie d'œuvres choisies de la science historique hongroise 1959–63', *Nouvelles études historiques*, publiée à l'occasion du XIIe Congrès International des Sciences Historiques par la Commission Nationale des Historiens Hongrois (Budapest, 1965), II, 463–629.

FAUSTO NICOLINI, 'Jean-Baptiste Vico dans l'histoire de la pensée', *Journal of World History*, VII (1963), 299–319.

D. S. NIVISON, *The Life and Thought of Chang Hsueh-ch'eng (1938–1801)* (Stanford, Calif., 1965).

ROBERTO RIDOLFI, *Vita de Francesco Guicciardini* (Rome, 1960).

L. SALVATORELLI, 'L'historiographie italienne au XVIIIe siècle', *Journal of World History*, VII (1963), 321–40.

HENRY WYVERBERG, *Historical Pessimism in the French Enlightenment* (Cambridge, Mass., 1959).

MIRIAM YARDENI, 'La conception de l'histoire dans l'oeuvre de la Popelinière', *Revue d'histoire moderne et contemporaine*, XI (1964), 109–26.

The Enlightenment and Social Thought

BERNARD BAILYN, 'Political Experience and Enlightenment Ideas in Eighteenth-Century America', *American Historical Review*, LXVII (1962), 339–51.

PAOLO CASINI, *Diderot 'philosophe'* (Bari, 1962).

ALFRED COBBAN, *In Search of Humanity, The Role of Enlightenment in Modern History* (London, 1960).

E. W. COCHRANE, *Tradition and Enlightenment in the Tuscan Academies, 1690–1800,* (Chicago, 1961).

——, 'French Literature and the Italian Tradition in Eighteenth-Century Tuscany', *Journal of the History of Ideas,* XXIII (1962), 61–76.

FREDERICK COPLESTON, *History of Philosophy,* Vols. IV to VI [from Descartes to Kant] (Westminster, Md., 1959–60).

L. G. CROCKER, *An Age of Crisis: Man and World in Eighteenth Century French Thought* (Baltimore, 1959).

——, *Nature and Culture, Ethical Thought in the French Enlightenment* (Baltimore, 1963).

——, 'Voltaire's Struggle for Humanism' in *Studies on Voltaire and the Eighteenth Century,* IV (1957), 137–69.

——, 'Recent Interpretations of the French Enlightenment', *Journal of World History,* VIII (1964), 426–56.

DURAND ECHEVARRIA, *Mirage in the West: a History of the French Image of American Society to 1815* (Princeton, N.J., 1957).

JEAN EHRARD, *L'idée de nature en France dans la première moitié du XVIIIe siècle* (Paris, 1963).

PETER GAY, *Voltaire's Politics: The Poet as Realist* (Princeton, N.J., 1959).

L. H. GIPSON, *The British Empire before the American Revolution,* Vol. X: *The Triumphant Empire: Thunder-Clouds Gather in the West, 1763–66* (New York, 1961).

RONALD GRIMSLEY, *Jean d'Alembert (1717–83)* (Oxford, 1963).

PIERRE GROSCLAUDE, *Malesherbes témoin et interprète de son temps* (Paris, 1961).

FRITZ HARTUNG, *Enlightenment Despotism* (London, 1957).

RICHARD HERR, *The Eighteenth-Century Revolution in Spain* (Princeton, N.J., 1958).

RICHARD HERR and HAROLD PARKER (eds.), *Ideas in History* (Durham, 1965).

A. O. LOVEJOY, *Reflections on Human Nature* (Baltimore, 1961).

ROBERT MAUZI, *L'idée du bonheur dans la littérature et la pensée française au XVIIIe siècle* (Paris, 1962).

S. T. MCCLOY, *The Humanitarian Movement in Eighteenth-Century France* (Lexington, Kentucky, 1957).

R. PORTAL et al., *La Pologne de l'époque des Lumières au duché de Varsovie,* special no. of *Annales historiques de la Révolution française,* XXXVI, No. 177 (July-Sept. 1964), 257–416.

JACQUES PROUST, *Diderot et l'Encyclopédie* (Paris, 1962).

ROBERT SHACKLETON, *Montesquieu: A Critical Biography* (New York, 1961).

LOUIS TREMARD, 'Pour une histoire sociale de l'idée de bonheur au XVIIIe siècle', *Annales historiques de la Révolution française*, XXXV (1963), 309–30 and 428–52.

I. O. WADE, *The Search for a New Voltaire, Studies in Voltaire Based upon Material Deposited at the American Philosophical Society* ('Transactions of the American Philosophical Society', Vol. XLVIII, Pt. 4; Philadelphia, 1958).

A. M. WILSON, *Diderot: The Testing Years* (New York, 1957).

CHAPTER X
LITERARY COMMUNICATION AND BELLES-LETTRES (1300–1500)

Manuscripts, Books, and Printing

PAUL CHAUVET, *Les ouvriers du livre en France, des origines à la Révolution de 1789* (Paris, 1959).

D. J. GEANAKÖPLOS, *Greek Scholars in Venice: Studies in the Dissemination of Greek Learning from Byzantium to Western Europe* (Cambridge, Mass., 1962).

K. M. SETTON, 'From Medieval to Modern Library', *Proceedings of the American Philosophical Society*, CIV (1960), 371–90.

The Development of Vernacular Languages

R. E. CHANDLER and KESSEL SCHWARTZ, *A New History of Spanish Literature* (Baton Rouge, Louisiana, 1962).

CH'EN SHOU-YI, *Chinese Literature: A Historical Introduction* (New York, 1961).

GEORGE SAMPSON, *The Concise Cambridge History of English Literature* (2nd ed. New York, 1962).

Poetry, Drama, and Story in Europe

NICOLA ABBAGNANO, 'Italian Renaissance Humanism', *Journal of World History*, VII (1963), 267–83.

CARLOS CLAVERÍA, 'Les mythes et les thèmes espagnols dans la littérature universelle', *Journal of World History*, VI (1961; special Spanish no.), 969–89.

W. K. FERGUSON, 'The Interpretation of Italian Humanism: the Contribution of Hans Baron' and HANS BARON, 'Moot Problems of Renaissance Interpretations: An Answer to Wallace K. Ferguson', *Journal of the History of Ideas*, XIX (1958), 14–34.

——, *Europe in Transition* (Boston, 1962).

RAYMOND QUENEAU (ed.), *Histoire des littératures* (3 vols.) (Paris, 1955–58).

MARTIN DE RIQUER MORERA, 'La culture au bas Moyen-âge', *Journal of World History*, VI (1961; special Spanish no.), 771–86.

I. O. WADE, *Voltaire and 'Candide'* (Princeton, N.J., 1959).

E. H. WILKINS, *Life of Petrarch* (Chicago, 1961).

Belles-Lettres in the Far East

FENG YÜAN-CHUN, *A Short History of Classical Chinese Literature*, tr. by Yang Hsien-yi and Gladys Yang (Peking, 1958).

HOWARD HIBBETT, *The Floating World of Japanese Fiction* (New York, 1959).

LU HSUN, *A Brief History of Chinese Fiction*, tr. by Yang Hsien-yi and Gladys Yang (Peking, 1959).

P. G. O'NEILL, *Early Nō Drama, Its Background, Character and Development, 1300–1450* (London, 1959).

SAIKAKU'S *'The Japanese Family Storehouse'*, tr. with an Introduction and Notes by G. W. Sargent (New York, 1959).

A. C. SCOTT, *The Classical Theatre of China* (London, 1957).

WU SHIH-CH'ANG, *On the Red Chamber Dream. A Critical Study of Two Annotated Manuscripts of the XVIIIth Century* (Oxford, 1961).

CHAPTER XI
LITERARY COMMUNICATION AND BELLES-LETTRES (1500–1775)

The Technical Apparatus of Literature

JOSEPH FRANK, *The Beginnings of the English Newspapers, 1620–60* (Cambridge, Mass., 1961).

FRANÇOIS FURET, 'La "Librairie" du royaume de France au XVIIIe siècle', XIIe Congrès International des Sciences Historiques, *Rapports* (Vienna, 1965) I, 423–50.

STANLEY MORISON and KENNETH DAY, *The Typographic Book, 1450–1935* (Chicago, 1964).

D. T. POTTINGER, *The French Book Trade in the Ancien Régime, 1500–1791* (Cambridge, Mass., 1958).

PH. SCHMIDT, *Die Illustration der Lutherbibel, 1522–1700* (Basel, 1963).

A. A. SIDOROV, 'Les anciens livres imprimés slaves en tant que documents de l'interaction culturelle', *Journal of World History*, special no. 'Contributions to Russian History' (1958), 126–54.

Poetry, Drama, and Fiction in Europe

DÁMASO ALONSO, 'The Spanish Contribution to the Modern European Novel', *Journal of World History*, VI (1961, special Spanish no.), 878–97.

GEOFFROY ATKINSON, *Le sentiment de la nature et le retour à la vie simple (1690–1740)* (Geneva, 1960).

DOUGLAS BUSH, *English Literature in the Earlier Seventeenth Century, 1600–60,* (2nd ed., 'Oxford History of English Literature', New York, 1962).

R. W. GIBSON et al. (eds.), *St. Thomas More: a Preliminary Bibliography of His Works and of Moreana to the Year 1750* [with a bibliography of Utopiana] (New Haven, Conn., 1961).

A. J. GUIBERT, *Bibliographie des œuvres de Molière publiées au XVIIe siècle* (2 vols.).

G. J. KOLB and C. A. ZIMANSKY, *English Literature, 1660–1800*, Vols. III and IV (Princeton, N.J., 1962). [Annotated bibliography.]

JULIAN MARÍAS, 'Contemporary Spain in World Culture', *Journal of World History*, VI (1961, special Spanish no.), 1006–22.

CHRISTOPHER MARLOWE, *Doctor Faustus*, ed. by J. D. Jump (Cambridge, Mass., 1962).

ANGEL VALBUENA PRAT, 'Le théâtre espagnol et ses rapports avec le théâtre européen', *Journal of World History*, VI (1961, special Spanish no.), 898–915.

G. W. STONE *et al.* (eds.), *The London Stage, 1660–1800* (8 vols. to date [1660–1776]; Carbondale, S. Ill., 1960–63).

FRANCO VENTURI (ed.), *Illuministi Italiani*, Vol. V: *Reformatori Napoletani* (Milan and Naples, 1962).

C. V. WEDGWOOD, *Poetry and Politics under the Stuarts* (New York, 1960).

BERNARD WEINBERG, *The Art of Jean Racine* (Chicago, 1963).

D. M. WOLFE *et al.* (eds.), *Complete Prose Works of John Milton* (4 vols. to date [to 1655] (New Haven, Conn., 1953–65).

Belles-Lettres around and in China

TS'AO HSUEH-CH'IN, *Dream of the Red Chamber*, tr. by Chi-chen Wang (New York, 1958).

ARTHUR WALEY, *Yüan Mei* (London, 1957).

Imaginative Literature in Japan

[CHIKAMATSU], *Major Plays of Chikamatsu*, by Donald Keene (New York, 1961).

KENNETH YASUDA, *The Japanese Haiku: Its Essential Nature, History, and Possibilities in English with Selected Samples* (Rutland, Vt., 1957).

CHAPTER XII
THE VISUAL ARTS AND MUSIC (1300–1775)

Note: The standard bibliography for the history of art is Mary W. Chamberlin, *Guide to Art Reference Books* (Chicago, 1959). Titles listed in that work are not given below.

Painting in Europe

SYLVIE BÉGUIN, *L'école de Fontainebleau; le maniérisme à la cour de France* (Paris, 1960).

BERNARD BERENSON, *Italian Pictures of the Renaissance. Florentine School* (London, 1963), (2 vols.).

ANDRÉ CHASTEL, 'La légende médicienne', *Revue d'histoire moderne et contemporaine*, VI (1959), 161–80.

——, *Italian Art*, trans. by Peter and Linda Murray (London, 1963).

COUNCIL OF EUROPE (sponsor), *Le triomphe du maniérisme européen de Michel-Ange au Gréco*. Catalogue of an exhibition held at Rijksmuseum, Amsterdam, July 1–October 16, 1965.

E. T. DEWALD, *Italian Painting, 1200–1600* (New York, [1961]).

ALBRECHT DOHMANN, 'Les événements contemporains dans la peinture hollandaise du XVIIe siècle', *Revue d'histoire moderne et contemporaine*, V (1958), 265–82.

MICHEL FLORISOONE, *Le dix-huitième siècle: la peinture française* (Paris, 1948).

S. J. FREEDBERG, *Painting of the High Renaissance in Rome and Florence* (Cambridge, Mass., 1961), (2 vols.).

——, *Andrea del Sarto*, (Cambridge, Mass., 1963), (2 vols.).

JAN GERRIT VAN GELDER, *Dutch Drawings and Prints* (London, 1959).

ENRIQUE LAFUENTE FERRARI, 'De Velasquez à Picasso, suggestions pour une compréhension de l'art espagnol', *Journal of World History*, VI (1961, special Spanish no.), 990–1005.

JAROMIR NEUMANN, 'L'art du baroque dans les pays tchèques', *Journal of World History*, IV (1958), 688–708.

MASSIMO PALLOTTINO *et al.* (eds.), *Encyclopedia of World Art* (New York, 1958), (10 vols. published to 1965).

ERWIN PANOFSKY, *Renaissance and Renaissances in Western Art* (Stockholm, 1960), (2 vols.).

NICOLAS POWELL, *From Baroque to Roccoo* (New York, 1959).

E. H. RAMADEN (tr. and ed.), *The Letters of Michelangelo* (Stanford, 1963), (2 vols.)

EARL ROSENTHAL, 'Changing Interpretations of the Renaissance in the History of Art', in Tinsley Nelton (ed.), *The Renaissance: A Reconsideration of the Theories and Interpretations of the Age* (Madison, Wisc., 1961), pp. 53–75.

SEYMOUR SLIVE, 'Realism and Symbolism in Seventeenth-Century Dutch Painting', *Daedalus, the Journal of the A.A.A.S.*, XCI (1962), 469–500.

GERALD VAN DER KEMP *et al.* (eds.), *Treasures of Versailles: A Loan Exhibition from the French Government Organized by the Art Institute of Chicago* (Chicago, 1962).

ELLIS K. WATERHOUSE, *Baroque Painting in Rome, the Seventeenth Century* (London, 1937).

JOHN WHITE, *The Birth and Rebirth of Pictorial Space* (London, 1957).

Sculpture in Europe

JOHN POPE-HENNESSY, *An Introduction to Italian Sculpture* (New York, 1955), (3 vols.).

WOLFGANG SCHOENE, *Über das Licht in der Malerei* (Berlin, 1934).

Architecture in Europe

PAUL FRANKL, *The Gothic, Literary Sources and Interpretations through Eight Centuries* (Princeton, N.J., 1960).

WERNER GROSS, *Die abendländische Architektur um 1300* (Stuttgart, [1948]).

WERNER HAGER, *Die Bauten des deutschen Barocks, 1690–1770* (Jena, [1942]).

HANS JANTZEN, *Die Gotik des Abendlandes* (Cologne, 1962).

GEORGE KUBLER and MARTIN SORIA, *Art and Architecture in Spain and Portugal and Their American Dominions 1500–1800* (Baltimore, 1959).

LEWIS MUMFORD, *The City in History: Its Origins, Its Transformations, and Its Prospects* (New York, 1961).

NIKOLAUS PEVSNER, *An Outline of European Architecture* (6th ed.; Baltimore, 1960).

EARL E. ROSENTHAL, *The Cathedral of Granada* (Princeton, N.J., 1961).

VICTOR-L. TAPIÉ, *Baroque et classicisme* (Paris, 1957).

RUDOLPH WITTKOWER, *Architectural Principles in the Age of Humanism* (2nd ed.; London, 1952).

The Decorative Arts in Europe

HUGH HONOUR, *Chinoiserie, the Vision of Cathay* (London, 1962).

E. POCHE, 'Le verre de Bohème', *Journal of World History*, V (1959), 434–62.

Theories of Art and the Role of the Artist

FRANCIS HASKELL, *Patrons and Painters* (New York, 1963).

RENSSELAER LEE, 'Ut Pictura Poesis: The Humanist Theory of Painting', *Art Bulletin*, XXII (1940), 197–263.

DENIS MAHON, *Studies in Seicento Art and Theory* (London, 1947).

NIKOLAUS PEVSNER, *Academies of Art Past and Present* (Cambridge, Eng. 1940).

GEORGES WILDENSTEIN, *Le goût pour la peinture dans le cercle de la bourgeoisie parisienne autour de 1700* (Paris, 1958).

——, *Le goût pour la peinture dans la bourgeoise parisienne au début du règne de Louis XIII* (Paris, 1959).

The Dance and Music in Europe

WILLI APEL, *Harvard Dictionary of Music* (Cambridge, Mass., 1958).

HOWARD MAYER BROWN, *Music in the French Secular Theatre, 1400–1550* (Cambridge, Mass., 1963).

A. GEOFFROY-DECHAUME, *Les 'secrets' de la musique ancienne. Recherches sur l'interpretation XVIe, XVIIe, XVIIIe siècles* (Paris, 1964).

DONALD GROUT, *A History of Western Music* (New York, 1960).

JOHN HAWKINS, *A General History of the Science and Practice of Music* (New York, 1963), (2 vols.).

ANSELM HUGHES and GERALD ABRAHAM (eds.), *Ars Nova and the Renaissance, c. 1300–1540* (Vol. III of the *New Oxford Dictionary of Music*, edited by J. A. Westing *et al.* (New York, 1960).

ROGER LONSDALE, *Dr. Charles Burney. A Literary Biography* (Oxford, 1965).

E. E. LOWINSKY, *Tonality and Atonality in Sixteenth-Century Music* (Berkeley, California, 1962).

ROLAND MANUEL (ed.), Histoire de la musique ('Encyclopédie de la Pleiade', Paris 1960–3), (2 vols.).

GUSTAVE REESE, *Music in the Renaissance* (rev. ed., New York, 1959).

The Arts in Islam

W. G. ARCHER, *Indian Miniatures* (Greenwich, Conn., 1960).

R. ETTINGHAUSEN, *Persian Miniatures in the Bernard Berenson Collection* (London, 1962).

Hindu and Buddhist Art

THEODORE BOWIE (ed.), *The Arts of Thailand: A Handbook of Architecture, Sculpture and Painting of Thailand* (Bloomington, Ind., 1961).

HERMAN GOETZ, *India—Five Thousand Years of Indian Art* (New York, 1959).

O. GOSWAMI, *The Story of Indian Music: Its Growth and Synthesis* (Bombay, 1957).

B. P. GROSLIER, *The Art of Indochina including Thailand, Vietnam, Laos and Cambodia* (New York, 1962)

RADHAKAMAL MUKERJEE, *The Culture and Art of India* (New York, 1959).

DIETRICH SECKEL, *Buddhist Kunst Ostasiens* (Stuttgart, 1957).

F. A. WAGNER, *Indonesia: The Art of an Island Group* (New York, 1959).

The Arts in China, Vietnam, and Korea

ANDREW BOYD, *Chinese Architecture and Town Planning, 1500 B.C.–A.D. 1911* (Chicago, 1962).

JAMES CAHILL, *Chinese Painting* (Cleveland, 1960).

R. H. VAN GULICK, *Chinese Pictorial Art as Viewed by the Connoisseur* (Rome, 1958).

G. R. LOEHR, 'The Sinicization of Missionary Artists and Their Work at the Manchu Court during the Eighteenth Century', *Journal of World History*, VII (1963), 795–815.

EVELYN MCCUNE, *The Arts of Korea, an Illustrated History* (Rutland, Vt., 1961).

OSVALD SIRÉN, *Chinese Painting: Leading Masters and Principles*, Part II: *The Later Centuries* (New York, 1960), (4 vols.).

CHIANG YEE, *Chinese Calligraphy* (Cambridge, Mass., 1958), 2nd ed.

The Arts in Japan

LAURENCE BINYON and J. J. O'BRIEN SEXTON, *Japanese Colour Prints*, ed. by Basil Gray (Rev. ed.; London, 1960).

W. P. MALM, *Japanese Music and Musical Instruments* (Tokyo, 1959).

J. A. MICHENER, *Japanese Prints, from the Early Masters to the Modern* (Rutland, Vt., 1959).

HUGO MUNSTERBERG, *The Arts of Japan: An Illustrated History* (Rutland, Vt., 1957).

The Arts outside Eurasia

ANGULO INIGUEZ, 'Caracteristicas generales de el arte hispano-americano.' *Journal of World History*, IV (1957), 59–82.

PÁL KELEMEN, *Baroque and Roccoco in Latin America in the Seventeenth and Eighteenth Centuries* (New York, 1946), (2 vols.).

DIEDRICH WESTERMANN, 'Cultural History of Negro Africa', *Journal of World History*, III (1957), 983–1004.

CHAPTER XIII

SCIENCE AND TECHNOLOGY (1300–c. 1530)

General Characteristics

MARIE BOAS [Hall], *The Scientific Renaissance, 1450–1630* (New York, 1962). (See also Hall.)

MARSHALL CLAGETT (ed.), *Critical Problems in the History of Science* (Madison, Wisc., 1959).

MAURICE DAUMAS (ed.), *Histoire de la Science* ('Encyclopédie de la Pleiade', Paris, 1957).

T. K. DERRY and TREVOR I. WILLIAMS, *A Short History of Technology: From the Earliest Times to A.D. 1900* (New York, 1961).

R. J. FORBES and E. J. DIJKSTERHUIS, *History of Science and Technology* (London, 1963), (2 vols.).

BERTRAND GILLE, 'Le developpement technologique en Europe de 1100 à 1400', *Journal of World History*, III (1956), 63–108. (English translation in Guy S. Métraux and François Crouzet [eds.], *The Evolution of Science* (New York, 1963), 168–219.

MARIE BOAS HALL, *History of Science* a bibliography, (2nd ed.; Washington, D.C. 1964). (See also Boas.)

R. HOOYKAAS, 'Science and Theology in the Middle Ages', *Free University Quarterly*, III (1957), 77–163.

FRIEDRICH KLEMM, *History of Western Technology*, tr. by D. W. Singer (London, 1959).

PEDRO LAIN ENTRALGO and JOSE M. LOPEZ PINERO, 'The Spanish Contribution to World Science', *Journal of World History*, VI (1961, special Spanish no.), 948–68.

ROBERT K. MERTON, 'Singletons and Multiples in Scientific Discovery: A Chapter in the Sociology of Science', *Proceedings of the American Philosophical Society*, CV (1961), 470–86.

J. H. RANDALL, JR., *The School of Padua and the Emergence of Modern Science* (Padua, 1961).

CHARLES SINGER, *A Short History of Scientific Ideas to 1900* (rev. ed.; New York, 1959).

CHARLES SINGER, E. J. Holmyard, *et al.* (eds.), *A History of Technology*, Vols. II–IV [from *c.* 700 A.D. to *c.* 1850] (Oxford, 1956–8).

JOSEPH R. STRAYER, 'The Promise of the Fourteenth Century', *Proceedings of the American Philosophical Society*, CV (1961), 609–11.

RENÉ TATON (ed.), *Histoire générale des sciences*, Vols. I and II [from the origins to 1800], (Paris, 1957–8).

LYNN WHITE, JR., *Medieval Technology and Social Change* (New York, 1962).

Mathematics in Europe

A. C. CROMBIE, 'Quantification in Medieval Physics', *Isis*, LII (1961), 143–60.

The Physical Sciences in Europe

MARSHALL CLAGETT, *The Science of Mechanics in the Middle Ages* (Madison, Wisc., 1959).

——, 'Nicole Oresme and Medieval Scientific Thought', *Proceedings of the American Philosophical Society*, CVIII (1964), 298–309.

EDWARD GRANT (with a commentary by Benjamin Nelson), 'Hypotheses in Late Medieval and Early Modern Sciences', *Daedalus, The Journal of the American Academy of Arts and Sciences*, XCI (1962), 599–616.

E. J. HOLMYARD, *Alchemy* (London, 1957).

ANNALIESE MAIER, *Zwischen Philosophie und Mechanik* (Rome, 1958).

The Biological Sciences in Europe

LOUIS DULIEU, 'La peste à Montpellier', *Montpellier Médical*, LI (1957), 787–810.

T. H. GRAINGER, JR., *A Guide to the History of Bacteriology* (New York, 1958).

L. S. KING, *The Growth of Medical Thought* (Chicago, 1963).

L. C. MACKINNEY, 'Medical Illustrations in Medieval Manuscripts of the Vatican Library', *Manuscripta*, III (1959), 3–8 and 76–88.

——, 'Medieval Medical Miniatures in Central and Eastern European Collections', *Manuscripta*, V (1961), 131–50.

——, 'The Beginnings of Western Scientific Anatomy: New Evidence and a Revisionary Interpretation of Mandeville's Role', *Medical History*, VI (1962), 233–39.

——, *Medical Illustrations in Medieval Manuscripts* (London, 1965).

V. L. SAULNIER, 'Médecins de Montpellier au temps de Rabelais', *Bibliothèque d'Humanisme et Renaissance*, XIX (1957), 425–79.

H. SCHIPPERGES, 'Mondino dei Luzzi: Anatomia (1316)', *Neue Zeitschrift für ärtzliche Fortbildung*, XLVIII (1959), 340–401.

Science and Technology outside Europe

JOSEPH NEEDHAM, *The Development of Iron and Steel Technology in China* (London, 1958).

JOSEPH NEEDHAM and WANG LING, *Science and Civilization in China* (Cambridge, 1954–65), 4 vols. [to be completed in seven volumes].

LYNN WHITE, JR., 'Tibet, India, and Malaya as Sources of Western Medieval Technology', *American Historical Review*, LXV (1960), 515–26.

The Beginnings of World Geography

LEO BAGROW, *History of Cartography*. Revised and enlarged by R. A. Shelton. (London, 1965).

C. R. BOXER, *Four Centuries of Portuguese Expansion, 1415–1825: a Succinct Survey* (Johannesburg, 1961).

ARMANDO CORTESÃO and AVELINO TEIXEIRA DA MOTA, *Portugaliae monumenta cartographia* (Lisbon, 1960), (6 vols.).

H. A. R. GIBBS (tr.), *The Travels of Ibn Battūta, A.D. 1325–54* (2 vols.: 'Hakluyt Society, Second Series', Numbers CX and CXVII; New York, 1958 and 1962).

F. C. LANE, 'The Economic Meaning of the Invention of the Compass', *American Historical Review*, LXVIII (1963), 605–17.

CARLOS SECO SERRANO, 'El siglo de los grandes descubrimientos geograficos', *Journal of World History*, IV (1958), 553–81. [With further comments *ibid.*, V (1959), 509–11.]

A. O. VIETOR, 'A Pre-Columbian Map of the World, circa 1489', *Yale University Library Gazette*, XXXVII (1962), 8–12.

W. E. WASHBURN, 'The Meaning of "Discovery" in the Fifteenth and Sixteenth Centuries', *American Historical Review*, LXVIII (1962), 1–21.

CHAPTER XIV

SCIENCE (*c.* 1530–*c.* 1775)

Scientific Epistemology and Methodology

HERBERT BUTTERFIELD, 'The Scientific Revolution', *Scientific American*, CCIII (Sept. 1960), 173–92.

C. C. GILLESPIE, *The Edge of Objectivity: An Essay in the History of Scientific Ideas* (Princeton, Mass., 1960).

A. R. HALL, *From Galileo to Newton* (New York, 1963).

R. HOOYKAAS, 'Pierre de la Ramée et l'empirisme scientifique au XVIe siècle', in *La science au seizième siècle*, Colloque international de Royaumont, 1–4 juillet 1957, of the Union Internationale d'Histoire et de Philosophie des Sciences (Paris, 1957).

A. KOYRE, 'Newton, Galilée et Platon', *Annales: Economics, Sociétés, Civilisations*, XVI (1960), 1041–59.

T. S. KUHN, *The Structure of Scientific Revolutions* (Chicago, 1962).

R. MORGHEN, 'The Academy of the Lincei and Galileo Galilei', *Journal of World History*, VII (1963), 365–81.

ROLAND MOUSNIER, *Progrès scientifique et technique au XVIIIe siècle* (Paris, 1958).

NETHERLANDS SOCIETY FOR THE HISTORY OF MEDICINE, MATHEMATICS AND EXACT SCIENCES, *Dutch Classics on History of Science* (The Hague, 1961-6), (15 vols. to date).

IGNACIO OLAGÜE, 'Les changements de climat dans l'histoire', *Journal of World History*, VII (1963), 637-74.

J. W. OLMSTED, 'The Voyage of Jean Richer to Acadia in 1670: A Study in the Relations of Science and Navigation under Colbert', *Proceedings of the American Philosophical Society*, CIV (1960), 612-34.

M. L. PERKINS, 'Late Seventeenth-Century Scientific Circles and the Abbé de Saint-Pierre', *Proceedings of the American Philosophical Society*, CII (1958), 404-12.

FRANÇOIS RUSSO, 'Role respectif du Catholicisme et du Protestantisme dans le développement des sciences au XVIe at XVIIe siècles', *Journal of World History*, IV (1957), 854-80.

LYNN THORNDIKE, *A History of Magic and Experimental Science*, Vol. VIII: *The Seventeenth Century* (New York, 1958).

A. A. ZVORIKINE, 'Remarques sur l'historie des inventions et de la pensée scientifique et technique russes des XVIIIe et XIXe siècles,' *Journal of World History*, special no. 'Contributions to Russian History' (1958), 183-211.

Mathematics in Europe

J. F. SCOTT, *A History of Mathematics from Antiquity to the Beginning of the Nineteenth Century* (London, 1958).

BENIAMINO SEGRE, 'The Rise of Algebra and the Creation of Algebraic Geometry', *Journal of World History*, VII (1963), 383-406.

The Physical Sciences in Europe

MARIE BOAS, *Robert Boyle and Seventeenth-Century Chemistry* (New York, 1958).

M. H. CARRÉ, 'New Heaven of Thomas Digges', *History Today*, XX (1961), 779-885.

MAX CASPAR, *Kepler*, tr. and ed. by C. D. Hellman (New York, 1959).

A. G. DEBUS, 'The Significance of the History of Early Chemistry [a review article]', *Journal of World History*, IX (1964), 39-58.

MICHELE GORTANI, 'Italian Pioneers in Geology and Mineralogy', *Journal of World History*, VII (1963), 503-19.

HENRY GUERLAC, *Lavoisier—The Crucial Year: The Background and Origin of His First Experiments on Combustion in 1772* (Ithaca, N.Y., 1961).

——, 'Quantification in Chemistry', *Isis*, LII (1961), 194-214.

BROOKE HINDLE, *David Rittenhouse* (Princeton, N.Y., 1963).

ALEXANDRE KOYRE, 'La dynamique de Nicola Tartaglia' in *La Science au seizième siècle: Colloque international de Royaumont, 1-4 juillet 1957* (Paris, 1960).

L. M. MARSAK, *Bernard de Fontenelle: The Idea of Science in the French Enlightenment* (*Transactions of the American Philosophical Society*, XLIX, Pt. 7 [1959]).

ANTONIO MARUSSI, 'Italian Pioneers in the Physics of the Universe; Third Part: Geodesy', *Journal of World History*, VII (1963), 471–83.

J. R. PARTINGTON, *A History of Chemistry*, Vols. II, III, and IV (London, 1961–4).

ANTONIO SIGNORINI, 'Contributions italiennes à la méchanique théorique de Léonard de Vinci à Levi-Civita,' *Journal of World History*, VII (1963), 419–33.

H. W. TURNBULL (ed.), *The Correspondence of Isaac Newton* (3 vols. to date [to 1964], Cambridge, Eng., 1959–61).

HARRY WOOLF, *The Transits of Venus: A Study of Eighteenth-Century Science* (Princeton, N.J., 1959).

FRANCES A. YATES, *Giordano Bruno and the Hermetic Tradition* (Chicago, 1964).

VASSILI PAVLOVITCH ZOUBOV, 'Vitruve et ses commentaires du XVIe siècle' in *La science au seizième siècle, Colloque international de Royaumont, 1–4 juillet 1957* (Paris, 1960).

World Geography

J. C. BEAGLEHOLE et al. (eds.), *The Journals of Captain James Cook on His Voyages of Discovery* (2 vols. from 1768 to 1775; New York, 1956 and 1961).

J. L. GIDDINGS, 'Seven Discoveries of Bering Strait', *Proceedings of the American Philosophical Society*, CVI (1962), 89–93.

J.–E. MARTIN-ALLANIC, *Bougainville, navigateur, et les découvertes de son temps* (Paris, 1965), (2 vols.).

ALAN MOOREHEAD, *The Blue Nile* (New York, 1962).

CHARLES E. NOWELL (ed.), *Magellan's Voyage around the World: Three Contemporary Accounts* (Evanston, 1962).

JAMES A. WILLIAMSON, *The Cabot Voyages and Bristol Discovery under Henry VII*, with a cartography of the voyages by R. A. Skelton (New York, 1962).

The Biological Sciences in Europe

A. G. DEBUS, 'Paracelsian Doctrine in English Medicine' in *Chemistry in the Service of Medicine*, edited by F. N. L. Poynter (Philadelphia, 1963).

ERNST EKMAN, 'Gothic Patriotism and Olof Rudlick', *Journal of Modern History*, XXXII (1962), 52–63.

BENTLEY GLASS et al. (eds.), *Forerunners of Darwin 1745–1859* (Baltimore, 1959).

——, 'Eighteenth-Century concepts of the Origin of Species', *Proceedings of the American Philosophical Society*, CIV (1960), 227–34.

GIUSEPPI MONTALENTI, "La pensée biologique en Italie depuis la Renaissance jusqu'à Spallanzani', *Journal of World History*, VII (1963), 523–46.

C. D. O'MALLEY, 'The Anatomical sketches of Vitus Tretonius Athasinus and Their Relationship to Vesalius' "Tabulae Anatomicae"', *Journal of the History of Medicine and Allied Sciences*, XIII (1958), 395–407.

——, *Andreas Vesalius of Brussels, 1514–64* (Berkeley, Calif., 1964).

WALTER PAGEL, *Paracelsus: An Introduction to Philosophical Medicine in the Era of the Renaissance* (Basel, 1958).

JACQUES ROGER, *Les sciences de la vie dans la pensée française du XVIIIe siècle: la génération des animaux de Descartes à l'Encyclopédie* (Paris, 1963).

MARIA ROOSEBOOM, 'Antoni van Leeuwenhoek vu dans le milieu scientifique de son époque', *Archives internationales d'histoire des sciences*, XII (1959), 27–46.

R. F. RUSSELL, *British Anatomy, 1525–1800. A Bibliography* (Melbourne, 1965).

C. SINGER, 'Eighteen Years of Vesalian Studies', *Medical History*, V (1961), 210–20.

Science outside Europe

FURUKAWA TETSUSHI, 'The Growth of Anti-Religious Rationalism and the Development of the Scientific Method in Japan', *Journal of World History*, VII (1963), 739–55.

YABUUTI KIYOSI, 'The Pre-History of Modern Science in Japan, the Importation of Western Science during the Tokugawa Period', *Journal of World History*, IX (1965), 208–32.

C. D. O'MALLEY, 'A Latin Translation of Ibn Nafis (1547) related to the problem of the circulation of the blood', *Journal of the History of Medicine*, VII (1957), 248–53.

G. WIET, 'Ibn an-Nafis et la circulation pulmonaire', *Journal asiatique*, CCXLIV (1956), 95–100.

CHAPTER XV
TECHNOLOGY AND SOCIETY (1300–1775)
Machines, Industry, and Power

CHARLES COULSTON GILLESPIE (ed.), *A Diderot Pictorial Encyclopedia of Trades and Industry: Manufacturing and the Technical Arts in Plates Selected from 'L'Encyclopédie ou Dictionnaire raisonné des sciences, des arts et des métiers' of Denis Diderot* (New York, 1959).

L. S. PRESSNELL (ed.), *Studies in the Industrial Revolution, presented to T. S. Ashton* (London, 1960).

R. S. WOODBURY, *History of the Gear-Cutting Machine* (Cambridge, Mass., 1958).

——, *History of the Grinding Machine* (Cambridge, Mass., 1959).

——, *The Story of the Lathe to 1850: A Study in the Growth of a Technical Element of an Industrial Economy* (Cleveland, Ohio, 1961).

Heating, Mining, and Metallurgy

JUAN FRIEDE, 'La introduccion de mineros alemanes en America por la compañia Welser de Augsburgo', *Revista de Historia de America*, no. 51 (June 1961), 99–104.

O. PAULINYI, 'Die Edelmetallproduktion der Niederungarischen Bergstädte, besonders jene von Schemnitz, in der Mitte des 16. Jahrhunderts', in E. Molnar *et al.* (eds.), *Nouvelles études historiques* (Budapest, 1965), 181–96.

C. S. SMITH, *A History of Metallography, the Development of Ideas on the Structure of Metals before 1890* (Chicago, 1960).

T. A. WERTIME, *The Coming of the Age of Steel* (Chicago, 1962).

Transport and Navigation

M. N. BOYER, 'Roads and Rivers: Their Use and Disuse in Late Medieval France', *Medievalia et Humanistica*, XIII (1960), 68-80.

J. J. MALONE, *Pine Trees and Politics, the Naval Stores and Forest Policy in Colonial New England, 1691-1775* (Seattle, Washington, 1965).

FRÉDÉRIC MAURO, 'Types de navires et constructions navales dans l'Atlantique portugais aux XVIe et XVIIe siècles', *Revue d'histoire moderne et contemporaine*, VI (1959), 181-209.

D. A. STEVENSON, *The World's Lighthouses before 1820* (New York, 1959).

E. G. R. TAYLOR, *The Geometrical Seaman: A Book of Early Nautical Instruments* (New York, 1962).

The Technology of Warfare

GEORGE CLARK, *War and Society in the Seventeenth Century* (New York, 1958).

ANDRÉ CORVISIER, *L'armée française de la fin du XVIIe siècle au ministère de Choiseul* (Paris, 1964), (2 vols.).

GARRETT MATTINGLY, *The Armada* (Boston, 1959).

CAPITAINE PICHENÉ, *Tactique et stratégie des origines à la guerre mondiale* (Paris, 1957).

ROBERT S. QUIMBY, *The Background of Napoleonic Warfare: The Theory of Military Tactics in Eighteenth-Century France* (New York, 1957).

THEODORE ROPP, *War in the Modern World* (Durham, N.C., 1959).

D. W. SINGER, 'On a 16th Century Cartoon concerning the Devilish Weapon of Gunpowder: Some Medieval Reactions to Guns and Gunpowder', *Ambix*, VII (1959), 25-33.

H. J. WEBB, *Elizabethan Millitary Science, the Books and the Practice* (Madison, Wisc., 1965).

The Methods of Agriculture

MICHAEL CONFINO, 'La comptabilité des domaines privés en Russie dans la seconde moitié du XVIIIe siècle. (D'après les "Travaux de la Société libre d'économie" de Saint-Petersbourg)', *Revue d'histoire moderne et contemporaine*, VIII (1961), 5-34.

GILBERT FREYRE, 'Impact of the Portuguese on the American Tropics', *Journal of World History*, IV (1958), 582-602.

Medical Practice, Public Health, and Sanitation

H. C. CAMERON, *A History of the Worshipful Society of Apothecaries of London*, Vol. I: *1617-1815*, edited by E. A. Underwood (New York, 1963).

GEORGE CLARK, *A History of the Royal College of Physicians*, Vol. I [to 1688] (Cambridge, 1965).

ALCIDE GAROSI, *Siena nella storia della medicina (1240-1555)* (Florence, 1958).

M. D. GRMEK, 'Ancient Slavic Medicine', *Journal of the History of Medicine and Allied Sciences*, XIV (1959), 18-40.

E. A. HAMMOND, 'Physicians in Medieval English Religious Houses', *Bulletin of the History of Medicine*, XXXII (1958), 105–20.

——, 'Income of Medieval English Doctors', *Journal of the History of Medicine and Allied Sciences*, XV (1960), 154–69.

RICHARD SHRYOCK, *Medicine and Society in America, 1660–1860* (New York, 1960).

Technology and the State

ED. ESMONIN, 'L'Abbé Expilly et ses travaux de statistique', *Revue d'histoire moderne et contemporaine*, IV (1957), 241–80.

The Impact of Science and Technology on Life and Thought

T. K. RABB, 'Puritanism and the Rise of Experimental Science in England', *Journal of World History*, VII (1962), 46–67.

RICHARD S. WESTFALL, *Science and Religion in Seventeenth-Century England* (New Haven, Conn., 1958).

CHAPTER XVI

EDUCATION (1300–1775)

European Educational Institutions

J. L. CATE, *The Scholars Got Bows and Arrows* (San Marcos, Texas, 1962).

KENNETH CHARLTON, *Education in Renaissance England* (Toronto, 1965).

COMITÉ INTERNATIONAL DES SCIENCES HISTORIQUES, XIth Congress, Stockholm, 1960, Vol. I: *Méthodologie—Histoire des universités—Histoire des prix avant 1750* (Göteborg, 1960).

L. J. DALY, *The Medieval University, 1200–1400* (New York, 1961).

M. S. FOSTER, *'Out of Smalle Beginnings . . .': An Economic History of Harvard College in the Puritan Period (1636 to 1712)* (Cambridge, Mass., 1962).

L. S. KHACHIKYAN, 'Mongols in Transcaucasia', *Journal of World History*, 'Contributions to Russian History' (1958), 98–125.

PEARL KIBRE, *Scholarly Privileges in the Middle Ages: The Rights, Privileges, and Immunities of Scholars and Universities of Bologna, Padua, Paris, and Oxford* (Cambridge, Mass., 1962).

E. KOVACS, 'L'Université de Cracovie et la culture hongroise aux XVe–XVIe siècles', in E. Molnar *et al.* (eds.), *Nouvelles études historiques* (Budapest, 1965), 197–218.

JACQUES LE GOFF, 'Les universités et les pouvoirs publics au Moyen-âge et à la Renaissance', *XIIe congrès international des sciences historiques, Rapports* (Vienna, 1965), III, 189–206.

Educational Methods and Theory in Europe

V. L. BULLOUGH, 'Medieval Bologna and the Development of Medical Education', *Bulletin of the History of Medicine*, XXXII (1958), 201–15.

A. B. FERGUSON, *The Indian Summer of English Chivalry; Studies in the Decline and Transformation of Chivalric Idealism* (Durham, N.C., 1960).

JAMES MULHERN, *A History of Education, a Social Interpretation* (2nd ed.; New York, 1959).

JOSEF POLIŠENSKY, 'Comenius and His Time', *Journal of World History*, VI (1960), 45–77.

L. V. RYAN, *Roger Ascham* (Stanford, Calif., 1963).

ALBERT THIBAUDET, *Montaigne*, ed. by Floyd Gray (Paris, 1963).

Education outside Europe

E. S. MORGAN, *The Gentle Puritan: A Life of Ezra Stiles, 1727–1795* (New Haven, Conn., 1962).

CLIFFORD K. SHIPTON. *Biographical Sketches of Those who Attended Harvard College in the Classes of 1746–50, with Bibliographical and Other Notes* (Boston, 1962).

TILEMANN GRIMM, *Erziehung und Politik im Konfuzianischen China der Ming-Zeit* (Wiesbaden, 1960).

A. S. TRITTON, *Materials on Muslim Education in the Middle Ages* (London, 1957).

L. L. TUCKER, *Puritan Protagonist: President Thomas Clap of Yale College* ('Institute of Early American History and Culture'; Chapel Hill, N.C., 1962).

Professional Training

ANNE BLANCHARD, ' "Ingénieurs du roi" en Languedoc du XVIIIe siècle,' *Revue d'histoire moderne et contemporaine*, IX (1962), 161–70.

HENRI HOURS, *La lutte contre les épizooties et l'École Vétérinaire de Lyon au XVIIIe siècle* (Paris, 1957).

K. A. KOENIG, 'Die Stellung der Anatomen unter den medizinischen Lehrern in Padua im 16 Jahrhundert. (Vesal und Fabrizio d'Acquapendente),' *Centaurus* (*Kbh*), VII (1960), 1–5.

CHAPTER XVII
SUMMARY AND CONCLUSION

PETER AMANN (ed.), *The Eighteenth-Century Revolution: French or Western?* (Boston, 1963).

HANNAH ARENDT, *The Human Condition* (Chicago, 1958).

——, *On Revolution* (New York, 1963).

PIETER GEYL, 'The Vitality of Western Civilization', *Delta, a Review of Arts, Life and Thought in the Netherlands* (Spring, 1959), pp. 5–19.

JACQUES GODECHOT, *Les Révolutions (1770–99)* (Paris, 1963).

M. B. JANSEN (ed.), *Changing Japanese Attitudes toward Modernization* (Princeton, N.J., 1965).

MARSHALL HODGSON, 'Hemispheric Interregional History as an Approach to World History', *Journal of World History*, I (1954), 715–23.

HIDEO KISHIMOTO, 'Modernization versus Westernization in the East', *Journal of World History*, VII (1963), 871–74.

KARL LOWITH, *Meaning in History* (4th impression; Chicago, 1957).

W. H. MCNEILL, *The Rise of the West* (Chicago, 1963).

R. R. PALMER, *The Age of the Democratic Revolution, a Political History of Europe and America, 1760–1800*, Vol. I: *The Challenge* (Princeton, N.J., 1959).

J. M. ROMEIN, 'The Common Human Pattern (Origin and Scope of Historical Theories)', *Journal of World History*, IV (1958), 449–70.

J. J. SAUNDERS, 'The Problem of Islamic Decadence', *Journal of World History*, VII (1963), 701–20.

INDEX

Names of persons are selected from the literary and visual arts, religion, science and technology.
Names omitted, apart from popes, rulers and politicians, are those mentioned briefly on one page only. Access to these names may be had by consulting the appropriate collective entries under place names and subject headings.

China—*continued*
644, 904; language 562–3, 589–91, 596, 641–2, vernacular 590–1, 642; literature 590–96, 641–6, 904–5; music, drama 590–1, 593–4, 642–4, 777; poetry 591–2, 642, 644; philosophy, *see* Confucianism; Neo-Confucianism
architecture 757–60, 787; crafts 705–7, 766–7; ceramics 764–7; painting 760–3; sculpture 763
alchemy 815; astronomy 816, 906; biology 815; chemistry 815; geography 815–16; mathematics 815–16, 904; medicine 815–17, 905
agriculture 51, 53, 58, 490, 531, 906; armaments 815–16; 905–6; engineering 816; metallurgy 932; mining 905; pottery 707, 764, 815, 905; printing 589–90, 815, 930–31; shipping 815–16, 942; textiles 60, 705, 758, 766, 905
Ching-t'u, Buddhist sect 133, 171
Chishtiyya, Ṣūfī order 152, 180, 184
Christian Brothers, teaching order 1004, 1013, 1043
Christianity 156–9; groups 156, 158; relations with state 161, 275–6, 303–10, 411, 458–9, 1052–4; theology 396–411, 438–55; *see* Orthodox, Protestant, Roman Catholic churches
Chrysoloris (d. 1415) 400, 554
Chu Chih-yü (1600–82), Neo-Confucian 427, 543
Chu Hsi (1130–1200) 176, 1029–30, 1032; writings 141, 387, 429, 498, 542–3, 1029–30; followers 389–90, 423, 426, 429–30, 432–4, 513, 542–3, 1032
Ch'u Yu (1341–1427), writer 591
Cherriguera, José (1656–1725), architect 698
Clairault, Alexis Claude (1713–65), astronomer 845, 851, 880
Cochin China, *see* Vietnam
Coducci, Mauro, architect 692, (Pl. 48)
Coeur, Jacques, merchant of Bourges 66, 72, 698; house 686, 698, (Pl. 43)
Coeurdoux, Gaston Laurent (1691–1779), Jesuit 607
Coiter, Volcher (1534–76), biologist 891, 892–3, 899; works 893
Colden, Cadwallader, scientist 454
Colet, John (*c.* 1467–1519), humanist 224, 992
Cologne cathedral 684, (Pl. 38); university 275, 995, 997, 1000
Colonna family 191–2, 194; pope 205
Columbus, Christopher (*c.* 1451–1506) 14, 806, 814, 819–20, 826, 1056; voyages 823–5

Comenius, John Amos (Komenský) (1592–1610) 299, 306, 606, 1058; on education 1010–11; works 1011
Commines, Philippe de, historian 494
commodities 4, 50, 52–3, 60, 63, 67, 69, 954–7, 979–80, 1054
Confucianism 136–43, 175–6, 363–4, 1063; State Cult 139, 141; Cult of the Scholars 141, 176, 363–4; school of Han Learning 364, 428–9; ancestor worship 137–8, 363; canon 140–1; ethical code 137, 139–41, 364, 422–3, 430–1, 435; philosophers 363–4, 390, 426–7, 435; temples 142, 176, 363–4
Confucius 140–2, 176, 363–4, 431
Constance, Council of (1414–18) 202–5, 217, 222; concordats 205, 206; church reform 204–6; representatives 203; trial of heretics 203, 205
Constantinople 150, 189; fall of (1453) 18, 183, 188, 211, 1056; Judaism 368, 371–2; Orthodox synod 156; patriarchate 156, 188, 191, 209, 335–6; architecture 738, 741; manuscripts 553–4; observatory 903
Contarini, Gasparo, cardinal 278, 279–81
Cook James (1728–79), explorer 837, 884–5, 1048
Copernicus, Nicolas (1473–1543), astronomer 440, 451, 802–3, 805, 839, 841; system 846, 848–9, 908; *De Revolutionibus* 830–1, 845–6, 1056
Coptic Christians 4, 158, 333
Cordus, Valerius (1515–44), botanist 872
Corneille, Pierre (1606–84), dramatist 619, 621–2, 624–5
Cortés, Hernando (1485–1547) 87–9, 322
Čosgi Odsir, Tibetan monk 590, 640
Cotte, Louis (1740–1815), meteorology 871
Coulomb, Charles de (1736–1806), physician 865, 867–9
Coysevox, Antoine (1640–1720), sculptor 681–2, (Pl. 36)
crafts 59–60, 62, 1036–37; arms 60, 777; carpets 60, 740, 766–7, 904; furniture 710–12, 742, 785, 904; glass 60, 708–9, 742, 928–9; jewellery 710, 742, 746, 757, 767, 780; lace 706; metal work 709–10, 742, 753, 767, 929; porcelain 707–8, 764–6, 777, 812, 904, 919–30; pottery 60, 707–8, 742, 764, 768, 782, 930, tiles 931–2; stained glass 704, 708, 785–6, 928; tapestry 547, 704, 706, 785, 928, (Pl. 58); textiles 60, 705–7, 742, 780–1, 926
Cranach, Lucas (1472–1553), painter 660, 714, (Pl. 76)
Cranmer, Thomas (1489–1556), archbishop 238, 244–5